# HANDBOOK OF PALEONTOLOGICAL TECHNIQUES

# OTHER BOOKS IN GEOLOGY

# HANDBOOK OF PALEONTOLOGICAL TECHNIQUES

Prepared Under the Auspices of the Paleontological Society

Edited by

BERNHARD KUMMEL, *Harvard University*

DAVID RAUP, *The Johns Hopkins University*

COORDINATORS OF SECTIONS

Jane Gray, *University of Oregon*
R. L. Langenheim, Jr., *University of Illinois*
Franco Rasetti, *The Johns Hopkins University*
J. Keith Rigby, *Brigham Young University*
H. B. Whittington, *Harvard University*
Ellis L. Yochelson, *U. S. Geological Survey*

 W. H. FREEMAN AND COMPANY

SAN FRANCISCO AND LONDON

# PREFACE

---

Effective field and laboratory techniques are essential to any work with fossils. The paleontological literature of the past century contains countless references to these techniques, and many excellent descriptions of them have been written. In the last decade, however, the literature on techniques has become so large, and so many new procedures have been introduced, that it has become increasingly difficult for the working paleontologist to find the techniques most appropriate to his particular material. This problem has been further complicated by the fact that many of the new techniques were developed first in disciplines other than paleontology. The basic literature is thus often inaccessible to most paleontologists. Clearly there is a need for an up-to-date and reasonably comprehensive sourcebook. With the *Handbook of Paleontological Techniques* we hope to satisfy this need.

The importance of techniques was expressed by Dr. G. G. Simpson at the meetings of the Society of Vertebrate Paleontologists in Pittsburgh in 1959. Dr. Kenneth Caster, then President of the Paleontological Society, seized upon this statement principally as a potential topic for establishing greater liaison between invertebrate and vertebrate paleontologists. He requested that the editors formulate some kind of program for the following meeting of the Paleontological Society (Denver, 1960). A committee was established to organize a session on techniques for the Denver meeting. It soon became evident that the topic was impractical for the facilities, etc., available at a national meeting. Widespread enthusiastic response, however, suggested that a Handbook was needed. Thus, the original committee was retained and this volume is its final product.

The Handbook consists of a series of essays and a set of bibliographies. Some of the essays deal with newly developed techniques; others summarize classical techniques. Most of the individual contributions have been written by those actively concerned with the techniques described.

The Handbook is divided into five parts:

Part I.   General procedures and techniques applicable to major fossil groups.
Part II.  Descriptions of specific techniques.
Part III. Techniques in palynology.

Part IV. Bibliography on paleontological techniques.
Part V. Compilation of bibliographies of use to paleontologists and stratigraphers.

Part I consists of 21 essays, each dealing with one of the major fossil
groups. These essays are intended as general introductions to the problems
usually encountered in working with particular taxonomic groups. They discuss *what* to do rather than *how* to do it. Wherever possible, reference is
made either to existing literature or to Part II of the Handbook for detailed
description of the actual techniques. Where very specialized methods have
been developed (e.g., in conodonts and ostracods), the essays have been expanded to cover the techniques as well.

Part II includes 51 essays divided into six sections. Here the principal
techniques having applicability over a wide taxonomic range are described.
We are particularly indebted to the coordinators who undertook the heavy
responsibility of organizing the sections and soliciting the manuscripts.

Part III deals with techniques in the expanding field of palynology and
was entirely organized by Jane Gray. This is the largest individual part of
the Handbook. We feel that because palynology is one of the newer branches
of paleontology, and one requiring highly specialized techniques, the extensive treatment is warranted. This was an exceptionally difficult part to organize, and the editors are extremely grateful to Dr. Gray for the great imag-
ination and energy which she gave to its preparation.

The bibliographies which make up Parts IV and V are not intended, in
any way, to be exhaustive. Space alone required that we be selective; we also
wished to balance the coverage of old and new literature.

Each coordinator was given complete freedom to develop his section. We
are entirely aware that the Handbook does not cover all subjects, but we are
satisfied that within the means available, we have achieved maximum coverage.

In addition to the authors who have contributed manuscripts, a large
number of individuals were most helpful to the project. We wish particularly
to acknowledge the thoughtful advice on organizational problems given by
J. T. Dutro, Jr., William S. Oliver, Jr., Allison R. Palmer, and Frank Whitmore, Jr. Finally, the long, tedious chore of compiling and checking all the
contributions was very ably done by Miss Victoria Kohler, to whom we are
most grateful.

*May 1964*

BERNHARD KUMMEL
DAVID M. RAUP

# CONTENTS

## PART I

### GENERAL PROCEDURES AND TECHNIQUES APPLICABLE TO MAJOR FOSSIL GROUPS

COORDINATOR: DAVID M. RAUP

# PART II

# DESCRIPTIONS OF SPECIFIC TECHNIQUES

## Section A.   Collecting Techniques

COORDINATOR: ELLIS L. YOCHELSON

## Section B.  Mechanical Methods of Preparation

COORDINATOR: R. L. LANGENHEIM, JR.

## Section C.   Chemical Methods of Preparation

COORDINATOR: H. B. WHITTINGTON

## Section D.   Radiation and Related Techniques

COORDINATOR: DAVID M. RAUP

## Section E. Casting and Molding

## Section F. Illustrations

# PART III

# TECHNIQUES IN PALYNOLOGY

## PART IV

## BIBLIOGRAPHY ON PALEONTOLOGICAL TECHNIQUES

BERNHARD KUMMEL

## PART V

## COMPILATION OF BIBLIOGRAPHIES OF USE TO PALEONTOLOGISTS AND STRATIGRAPHERS

BERNHARD KUMMEL

# Part I

GENERAL PROCEDURES
AND TECHNIQUES
APPLICABLE TO MAJOR
FOSSIL GROUPS

*Coordinator:* DAVID M. RAUP

# Calcareous Nannofossils

WILLIAM W. HAY

*Department of Geology, University of Illinois, Urbana*

Calcareous nannofossils constitute a heterogenous group of objects that range in size from $\frac{1}{4}\mu$ to $20\mu$. The most common calcareous nannofossils are coccoliths—complexly constructed, button-shaped skeletal elements produced by chrysomonad flagellates called coccolithophores. In the living organism, the coccoliths are arranged in the form of a hollow sphere, called a coccosphere, just within the cell membrane. The coccoliths of a coccosphere may all be alike or they may be dimorphic, the circumflagellar cycle being different from the rest. Parke and Adams (1960) have noted that the life history of coccolithophores may be complex, and have demonstrated that one coccolithophore may produce different kinds of coccoliths during different phases.

Calcareous nannofossils have been divided into two main groups according to the arrangement of the structural elements composing them: (1) heliolithid forms, such as coccoliths, in which the carbonate elements are arranged so that a swastika-like negative uniaxial pseudofigure is seen in polarized light; and (2) ortholithid forms, such as discoasters, in which the *c*-axes are oriented perpendicular to the plane of the disc so that the object is in extinction in polarized light. Rhabdoliths are heliolithid skeletal elements produced by organisms called rhabdosphaerids. They differ from coccoliths in having a long rod rising perpendicularly from the coccolith-like basal disc. Braarudo-sphaerids construct modified ortholithid skeletal elements called pentaliths, made of five crystals of calcite, each with a different orientation.

Most present-day coccolithophores live in oceanic waters, the species there producing large, strong coccoliths. The species that dwell in shallow waters generally have smaller, more delicate coccoliths. Fossil calcareous nannofossils seem to have been produced chiefly by oceanic plankton, as they are commonly associated with the tests of other planktonic organisms.

## COLLECTING NANNOFOSSILS

Because of their small size, nannofossils cannot be observed in the field unless a high-powered microscope is taken along. The Cooke-MacArthur field microscope can serve this purpose well, and rough preparations can be made on the spot to determine whether a sample contains nannofossils.

A field microscope is usually not available, so that samples must be taken "blind" and examined later in the laboratory. Calcareous nannofossils are most abundant in fine-grained pelagic sediments and are commonly associated with planktonic foraminifera. In clays containing abundant planktonic foraminifers, the concentration of coccoliths and similar nannofossils often exceeds one million specimens per cubic centimeter. Clayey rocks containing abundant nannofossils often feel soapy or talc-like. Nannofossils are rarely found in clastic deposits in which the main components are coarser than silt. In formations composed chiefly of sand-sized material, calcareous nannofossils may be found in shaly partings between the beds. In flysch deposits, the uppermost millimeters of graded beds are sometimes rich in nannofossils. They occur in chalk in great numbers, but they are better preserved in clayey partings. Occasionally coccoliths can be seen in thin sections of indurated limestones, but they cannot ordinarily be isolated or identified.

Samples need not exceed 25 grams. A few grams will suffice to make a number of preparations, therefore a 25-gram sample will provide plenty of extra material for later reference. Since such small samples are used, it is possible to collect large numbers of samples in remote field areas with relatively little inconvenience.

In taking samples, care must be exercised to avoid contamination. The nannofossils are so small that they can become lodged in scratches on the surface of a hammer or knife, or between the ridges of the skin. The easiest way to avoid contamination and obviate the necessity of washing hands and hammer after taking each sample is to use a sample bag, usually a small manila envelope, as the sampling device. It is wise to note field relations carefully, as running water during storms may contaminate the surfaces of outcrops with nannofossils from higher exposures on a slope.

## PREPARATION OF SAMPLES

Rough preparation of a sample to determine whether nannofossils are present takes only a few minutes (Hay, 1961). Crush several grams of the sample in a mortar and pestle, and add a few drops of water to make a muddy suspension. Place a drop of this suspension on a glass cover slip (soda straws make cheap disposable pipettes), add a few drops of water to dilute it, and dry the suspension on a hot plate. Place a drop of Caedax or other suitable mounting medium on a glass slide. Touch the Caedax drop to the dried suspension on the cover slip, and immediately invert the glass slide and place it on the hot plate. In a few seconds the Caedax will have run to the edges of the cover slip, resulting in a clean mount. The slide can now be inspected under the microscope. The simplest way to determine whether calcareous nannofossils are present is to view the slide at 800× with crossed nicols. If heliolithid nannofossils (usually far more abundant than ortholithid forms) are present, they can be readily recognized by the swastika-like negative uniaxial pseudo-figures they produce.

If rough preparation reveals nannofossils, then a cleaner concentration can be made for more convenient study. Break down several grams of the sample by soaking and swirling in water, by ultrasonic treatment, or by crushing if necessary. Addition of a small amount of sodium hexametaphosphate (Calgon) will help to disperse the clays and will also insure an even distribution of the particles in the final mount. Short-centrifuging, as described by Edwards (1963), can be used to remove clay. Pour the suspension into a 50-ml centrifuge tube, add distilled water, and short-centrifuge the sample at 300 rpm for 15 seconds. Then decelerate the centrifuge, decant the suspension, and set it aside. Repeat the process several times until the decantate is nearly clear. Then short-centrifuge the decantate at 850 rpm for 30 seconds. The residue will contain particles from $3\mu$ to $25\mu$ in size, and will include those nannofossils most easily studied under the light microscope. Longer centrifuging will settle the abundant tiny coccoliths, which are of particular interest to the electron microscopist.

Slides can be made from the centrifuge residue in the same manner as the rough preparations described above. Stradner and Papp (1961) have suggested mounting assemblages between two cover slips so that oil immersion techniques may be used to study both sides of the same permanently mounted specimen. Permanent mounts should be cured in the drying area for a number of hours to insure that the cover slip will not drift and disorient specimens. If vernier scales on a microscope stage are to be used in recording the location of a specimen, the mounts should be stored horizontally, as even long curing of mounting media does not fully prevent drift. If the microscope is not equipped with vernier scales, the specimen may be marked by a ring drawn in India ink. Leitz manufactures a diamond-tipped marking device which screws into one of the holes in the objective turret and can be used to scratch very small rings around nannofossils.

To study nannofossils in side view, viscous mounts are needed (Bramlette and Sullivan, 1961). The 15-minute fraction is used once again. Place a drop of mounting medium on a glass slide, and allow it to dry. Then add a small amount of a silicone or other nondrying oil. Scrape the sedimented particles from the glass, mix them into the silicone with a toothpick, and mount a cover slip in place. The nannofossils can be made to roll up on their sides by pushing the cover slip around with the eraser of a pencil.

Caedax and viscous mounts can be studied under a light microscope. For scanning slides, $800\times$ is a convenient magnification, but for studying details $1200–1600\times$ with double oil immersion is needed. A polarizer and analyzer with a mechanical stage mounted on a centered revolving stage are indispensable for the study of heliolithid nannofossils. Phase optics and dark-field illumination techniques may reveal detail that is otherwise obscure.

Shadowing of the nannofossils with heavy metals, such as gold or platinum, in a vacuum evaporator prior to mounting can bring out structural details that cannot ordinarily be observed.

For electron microscopy, the nannofossils can be allowed to settle directly on Formvar-coated grids. However, only transmission electron micrographs can be obtained, because the nannofossils are silhouetted against a light background. The transmission micrographs are not particularly useful, and to take advantage of the electron microscope, carbon replicas must be prepared (Deflandre and Durrieu, 1957; Black and Barnes, 1959; Hay and Towe, 1962).

To make a good carbon replica it is necessary to get rid of as much extraneous material as possible before replicating. Treat the centrifuged fraction of the sample to be studied with a weak solution of Clorox, and allow it to stand for 24 hours to remove organic matter. Then clean the sample in an ultrasonic cleaner to break down any remaining clay and to clean the surfaces of the coccoliths. Short-centrifuge the sample, and check the residue under the light microscope to see that the coccoliths are indeed clean. (If necessary, ultrasonic cleaning and short-centrifuging may be repeated several times.) Spread a few drops of the suspension on a freshly cleaved surface of muscovite, and place it gently under a heat lamp. When the suspension is dry, place the mica sheet in a vacuum evaporator with carbon rods located about 12 cm above the sample. A drop of glycerin on the tip of each carbon rod aids later removal of the replica from the mica. When a vacuum of $5 \times 10^{-5}$ mm Hg has been obtained, evaporate carbon onto the specimen in four 15-second bursts. Remove the mica sheet from the evaporator, and use a knife to score the carbon film into squares the size of an electron microscope specimen support screen. Then float the squares of carbon off into water. Very slowly and gently, add HCl to the water to make a 1 percent solution, and allow the replicas to float on this for several hours to remove all $CaCO_3$. Then transfer the replicas to a polyethylene dish containing distilled water. Slowly add HF to produce a 10 percent solution, and leave the replicas in this solution for about 8 hours while the clay particles dissolve. Transfer the replicas to another dish containing distilled water, and pick them up with electron microscope grids. If the carbon film is heavy enough it will support itself, so that Formvar backing is not necessary.

## REFERENCES

Black, M., and B. Barnes (1959). The structure of coccoliths from the English Chalk. Geol. Mag., v. 96, p. 321–328, pls. 8–12.

Bramlette, M. N., and F. R. Sullivan (1961). Coccolithophorids and related nannoplankton of the early Tertiary in California. Micropaleontology, v. 7, p. 129–188, pls. 1–14, table 1.

Deflandre, G., and Durrieu (1957). Application de la technique d'empreintes de carbone à la systématique des coccolithophoridés fossiles. C. R. Acad. Sci. Paris, v. 244, p. 2948–2951, 2 text-figs.

Edwards, A. R. (1963). A preparation technique for calcareous nannoplankton. Micropaleontology, v. 9, p. 103–104, 2 text-figs.

Hay, W. W. (1961). Note on the preparation of samples for discoasterids. J. Paleontology, v. 35, p. 873.

——, and K. M. Towe (1962). Electron-microscopic examination of some coccoliths from Donzacq (France). Eclog. Geol. Helvet., v. 55, p. 497–519, pls. 1–10, 2 text-figs.

Parke, M., and I. Adams (1960). The motile (*Crystallolithus hyalinus* Gaarder and Markali) and nonmotile phases in the life history of *Coccolithus pelagicus* (Wallich) Schiller. J. Marine Biol. Assoc., U.K., v. 39, p. 263–274, pls. 1–4.

Stradner, H., and A. Papp (1961). Tertiaere Discoasteriden aus Oesterreich und deren stratigraphische Bedeutung. Jahrb. geol. Bundesanst., Sonderband 7, p. 1–160, 42 pls., 24 text-figs., 4 tables.

# Radiolarians

BENJAMIN H. BURMA

*Sunnyvale, California*

The method discussed here was developed to obtain radiolarians from indurated tuffs, which break down with difficulty. Rocks more easily broken down can be treated more gently and some of the directions abbreviated or possibly omitted. The method is presented in more detail than is usual. Our experience has been that it is far commoner for presentations of technique to err on the side of too little rather than too much detail. Attention is paid to factors important to processing samples with maximum efficiency, minimum man-hours expended, and minimum cost consistent with good results.

## OCCURRENCE OF RADIOLARIA

Radiolarians are, at the present, creatures of the open sea and rarely come inshore. They are, accordingly, uncommon in present-day sediments except those from the continental slope and the adjoining bathyal to abyssal regions. Their distribution in ancient sediments is in general accord with this, though they are well known in sediments that must have accumulated in shelf waters.

Thus, one can say that, in general, the best place to look for radiolarians is in sediments which accumulated on the deeper parts of the shelf or at greater depths under open-sea, or maximum-marine, conditions. In the Cretaceous and Tertiary, sediments in which the fauna consists preponderantly of planktonic Foraminifera should be regarded as most favorable.

I have found that, for fairly indurated sediments, preparation of thin sections is often a good way to determine which parts of the stratigraphic section contain useful concentrations of Radiolaria. It is usually easier and quicker to prepare thin sections of such sediments than to break down samples for examination. Since only rarely can radiolarians definitely be identified in the field, collection of them is generally done "blind."

## STUDYING THIN SECTIONS

Much of the work that has been done on Radiolaria, especially in pre-Tertiary rocks, has been done on specimens in thin sections. This is not a method of choice for radiolarian studies, but it may be necessary if the containing rocks have been thoroughly silicified. The preparation of samples of such rocks involves making thin sections, according to standard methods.

In making such thin sections only two points should be particularly kept in mind. First, the section should be made as *thick* as is practicable, so that as much of the radiolarian as possible will be contained within the thickness of the section. Second, careful polishing of both surfaces of the section will be amply repaid. The commonest mistake in preparing thin sections of fossils consists in not polishing the section with a sufficient number of grades of fine enough abrasive powders.

## RADIOLARIA PRESERVED AS OTHER THAN SILICA

Radiolaria which have been preserved by such substances as pyrite can often be recovered from sediments by the methods given here or by those used in the preparation of foraminiferal samples. Such specimens are only rarely worthy of serious study, as they will usually be found to be steinkerns. For this reason, no special attention will be paid to them here. In general, only well-preserved Radiolaria will repay the time spent in preparing and studying them.

## THEORY OF RADIOLARIAN SAMPLE PREPARATION

Radiolaria (hereafter called rads) are composed of opaline silica, and advantage is taken of this relatively resistant composition in isolating them. Any acid other than hydrofluoric may be used to assist in breaking down the containing rock or to aid in concentrating the rads by dissolving carbonates.

Alkalis are useful to help break down and disperse clays, but solutions too strongly alkaline will attack the rads. Care must therefore be taken when boiling rads in alkalis to ensure that the solutions do not evaporate to a greater extent than indicated in the directions below. If the rads appear corroded after sample preparation, over-strong alkali should be suspected.

Treatment with $H_2O_2$ (30 percent) or $HNO_3$ is designed to oxidize any organic matter in the sample. Organic matter can cling to or cause clay to cling to the rads and obscure them. The $H_2O_2$ also serves as a vigorous mechanical agent in cleaning rads and should be used if available.

Rad samples washed with water will often stick together when dried, apparently as a result of traces of salts or clay remaining in the sample. This trouble is eliminated by dehydrating the sample with acetone as indicated below. *Absolute* methyl or ethyl alcohol can be substituted, but neither is recommended. If none of these are obtainable, this step can be omitted, but results will not generally be as good. (We use this treatment routinely for foram samples as well.)

### DIRECTIONS

1. Break the sample into pieces less than ¼ inch in size. An iron mortar is recommended. Crush, using an up-and-down motion of the pestle. *Do not grind* or try to treat more than ½ to 1 cubic inch of sample at a time, as this will produce undesirable powdering. For maximum efficiency always thoroughly clean the crushing equipment immediately after use.

2. In a 400-ml glass beaker, put enough sample to cover the bottom (25 to 30 grams). Add about 50 ml of alcohol followed by about 50 ml of concentrated technical grade HCl. (If the alcohol is omitted, the HCl must be added slowly to avoid undue effervescence in calcareous rocks.) If the rock is not particularly calcareous, the alcohol may be omitted. When the first reaction has slowed, fill the beaker about half full with water, cover it with a watch glass, and place it on a hot plate. Boil the contents for 10 to 30 minutes. *Note:* Beakers may tend to bounce on the hot plate due to explosive boiling in this or later steps. To avoid this, fit the hot plate with a removable rim of metal about ½ inch high. Explosive boiling is usually less of a problem if the hot plate is kept really *hot*. Sometimes it helps to interrupt the boiling and wash out accumulated clay (washing directions below).

3. Remove the beaker from the hot plate and allow it to stand for 10 minutes. Decant the acid as completely as possible. Fill the beaker about ⅔ full of water, stir vigorously, and let it stand for 5 to 10 minutes. Decant again, and add water until the beaker is about half full.

4. Cautiously add solid powdered $Na_2CO_3$ while stirring vigorously until the acid is neutralized, as will be shown by the stopping of effervescence. Then add a slight excess of $Na_2CO_3$ (about ½ teaspoon or a little more). Now add 10 to 12 pellets of NaOH. (*Caution:* Too much NaOH will attack the rads.) Add water until the beaker is two-thirds full. Cover the beaker with a watch glass, and place it on the hot plate. Even the most amenable samples need to be boiled for at least ½ hour. Our samples of tuff showed almost no effect after this amount of boiling, but had to be boiled for 24 hours (three working days). This did not completely break down the sample, but freed enough rads to produce a good suite. We doubt whether samples not yielding results after such a period of time are usable. (*Caution:* Do not allow the water level to fall below *half full* at any time while boiling, as the solutions will become too strongly alkaline and corrode the rads.)

5. When the sample is sufficiently disintegrated, remove it from the hot plate and float it onto a 200-mesh screen (no coarser!). Pick out any large undisintegrated fragments. Wash the residue *very gently* with a spray of water until the

water coming through the screen is clear. *Do not rub* the residue against the screen as is sometimes done with forams. (If a 200-mesh or finer screen is not available the sample must be washed by decantation. This is tedious, and the smallness and lightness of the rads makes the separation more difficult than washing forams on a screen. Decantation is definitely not recommended. If the sample is washed gently on the screen, rads will not be broken in the process. A 200-mesh screen in good condition will hold even the smallest intact rads.)

6. Using a *gentle* spray of water, float the washed residue back into the same beaker. Let the sample stand, then decant as much water as possible.

7. Add a volume of acetone equal to twice the volume of the residue, *gently* mix, and decant. Repeat this step.

8. Dry the residue with gentle heat. (*Caution: Avoid open flames. No smoking.*)

9. Add sufficient 30 percent $H_2O_2$ to more than cover the residue. Warm the contents until vigorous effervescence starts, then remove the beaker from heat, and wait until bubbling stops. Add water to produce a 10 percent $H_2O_2$ solution. Cover the beaker with a watch glass, and boil the contents for 30 minutes. (*Caution: 30 percent $H_2O_2$ is dangerously corrosive. Handle only when wearing goggles or face mask and rubber gloves.*)

If 30 percent $H_2O_2$ is not available, add concentrated $HNO_3$, about twice the volume of the residue. Cover with a watch glass and boil for 5 minutes in a fume hood or with good ventilation. Add water to make about a 50 percent $HNO_3$ solution, and boil for 30 minutes.

10. Repeat steps 5, 6, 7, and 8, but in step 6, float the residue into a petri dish. The sample is ready for study.

11. If a distillation setup is available, the acetone used in steps 7 and 10 should be decanted into a bottle and saved. It can be recovered by distillation with minimal loss.

12. *Never* use filter paper to collect rad residues. The rads will stick to the paper.

## SLIDE PREPARATION—STREWS

When dealing with a known fauna, you will probably prefer to prepare strews of the washed residue. Many workers use strews for research phase studies as well. My own experience is such as to indicate the desirability of studying individually mounted specimens (see below) in the research stage, and restricting the use of strews to the routine study of established faunas.

1. Clean a 1 by 3 inch glass microscope slide. Put five dots of gum arabic or gum tragacanth solution on the slide in such a position that when the cover glass is in place, four dots will be about $\frac{1}{8}$ inch from each corner of the cover glass and one in its center.

2. In each dot mount a 50-mesh Carborundum or Alundum grain (as one would mount a foram) to hold the cover glass off the fragile rads. (If the residue contains sand grains of comparable size, steps 1 and 2 can be omitted.) Allow the slide to dry.

3. In a clear space between the Carborundum grains, put enough mounting medium to more than fill the space under the cover glass. It is generally impractical to use a medium that must be cooked or melted, such as canada balsam. I recommend Technicon Mounting Medium (Technicon Chemical Co., Chauncey, New York).

4. On the pool of mounting medium, place enough washed residue to make a layer no more than one grain or fossil thick when spread out under the cover glass. Too much residue will cause specimens to be piled one atop the other, and will hamper identification. Use too little rather than too much. If the residue contains coarse fragments, these must be sieved out before beginning this step.

5. Using a clean needle, carefully but thoroughly mix the residue into the mounting medium. Break any bubbles.

6. Clean a cover slip and carefully lower it into position. Use an excess of mounting medium so that it squeezes out around the cover slip. If none squeezes out, add some around the slip with a glass rod or medicine dropper.

7. Allow the completed slide to sit overnight. This allows the medium to penetrate the rads and the excess medium to dry somewhat.

8. Store the slides horizontally. If the slides are stored on edge, the rads will gradually slip down to the lower edge of the slide, ruining the preparation.

## SLIDE PREPARATION—PICKED SLIDES

These slides are preferred for research or reference material, although they take considerably longer to prepare than strews. Specimens can be mounted one to a slide, but one would soon accumulate an impossibly large number of slides. If a large number of specimens are to be mounted on a single slide, efficient reference will demand a systematic and uniform method of arranging specimens. This can be done in a number of ways. The method described below has been found practical.

1. Prepare a slide holder, using cardboard as close as possible to the thickness of the slides being used. With a razor blade cut out two 4 by 9.5 cm pieces of this cardboard. In the center of one piece, cut out a rectangle to hold a 1 by 3 inch glass slide, using a slide as the pattern. In one end of the other piece, cut a small semicircular indentation. Cement the two cardboard rectangles together with a nondistorting cement such as Kodak Rapid Mounting Cement, sold in camera shops. Rubber cement can be used, but will deteriorate. Paint a large gummed label with India ink. When dry, rule onto it, with white ink and a crow quill pen, a rectangle 18 by 35 mm. Rule this rectangle into six divisions horizontally and fifteen divisions vertically, making ninety rectangles in all. When the ink is dry, trim the rectangle, and paste it into the cavity of the slide holder. The ruled rectangle should be equidistant between top and bottom of the cavity and 27 mm from one end, hereafter to be the *left* end of the slide holder. Paste a small square of gummed label in either end of the slide holder recess, not covered by the ruled label. Now carefully paint the entire slide holder with India ink except for the part covered by the ruled rectangle.

2. Place a glass slide in the slide holder and put the whole under a stereoscopic microscope set at about 50× magnification. Carefully focus on the top surface of the slide.

3. Take a regular cardboard micropaleontology slide with a large ruled rectangular recess. Cut a piece of cardboard, as in step 1, to the same size as the cardboard slide, and put it under this cardboard slide. Put both together on the microscope stage, snugly against the slide holder, holding all together with one hand. With the focus set on top of the glass slide, move the cardboard slide under the microscope and see if the bottom of the recess is in good focus. If it is not, build up the cardboard under the micropaleontology slide until the two surfaces are at the same level. This part of the apparatus is now ready for use and is put to one side.

4. It is generally advisable to sieve the washed residue for ease in picking. We have found 60-, 100-, 150-mesh screens, and pan, in the 8-cm diameter size, most useful. The 60-mesh screen almost never retains rads on it, but should always be checked. The 100-mesh screen will occasionally retain some large rads. Most of the rads will be found on the 150-mesh screen. The pan should always be checked for smaller rads. These are *not* juveniles, but small genera and species. Do not ignore them.

5. I have never found reason to pick rads with other than a No. 000 sable brush, as used on forams. You may have to check several brushes before finding a good one. The point should be short but sharp. Generally, moistening the brush in the mouth is the best way to check this. You will find that the moistness of the brush must be rather closely controlled for most effective use. If you wish to try tweezers for handling the rads, see Frizzell and Middour, Mo. Sch. Mines Tech. Ser. Bull. 77, 1951. However, I have never found rads which could not be manipulated with a brush.

6. Sprinkle some of the washed residue onto a ruled, rectangular-recess micropaleontology slide. If you are making a detailed faunal study, you will probably want to pick every usable rad. If so, use a slide having 60 to 100 numbered rectangles so that you can keep track of what part you have picked. In any case, the slide you use should be of this type, and the recess should be lightly coated with gum tragacanth or gum arabic solution. Put these two slides, one in front of the other and in contact, on the stage of a stereoscopic microscope. I would suggest trying about 50× magnification for picking. Locate a rad in the residue. Moisten the No. 000 sable brush and touch it to the rad. While viewing through the microscope, raise the brush enough to clear the slides while holding the slides together with one hand. Move the other slide into the field of view, and while you watch through the microscope, place the rad onto the gummed slide. This *must* be done while you watch through the microscope, as the rads are so small you will lose them otherwise. Continue picking in this manner until you think you have what you need of the fauna. This phase of the work can be turned over to "bug-pickers," who can also readily be trained to segregate superfamilies into different areas of the gummed slide. These positions should be standardized. The pickers, or you, should make whatever breakdown is possible within the superfamilies at this stage, but remember that you can do relatively little in the way of generic, and sometimes even family, identification with a stereoscopic microscope.

7. Put the gummed slide on the stage of a stereoscopic microscope. It should be

resting on its cardboard platform and be in front of the previously prepared slide holder.

8. Using a diamond pencil, or similar instrument, write the sample identification on the 1-inch square at the left end of a 1 by 3 inch glass microscope slide. Clean the glass slide. Paint a layer of a heavy solution of gum tragacanth or gum arabic on the other two inches of the slide, and allow this to dry. Put the glass slide into the recess of the slide holder, left end of slide in left end of holder. You can now transfer the rads from the gummed slide to the glass slide, using a brush as before. The *ruled* area of the slide holder will show through the glass slide. You can place as many as 9 rads in each rectangle. Arrange them in rows and columns of three. Looking down on the slide with its left to your left, squares 1 to 15 are the top row of squares, 16 to 30 the second row, and so on to 90. Within each *rectangle,* the specimens are, from left to right: 1 to 3 in the top row, 4 to 6 in the middle row, and 7 to 9 in the bottom row. Thus, any specimen can be quickly identified and located on the slide. Specimen 21-5, for example is in the sixth rectangle from the left in the second row, and in position 5 within that rectangle (middle of the middle row). If, when you study the slide under a high-powered microscope, you put the *left* end of the slide on the *right* side of the microscope stage, you will *see* the specimens in the way they were placed on the slide. While putting specimens on the glass slide, mount at least one specimen in each square in numerical order to facilitate later numerical identification. Use care in mounting and orienting the rads on the slide. It will greatly facilitate later study. With patience, you can soon learn to mount a conical rad on one lip of the mouth of the cone and with the upper surface of the cone horizontal. In general, the transfer of rads to the glass slide should be done by the paleontologist. An attempt should be made to segregate species into some kind of taxonomic order at this stage.

9. When all the specimens have been transferred to the glass slide, affix a grain of 50-mesh Carborundum to each corner of the ruled rectangle and one in the center in order to hold the cover slips off the rads and keep them from being crushed.

10. Remove the slide from the slide holder. Using a medicine dropper, *flow* Technicon mounting medium, or equivalent medium, onto the slide to suffice. *Do not* allow the medium to drop onto the slide, as this will probably dislodge specimens. I would suggest using a dropper which is affixed to the cap of a small bottle. If you put enough xylene in this bottle to cover the tip of the dropper when the cap is screwed on, the dropper will automatically be cleaned after each use.

11. Gently lower a clean 24 by 40 mm cover slip into position. Sufficient mounting medium should have been used so that it squeezes out all around the cover slip. Add more if necessary. The Technicon shrinks as it gradually dries, and if an excess is not present around the cover slip, bubbles will be pulled under the slip by the shrinkage.

12. Allow the slide to dry overnight before study to allow the medium to penetrate the rads. *Always* store slides horizontally.

## STUDYING RADIOLARIA

Rads *must* be studied by transmitted light at fairly high magnifications, which requires a biological or petrographic microscope. No compromise should be made on the quality of the optical system, since studying rads involves the detailed examination of structures as small as a micron or less across. A magnification as low as 100× will be found useful for scanning slides, but actual study is not very profitable at less than 400 to 500×. I have tried vertical illumination (metallographic type) but have found that it offers no particular advantage.

Rads must be absolutely clean for profitable study. It is a waste of time to mount dirty ones. If the stereoscopic microscope does not show the rads to be shining clean, the residues should be boiled further in alkali. Do not temporize in this respect.

If you wish to use a detergent, I would suggest adding to the alkaline boiling solution $\frac{1}{2}$ to 1 ml of a 10 percent solution of Dowfax 2Al, manufactured by the Dow Chemical Co. This detergent has very low foaming and retains its activity in alkaline solutions.

## ACKNOWLEDGMENTS

The sample preparation techniques described are based on those developed in earlier work on radiolarians and have been modified and adapted by T. A. Edison, D. F. Schaefer, A. A. Graffham, and B. H. Burma. The slide preparation methods are mine. I wish to thank the management of the California Exploration Company for permission to publish these notes.

# Smaller Foraminifers

RUTH TODD, DORIS LOW, and JAMES F. MELLO

*U. S. Geological Survey, Washington, D.C.*

Any investigation of microfossils must, of course, begin with the careful collection of samples from suitably spaced stratigraphic intervals. Although there is no universally practiced method of stratigraphic sampling for microfossils— the sampling techniques used will depend on the unique requirements of the investigation—it is possible to offer some sampling guides that have general application. The most important general comment we can offer is to be as sure as possible that the collected material is uncontaminated. Effort expended in getting to fresh material through weathered mantle or in finding fresh exposures is amply rewarded by the increased confidence that can be placed in the results of an investigation. When it is impossible to obtain unquestion-

Publication authorized by the Director, U. S. Geological Survey.

ably uncontaminated material, samples should be clearly labeled as doubtful, both in the field notes and on the sample bags.

## SAMPLE COLLECTION

Two basic sampling methods have received wide acceptance: channel sampling and spot sampling. Channel samples are taken by first trenching the outcrop or otherwise exposing a surface and then collecting chunks of rock from all levels within predetermined stratigraphic intervals (usually 2 to 10 feet). Channel sampling assures the inclusion of fossils from all layers in the interval sampled but increases danger of contamination. Spot samples are taken at predetermined stratigraphic levels and permit more accurate sampling of faunas from specific layers. They are generally easier to take, and contamination is more easily avoided because of the reduced surface area from which samples are taken. But the intervening lithology remains unsampled, therefore there is no assurance that the samples will contain all faunal elements in the interval. Neither spot samples nor channel samples can give a true picture of the microfossil assemblage that dwelled on an ancient sea bottom at any particular moment in time because both are collected from a stratigraphic interval representing an unknown period of time, though for spot samples this period of time is considerably less. Under unusual circumstances it may be possible to collect from a single time plane—for example, beneath a bentonite bed—but even when this is possible, at least a few millimeters of stratigraphic thickness must be collected. Such a sample may contain many generations of microfossils, possibly reflecting several minor environmental changes.

The scope and purpose of the microfossil study must be considered in determining sampling interval and sample size. For a reconnaissance study of a large stratigraphic interval, widely spaced spot samples (10 to 50 or 100 feet apart) of relatively small size (about 1 pound) may suffice, whereas a detailed analysis of faunal changes within a small stratigraphic interval may require 10- to 20-pound samples taken only a few feet or even a few inches apart. A logical way to determine sampling interval and sample size is to sample each lithology in the section to be studied at several locations. Examination of these samples will, for each lithology, reveal the uniformity of fauna and abundance of specimens and will permit reasonable decisions to be made on the proper sampling interval and sample size.

## PREPARATION

Foraminifera occur in a wide variety of rock types, and the task of freeing specimens from various rocks has engaged the ingenuity of many people. The result is a large body of literature pertaining to methods of obtaining intact foraminifers from many different rock types. Many of the methods for harder rocks are quite involved and cannot be discussed here. Many rocks, however, especially Cretaceous and Tertiary rocks, will break down without elaborate treatment. Some rocks are friable and clean enough to be merely sifted dry and studied without being washed. The principal hazard involved in preparation is possible contamination due to dirty equipment or carelessness, hence it is imperative that screens, brushes, trays, and other equipment be checked both before and after processing any sample. Sinks must be kept clean, otherwise sediment from previously washed samples may be accidentally splashed up into the screen.

Size of a sample may vary from a fraction of an ounce to several pounds. Usually only a portion of each sample is prepared, leaving the balance as a reserve for possible search for other microfossils.

### Washing

Some samples can be washed without being soaked for any appreciable time; others may have to be soaked several hours or overnight. Gentle boiling for an hour or so often hastens breakdown, either in plain water or in water to which a small amount of soda ash has been added.

Hydrogen peroxide (30 percent solution diluted to 15 percent with water) has proved very effective as a soaking solution, especially for shale samples. *Warning:* Hydrogen peroxide should not be stored at full strength because of the danger of explosion.

Use a flexible rubber hose about $\frac{3}{8}$ inch in diameter to control the force and direction of the stream of water on the washing screen. Ordinarily the material is placed directly on a 200-mesh screen, but if the material contains comparatively large pebbles or coarser shell fragments that would damage the screen or deflect the washing stream, a 10-mesh screen is placed above the 200-mesh screen. The 10-mesh screen may also be used with samples that are more difficult to break down. The large fragments can be broken by hand over the coarser mesh and the smaller pieces washed through to the fine screen. Care must be taken to wash the sample toward the center of the screen; too much pressure toward the rim may splash the sediment out of the screen.

To transfer the material from the screen to a container for drying, concentrate the sample at one edge of the screen with a very gentle stream, and wash it into the dish or pan. *Do not decant the excess water into the sink,* as hollow shells of forams usually float, and the best part of the sample could be lost. Decanting may be done if the water is poured back into the screen. Then wash the residue back into the pan with a very light trickle of water, leaving a minimum of excess water in the drying vessel.

If it is necessary to dry the sample rapidly, separate the sample into two containers, one for the greater part, from which water has been decanted, and another for the lesser part, which includes excess water. For samples of one ounce or less, use a porcelain evaporating dish about 4 inches in diameter. Use enamel pans for drying larger samples. Label the containers with a pencil crayon designed for use on glazed surfaces.

tromagnet. The Frantz Isodynamic Separator, a device most frequently used to separate various mineral types, can be used for this task. The machine can be adjusted to a wide range of tilt and slope, and the intensity of the magnetism can also be varied so that it is possible to make quite good separations of particles which differ only slightly in content of magnetic materials. No standard settings can be given here for the separation of Foraminifera because different lithologic types, and even different samples from the same lithology, may require settings and adjustments which can be learned only through experience. It is, of course, necessary to ascertain whether all specimens of forams are being separated, because most or all of the specimens of some species may be filled with pyrite and thus will react differently from empty tests; moreover, arenaceous forams may be unintentionally separated from calcareous specimens by this method.

### STAINING

The critical features of some fossil specimens are hard to see, owing to various processes undergone during preservation, or to abrasion before fossilization. These features may be brought out by using a water-soluble vegetable stain, such as those used in tinting cake frostings. The degree of coloration is easily controlled by dilution with water, and the stain may be completely removed by water if desired. This process is not to be confused with the use of the rose bengal protein stain to distinguish between living specimens and empty shells in Recent collections (see Walton, 1952).

### ELIMINATION OF PLANT DEBRIS

Sometimes forams are associated with fibrous plant debris. Clorox may be useful in decomposing such material so that it may be separated by washing. Another method of separating forams from such material involves the use of several water-filled porcelain dishes. The floating strands of material are lifted out of one dish by means of a needle and put into a second dish where they are stirred for a moment to free the entangled specimens which drop to the bottom. Then the mass of strands is lifted out again and put into a third dish and stirred again, and so on, using as many dishes as necessary. The sediment remaining in the dishes is concentrated by washing it through a screen. This method has been referred to as the Parker Pin Method by Frances L. Parker, who devised it and described it to us. Though it may seem tedious, this method is quite effective in obtaining specimens that might otherwise be overlooked

### HEAVY-LIQUID SEPARATION

Carbon tetrachloride may be required for separation in samples where the proportion of specimens to sediment is very small. It may also be used to concentrate the specimens and thus speed the picking process.

In using carbon tetrachloride, the entire process must be conducted under a hood. Place the dried, washed, and sifted sample in a beaker, and add a volume of carbon tetrachloride equal to two or three times the volume of the sample. Stir the sample to facilitate the rising of the lighter shells to the surface. Float the portion that rises to the surface into a filter-lined funnel. To obtain a good separation, it is usually necessary to repeat this operation until further stirring of the sediment in the liquid no longer causes shells to rise to the surface. Pour the balance of the carbon tetrachloride through the filter and shake out the remaining wet sediment onto papers to dry under the hood. Neither filter paper nor drying sediment should be removed from the hood until each is completely dry and odorless. If any odor is detectable, then there is still danger from breathing the gas.

### EXCAVATION BY NEEDLE

If a rock has resisted all methods of disintegration, individual specimens visible on its surface can be excavated with a fine needle and a sharp knife. Using these tools, and by watching the process through the microscope, one can rather successfully free the specimens one at a time. This work is best performed under water or on a surface kept wet by frequent additions of water to prevent the specimen, once it is free of the rock, from being lost. Individual specimens excavated in this way commonly have matrix adhering to them, which must be cleaned off by further use of the needle or knife blade. To hold the specimen firmly while this is done, a piece of gum eraser, sharpened to a wedge, is helpful in preventing loss of the specimen.

### REFERENCES

Walton, W. R. (1952). Techniques for recognition of living Foraminifera. Cushman Found. Foram. Res. Contr., v. 3, p. 56–60.

# Larger Foraminifers

RAYMOND C. DOUGLASS

*U. S. Geological Survey, Washington, D.C.*

Larger Foraminifera range in size from less than 1 millimeter to more than 10 centimeters. The methods of locating and collecting samples of these forms vary with the size of specimens sought and the nature of the containing rock.

Publication authorized by the Director, U. S. Geological Survey.

Two general working rules should be observed: (1) all contamination should be avoided, and (2) the geographic and stratigraphic location of each sample should be noted as accurately as possible before leaving the outcrop. Without these precautions the collection is worthless.

The method of collecting depends on the containing rock. If the rock is solid limestone, the problems of contamination are minimized. Fresh samples should be broken from ledges of the outcrop, even though loose pieces of rock may appear to contain more-abundant or more-varied fossils. Weathering enhances the appearance of the fossils and may heighten the contrast with the matrix, but loose pieces are suspect as float from higher beds in the section. If the bed is of marl, shale, or other friable material, special care must be taken to be sure that fresh outcrop material is obtained and that no contaminants which have been washed onto the bed are included. Again, the weathered and partly washed surficial material may appear to be much richer in fauna than the freshly excavated bed, but clean collecting is mandatory for significant reproducible results. The tool used for excavating should be cleaned before and after use to minimize contamination.

Each sample must be separately wrapped and accurately labeled. Samples of hard rock can be treated more roughly than those of friable rock. Friable material should be placed in a canvas or other fine-mesh bag which can be tied securely at the neck to prevent loss or mixing of contents. Labels should include geographic and stratigraphic data as well as name of collector and date. An outside label on each bag permits sorting samples without opening the bags, and an inside label ensures against loss of sample identification if the outside label is obliterated or torn off.

The amount of material collected will be determined by such factors as the purpose of study and the distance to your vehicle. It is much easier to throw away an extra piece of rock than it is to climb back up a mountain to obtain another piece to supplement an inadequate sample. In general, the richer the material, the smaller the sample. A pound or two of sample is generally adequate when the specimens are easily visible on the surface. Biological studies may call for more material; generalized age determinations are often made on less material.

The larger foraminifers can be considered in two categories, the Paleozoic and the post-Paleozoic. Each poses its special problems for the collector. The Paleozoic larger foraminifers consist dominantly of fusulinids. The post-Paleozoic larger foraminifers consist dominantly of orbitoids and nummulitids.

## PALEOZOIC LARGER FORAMINIFERS

All the Paleozoic forms are limited to the upper part of the Paleozoic. They apparently originated during Mississippian time, reached their maximum development in Pennsylvanian to early Permian time, and became extinct before the close of the Permian. All the forms are marine and seem to be restricted to fairly shallow-water environments. The forams are found in many lithologies, from fine-grained mud and siltstones through fine sands to coarse sands of various composition. They are even found in volcanic rocks that were deposited in marine waters.

The earliest fusulinid foraminifers are the smallest, and in general, they increase in size with time. The detection of fusulinids in rocks older than Middle Pennsylvanian is exceedingly difficult in the field. Thin sections of random samples of fine-grained carbonates of this age will often reveal forams, even though none were detectable in the field. Where thin limestone beds alternate with silty beds, the limestone beds commonly contain foraminifers. Where thick-bedded limestones occur, the upper few inches of the massive beds and the intervening thin limestones commonly contain foraminifers. Middle and Upper Pennsylvanian fusulinids are easily detectable with the unaided eye if their color contrasts with that of the matrix. Commonly, however, there is no color difference, so that the rock must be carefully searched with a $10\times$ or more powerful hand lens. Weathered surfaces may expose the forams in relief, but weathering often obscures rather than accentuates their presence. A freshly broken surface moistened with the tongue or etched lightly with dilute acid may display the foraminifers quite well. Direct sunlight is an asset. Forms too small to be seen on cloudy days are commonly visible in bright sunlight.

In detecting foraminifers, nothing helps more than knowing what one is looking for. Study of illustrations, generally of oriented sections, should be supplemented with the examination of hand specimens known to contain the foraminifers.

Silicified specimens often stand out in relief on limestones and may be attractive. As the study of larger foraminifers is largely dependent on structures seen in thin section, collections of silicified specimens are less useful than those of unaltered material. If both silicified and unaltered material are available, a few silicified specimens might be of interest for supplemental information, but the bulk of the sample should be taken from unaltered material.

## POST-PALEOZOIC LARGER FORAMINIFERA

Most of the post-Paleozoic larger Foraminifera are found in rocks of Cretaceous and Tertiary age. All were originally marine forms and are thought to have dwelled in relatively shallow warm-water environments. A great number of unconsolidated post-Paleozoic sediments yield specimens.

The external features of many post-Paleozoic forms are of taxonomic value. Large individual specimens or slabs showing exposed specimens should be wrapped for protection. Other specimens are usually cushioned and protected by the loose matrix and will not be damaged in the bag during transportation.

PREPARING LARGER FORAMINIFERS FOR STUDY

The larger foraminifers are studied principally in thin section. External characters shown on free specimens are used when such specimens are available. Samples of forams in loose matrix are washed in the same manner as are the smaller foraminifers, and no special techniques are necessary. The dried specimens are ready for study of the external characters and then for sectioning. Sectioning in any plane through a specimen gives some information about its internal structure, but the angle at which a specimen is cut will affect its appearance, especially if it has a rather complicated internal structure. For the purposes of description and illustration several standard cuts are made. Common names for some of these cuts, or views, are:

*Axial,* through the axis of coiling, or along the axis of growth. This is also known as *vertical* or *transverse.*

*Equatorial,* perpendicular to the axis of growth or in the plane of coiling or equatorial layer. This is also known as *horizontal* or *median.*

*Tangential,* tangential to a surface which may be specified.

*Oblique,* in any plane other than those specified above.

When free specimens are available, it is relatively easy to prepare oriented sections. Put a drop of canada balsam or a small chip of thermoplastic on a glass slide and heat it. Then place a specimen in the medium. Put the slide on the stage of a low-powered microscope or view it through a hand lens, and align the plane of the desired section so that it is parallel with the glass by using a teasing needle or a toothpick for manipulation. (Ordinarily there is time to orient the specimen before the mounting medium cools and hardens, but it may have to be reheated slightly to complete the orientation. When oriented, the specimen can be ground down to the desired plane.) Frequent observation of the grinding progress is generally necessary. If the need is detected early enough, corrections in orientation can be made by slightly reheating the slide and adjusting the specimen. When the specimen has been ground to a desired plane, the slide is reheated and the specimen turned over. If the medium has become clogged with abrasive, the specimen can be transferred to a clean side with fresh mounting medium. It is important to try to eliminate all bubbles at this stage and to ensure contact between the slide and the ground surface of the specimen. The mounting medium will boil if overheated, causing bubbles to form, or it will become so brittle that it will shatter before the final section can be ground thin enough. Final grinding, as in other sectioning, involves carefully thinning the specimen until maximum detail is visible. Final thickness generally will be slightly greater than required for petrographic studies, but will depend on the composition and preservation of the specimen. When all details of the wall structure are visible, the section is generally thin enough. Covering, sealing, and labeling are the same as for other thin sections.

Sectioning of specimens in hard matrix presents more problems. If abundant material is available it may be feasible to slice the rock with a diamond saw, giving some attention to general orientation of the specimens. The slices can be smoothed on a lap and then searched under the microscope for oriented sections. If sufficiently oriented sections are found, the slices can be cut to include the specimens in pieces small enough to fit on a slide. The pieces can then be mounted and finished as for regular sections. If few oriented sections are found in the slices, specimens showing approximate orientation can be cut as individual specimens and treated as free specimens. If individual specimens are uncommon in the rock, they can be cut or excavated with a vibrating needle and treated as free specimens.

A method of preparing more than one section from a specimen of *Orbitolina* was described by Douglass (1960, p. 25–26). The technique of multiple sectioning could be applied to other larger Foraminifera as well. This technique consists in cutting the specimen in the principal desired plane with a fine diamond-bonded blade and using the remaining chips for auxiliary sections. Ten thin sections from part of one specimen of *Parafusulina* have been obtained by means of this technique.

Occasionally, delicate or extra-fine specimens must be ground. It is preferable to view such specimens under the microscope almost continuously during the grinding. This can be done by mounting the specimen as usual on a glass slide and then placing it on the microscope stage and grinding it with another glass slide which has been "frosted" on one surface. The grinding slide is frosted with coarse or fine Carborundum, depending on the speed with which it is to cut the specimen. Several slides of varying roughness can be prepared for grinding and finishing the specimen. They are used, with or without abrasive powder, by dipping them in water and then moving them about on the specimen with light pressure. The specimen will remain visible at the point of contact, and the progress of grinding is observed continuously through the microscope.

The use of peels has proved helpful in the study of some kinds of foraminifers. The peel technique promising the most detail is that described by Honjo (1960, p. 457–459), in which details visible in planes separated by less than $10\mu$ are recorded on a treated Bioden plastic after etching the surface of the specimen with an inorganic salt solution. The amount of etching is more accurately controlled by using the salt solution than it is with the usual weak acid method, and the Bioden plastic reproduces more detail than is generally visible on thin sections.

Some structures are too fine or too delicate to show in ordinary thin sections. Some of these can be brought out by staining the cut or ground surfaces. Occasionally, ink will reveal such structures satisfactorily, but usually more detail is brought out by such stains as methylene blue, malachite green, or alizarine red (Dunbar and Henbest 1942, p. 72–73). Another technique commonly used on post-Paleozoic larger foraminifers is the preparation of canada balsam "negatives" of decalcified specimens. One relatively easy method of making such preparations is to prepare a thicker-than-normal thin section in the usual way. The specimen is then boiled in canada balsam. The impregnated specimen is removed to a slide, ground on one surface to remove excess balsam, and then etched with dilute acid. The canada balsam negative cast can then be preserved in glycerin gelatine.

Glass slides can be labeled by frosting the unused areas on each side of the specimen with fine abrasive and writing on the frosted area with India ink. Locality data can be written on one end and taxonomic data on the other. The back of the slide should be labeled with a diamond scriber or similar tool as soon as the specimen is mounted.

## REFERENCES

Douglass, R. C. (1960). The foraminiferal genus *Orbitolina* in North America. U. S. Geol. Survey Prof. Paper 333, p. 1–52.

Dunbar, C. O., and L. G. Henbest (1942). Pennsylvania Fusulinidae of Illinois. Illinois Geol. Survey Bull. 67, p. 35–218.

Honjo, Susumu (1960). A study of some primitive *Neoschwagerina* by a new serial section technique. J. Faculty Sci., Hokkaido Univ., ser. 4, Geology and Mineralogy, v. 10, no. 3, p. 457–470.

# Sponges

ROBERT M. FINKS

*Queens College, New York*
*American Museum of Natural History, New York*

Fossil sponge skeletons are often large objects of rather intricate outline penetrated by canals of various sizes which terminate on the exterior as pores. The skeleton is built of microscopic elements (spicules) united into a more or less continuous three-dimensional network or lattice. The shape of the individual spicules and the geometry of their mutual arrangement are as diagnostic as the grosser features of sponge form. Thus, sponges must be prepared and studied both at the megascopic and the microscopic levels.

The following features should be observed, recorded, and illustrated in any taxonomic work on fossil sponges:

1. The shape of individual spicules—usually significant at taxonomic levels higher than family.

2. The geometric arrangement of the spicular net—generally significant at about the family level.

3. The overall arrangement, in three dimensions, of the internal canal system —commonly useful in determining genera, and is partly related to the following item.

4. The organization and distribution of pores and grooves on the outer surface —a generic and specific character, but one which is subject to some individual variability under ecologic control.

5. The shape of the whole sponge—suggestive at the family level, it is often diagnostic for genera and species but is subject to environmentally controlled individual variation and is thus an ecologic indicator.

Different techniques are sometimes necessary to study each of the features listed. In addition the intricacy and fragility of sponge skeletons often give rise to special problems of conservation.

## COLLECTING

### OCCURRENCE

Nearly all fossil sponges occur in marine sediments. The only known exceptions are members of the family Spongillidae, whose monaxonic spicules are known from lacustrine deposits of Cenozoic age. Fossil marine sponges occur in sediments of every lithologic type and may be either calcified or silicified. Originally the sponge skeletons were composed of either hydrous silica or calcite. Although sponges that were originally siliceous are more commonly preserved by silica and sponges that were originally calcareous preserved by calcite, it is by no means uncommon to find calcified silicisponges and silicified calcisponges. Furthermore, both types of preservation may occur at a single collecting locality and, indeed, within a single specimen. Fossil sponges may be expected in almost any marine deposit, but their distribution tends to be more patchy than that of shelly fossils, with local spots of great abundance.

Chert nodules in limestone suggest the presence of silicisponges. Among the most common fossils found in such concretions, they may also occur in the limy matrix outside the nodules. Spiculite beds and beds containing root tufts also suggest the presence of silicisponges, particularly hexactinellids, and invite search for whole sponges. Very delicate, sack-like sponges may be found flattened on the bedding planes of fine-grained shales and limestones that were deposited in low-energy environments. The more robust forms of sponges, whether calcified or silicified, will weather out of shales, but only those that are silicified will weather out of limestones. Calcisponges and calcified silicisponges occurring in limestone matrix are most often seen in section on weathered surfaces.

### REMOVAL

Sponges that have not weathered entirely free from an outcrop should be removed with care so as to secure the entire specimen, which may be of quite irregular outline. In dealing with silicified material in limestone matrix, as large a block as practicable should be removed and prepared in the laboratory with acid. Calcified specimens in limestone are difficult to remove and, because of their irregular outline and many pore spaces, cannot be hammered free of the matrix as easily as shelly fossils. A portable, power-driven circular saw with Carborundum blade can be used to saw out a desirable specimen with a minimal amount of adherent matrix. The process is tedious and time-consuming, but may be the only way to secure a desirable specimen.[1]

Wherever possible the orientation of the specimen in the rock should be recorded in the field notes and the specimen marked to indicate the stratigraphic top as well as a compass direction. This is important, because the form of sponges is affected by currents and other vectorial elements of the environment, and most have not been transported far from their site of growth. Care should be taken to preserve any other fossils to which a sponge is basally attached or which are attached to it, as these provide evidence of the local biocoenosis.

## PREPARATION AND STUDY OF WHOLE SPECIMENS

The skeleton of a sponge is a complex structure. In addition to having a highly irregular external surface, full of pores and canals, it is completely penetrated by interconnecting spaces, ranging in size from large canals several millimeters in diameter down to microscopic interstices between individual spicules. Preparation of a fossil specimen requires either that the rock matrix be removed from these spaces to free the skeleton or that the specimen be sampled by cutting it in oriented sections. The former alternative is practicable only if the matrix is unconsolidated or if the skeleton is silicified in a limestone matrix. In such cases it may be necessary to strengthen the freed portions of the skeleton by special treatment in order to prevent its disintegration. The sponges that have been preserved are usually those whose spicular network was firmly united in life, but such sponges may also bear loose flesh spicules which can be lost in preparation unless precautions are taken.

### CHEMICAL PREPARATION

A fossil sponge whose skeleton was originally siliceous or is replaced by silica, and is enclosed in an acid-soluble matrix, may be freed by the use of acid (except hydrofluoric). So far as possible each individual specimen should be treated in a separate container so that loose spicules belonging to it may be recovered from the insoluble residue by filtration. The progress of the treatment should be closely observed, for the freed portions of the skeleton may be so loosely united that it will disintegrate when the matrix is dissolved. For this reason it is advisable to use a weak organic acid (formic or acetic) rather

---

[1] This technique was pioneered by Max F. Pitcher of Columbia University and was successfully employed by him and the writer in removing fossil sponges from massive limestone.

than the strong mineral acids. Not only does this permit better control of the process but it also reduces the rate at which mechanically disrupting gas bubbles are evolved. In the event that the freed portions of the skeleton show signs of disintegrating, it may be possible to save them by carefully removing the specimen from the acid, gently rinsing it in several changes of water, drying it in an oven, and dipping it in Alvar or some similar solution. The specimen may be then returned to the acid, more of the skeleton freed, and the strengthening process repeated on the newly exposed portions. If the emerging sponge appears to be so fragile that it would not be likely to support its own weight when completely or nearly completely freed from the matrix, it may be possible to save the specimen by embedding the exposed portions in paraffin and then carefully dissolving the remainder of the matrix, by hand if necessary, down to the outer surface of the sponge. Thus, the external details may be revealed even though matrix must be left on the interior of the sponge. Each specimen is likely to be unique, requiring individual treatment.

MECHANICAL PREPARATION

Surface features such as pores and grooves may often be studied adequately after such minimal mechanical treatment as gentle washing with toothbrush and detergent or a short stay in the ultrasonic vibrator. Care must be taken not to dislodge loose dermal spicules, and the solid material removed from the surface should be retained and examined under the binocular microscope for spicules. More extensive patches of adherent matrix may be removed with needles, Vibro-tool, or dental drill in the usual manner. This is absolutely necessary in the cases of specimens imbedded in rock. In the final stages of preparation, details may be brought out through brief washing (under the binocular microscope) with very dilute HCl, if either the matrix, the fossil, or both are calcareous.

Since the internal arrangement of the canals and the skeletal net is of great taxonomic importance, the sponge must be sectioned in some way. Simple polished sections often suffice; if the sponges are highly symmetrical, three sections at right angles may define these structures adequately. Serial sections (either polished sections or thin sections) may be necessary to study more complexly organized sponges. A technique for constructing a model from serial sections is outlined below. If the sponge skeleton has been completely freed from the matrix by chemical treatment, it may be possible to see some of the internal structures from the outside. But only rarely will all the inner structures be visible. Two techniques are used to reveal details of inner structure: one may embed the specimen in one of the standard transparent thermosetting plastics and then prepare polished sections or thin sections in the ordinary manner; alternatively, one may mechanically dissect away part of the skeleton with fine-pointed forceps, needles, or dental tools to expose the internal structures. The latter alternative is preferred, if feasible, as it reveals the structures directly in three dimensions and renders them available for photographic illustration. It is also much less time-consuming than embedding in plastic and sectioning. Before dissection it may be desirable to strengthen the specimen by means of the techniques described below.

### SECTIONING

Reconaissance studies of sponge skeletal structure can be made using simple polished sections viewed in reflected light. Ground thin sections reveal greater detail of microstructure; if they are made somewhat thick the three-dimensional structure of a spicular net can sometimes be worked out from one or two oriented thin sections. Thin sections generally reveal the most detail of the internal structure of spicules. Peels, on the other hand, made either by wet or dry techniques, may reveal more of the surface ornament of individual spicules, and may also reveal a considerable amount of three-dimensional structure of the spicular net. Much depends on the mode of preservation of the fossil, and experimentation is desirable. For a thoroughgoing study of sponge skeletal construction in three dimensions, serial sections are necessary. When made at constant spacing, carefully measured, it is possible to reconstruct an accurate model of the structure of the sponge. Devices of varying degrees of elaboration are commercially available, or may be constructed, to control the spacing of sections (see Croft, 1953, Seilacher, 1962, and the Gillings-Bronwill Thin Sectioning machine).[2] For serial sections, peels or photographs of polished surfaces (depending on the degree of resolution desired, time available, and factors of preservation) are altogether satisfactory and less time-consuming than ground thin sections.

### CONSTRUCTING A MODEL FROM SERIAL SECTIONS

Seilacher (1962, p. 732) describes a technique for constructing a transparent model of sponge structures from serial sections. Peels or photographic negatives of uniformly spaced sections are projected through a photographic enlarging apparatus onto glass plates of uniform thickness (old photographic plates are suggested) and the structures traced with ink upon the glass. The thickness of the glass plates corresponds, of course, to the spacing of the actual sections, so that the ratio of the two will determine the appropriate magnification of the projected image. Thus, an undistorted, transparent model of the interior of the sponge will be obtained by the simple superposition of the glass plates. Seilacher illustrates stereophotographs of such models (Seilacher, 1962, figs. 1, 2) as well as a drawing made therefrom (*ibid.,* fig. 3).

### EMBEDDING FRAGILE MATERIAL FOR SECTIONING

Silicified material that has been freed from limestone with acid must be embedded in a solid substance before sectioning. The commercially available

---

[2] Gillings-Bronwill Thin Sectioning Machine, manufactured by the Will Corporation, Rochester, New York.

thermosetting transparent resins are best for this purpose. It is important to remove all air bubbles from the interior spaces before polymerizing the resin. Sponges may be more troublesome in this respect than other types of fossils. Completely immerse the sponge in the unpolymerized liquid resin, preferably in its final container, and place it under an air-tight bell jar attached to a pump. A simple sink pump or Bernouilli pump may be satisfactory. Too rapid a reduction in air pressure should be avoided, because rapidly escaping air bubbles may disrupt a delicate sponge skeleton. When bubbles cease to come off the specimen it may be removed, the catalyst added, and the specimen placed in an oven for curing. Thin sections and polished sections may be made from the finished product in the usual manner. I have not tested the possibility of making peels from specimens embedded in plastic; this may prove to be difficult.

### STRENGTHENING FRAGILE MATERIAL

The addition of strengthening coatings is to be avoided if possible, as their use may obscure fine details of spicules and may make it impossible to remove single spicules from the skeletal net for study. If, however, the skeleton is in imminent danger of disintegration, several sprayings with a transparent acrylic resin of the sort sold as an aerosol may be sufficient to increase its cohesiveness without adding too much extraneous material. Spraying minimizes handling of the specimen and is preferred over immersing extremely fragile specimens in a liquid. The latter procedure, however, permits more complete penetration and more even distribution of the strengthening material on the interior. A thin solution of Alvar is recommended for this purpose. If part of the specimen is to be dissected to reveal internal structures, strengthening may be necessary to prevent extensive shattering.

### RECOVERY OF LOOSE FLESH SPICULES

Even in sponges whose principal skeleton is rigidly fused there may be additional unattached spicules, once suspended in the flesh and now free in the matrix-filled spaces within the sponge. One should make an effort to search for these in preparing any entire sponge fossil. If a silicified sponge is removed from a limestone matrix with acid, a careful watch should be kept on the progress of removal and the surface should be examined under magnification for the presence of loose spicules in the interstices of the principal skeleton. They may then be removed for study and their position noted. Removal should be carried out in a small container, and when complete the insoluble sediment may be filtered out and examined for isolated spicules. The specimen itself should be washed with a very gentle current of water in another container to minimize loss of other loose spicules, and any remaining sediment on the bottom of this vessel may be similarly examined for spicules. Sponges which cannot be prepared in this way may still yield some information on loose spicules through study of sections. It should be noted that in no case can one be certain that the loose spicules found actually belonged to the sponge.

## STUDY OF INDIVIDUAL SPICULES

### SURFACE FEATURES

The study of such surface details as spines, tubercles, branching outgrowths, and similar features is best done on spicules isolated from the matrix and from the skeletal net. A binocular microscope is indispensable. The spicules should be mounted for observation so that they may be readily turned about. Best for this purpose is a glass well-slide in the well of which a drop of glycerin may be placed and the spicule introduced. The viscous fluid permits the spicule to be moved about but damps its motion so that its position may be adjusted more easily. A thin, flexible, sable-tipped brush is best for manipulating the specimen. Various combinations of transmitted and low- and high-angle reflected light may be employed to bring out particular features.

In types of preservation where spicules cannot be freed from the matrix, a single thin section may permit much of the spicule to be seen in three dimensions; a fairly thick section is required, and the matrix must be relatively transparent. Serial sections made by the peel technique, in which the spacing of sections is very close, may permit reconstruction of the surface details of a spicule.

For determining angles between rays a Universal-Stage may be useful. If the spicules are isolated they would, of course, have to be mounted in a solid medium such as balsam.

### INTERNAL FEATURES

Observation of the axial canal of a siliceous spicule may permit one to determine the basic number of rays in a spicule whose external form is highly modified; for example, whether a particular lithistid desma is monaxial or tetraxial, or whether a monaxon is of hexactinellid or demosponge origin. The complete form of the canal may be hard to determine in a thin section. Isolated spicules are more easily studied. In order for the axial canal to be seen, the spicule must be viewed with transmitted light. Isolated spicules must be placed in some liquid medium.

Orientation of crystallographic axes may be of interest in studying spicules of calcareous sponges, each of which is a single calcite crystal. A petrographic microscope is, of course, necessary for such study.

## ILLUSTRATION

### DRAWINGS

Line drawings shaded with stippling are probably the best method of illustrating individual spicules or small portions of the spicular net. They are most accurately made with the aid of the camera lucida. If thin sections, peels, or photographic negatives are available, these may be projected through an enlarger onto a sheet of paper and the outlines traced. Although the simple outline may suffice, the three-dimensional form is best indicated through the use of stippling. Line drawings in the form of stereopairs have not, to my knowledge, been published in works on fossil sponges, but they might provide a means of illustrating a skeletal net when photographic reproduction is not possible. The stereo-pair may be made by drawing the same structure with a camera lucida, first through one eyepiece and then the other of a binocular microscope.

### PHOTOGRAPHY

Where possible this is the most satisfactory method of illustration. Sponges present particular problems because of their irregular form, fine detail, and great extent in depth. Careful adjustment of lighting will bring out much of the three-dimensional form of the sponge structures, and time spent in experimenting with lighting arrangements for each individual specimen will not be wasted. The judicious use of shadows produced by low-angle light will reveal many details. In order to obtain as great a depth of focus as possible it may be desirable to photograph the specimen at a low magnification and enlarge it further in making the positive print. In photographing spicules or small portions of the spicular net at high magnifications it is neither necessary nor desirable to coat the specimen with ammonium chloride. Spicules, as commonly preserved, are naturally white and highly reflective; moreover, a coating of ammonium chloride may be so granular as to obscure fine details. In photographing sponges at grosser levels of magnification ammonium chloride is desirable and will help bring out surface details such as pores, grooves, and the general form of the spicular net. Because of the importance of fine detail, photographic illustrations should be reproduced as collotypes or as finely screened halftones.

The use of photographs in stereopairs is a particularly effective way of presenting magnified views of complex spicular networks, but the technique seems to have been unanimously eschewed, at least for direct views of actual fossils. However, the previously described method of forming a transparent three-dimensional model by superposing tracings of serial sections on glass was used to make photographs by transmitted light that were published as stereopairs (Seilacher, 1962, figs. 1 and 2).

## MEASUREMENT

### MEASURABLE CHARACTERS

Measurable structures on a fossil sponge may include some or all of the following: height and diameter of the whole sponge; diameter of the cloaca; diameter of parietal gaps or of internal cavernous spaces; diameters of incurrent and excurrent pores and canals; length of surface canals; diameters of pore clusters; numbers of pores of a particular kind per unit area or per cluster; spacing of pores and canals; thickness and spacing of vertical and horizontal spicule-bundles or tracts; length and diameter of each kind of spicule, of their rays, and of their surface ornament; angular relationships between spicule rays; length and diameter of projecting spicule tufts, including root tufts; and thickness of body wall and of any specialized dermal and gastral spicule layers. In addition, certain derived measurements may be determined, such as the ratio of cloacal diameter to sponge diameter. For more specialized studies such measurements as total incurrent or excurrent pore area per unit surface area may prove of interest or significance.

### VARIABILITY

Many of these structures occur in large numbers on each sponge, and their dimensions are commonly variable. We are faced, therefore, with the task of recording variability within a specimen as well as variability among the individuals of a population. The extent to which variability is to be analyzed depends on the scope of the study. The total range of variation may generally be determined by simple inspection and measurement of the extremes. To obtain size distributions or to measure total pore area per unit surface area, some form of sampling technique is essential, since it is impractical to measure every single pore or spicule of a sponge. Sampling is complicated by the fact that dimensions, as well as variability itself, may show systematic variation according to position on the sponge, because of functional or ontogenetic differences.

### MEASUREMENT TECHNIQUES

For measurement of pores and spicules a scale mounted in the eyepiece of the microscope (ocular micrometer) will give the most accurate results; a reticule is almost as satisfactory. For larger structures, which still must be viewed through the microscope, a short length of an accurately ruled millimeter scale, which can be grasped with forceps and held beside the structure, will make a very convenient measuring tool. If the specimen rests in a tray of sand it may be turned easily to the desired position and supported there while the microscope is focused and the measurement taken; unfortunately the sand may clog the pores of the sponge, but it is to be preferred to adhesive plastic substances. For measuring thin-sections a mechanical stage equipped with a micrometer will be satisfactory. For all these measurements a binocular microscope, with wide-field oculars and a wide range of magnification (up to sixty diameters) is most satisfactory. For very small spicules higher magnifications may be necessary.

Where statistical sampling of pore diameters is desired, a mechanical stage will permit one to measure the pores which fall along a series of evenly spaced parallel lines. If the surface of the sponge is highly curved this may prove to be difficult. Alternatively, a square may be marked on the sponge and all the pores within it measured.

## MORPHOLOGIC DESCRIPTION

The measurable characters listed in the preceding section, so far as they are present on the sponge, are essential to a complete description. The range of variation and an estimated modal value should be given for each, together with some indication of intra- and interindividual variability. More elaborate statistical analysis usually is not necessary in ordinary taxonomic work. The variation in overall shape of the sponge should be described and illustrated, for this is often great within a single population collected at one locality; external form may be of value in paleoecologic reconstructions. Ontogenetic changes in shape should also be noted.

## CURATING AND CONSERVATION

Sponges are particularly efficient dust-catchers because of their porous surfaces, and should be stored under cover. Fragile specimens, such as acid-prepared skeletons, are best stored in sturdy covered boxes so that they will be protected against accidental crushing. Transparent plastic containers are best for this, as the specimen can be seen without opening the box. It is best not to place any cushioning material in the box. I have found that cotton and similar fluffy materials tend to catch on the spicules and may cause the specimen to be torn when removed or cause it to become covered with lint.

Isolated spicules are best stored by fastening them to paper well-slides with a water-soluble gum such as gum tragacanth. They may easily be removed for study by touching them with a wet brush. If all the spicules have been removed from an individual, it is probably best to keep them with the parent specimen. For the sake of safety, however, such slide-mounted spicules, as well as thin-sections, may be kept in a separate storage box for slides; if this is done, their whereabouts should be noted on the label of the whole specimen to save time for subsequent workers.

Loose spicules that have not actually been removed from a specimen, and small fragments of skeletal net, present a particular problem in curating, as they can rarely be identified generically or specifically, yet may be of stratigraphic value and should not be thrown away. If they have been specifically named and belong to the type lot, they can easily be integrated into a biologically arranged collection. The practice of giving binomials to individual spicules should, I feel, be avoided. It is better to label loose spicules according to the name of the spicule form (an elaborate descriptive nomenclature exists; see Scott, 1944). If the collection is biologically arranged it is probably best to set aside a separate section for isolated spicules, as it is sometimes impossible to identify them even by class.

## PALEOECOLOGICAL OBSERVATIONS

The use of fossil sponges as paleoecological indicators may require special techniques beyond those ordinarily used in collecting, preparing, and studying invertebrate fossils. The orientation of the sponge in relation to the bedding should be recorded in the field, as should any observations on the variability of form at a single locality or on the variability of form in relation to a sedimentary structure such as a reef. Documented with photographs this may be a useful supplement to even the largest of collections. A 1 by 1 foot metal frame strung with wire to form a grid of 1-inch squares is a useful device for making point counts of various organisms, including sponges, and may be used to study the spatial distribution of sponges in a reef or similar organic structure.[1]

Because sponges encrust other organisms and are in turn overgrown, a single specimen or a series of them may provide an indisputable record of the local biocoenosis. If an organism both overgrows and is overgrown by the same sponge or another sponge of the same species, such evidence is at hand. Some sponges also encrust so much of the bottom sediment, including shell fragments and inorganic sand, that they contain a veritable sample of the sea floor at the time they were alive. For this reason care should be taken to preserve the surrounding organic material and sediment when removing a sponge from matrix with acid. If the sponge is very delicate it is likely not to have been transported far, and thus may be interpreted as an indicator of the environment in which it was preserved (Finks, 1955, 1960, p. 30ff.).

## REFERENCES

Croft, W. N. (1953). A simplified parallel-grinding instrument. Ann. Mag. Nat. History (London), ser. 12, v. 6, p. 915–918, figs. 1,2.

Finks, R. M. (1955). *Conularia* in a sponge from the West Texas Permian: J. Paleontology, v. 29, p. 831–836, pl. 82.

——— (1960). Late Paleozoic sponge faunas of the Texas region, the siliceous sponges. Am. Mus. Nat. History Bull., v. 120, art. 1, p. 1–160, figs. 1–77, pls. 1–50.

Seilacher, A. (1962). Die Sphinctozoa, eine Gruppe fossiler Kalkschwämme. Abh. Mathem.-Naturwiss. Klasse der Akad. Wiss. u. Lit. (Mainz), Jahrb. 1961, no. 10, p. 723–790, figs. 1–8, pls. 1–9.

---

[1] Such a grid, designed by Donald F. Toomey of Shell Development Company, was used by him and the writer to study distribution of fossil sponges in Ordovician reef limestones.

# Corals: As Illustrated by Paleozoic Forms

WILLIAM A. OLIVER, JR.

*U. S. Geological Survey, Washington, D.C.*

From the point of view of the specialist in Paleozoic corals, the ideal specimen for study is one preserved without any recrystallization or replacement of
original calcareous tissue, and free of any matrix. Most Paleozoic corals are
within rock and are not perfectly preserved when found, so the problem becomes one of obtaining as much biological information as possible, through
the proper sequence of collecting and laboratory procedures. In stratigraphic
units where preservation of corals is poor, considerable biologic and stratigraphic information may still be obtained if the specimens are properly
handled.

The most important features of fossil corals are internal. A knowledge of
the nature, arrangement, and dimensions of the septa, tabulae, dissepiments,
axial structures, outer wall, and other features is prerequisite to identification
of most genera and species. It follows that external molds cannot ordinarily
be generically or specifically identified, but these may give information which
will allow assignment to a group of genera or higher taxon. Such suprageneric
groups may be time-limited and of some index value. Poorly preserved specimens may give ecologic information through their general growth form or
taxonomic grouping.

The microscopic structure of septa and other parts of the coral skeleton is
now recognized as being very important in understanding the relationships of
many corals. The preservation of microstructure varies from excellent to poor
in "well-preserved" specimens.

External features are less important than internal ones, but are needed for
complete description. If the specimen cannot be removed from the enclosing
rock, the size and general shape of the corallum and the calice and an indication of longitudinal and encircling markings can be obtained from sections.

## COLLECTING

So far as is possible and practical, complete specimens or colonies should be
collected. Individual corals vary in morphology from early to late stages, and
colonial forms vary from bottom to top and from side to side in the colony.
Since incomplete specimens of either may be misleading, large blocks of rock

Publication authorized by the Director, U. S. Geological Survey.

must often be collected for later laboratory handling. Trimming in the field cuts down on the shipping expense, but this must be balanced against the danger of breaking off and losing parts of specimens.

If colonies have fallen apart, or are so large that only fragments can be collected, the collector should keep pieces of each colony together and note how they fit, or note what parts of the large colony they represent. If corals show evidence of abrasion, effort should be made to find some specimens in which the outer zone and wall are preserved. Certain dissepimented horn corals are especially prone to decortication as a result of wear, either before burial or after exposure.

Some fully grown corals, and immature individuals of many types, are so small that they rarely will be found unless they have been silicified and etched or washed from decomposed rock and picked by standard micropaleontological techniques.

Individual variation in Paleozoic corals is extreme. Species descriptions should be based on large samples whenever possible and should ideally include statistical characterization of important measurable and countable characters. A colony comprising one hundred individuals is not a sample of a species. Rather, in variation analysis it is necessary to consider the colony as an individual, because individual variation within colonies is frequently much less than variation between colonies. In short, collections of corals should be large.

There are practical limits to the application of the collecting principles set out in the previous paragraphs. Incomplete fossils should not be neglected, as they can give valuable information or supplement the information obtained from other specimens. Variation in adult morphology can be studied in a collection of corals in which only a few are complete at their lower ends. If a species has been adequately described, it may be possible to recognize only fragments. Specimens of some species are extremely rare; such species should be described even though material is sparse and the description incomplete.

## SECTIONING CORALS

Because of the importance of internal structure, sectioning is the technique most frequently used in the study of Paleozoic corals. Two orientations are basic, but others are used for special purposes. In solitary corals, the transverse section (taken at right angles to the axis, and normally circular in outline) and the longitudinal section (passing through the axis, and conical or rectangular in outline) are most important. In general, longitudinal sections are cut along the plane of the cardinal-counter septa; but in forms having axial structures or marked bilateral symmetry, longitudinal sections cut at right angles to the cardinal-counter plane are needed. To show ontogeny, several closely spaced transverse sections are desirable. Tangential sections (parallel to the axis but eccentrically located) are sometimes needed to interpret details of the septa, wall, and other parts of their structure.

The same basic sections are used for colonial corals (rugose and tabulate). In loose colonies (dendroid or phaceloid) corallites may be treated as solitary corals except that the connection with the parent individual should be included in the sections. In massive colonies and in most phaceloid colonies a horizontal (transverse) section can be cut at right angles to the axes of several corallites. This may require large sections, but will give a much more adequate picture of the specimen. Similarly, a well-oriented vertical section through the colony may show several longitudinal sections of individuals, although many corallites will inevitably be seen in tangential section. In colonies with large corallites, it may be necessary to make a vertical section for each individual longitudinal section desired.

Serial sectioning is the process of taking several more or less parallel sections through an individual or a colony. These may be closely or widely spaced, depending on the coral and on the goal of the specialist. Serial transverse sections are most commonly used to show either the development of a corallite from its earliest to its latest stage of preservation or the development of offsets in a colony. Serial longitudinal or other sections are used wherever the details one wishes to observe do not lie in a single plane. A thin axial structure can best be studied with closely spaced serial longitudinal sections cut from one side of the axial region to the other.

Thin sections are the most important type of section. They are best for studying microstructure and for photographing gross structure as well. With even the best equipment, however, thin sectioning destroys a significant portion of a small specimen, and very close spacing of sections is difficult or impossible. Peel sections are ideal for close-spaced serial sectioning. Section intervals can be small enough so that an almost continuous record of ontogenetic or other change can be made. Peel sections take much less time to prepare than thin sections, but allowance for variation in preservation is more difficult and peels are not as satisfactory for photography.

Polished sections are easily made and used. Fine polishing is not necessary, as the same effect may be had by lightly etching a surface ground with a No. 600 to 800 compound and covering it with glycerin or water. Polished sections are excellent for studying the gross structures of large numbers of moderately well-preserved and well-preserved corals. They are difficult to photograph and rarely show microstructure.

## CORAL EXTERIORS

Not uncommonly, fossil corals occur within a matrix that contrasts with the coral itself in chemical and/or physical characteristics. Such specimens can often be separated from the matrix by chemical or mechanical means.

Well-silicified specimens can be etched from limestones or dolomites to reveal their exteriors, but once etched, such specimens are more difficult to section. If silicification is only local, it may be found that the interior of the coral has been dissolved with the rock matrix and that sectioned specimens would have revealed more morphologic information than etched specimens. Etched specimens facilitate the study of size, shape, calicular details, and other external features, and should be combined with sectioned specimens for best results.

Corals preserved in a relatively soft matrix can be cleaned by mechanical means. Some shales can be softened or removed chemically, but this must be done with great care, as the chemicals commonly used attack calcitic specimens also.

If the fossil is similar to the matrix in composition or physical characteristics, it may not be practical to clean its exterior. Many external features, such as shape, size, longitudinal or transverse ribbing, calice depth, can be determined from sections of specimens in matrix.

## PRESERVATION

The mode of preservation of Paleozoic corals varies widely. As this influences collecting and preparation techniques, methods of treatment are discussed briefly in the following paragraphs.

### PRESERVATION OF ORIGINAL STRUCTURE

Many calcitic Paleozoic fossil corals are preserved in such microscopic detail as to suggest that they are essentially unaltered. These fossils can occur in any kind of rock, but are most common in limestones and calcareous shales. Specimens can either be left in the matrix or be removed with great care by mechanical means. They are studied primarily by means of thin sections and accessory polished sections and peel sections. Microstructure, gross internal structure, and exteriors should be described.

### PRESERVATION OF ORIGINAL FORM THROUGH VARIOUS TYPES OF REPLACEMENT

The original skeleton of Paleozoic corals can be recrystallized so that the fossil is calcite, but with the microstructure obliterated. Other specimens are dolomitized or silicified or replaced by some other mineral, retaining the gross form, but not the microscopic details. Such specimens can be fully described except for microstructure. Well-silicified specimens can be etched from limestones to reveal their exteriors.

### COARSER REPLACEMENT

Replacement by new minerals may be partial and may alter the dimensions and/or reduce the contrast between the specimen and the rock. Some dolomitized specimens appear as shadows and may seem to disappear in thin sections. Thicker thin sections often increase contrast; these or polished sections can sometimes be improved by etching with weak acid to bring out subtle contrasts. Resolution of detail can often be further increased by applying glycerin to the etched surface of the thin section or polished section.

MOLDS AND CASTS

Impressions of corals in fine-grained rocks commonly preserve in considerable detail the configuration of the exterior and the calice. Some corals have such characteristic shape, ornamentation, or calice that they can be identified from such specimens. A latex or plastic cast of a mold may be easier to interpret, as it is a positive rather than a negative replica of the coral. The species of most coral specimens cannot be identified from molds or casts. They can, however, often be assigned to genera or higher taxa, and some ecologic or stratigraphic information will result. Molds and casts should not be used as the basis for new species except under the most unusual circumstances.

## ACKNOWLEDGMENTS

The techniques summarized above are in general use by specialists in Paleozoic corals. This evaluation of ways and means is based on the experience of many individuals in addition to myself. Teachers and co-workers who first introduced me to the techniques are too numerous to list. I am especially grateful, however, for the suggestions of Helen Duncan, W. J. Sando, and J. W. Wells, who critically read the manuscript. Coral terms used are all included in the glossary of the *Treatise on Invertebrate Paleontology,* Part F on Coelenterata (p. 245–251).

# Bryozoans

JUNE R. P. PHILLIPS ROSS

*Department of Geology, University of Illinois, Urbana*

CHARLES A. ROSS

*Department of Geology, Western Washington State College, Bellingham*

Only the calcareous skeletons of marine bryozoans are preserved as fossils. The fossil colonies, commonly fragmented into small twigs and branches, are found in rocks of early Ordovician to Recent age, and they have many diverse shapes and sizes. Colonies may be slender sticks 1.0 cm in length and 0.8 mm in diameter or bush-like growths of large cylindrical branches extending laterally to six feet or more. There is no relation between their size and their geologic occurrence.

Fossil Bryozoa are commonly abundant in alternating sequences of thin-bedded marine limestone and calcareous shale. They may be numerous in bedding planes. Weathered limestone surfaces readily reveal bryozoan fragments which may be very difficult to spot on freshly broken outcrops. In shale, ramose bryozoan colonies are readily observable, but microscopic cryptostomes commonly cannot be seen and are obtained by collecting and washing shale samples in the laboratory. Bryozoa are generally rare or absent in noncalcareous rocks, such as terrigenous sandstone and conglomerate. In silicified limestones bryozoan colonies may show up in distinct relief on the weathered surfaces. Etching with acetic acid generally reveals that silicification is limited to the outer regions of the bryozoan colonies and usually removes the remainder of the skeletal structures. Etching may, however, reveal the form of many delicate colonies that could not otherwise be observed. Bryozoa are also preserved as molds and casts, but since this mode of preservation shows no details of the skeletal structure of the colonies, few features are available to identify the colonies.

On weathered limestone surfaces fossil bryozoans may appear as slender white, or light or dark gray, branches. These may be mistaken for tabulate corals or fenestrate funnels and fans like those commonly found in late Paleozoic rocks. On shaly slopes bryozoans may lie crowded together where they have been washed into small nooks or they may lie on the more gentle part of the shale slope. A 10× or 15× lens is useful in spotting bryozoans on the weathered rock surfaces and in observing the zooecial openings, the fenestrules of fenestrate colonies, and the zooecial tubes on broken longitudinal surfaces. Locating Bryozoa in the field requires that the geologist focus his attention on objects about 1 cm or less in diameter, hence close scrutiny of rock surfaces is necessary.

## SAMPLING BRYOZOAN-BEARING ROCKS

In sampling bryozoan localities, complete bryozoan colonies should be collected where possible, and in order to obtain good representation of the fossil assemblages, numerous slabs should be collected. These slabs should be wrapped in paper (e.g., newspaper) in order to protect the bryozoans on the surfaces of the slabs from being abraded and broken.

## PREPARATION OF BRYOZOAN-BEARING SAMPLES

Paleozoic Bryozoa (orders Trepostomata, Cryptostomata, and Cyclostomata) are identified by study of thin sections, whereas Paleozoic Ctenostomata and Mesozoic and Tertiary Cyclostomata and Cheilostomata are generally studied by means of their external features, and supplementary thin sections are used in studying the frontal wall of cheilostomes and the internal structures of cyclostomes.

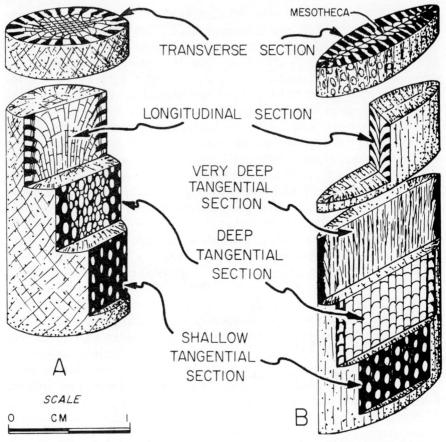

**Fig. 1.** (*A*) *Orientation of different sections cut from a Paleozoic trepostome.*
(*B*) *Orientation of different sections cut from a Paleozoic cryptosome.*

Identification of Paleozoic Bryozoa (orders Trepostomata, Cryptostomata, and Cyclostomata) is based primarily on internal microstructures and requires a minimum of four differently oriented thin sections from each colony. Transverse, longitudinal, and tangential sections (fig. 1,A) are necessary for trepostomatous and cyclostomatous bryozoans that have radial symmetry around an axis of growth. For bilaterally symmetrical colonies and colonies of reticulate or fenestrate expansions, including many of the cryptostomes, very deep tangential sections are required to show structures in the mesotheca and near the bases of the zooecial tubes (fig. 1,B). The inner and outer (thickened regions of the bryozoan colonies have significantly different features, and several tangential sections at successive depths are commonly needed to study these colonies completely. In order to be familiar with the morphology of a colony, several parts—that is, the basal (older), medial, and upper (younger) parts of the same colony—need to be studied in each of these different orientations. In studying Mesozoic and Tertiary cheilostomes, two or more tan-

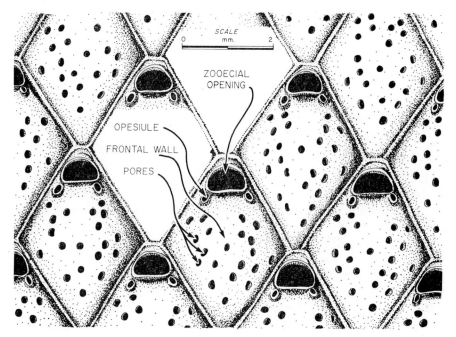

**Fig. 2.** *Surface features of a Tertiary cheilostome. Frontal wall structures observed in tangential section in plane of the colony.*

gential sections at successive depths are necessary to observe all features of the frontal wall (fig. 2).

### MAKING THIN SECTIONS

1. Use end cutters to snip free specimens into small (1- to 2-cm) fragments.

2. Mount a single fragment on a glass slide with a thermal plastic cement or slowly cooked canada balsam.

3. Grind the fragment to the desired plane, and polish it with fine (1000-mesh) Carborundum and water on a glass plate.

4. Wash and heat the fragment, then free it from the cement and turn it over. Mount the fragment in thermal plastic or canada balsam on a glass slide so that the polished surface is against the slide. It is essential that the ground surface and the surface of the glass slide be parallel and separated by a minimum of cement and that no air bubbles remain in the cement.

5. Grind the exposed surface of the mounted fragment with medium (400- to 600-mesh) Carborundum on a flat, rotating lap. The thin slice should be kept uniform in thickness during grinding. Continue grinding until light is transmitted through the bryozoan fragment.

6. The final grinding is done by hand on a glass plate with fine Carborundum (1000-mesh) and water. Continue grinding until the thickness of the mounted fragment is about 0.3 mm. The thickness is checked in the final stages of grinding by observing, through a microscope, the amount of light transmitted by the fragment.

7. Wash the ground section free of grinding compounds.

8. Remove excess cement around the bryozoan fragment with alcohol.

9. Smear canada balsam or Permount over the surface of the ground bryozoan fragment and place a cover glass on it.

10. In Permount preparations the thin section is cured at room temperature for about 24 hours and is then cooked in an oven at 35°C for about 24 to 36 hours.

11. Excess canada balsam or Permount is dissolved with xylol or toluol.

12. After a couple of weeks have elapsed, seal the edge of the cover glass with clear varnish.

Bryozoans firmly embedded in rock can be thin-sectioned by using the same techniques; only the preparation of the oriented specimens is different. As bryozoans commonly lie parallel to bedding planes, several thin slices (1 cm thick) are cut, with a diamond saw, from the rock parallel to the bedding plane and are polished with 1200-mesh carborundum. These slices commonly yield either longitudinal or tangential sections of bryozoan specimens that may be selected under a microscope and oriented with a minimum of additional grinding. If the bryozoans show a preferred lineation in the rock, slices cut perpendicular to such a lineation usually produce specimens that require only slight additional grinding for orientation as transverse sections.

Randomly oriented specimens in rock matrix are commonly difficult to section, and a larger quantity of material is usually necessary. The rock is cut into thicker slices (3 to 4 cm), the slices polished, and the bryozoan specimens traced from one surface of the slice to the opposite surface. After a thick slice has been examined under a microscope, it is marked for additional saw cuts with a waterproof marking pencil and cut into smaller pieces containing the desired specimens. The specimens are then mounted according to the steps outlined for free specimens.

For cleaning the surfaces of bryozoans, particularly Mesozoic and Tertiary cheilostomes and cyclostomes, use of ultrasonic vibration may expedite preparations.

# Brachiopods

J. T. DUTRO, JR.

*U. S. Geological Survey, Washington, D.C.*

Fossils in general, and brachiopods in particular, are collected for many purposes. Complete or well-preserved shells are prized for the light they shed

Publication authorized by the Director, U. S. Geological Survey.

on the morphology of the various genera. Large quantities of measurable specimens of a single form from a single locality are invaluable for population studies that may lead to sophisticated and biologically sound species concepts. Suites of shells, examined particularly in relation to other fossil organisms and sediments representing one place in space and time, are the bases for ecologic and paleogeographic interpretations of ancient seas. To avoid erroneous age assignments of rock units in geologic mapping, the full variety of genera and species present must be collected from well-documented stratigraphic sections.

All these are valid uses of fossils; each calls for a different kind of collection and a different way of collecting. For some problems, two or more approaches may be combined; seldom can the full potential of fossils be realized, because of limitations of time and ingenuity.

Brachiopods are so abundant in Paleozoic strata that many paleontologic, stratigraphic, and general geologic studies depend on the accurate identification and careful zonation of these fossils. It is important, therefore, that as complete and as diversified collections as possible be made from all brachiopod-bearing beds.

Proper study of brachiopods requires more than well-preserved shells showing external features and general shape. Many genera are distinguished by subtle differences inside the valves, especially within the brachial valve. All collecting should be aimed at getting adequate material for morphologic study. This usually means collecting single valves as well as whole shells to make certain that internal features can be examined either directly or after additional preparation in the laboratory. Hingement features are most important; special care should be taken to assure collection of the hinge of the brachial valve. Shell composition and structure, both important in classification, place a premium value on original shell material.

Brachiopods live today in many environments, but always in the marine realm. They most certainly occupied a similar variety of ecological niches in past geologic epochs. Most apparently are gregarious creatures, living in clusters attached by a fleshy pedicle to rocks, other shells, themselves, or the sea floor. Some, like *Lingula,* live in burrows in sandy littoral or sublittoral regions. Others cement themselves to firm surfaces, rock or shell. Among these were the irregular shaped *Leptodus,* a Permian genus, the shells of which are found cemented together quite like the shells in a modern oyster bank. Other peculiar modifications in the Permian were the richthofenids that assumed a coralline habit, grew a conical pedicle valve, and attached themselves to each other or to the substrate with long spines. Whole groups of brachiopods (for example, late Paleozoic productoids) lost the pedicle attachment and lived free on the sea floor, supported by an amazing array of spines.

Because of the great range in shell shape and the variety of environments occupied, brachiopods were widely dispersed; the search for fossil brachiopods is not too difficult. They are found in many places where marine fossils are preserved. Extracting them from the rock in usable condition for study is a more demanding task. Patience is the fossil hunter's most rewarding virtue.

If good fortune permits the exposure of calcareous shaly rocks rich in brachiopods, shells may be found weathered free in the soil or along shaly bedding surfaces. The wonderful Upper Ordovician localities in the vicinity of Cincinnati, the Silurian Visby Marl on Gotland, the Three Forks Shale in southern Montana and the Sly Gap beds near Alamagordo, New Mexico, are well-known examples of this kind of preservation. There are many others. Natural etching of silicified fossils sometimes results in a concentration of shells in the soil or rock residuum. Collecting techniques for these two kinds of preservation are quite similar.

When fossils are plentiful the collector must resist an urge to accumulate too many shells of the more common forms. *Atrypas* and *Rhychotremas* are beautiful shells when found free, but concentration on them can divert the collector from rarer, more significant genera. A rule of thumb to follow when confronted with an embarassment of fossil riches is to collect all the different kinds first, searching especially for rare and unusual shells. If several hours have been spent at one spot and no new kinds of shells have been collected in the last half hour or so, the collector can then turn to enrichment of his collection in the more abundant species.

To assure complete coverage of a fine outcrop, it is sometimes advisable to lay out a grid, dividing the exposed area into squares—perhaps three feet on a side. These can then be systematically examined, preferably on hands and knees, until all have been carefully covered. If more than one person is collecting, a modified "gang-plowing" technique will produce noticeably richer collections. Several collectors also help eliminate bias that may influence the collecting of a lone paleontologist with a definite specialty in mind. Basket-ball knee guards save wear and tear on trousers.

Lighting is critical for this kind of collecting. In the early morning or late afternoon, long shadows obscure many of the smaller shells. Peculiar shadow effects are also produced by the winter sun, low in the sky in the northern latitudes. Full sunlight for the four to six hours near midday is best. Needless to say, both efficiency of collector and comprehensiveness of collection are impaired on wet, cloudy, or cold days.

Sieving the fossiliferous residue in the field will generally yield a large quantity of small fossils that may have been overlooked in hand picking. If a stream is nearby, the material can be washed on the spot and the fossil concentrates saved. A standard set of sieves can be used, but wire screening tacked to a wooden frame serves very well. McKenner discusses a similar technique elsewhere in this volume.

Marine siltstones, sandstones, and more exotic clastic rocks such as tuf-faceous breccias, can yield fine brachiopods. The fossils are preserved as molds and casts by the solution of shell material, either by natural weathering or by acid etching in the laboratory. The shelly beds can be identified as streaks of holes, generally parallel to the bedding. Undissolved layers may reveal exquisite fossils in which shell ornament and other morphologic features are preserved in remarkable detail.

Molds and casts present a problem in interpretation that may baffle the novice. In order to secure an accurate representation of a single brachiopod, four different molds are needed. Interiors and exteriors of both the pedicle and brachial valves must be collected. Latex casts can be made later to reconstruct the form of the original shells.

Preservation of this type is common, for example, in rocks of the Chemung facies in New York, Devonian tuffaceous breccias in Maine, and Upper Mississippian siltstones in southeast Idaho. Similar molds and casts are found in some cherty formations; the Boone Formation of northwest Arkansas is a fine example.

Sandstones may be split and chert cracked on the outcrop until a wide variety of fossils is secured. Often, time does not permit such extended effort. Frequently, better collections can be obtained by taking large blocks back to the laboratory and preparing the material there with rock splitter, hammer, and chisel.

A word of caution about fossils in dolomite is in order here. Brachiopods are commonly preserved as molds and casts in dolomite. If any shell material is present, it is generally made up of replacement minerals. Some useful information can be had from a study of molds (for example, the pentameroids contained in Silurian dolomites in many parts of the United States). However, preservation is often poor, and morphologic interpretations based on fossils from dolomites should be made with caution. Unless some special condition exists, such as silicification of shells, time spent collecting brachiopods from dolomitic beds could be better spent elsewhere.

A special type of preservation is responsible for the occurrence of *Lingula, Leiorhynchus,* and other brachiopods in black shales. Fossiliferous layers can frequently be spotted as ferruginous weathering zones, and careful splitting of such shales may reveal these fossils either along bedding planes or, as some Lingulas and Cranias have been found, in the position of growth.

Perhaps the most difficult collecting is in massive carbonate rocks which, unfortunately, are widely distributed and are frequently the subject of inquiry in stratigraphic and mapping projects. Fossiliferous layers are not difficult to locate; generally there are texture and color differences between shells and matrix. Cracking with a 2- or 3-pound sledge will reveal the character of the fossils and their mode of preservation. Often, considerable effort must be expended to secure a reasonably complete representation of the fossil assemblages. The Mississippian carbonate sequences of the Rocky Mountain region (Redwall Limestone, Madison Group, etc.) offer fine opportunities for this kind of collecting.

Fortunately, massive carbonates may yield silicified fossils in great numbers and of superb preservation. Because of the normally difficult collecting conditions in carbonate rocks, silicified layers and blocks should be looked for assiduously. When a layer is found, the silicified shells usually stand out in relief and are a different color from the matrix. Blocks of reasonable size can be freed by sledge or crowbar. The blocks should be examined on all surfaces to ascertain the extent of silicification. A small bottle of hydrochloric acid is useful in testing for silicified material, and a good strong glue or cement is essential for piecing together fragments of fossils broken during their extraction from rocks. Blocks about 18 inches to 2 feet on a side can be handled by two men and will produce amazing quantities of material. Elsewhere in this book, Cooper and Whittington provide a detailed explanation of methods and techniques for securing and preparing silicified fossils.

In addition to sharp eyes, a keen mind, and perseverance, the collector will need a geologic hammer ("shale" type) or a bricklayer's hammer. Smaller hammers and various chisels are useful for more delicate shale splitting and trimming. A 2- to 4-pound sledge is needed for collecting from massive carbonate rocks and cherts. An 8-pound sledge and wrecking bars may be necessary for more ambitious quarrying projects and for collecting silicified blocks. Hand lenses aid in examining details of shell morphology and ornament. Those having a large field of view ($3\times$ to $5\times$) are best. A $10\times$ lens may be useful; stronger lenses are a nuisance.

Fossils should be wrapped as soon as possible after collecting to prevent wear and tear on the delicate shells. Old newspaper is excellent wrapping material; toilet paper may be used for more fragile fossils. The wrapped fossils from each locality should be carefully bagged and labeled with as much information as necessary to give an accurate geographic and stratigraphic location of the collecting spot. Blocks for acid etching or splitting should be wrapped in burlap and bound with wire or strap binders. Used feed bags are fine for this purpose and can be shipped easily by freight.

Collecting brachiopods, like collecting any group of fossil animals, depends on experience, training and, often, luck. It is difficult, or impossible, to make adequate collections without knowing in detail the shell that is being sought and under what conditions it might be preserved as a fossil. In order to fully appreciate a good fossil locality, the collector must know what he is looking for. A little knowledge is a safeguard to adequate collecting. A comprehensive understanding of the fossil assemblages and the stratigraphy of a given area will more than pay for itself in superior collections.

# Gastropods and Pelecypods

NORMAN F. SOHL, ELLIS L. YOCHELSON

*U. S. Geological Survey, Washington, D.C.*

ERLE G. KAUFFMAN

*U. S. National Museum, Washington, D.C.*

Since the Cambrian, gastropods and pelecypods have made up a significant proportion of marine faunal assemblages, becoming increasingly abundant and diverse with time. During the Paleozoic these mollusks were only locally abundant, but displayed great diversity. Their biostratigraphic value in Paleozoic rocks has not been adequately tested. Although Mesozoic biostratigraphy is based predominantly on ammonites, many groups of pelecypods and gastropods play a significant role in correlation. In the Cenozoic, however, clams and snails are the primary macrofossils used in biostratigraphy. Nonmarine mollusks, first known from Devonian rocks, have also increased in abundance and variety with time.

In marine assemblages of all ages, pelecypods generally outnumber gastropods, but are generically less diverse. In a single fauna numerous gastropod groups are commonly represented by relatively few individuals. This may reflect the carnivorous habit of many gastropod groups (some mesogastropods, most neogastropods and euthyneuran snails) and the common ecologic situation, wherein a large variety of carnivores, represented by relatively few individuals, coexist with large numbers of noncarnivores (filter-feeding pelecypods and herbivorous snails). This possible explanation may not, however, be applicable to the Paleozoic faunas.

## COLLECTING

Pelecypods and gastropods appear to have inhabited a wide range of environments during much of their history, but individual species of gastropods are usually restricted in their range and are sensitive to environmental control. Individual species of pelecypods are generally more widespread and occur in a broader range of environments; some attained intercontinental to cosmopolitan distribution during the Jurassic and the Cretaceous. Despite their wide overall distribution, marine clams and snails have been predominantly shallow-

Publication authorized by the Director, U. S. Geological Survey, and the Secretary of the Smithsonian Institution.

water shelf dwellers throughout their history, as reflected by their relative abundance and distribution in ancient sediments. As a first step the interested collector should seek out sediments representing these environments.

The diversity of gastropods and pelecypods in fossil accumulations, and the restricted occurrence of the former, require that large collections be made over a broad geographic area in order to develop a relatively complete picture of any time-restricted assemblage. Large collections are also needed to define accurately the broad variability limits of many pelecypod and gastropod taxa, and to identify species. Immature forms and small species are poorly known and should not be overlooked during collecting. As the finer classification of many gastropod and pelecypod taxa is based on such delicate structural features as dentition, muscle scars, and detailed ornamentation (in clams), or apertural features, protoconch, and siphons (in snails), well-preserved material is essential for their study.

The best Paleozoic gastropod and pelecypod faunas are obtained from undisturbed marine siltstones, fine-grained sandstones, clay shales, calcareous shales, and limestones deposited in relatively shallow water on the continental platform. Mesozoic and Cenozoic species are similarly distributed and, in addition, are exceedingly common in near-shore siltstones and sandstones. Similarly, in Recent platform deposits, the number and diversity of clams and snails decreases offshore. Limestone and siderite concretions are an important source of mollusks in rocks of all ages, and preservation within them is usually superior to that in the host rock. The concretions commonly contain a more diverse assemblage, preserving thin-shelled and ornate species that were destroyed or distorted in the surrounding sediment.

The best specimens for study are complete, original shells (or a finely crystalline replacement) that can be easily freed from the matrix. Details of the apeture in most snail groups, and hinges in pelecypod groups, are essential for study. Usually the best fossils are collected from weathered rocks. This is particularly true of the gastropods, because their irregular shape and the ease with which the shell exfoliates make it difficult to split them out of a hard matrix. Unconsolidated or semiconsolidated sediments (such as those of the Tertiary) also yield quantities of well-preserved fossils which are easily removed from the matrix by washing techniques or mechanical cleaning. Silicified limestones are another primary source of clams and snails, and may contain a tremendous wealth of finely preserved material which can be successfully recovered by acid etching techniques. Well-preserved pelecypods can also be collected in great numbers from other types of sediments, such as dense limestones, sandstones, and argillites. Because of their planar surfaces and the greater stability of their shells, pelecypods are more easily recovered than gastropods from such well-consolidated rocks.

Locally, leached sandstones, siltstones, carbonates, and other sediments contain numerous external molds of both clams and snails, preserving the fine details of the outer shell surface. Internal molds, particularly of gastropods, are less usable; unless they are the only fossils present, they do not warrant a great deal of time and effort. Internal molds of pelecypods commonly preserve impressions of the dentition and muscle scars, and can generally be identified by genus. Natural and artificial cross sections are useful in determining genera or species in a few groups of mollusks, such as the rudistids and the acteonellid and nerineid gastropods.

## PREPARATION

Methods of preparation must be suited to the specimen's size, shape, preservation and to the nature of the matrix. Preparation is tedious and time consuming and must be done with care and patience. Thus, an estimation of the specimen's value is an important first step; is the specimen worth the effort necessary to clean it? It is important to bear in mind that preparation is a means to an end, and not an end in itself.

Before attempting to remove a specimen from matrix, it is necessary to understand the shell form and to know what to expect in covered areas. This requires some knowledge of the major pelecypod and gastropod groups, and an appreciation of the wide range of molluscan shell forms. Shells of most gastropods are asymmetrical. The outer lip of the aperture, the apex, and extended siphonal canals are particularly fragile and must be cleaned with great care. In some groups (Strombacea) the outer lip is expanded and commonly spinose. Other snails are highly ornamented and have delicate external spines. Unless the collector knows about these structures, he may ruin the specimen during preparation. In general, pelecypods are easier to prepare, being most commonly rounded or ovate, with smooth exterior surfaces. Some, however, have an unusual shape (*Leda, Pteria, Cuspidaria, Pholas*) and nodes or spines (*Pitar, Spondylus, Echinochama*) which must be considered before cleaning is attempted. The hinge area presents the most delicate cleaning problem in pelecypods.

Most methods of preparation applicable to other fossils can be used on the mollusks. The matrix will determine what methods to employ. The gentler the method used, the less chance there is of ruining the specimen.

In clay, shale, chalk, or unconsolidated silt and sand, specimens may be washed free in water or in some disaggregating agent such as hydrogen peroxide, the type of agent being determined by the nature of the sediment. Washing may be accompanied by gentle agitation to speed up the removal of sediment from the specimens. If washing fails, try boiling. Most original mollusk shells will not survive long-term soaking, but this technique may be used satisfactorily if the shells are not fragile and have been replaced by some stable mineral. A little-tried method for the recovery of mollusks from poorly consolidated sediments is the hydrofluoric acid treatment. The potential of this method is especially great for recovering numbers of small specimens.

Many mechanical processes may be used to remove specimens from a soft matrix. In some deposits, the shells are strong enough so that the matrix may be removed with a stiff brush. In hard, well-cemented sediments (limestone, sandstone, siltstone, argillite) mechanical cleaning devices are most successful. Standard manual tools—hammers, chisels, picks, and needles—may be supplemented by various power tools which take much of the labor out of preparation: rock crushers; electric vibrating needles and chisels; standard dental drills, which can be fitted with a variety of burrs, grinding wheels, saws, and brushes; and even sonic vibrators. The use of mechanical cleaning devices takes practice, however, and in careless hands they are capable of doing great damage to the specimens.

Specimens contained in dense, hard matrix are usually less fragile than those in unconsolidated sediments, where the specimens have been leached, but some difficult cleaning problems commonly arise. In many rock types, the bond between the exterior surface of the shell and the matrix is stronger than that between the internal surface and the steinkern (internal mold), and the rock most readily splits around the steinkern, tearing away the shell, and ruining the specimen. If the shell layers have been altered, they tend to spall, one layer pulling away from another as the enclosing matrix is removed. Spalling ruins most fossils for refined paleontologic study unless all the shell material can be removed from the external and internal molds. These may then be cast to give replicas of the shell surfaces.

Some of the most beautifully preserved mollusk faunas known are those obtained from limestones in which the shells have been replaced by silica. These are removed by dissolving the matrix in acetic or hydrochloric acid. Great care must be taken in handling etched silicified mollusks, as they are commonly incompletely replaced by silica and are very fragile. Residues of etched blocks should be washed thoroughly before they are allowed to dry. The quality of silicification varies with the animal group, the degree of silicification, and the coarseness of the silica replacement. In some specimens, only a single shell layer is replaced, and interpretation of shell morphology is difficult.

Following any liquid preparation treatment, fossils should be allowed to dry thoroughly before they are sorted. Wet shells are several times more fragile than dry ones. Flexible tweezers or a wetted brush are the best tools for picking dried washings and etched residues.

Large, individual specimens embedded in clay or shale may be cleaned by applying a strong base (such as potassium hydroxide in the form of pellets or powder) to the covered surfaces. To prevent damage to the specimen, the pellets should be removed frequently and the surface washed. Thin sections and polished sections are used sparingly in the study of mollusks, but certain groups cannot be properly studied without them. Such groups as the rudistid pelecypods and nerineacean and acteonellid gastropods have a complex internal structure, and it is necessary to section them for identification. There is some indication that this technique could be applied successfully to the study of many more groups of gastropod and pelecypod taxa. Shell structure may be useful in the classification of certain groups, as it is in the Ostreidae. Serial sectioning of pelecypod dentition in dense matrix is rarely used, but may be the only way of obtaining this information. Similarly, columellar plications in gastropods may be studied by making thin or polished sections parallel to the axis of coiling. Acetate peels are an extremely useful supplement in serial sectioning.

Many types of fossil mollusks, once they are free of matrix require no further preparation. On the other hand, extremely fragile specimens, leached or porous shells, or those which tend to exfoliate, need to be strengthened before being handled to any extent. This may be done by soaking or coating the specimens with a very thin varnish, such as dilute Alvar, or by applying a thin coat of protective plastic from a spray can. These must be applied with care, as a thick coat may obscure structural details. Most sprays and varnishes may be removed from the specimen or thinned with acetone. It is also useful to have a thin varnish on hand during the process of cleaning matrix from the specimen. Application of the varnish to exposed surfaces and to cracks in the specimen will strengthen it against breakage during further preparation.

In some rocks, the best specimens are obtained by casting external molds. Internal molds of pelecypods may be cast to obtain hinge and muscle attachment structures. The best overall material for this is liquid latex (generally mixed with lamp black or black ink to darken the cast). The mold is coated with water or a wetting agent and the latex applied in such a manner that it slowly flows across the surface, filling all the fine recesses and pushing air ahead of it. Recently developed silicone latex may be used similarly and dries in a much shorter time, but it must be mixed in small lots and used quickly. Clay, dental wax, and plaster are less satisfactory casting materials. Many other plastics may prove to be useful in this process.

# Cephalopods: As Illustrated by Early Paleozoic Forms

ROUSSEAU H. FLOWER

*New Mexico Institute of Mining and Technology, Socorro*

The greatest problem presented by the cephalopods is their relatively large size. Casual collectors are inclined to be content with fragments. Another serious problem stems from the fragmentary condition of remains of many of the forms. It is commonly necessary to piece together a concept of a species from discrete remains; one fragment may show the general form of the phragmocone, another may show only a living chamber. Siphuncles, or fragments of siphuncles, may occur separately, particularly in the Actinoceratida and Endoceratida, whose remains are commonly solid and heavy. These situations combine to make the study of casually made collections, without supplementary collecting and attention to the particular type of material needed for study, most hazardous, though such study is often necessary.

Edgar Stillman Kelley, in his *Instruments of the Orchestra,* tells the story of a violinist who complained to Wagner that though he sat up late nights practicing he could not get the thirty-second notes of the Fire Music perfectly. Wagner replied that he didn't care; what he wanted was the general effect, that the parts one player missed another would get. The study of cephalopods is like that; often it takes a considerable suite of fragments, each in itself inadequate, to form the basis of the concept of a species.

The best cephalopod material often occurs in hard limestones; thus, whenever possible, it is best to remove large blocks containing the specimens and to leave finer extraction for the laboratory. Cephalopods are commonly found on flat, weathered surfaces. Where the rock is massive and one cannot separate readily the layer containing the specimen from the one below, it is necessary to dig channels along either side of the specimen with hammer and chisel, and then to work below the specimen from either side. This method does not always work.

Weathering is a valuable aid. Where moisture tends to run downdip through bedding planes, specimens will pop out easily. In collecting from one side of a stream at Loretteville, Quebec, I easily obtained good specimens where the beds dipped down away from the stream, but found it almost impossible to extract specimens on the other side, where the strata dipped down into the stream. Where limestones are dense and fine-grained, prolonged weathering may be an aid in the selection of extractable material. Along the shore of Valcour Island in Lake Champlain, some of the Fort Cassin Formation weathers nicely, so that extraction of the cephalopods is relatively easy, but about 10 feet back, where the rock is not constantly exposed to moisture, it tends to break uniformly through the specimens rather than around them. Again, where the outcrop failed to weather properly, as in the *Lecanospira* beds (Rochdale Limestone) of the Millbrook quadrangle, chopping boulders that had weathered for a long time under the soil yielded some fine material which separated quite readily along the surface of the specimen.

In the older cephalopods, living chambers alone seldom reveal the taxonomic position, except, of course, in the more specialized brevicones. Ordinarily, phragmocones contain the crucial structures, and a little observation will usually show if the surface of a weathered specimen is likely to contain the essential siphuncle. Happily, the siphuncles are usually the heavy part of the shell, and shells commonly are found oriented with the siphuncle below. This is commonly true of the forms that have large, heavy siphuncles—the Endoceratida, the Actinoceratida and some Discosorida—but is not as generally true of other groups.

Chisels are usually necessary for extracting good materials; sometimes a crowbar and a heavy sledge are needed. No laws can be laid down as to the best way to attack the rock. Separation along bedding planes is probably generally an advantage, but I found it to be of no advantage in the *Maclurites* ledges of the Chazyan; pieces came out only in small chunks, and I found that excellent specimens could be obtained by hitting the top surface of the rock. This was successful, however, only if the piece was considerably weathered.

If specimens can be obtained in blocks, but not separated from the matrix, they may still be useful. Such an approach has been necessary in the southwest, where there is no weathering under the dry soils. Most cephalopods show a good bilateral symmetry, and concepts of the species can be obtained by making cross sections and longitudinal sections of such material.

Silicified material is of variable value. The chert steinkerns representing cephalopods in many of the dolomites of the Canadian permit specific evaluation, but it remains for material in limestones to show the crucial morphology of the forms. Gentle and incomplete silicification may replace and retain such original structures as the endosiphoblades of the Endoceratida, which may be lost by replacement of the original aragonite by calcite. Such material extracted from limestones has produced most significant specimens.

Material flattened in shales is of little value, and much of it is undeterminable. Proper generic assignment of much of the New York Devonian material has depended on study of specimens in calcareous or pyrite concretions, rare limestone horizons or lenses. In the higher Upper Devonian, where beds are largely sandy, chance calcareous lenses or rare calcite-filled specimens supply the exceptionable forms that show enough structure to allow generic determination.

Special groups and types involve special considerations. The Ellesmeroceratida, the primitive order, usually is represented by small shells that do not offer particular problems in collecting. Limestone material showing the siphuncles and, particularly, early parts of the siphuncle, to which diaphragms are commonly confined, is most significant. Further study of well preserved siphuncle walls is needed; curiously, black calcarenites of calcilutites which are not too fine yield the best material for study; the finest calcilutites commonly show too extensive a recrystallization of the shell parts to be of great value.

The Endoceratida present special problems, both in collecting the badly needed, large, complete specimens and in the matching of fragments at the specific level. In this group, siphuncles are all-important; specimens in which the siphuncle wall can be studied (thin sections are commonly necessary) and which show the endosiphocone and endosiphotube are most important. Apical ends of siphuncles, which vary in shape and have inadvisably been given generic names, are of considerable significance, but anterior ends of specimens showing only empty siphuncles in phragmocones or living chambers will not yield ready determinations. Shell form is important only in the piloceroids, but complete shells are so rare that taxonomy rests primarily on the shape of the siphuncle, an easy basis for general recognition, but not fundamental to taxonomy. Genera based on shape have little real value.

In the Endoceratida, endosiphuncles are highly specialized—indeed, their specialization is sometimes bizarre. Such parts alone may be diagnostic of genera. It is well that this is so, for particularly in the Canadian, these are the only parts preserved and obtainable. It is well to note that such parts alone may yield information of faunal and stratigraphic value.

The crucial generic features of the actinoceroids are found in the siphuncles. Here there is a particular need for collecting specimens that are as complete as possible, for the siphuncle segments may change so in ontogeny as to appear to belong to different genera. The pattern formed by the radial canals is also significant, and the Wutinoceratidae, characterized by particular canals, are, as far as is now known, confined to the Whiterock Formation. *Leurorthoceras* is a genus based on what are now known to be anterior slender siphuncle segments developed in some species groups of Actinoceras. Complete specimens give meaningful results; mere fragments may not.

The large group of orthocones of the Michelinoceratida, which a generation ago was lumped as *"Orthoceras"* having relatively small siphuncles, presents the greatest taxonomic problem, for typical and conspicuous specimens may not show shell features adequate for classification. Those flattened in shales cannot ordinarily be identified, except by inference, and even then only where shell surfaces prove diagnostic, as in *Spyroceras* or *Dawsonoceras*. Internal deposits of the camerae and siphuncle show meaningful and diagnostic patterns, which characterize certain families and genera. Such features are found in the apical parts of phragmocones, but are immature or altogether wanting in adoral parts.

The coiled cephalopods, appearing as the Tarphyceratida in the Middle Canadian, largely replaced by the Barrandeoceratida in the Ordovician, and that group largely replaced by the Rutoceratida and the Centroceratina (the first of the Nautilida) in the Devonian, offer few special problems. Recognition depends on proportions and as is true for many other fossils, requires that the material collected be as complete as possible. The siphuncles are particularly important in distinguishing the archaic Tarphyceratida, which has thick, complex rings, from the younger Barrandeoceratida, which has thin homogeneous rings. If determinations are to be meaningful, material showing siphuncles that retain original structures, rather than recrystallized replacements, is needed.

It is of significance to know that, in the Early Paleozoic, cross section of the whorl and the position and structure of the siphuncle are all important; surfaces are not as simple as was believed, but taxonomy was built upon specimens in which good shell surfaces are not commonly shown. It is not until the Devonian that coiled cephalopods are found in which complexities of frills, spines, nodes, and growth lines are generally of great practical value in taxonomy.

Shape is important in the Oncoceratida; indeed, shape and form of aperture are now relied on in distinguishing genera and species. Siphuncles show varied structures, and are important, both for form of segment and possible deposits.

The Oncoceratida and the Discosorida are largely homeomorphic, both being dominantly breviconic shells. The fundamental features by which the Discosorida are distinguished are found in the specialized regions in the connecting ring. In this group, supplementary deposits—annuli or Endocones or both—may be confined to the apical half of the phragmocone, a good matter to keep in mind when collecting significant materials; curiously, actino-siphonate deposits of the oncoceroids are less commonly confined.

# Echinoderms

J. WYATT DURHAM

*Department of Paleontology, University of California, Berkeley*

The Echinodermata are characterized by a skeleton or test of mesodermal origin in which each plate is a single calcite crystal and has a distinctive reticulate microstructure. Because each plate is a single crystal, they readily display characteristic rhombic calcite cleavage when weathered or fractured. The fenestrate microstructure and single crystal habit of each skeletal element (plate) distinguish the remains of echinoderms from those of all other organisms. The microstructure is somewhat similar to that found in the bones of vertebrates, but usually on a smaller scale. So far as known, however, vertebrate skeletal elements are never single crystals.

The reticulate microstructure (fig. 1) is invariably present in all echinoderm skeletal elements except the teeth (characterized by a "cone in cone" structure) of the echinoid lantern, small spicules and discs that occur in various organs, some parts of the larval skeleton (fig. 2), and the primordia of the adult elements. Deposition of calcite in the skeletal elements begins with a small granule which becomes triangular and then forms a triradiate spicule. Each branch of the spicule branches dichotomously and by repetition forms an open meshwork, with the branches that come in contact fusing together. Although the rods of the meshwork may have a considerably greater diameter

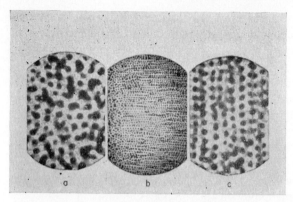

**Fig. 1**

*Echinoderm plate micro-structure. Coronal plate of echinoid* Strongylocen-trotus *under crossed nicols. (a) Irregular meshwork (100×), detail of left side of b. (b) General view of part of plate (25×). (c) Detail of regular mesh-work of b (100×).*

in the adult, an early triradiate spicule may be only about $10\mu$ in maximum dimension. It seems probable that the lack of reticulate meshwork in the various small structures noted above is a function of their minute size. As far as is known, the tooth of the echinoid lantern is the only large skeletal element

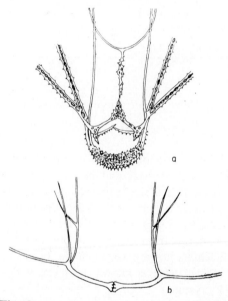

in which the characteristic micro-structure is not found. During fossilization secondary calcite is often deposited within or around the individual plates. This calcite is always in crystallographic con-tinuity with the elements of the meshwork.

Echinoderms are found in rocks of all ages from Early Cambrian on. They range in size from microscopic larval skele-tons to some very long crinoid stems (up to 20 meters), but most adults are in the range from 5 to 25 mm. The major elements of the skeleton (or test) are often well preserved, but the various appendages, rainging in size from microscopic to macro-scopic, are commonly either dis-sociated or broken off. The re-mains of easily disarticulated types, such as starfish, or the nonarticulated plates of holothu-

**Fig. 2**

*Skeleton of pluteus larva (full length of arms not shown). (a) Echinoid,* Echinodiscus auritus *(100×). (b) Ophiuroid,* Ophicoma erinaceus *(80×). [Both from Mortensen (1937).]*

rians, usually occur as dissociated elements. The coarser fraction of microfossil washings and screenings sometimes is a prolific source of disassociated plates and disarticulated skeletal elements. Rarely are specimens found with all appendages, both large and small, attached. Special attention should be given to such material, for complete complements of appendages often yield previously unsuspected clues to systematic relationships or differences.

The morphology of the echinoderm test varies greatly from one major group to another, ranging from the more or less globular test of some echinoids, with the individual plates strongly sutured together, to soft-bodied holothurians, in which the individual plates are dispersed in the mesodermal tissues. Consequently, the remains found in the fossil record vary from isolated dissociated elements to dissociated plates and/or columnals so abundant as to be the dominant constituent of limestones, to complete tests with all parts associated in normal relationships.

The carbonate of echinoderm tests is mostly calcite (Revelle and Fairbridge, 1957, p. 265–266) but may contain a varying percentage, up to about 16 percent, of magnesium carbonate. As a result, the tests of echinoderms are often one of the more durable kinds of fossils in environments where the remains of other organisms are removed by solution.

Echinoderms are often gregarious and always live in a marine environment, never being found in waters of very low salinity. For this reason their fossil remains are found only in marine sediments. Their gregariousness often leads to a very local distribution. A species may occur in great abundance in a few localities yet not be found in intermediate areas. This usually results in numerous individuals occurring near one another in the fossil record. Thus, if one specimen is found, the immediate vicinity should be searched for others. This gregarious habit is not a universal rule, however, and occasional isolated specimens, even of normally highly gregarious species, may be found.

As is true of many other invertebrates, the life history of echinoderms (Hyman, 1955) is characterized by two phases: the larvae are usually planktonic; but most postlarval echinoderms are bottom dwellers. However, a number of crinoids and at least one holothurian are pelagic. Many (most of the Pelmatozoa) are attached by a stem, thus they may occur wherever a suitable substrate is present. Others are free living: some dwell on the sea floor (or on other organisms); others burrow in the sediments. The postlarval stages of echinoderms occur from the intertidal to the hadal zones. Because of this diversity of habitat and mode of life, fossil echinoderms (see: Berry, 1957; Clark, 1957; Cline and Beaver, 1957; Cooke, 1957a,b; Cooper, 1957a,b; Deichmann, 1957a,b; Frizzel and Exline, 1957; Laudon, 1957; Sinclair, 1957) may be found in almost any type of sediments, but are most common in sandstones, limestones, and chalks. In some rocks their abundant skeletal remains are the dominant constituent (e.g., crinoidal limestones). The characteristic microstructure is easily observed in thin sections of limestones of this type; sometimes it is recognizable in coarsely crystalline and/or partially recrystallized limestones.

Any large plate or fragment of a fossil that shows well-developed, uniformly oriented calcite cleavage should be suspected of being an echinoderm. Well-developed cleavage of this type occurs in other fossils only when the calcite has been replaced or recrystallized. This cleavage is the most useful field criterion (other than morphology) for recognition of echinoderms. This same cleavage, however, renders these fossils more susceptible to fracturing than many others. Particular care must therefore be taken in collecting and preparing to avoid hitting fossils too hard. Sometimes even blows on the adjacent matrix of a well-indurated rock will shatter a fossil. In thin section, the reticulate microstructure affords an excellent clue to the presence of echinoderms. Spines have a characteristic radial pattern and, as a result, have sometimes been mistaken for corals.

Once an echinoderm has been recognized, preparation proceeds according to the character of the enclosing sediments. Noncemented materials may be brushed or washed away. More commonly, however, it is necessary to resort to careful mechanical preparation with well-sharpened needles and small chisels. A needle with a fine chisel point, when carefully used under low powers of a binocular microscope, will produce excellent results. This technique is, of course, time-consuming. In well cemented rocks, it is sometimes necessary to remove all but a thin layer of matrix with a motor-driven grinding wheel or drill and to remove the final layer under the microscope with a chisel-pointed needle. Where the surface of the test has inadvertently been scratched or ground, careful application of a weak solution of an acid will often bring out surface details. In echinoids and other types that have solid tests, acid will sometimes clarify the individual plate relationships. Ultrasonic treatment will produce surfaces with unrivaled clarity of detail if the matrix is amenable to breakdown by this method. However, care needs to be exercised in its use if skeletal elements are not cemented or sutured to one another, or else the individual plates will be dissociated. In sediments that have been well-cemented with a noncalcareous cement, outstanding results can sometimes be obtained by dissolving away the calcite test with a weak acid, and then making latex or plastic impressions of the resulting molds. Excellent fidelity of surface detail can sometimes be obtained in some instances with this method. Serial sectioning is often necessary to obtain details of internal morphology or structures.

## REFERENCES

Berry, C. T. (1957). Asterozoa of the post-Paleozoic, *in* H. S. Ladd (ed.), Treatise on marine ecology and paleoecology. Geol. Soc. America Mem. 67, v. 2, p. 975–978.

Clark, Ailsa M. (1957). Crinoids, *in* J. W. Hedgepeth (ed.), Treatise on marine ecology and paleoecology. Geol. Soc. America Mem. 67, v. 1, p. 1183–1185.

Cline, L. M., and Harold Beaver (1957). Blastoids, *in* H. S. Ladd (ed.), Treatise on marine ecology and paleoecology. Geol. Soc. America Mem. 67, v. 2, p. 955–960.

Cooke, C. W. (1957a). Echinoids, *in* J. W. Hedgepeth (ed.), Treatise on marine ecology and paleoecology. Geol. Soc. America Mem. 67, v. 1, p. 1191–1192.

———— (1957b). Echinoids of the post-Paleozoic. *Op. cit.,* p. 981–982.

Cooper, G. A. (1957a). Asterozoa of the Paleozoic, *in* H. S. Ladd (ed.), Treatise on marine ecology and paleoecology. Geol. Soc. America Mem. 67, v. 2, p. 973–974.

———— (1957b). Echinoids of the Paleozoic. *Op. cit.,* p. 979–980.

Deichmann, Elisabeth (1957a). Asteroids and Ophiuroids, *in* J. W. Hedgepeth (ed.), Treatise on marine ecology and paleoecology. Geol. Soc. America Mem. 67, v. 1, p. 1187–1190.

———— (1957b). Holothurians. *Op. cit.,* p. 1193–1195.

Frizzell, D. L., and Harriet Exline (1957). Holothurians, *in* H. S. Ladd (ed.), Treatise on marine ecology and paleoecology. Geol. Soc. America Mem. 67, v. 2, p. 983–986.

Hyman, Libbie H. (1955). The invertebrates: Echinodermata. New York, Mc-Graw-Hill, 763 pp.

Laudon, L. R. (1957). Crinoids, *in* H. S. Ladd, Treatise on marine ecology and paleoecology. Geol. Soc. America Mem. 67, v. 2, p. 961–972.

Mortensen, Th. (1937). Contributions to the study of the development and larval forms of echinoderms, III. Kongl. Danske Vid. Selsk. Skrift., Nat. og Math., 9 Raekke, v. 7, no. 1, p. 1–65, 15 pls.

Revelle, Roger, and Rhodes Fairbridge (1957). Carbonates and carbon dioxide, *in* J. W. Hedgepeth (ed.), Treatise on marine ecology and paleoecology. Geol. Soc. America Mem. 67, v. 1, p. 239–296.

Sinclair, G. W. (1957). Cystoids, *in* H. S. Ladd (ed.), Treatise on marine ecology and paleoecology. Geol. Soc. America Mem. 67, v. 2, p. 953–954.

Valentin, G. (1841). Anatomie du genre Echinus: Mon. d'Echinodermes, v. 4, $x + 126$ pp., pls. 1–9.

# Trilobites

FRANCO RASETTI

*Department of Physics, Johns Hopkins University, Baltimore, Maryland*

ALLISON R. PALMER

*U. S. Geological Survey, Washington, D.C.*

Trilobites may be prepared by either chemical or mechanical techniques. Chemical techniques are effective if the trilobite exoskeleton is in a carbonate

Publication authorized by the Director, U. S. Geological Survey.

matrix and has been replaced by an insoluble mineral such as silica. Although hydrochloric acid will usually dissolve a carbonate matrix, organic acids such as acetic or formic acid do so more gently and are less likely to damage fragile specimens by violent bubbling. Trilobites from some Cambrian limestones seem to have a phosphatic exoskeleton that is soluble in hydrochloric acid. Thus, although the expense is greater, the chance of success in the chemical preparation of trilobites from a carbonate matrix is best if organic acids are used. All limestone samples should be checked for insoluble fossils even if none are apparent on weathered surfaces. Some of the best silicified trilobites have been obtained unexpectedly in this manner.

Another effective chemical technique is used to remove calcareous trilobite exoskeletons from a siliceous matrix. By soaking the siliceous rock in hydrochloric acid and dissolving the calcareous exoskeleton, exquisite casts and molds of exoskeletal surfaces can often be obtained. After being soaked in acid, the specimens in the dried rock must be prepared by mechanical techniques. Both internal and external molds must be saved when this technique is used, as the upper and lower surfaces of the trilobite exoskeleton are not identical, and both provide useful morphologic information.

If the trilobites are collected as natural molds, as impressions in shales, or as calcareous specimens in a calcareous matrix, mechanical techniques must be used. The first task is to uncover the fossils contained in the rock. The proper tool for this is the rock trimmer, preferably of small size, with steel edges $\frac{1}{2}$ inch in length that can be separated to a distance of 4 to 6 inches. Small pieces can be broken more accurately with this instrument than with the larger ones commonly used. A lightweight hammer with a chisel edge and a small anvil are also useful tools for preliminary breaking of the rock. The object is to break the rock along planes parallel to the bedding, the better to reveal enclosed specimens. Both surfaces produced by each fracture should be examined under a binocular microscope at a magnification of 10× or 15× and specimens of interest circled with a red pencil. How far one should go in the fragmentation of the rock and search for specimens depends chiefly on the amount of rock available, the number of species present, and their size and scientific potential.

The initial breaking of the rock with rock trimmer or light hammer seldom exposes all that is preserved of the fossil. This is particularly true for trilobite parts that have considerable relief. For such specimens the most desirable thing to do is to uncover only the tops of the most prominent parts—for example, the glabella of a cranidium. Then the rest of the fossil can be prepared as discussed below. However, the fracture may leave a small part of the specimen in one half of the broken rock and the rest in the other half. An important specimen may warrant restoration. In this event, the piece of rock containing the small part should be further trimmed until the skilled technician can break the fossil free. It may be convenient, in the last stages of this operation, to break the matrix by means of cutting pliers under the binocular microscope. The small part can then be cemented to the rest of the specimen.

To cement broken fossils, try using a thin solution of Duco or Ambroid in a slowly evaporating medium such as amyl acetate. Excess cement that may cover the surface of the fossil can be removed after the cement has hardened by rubbing with a small acetone-soaked sponge or brush. The use of water-soluble glue for cementing fossils is not recommended because such glues deteriorate with time and it is often desirable to wash specimens in water during the course of study.

More refined mechanical preparation of trilobites uses two principal tools, a high-speed rotating abrasive wheel and a Vibro-tool. Silicon carbide and boron carbide abrasive wheels from $\frac{1}{4}$ to $\frac{3}{4}$ inch in diameter and $\frac{1}{16}$ inch thick are inexpensive and effective in removing matrix from a trilobite specimen. An even more effective wheel, although expensive, is a metal wheel 1 inch in diameter and 1/25 inch thick impregnated with diamond dust. The thin metal blade allows more precise cutting and grinding than is possible with the thicker carbide wheels. Aluminum oxide abrasives are worthless for this purpose. Many paleontologists use regular dentistry equipment with pulleys and belts to operate these tools. It may be simpler and equally effective to mount the abrasive wheel on the shaft of a small hand motor revolving at about 4000 rpm.

Although a grinding wheel can often be used to prepare most of a trilobite specimen, details of delicate parts must be prepared further with either a hand needle or a Vibro-tool. Usually, a Vibro-tool with a short stroke and a sharp needle will suffice for cleaning even the most fragile structures. However, successful use of the Vibro-tool requires that the matrix and the exoskeleton part cleanly at their contact. When the matrix and exoskeleton do not part cleanly, a needle with a chisel edge can be used to scrape away the matrix. This tool is usually effective only if the surface is wet and there is a color contrast between specimen and matrix.

All preparation work with needle and Vibro-tool, and much grinding, should be done under a binocular microscope at magnifications of 15× or more.

Most trilobites should be coated with a white deposit of either ammonium chloride or magnesium oxide prior to study, and especially in preparation for photography. It is amazing how much unsuspected detail is revealed by such coating, especially when the fossils are originally dark-colored. Ammonium chloride has the advantage of easily allowing uniform coating of large areas and should be used for large specimens. Its drawbacks are that it is more complicated, produces irritating and corroding fumes, and the deposit is hygroscopic, quickly dissolving in damp weather. For these reasons, magnesium oxide is preferable for whitening small specimens. A chemically stable, very fine-grained coating is produced by inverting a specimen in the smoke from a burning 1-inch length of magnesium ribbon. The coating may be removed with water or a jet of compressed air unless the specimen is silicified. The oxide layer is best removed from delicate silicified specimens by immersing them in acid.

After preparation, specimens should be trimmed of all excess rock to provide most efficient storage. This can be accomplished by careful use of the rock trimmer and cutting pliers, or with less danger of unwanted breakage by using a thin-bladed, 6-inch diameter, diamond-disk saw. The specimen may be held by hand, as the disk does not cut the skin and is entirely harmless. A small specimen is cut in a few seconds, and the disk will have almost unlimited life if used only on limestone and shale.

# Arthropods with Chitinous Exoskeletons

## H. K. BROOKS

*Department of Geology, University of Florida, Gainesville*

Arthropods are the most abundant and diverse multicellular animals on Earth, and have apparently been so since the beginning of the Cambrian. Trilobites and ostracods, whose living exoskeletons were calcareous, have left a prodigious fossil record, whereas their relatives, whose skeletons were composed of organic material, occur rarely or sporadically. Some major arthropod taxa have not even left a trace of their former existence; for example, the euphausid crustaceans.

The arthropod skeleton covers the whole external surface of the body and consists essentially of a chitin-protein structure. It is usually stiffened over most of the surface by deposition of other organic matter or by calcium or phosphatic salts.

Because destruction of protein and chitin rapidly occurs after death of the creature under most natural conditions, the stratigraphic occurrence of arthropods with only these skeletal materials is most limited. For their entombment and preservation, special environmental conditions are required. Since such ecological conditions are rarely represented in stratified rocks, a good crustacean, merostome, arachnid, myriapod, or insect fossil is indeed a choice possession. Considering how few deposits contain chitinous fossil arthropods, it is surprising that so many specimens display exquisite details of the external morphology as well as of such minute structures as pores and setae.

It can safely be stated that through chance discovery and diligent collecting, new and unique fossil arthropods will continue to be unearthed; our known fossils are but a poor sample of the multitudes of species that have flourished during the past. Just as important as collection and description of these new fossils is the proper interpretation of the museum specimens that have been known for many years. Obvious gross characteristics were described by the earlier workers. To disclose and describe the morphological details preserved on these fossils through the employment of proper paleontological techniques must be the principal objective of the paleocarcinologist, arachnologist, and entomologist.

## CHITINOUS REMAINS: THEIR PRESERVATION AND STRATIGRAPHIC OCCURRENCE

At one time or another we have been impressed with the toughness and seemingly indestructability of chitin. It is true that chitin is an extremely stable organic polysaccharide. That it can endure without significant degradation for vast periods of time is proven by the existence of fossils dating from Early Paleozoic rocks in which the chitin is still translucent. Prevailing opinion to the contrary, chitin is rapidly destroyed in soils, and in the sediments of lakes, rivers, oceans and their estuaries. Chitinoclastic bacteria, actinomycetes and fungi, which utilize enzymes, are extremely efficient in the destruction of this seemingly indestructable material. If this were not so, available carbon and nitrogen for the life cycle on earth would have been tied up long ago in arthropod skeletons littering the earth.

Ecological factors and selective preservation and destruction of chitin have influenced the stratigraphic occurrence of fossil arthropods, and misconceptions have resulted. One has only to cite the fossil record of the limuloid chelicerates (Brooks, 1957, p. 896). Recent *Limulus* and its congeners are marine animals. In the breeding season they migrate to the beaches, invading lagoons, estuaries, and swamps and sometimes wandering for considerable distances up rivers. Undoubtedly, the Tertiary as well as the Mesozoic limuloids behaved in a similar way. It is interesting to note that not one reported fossil limuloid has been found in typical marine sediments. Fossil limuloids are found in association with trachaeophytes in fresh or brackish water, in lagoonal and swamp deposits, and in sediments that contain evidence of supersaline conditions. The only marine deposit in which fossil limuloids have been found is the lagoonal Solnhofen limestones of Bavaria. These are Jurassic back reef deposits in which marine organisms, including several genera of decapods that have chitinous skeletons are associated with terrestrial animals —that is, insects, arachnids, and vertebrates. The fossil record of the limuloids and all other fossil arthropods whose exoskeletons were composed only of organic material imposes a paleoecological paradox unless their restricted stratigraphic occurrences are the result of selective preservation. Environmental conditions under which chitin is not destroyed are usually beyond the tolerances of most arthropods for prolonged existence. Lithologic, stratigraphic, and paleontological evidence always indicates some peculiarity of the lithotope of preservation, such as supersalinity or stagnation of the water, catastrophies, volcanic ash falls, and even entrapment in bitumen of oil seeps or the extruded resin of trees.

Except for ostracods and trilobites, in which calcareous materials dominate over organic skeletal materials, the arthropods whose skeletal compositions lend themselves to preservation are the barnacles and some decapod Crustacea.

The mineralization of the integument of decapods is usually not sufficient to withstand the tribulations to which materials are subjected on and within sediments of the open sea floor. For example, Mesozoic and Cenozoic lobsters have left a fossil record consisting mostly of chelae. Crabs, in general, are more heavily calcified, thus their remains are more frequently collected and in a better state of preservation, especially from limestone and other highly calcareous deposits. Certain zones of the Eocene bioclastic Ocala Limestone of Florida have yielded several different species of crabs. The species most frequently collected, with consistent excellent preservation, is *Ocalina floridanum*. This species has a massive calcareous exoskeleton.

Only a few Paleozoic malacostracan Crustacea of both the Phyllocarida and the Eumalacostraca have been found with mineral reinforcement of their skeleton (Rolfe, 1962, p. 33; Brooks, 1962, p. 259), and it is these that are found in marine deposits.

That preservations of fossil arthropod remains in open shelf marine sediments is dependent largely on mineral impregnation is best proven by the occurrence of barnacles. Both pedunculate, ("goose") and operculate ("acorn") barnacles have heavily calcified plates. These plates are not uncommonly found in deposits representing considerable wave or current action, and they may represent a dominant element of the shell fauna.

Among other arthropods, only the Early Paleozoic aglaspids of the chelicerates are known to have had any significant degree of mineral fortification. According to Raasch (1939, p. 87–116) the weakly phosphatized skeletons of aglaspids are absent or are rare in sandstone, limestone, and dolomite, and are typically found in fine-grained clastic sediments that were accumulated in shallow, tranquil, poorly aerated marine embayments.

Except for the rare, single, individual fossil that is found by chance, the remains of the chitinous Trilobitomorpha, Crustacea, Chelicerata, Myriapoda, and Insecta occur together in various combinations. Their most frequent stratigraphic associates are fish and terrestrial plant remains. The collection and preparation of all of these arthropod fossils imposes the same problems. It is not within the scope of this work to cite all known occurrences, but it will be instructive to discuss briefly the types of fossiliferous deposits most frequently encountered and to cite representative examples and modes of preservation.

Fossils of chitinous arthropods have been reported from many more black shale deposits than from any other rock type. The residual films of soft-bodied organisms on the bedding planes of the incomparable Burgess Shale of Middle Cambrian age in Canada represents a numerous and diverse arthropod fauna. At most other known sites the occurrence of compressions of chitin, residual films, impressions, and pyritized replacements are confined to a single or a few specimens. These have usually been discovered as a result of collecting for other types of fossils. Compressions and impressions of chitinous fossils are rarely found in dark gray to black fine-grained sandstone and siltstone. They are never abundant, and the preservation is generally poor except when the fossils occur in sideritic nodules.

The most beautiful arachnids, myriapods, and crustacean fossils known from the Paleozoic occur in ironstone nodules from siltstone associated with Carboniferous coal swamps in Illinois, Kansas, and England. Any small concretionary nodule should be suspect of containing remains of a chitinous arthropod. Most decapod fossils have been collected from calcareous concretions in marine sandstones, shales, and greensands. Palmer (1957) has recently described silicified remains of an anostracan crustacean associated with similarly preserved arachnids and insects from calcareous nodules occurring in a Miocene lacustrine bed in California.

Remains of the exoskeleton of arthropods, chitinous or poorly fortified with some mineral matter, are sometimes found in green clayey sandstones and shales. Preservation may be excellent, especially when the specimens are enclosed in phosphatic concretions, as are the crustacean fossils from the Lower Mississippian of Kentucky.

Thinly bedded lagoonal limestones and dolomites accumulated behind barriers, especially reefs, are famous for eurypterid, crustacean, and insect fossils. In association, an occasional arachnid has also been collected. Many examples could be cited, but the compressions in the Bertie Waterlime of Silurian age in New York and the Solnhofen plattenkalk of Jurassic age in Germany are best known.

Though red beds are notoriously barren of fossils, certain limited horizons of fine-grained, thinly bedded materials contain prodigious numbers of compressions and impressions of Conchostracea and other arthropods such as notostracans and insects with which they are rarely associated. In a few examples, the red color is the result of postdeposition oxidation, but usually the color is inherited from the environment of erosion and deposition. Most red beds are fluvial terrestrial deposits, and it is these that are typically barren. Usually when oxidized terrestrial sediments are carried into lakes or into the sea, enough organic matter accumulates within the sediment to alter its color through bacterial activity and the reduction of the iron. Gray, green, and black are the colors of normal fine-grained marine rocks. Therefore, lacustrine or marine red beds would indicate that some environmental factor inhibited the production of organic-rock sediment. This could be due to temporality or intermittency of lakes or to supersalinity in restricted basins.

Though commonly associated with coal-swamp deposits, remains of chitinous arthropods are unknown in bituminous coal. Beetle remains are known to occur in Pleistocene peats. In lignites it is only within amber that insects, myriapods, arachnids, and terrestrial crustacean remains are sometimes found. The fauna of the Baltic amber is legendary. Amber occurs so sparcely within lignitic deposits that it is only practical to collect where recent erosion and deposition has secondarily concentrated the fossiliferous particles.

Compressed residual films of insects, arachnids, and other animals and plants are found on bedding planes with volcanic ash deposits. In the Florissant shales of Colorado, the fossiliferous beds are thinly laminated, and the ash has obviously been reworked.

The fabulous Rhynie Chert of Scotland, in which Devonian plants and a limited number of Crustacea have been found, is allegedly a siliceous spring deposit. This may be true in that insects and spiders have been found (Chamberlin, 1949) in an onyx marble spring deposit of Late Cenozoic age in Arizona.

A few arthropods have been obtained from the asphaltum accumulation of oil seeps; for example, the La Brea tar pits of Pleistocene age in California.

## PREPARATION

Because of the diversity of sedimentary materials and the many types of preservation that are encountered in the study of fossil arthropods there will be times when more than one of the methods discussed here will be applicable. The objective of the preparator should be to disclose the greatest amount of morphological detail. If many specimens are available, one should experiment with different methods and even sacrifice a specimen or two for thin sectioning or maceration with an appropriate chemical. Destructive techniques should be minimized unless information about some specific structure, or structures, warrants the chance of failure, destruction of the individual fossil, and the time and effort of the tedious techniques that must be employed.

### SPLITTING

Arthropod fossils in sedimentary rocks occur at or on bedding planes, and even in concretions. The chitin, carbonized residue, residual film, or cavity of a natural mold of the flattened or uncompressed exoskeleton (in some concretions) contribute even greater weakness to the bedding plane, and the rock specimen will nearly always cleave in such a way that any fossil present will be exposed. This is also true in quarrying. Fossils on bedding planes not cleaved in the quarrying operation can be best exposed by holding the rock on its side and hitting it with a hammer. The plane of bedding can usually be seen in nodules, and the same rule applies to breaking them open. It may be convenient to note that the axis of intermediate length of the nodule is parallel to the bedding. Splitting will occasionally expose a fossil that cannot be improved upon by mechanical or chemical preparation.

Collectors should be warned that the skeletons of crabs and other calcified Crustacea are usually friable. Upon discovering such a fossil, no further matrix adjacent to the specimen should be removed in the field. Instead, a minimum-sized rock specimen containing the fossil should be collected for the delicate laboratory preparation that is required.

In the laboratory study of the crustacean, *Lepidocaris rhyniensis,* Scourfield (1926) took advantage of the transparency of thin slivers of the Rhynie Chert. The fossils were discovered and studied by microscopic examination of thin chips of the chert under transmitted light.

The surface of particles of amber are such that they may require chipping, grinding, or emersion in a suitable liquid so that the fossil within can be detected.

HAND TOOLING

In general, chipping to remove matrix from a specimen is preferred to grinding. Coarse preparation is best achieved with a hydraulic rock trimmer and completed with a chisel mounted in a Vibro-tool. Final preparation requires minutely chipping away matrix obscuring the specimen with a sharpened needle. Experience has proven that both a pin vise for delicate manual manipulation and a pin vise chuck mounted in a Vibro-tool, may be utilized to advantage. To insure the greatest perfection of preparation with the least damage to the fossil, the final preparation should be carried out with the aid of a stereoscopic microscope. Debris must be removed as it is produced, by blowing or brushing it away. In some compressions and carbonizations it is best to wet the specimen frequently with alcohol to check on the progress of preparation. Many museum specimens show that the preparator carried his removal of materials too far.

Except for shaping rock specimens containing fossils, grinding is of little use in preparing the fossils discussed here. The one example that can be cited where excellent results have been obtained by abrasive methods is the pyritized remains in the Hunsrück shales. Preparators have taken advantage of the greater hardness of the pyrite. Brushes composed of brass bristles softer than the pyrite but harder than the shale matrix have been employed in abrading the matrix from the fossils. Possibly blasting with a suitable abrasive would achieve equally good, or better, results.

MOLDS AND CASTS

Many of the specimens in concretions have retained all or part of their original relief. Ironstone concretions break so that the dorsal and ventral sides of the specimen are on opposite sides of the break. For the most part, the fossils consist of the mineral matter that has been introduced into the body space of the arthropod. This material is predominantly kaolin and can easily be removed with a sharpened needle held in a pin vise. Petrunkevitch (1913) preferred to study the natural molds or impressions of these fossils after removing the mineral-filling and any remnants of chitin. Because of the difficulty of studying negative impressions, I have resorted to preparing casts with a latex molding compound (Brooks, 1962, p. 165). The most minute detail can be reproduced on the surface of the latex if the specimen is properly prepared. Not only is it easier to study the rubber casts, but excellent photographs can be obtained if red latex is used in making the cast, if the surface of the reproduced fossil is coated lightly with ammonium chloride, and if orthochromatic film is used in taking the pictures.

CHEMICAL PREPARATION

It is routine paleontological procedure to remove silicified fossils from calcareous matrix with hydrochloric, acetic, or formic acid. Possibly more silicified specimens of chitinous arthropods should be searched for, but so far only a few remarkable specimens of crustaceans, arachnids, and insects have been obtained from calcareous concretions in a Miocene lacustrine deposit. Palmer (1957) freed these specimens from the matrix with formic acid diluted with four parts water.

Chitin and its carbonaceous residue are practically inert to most mineral-dissolving acids. Therefore, it should be possible to remove these organic skeletal remains from the matrix by digesting the rock in acid. In practice one might call this procedure paleontological maceration, for that is exactly what happens. Cracks in the fossil, and its tendency to dissociate and break up further, will reduce the specimen to a multitude of unrecognizable pieces. By taking great care in procedure and by providing structural support for the free skeletal pieces, Wills (1959, p. 263–265) has been most successful in freeing chitinous remains from sideritic concretions with hot hydrochloric acid. Since the technique is not generally known, its description is reproduced here verbatim.

1. Trim the sides of the specimen if possible so that it becomes roughly rectangular. With waterproof ink rule two lines across the matrix at right angles, and if possible, a third, parallel to and 1 inch from one of these. Continue these lines as sawcuts on the sides and back of the specimen. The lines should be close to the exposed fossil and parallel to the sides of the specimen if it has been squared up, or to the intended sides of the Marco block in which the fossil is to be embedded. The object of the lines and sawcuts is to enable one to locate the position of anything revealed on the back of the nodule in the correct relation to the original fossil.

2. Examine, photograph under alcohol, and sketch the fossil.

3. Make several enlargements of the photo, ×4, printing one from the front of the negative and several from the back.

4. Prepare a grid of ¼ inch squares on a sheet of celluloid, big enough to cover the whole piece of ironstone and the block of Marco; also a similar grid with 1 inch squares on paper, several copies of which will be needed.

5. Prepare a shallow metal box, big enough to take the specimen easily and

deeper than its thickness. Melt a little paraffin wax in it, and on this lay the specimen face upwards as level as possible. Add wax until the lower part of the ironstone is embedded in it. Now mix enough of the transparent polyester plastic Marco (supplied by Scott Bader and Co., Ltd., 109 Kingsway, London, W.C. 2) or similar plastic that polymerizes at room temperature, to fill the space above the wax and to cover the exposed surface of the fossil to a depth of 2–3 mm. Pour this and allow to polymerize. Cement down a glass cover-slip about the same size as the box, using fresh Marco. This glass usually falls away during the etching, but produces a smooth surface through which the specimen may be viewed. If the specimen is deep, pour only enough Marco to give a layer 6 to 8 mm. thick, and allow this to polymerize before pouring another layer. Allow the Marco to stand for two or three days, wipe off any sticky residue and remove the wax.

6. If thought advisable, grind the back of the specimen roughly parallel to the front, in order to reduce the amount of matrix to be dissolved.

7. Heat 10 percent, HCl in a basin on a water bath and in it place the Marco block and specimen with the exposed surface of ironstone upwards. Etch with pauses to examine the surface until some part—perhaps the claws—begin to appear. The first examinations can be made by lifting the specimen out of the acid and turning upside down in a basin of water to remove the scum and mud, but as soon as any chitinous part appears examination should be made thus: take the specimen carefully out of the acid and, keeping the exposed surface upwards, slide it slowly into a basin of warm water deep enough to cover it easily. The scum of mud floats away, and the specimen is withdrawn slowly, still with the exposed surface upwards. By this time it will probably lie at the bottom of a shallow well surrounded by Marco. If there are delicate parts exposed, the water in this well should be drawn off by a pipette until the ironstone is only moist. The specimen can then be safely carried to the dissecting microscope where water is restored by a pipette and an examination can be made. Never carry the specimen in water enough for loose bits to be washed out of position.

8. Place the ¼-inch celluloid grid over the well and, looking vertically through it, note the position of any object worth recording and sketch in the same on the 1-inch grid (which will ultimately be related to the lines on the exposed surface and the ×4 enlargement printed in reverse). A separate 1-inch grid is needed after each etch—at any rate, when much is emerging. It is often advisable to photograph at this stage and print ×4 to supplement one's sketch.

9. Suck off the water again and invert the moist, but not wet, specimen in a basin of water at the bottom of which are one or two 3 by 1 slides to catch, if possible, anything which has etched loose and any of the matrix which has not floated off with the waxy bubbles. If the specimen was originally thick, the well may now be deep. If so, drill a small drainage hole in the side of the Marco; otherwise air gets trapped in the inverted well. The hole is also useful to drain off the acid before the descumming described in (7).

10. Remove water from the specimen as before, transfer to microscope and re-examine under water. Photograph if necessary and note on 1 inch grid anything that now appears for the first time, having been obscured previously by debris.

11. Maneuver any bits of chitin left in the basin on to a 3 by 1 slip using a

pipette or brush or feather. Get the slip out of the water, wash off obvious mineral particles, examine the rest. If possible arrange the bits of chitin as they had appeared in (8). If a piece has to be turned over, always do this under water deep enough to cover the specimen in every position. If unrelated, put each bit on a separate slip. In every case label the slip with the number of the etch and position on the grid or otherwise relate the mount to the grid (the grids must also bear the number of the etch). Also, if possible, note which aspect is uppermost as mounted.

In some cases a bit first seen in an early etch may not become detached from the matrix until a later etch, and occasionally may remain throughout, being ultimately found to be attached to the Marco-cast.

12. Repeat (7) to (11) until all the matrix has disappeared (in some cases it may be well to stop the etching before this stage has been reached), numbering carefully each etch or group of etches on 1-inch grids, the photos and the mounts. There will then remain the mould in Marco of the parts originally exposed together with any chitin embedded in or attached to it. This, "the Marco-cast," will now show the ink lines and/or sawcuts made in (1) and it will be possible to relate the grid sketches and progress photos to it and to the reversed $\times 4$ photographs of the original exposed fossil. The Marco must now be thoroughly soaked in water to remove any acid.

13. Cement a cover-slip on to the flat side of the Marco-cast using either Xylol Balsam or Marco to replace the original slip which will almost certainly have flaked off during the etching.

The Marco-cast can now be examined from both sides by reflected or transmitted light, provided that the well has some water or alcohol put into it. It may be advisable to photo the side exposed by the etching.

Finally, in some cases where there is plenty of chitin embedded in the Marco-cast, the well after complete drying may be filled with Marco. After this has set and matured the surface must be ground flat and either polished or covered by a glass slip. When this is done all the skin that was originally exposed in the iron-stone together with other bits of skin that have remained attached to the Marco are revealed inside a transparent block.

14. In mounting the pieces remember that the chitin is very delicate and fragile, and must always be moved under water. The bits can be wetted and dried indefinitely. If any piece needs to be turned upside down, do this in water deep enough to cover it in every possible position it may take up. A dodge that sometimes succeeds is to place a 3 by 1 slip in a shallow basin of water, drain off the water from the specimen, invert it and the slip it is on; then just dip them into the water in the basin, then the specimen may drop on to the waiting slip the right side up.

*a.* If the specimen is in one piece it can be allowed to dry off under a bell jar to protect it from dust and draughts. When completely dry, damp it with benzol, remove any air bubbles and mount under a cover-slip, using Balsam in Xylol, Euparol, or Marco.

*b.* If the specimen is broken or consists of several pieces, arrange these in appropriate positions under a film of water. Allow to dry almost completely, run in a little dilute seccotine, allow this to dry completely, damp with benzol, and mount as above. Unless the bits are thus stuck to the slip they float apart during the covering process. On the other hand air may be trapped during the drying of the seccotine, and this mars the final result. This is obviated by using very dilute seccotine.

*c.* Balsam in Xylol and Euparol are easy to use but have the disadvantage that they take years to dry, especially if the mount is a thick one. Marco, on the other hand, sets completely, but with some contraction which may draw in air bubbles, if any are trapped under the cover-glass. After polymerization it is almost insoluble in any ordinary reagent, so that a remount is virtually impossible, whereas Balsam and Euparol are soluble in benzol and ethyl alcohol respectively, even after a year or more has elapsed.

*d.* If the specimen is thin it can be mounted in any of the above under a cover-slip without any spacing between the cover-slip and the 3 by 1 slide; but if it is moderately thick spacing must be provided such as strips of glass or a ring of some sort. Marco is best for both moderately thick and very thick specimens, but it is very mobile before polymerization and a ring of wax should surround the specimen to prevent it flowing out from under the cover-slip. If the specimen is very thick a glass or plastic spacing-ring or washer should be cemented carefully, with no gaps below it, on to the 3 by 1 glass. When this has set, pour in the Marco to the brim and allow it to polymerize nearly or completely. A meniscus will form on its surface, which should be carefully filled with Marco and covered with a cover-glass, making certain that there is no bubble below the cover. Should one be found, take off the cover-slip, re-fill and re-cover.

Hydrofluoric acid can be used to free chitinous remains from siliceous matrix. Great care must be exercised in handling this corrosive acid. Acetic acid has been used to liberate scraps of phosphatic cuticle from a calcareous matrix.

One should be warned that it is not possible to remove the seemingly perfectly preserved arthropod specimens from amber. The specimens crumble to dust when the support of the amber is removed by use of organic solvents.

X-RAY

X-ray can be used to observe morphological parts of fossils while they are still within the matrix if copper or iron salts have impregnated or replaced the skeletal materials. This method has been employed as a supplement to the study of the pyritized fossils from the Hunsrück shales of Germany.

POLISHED SURFACES AND THIN SECTIONS

Cut and polished surfaces are made on particles of fossiliferous amber to facilitate study of the enclosed remains. Cut and polished surfaces have also been employed in the study of the arachnid and myriapod fossils in onyx marbles (Chamberlin, 1949). The interlaminated figures in the compartmental plates of the shells of barnacles may be useful in distinguishing species. To prepare a polished surface, Cornwall (1962) embeds the shell in plaster of paris to hold the plates during the grinding and polishing process. Wetting the finished surface with benzyl alcohol makes the structures more visible.

Thin sections have rarely been attempted in the study of chitinous arthropods. With appropriate techniques employing serial sections or peel sections, it may be possible to reconstruct the appendages of some of the Paleozoic crustaceans, as Størmer (1939) has done with the trilobites.

MISCELLANEOUS TECHNIQUES

The outline of chitin and residual films can sometimes be better studied and photographed when the specimen is wet. Wetting increases the contrast between the specimen and the matrix. Various liquids have been used, including water, but alcohol or glycerin is recommended.

Because fossil chitin and its carbonaceous residue have a tendency to chip and spall, extra caution must be exercised in the collection, shipping, storage, and preparation of these specimens. In the past it has been a common museum practice to coat specimens with a surface film of lacquer or other material. Not only does the film render the fossil less useful for scientific study by obscuring it, but as the film ages, it shrinks and pulls away, actually damaging the specimen. If a cement is required to indurate or harden the specimen, a very thin binder such as thinned Duco cement, Alvar, or other stable nitrocellulose may be employed.

Many of the compressions and impressions of fossil arthropods are very nearly flat. Any technique that will emphasize the relief, to bring out the outline of the fossil, individual skeletal sclerites and ornament must be used. Experiments with infrared and ultraviolet photography have so far proved worthless. Oblique lighting will emphasize relief as well as a thin coating of ammonium chloride. Further contrast can be obtained on photographic prints by using appropriate films and paper. Vaguely preserved morphological features can often be more easily detected on a photograph than on the specimen.

## CONCLUSION

Fossil arthropods whose exoskeletons are not preserved by minerals are uncommon. In search for them the collector should examine deposits other than the typical marine sandstones, limestones, and shales. Unless a specific fossiliferous bed is known, the collector must not be disappointed if a diligent search fails to yield fossils even from a proved locality. Practically all chitinous arthropod fossils have potential scientific value. If you discover one, be sure that you have the steady hand, patience, skill, and knowledge to properly prepare it; even better, hand it over to a specialist.

## REFERENCES

Brooks, H. K. (1957). Chelicerata, Trilobitomorpha, Crustacea (Exclusive of Ostracoda), and Myriapoda, *in* H. S. Ladd (ed.), Marine ecology and paleoecology. Geol. Soc. America Mem. 67, v. 2, p. 895–930.

—— (1962). The Paleozoic Eumalacostraca of North America. Bull. Am. Paleontology, v. 44, p. 163–338.

Chamberlin, R. V. (1949). A new fossil chilopod from the Late Cenozoic. San Diego Soc. Nat. Hist. Trans., v. 11, p. 117–120.

Cornwall, I. E. (1962). The identification of barnacles with further figures and notes. Canadian J. Zoology, v. 40, p. 621–629.

Palmer, A. R. (1957). Miocene arthropods from the Mojave Desert, Calif. U. S. Geol. Survey, Prof. Paper 294-G, p. 237–280.

Petrunkevitch, A. (1913). A monograph of the terrestrial Paleozoic Arachnida of North America. Connecticut Acad. Arts Sci. Trans., v. 18, p. 1–139.

Raasch, G. O. (1939). Cambrian Merostomata. Geol. Soc. America Spec. Paper 19, 146 pp.

Rolfe, W. D. I. (1962). The cuticle of some Middle Silurian ceratiocaridid Crustacea from Scotland. Paleontology, v. 5, p. 30–51.

Scourfield, D. J. (1926). On a new type of crustacean from the Old Red Sandstone (Rhynie chert bed, Aberdeenshire), *Lepidocaris rhyniensis,* gen. et sp. nov. Roy. Soc. London Philos. Trans., ser. B., v. 214, p. 153–187.

Størmer, L. (1939). Studies on trilobite morphology; 1. The thoracic appendages and their phylogenetic significance: Norsk Geol. Tidsskr., v. 19, p. 143–273.

Wills, L. J. (1959). The external anatomy of some Carboniferous scorpions. Paleontology, v. 1, p. 261–281.

# Ostracods

I. G. SOHN, JEAN M. BERDAN

*U. S. Geological Survey, Washington, D.C.*

RAYMOND E. PECK

*University of Missouri, Columbia*

Ostracods are small, bivalved crustaceans whose range extends from Cambrian to Recent times. With the exception of the order Leperditicopida of the lower Paleozoic, which may reach a length of more than a centimeter, fossil ostracods rarely exceed more than one or two millimeters in length. In general, those from the lower Paleozoic systems tend to be somewhat larger than those from younger rocks, and are more easily recognized in the field. Fossil ostracods occur as separate valves, or with both valves together as complete carapaces. In lateral outline they are subelliptical, subovate, or reniform, and are frequently described as looking like beans. Some have elaborate spines or frills, and many are nodose. In general, the more highly ornamented forms

Publication authorized by the Director, U. S. Geological Survey.

are the most useful in correlation. The appendages are almost never preserved.

A 10× to 15× hand lens will aid in identifying the larger forms, and will help in the recognition of smaller ostracods. Samples of hard rock may be collected with a hammer; samples of unconsolidated rocks, with a clean trowel or shovel. As with any microfossils, the collecting bags should be clean, to prevent possible contamination.

Present-day ostracods live in marine, brackish, hypersaline, and fresh-water environments, and apparently did in the past. Consequently, their remains may be found in almost any type of sedimentary rock, although none have been reported from rocks of unquestioned fresh-water origin older than Mississippian. Possibly as a result of wide salinity tolerance, they may occur in rocks where no other fossils are present.

## COLLECTING OSTRACODS

The type of collecting technique depends primarily on the type of containing rock. With hard limestones or sandstones, the best procedure is to break the rock and examine both the fresh and weathered surfaces with a lens. If ostracods are seen, a sample of several pounds of rock should be taken, as more specimens will be found in laboratory preparation.

Because of their small size, ostracods are sometimes difficult to recognize in the field. They may easily be overlooked, or confused with rounded sand grains, worn crinoid columnals, and oolites. As fossil ostracod faunules are rarely composed entirely of complete carapaces, one of the best criteria for distinguishing them from oolites is the presence of separated valves, which may be seen in cross section on a broken surface, or as fragments, or weathered in relief on the surface of the rock as small arcuate traces. If large numbers of complete carapaces are present, the contact between the valves can usually be observed as a line. In cross section, the presence of an overlap distinguishes them from small pelecypods, brachiopods, and whorls of gastropods.

Paleozoic ostracods tend to be preserved in the same way as the trilobites in the same rock. For example, in rocks where trilobites are preserved as black or dark fragments against a gray matrix, the ostracods are also commonly black. Hence, it is sometimes helpful to check the type of preservation of the larger and more easily recognized trilobite fragments in order to spot the much smaller ostracods.

Ostracods are often visible on the weathered surfaces of thin-bedded calcareous rocks. Unfortunately, the weathering which makes the specimens noticeable tends to destroy the surface detail on which the identification of ostracods largely depends. Thus it is desirable to collect chunks of limestone at least three inches thick, as it is usually possible to obtain well-preserved specimens on the freshly broken surfaces of such pieces, especially since the individuals are apt to be randomly oriented in the rock. Thin slabs should also be collected, as surface silicification of such small objects—more likely to be developed on thin slabs—may yield excellent specimens when prepared in the laboratory.

Among the more indurated rocks, those that are least likely to contain well-preserved ostracods are oolites and coarsely crystalline dolomites in which recrystallization has destroyed or obscured the specimens. Shales in which the clay minerals tend to be micaceous may contain many specimens, but are poor sources of material for study. The clay particles tend to wrap around and obscure the details on small fossils such as ostracods, and the coating of clay particles is exceedingly difficult to remove without damaging the specimens.

Excellent ostracods have, however, been taken from calcareous shales and marls, where they are usually associated with varied fossils of other groups. Collectors of megafossils from such beds are advised to fill their collecting bags with the matrix in which the larger fossils occur. This protects the larger fossils and may later be washed for microfossils.

In sections composed of alternating limestones and shales, such as much of the upper Paleozoic, shale breaks between limestones are a productive source of ostracods. These are easily processed, and may contain well-preserved fossils; just above and just below the limestones, the shales are favorable for ostracods.

With few exceptions, the post-Paleozoic ostracods are smaller than Paleozoic forms. They occur in greensands, marls, clays, and shales, as well as in more indurated rocks. Shell beds and beds containing debris of larger fossils usually yield well-preserved ostracods. Ostracods are sometimes found as coquinas; in some of these the specimens are well preserved, in others the specimens are not as well preserved as those found in other rock types. In addition to the coquina lenses, it is wise to collect the sediments enclosing them in case they contain better-preserved specimens.

The distribution of ostracods varies considerably, both laterally and vertically, in the sedimentary sequence. It is therefore advisable, for preliminary collecting where ostracods cannot be seen in the field, to take consecutive channel samples of the principal beds or groups of beds exposed in the section. Subsequent collecting in the promising beds can then be done to determine the precise ostracod-bearing horizon.

In general, nonmarine stratigraphic units are thick, and fossils are scarce. Random or casual sampling for microfossils in such sediments is almost sure to be discouraging, and may lead to the conclusion that they are unfossiliferous.

The best lithologies for collecting nonmarine ostracods are gray calcareous shales associated with fossiliferous limestones. However, many shale partings

from nonfossiliferous limestones yield microfossils, whereas some shale partings in fossiliferous limestones yield none.

Shales and sandy shales containing fresh-water molluscan fossils are almost
sure to yield microfossils in abundance. Calcareous shales of various shades
of gray have a good potential for microfossils even when not associated with
limestones. Some red and green shales yield ostracods, but the percentage
of those that do is small.

The fossiliferous zones in nonmarine sediments may be thin. In order to
find them without handling a great bulk of material, it is sometimes necessary
to select an exposure that appears favorable and let one sample represent a
considerable thickness of strata. An exposure is as well represented as possible by taking a small amount of material from each parting or zone until
a sample of convenient size is obtained. The stratigraphic thickness included
in any one sample will vary widely and will depend on such factors as number
of favorable zones, size of sample taken from each, thickness of outcrop, and
accessibility of outcrop to collector. If the sample contains microfossils the
outcrop should be revisited and detailed collections made. This method has
obvious disadvantages, in that the collector may not be able to return to the
outcrop, but it does enable the collector to find the fossiliferous zones more
quickly and keeps him from getting bogged down with a large number of
unproductive samples.

## PREPARATION OF SAMPLES

The purpose of this section is to describe the techniques used in preparing
ostracods for study. These depend to a large extent on the type of containing
rock, and the first step in laboratory preparation is to examine the matrix to
decide on the appropriate procedure. Once this has been done, a portion of
the sample should be tested to see whether it contains good specimens. For
several reasons, an entire sample should never be used in trying out any one
technique; for example, limestone in which the fossils appear to be silicified
may dissolve completely. In general, hard rocks, such as limestones, dolomites, sandstones, and some shales, will yield fossils only to hand tooling,
crushing, or if silicified, treatment with acid. Soft rocks, such as most shales,
clays, marls, and some sandstones, may be treated by the schedule of operations given here, which is a modification of the section published in the
*Treatise on Invertebrate Paleontology,* part Q (Sohn, 1961, p. 64–70), and
of the section on preparation and study of Ostracoda in a paper on the Lower
Tertiary ostracods from western Pakistan (Sohn, in press). The same methods
are applicable to the preparation of other microfossils; most of these, as
well as additional methods, have been described previously by Pokorny
(1958); Triebel (1958); Witwicka, Bielecka, Styk, and Sztejn (1958); and
Jekhowsky (1959).

### BOILING IN WATER

Most soft sediments break down by boiling them in water to which one or two tablespoons of soda ash have been added. Stir occasionally in order not to burn the pot. Sediments containing interstitial water do not break down as readily as those that are dry, consequently it is common practice to air-dry collections prior to boiling. To check whether a particular sample will break down by boiling, bite off a small piece and put it in the mouth; if it disintegrates, it will break down. Add a tablespoon of salt to bentonitic sediments in order to inhibit swelling.

### WASHING

Wash the broken sample through a set of sieves. This operation reduces the volume in two ways: unbroken pieces and larger fossils are separated from the microfossiliferous fraction, and finer material is removed. Sieves become clogged when fine sediment clogs the holes of the mesh and when too much material is put in the sieve.

For convenience in washing, two sieves (A and B) are used. Sieve A is 10 inches in diameter and 5 inches deep, with 200-mesh copper screen reinforced on the bottom by 16-mesh copper screen. Below the screen is a 1-inch sleeve which protects the mesh and prevents contamination from the bottom. The lower edge of this sleve is perforated by $\frac{1}{4}$-inch semicircular holes $2\frac{1}{2}$ inches from center to center. These holes permit the water to flow out from beneath the screen. Sieve B is 9 inches in diameter and 5 inches deep, with a 16-mesh copper screen. This sieve fits into sieve A and removes particles that are larger than most microfossils. Three copper angles are soldered on the outside of sieve B, $1\frac{1}{2}$ inches from the top, in order to keep the bottom of this sieve well above the screen of sieve A, and three legs 1 to 2 inches long protect the screen. The mesh is attached on the inside of the sieves by smooth solder for ease of cleaning.

Standard screens of 16- and 100-, or finer, mesh can be used. For Foraminifera, a 200-mesh screen is necessary. Tilt the standard screens by propping one end with a spoon handle or piece of wood in order to permit the water to escape from under the screen.

Wash the sample with a hose. If the fine sediment clogs the screen, pinch the end of the hose in order to increase the velocity of the water and hold it close to the screen; this breaks the seal and the fine sediment can then be washed out. Continue washing until the water escaping from the screen is clear. Then dry the concentrate.

### DRYING

The washed sediment can be dried either in the sieve, if the sieve is not needed for a second sample, or transferred to newspaper for drying. Spread several thicknesses of newspaper and turn the sieve over on the paper; most of the wet sediment will fall on the paper. With the hose, wash the remaining sediment to the center of the screen, then turn it over and drop it gently on the newspaper. The remaining sediment will fall out of the screen. Repeat if necessary. Fold the newspaper over several times, insert an identifying label, and set the sample aside to dry. The plus-16 fraction can be discarded, dried in the same manner as the minus-16 fraction and stored, or subjected to other methods of disaggregation.

### HYDROGEN PEROXIDE AND GASOLINE METHOD

Dry the sample, cover it in a sauce pan with 15 percent hydrogen peroxide, and let it soak from 2 to 24 hours. Add more water and boil. Most samples will break down, but those that do not can be treated as follows: When dry, place the sample in a porcelain evaporating dish on a warm hot plate. When warm, add a few drops of 15 percent hydrogen peroxide. Usually a vigorous reaction will take place and the shale will break down. Add water and boil. Wash. Some calcareous fossils are corroded by hydrogen peroxide, consequently its use is limited.

Sodium hypochlorite, obtained in 5.25 percent solution as a common household bleach, can be used instead of hydrogen peroxide (Hoffmeister, 1960). It is less expensive, does not injure calcareous fossils, and is safer to use.

Dry the sample, cover it in a sauce pan with commercial gasoline (store in a metal container), and soak from 15 minutes to 1 hour. Filter the gasoline back into the container, add two tablespoons of soda ash, cover the sample with water, and boil. Varsol, which is not as flammable as gasoline, and also less expensive, may be substituted for gasoline.

### SODIUM ACETATE

Rocks are comminuted in nature by freezing and thawing. The forces exerted by the formation of ice crystals in pores break up the rock. This is accomplished in the laboratory by use of sodium acetate. Break the dry rock into about one-inch cubes, place in a beaker or a crucible, and cover with sodium acetate. Add 4 to 5 drops of water, cover the beaker, and place it over low heat. The sodium acetate will melt and soak into the pores of the rock. Remove from heat and cool by placing in a pan of water. The sodium acetate will crystallize and rupture the rock. Add a few drops of water and repeat the process. The first crystallization will weaken the rock so that it will subsequently break down more readily. Continued melting and solidifying will not only disintegrate the rock, but also will break up the fossils, consequently it is best to decant the melted solution of sodium acetate into a second beaker to which are transferred the larger remaining pieces of rock, and repeat the process. The sodium acetate that remains with the broken sediment will be dissolved when the sediment is boiled.

Occasionally the force of crystallization will break the glass beaker, but if the pan of cooling water is clean, the uncontaminated sediment can be recovered. Stainless steel beakers may be substituted for those made of glass. Crystallization is accelerated by adding a few grains of sodium acetate to act as nuclei for the crystals.

The same results are obtained by the slower method of freezing and thawing in a refrigerator. The broken sediment should be removed after each thawing to prevent breakage of the fossils. The sediment is then boiled.

## MECHANICAL CRUSHING

The process consists in applying a crushing force rather than a breaking force to the rock fragments by using an electrically driven rock crusher. The same results can be obtained with an iron mortar and pestle, or by placing small chunks of rock in a canvas bag and applying a crushing force by using a wood mallet or the handle of a hammer. Electric blendors have been used to break sediments and release fossils.

## ACID ETCHING

Silicified fossils can be removed from limestone by etching with hydrochloric acid. Certain fossils are more successfully removed by use of acetic acid, or the more expensive but faster acting formic acid.

Wash the rock to remove all adhering mud, break it into chunks, and place it in an acid-resistant vessel. Cover it with water and add sufficient acid to start bubbling. Periodically decant, replacing water and acid. Many apparently silicified fossils contain an appreciable amount of calcium carbonate; consequently, it is advantageous to harvest the fine material between changes of acid. Neutralize the residue with soda ash and boil it in order to remove any fine mud from the specimens. Should the silicified specimens be exceptionally fragile, or should the residue be relatively clean of mud, it is not necessary to boil them.

## HAND TOOLING

Many ostracods are so fragile that they are destroyed by boiling; other specimens have ornament that breaks when crushed from hard rocks. These must be handled individually. Slabs of rock are broken along and across the bedding planes and the surfaces examined with a microscope. If the fossils are nearly the same color as the matrix, it is sometimes advisable to coat the surface to be examined with either ammonium chloride (p. 85) or magnesium oxide (p. 86) to accentuate the fossils. When a specimen is found, it is either circled with a colored pencil or stained with malachite green to aid in finding it again. The specimen is then cleaned with a needle or a Vibro-tool to determine whether it is sufficiently complete to be worth extracting. The use of a Vibro-tool speeds up this part of the operation, but excellent preparation may be done with an ordinary sewing needle held in a pin vise. It is essential, however, that the needle in the Vibro-tool or pin vise be kept sharp, and a whetstone or a grinding wheel should be available. When using a Vibro-tool, it is important not to exert too much pressure; not only may the point slip and damage the specimen, but the matrix can be split or chipped more effectively if the instrument is held loosely. Kesling (1954) described an instrument used for cleaning small fossils that was based on the principal of a microdissector.

Once the specimen has been cleaned, if it is to be removed from the rock, a groove is scraped (with a needle) or chipped (with a Vibro-tool) around it, far enough removed to insure against accidental breaking. This groove may be cut below the specimen so that it can be chipped from the rock. As the specimen may pop off at this stage it is a good idea to have a clean sheet of paper beneath the microscope so that the specimen may be readily recovered. Some specimens may be extracted by sawing around them with separating discs attached to a dental drill, so that a square of rock is cut out, which can be cemented to a slide.

### SIEVING

The dried sample is conveniently separated into fractions of different sizes by sieving through nested screens. The minus 16- plus 200-mesh sediment is dry-sieved through a series of 40-, 60-, 80-, and 100-mesh screens. A 150-mesh screen can be added if very small fossils are expected. The combination of screen sizes is a matter of individual preference. Screens should be thoroughly cleaned after each sieving.

In order to avoid contamination, the screens should be dipped for a few minutes after each use in an aqueous solution of methylene blue. Any specimens (except pyritized fossils) caught in the screens will then be colored blue and will be easily recognized as contaminants should they become incorporated in subsequently sieved samples (Beckmann, 1959). An alcohol solution of methylene blue dries faster than a water solution.

Some laboratories in the U. S. Geological Survey clean sieves by using ultrasonic vibration. The sieves are immersed in water in the ultrasonic cell and are cleaned by several minutes of treatment.

### HEAVY-LIQUID SEPARATION

Many types of microfossils can be concentrated by use of heavy liquids, and various techniques for accomplishing this have been described. Ostracods do not usually lend themselves to such treatment, but must be hand picked under a binocular microscope. Howe (1941) described a method of floating microfossils, including ostracods, by use of soap suds in warm water.

### PICKING

Samples obtained from the 40- and 60-mesh screens are conveniently picked under a low-power microscope, whereas those from smaller size screens require medium power.

Various picking trays have been described. The simplest is a flat-bottomed black-painted tray with 0.15-inch or higher sides and open on one end. Horizontal and vertical lines are painted or grooved on the picking surface. The distance between the lines should correspond approximately to the field of view seen through the microscope. Scatter an evenly distributed layer of prepared sediment on the tray so that each particle can be seen. By moving the tray back and forth under the microscope, every grain can be examined and the fossils picked out.

For picking up fossils and placing them in well-slides or other receptacles, it is best to use a No. 00, or finer, sable or camel's-hair brush. Dip the brush in water and pass it over the back of the other hand, rolling the handle between the fingers. This removes excess water and makes a point on the tip of the brush. Some workers wet the brush with saliva, but this is not advisable because the brush may be contaminated with harmful substances such as dyes and carbolic or other acid used to inhibit bacterial growth in the glue —not to mention that specimens adhering to the brush may be swallowed. Always examine the brush under the microscope before dipping it in water in order to insure that specimens inadvertently picked up by the brush are not dropped into the water.

### PREPARATION OF INDIVIDUAL SPECIMENS

Although the various methods of disaggregating and washing sediments commonly result in clean specimens, matrix sometimes adheres to the outside of specimens or remains inside the valves. This extraneous material needs to be removed in order to observe shell structures. Such cleaning may be done by manual, chemical, or mechanical methods.

For manual cleaning, place the loose specimen on a cardboard slide, cover it with a drop of water, and remove the matrix with a sharp needle. A small glass dish with a thin layer of beeswax on the bottom can be used instead of a slide. The drop of water, in addition to possibly softening the matrix, prevents the specimen from popping out of the slide when touched with the needle. A chewed wooden toothpick makes an excellent stiff-bristled broom to sweep matrix from a valve. A sharpened toothpick can be used instead of a needle on fragile specimens.

For chemical cleaning, matrix can be removed from individual carapaces or valves by soaking them in a 15 percent solution of hydrogen peroxide in a concave glass slide, observing progress of the reaction through a microscope. A toothpick may be used to sweep away the matrix. Hydrofluoric acid will remove siliceous matrix from calcareous specimens and at the same time render the specimens translucent (Sohn, 1956). The valves of hollow carapaces are sometimes dissociated by the gas pressure that is generated in this process.

Experiments in the use of ultrasonic vibration have proved successful in mechanically cleaning individual ostracod specimens, but if incipient fractures are present, the specimens tend to break. In ultrasonic treatment, high-frequency acoustical waves are transmitted to water or other liquids by means of electrostrictive or magnetostrictive devices called transducers. The transducers are designed for various industrial uses, either as integral parts of stainless steel tanks or as separate units that can be immersed in tanks available in the laboratory. This process works well for disaggregating such groups of fossils as diatoms and foraminifers but usually cannot be used for recovering and cleaning ostracods, because they tend to break (Sohn, 1960).

For ease in ultrasonic treatment of individual specimens the following procedure is recommended. Cover the fossils with about $\frac{1}{4}$ inch of water in a beaker that is about $\frac{1}{2}$ inch in diameter. Place this beaker in a larger beaker, and add water in such amount that the small beaker does not float and tip over. Then place the larger beaker in the tank with the transducers. Control the depth of water to prevent the large beaker from floating and tipping. About one minute of ultrasonic treatment is sufficient to clean most specimens.

### MOUNTING SPECIMENS

It is customary to glue ostracod specimens to micropaleontology slides, and for this purpose all types of glue, including Duco cements, have been used. Duco cement and most glues may in time contract upon hardening and thus rupture some specimens. Experience has shown that a dilute solution of gum tragacanth, to which a few drops of phenol or oil of cinnamon are added to prevent the development of mold, is admirably suited for the purpose of mounting small fossils. The specimens can be easily unglued by wetting them with a brush. Should it be necessary to remove all traces of the gum tragacanth from a specimen, immerse it in alcohol; the gum tragacanth will then form a milky, cohesive, gel-like substance that can be teased away easily with a needle.

## ILLUSTRATION AND STUDY

Ostracods can be illustrated by drawings, photographs, or a combination of both. The diagnostic features used in their classification may be external, such as shape and surface ornament; internal, such as type of hinge, muscle-scar pattern, pore canals, and marginal structures; or a combination of both. Consequently, the method of illustration and the magnification used vary with the individual taxon. Magnifications of $10\times$ to $600\times$ or more have been used. Choice of magnification depends on the size of the specimen and the features to be illustrated. Moreover, these features determine whether reflected or transmitted light should be used.

Ideally, an ostracod should be shown in lateral, dorsal, ventral, posterior, and/or anterior views. When the two valves differ, both should be shown.

Often, the interior structures should be illustrated. It is sometimes necessary to illustrate cross sections either as polished surfaces or thin sections.

Because of their small size, orienting and posing individuals for drawing and photography is a problem. Specimens may be attached to a needle inserted in a cork or other material and oriented as desired. Satisfactory results can be obtained by posing the specimen on a paper slide. For dorsal or end views, the specimen can be mounted on its lateral surface on a slide prepared as follows: Cut a single-hole, 16-gauge paper slide in half, and trim it to fit into a 26-gauge or larger faunal slide. Paint the cut edge below the black paper and the rim surrounding the semicircle with black India ink. Attach the specimen by its side near the edge of the slide, oriented so that the view desired is parallel with the cut edge. This slide can then be posed on a shelf if a horizontally mounted camera is used, or in a slot if a vertically mounted camera is used, so that the desired view is normal to the camera.

The mounted specimen can be safely transported or stored in a faunal slide in which a thin, short strip of paper is glued to act as a spacer to protect the specimen from damage by touching the side of the faunal slide.

The plastic cleaning material available for cleaning typewriter type is a suitable medium to use for posing specimens. A specimen picked up with a moistened brush and placed on this substance will adhere and remain oriented. The substance is not affected by ammonium chloride or alcohol and does not adhere to the specimen. When some specimens are left on this substance for more than two days, oil from the substance penetrates them and prevents proper coating with ammonium chloride.

STUDY WITH REFLECTED LIGHT

Ostracods usually are examined with reflected light. Finer details are better seen when the specimen is either coated or stained. For best results in photography specimens should be coated. Triebel (1958) describes methods of preparing specimens for photography.

*Ammonium chloride coating.* Bassler and Kellett (1934, p. 9, fig. 2) describe an apparatus that will coat specimens with a thin film of ammonium chloride sublimate through the combination of fumes of concentrated hydrochloric acid and ammonia. This method is not satisfactory for microscopic specimens because high humidity commonly causes the grain size of the sublimate to be too large. Hessland (1949, p. 115) describes a method which is an improvement on that reported by Branson and Mehl (1933, p. 17), and by Cooper (1935, p. 357), for obtaining a fine-grained deposit of ammonium chloride sublimate. A simplification of Hessland's method consists in drawing out one end of a 4-inch piece of glass tubing (2- or 3-mm inside diam.) to form a fine nozzle, and filling it with ammonium chloride powder through the other end. This end is then sealed with plastic wood or plaster of paris. When the tube is heated, a jet of ammonium chloride is released through the nozzle. The vapor can then be directed over the specimen and a fine-grained sublimate deposited on the specimen. I have used a vial prepared in this manner for several years.

*Magnesium oxide coating.* Specimens can be coated by passing them through the fumes from a piece of burning magnesium ribbon held with forceps. This method is advantageous in that the film remains on the specimen until it is brushed off. *Caution:* The light emitted by burning magnesium can be injurious to eyesight; avoid looking directly at the light.

*Staining.* Stains cause fine detail to stand out on specimens, and almost any kind of ink or food-coloring can be used for this purpose (Artusy and Artusy, 1956). Malachite green (Henbest, 1931, p. 358) dissolved in alcohol has proved to be most suitable for staining ostracods because it dries rapidly. This stain can be removed with alcohol.

*Silver nitrate coating.* Levinson (1951) described a technique for depositing a metallic film of silver nitrate on ostracods. This method involves heating a clean specimen for about three seconds, allowing it to cool to room temperature, and then painting it with 5 percent silver nitrate solution. After 15 seconds draw off the excess with filter paper and reheat the specimen over a bunsen flame for 1 minute. The resulting metallic film is permanent, but has the disadvantage of obscuring pore-canals and muscle scars.

### STUDY WITH TRANSMITTED LIGHT

The muscle scars, pore canals, and duplicature of ostracods are best observed in transmitted light, and methods of making the valves translucent have been devised. The same methods can be used to observe certain structures with reflected light.

*Liquid immersion technique.* Sometimes water is adequate to observe the structures in transmitted light, but usually glycerin or an immersion oil is used. Wagner (1957, p. 17) soaked ostracod specimens for several hours in castor oil in order to make them translucent.

*Canada balsam technique.* Specimens mounted in canada balsam will show structures in transmitted light that are not seen on dry specimens.

*Hydrofluoric acid technique.* Calcareous specimens can be converted to fluorite by use of hydrofluoric acid (Sohn, 1956). Fluorite is more translucent in water or glycerin than calcite, and many calcareous specimens that show no shell structure will exhibit muscle scars and marginal structures when converted to fluorite.

### STUDY WITH POLISHED SECTIONS AND THIN SECTIONS

Overlap, certain types of hingements, and duplicatures of ostracods can be observed on polished surfaces and in thin sections. The specimen is mounted on a glass slide in canada balsam, bioplastic, or other suitable medium and ground in the same manner as thin sections of rocks. When the specimen has been ground to the desired plane, it is turned over on the slide and the other side ground until the section is of the required thickness.

It is possible to reconstruct the structure of a complete ostracod carapace by means of a series of polished surfaces (Kesling and Sohn, 1958, p. 518), records of which can readily be made photographically and by aid of camera lucida. When canada balsam is used, the specimen is oriented with a tooth-pick or a warm needle. It is easier to observe wall structures if the specimen is stained prior to mounting in the cement. The stain sometimes penetrates the shell material so that the inside border of the shell can be seen.

Sylvester-Bradley (1941, p. 6) obtained excellent results in reconstructing large specimens with thin shells by first making a drawing of the specimen to be studied and then breaking the specimen with a needle and recording the lines of fracture on the drawing. Each fragment was then mounted on its edge with a gum tragacanth smear, and examined.

MEASUREMENT

Ostracods are sometimes difficult to measure because of their convex lateral surfaces and also because many genera overhang on the dorsal margin, the ventral margin, or both. Dissociated valves can be measured on the in-side. The valve is attached along its contact margins with gum tragacanth to a glass slide, and the slide is inverted so that the specimen hangs in a paper slide. Any chosen parameters, such as height, greatest length, or hinge length, can then be measured by focusing through the glass, using a micrometer ocular.

Complete carapaces that have straight ventral or dorsal margins can be posed with those margins attached to a glass slide, and greatest length, hinge length, and width measured. In order to measure the height of such carapaces and the width of single valves, stand the glass slide on edge, and focus the microscope on the plane to be measured. To hold the glass slide steady and to keep it oriented parallel to the line of sight, back the slide with a firm support. A support with a square cross section can be made by taping 20 glass slides with scotch tape. Press the glass slide that holds the specimen against the supporting block and focus the microscope on the specimen. Carapaces without straight sides can be oriented for precise measurement by use of a Goldschmidt two-circle goniometer (Sohn, 1962).

## REFERENCES

Artusy, R. L., and J. C. Artusy (1956). The use of food coloring as a new technique for staining microfossils. J. Paleontology, v. 30, p. 969–970, 1 text-fig.

Bassler, R. S., and Betty Kellett (1934). Bibliographic index of Paleozoic Ostracoda. Geol. Soc. America Spec. Paper 1, 500 pp., 24 text-figs.

Beckmann, von, Heinz (1959). Verunreiningung von Mikroproben beim Schlämmen. Paläont. Zeitschr., v. 33, no. 1/2, p. 124.

Branson, E. B., and M. G. Mehl (1933). Conodont studies no. 1; Conodonts from Harding sandstone of Colorado; from the Bainbridge (Silurian) of Missouri; from the Jefferson City (Lower Ordovician) of Missouri. Missouri Univ. Studies, v. 8, no. 1, 72 pp., 4 pls., 1 text-fig.

Cooper, C. L. (1935). Ammonium chloride sublimate apparatus. J. Paleontology, v. 9, p. 357–359, 2 text-figs.

Henbest, L. G. (1931). The use of selective stains in paleontology. J. Paleontology, v. 5, p. 355–364.

Hessland, Ivar (1949). Investigations of the Lower Ordovician of the Siljan district, Sweden: 1. Lower Ordovician ostracods of the Siljan district, Sweden. Geol. Inst. Univ. Uppsala Bull., v. 33, p. 97–408, 26 pls.

Hoffmeister, W. S. (1960). Sodium hypochlorite, a new oxidizing agent for the preparation of microfossils. Oklahoma Geol. Notes, v. 20, p. 34–35.

Howe, H. V. (1941). Use of soap in the preparation of samples for micropaleontologic study. J. Paleontology, v. 15, p. 691.

Jekhowsky, B. de (1959). Une technique standard de preparation des roches pur l'étude des microfossiles organiques. Inst. Française Pétrole., Rev., v. 14, no. 3, p. 315–320.

Kesling, R. V. (1954). An instrument for cleaning small fossils. Michigan Univ. Mus. Paleontology Contr., v. 11, no. 10, p. 193–199, 2 pls.

———, and I. G. Sohn (1958). The Paleozoic ostracod genus *Alanella* Boucek, 1936. J. Paleontology, v. 32, p. 517–524, pl. 78, 3 text-figs.

Levinson, S. A. (1951). The Triebel technique for staining ostracods. Micropaleontologist, v. 5, p. 27.

Pokorny, Vladimir (1958). Grundzüge der Zoologischen Mikropaläontologie. Deutsche Verlag Wiss., Berlin, v. 1, 582 pp., 549 text-figs.

Sohn, I. G. (1956). The transformation of opaque calcium carbonate to translucent calcium fluoride in fossil Ostracoda. J. Paleontology, v. 30, no. 1, p. 113–114, pl. 25.

——— (1960). Cleaning ostracod valves with ultrasonic vibrations (abs.). Geol. Soc. America Bull., v. 71, p. 1982.

——— (1961). Techniques for preparation and study of fossil ostracods, *in* R. C. Moore (ed.), Treatise on invertebrate paleontology, Part Q, Arthropoda 3. Geol. Soc. America and Univ. Kansas Press, p. 64–70.

——— (1962). Stratigraphic significance of the Paleozoic ostracod genus *Coryellina* Bradfield, 1935. J. Paleontology, v. 36, p. 1201–1213, pl. 167, 3 text-figs.

——— (in press). Lower Tertiary ostracods from Western Pakistan with a section on the preparation and study of Ostracoda. Pakistan Geol. Survey, Mem. Palaeontologia Pakistanica, v. 3, pt. 2.

Sylvester-Bradley, P. C. (1941). The shell structure of the Ostracoda and its application to their paleontological investigation. Ann. Mag. Nat. Hist., ser. 11, v. 8, p. 1–33, 18 text-figs.

Triebel, Erich (1958). Ostracoden, *in* Hugo Freund (ed.), Handbuch der Mikroskopie und der Technik. v. 2, pt. 3, p. 193–236, 8 pls.

Wagner, C. W. (1957). Sur les ostracodes du Quaternaire Récent des Pays-bas et leur utilisation dans l'étude des dépots Holocènes. The Hague, Mouton Co., 259 pp.

Witwicka, E., W. Bielecka, O. Styk, and J. Sztejn (1958). The methods of working out microfossils. Poland Inst. Geol., Bull., 156 pp., 1 pl., 69 text-figs.

# Branchiopods

PAUL TASCH

*Department of Geology, University of Wichita, Wichita, Kansas*

Branchiopod fossils have been used in correlating parts of the European Carboniferous and parts of the American Midcontinent Leonardian, as well as Asiatic Mesozoic beds. They also have many other important applications. Such fossils can contribute new data on certain aspects of crustacean evolution (Tasch, 1962b). They can provide otherwise inaccessible paleolimnological data on such items as: depth of water, temperature, salinity, pH and eH of water and bottom muds, or permit evaluation of seasonal changes in a Paleozoic puddle, pond, or lake. In addition, conchostracan-bearing beds constitute a sensitive crustacean clock on which *months* of time in the geologic past can be distinguished (Tasch, 1961, text-fig. 3).

The crustacean subclass Branchiopoda embraces seven orders, three of which are extinct and all of which have a fossil record. One can place the orders into three large groups (superorders) in each of which the subtended orders show close affinities. Group I: Acercostraca (Dev.), Kazacharthra (L. Jur.), and Notoscraca (Carb.–Rec.). Group II: Conchostraca (L. Dev.–Rec.) and Cladocera (Olig.–Rec.). Group III: Anostraca (Carb.–Rec.) and Lipostraca (M. Dev.). Each of these groups will be discussed in greater detail. Specific emphasis will be given to the question of where to look for, and what techniques can aid in the discovery of, specific fossil branchiopods. Detailed methodology applicable to nonmarine biofacies in general is given in Part II of this book.

## GROUP I: ACERCOSTRACA, KAZACHARTHRA, AND NOTOSTRACA

Fossils belonging to any of the orders in this group are generally characterized by a chitinous dorsal shield (cephalothorax) and/or a telson and a supra-anal plate. Occasionally, impressions of a particular part, such as the shell-gland, may constitute the only fossil evidence for a notostracan, as is the case for *Triops beedei* from the Permian in Oklahoma.

Notostracan are 30 mm or less in size. A half-bushel of living *Triops* can be found in a shallow, dried depression that was once a pond some twenty feet in diameter. Since notostracans are burrowers and inhabit temporary basins, one can expect to find fossil notostracan dorsal shields strewn on horizontally restricted bedding planes of thin shale, silty shale, or argillaceous sandstone. Trusheim (1938) found thousands of *Triops* fragments in a thin zone of green shale and sandstone of Middle Keuper (Triassic) age.

The two living genera of notostracans, *Triops* and *Lepidurus,* have fossil representatives closely similar morphologically. Species of *Lepidurus* are known from the Triassic of South Africa, the Lower Cretaceous of Turkestan, and the Pleistocene of England. Species of *Triops* are particularly prominent in certain zones of the German Carboniferous and Triassic.

American Lower Devonian shales, similar to the Hunsrück of Germany, may contain equivalents of the acercostracan *Vachonia* (Lehmann, 1955). Lower Jurassic beds, such as the Sundance Formation[1] of Southwestern Wyoming, may be expected to yield branchiopods. The lithic-biotic evidence from the Kazakhstan Lower Jurassic (Novojilov, 1957) indicates a crustacean horizon in a gray, slaty, gypsiferous clay in which hundreds of kazacharthran fossil shields, telsons, and isolated body parts occur. Below that bed there is a carbonaceous bed containing characteristic plants, insects, and conchostracans. If fossil branchiopods are to be found in the American Jurassic, argillite sequences characterized by carbonized and evaporite zones should be favorable sites to search.

## GROUP II: CONCHOSTRACA AND CLADOCERA

Fossil conchostracans will generally be represented by left or right valves, concave upward, flattened and/or crushed. Numerous valves are commonly found overlying one another, the whole array impressed on a bedding plane of thin argillites and argillaceous limestone. Mesozoic conchostracans will often be represented by hollow, external valve casts or internal molds, although original chitinous valves flattened on thin, papery shales or slatey shales are not uncommon.

Living conchostracans inhabit temporary depressions of any size, ranging from puddles to large ponds, in open fields and in dried-out creek beds, or isolated patches of water on river flood plains. The forms found as fossils once inhabited such restricted bodies of water, living in the shallow margins only a few inches deep.

In life, fossil conchostracans inhabited a broad array of environments. Marine environments are indicated for some conchostracans in the German Devonian, where they were fossilized with marine ostracods, and in the

---

[1] A poorly preserved fossil from this formation studied by the writer was found to be closer to the conchostracans than any other group. Conchostracans occur in the Russian Jurassic below the horizon bearing the branchiopod order Kazacharthra.

German Carboniferous, where they were fossilized with trilobites. The Carboniferous of Ireland contained a form *Limnestheria ardra* that clearly inhabited an estuarine environment. The Williston Basin *Rhabdostichus*-type conchostracan (Wilson, 1956) apparently lived in a brackish-marine environment, and was found to extend around the basin. Conchostracans from the North American Mississippian through the Triassic are frequently fresh- to brackish-water forms, as indicated by floral and faunal associates.

The Russian and Asiatic Cretaceous have yielded a large number of conchostracan fossils, but no American forms of this age have yet been reported. Ribbed conchostracans (an extinct group called leaiids) are common in the Permo-Carboniferous of Europe and North America, and are useful stratigraphic and paleoecological indicators (Mitchell, 1925; Tasch, 1962b; Guthörl, 1934).

The American Mesozoic, particularly the Jurassic-Cretaceous, seems to offer especially promising possibilities for the discovery of fossil conchostracans. Beds containing plant and/or insect fossils, coals, or evaporites are the most likely to sample for this purpose (Kobayashi, 1954; Novojilov, 1954).

Curiously, no fossil conchostracans have been reported from the Tertiary of any continent, although it is apparent that conchostracans alive today derive from Pleistocene and pre-Pleistocene ancestors. Here again, plant and insect beds, Tertiary coal and evaporite deposits (particularly interbedded evaporitic shales) are the places to search for such fossils.

Fossil cladocerans are known predominantly from late glacial and postglacial deposits (Frey, 1958). However, there is a Tertiary record as far back as the Oligocene, when daphniid ephippia were preserved. Recently, fossil caldoceran ephippia were reported from lacustrine deposits of the Miocene Humboldt Formation (Dickinson and Swain, 1961). The folded chitinous univalve of cladocerans appears to be bivalved in lateral view. In several species, the valve has a portion called the ephippium, which contains two eggs. The ephippium separates from the valve when extreme conditions such as freezing or drying occur. Ephippia often accumulate along the shore and, in such condition, are readily subject to burial and fossilization.

Living cladocerans and their fossil equivalents in life also inhabit fresh to brackish and slightly alkaline waters of all types. Today they are found in the marginal vegetation of rivers, the weedy margins of lakes and swamps, in shallow, silty, and muddy ponds, in both permanent ponds and temporary rainwater ponds. Some species live in the shallow ditches of rice paddies. A few marine genera are known (Tasch, 1962b).

In addition to ephippia, interglacial (Frey, 1960) and postglacial deposits may contain the following cladoceran fragments: complete empty valves, head shields, detached abdomens, mandibles, claws, setae. Such parts may occur with pollen and/or spores, diatoms, and testate protozoans in bottom cores of silty clay from existing lakes (Swain, 1956).

Cladoceran fossils need not be sought in the Paleozoic or Mesozoic sediments, as present evidence suggests a post-Cretaceous–pre-Oligocene first appearance of the order (Tasch, 1962a). In Tertiary and Pleistocene lacustrine deposits, however, they should be found more frequently if field geologists are oriented to search for and recognize their fossil remains.

## GROUP III: ANOSTRACA AND LIPOSTRACA

One can find very few reports in the literature on fossil anostracans. Nevertheless, these few published discoveries are of great interest. The oldest presently known anostracan is from the Upper Devonian of Germany (Van Straelen, 1943). They are also known from the Carboniferous of Germany and England and the Tertiary of England and the United States (Palmer, et al., 1957).

Generally, the cephalon, segmented body, and appendages are preserved as fossils in whole or in part. The fossils occur in lacustrine deposits in argillites or argillaceous limestones. Palmer's fauna occurred in calcareous nodules associated with borate beds. The nodules themselves were found in brown, paper-thin, laminated siltstones and thin limestone beds.

Plant and insect fossils are common biotic associates. Experimental evidence indicates an insect predator-anostracan prey association (Mathias, 1937). Accordingly, any Tertiary deposit bearing insect fossils is a likely place to search bedding planes for impressions of anostracans. As noted earlier, carbonized zones and evaporite zones are also promising sites.

Living anostracans thrive in small, temporary, alkaline water ponds. Rain pools and temporary ponds formed in melting snow and ice are the most usual habitat (Dexter, 1959). Fossil brine shrimp or their fecal pellets may be sought in interglacial deposits (Tasch, 1962a).

The Lipostraca, known only from the Middle Devonian Rhynie Chert of Scotland, were found fossilized in silicified peats. (Details of the paleoecology and paleontology are given in Tasch, 1957.) All soft parts and all growth stages of this branchiopod that lacked a carapace of any kind were preserved in the carboniferous chert. Flakes of Rhynie Chert covered with a thin layer of oil and observed microscopically bring out almost as much detail as might be obtained from a biologic study of a living specimen. Discovery of this form added important information on crustacean evolution. Associated with it in the cherts were a variety of fossil arachnids and plants, including fungi.

Although there is little likelihood of finding more lipostracans in the American or European Devonian, we can, nevertheless, be especially alert for Devonian and later Paleozoic carbonized and organically rich cherts, cherty sandstones containing carbonaceous material, silicified peat beds, plastic clays grading up to carbonized beds, and siliceous sandstones. Other branchiopods or possibly proto-lipostracans may be found.

## PRE-DEVONIAN BEDS

Present evidence points to an adaptive radiation during Silurian time that led to the three Devonian branchiopod orders, Conchostraca, Anostraca, and Acercostraca (Tasch, 1962b). Therefore, particular Silurian beds anywhere in the world may contain crucial evidence bearing on the evolution of branchiopods in particular, and post-Silurian crustaceans in general.

It is highly probable that Silurian branchiopods were dominantly marine forms. Hence, the marine Silurian, especially the shallower inshore brackish-water facies, appears to be the most promising place to search for such fossils. They can be expected to be found with such marine associates as trilobites, ostracods, and mollusks.

## REFERENCES

Dickinson, K., and F. M. Swain (1961). Ostracoda and Cladocera of the Late Tertiary Humboldt Formation, northeastern Nevada (abs.). S.E.P.M. Program (Denver), p. 91.

Dexter, R. W. (1959). Anostraca, *in* H. B. Ward and G. C. Whipple (eds.), Freshwater biology (2nd. ed., edited by W. T. Edmondson), p. 558–570.

Frey, D. G. (1958). The late glacial cladoceran fauna of a small lake. Archives Hydrobiology, v. 54, p. 14–270, pls. 35–41, 113 text-figs., 6 tables.

——— (1960). Cladocera from the Eemian Interglacial of Denmark (abs.). G.S.A. Program (Denver), p. 100.

Guthörl, P. (1934). Die Arthropoden aus dem Carbon und Perm des Saar-Nahe-Pfalz Gebietes. Berlin, Preuss. Geol. Landesanst. Abh., N.F., no. 164, p. 3–219, pls. 1–30.

Kobayashi, T. (1954). Fossil estherians and allied fossils. J. Faculty Sci., Univ. of Tokyo, v. 9, sec. 2, pt. 1, p. 1–192, 30 text-figs.

Lehmann, W. M. (1955). *Vachonia rogeri, n. gen., n. sp.,* ein Branchiopod aus dem unter-devonischen Hunsrückschiefer. Paläont. Zeitschr., v. 29, p. 126–130, pls. 11, 12, text-figs. 1, 2.

Mathias, P. (1937). Biologie des Crustacés Phyllopodes. Paris, Hermann et Cie, 106 pp., 8 text-figs.

Mitchell, J. (1925). Descriptions of new species of *Leaia*. Linnean Soc. New South Wales, v. 1, pt. 5, p. 438–447, pls. 51–53.

Novojilov, N. (1954). Crustacés Phyllopodes du Jurassique supérieur et du Crétacé de la Mongolie. Trav. Inst. Paléont. Acad. Sci., U.S.S.R., v. 48, p. 7–124, 75 figs., 17 pls.

——— (1957). Un nouvel ordre d'Arthropodes particuliers; Kazacharthra du Lias des monts Ketmen. Kazachstan, W.E., U.S.S.R., Soc. Géol. de France Bull., ser. 6, v. 7, p. 171–184, pls. 14, 15.

Palmer, A. R., and A. M. Bassett (1954). Non-marine Miocene arthropods from California. Science, v. 120, p. 228–229.

Swain, F. M. (1956). Stratigraphy of lake deposits in central and northern Minnesota. Am. Assoc. Petrol. Geol. Bull., v. 40, p. 600–653, 29 text-figs.

Tasch, P. (1957). Flora and fauna of the Rhynie Chert; a paleoecological reevaluation of published evidence. Univ. of Wichita Bull., v. 32, Univ. Studies no. 36, p. 1–24, text-figs. 1–7, app. 1, 2.

——— (1961). Paleolimnology, Part II; Harvey and Sedgwick Counties, Kansas, stratigraphy and biota. J. Paleontology, v. 35, p. 136–865, pls. 97–98, 6 text-figs.

——— (1962a). Evolution of the Branchiopoda. Harvard Mus. Comp. Zool. Bull. In Press.

——— (1962b). Branchiopoda, *in* R. C. Moore (ed.), Treatise on invertebrate paleontology. Kansas Univ. Press. In Press.

Trusheim, F. (1938). *Triopsiden (Crust. Phyll.)* aus dem Keuper Frankens. Paläont. Zeitschr., v. 19, p. 198–216, pls. 13–14, 10 text-figs.

Van Straelen, V. (1943). *Gilsonicaris rhenanus* nov. gen., nov. sp., Branchiopode Anostracé de l'Éodévonien du Hunsruck. Mus. Royale d'Histoire Nat. de Belg. Bull., v. 19, no. 56, p. 1–10, 1 pl.

Wilson, J. L. (1956). Stratigraphic position of the Upper Devonian branchiopod Rhabdostichus in the Williston Basin. J. Paleontology, v. 30, p. 959–980.

# Conodonts

## CHARLES COLLINSON

*Illinois State Geological Survey, Urbana*

Conodonts are minute, toothlike microfossils that may be cone-, bar-, blade-, or platform-shaped; are composed of concentric layers or longitudinal fibrous bundles of calcium metaphosphate; and range in size from less than 0.1 mm to more than 4 mm. When unaltered the fossils are translucent amber-brown and have a waxy luster. When altered they range in color from translucent gray through opaque white and gray to opaque black.

The biologic affinities of conodonts are unknown (Rhodes, 1954; Müller, 1956) but their internal structure, shape, and composition suggest that they may be hard parts of soft-bodied primitive vertebrates. The fossils are so widely distributed in marine Paleozoic rocks (Collinson, Rexroad, and Scott, 1959) and are so independent of facies that they are almost certainly the remains of pelagic—probably nektonic—organisms. Because they are highly resistant to chemical weathering, conodonts are commonly concentrated in the residum from rocks that originally contained them, and may be found reworked into younger sediments and admixed with younger faunas.

Conodonts are rarely seen in the field, although some early workers

(Ulrich and Bassler, 1926; Huddle, 1934) made collections using a hand lens. Where conodonts are visible to the naked eye, the fossils are usually exceedingly abundant and occur on bedding planes or as thin layers where great numbers have accumulated. On bedding surfaces of black shale they or their molds appear as shiny black objects or, if oxidized, as tiny white figures showing against the dark background. In lighter colored rocks conodonts appear as dark irregular grains that reflect light from their broken surfaces.

In modern collecting practice, rocks believed to contain conodonts are generally collected and returned to the laboratory, where they are disaggregated and the conodonts removed. Thus, the collector must have some advance knowledge of where conodonts are likely to be found and must formulate a plan for sampling the area and the stratigraphic interval to be studied.

## OCCURRENCE OF CONODONTS

Two erroneous beliefs about the occurrence of conodonts are widely held: that they occur most commonly in shale and that they occur most abundantly in "black" shale. As will be seen in the following discussion, neither is true.

Conodonts may be found in fair abundance in almost any marine rock ranging in age from Upper Cambrian through Middle Triassic. Nearly all limestones, dolomites, and shales (generally excluding "black" shales) respond to petroleum solvent or acid digestion (Beckmann, 1952, 1958; Müller, 1956; Bischoff and Ziegler, 1957; Thursch, 1958; Collinson, Rexroad and Scott, 1959; Hass, 1962; Collinson, *in press*) and in most cases permit processing quantities of material in relatively few hours. Calcareous and argillaceous sandstones are amenable to the same standard techniques but yield fewer specimens. At present no practical mass technique is known that will disaggregate "black" shales without destroying the contained conodonts.

## ABUNDANCE OF CONODONTS

During the past several years the paleontological staff of the Illinois State Geological Survey has processed many thousands of samples containing conodonts and for the last five has kept records of the amounts and kinds of rocks processed and the numbers of conodonts recovered. These figures, based mainly on samples from Silurian, Devonian, and Mississippian rocks of the central United States but also representing several hundred samples from the western and the eastern United States as well as southwestern Canada, show that significant numbers of conodonts occurred in more than half of all samples examined.

### LIMESTONE SAMPLES

Of the rock types processed, limestones have been the most reliable and productive. For example, more than 85 percent of the limestone samples of late Mississippian age have yielded at least 10 conodonts per kilogram. Several beds yielded more than 100 per kilogram. Of 70 consecutive samples of Middle Devonian age recently taken from a single outcrop, all yielded conodonts and more than 75 percent yielded more than 15 conodonts per kilogram and several contained more than 100 per kilogram. More than 5000 specimens were obtained from this section, which is considered average—not exceptional. There are, however, notable exceptions to the productivity of limestones. Some fine-grained limestones, such as the Upper Devonian Louisiana Limestone and the lower Mississippian McCraney Limestone of the Mississippi Valley, apparently represent rapid chemical precipitation and carry less than 5 conodonts per kilogram.

In general, bioclastic limestones contain the most fossils. Oolitic limestones may or may not contain identifiable conodonts, because specimens are commonly rounded and unidentifiable.

### SHALE SAMPLES

Shales are generally excellent sources for conodont faunas; the abundance of specimens is frequently spectacular. Yields exceeding 1000 specimens per kilogram are known, but occurrences are generally sporadic and beds containing great numbers are interspaced with intervals carrying relatively few or none. In overall aspect shales do not yield as consistently as limestones, nor is the average yield as high. But because shales are more easily processed, and because shales have for many years been considered the primary source of conodonts, enormous quantities have been recovered from them, with the result that more conodonts have been collected from gray, green, buff, or brown shales than from any other kind of rock.

Red marine shales, as in the Fern Glen Formation of Missouri, yield significant numbers of specimens, but nonmarine or brackish-water shales, as in the red beds of the Chesterian Series, yield none.

The very dark brown or gray shales widely referred to as black have long been considered excellent sources of conodonts; in actuality, they are among the poorest. This is due to the lack of a satisfactory mass technique for separating conodonts from them. Their high reputation arose from the fact that the well-known faunas described by Ulrich and Bassler (1926), Huddle (1934), and Branson and Mehl (1934) were reputed to have come from such lithologies. However, the first two of these faunas were found on bedding planes of "black" shale, and the third came mainly from gray-green shale.

### DOLOMITE SAMPLES

Although considerably fewer samples of dolomite than limestone have been processed, several hundred samples from the Silurian, Devonian, and Mississippian indicate that conodonts are somewhat less regularly distributed in dolomite than in limestone and that they are less abundant in dolomite than in shale or limestone. Some of the apparent difference may be due to processing difficulties, as dolomite is less soluble than limestone, and residues are commonly clogged with dolomite rhombs that may be difficult to separate cleanly in heavy liquids. Nevertheless, conodonts are common in dolomites and frequently exceed 50 specimens per kilogram.

### SANDSTONE AND SILTSTONE SAMPLES

The occurrence of conodonts in sandstones and siltstones is extremely variable for a variety of reasons. Highly indurated or quartzitic sandstones cannot be adequately disaggregated except with hydrofluoric acid, which is not suited to mass techniques, whereas friable, calcareous, and argillaceous sandstones usually can be. The rates and conditions of deposition of various sand bodies may have differed considerably. Lag sands deposited slowly over long intervals of time often yield large faunas. Channel, bar, and beach sands, however, accumulated fairly rapidly, and, even though marine, contain few conodonts.

In summary, one can say that limestones are the most favorable rock type for the collection of conodonts. Distribution is more regular than in other rock types, and the average number of specimens contained is higher. Specimens from limestones usually are better preserved, have undergone less breakage, and are cleaner. Most shales are more easily disaggregated than limestones, and some beds produce prodigious collections. Distribution is very uneven, however, and the average yield of specimens per kilogram is lower than for limestones. Sandstones and siltstones yield specimens only sporadically, and generally in relatively low numbers.

The stratigraphic distribution of conodonts and the relationship of occurrence to lithology indicate that the conodont-bearing animal was almost continuously present and uniformly abundant in Paleozoic and early Mesozoic seas and that the rate of deposition apparently governed the present-day occurrence. Sea-bottom environment seems to have been a minor factor.

## PHILOSOPHY OF CONODONT COLLECTING

Modern collecting and processing techniques make practical the collection of abundant faunas from continuous or nearly continuous consecutive samples in the greater part of the Paleozoic. As a direct result, collections from unrelated, short stratigraphic intervals or isolated outcrops can no longer be considered adequate for taxonomic or biostratigraphic determinations. Exceptions, of course, are collections for comparative material or for reference to previously well-known sequences.

The large, correlated collections now available suggest that conodont taxa should be considered deficient unless related in time to ancestor and descendant as well as to contemporaneous variants. Biostratigraphic zones, correlations, and age determinations should be considered uncertain unless sequences of faunas above and below the units in question are known. This is vitally important, since the elements that make up the fauna from any particular horizon represent increments of numerous phylogenetic lineages and must be related to major portions of these lineages to be useful biostratigraphically. Many a fauna described in the literature as representing a specific stratigraphic unit actually represents only one of many integrading faunas contained therein and may be quite unlike faunas from other stratigraphic horizons in the unit. A number of well-known formations that have for years been assigned to a specific series or period are now recognized to extend beyond that unit and are largely referable to a unit above or below.

For these reasons, any study undertaken other than for the collection of comparative material should be based on a predetermined, orderly, comprehensive sampling scheme that will give adequate geographic as well as stratigraphic coverage and assure that the information secured can be duplicated by subsequent workers. So many aspects of conodont occurrence remain unstudied that preoccupation with short sequences, incompletely known faunas, and isolated faunas serves only to dilute and delay progress toward adequate knowledge of conodont biostratigraphy and the paleogeographic refinement it will bring.

## A PLAN FOR COLLECTING CONODONTS

Some of my colleagues and I have developed a sampling routine for conodont collection that has been used for several years. Offered here as a practical approach to systematic conodont collecting this routine involves three phases:

1. *Reconnaissance*—Continuous channel sampling of the largest and best-exposed sections available consistent with good coverage of the stratigraphic units represented.
2. *Selective re-collecting*—Zones of especial abundance are re-collected in order to gain comprehensive knowledge of representative faunas.
3. *Bulk re-collecting*—Re-collection of large quantities of material in parts of the section where faunas are sparse but are of special significance.

## RECONNAISSANCE

### DISTRIBUTION OF COLLECTING LOCALITIES

In the reconnaissance phase emphasis should be placed on careful collecting of samples from a few of the thickest, best exposed, and most nearly complete sections available. Uniform geographic spacing is not as important as adequate representation of the facies, members, or formations of the stratigraphic interval under study. The thickest and best sections in which they are exposed should be sampled in such a manner that their faunal sequences may serve as references for later work. After the faunal sequences of the reference sections are well known, the need for additional localities will become apparent and the location of zones where conodonts are lacking or where stratigraphic units are missing will dictate the location of additional sampling localities.

DISTRIBUTION OF SAMPLES

The thickness of stratigraphic section to be studied, the capacity of facilities available for processing samples, and the amount of time available for collecting and processing determine the sampling pattern that will be most useful in any given study.

Where the geologic column is relatively short, as in the central United States, outcrop, core, or well sections seldom exceed two or three hundred feet in thickness, and continuous channel sampling is recommended. Processing techniques are such that very large quantities of material can be handled even in laboratories of modest size and one or two hundred samples (two to four hundred pounds) per reference section are not excessive.

Where the geologic column is long and sections may be several thousand feet thick, 100 to 200 samples must be distributed in such a manner that maximum information can be derived. In sections composed mainly of limestone, conodonts should be rather uniformly distributed throughout, and collection of uniformly spaced composite channel samples should give optimum results. In sandstone, shale, or siltstone sequences conodonts are generally irregularly distributed; the most effective plan is to take a concentration of samples above and below formational or member contacts or where special problems exist. For example, if one hundred samples are the maximum that can be efficiently handled in the time available and there are five formational boundaries in a 1000-foot section, 10 composite channel samples above and below each formational boundary should give optimum practical coverage.

Of special importance in collecting reconnaissance samples is the accurate geographic and stratigraphic location of all samples. Whenever possible, the outcrop or core should be permanently marked. If the sample is from soft sediments a survey stake will serve as a reference point. *It is imperative that the collector be able to re-collect any particular sample with accuracy.*

SAMPLE INTERVAL

Reconnaissance samples should be of the consecutive composite channel type, in which every inch of the sampled interval is represented. Where natural beds are generally less than 5 feet thick each sample may represent one bed or any shorter interval. Where beds are thicker, or where bedding is not significant, as in shale sections, $2\frac{1}{2}$- to 5-foot intervals may be necessary. In special situations, 10-foot intervals are useful, but the strong possibility that faunas of significantly different aspect and age may be intermixed must be considered.

SIZE OF SAMPLE

Extensive experience in collecting samples for conodont recovery has shown that a 2000-gram sample is eminently satisfactory for both biostratigraphic and taxonomic studies. A 7 by 12 inch cloth sample bag will hold slightly more than 2000 grams. Past collecting from middle Paleozoic rocks has demonstrated that this size of sample will contain, on the average, 10 to 20 conodonts in more than half of all samples. Such amounts are more than adequate for reconnaissance as well as for age determinations where the faunal sequence is well known.

In zones where the concentration of conodonts exceeds one specimen per 1000 grams of sample, the chances are 9 out of 10 that a 2000-gram sample will contain at least one specimen. This allows the collector to remove from consideration zones of low concentration and thereby to devote further efforts to zones of promise.

## SELECTIVE RE-COLLECTING

After the reconnaissance samples have been processed and zones of low, common, and abundant occurrence have been outlined, it is generally necessary to re-sample zones of abundance. This is done in order to expand the collections to a point where they are representative of the entire fauna. Percentages represented by various genera and species can be reliably determined, along with the intraspecific variability of more important species. This phase also verifies the original collection in some degree by repetition.

Samples for re-collecting are of the standard 2000-gram size and are commonly taken at 6-inch or shorter intervals in the zones of abundance. Such distribution determines the variation of occurrence within the zone and pinpoints the horizons of greatest abundance. Such horizons may later be invaluable for detailed taxonomic studies.

## BULK RE-COLLECTING

After a sequence of conodont faunas is fairly well known, certain stratigraphic or taxonomic problems commonly remain that must be resolved in order to complete the study. Usually these problems must be resolved by re-examining parts of the section where occurrences were very low, since information from most other zones is already sufficient. It is necessary to collect and process very large quantities of material. Several times in the recent past I have found it necessary to collect and process 400 or 500 pounds of material from a single bed in order to resolve a stratigraphic boundary problem. In cases where answers are not forthcoming from one section, collections from nearby sections may hold the sought-for faunas.

## COLLECTION OF SUBSURFACE SAMPLES

### CORES

Cores often represent irreplaceable material and should therefore be subdivided into the smallest practical sample increments. A 250-gram sample is suggested as the smallest unit that can be processed efficiently. In a 3-inch core of bioclastic limestone this would represent approximately 1/10-inch increments. Such short intervals have been used in our laboratory for cores from the Chappel Limestone of Texas and have proved to be very practical.

If the core is about 100 feet long or more one- or two-foot intervals are recommended. It must always be kept in mind, however, that samples can be combined after processing but not redivided.

### WELL SAMPLES

The size of sample normally taken at the well for microscopic study is too small for conodont studies, and it is therefore necessary to make special collections at the well site. Because well cuttings are finer than samples crushed for processing of conodonts, approximately twice as much well-cutting material must be collected per stratigraphic unit as would be used for a similar outcrop study. Approximately 4000 grams should represent the practical minimum to be collected at the well, and all fine material should be washed from the sample before processing. When well-sample sets are already available for conodont studies, it is recommended that individual samples be combined to make up 250-gram samples.

## CONTAMINATION

Because of the unusual durability of conodonts, extra measures must be taken to guard against contamination. Sample bags should never be reused. Tools such as picks, trowels, and shovels should be cleaned before each sample is taken, and sample bags must be tightly sealed and inspected for rips or punctures. Whenever there is the slightest possibility of contamination, the suspected samples should be discarded.

In collecting from outcrops it is wise to take the lowest samples first and work uphill, cleaning the site carefully before sampling. Because conodonts characteristically accumulate in weathered material, great care should be taken to secure samples from fresh exposures. Contamination is particularly to be anticipated on shale slopes where slope wash and slump are active. Often it is necessary to dig the slope back 2 or 3 feet. Flat areas at the base of shale slopes should be avoided. Reworked material there may be very difficult to recognize, and the possibility of its occurrence is very high.

## REFERENCES

Beckman, Heinz (1952). The use of acetic acids in micropaleontology. Micropaleontologist, v. 6, p. 39.

—————— (1958). Arbeitstechniken und Erfahrungen der Mikropaläontologie in Palaozoikum, *in* Freund, H. (ed.), Handbuch der Mikroskopie in der Teknik. Frankfurt, M., v. 2, pt. 3, p. 147–165.

Bischoff, Gunther, and Willi Ziegler (1957). Die Conodontenchronologie des Mitteldevons und des tiefsten Oberdevons. Hess. Landesamt. Bodenf., Abh., v. 22, p. 1–136, pls. 1–21.

Branson, E. B., and M. G. Mehl (1934). Conodonts from the Grassy Creek shale of Missouri. Univ. Missouri Studies, v. 8, p. 171–259, pls. 13–21.

—————— (1933). Conodont studies number 1: Univ. Missouri Studies, v. 8, p. 1–72, pls. 1–4.

Collinson, Charles (1963). Techniques for the collecting and processing of conodonts. Illinois Geol. Survey Circular 343, 16 pp.

——————, C. B. Rexroad, and A. J. Scott (1959). Abundance and stratigraphic distribution of Devonian and Mississippian conodonts in the upper Mississippi Valley: J. Paleontology, v. 33, p. 692–696.

Ellison, Samuel P., Jr. (1962). Annotated bibliography and index of conodonts. Univ. Texas Publ. 6210, p. 1–128.

Hass, W. H., Walter Häntzschel, D. W. Fisher, B. F. Howell, F. H. T. Rhodes, Klaus J. Müller, and R. C. Moore (1962). Conodonts, conoidal shells of uncertain affinities, worms, trace fossils and problematica, *in* Treatise on invertebrate paleontology, Part W, Miscellanea, p. W1–W259.

Huddle, J. W. (1934). Conodonts from the New Albany shale of Indiana. Bull. Am. Paleont. (Paleont. Res. Inst.), v. 21, no. 72, p. 1–136, pls. 1–12.

Müller, Klaus J. (1956). Zur Kenntnis der Conodonten-Fauna des europäischen Devons, 1—Die Gattung *Palmatolepis*. Senckenbergischen naturf. Gesell., Abh., no. 494, p. 1–68, pls. 1–11.

Rhodes, F. H. T. (1954). The zoological affinities of the conodonts. Biol. Rev., v. 29, p. 419–452.

Thursch, Horst (1958). Ein neues Verfahren zur Preparation von Kalkproben mit Essigsaure. Neues Jahrb. Geol. Paläont., Monatsh., Jahrg. 1958, p. 283–284.

Ulrich, E. O., and R. S. Bassler (1926). A classification of the toothlike fossils, conodonts, with descriptions of American Devonian and Mississippian species. U. S. Natl. Mus. Proc., v. 68, art. 12, p. 1–63, pls. 1–11.

# Graptolites

WILLIAM B. N. BERRY

*Department of Paleontology, University of California, Berkeley*

Most fossil graptolites are flattened and need little special treatment to adequately study them. The complexities of graptolite morphology, however, must be worked out primarily from uncrushed specimens freed from their matrix. Although little mention has been made in the literature of how to collect graptolites and how to work with flattened specimens, Gumbel, as early as 1878, described acid technique for freeing graptolites from rock matrix. A few years later, Wiman (1895) gave a complete account of techniques for freeing graptolites from various types of rocks and for working with them, once isolated. Wiman's is perhaps the most detailed account recorded—an account the reader should examine. Kraft (1926) also carefully described methods for freeing graptolites from their matrix. Bulman (1927, 1955) summarized the techniques for working with uncrushed graptolite specimens, including a description of serial sectioning to study detailed morphology of specimens that cannot successfully be removed from their matrix.

## COLLECTING GRAPTOLITES

Graptolites may occur in any kind of sedimentary rock and in some metamorphic rocks. Classically, many graptolite collectors have restricted their search to black shales only. Admittedly, these are the most prospective rocks in which to hunt for graptolites, but they are by no means the only ones. Many fine collections have been long overlooked by collectors interested solely in the most likely looking black shales. In addition to these, many limestones (especially the fine-grained or argillaceous types), sandstones (including even coarse-grained graywackes), mudstones, argillites, cherts, and slates have yielded good collections. Assemblages from slates are sometimes particularly important to a determination of the geologic structure of an area, and such rocks should not be passed over lightly in the search for graptolite remains.

Graptolites are commonly preserved as flattened carbon films on bedding surfaces. In many instances their skeletal parts have left nothing but an imprint upon the bedding. Some imprints may have carbon clinging to them; general practice is to remove the carbon film and study the imprint directly.

Because graptolites are commonly preserved as shiny films upon bedding surfaces, the surfaces should be carefully examined at many different angles with as bright a light as possible reflected from them. At some angles of reflection the films may not be apparent at all, but will become readily apparent at others. Because their appearance varies with the angle at which light is reflected from bedding surfaces, searching for graptolites is best undertaken in strong sunlight or at least in as bright a light as possible. A general guide in examining exposures of argillites and mudstones is to study the surfaces of weathered chips carefully. Many of the best specimens may be found on them. If graptolites are common on weathered chips, then the exposure should be searched assiduously.

As graptolites are plentiful on certain bedding surfaces and not on others, best collecting is accomplished by carefully splitting layers with chisels. A variety of small and medium-sized, well-sharpened chisels is quite useful when hunting for graptolites. A good procedure is to quarry out from an exposure many large chunks of rock, then split them carefully. Repeated searching of this sort, even in the most highly contorted shales and argillites, often will result in at least a small collection. A fact to be emphasized, particularly when collecting compressed material, is that care taken to obtain good, complete specimens will pay considerable rewards later when the material is taken to the laboratory to study. If time is short and space and weight are not a problem, then large blocks can be taken from layers ascertained to contain graptolites at the outcrop. The blocks can be split in the laboratory.

Uncrushed material is most commonly encountered in cherts, limestones, and some mudstones. All such rocks should be examined with a hand lens to see whether uncrushed graptolites may be present. Where uncrushed or apparently uncrushed material is present, large blocks should be collected for later treatment in the laboratory. Nodules, as well as bedded rocks, should be examined carefully.

## PREPARATION

Preparation of graptolites involves two rather distinct sets of techniques: those for use with flattened specimens and those useful in working with uncrushed or partially crushed material. The latter types of specimens yield information about morphological detail that it is not possible to obtain from flattened specimens in general.

### CRUSHED MATERIAL

Flattened or crushed specimens are by far the most commonly encountered. In the laboratory, pieces of graptolite-bearing rock may be carefully split with small, well-sharpened chisels. Once specimens are exposed, use of a Vibro-tool or an air-driven dental grinding tool is often necessary to remove small flakes of rock still covering parts of the specimens. Some specimens may have to be partly excavated by using such tools.

Once the specimens are uncovered and free to be studied, a strong light is needed; it should be permitted to reflect from the bedding surface at several different angles until one is found that most clearly reveals the details of the rhabdosome. Commonly, a low angle of reflection will be found to reveal detail most clearly. Details of morphology may be more clearly seen by wetting the specimens. Water, alcohol, and glycerine have proved to reveal detail most clearly. These liquids may be applied with a small brush. All fragile specimens that need to be wetted for closer study should be examined under alcohol, as it has been found to evaporate quickly with least possibility of damage to the specimen or the rock.

When graptolites are preserved as impressions, a latex rubber peel of the rhabdosome will reveal more structural detail than is readily seen by simply examining the specimen under reflected light. Where the imprint is distinct, it may first be scrubbed with a toothbrush under running water to rid the surface of dirt and other substances. Even the carbon film of the rhabdosome, if any remains, should be scrubbed off. (I am indebted to R. J. Ross for this suggestion, as common practice in the past has been to leave all remains of the periderm in place.) The specimen should next be washed in distilled water before self-vulcanizing latex is applied over it. Clearest results are obtained by using a black latex. White latex can be made black simply by adding India ink. I have used a latex molding compound thinned with distilled water or ammonia and made black with India ink. This is applied to the specimens from which peels are to be made. After one application has been made, it should be permitted to harden for 3 to 5 hours, then another coating can be applied. Peels for quick inspection may often be made with but two or three coats of latex. For more durable peels, several coatings should be built up with a layer or two of fine gauze applied when the last two or three coats of latex are put on. Latex peels so formed may be made not only from imprints but also from partly crushed and completely crushed specimens. Some completely crushed specimens will yield peels revealing more details than can be seen by examining them directly.

### UNCRUSHED MATERIAL

Although flattened specimens are by far the more common, they seldom reveal morphological details. Uncrushed specimens are virtually essential to ascertain rhabdosome structure and development. Such information can almost always be obtained by freeing the rhabdosome from its matrix. This is done by dissolving the matrix and, in most instances, by making the specimens to some extent transparent by the use of oxidizing agents.

The matrix may be removed in one of two ways: (a) by dissolving all of it at once or (b) by dissolving it from one side until the graptolite is exposed and then cementing the exposed portions of the graptolite to a glass plate for support and dissolving the remainder. The first method is best for unbranched members of the order Graptoloidea and for stipe or rhabdosome fragments of the other kinds; the second method is best for branched specimens.

Pure or nearly pure limestone matrix may be dissolved with hydrochloric, acetic, or formic acid. Acetic is perhaps the most preferable, although formic is desirable to use on fragile specimens. The concentration of the acid should be adjusted so that bubbling or effervescence is only moderate. After bubbling ceases, and if the block remains undissolved, some of the liquid may be decanted and more acid added until the rock has been broken down. Sometimes, graptolites freed from the matrix float on the liquid. They may be removed with a pipette or a small brush.

Once the block has been dissolved, the residue should be washed with water, then taken in small amounts in a watch glass and examined under a binocular microscope. Graptolite fragments may be picked from the residue with a pipette or a fine brush. They should be stored in water or glycerine until further treated and studied.

The graptolite periderm may be so brittle that it will fall apart when released from its matrix. Some rhabdosomes may have been filled in and maintained in an uncrushed condition, but freeing them from the matrix may dislodge the supporting substance and the remains may crumble. Many seemingly good uncrushed specimens literally fall apart once the matrix has been dissolved away from around them. This is always a potential hazard when trying to free specimens, therefore it is best to attempt to free only a small part of a collection at first to find out whether the specimens will withstand being released from their matrix.

Impure limestones commonly need a two-fold acid treatment. The calcareous material can first be dissolved with hydrochloric acid. The remaining portion of the rock should be thoroughly washed in water, preferably by letting it stand in water for a few days to a week. Then hydrofluoric acid may be used to dissolve the siliceous matter. The remaining sludge should be washed thoroughly and then transferred in small amounts to a watch glass and the graptolite remains picked out.

Mudstones and some shales can be treated with hydrofluoric acid directly. After a few days to a week, the matrix may dissolve in part or completely leaving a residue which, when washed, may be picked in the usual manner. Chert should also be directly treated with hydrofluoric acid.

CLEARING

Graptolite rhabdosomes freed from their matrix are commonly black in appearance because an amount of carbonaceous material is present. An oxidizing agent should be employed to remove this carbon covering from the periderm and thus render the rhabdosomes transparent, permitting close study of the periderm and other structures. Hydrogen peroxide can be used, but it may not be strong enough. The best reagent for clearing is potassium chlorate and concentrated nitric acid. A small amount of each should be mixed in a watch glass and several specimens to be cleared placed in the solution. Because the period required to clear the rhabdosomes varies with the individual specimens, the results of the process should be followed by observing the material through a microscope. Some specimens will withstand only a small amount of clearing before becoming brittle and falling apart. About half an hour is long enough for fragile material. Other specimens, however, will withstand clearing for many hours. Skoglund (1961) has recorded clearing times as long as six days. Some specimens are so highly carbonized that they cannot be cleared at all. Other specimens are so fragile when freed from their matrix that they do not withstand the clearing treatment. Only experience with individual specimens will indicate which specimens will withstand treatment and which will not.

MOUNTING

Freed specimens that are highly carbonized and those that will not withstand the clearing treatment are best mounted dry, because their features are more easily visible than when they are placed in any mounting medium. They may be glued to a slide with gum tragacanth. Cleared specimens may be mounted in a hollow ground area in a glass slide in canada balsam, or in a mounting medium supplied by the Technicon Chemical Co., New York, following the technique described by Whittington (1954, p. 613). Thorsteinsson has had considerable success mounting specimens in clear plastic. Before specimens are mounted, they must be dehydrated by taking them through the usual alcohol series and xylol. Cleared specimens may also be floated in glycerin in tiny glass vials. If this is done, the drying procedure may be avoided, and the specimens can be washed in water after removing them from the clearing solution and placed directly into glycerin.

BRANCHING SPECIMENS

Branching and fragile specimens can, when one side has been exposed, be cemented to a glass slide with Lakeside 70 or canada balsam. Then the other side can be freed from the matrix by carefully dissolving it away. Such material cannot be cleared, because the cement will not withstand the clearing solution.

## STUDY OF UNCRUSHED SPECIMENS

Specimens freed from their rock matrix may be studied directly under the microscope. Those in glycerin and in plastic have the advantage that they may be readily viewed from any direction, and those in glycerin can be placed in a watch glass and carefully dissected with needles. Another way to study freed specimens is in microtome section. Some workers have successfully used only paraffin wax as the embedding medium, but better results are obtained by first using collodion and then paraffin. Standard zoological microtome techniques can then be utilized.

Specimens that cannot be successfully removed from their rock matrix but are uncrushed or only partly crushed can be studied by grinding serial sections. In a technique described by Bulman (1927), the specimen selected for study can be embedded in plaster and then mounted on the grinding plate of a Croft Parallel Grinder and sections ground off at selected intervals. If the matrix is limestone, acetate or parlodion peels can be taken of the exposed surface before another is ground. In other materials, and alternatively in limestones, a photograph or camera lucida drawing can be made of each surface. Once a sequence of drawings or photographs has been made, they may be studied individually, but a better and more comprehensive record of what they reveal can be had by making a wax model. These are particularly useful in the study of proximal end development. Drawings of each of the intervals studied in the sectioning process are made, then wax templates, like model airplane templates, are constructed from them. The thickness of the wax template used is determined from the frequency at which the sections were ground and the magnification employed. Once the wax templates have been made by pouring out a sheet of wax of the proper thickness onto a piece of stone or metal and letting it cool and then embedding the drawings of the sections on it, the drawings may be cut out and stacked one on top of the other. They can be held together with pins and by smoothing the edges of the several templates together with a hot knife. The thickness of wax representing the thecal walls is cut away during the construction of the wax model so that the final form is one of a sequence of thecal cavities, or an internal cast. Study of such a wax model can lead to elucidation of the details of proximal end structures like that executed by Bulman (1936) for *Oncograptus*.

**ILLUSTRATION**

Graptolite illustration has always proved to be a problem, because details of the rhabdosome as well as its overall form need to be seen. The most satisfactory illustrations are photographs, for they can be shown at natural size and can also be enlarged to show details. Isolated material and flattened specimens can be photographed either dry or in glycerin. Immersion in glycerin commonly yields clearer pictures of details. Whittington (1954) used infrared film to obtain pictures showing details of the proximal end clearly at a magnification of 80×. Flattened specimens have to be turned and studied through the camera to get the best possible reflection from them. Low angles of light incidence are usually best. Depth of focus may prove to be a problem with those specimens that must be tilted to steep angles to give good reflections. At least the proximal ends of such specimens can be included in sharp focus. R. J. Ross (personal communication) reports good results photographing the latex peels taken from imprints. In many instances, pic tures obtained from the peels are better than those from the specimens. Photographs may have to be retouched, but proper care in obtaining a clear image before taking the picture will usually produce an acceptable result.

For graptolites that are not amenable to photographic reproduction, and in those cases where a less expensive method of illustration is necessary, line drawings can be used. They can be made with the aid of a camera lucida, or they can be drawn on an enlarged photograph which is subsequently reduced to the desired size and bleached.

Figures at natural size are valuable for comparison of general rhabdosome form. Enlargements also should be included to show details of thecal and, where needed, proximal end structures. Magnification of $5\times$ to $10\times$ are acceptable for standard descriptive work, but if detail of the periderm is being shown, or certain other features, magnifications up to $100\times$ or $200\times$ may be necessary.

Flattened specimens prove to be the most difficult to photograph well because not only does the background vary from specimen to specimen but so do the reflective properties of the specimens. Because a wide range of backgrounds and different preservations may be present in a fauna being illustrated, uniformity of tone in plate composition is sure to be difficult, if not almost impossible, to attain. Photographs are, however, the most accurate record of the material studied and should be attempted.

## REFERENCES

Bulman, O. M. B. (1927). A monograph of British dendroid Graptolites, Part I. Palaentogr. Soc. London, p. 1–28.

——— (1936). The structure of *Oncograptus* T. S. Hall. Geol. Mag., v. 73, p. 271–278.

——— (1955). Treatise on invertebrate paleontology, Part V, Graptolithina. Geol. Soc. America and Univ. Kansas Press, p. V1–V101.

Gumbel, C. W. (1878). Eininge Bemerkungen über Graptolithen. Neues Jahrb. Geol. und Paläont., Jahrg. 1878, p. 292–296.

Kraft, P. (1926). Eine neue Methode zür Entfarbung des rezenten und fossilen Chitins. Naturwissenschaften, 14 Jahrg., p. 85–86.

Skoglund, R. (1961). *Kinnegraptus,* A new graptolite genus from the Lower *Didymograptus* Shale of Västergotland, Central Sweden. Bull. Geol. Inst. Univ. Uppsala Bull., v. 40, p. 389–400.

Whittington, H. B. (1954). A new graptolite from Oklahoma. J. Paleontology, v. 28, p. 613–621.

Wiman, Carl (1895). Über die Graptoliten. Bull. Geol. Inst. Univ. Uppsala Bull., v. 2, p. 239–316.

# Fishes

BOBB SCHAEFFER

*American Museum of Natural History, New York*

The factors involved in the preservation of a fish skeleton as a fossil are complex and poorly understood. Although various kinds of fishes have presumably invaded an increasing variety of aquatic environments from the Ordovician on, conditions favoring preservation have been limited mostly to lacustrine, swamp, lagoonal, epicontinental sea, and coastal environments. Fluvial forms are rarely preserved. Oceanic and deep-water marine forms are found mainly in uplifted coastal sediments, usually mixed with coastal types. (See David, 1957; Denison, 1956.)

Fishes are killed individually or in large numbers by a variety of physical and organic causes. Unless consumed by predators, a carcass may be washed ashore or it may float above the bottom until the gases of decomposition rupture the body cavity. Death resulting from asphyxiation and/or desiccation is frequently indicated by concentrations of fish remains in stagnant pond deposits, and by specimens preserved with open mouths and showing signs of shriveling prior to burial. When a carcass settles to the bottom, the soft tissues and skeleton are usually rapidly consumed by benthic scavangers and by bacterial action. If bottom conditions are not suitable for scavangers, and particularly if the neritic environment is nearly anaerobic, the probability of preservation is greatly increased. Fish remains tend to be scarce or absent in layers containing an abundant benthic invertebrate assemblage, but bone beds composed mostly of fish remains may include abundant invertebrate fragments. Aggregation and sorting are particularly evident in bone beds and in near-shore deposits where fishes and invertebrates are commonly intermingled.

Population density for all types of fishes varies greatly in any given environment, depending on food supply, temperature, salinity, and many other factors. Fishes may be locally abundant around reefs and in other environments where, unfortunately, they are rarely or never preserved. It is probable that many ancient epicontinental seas (e.g., the Niobrara and Pierre) and extensive lakes (e.g., the Green River lakes) supported large populations and that, during intervals when bottom conditions were suitable for preservation, numerous individuals were entombed over a wide area. Nevertheless, core and dredge samples, as well as direct inspection of the bottom, show that fish bones are generally rare. Isolated teeth and scales are relatively more common, as in bone beds, indicating that the "enamel" and dentine are the most resistent parts of the skeleton. Cartilage is never preserved unless it is well calcified, and even then it is rarely preserved, except in certain formations (e.g., pleuracanth remains in the Texas Lower Permian).

Paradoxically, some fossil fish assemblages include or are composed mainly of bottom dwellers. Most ostracoderms and some placoderms were undoubtedly detritus feeders, and many placoderms, chondrichthyans, and osteichthyans with crushing or shearing dentitions must have fed on benthic organisms. Even if these organisms were not all scavangers, they would require aerobic bottom conditions to exist. The usual sporadic occurrence of fossil fishes, and in fact of all fossil vertebrates, indicates a complicated and variable interrelationship between population density, mortality, and preservation factors. Death associations usually include fishes from various zones and habitats. Deductions about the environment inhabited during life must therefore be based mostly on the structure of the feeding mechanism and on body form.

Fossil fishes occur most commonly in shales, perhaps less commonly in limestones and most rarely in sandstones. Fragmentary remains are often found, and may be locally abundant in unconsolidated silts, clays, marls, and conglomerates. Associated skeletons are most common in sapropelic, fine-grained sediments and in concretions. It is important to note, however, that a delicate bony skeleton may be scattered by the slightest current action prior to burial. Skull elements, in particular, are subject to dispersal, and teleost skeletons minus the skull are by no means rare.

Complete specimens or skulls "in the round"—that is, with little compression or distortion—represent the rarest sort of preservation, but they are the most desirable for detailed morphologic investigation. They occur most commonly, but not exclusively, in concretions, indicating that the cavities in the skull and body were filled with sediment, and that the concretion was nearly completely formed prior to compression of the surrounding sediments. In some concretions (as from the Lower Triassic of Madagascar) the skeleton has completely disappeared, but a sharply defined mold of the body remains.

The great majority of fossil fishes are compressed, usually to the extent that the bone or calcified cartilage will allow. Individual skeletal elements that are well ossified usually retain their original shape and thickness, but they may be badly fractured or comminuted. Specimens in partly metamorphosed rocks such as argillites may be identifiable, but they are commonly distorted and nearly useless for detailed study. Individuals in which the skull elements are somewhat separated will show more exactly the shape of the dermal elements; the brain case and the ossified components of the visceral skeleton may also be exposed.

## COLLECTING FOSSIL FISHES

Even if a particular rock unit is known to contain fossil fishes, "blind" prospecting can be very time-consuming and discouraging. Since fishes are rarely distributed throughout a formation, the pertinent literature in paleontology and stratigraphy should be checked for specific localities and horizons. Persons acquainted with the regional geology, local "rock hounds," and landowners may provide important clues. A high percentage of the good fossil fish localities have been discovered fortuitously by amateurs and stratigraphers.

When prospecting continental deposits, particular attention should be paid to pond and lake deposits. Shales, mudstones, and fine-grained sandstones containing eurypterids, myriapods, ostracods, phyllocarids, fresh-water mollusks, and plant remains may contain fish remains. Cannel deposits are always worth examining. In a carbonaceous shale sequence, fishes are frequently most abundant in the layers having the highest carbon content. Concretions containing recognizable organic remains should be cracked open, in quantity if possible, before deciding that fish remains are probably absent.

Marine and brackish-water beds present a somewhat greater problem for the collector, even though fishes are generally encountered more frequently in these beds than in fresh-water beds. Shales, limestones, and fine-grained sandstones containing an impoverished benthic invertebrate fauna usually offer the best possibilities. Cephalopods and fishes are frequently associated in Mesozoic sediments. As in continental deposits, concretions in shale, marl, and argillaceous limestone facies of stagnant-water origin warrant examination. Shales and limestones of nearly uniform lithology may contain widely scattered specimens, but more frequently the fishes are restricted to one or a few horizons ("fish beds") perhaps only a few centimeters in thickness (Rayner, 1958). Bone beds are always thin, frequently widespread, sometimes lenticular, and not always at exactly the same stratigraphic level throughout their extent (Denison, 1956, p. 389).

Surface prospecting is the only way to discover rock layers containing fishes. Unconsolidated sediments can be screened or sorted by hand, but remains should first be found on the surface. If a specific rock type in some stratigraphic unit is known to contain fishes (e.g., paper shales in the Green River Formation), specimens may be found by "blind" digging.

Always collect scattered remains on the surface before beginning excavation of the source bed. If at all possible, a fish-bearing layer situated below the surface should be approached from above, even when partly exposed in a gorge or wash. Remove the overburden in a circumscribed area and work down to the predetermined horizon. If the layer extends into a bank, the excavation will resemble a big step, or shelf. This approach is particularly desirable for specimens in shale or mudstone, since it will permit the removal of large slabs and thus increase the probability of locating complete specimens with a minimum of damage. It is also useful for uncovering specimens in chalk and for removing large, embedded concretions.

A variety of sharp, well-tempered, cold-rolled steel chisels from 6 inches to 2 feet in length should be available for working in any sort of consolidated matrix. Flat chisels made from automobile springs are useful for splitting shale. Other tools necessary in the field are a shovel, crowbar, pick, Marsh pick, plus awls, sledge hammers (2- and 3-pound), whisk brooms, and paint brushes (for cleaning an exposed layer).

Specimens in shale or mudstone usually require little treatment in the field. Excess matrix can be removed there, but it is generally safer to do this in the laboratory with a rock saw. Coat delicate or fragile specimens damaged by splitting (usually unavoidable) with a very thin solution of Alvar or a similar plastic cement. Shellac is not recommended, as it is extremely difficult to remove in the laboratory. Broken specimens with delicate edges should be cemented together in the field to prevent further damage. Always save part and counterpart and give them the same field number. Wrap each piece separately and cover fragile specimens with padding. Quilting cotton is inexpensive, makes excellent padding material, and can be arranged in layers in a carton for transporting very fragile specimens, including those in paper shale.

Associated fish remains in marl, soft crumbly shale, soft limestone, and chalk, unless small and easily lifted as a unit after "hardening" with Alvar solution, are best removed in a block of matrix securely covered by a plaster and burlap jacket. If the matrix is dry, paint the exposed parts of the skeleton with thin Alvar solution; if damp, use gum arabic solution. Cover the upper surface of the block with a thin separating layer of toilet paper well soaked in gum arabic solution, and allow this layer to dry thoroughly before applying the burlap jacket. Only enough of the skeleton should be exposed to determine its limits. Never attempt to prepare a specimen in the field. Without proper laboratory equipment, there is always great risk of irreparable damage.

Large specimens in soft limestone or chalk (e.g., from the Niobrara) have been collected by preparing the upper side while still in place, trenching around the specimen, and surrounding it with a wooden frame which projects well above the specimen. Molding plaster is poured into the frame, allowed to harden, and the upper side covered with boards. The trench is then deepened and extended under the frame so that the entire block is finally freed and turned over. The matrix on the lower side is shaved down to the level of the frame and that side boarded up. In the laboratory, the lower side is always exposed so that the specimen remains embedded in plaster. This technique requires a great deal of time and labor in the field and is used mostly for specimens of exhibition quality. The jacket method is therefore usually preferred, even if the specimen and matrix must be divided into several parts with a hand saw.

## PREPARATION

An uncrushed specimen provides the best evidence on head morphology and body form. If well preserved, the internal anatomy of the skull can be revealed either by acid preparation or by the serial grinding technique. For detailed study of skull structure, the peel technique is unsurpassed. Peels can be studied directly, or used to make wax-plate reconstructions of the skull elements and of the endocranial cavity and its associated canals. A detailed cast of the skull should be made before it is destroyed by grinding.

Stensiö (1927) has studied the internal anatomy of the cephalaspid head shield by manually removing the matrix from the orobranchial chamber and flooding this area with a refringent liquid (alcohol, xylol, or oil of anis). The contrast between matrix and bone is greatly increased, and the perichondral bone lining the chamber becomes translucent, permitting examination of the endocranial structures. Alcohol and acetone are particularly useful for increasing contrast between bone and matrix during microscopic examination.

Casts of specimens preserved as molds in shale or in concretions can be made with latex or some other elastic casting compound such as SP 16 (Cementex). The surface of the mold should be as clean as possible, and secondary deposits of iron oxide or other minerals removed under the microscope with needle and brush. If the matrix is hard, try a soft wire brush, such as dentists use to burnish inlays. Soak the surface of the mold in a thin Alvar solution if it is at all delicate. Latex does not require a separator, but a separator must be used with most of the synthetic casting compounds in order to facilitate removal of the casting compound. Deep molds in concretions (as in the nodules from the Lower Triassic of Madagascar) can produce casts "in the round" by filling each half of the concretion with latex and rejoining the halves until the latex is set. Any deep cracks in the mold not related to the morphology of the specimen should first be filled with plasticine.

If the matrix separates readily from the surface of the specimen, preparation with needles (ground flat on one surface) will usually suffice to prepare all but the most delicate structures. The needle should be held in a pin vice and the point ground flat or to a taper. This work must be done under a dissecting microscope and with good illumination. A dental grinding machine is useful for removing most of the rock, but the final film of matrix must be cleaned from the specimen with a needle to preserve the bone surface. Compressed specimens, particularly in shale, are frequently well exposed in the field, either by weathering or splitting, and a few hours or days of manual preparation will expose the covered parts without resorting to more elaborate methods.

For small specimens or limited areas of large ones in hard, well-cemented matrix, the Airbrasive Machine can produce excellent results (Stucker, 1961). If the bone is harder than the matrix (as in the fishes from the Tessin fauna or the Newark Series), small, thinly covered specimens can be beautifully cleaned in several days. The abrasive is ejected under high pressure through a tiny nozzle at the end of a hand piece. The eroding action can be controlled by selecting the proper abrasive, by regulating both the quantity of abrasive ejected and the gas pressure (carbon dioxide), by changing the nozzle and the specimen, and by varying the time the abrasive jet is held at one spot. With all these variables, it is also possible to prepare well ossified specimens in quite soft matrix. Fishes in calcareous Green River shale have been perfectly cleaned, including isolated brain cases, in a fraction of the time required for manual or even acid preparation and with less damage to the bone. Of course, only surface structures can be prepared in this way. Practice is necessary!

Vibro-tools, both homemade and commercial have been used successfully to expose ostracoderms and other types of fishes when the structure is not too delicate. High-frequency (ultrasonic) equipment, such as the Cavatron, will remove hard to soft matrix rather quickly, but the Airbrasive Machine is usually recommended for final preparation.

Acid techniques, when applicable and properly controlled, will produce superior specimens. Matrix containing calcium carbonate can be removed with acetic acid (15 percent or less), even though the acid may only dissolve the cement and facilitate manual removal of the residue. Compressed specimens in rock having a high carbonate content may be completely freed of matrix by the "transfer method" of Toombs and Rixon (1950, 1959). The original exposed surface of the specimen, well cleaned with acetic acid, is embedded in clear plastic. The remainder of the matrix is then dissolved so that the skeleton is supported only by the plastic and is thus visible from both sides.

Formic acid may work if the matrix will not respond to acetic, but in concentrations above 10 percent, this acid frequently attacks bone. It is always advisable to test the action of an acid on a fragment of bone and matrix before attempting the preparation of a good specimen.

In flattened specimens the skull is often badly crushed or comminuted, so that individual bones and sutures cannot be recognized, but the impression of the bone pattern in the matrix is frequently sharp and far more informative. If the matrix contains little or no carbonate, the bone can be dissolved by local applications of dilute hydrochloric acid. The bone fragments can also be removed with a needle, but surface ornamentation and undercuts may make manual preparation difficult. If much of the head skeleton is crushed together, the bone fragments and intervening matrix must be carefully removed to reveal the entire mold of the outer dermal bones on one side. Thin Alvar solution applied to the mold surface will help to preserve sharp ridges and undercuts during the preparation of latex peels.

Fish skeletons infiltrated and covered with selenite (as in the Pierre Formation) are difficult to clean, and the best specimens are usually those that have been exposed by natural weathering, provided that this has not gone too far. Small, delicate skeletons are almost impossible to prepare, except by careful scraping. The gypsum can be removed rather easily from the outer surfaces of large, well-ossified skulls and skeletons, but attempts to disarticulate a skull for additional cleaning are rarely successful. Heating the specimen in an oven at 260°F for about one hour, or applying heat locally with a small alcohol torch, will remove the water from the gypsum and reduce it to powder, but the specimen may fall apart, as the cracks are usually also filled with this mineral. Cleaned specimens should be stored on plaster beds to prevent breakage.

Large actinopterygian skeletons in a soft friable matrix are best preserved by preparing the upper side, embedding that side in plaster reinforced with metal rods, and removing the matrix from the lower side. If the specimen is transported to the laboratory in a jacket and is in a crumbly matrix, the jacket should be removed from the upper surface first (the usual procedure), that surface prepared, and a plaster base applied before the rest of the jacket is lifted off.

Latex, properly thinned and ready for use, can be exceedingly useful on a study trip. A satisfactory peel of a compressed specimen can be made with a single application of latex. When time permits, two or three coats will produce a more durable peel, but one coat, spread evenly, even if less than 2 mm thick, will record all the details and serve later as the mold for a plaster cast. A thin peel with considerable relief should be supported in sand to prevent distortion of the cast. Keep the fresh peels between sheets of paper and dust them with powder to eliminate stickiness.

Paleohistology has recently become an important phase of paleoichthyology (see Ørvig, 1951, for general summary). Thin sections of calcified cartilage, bone, teeth, and scales are useful in identification, in determining affinity, and in unraveling the complex history of the calcified tissues. Unless a special technique such as vacuum infiltration is required to prevent crumbling, a specimen can be embedded directly in canada balsam or, preferably, in some synthetic embedding medium. Excellent results have been obtained with a thermoplastic called Lakeside 70 (available from Hugh Courtright and Co., 7600 Greenwood Ave., Chicago 19, Ill.). To prevent the formation of bubbles, it should be melted between 120° and 140°C. Pour a small amount into a paper container of suitable size, and orient the specimen on this layer before it solidifies. Then cover the fragment completely. Lakeside 70 hardens quickly at room temperature, and if orientation of the fragment is important, the paper cup should be placed on a hot plate until the operation is completed.

Grind one selected surface of the block on a glass plate with Carborundum powder, grade 180, until the desired plane is reached (with practice, this step can also be accomplished with a thin rock saw or a fine lapidary wheel), then grind briefly with grade 240, and finish with emery powder. Fasten the ground surface to a glass slide, warmed to about 120°C, with a small amount of the melted thermoplastic, taking care not to trap air bubbles under the specimen. When the block is firmly cemented to the slide, repeat the operation until the desired thinness is attained. Place a small amount of Permount (available from Fisher Scientific Co., Fairlawn, N. J.) or a similar synthetic resin on one side of the section, and lower the cover glass from that side to exclude air bubbles. The optimum thinness of a section should be determined by repeated examination under a microscope during the final stage of grinding. If the section is too thin, important details may be lost.

Photographs of fossil fishes are important for purposes of documentation, but their usefulness is limited because morphologic details are frequently obscured and confused. Accurate line drawings of specimens as preserved can show significant features that may not be visible in photographs without retouching. Graphic reconstructions of the skull and body are commonly based on a number of specimens, and in a real sense they represent a visual summary of the information available on a particular form. The initial sketches may be made with a camera lucida, by tracing photographs, or by projecting a flattened specimen on paper with an opaque projector.

Although the general shape of the head can frequently be determined directly from the specimen, a more accurate restoration of a flattened skull may be obtained by first making a three-dimensional model. Sheet lead cutouts have been used for models of the head and shoulder armor of placoderms (Denison, 1950, p. 577–578). The dermal bone pattern can also be drawn on tracing paper and stuck to a sheet of plasteline or wax. The pattern is then cut out along the outer edge of the drawing and molded into the shape of the skull. By bringing the snout, mandibles, and other ventral elements into proper relationship, the form of the skull is practically self-determining.

The depth of the trunk region in life may be approximated by utilizing the data on the geometry of scale arrangement provided by Breder (1947, p. 383 ff.). If the squamation is well preserved, one can determine the angle of intersection of the geodesic lines followed by the scale rows as they spiral around the body both anteroposteriorly and posteroanteriorly. By referring to the table of angles on page 394 of Breder's paper, compiled for a number of actinopterygians, the body depth can be determined as being about equal to that for the forms listed in the same angle range. Treating the scale rows as spirals around the body is also a useful technique for restoring areas lacking scales, for improving perspective, and, in some cases, for estimating the length of the trunk region.

Good detailed photographs of fossil fishes are difficult to take mainly because of the poor contrast between specimen and matrix or within the specimen itself. Dusting with ammonium chloride is usually not desirable, as it covers both bone and matrix. Submerging a specimen in alcohol may increase the contrast considerably. Large specimens can be coated with glycerin; if reflections cause trouble, use polarizing filters. In general, illumination must be regulated according to the relief in the specimen. If the bone is fluorescent under ultraviolet, excellent detailed photographs can be made by using ultraviolet light; combining ultraviolet and white light will also record any relief in the specimen (Colbert and Tarka, 1960). X-rays of fossil fishes, either prepared or covered with matrix, can be very useful. The success of this technique depends to a large extent on the nature and thickness of the matrix both around and within the specimen.

## REFERENCES

Pertinent data on the occurrence, collection, and preparation of fossil fishes are scattered widely throughout the literature, and only a few references can be listed here. For further information on preparation techniques, the reader should refer to Part II of this volume.

Breder, C. M., Jr. (1947). An analysis of the geometry of symmetry with especial reference to the squamation of fishes. Amer. Mus. Nat. Hist. Bull., v. 88, art. 6, p. 321–412.

Colbert, Edwin H., and Chester Tarka (1960). Illustration of fossil vertebrates. Medical Biol. Illus., v. 10, no. 4, p. 237–246.

David, Lore Rose (1957). Fishes (other than agnatha), *in* H. S. Ladd (ed.), Treatise on marine ecology and paleoecology. Geol. Soc. America Mem. 67, v. 2, p. 999–1010.

Denison, Robert H. (1950). A new arthrodire from the New York State Devonian. Am. J. Sci., v. 248, p. 565–580.

———— (1956). A review of the habitat of the earliest vertebrates. Fieldiana, Geology, v. 11, no. 8, p. 361–457.

Ørvig, Tor (1951). Histologic studies of placoderms and fossil elasmobranchs. Arkiv för Zool., ser. 2, v. 2, no. 2, p. 321–454.

Rayner, Dorothy H. (1958). The geological environment of fossil fishes, *in* T. S. Westoll (ed.), Studies on fossil vertebrates. London, The Athlone Press, p. 128–156.

Stensiö, E. (1927). The Downtonian and Devonian vertebrates of Spitsbergen, Part 1, Family Cephalaspidae. Skrift. Sval. Nord., no. 12, p. 1–391.

Stucker, Gilbert F. (1961). Salvaging fossils by jet. Curator, v. 4, no. 4, p. 332–340.

Toombs, H. A., and A. E. Rixon (1950). The use of plastics in the transfer method of preparing fossils. Mus. J., v. 50, no. 5, p. 304–312.

———— (1959). The use of acids in the preparation of vertebrate fossils. Curator, v. 2, no. 4, p. 304–312.

# Tetrapods

NICHOLAS HOTTON III

*U. S. National Museum, Washington, D.C.*

Tetrapods first appear in terrestrial shales and sandstones of Mississippian age, and are found in deposits of every period since that time. Although their remains are scarce, compared with those of invertebrate animals, they are found in clastic rocks of all kinds, including pyroclastics, and locally may be very abundant. Tetrapods are most frequently found in shales, especially those containing channel conglomerates, and in sandstones of fine to medium grain size.

The sediments in which bones are found vary from unconsolidated to highly indurated. The degree of induration corresponds only roughly to the age of the sediment. Well-preserved bones show little evidence of replacement, but like the matrix, they vary in hardness. Bones thoroughly impregnated by calcite or silica may be harder than the surrounding matrix; unimpregnated bones are usually much softer. Often the matrix next to the bone is infiltrated with calcite, hematitie, or silica, and helps protect the bone against weathering. When this type of crust is highly developed, the bone or skeleton is completely encased in a large nodule of matrix that is harder than the rest of the deposit in which it occurs. All fossil bones, even the hardest, are to some extent subject to cracking and checking, and tend to weather out in small fragments.

The relationship between hardness of matrix and hardness of bone is the major determinant of techniques of search, collection, and preparation of tetrapod fossils. Probably the most common occurrence is one in which the matrix consists of a moderately well-indurated shale or very fine-grained sandstone, and in which the bone is hard enough, or well enough protected by a nodular crust, that it is a little more resistant to weathering than the matrix. In these circumstances one follows the drainage, walking up draws and ravines, looking for tell-tale fragments of bone in the loose rubble along the foot of slopes. If the fragments become more frequent in any direction upslope, they can be followed to their source. Productive beds may be worth collecting about one time in ten.

The first thing a collector does upon finding such an occurrence is to sit down and have a smoke. He then proceeds to delimit the extent and nature of his find, using small tools. A stout-bladed jackknife, a putty knife or a shoemaker's awl, and a varnish brush or a whisk broom do nicely for this sort of work on anything smaller than an elephant.

Exposed bone is very fragile. To avoid breaking it up while working on it, the collector uses some sort of liquid cement which can be flowed or painted onto the specimen as it is being exposed. For some reason, expert opinion is violently divided over the nature of the material to be used for this purpose. Proponents of gum arabic do not speak to proponents of shellac, and those who favor the nitrocellulose cements, such as Alvar, Duco, Ambroid, or Glyptal consider themselves well above the proponents of gum arabic and shellac, and do not speak to each other, either. All of these materials, however, serve the same purpose and have the following features in common: they are liquid and can be applied in any degree of fluidity according to the amount of solvent used; they dry quickly; and they form a strong cement and film which holds the bone in place effectively while it is being worked on in the field. The solvent for gum arabic is water, that for shellac is alcohol, and that for all of the nitrocelluloses except Glyptal is acetone; Glyptal is dissolved in lacquer thinner. Gum arabic is the slowest-drying, and is probably not as strong as the others, although in dry weather it is as effective as any. All of these cements except gum arabic have the drawback that in wet weather or in a humid climate they do not harden properly but remain sticky and thereby lose a great deal of their strength. When they are sticky, they foul up the cleaning process in the field by accumulating a crust of dust and small fragments of matrix. Gum arabic does not have this disadvantage, but in wet weather it takes a long time to dry and may not be effective at all.

Once the specimen has been properly exposed and delimited it must be prepared for removal. For all but the smallest specimens in hard matrix, this involves preparing a plaster jacket. The fossil must be protected against accidental damage by the application of whatever cement is used. If the cement cannot be brushed on without displacing bones, it may be flowed onto exposed surfaces. After the first application has hardened, a few layers of any kind of soft tissue such as rice paper, tissue paper, toilet paper, or facial tissue (in order of preference) should be applied to the specimen. Another coat of the preferred cement is painted on, and the paper applied sheet by sheet, each layer being tucked carefully and firmly around surface irregularities. Three or four layers are adequate. In addition to protecting the specimen, this step insures a clean separation between the specimen and the jacket in the laboratory, and should never be omitted or skimped. Sheets of wet newspaper can be used for large fossils. After the specimen has been treated with preservative and the preservative allowed to harden, the surface is wetted and wet sheets of newspaper are laid down in separate layers, each layer being tucked carefully around irregularities. Here again three or four layers are adequate.

The next step is to dig a trench all the way around the specimen. It should be wide enough to work in comfortably and deep enough, one hopes, to include all of the specimen. The trench should be dug well away from the specimen; the softer the matrix, the farther away. Many good specimens in soft matrix have been wrecked when jarred by repeated pick-blows too close to them. The depth of the trench depends upon how deeply the specimen is buried in the ground. Most specimens of moderate size extend no more than 10 inches below the surface; a safe depth for the trench is about two or three times that. Hardness of matrix will govern depth of the trench and distance from the specimen. To be on the safe side, it is better to dig the trench farther away and deeper than necessary. Excess matrix can always be cut away after the heavy work of digging the trench is finished and before jacketing is started. The sides of the trench adjacent to the specimen should be vertical or only discreetly undercut.

The materials required to make a plaster jacket are burlap, plaster of paris, and water. Old burlap, from which the sizing has been washed, is better than new, because new burlap is stiff and cannot be fitted easily to the contours of the fossil. Old burlap bags are convenient to use and can usually be obtained at local feed or hardware stores. When in Texas or Oklahoma ask for tow sacks. Plaster of paris or molding plaster are best and can be found in builders' supply stores. Dental plaster is excellent, but is ridiculously expensive. Do not try to use finishing plaster or any kind of wall plaster, because these contain an aggregate that makes them slow to set and limits their strength.

The burlap is first cut into strips about three inches wide. The strips should be long enough to cover the specimen on top and reach down the sides to the estimated depth of burial. Enough strips should be cut so that, allowing a $\frac{1}{2}$- to $\frac{3}{4}$-inch overlap between strips, the top and sides of the block will be completely covered. It is better to make the burlap too long than too short, and better to cut too much than not enough. For a specimen no larger than a foot or two across, a single layer of burlap is entirely adequate, even if the matrix is quite soft. For larger specimens, very thin specimens, or completely unconsolidated matrix, two layers of burlap, strips of the second layer running at right angles to the first, may be advisable. Packages so cumbersome or weak as to require two layers of burlap may be further strengthened by including sticks or other stiffeners running the full length of the block and encased between the layers of burlap.

The plaster should be mixed with water to the consistency of thick cream, the plaster being added to the water and mixed in with the hands to insure breaking up lumps. From here on, one has to work fast because the plaster sets rapidly, especially in hot, dry weather. Each burlap strip is dipped into the plaster and squeezed so that the plaster will penetrate it completely. The burlap strip is removed from the plaster with one hand and drawn gently between two fingers of the other hand to wipe off excess plaster. Place the first strip in the middle of the specimen and work out to the end of the block alternately, overlapping adjacent strips by $\frac{1}{2}$ to $\frac{3}{4}$ inch. The most important aspect of this process is to be sure that the burlap is worked snugly into the irregularities of the surface. Let the ends of each strip hang slack while you are working on the top; afterwards pat them into place at the sides of the block without exerting any tension on the top. If the plaster is good and fresh, there is no need to apply any more than what is carried in the wiped burlap bandages. It is far more important to be sure of a good fit between the specimen and the first layer of bandages and to have enough bandages to cover the specimen.

The importance of a snug fit between the jacket and specimen cannot be overemphasized. The plaster jacket is rigid, and if it does not fit the block exactly, vibration may cause the matrix to disintegrate inside the jacket. It is disappointing to open a package and find nothing but shale-and-fossil hash.

If splints are necessary, they should never be applied between the specimen and the first layer of burlap, because this will spoil the fit between the specimen and the jacket, with the same tragic results. Always place the splints between the inner and outer jackets, fitting the outer strips carefully around the splints.

The most critical part of the whole operation is getting the specimen out of the hole and turning it over, preparatory to bandaging the underside. When the trench has been dug deep enough, the matrix is undercut below the level of the ends of the bandages, until the specimen is standing on a pedestal, like a toadstool. For large specimens or poorly consolidated matrix, it may be necessary to bandage beneath the undercut before turning the block. Be sure to prepare a flat surface onto which the block can be rolled as it comes off the pedestal. It is not good to have to lower it or raise it any distance, and it must be turned quickly but smoothly. If the matrix is unconsolidated or weathered, there is great danger at this point that the entire specimen might drop out of the bottom of the package; speedy and gentle handling are therefore essential.

Once the uncovered surface of the block has been turned over without dumping the specimen, the rest is gravy. Matrix is dug away from the underside of the block with small tools to reduce weight. A great weight of matrix does not add materially to the strength of the block, so it is advisable to remove as much as possible without encroaching on the specimen. The free ends of the bandages can be cut away flush with the edges of the matrix retained. The underside of the block is bandaged in exactly the same way as the top was, the bandages of the bottom overlapping those of the top. One must be equally finicky about being sure that the bandages fit the irregularities of the bottom of the block. They must fit tightly all the way around, because the matrix will jar loose just as easily if the bottom jacket doesn't fit closely as it will if the top doesn't.

This technique is applicable primarily to reasonably complete specimens or to large specimens which may be stratigraphically diagnostic. It is time consuming, however, and the necessary plaster and water is much too bulky a load to be carried routinely by the exploring geologist. Occasionally, straightforward collecting of weathered-out fragments of bone will provide useful information and may enable the paleontologist to tell whether the source of the fragments is worth further investigation. The most diagnostic fragments of any animal are pieces of skull, particularly if they contain teeth. Individual teeth are fairly useful in identifying mammals, considerably less so in identifying reptiles. A partial or complete dentition is, of course, always better than single teeth in identifying any animal. Vertebral fragments are generally more useful in identifying amphibians and reptiles, particularly those of Paleozoic age, than they are in identifying mammals. But limb and foot bones are more useful for identifying mammals than they are for reptiles and amphibians. Fragments of ribs are no good for identifying anything (except turtles!), although complete ribs may sometimes indicate what one is dealing with. Isolated fragments may be wrapped in tissue and stowed in standard sample bags.

The so-called nodular occurrence, in which bones are protected by a limy or ferruginous coating and tend to weather out intact, is much more useful from the standpoint of the perambulatory geologist, who must travel light. In this type of occurrence the surface of the ground is often littered with intact or nearly intact bones instead of fragments of bones. These can be collected, wrapped securely in soft paper, and bagged, in which condition they will withstand considerable traveling. If a nodule contains a small animal, it may be possible to dig the entire specimen out of the rock by quick and dirty methods, and elaborate bandaging can be dispensed with. Larger nodules have a tendency to crack, however, and often have to be bandaged like a specimen in loose shale. In some nodular occurrences the ground may be littered with nodules which show no bone at all on their surfaces. The only way to tell if such objects have bone in them is to break them with a hammer, but a little time spent in making little ones out of big ones may reveal superior specimens. Most nodules break cleanly, and if they contain bone can be glued back together again with minimal damage to the specimen. When they are firmly glued together with some sort of nitrocellulose cement, such nodules tolerate transportation very well.

The most difficult type of tetrapod fossil occurrence is that in which the matrix consists of soft shale and the bone is even softer. Because the bone weathers and disintegrates faster than the surrounding matrix, the geologist is not likely to encounter the bone in the field. Discovery of this type of occurrence is usually the result of commercial activity, such as strip mining or road building, which exposes unweathered rock. The best way to collect this material is to dig out as large chunks of the matrix as possible with a heavy pick. If unweathered bone shows up frequently on the surfaces of such large chunks, let them dry, wrap them carefully in newspaper, and send them without further ado to the laboratory for closer scrutiny. Except in rare cases, however, fossils are scarce in such beds, and it is usually not worthwhile to ship chunks of matrix to the laboratory without first checking them in the field. If the shale is well bedded, the laminae can be split apart carefully with a jackknife; fine specimens may thus be revealed. If the shale is not well bedded, it is necessary to break up the larger chunks carefully to expose unweathered fossils. With patience and care this technique will produce good material. Artificial preservation of the material is the same whether the shale is laminated or not. After the bone has been exposed and prayers said, the specimen is allowed to dry thoroughly and is then coated with a preservative. Because these specimens are usually of a size that can be handled easily and can be placed in a safe place to dry, the nitrocellulose cements are much more practical. The solution should be very dilute and should be dripped carefully onto the specimen rather than painted on in order to avoid displacement of delicate bone. Nitrocellulose cements are strong even when very dilute, and a coat or two should stick the bones firmly in place. Once this is accomplished and the bones show little tendency to shift, several thicknesses of soft paper should be applied directly over the bones with cement. Unweathered matrix often hardens thoroughly upon drying and may travel well without further treatment, but each piece should always be heavily wrapped in newspaper before packing. Laminated sheets of shale, which may be so broad as to be flimsy, can be reinforced on the side opposite the fossil by a couple of coats of plaster.

Fragmentary but useful tetrapod fossils are sometimes recovered from very hard channel sandstones or fine grits. If the bone is so hard that it hasn't been damaged by weathering, it can be collected by cutting the matrix around it with a cold chisel and removing the bone and some of the surrounding matrix. Before removing it, however, the exposed bone should first be carefully painted with preservative, covered with paper, and allowed to dry, because even though it seems very hard and has resisted weathering to a remarkable degree, it will tend to crack and pop out of its bed under the vibration of hammering. This procedure is much like the initial stages of taking a specimen out of its plaster jacket, except that the matrix is much harder and the operation is only practical on a small scale. As in trenching, it is much better to work too far away from the specimen than too close.

To sum up, the basic equipment needed by the geologist who hopes (or expects to be obliged) to collect vertebrate fossils during his field season should add little to his normal load. An ordinary geologist's hammer is suitable for digging in tough shales. A Marsh pick is much faster for clearing away unconsolidated sediment, but is too light for work on indurated materials. In addition to a hammer, the field worker will need a couple of different sizes of chisels—for example, a $\frac{1}{4}$-inch and a $\frac{1}{2}$-inch. Pieces of tool steel of the same diameter but ground to conical points instead of chisel edges will also be useful. A jackknife is a necessity. A whisk broom and a 1-inch varnish brush for sweeping away weathered debris, and additional smaller brushes for applying preservative, will also be needed. A half-pint or pint screw-top jar of dilute nitrocellulose cement and a supply of tissue and news-paper complete the list of personal portables. A number of stout cardboard cartons and plenty of newspapers should be stowed in the vehicle.

Plaster, burlap, and water are omitted from this list because of their bulk and weight. They are obviously never carried during prospecting; specimens requiring a plaster jacket are usually marked, and a special trip made to plaster them out. If needed, materials for plaster jackets can be obtained locally.

Almost anyone who has the time, the inclination, and, above all, the pa-tience, can do an adequate job of collecting vertebrate fossils. No one in a hurry should ever tackle such a project, and if there is any doubt in the geologist's mind as to the proper technique to use, the rule is to do it the hard way. If there is not time to do it the hard way, mark the spot and try to get a vertebrate paleontologist interested in the project.

# Otoliths

DON L. FRIZZELL

*Department of Geology, University of Missouri School of Mines and Metallurgy, Rolla*

Fossil otoliths of teleost fishes are only incompletely collected in the usual search for megafossils and are rarely found in conventional microfossil sam-ples. They are to be sought in restricted facies of marine formations of Triassic age and younger. Collections worthy of study result from the appli-cation of special field and laboratory techniques. Collecting otoliths is there-fore largely a task for the specialist.

## LITHOLOGICAL RESTRICTION

Otoliths have been extracted from fossil skulls and even studied in preserved skeletons. The great bulk of material, however, occurs as isolated specimens in various rock types: greensand marl, shell marl, glauconitic shell marl, rolled shells, shell debris, and storm beach deposits. Otoliths are concentrated at sedimentational discontinuities and, to a lesser extent, adjacent to them. They occur in abundance in small stringers and lenticles, as well as in shell pockets and sand pockets, and in places are widely and randomly dissemi-nated within a stratum.

## FIELD COLLECTING

Large specimens are collected individually in the field. Some lie free on the surface of the outcrop or on alluvial wash. Others may be dug from the rock with a pocket knife. Forceps, labels, cotton, and vials are essential equipment.

Small specimens constitute the large majority of the otoliths of any fauna. Two quarts of material from a sand pocket may yield hundreds of specimens. More commonly, though, bulk samples of 1 to 5 hundredweight are required, as many species are extremely rare.

Some otoliths usually may be observed on the outcrop, especially if they occur in relative abundance. Sparse occurrences, require a pilot-test wash and examination to determine whether they warrant further study. Preservation also varies, but fresh exposures usually yield the best specimens.

## SEGREGATION IN THE LABORATORY

Bulk samples are soaked, for hours or days, in water *without reagent*. (Bases such as sodium carbonate or bicarbonate deteriorate the organic fibers of otoliths.) After soaking, samples are wet-sieved on 10-, 20-, and 30-mesh screens.

The 10-mesh fraction is best picked wet, in a shallow pie tin under a large 4×-magnification crane magnifier. Specimens are removed with Turdox Microdissection Forceps. (All other types used have resulted in breakage of delicate specimens.) The remaining screen fractions are dried and subsequently examined under a stereoscopic microscope at 6× or 10× magnification. Specimens are transferred to cardboard slides with a moistened brush.

## PREPARATION OF SPECIMENS

Most otoliths must be cleaned before study. Encrusting debris may be removed, in a Syracuse watch glass under water, with fine brushes and needles. Preliminary treatment of *individual specimens* in an ultrasonic cleaner for one or two seconds is especially beneficial. A household detergent in water has proved satisfactory for this purpose.

Cleaned specimens are hardened by painting them with a very dilute solution of white shellac or with thin collodion. Fragments, if of sufficient interest, are assembled and glued together with collodion prior to hardening (if shellac is used).

Large specimens are stored in plastic boxes (1 by 1 by 1 inch, 1 by 1 by 2 inch, and 1 by 2 by 2 inch). Small specimens are stored on standard cardboard micropaleontology slides, and are glued in place with gum tragacanth.

The importance of precise labels, at all stages of work, cannot be overemphasized. Minimum data for a specimen label consists of: (1) system,

(2) group and formation, (3) collector's notebook symbol, (4) general description of locality, and (5) collector's name and date of collection.

# Plants: Mesozoic and Cenozoic Forms

---

ERLING DORF

*Department of Geology, Princeton University,*
*Princeton, New Jersey*

Most of the megascopic nonmarine plant remains preserved in rocks of Mesozoic or Cenozoic age are fossil leaves. Less common are the remains of fruits and seeds, cones and catkins, and petrified wood; very rare indeed are fossil flowers or parts of flowers.

Rocks of Triassic, Jurassic, and Lower Cretaceous age are apt to yield mainly the leafy fronds of ferns, the needle-like or scaly leaves of conifers, the spreading palm-like leaves of cycads and cycadeoids, and the fan-shaped leaves of ginkgos (fig. 1). In the rocks of the Upper Cretaceous, the Tertiary, and the Quaternary, the plant remains are chiefly the leaves of hardwood, deciduous trees, with conifers and ferns still fairly common; more unusual are large palm leaves, cones of various sorts, and fruits and seeds (fig. 2).

## KINDS OF ROCKS CONTAINING FOSSIL PLANTS

Nonmarine sedimentary rocks of nearly all types, from coarse sandstones to fine shales and limestones, have been known to contain well-preserved plant remains of one sort or another. Even rocks of marine origin may contain a few remains of land plants, though these are usually fragmentary and torn as the result of wave and current action. Only very rarely indeed have recognizable fossil plants been recovered from igneous rocks (e.g., the basal beds of lava flows) or from metamorphic rocks (e.g., slates and quartzites).

Excellent specimens can often be obtained from the dark, fine-grained, nonmarine shales associated with coal beds. The shale beds immediately above the coals are usually more productive than the beds between or below the coals. Coal mine dumps, which are usually made up largely of shales from the mine roof or from partings within the coal, often contain easily obtainable plant remains of excellent quality. Shaly interbeds or sandy lenses in nonmarine conglomerates are good prospects for fossil plants. The finer grained pyroclastics, from tuffaceous sandstones to fine vitric tuffs, are excellent sediments for the preservation of a great variety of plant remains, especially if

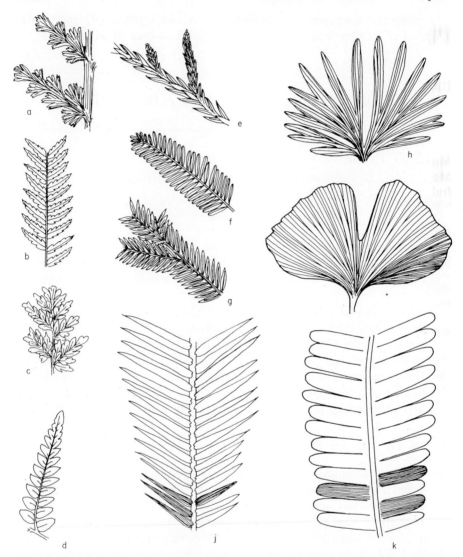

**Fig. 1.** *Sketches of typical representatives of ferns (a–d), conifers (e–g), ginkgos (h, i), and cycads (j, k).*

they were originally deposited directly from the atmosphere upon a region supporting a living forest. Nonmarine clay beds are also well suited for the preservation of fossil plants, sometimes in remarkably unaltered condition.

Somewhat less fruitful though possible sites for the occurrence of plant remains are (1) massive sandstones, in which the plants are usually widely scattered rather than concentrated in lenses or pockets, (2) concretions, in which the plant remains are usually fragmentary, (3) limestones, either fresh-

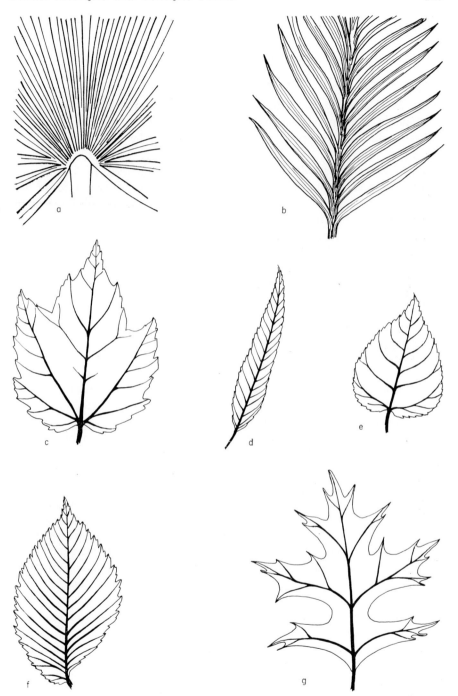

**Fig. 2.** *Sketches of typical representative of palms (a, b), and of hardwood, deciduous trees (c, maple; d, willow; e, poplar; f, elm; g, oak).*

water or marine, in which the plants are ordinarily widely scattered as well as fragmentary.

## LOCATING PLANT-BEARING BEDS

Many fossil plant localities are rediscovered, so to speak, on the basis of information from previously published reports. Others may be located by following directions supplied by other geologists or by natives familiar with the region.

When previous knowledge of them is lacking, the task of locating new plant-bearing zones usually begins with the careful search for pieces of float containing recognizable fragments of plants of any sort. By diligent sleuthing these fragments can usually be traced back upstream or upslope to the bed from which they came. In such exploratory work every effort should be made to locate as many plant-bearing beds as possible. It should never be assumed that an unfossiliferous bed in one exposure will be barren at adjacent outcrops. Well-preserved plant remains are notoriously localized in pockets or lenses.

## QUARRYING FOR GOOD SPECIMENS

The plant fossils ordinarily obtained from float or talus in the vicinity of a plant-bearing bed are generally not satisfactory for identification and correlation. Such specimens are usually badly weathered and fragmentary. They should be retained for study only if the fossil-bearing bed cannot be found in place or cannot be reached because of unfavorable topographic location. Sometimes, however, the float materials may yield a few unique specimens not subsequently collected in place, in which case they should be saved for study, even though imperfectly preserved or incomplete.

Assuming that the fossil-bearing bed has been located in place, the next objective is to secure large slabs of the unweathered rock containing the plant remains. For best results the barren strata lying above the fossiliferous beds should be carefully quarried and discarded. This should result in exposing as large a surface as possible of the plant-bearing bed. This undertaking may require much time and effort, depending upon the hardness, attitude, and thickness of the barren beds. In addition to the ordinary geologist's hammer, a crowbar, a large pick, a sledge, and a shovel are usually of great help, as are a few large, muscular, energetic field assistants.

When the quarrying has been completed and excess debris discarded, the plant-bearing bed is removed in large slabs up to 2 square feet or more in area if possible. These slabs are then carefully split along bedding planes or along laminae parallel to the bedding planes. Ordinarily this splitting is facilitated by the natural cleavage produced by the plant remains within the rock.

Wide-edged chisels of various sizes are usually necessary for most effective splitting. So far as possible it is generally best to split the slab first into half-thicknesses, and then into quarter-thicknesses, and so on until further splits are not possible or until satisfactory specimens have been obtained. It is advisable to wear protective goggles or nonbreakable glasses during this operation.

## WHAT TO COLLECT

Generally speaking, most of the fossils encountered in a plant-bearing bed of Mesozoic or Cenozoic age will be fossil leaves. These are either (1) compressions, in which part of the carbonized leaf substance is still present, giving the fossil a brown, dark gray, or even black color; or (2) impressions, in which the original leaf substance has been completely removed, leaving only an imprint. Of the two types the compressions are the more valuable since they are more apt to preserve important details of texture and epidermal characters.

For purposes of identification it should be kept in mind that a single complete fossil leaf showing shape, marginal characters, tip, base, and petiole, as well as clearly defined veins within the leaf blade itself, is worth a dozen fragments of the same species. The most fortunate find—rare and precious— is the specimen in which complete leaves or leaflets are found still attached to the stem or leaf stalks on which they were originally borne. Other rarities for which a diligent search should be made on every newly exposed surface are compressions or impressions of (1) cones of conifers or cycads, easily recognized by their resemblance to the modern cones of pines, spruces, hemlocks, and other trees; (2) seeds and fruits of various shapes and sizes; (3) flowers or parts of flowers; (4) catkins, usually long and narrow like those of modern alders or birches; and (5) fern leaflets (pinnules) on which are preserved the small, rounded fruiting structures.

If only a portion of a leaf or other plant fossil is exposed because of an uneven rock split, the rest of the specimen can usually be uncovered by carefully chipping away the matrix with a small chisel. Specimens that are accidentally cracked should not be discarded; unless the broken pieces are very small or are unavoidably scattered and irretrievable, they can usually be adequately mended with ordinary glue or household cement. It is generally advisable to delay most of the finer repair work and preparatory tasks until the specimens are in the laboratory. If this is done the broken portions of a single specimen should be properly labeled as parts of one fossil for subsequent reunion or repair.

Counterparts of either compressions or impressions, if they are well preserved, should be kept along with the originals. These reverse impressions often show details not seen or preserved on the originals. Neither originals nor counterparts should be coated with any kind of varnish, shellac, or plastic cement unless the plant remains are so very fragile that they must be held together by something.

Both judgment and care must be exercised in reducing specimens to convenient and reasonable sizes for transportation back to field headquarters, and for ultimate shipment to the laboratory. With a fissile shale, for example, very little trimming should be attempted in the field; with a firmer matrix, however, a great deal of reduction can be accomplished by careful chipping along the edges with a regular geologic hammer. Very soft shale or clay may often be effectively trimmed to desired size with a large knife.

## FIELD SORTING OF SPECIMENS

As soon as they are properly trimmed the plant specimens should be neatly piled side by side on a flattish surface at least 20 feet away from the working quarry. Specimens should never be placed on top of one another because of the danger of scratching or abrading the delicate plant remains. If the collection has to be left overnight, it should be covered by a canvas or tarpaulin properly anchored down with rocks. Collecting at each locality should continue as long as possible in order to insure as adequate a sample of the ancient forest as possible. Assuming that the fossil bed does not suddenly pinch out or become barren, as often happens, it is not an unusual practice to collect as many as 500 or 1000 individual specimens from each plant locality. Such amounts make quantitative data not only easier to determine but more meaningful.

If time permits, the sorting of specimens into different morphological "species" should be attempted in the field at each plant locality. For such tentative separation the collection is first re-sorted into individual piles of plant forms which look alike. Each pile then is presumed to represent a different "species." After this task is finished, a careful count is made of the number of specimens of each "species" in the collection at each locality. These may be distinguished from each other by tentative names, by letters, or by numbers, care being taken to get a full representation of all the "species" present. Then follows the discarding of fragmentary, broken, or abraded specimens, and the retention of an adequate number (a dozen at least, if possible) of each "species" encountered. Field labels should be provided for each specimen. Labels should include the stratigraphic position of the plant-bearing zone in the section in order to prevent future mixing of collections, as well as relations to both invertebrate and vertebrate zones, if present.

## WRAPPING SPECIMENS

Each specimen should be carefully wrapped in the field for safe transportation to field headquarters. Ordinary newspaper is by far the best for this purpose. Small, delicate, or fragile specimens are usually first wrapped in soft tissue paper and then further wrapped in newspaper. Care should then be taken to pack specimens as tightly as possible in collecting bags or knapsacks to prevent damage to the fossils by rubbing, shifting, or bouncing in transport—especially when transported by pack horse or by Jeep.

Final packing for shipment to the laboratory should be done with utmost care. Strong wooden boxes, preferably not too large, should be constructed from new, strong lumber. Some of the specimens will probably require additional wrapping in newspaper. All specimens should be carefully fitted together as tightly as possible in successive layers in each box. In addition to firmly nailed covers, the boxes should be bound in a good grade of wire to prevent breakage during transport, usually by railway freight.

## LABORATORY PREPARATION OF SPECIMENS

Assuming that the plant collections have arrived at the laboratory with a minimum of breakage enroute and have been carefully unwrapped, the specimens should first be sorted according to zones and localities and placed in adequate drawers or trays. Each specimen should then be numbered according to locality, preferably in India ink on a painted white rectangle. Extreme care should be taken to be certain that specimens from one zone or locality are not inadvertently mixed with specimens from another.

Preparation of compressions or impressions for final study and identification may often require further chiseling away of rock to expose the complete plant remains. Such chiseling should be done with the specimen carefully placed on a small sand bag. Chisels of various sizes and shapes may be found very useful, and Vibro-tools are often very effective; any hammering on the specimen should be done gently with a very small hammer. Glasses should be worn as a protection against flying chips. Broken specimens should be repaired as soon as possible with ordinary glue or household cement.

Compressions of leaves or other plant remains often preserve enough of the original plant materials, usually carbonized, to warrant their removal from the rock matrix for further study under the microscope. There are two common methods of removal:

1. *Maceration.* When plant fragments are especially abundant and well preserved, the enclosing matrix is usually removed by bulk maceration in hydrofluoric acid, Schultz's mixture, or other highly oxidizing agents. The residual fragments, which may include fragments of leaves, wood, cone scales, seeds, and so on, are cleaned, screened, and mounted for final study, usually on glass slides.

2. *Peel transfers.* When the compressions occur as flat carbonaceous films along bedding planes, they are usually removed intact from the rock matrix by transferring the plant materials to a peel of one sort or another and subsequently removing the matrix by trimming and by using acids. The various transfer techniques include

the Walton method, the Ashby method, and the Abbott method. The peels are more easily stored than the original rock specimens and are usually more satisfactory for both megascopic and microscopic study.

The laboratory preparation of petrified plant remains is discussed in detail in Part II of this Handbook. The specialized maceration techniques applied to the study of fossil spores and pollen are thoroughly covered in Part III.

# Part II

DESCRIPTIONS OF
SPECIFIC TECHNIQUES

# SECTION A

## COLLECTING TECHNIQUES

*Coordinator:* ELLIS L. YOCHELSON

# Sampling in Paleontology

## W. C. KRUMBEIN

*Northwestern University, Evanston, Illinois*

The sampling problem in paleontology has several aspects. One is *search sampling,* in which the objective may be to locate fossiliferous horizons in thick sequences of rock layers; or to find certain diagnostic organisms within a horizon known to be fossiliferous. The latter is an example of *purposive selection,* in which the objective is wholly substantive, as in stratigraphic correlation. In contrast to search sampling and purposive selection is *statistical sampling,* which includes an element of randomization as an essential part of the sampling plan. The objective here is to obtain unbiased samples as a basis for statistical inference about some specified population.

These and other aspects of paleontological sampling have been discussed in detail or in passing by many paleontologists. This paper reviews some conventional sampling procedures in an expository manner, with emphasis on the interplay between paleontologic judgment and statistical inference in the choice of a sampling plan. A selected annotated bibliography covers some of the procedures and principles treated in the text.

## RANDOMIZATION AND BIAS

Randomization is a formal procedure that assures the paleontologist that he will not unintentionally introduce a bias into his statistical samples, either by selecting favored specimens or by neglecting the principle that, for rigorous statistical inference, each individual in the population must have some chance of being included in the sample. Randomization definitely is not a haphazard process equivalent to blindfolding a paleontologist before he gropes about on an outcrop.

A simple parallel in randomization is afforded by shuffling a deck of cards. Shuffling is independent of the particular game played; it is a formal procedure to assure an equal chance for any card to appear in the hands of any player. In paleontological sampling for statistical purposes randomization plays a similar part in eliminating bias.

There is no bias in purposive selection, inasmuch as the intent is to obtain fossils for a particular paleontological purpose, such as selecting well-preserved fossil corals for thin sections. Bias may enter the picture if at some later stage these carefully and purposively collected specimens are used as a "typical sample" of the taxa. If this is done the statistical inferences arising from the sample may be quite different from what they would have been if a randomization procedure had been followed.

## SEARCH SAMPLING AND PURPOSIVE SELECTION

In search sampling for fossiliferous rock layers, the outcrop is scanned for changes in color, bedding, or calcareous content that may suggest the presence of fossil organisms. Where visual indications are absent, and it is desirable to locate all horizons that contain fossils, a relatively rapid search procedure can be based on a channel sample extending through the whole section normal to the bedding. Consider a horizontally bedded shale section 300 feet thick to be searched for microfossils. A single continuous channel is divided into, say, five segments, each 60 feet thick. The five bags are separately examined in the field for fossils. If none are found in a given bag, that part of the channel is eliminated. If fossils are found, the vertical outcrop interval in the channel segment is examined more closely to locate the fossil-bearing beds. This is a form of batch sampling, in which batches (here channel segments) are discarded when results are negative.

Search procedures are not infallible. In the example given, the position of the channel sample may be such that a given bed, fossiliferous elsewhere along the outcrop, is barren in the channel. The paleontologist judges, from contributing geological evidence, whether one vertical channel divided into five segments constitutes a sufficient search; and if so, where to position the search channel.

A second aspect of search sampling, that of purposively seeking organic remains to establish stratigraphic position, does not involve an element of randomization. It is a substantive procedure in which, conceivably, the finding of a single critical fossil may provide the information sought. A third aspect of search sampling is the collection of well-preserved specimens of some taxon for detailed morphological studies. As stated, the statistical inferences and frequency distributions that arise from measurements of these selected fossils may be notably different from those of the population as a whole.

## STATISTICAL SAMPLING

A principal attribute of statistical sampling is its element of randomization, which assures each individual in the population some chance of being included in the sample. If this chance is equal for all individuals in the population, the sample is a *simple random sample*. Complexities in obtaining statistical samples from a paleontological population are mentioned later; nevertheless, on any one outcrop it is possible to collect various kinds of statistical samples. These are discussed here in terms of a single outcrop, to make clear what the procedures are. For this purpose the outcrop may be considered as a subpopulation within some larger population representing the rock body as a whole.

An outcrop of calcareous shale, a few feet thick, and continuous for 500 feet, is used as the example. The fossils present are all microforms. There may be local variability in numbers and kinds of fossils, but no systematic changes are evident from a preliminary qualitative search.

The first step in choosing a sampling plan is to define the subpopulation being sampled, in terms of its physical limits and of the individuals that make it up. In this example the objects of direct interest are fossils, but the population to be sampled may be defined in any of several ways. One way is to define a population of fossils directly, and the other is to define a population of unit volumes of shale, each of which contains some fossils. This second plan offers the advantage that the sampling elements can be conveniently defined as consisting of all possible channels (say 6 inches wide and 2 inches deep) extending from top to bottom of the bed. This would generate a practical population of 1000 individual elements along the 500-foot outcrop.

It is to be emphasized that setting up a population, defining its individuals, and devising a sampling plan all involve a number of purely paleontological decisions. Once these have been made (as, for example, in deciding on the dimensions of a channel sample) the statistical model that is to be used in analyzing the data is in turn evident, and this model controls to some extent the kind of samples that are to be collected. There is no assurance that an arbitrarily selected sampling plan will be equally appropriate for different kinds of arbitrarily chosen statistical models.

In the example under discussion, the precise edge of the initial channel strip can be set at the extreme left end of the outcrop, or it may be placed even farther left in a random manner by uncovering a portion of shale shallowly buried. Thus, an essentially infinite number of randomized starting points is available. Once the first strip is designated, however, all others fall into place, and the situation becomes in practice a finite sampling problem involving 1000 6-inch strips along the 500-foot outcrop. It is to be emphasized that some of the sampling plans described here are designed for finite populations.

For convenience, let $N = 10$, so that the task is to collect ten shale strips from the outcrop. Since the kind of samples to be collected depends on what is to be done with them, and this in turn depends on the purposes of the paleontological study, four main sampling variants are described for this example.

### SIMPLE RANDOM SAMPLING

Suppose that the problem of paleontological interest is to estimate the mean size of adults in species I of genus A in the shale subpopulation. Here simple random sampling is appropriate, though in practice $N$ may be different from 10.

A table of random numbers is used to select ten 3-digit numbers lying between 000 and 999, omitting duplicates. Then, calling the first strip 000, the distance along the outcrop is measured in 6-inch units to locate the initial edges of the correspondingly numbered strips. In this plan each shale strip is an individual in a subpopulation of 1000 strips, but within each strip is a cluster sample (see below) of the subpopulation of microfossils. That is, the population that is sampled satisfies the condition that each shale strip has an equal chance of being included in the sample. Presumably each individual referred to this particular taxon also has an equal chance of being included in the sample, but there may be a technical difference, in that the shale strips are collected by a randomization procedure, but there is no randomization of the fossils in each strip. Whatever fossils are present are automatically part of the strip sample.

The paleontologic procedure may be to measure all adult specimens of this taxon, using all the fossils of this category in the sampled shale strips. This provides a *census* in each of the channels collected. If the number of adults referred to the taxon is very large in each shale strip, a subsample of size $n$ may be taken from the prepared material by a randomization procedure. If this is done, the census of all adults in each strip now becomes a simple random sample of adult fossils from each shale strip. Moreover, by focusing on the fossils in the shale, a new kind of population is generated. The shale strip is an individual in a population of shale strips, but the fossils are individuals in a population of fossils. The decision to use one kind of population for sampling and another for measurement is quite valid when the individuals in the population to be sampled contain within themselves individuals in the population of direct interest.

These two subpopulations have some interesting relations. A sedimentary petrologist has his samples directly as shale strips; the paleontologist has his included within the shale strips. Since both subpopulations have an element of randomization, the paleontologist interested in the properties of the shale that contains his fossils has statistical data available for paleoecological analysis. The petrologist interested in the environment of shale deposition has statistical faunal data for augmenting his physical interpretations.

With megafossils exposed to view on an outcrop, simple random sampling of the fossils in, say, species II of genus B would technically require numbering all the individuals on the outcrop, and randomizing a sample of, say, $N = 100$ from these numbered individuals. This procedure would be extraordinarily laborious, so that the practical solution is not unlike that for microfossils. Again, strips of the shale (perhaps of such size that each contains a fair number of fossils) are defined as individuals in a population of strips, and all fossils in the randomized shale strips are then taken. For some kinds of studies, where population density is of interest, all the fossils exposed in each randomly selected area or along randomly selected intercepts on the outcrop may be counted or collected.

Figure 1,*a,* shows the positions along the outcrop of ten random shale strips obtained by the procedure outlined earlier. In simple random sampling some samples are taken in clusters and others are widely spaced. As long as the population is homogeneous, showing no trends or gradients, and as long as all individuals in the subpopulation are equally accessible, simple random sampling is a standard procedure for estimating the population mean and variance of measured attributes.

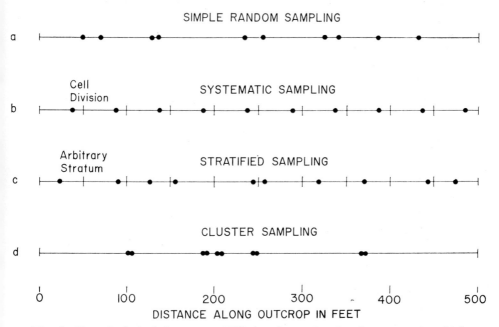

**Fig. 1.** *Hypothetical shale outcrop 500 feet long, showing four ways in which statistical samples may be collected.*

SYSTEMATIC SAMPLING

Most geologists and paleontologists intuitively prefer a sampling plan in which the individuals are spread fairly evenly over the area to be sampled. Systematic sampling provides such a plan. The 500-foot outcrop is divided into ten nonoverlapping segments, each of which includes 100 consecutive shale strips. One number in the range 00 to 99 is chosen at random to locate the individual shale strip in the first segment. Say the number is 72. Then, from each segment, the shale strip bearing this number is collected to obtain a *systematic sampling* of each segment.

Figure 1,*b,* shows this arrangement. The samples satisfy the condition of equal spacing, but there is no assurance that they will fall close to the center of each segment. One may arbitrarily take the middlemost strip in each segment without affecting randomization if the starting point of the whole system (i.e., the exact edge of the first shale strip on the outcrop) is itself randomized.

Systematic samples satisfy the condition of equal spacing, but statistical models related to systematic sampling may differ from those based on simple random samples. Regression models for detecting trends are conveniently used with systematic samples, whereas estimates of population means and variances and of statistical correlation among variates are commonly based on simple random samples. As is true of all sampling procedures, the decision to use one or another depends on the paleontological objectives and the selection of statistical models. Interestingly enough, systematic samples may give better estimates of mean values (because the whole outcrop is involved) than simple random samples will; but estimates of population variances may be larger for systematic than for simple random samples. This arises because systematic samples force the individuals into a fixed spacing, whereas simple random samples allow some clustering, and thus include in the variance estimate the balancing influence of greater resemblance between neighbors, and less between individuals farther away.

In the example under discussion it was assumed during random sampling that preliminary search sampling had suggested homogeneity of the shale along the 500-foot outcrop. This is also implied in the systematic samples, where the intention was to obtain more evenly spaced samples. The systematic samples, however, furnish an opportunity for testing this point, in that if the subpopulation does have a gradient or trend, regression analysis can commonly detect it. This might be particularly applicable to detection of slight ecological gradients in an otherwise apparently homogeneous shale or clay matrix.

STRATIFIED SAMPLING

In this method of statistical sampling, some control can be exerted on the spacing of the samples by setting up two or more *sampling strata.* These may be selected arbitrarily, or they may be selected on the basis of geologic or paleontologic criteria. A common geological example is the division of a vertical carbonate sequence into several kinds of limestone. The paleontological problem may be to see whether a given species common to the sequence responds to slight environmental changes. The appropriate sampling procedure may be to collect simple random samples from each stratum, to obtain a set of *stratified samples.*

The word *stratum* as used in statistical sampling is similar to its use in geology. In the social sciences, for example, a population of people may be subdivided into sampling strata according to annual income, educational background, size of family, and so on. Thus, the population is "sliced" into categories or subpopulations much as geological strata "slice" a stratigraphic section into parts. Stratified sampling permits the variability in each sampling stratum to be evaluated separately, in contrast to evaluation of the overall variability in the whole population.

The paleontologist may decide to use arbitrary sampling strata even in a single geological stratum. Thus, in the shale example of fig. 1, the 500-foot outcrop can be arbitrarily divided into ten statistical sampling strata of equal horizontal length, with a shale strip randomized from each. As shown in fig. 1,*c,* this tends to spread the samples over the outcrop more regularly than in simple random sampling, but less so than that in systematic sampling. This is a rather special case, in which a single sample is taken per stratum. More commonly, when the sampling strata coincide with rock strata, the number of samples taken per stratum may be proportional to the stratum thickness.

Stratified sampling—especially when more than a single sample is collected per geologically relevant rock stratum—yields a better estimate of the overall population mean than simple random samples collected over the rock face without regard to strata, because the variability in each sampling stratum is taken into account in setting confidence limits on the population mean.

## CLUSTER SAMPLING

Cluster sampling is a procedure by which more than one individual in the population being sampled is taken at each randomized position. In terms of the shale strips, as shown in fig. 1,*d,* five random points are selected along the outcrop. Using these as centers, those shale strips immediately adjacent to the randomized position are taken. Thus, if the randomized position is 214; shale strips 213 and 215 are collected. This procedure yields five clusters of two samples each, in which the spacing between major positions is random, but the spacing between individual shale strips making up the *cluster sample* is fixed at 12 inches from center to center.

In this example the total variability of the measurements made on some taxon can be divided into two parts. The first provides an estimate of the variability associated with a fixed spacing of 12 inches between samples, and the second gives an estimate of the variability at the average spacing of the major sampling points. In fig. 1,*d,* for example, there is an average spacing of 60 feet between succeeding pairs of main sampling points.

Cluster sampling can be extended to more than two levels, and can be designed as *nested sampling,* in which each sampling level is nested within a higher level. This can be illustrated in areal sampling, where, for example, the study area may have townships as the top level, square-mile sections within townships as the second level, outcrops within sections as the third level, and cluster samples on outcrops as the fourth level. This kind of sampling, also called *hierarchical sampling,* is very useful when questions of geographic scales of variability are part of the paleontologic study.

CHANNEL, COMPOSITE, AND GRAB SAMPLES

The varieties of statistical samples shown in fig. 1 emphasize the randomization aspects of sampling. The kind of sample to be taken at each randomized position also deserves comment. *Grab samples,* defined as relatively small fixed volumes of rock, or collections of megafossils from within relatively small areas on an outcrop, are distinguished from *channel samples,* in which the sample is an elongated strip, extending one or more feet normal to the bedding.

Channel samples differ in their use as search samples from their use as statistical samples. In the former the intent is to find a fossiliferous zone; in the latter it is to include a known fossiliferous zone in a single statistical sample. Once the statistically sampled material is put into a single bag, all information regarding vertical variability of fossils within the channel is lost. Grab samples, on the other hand, retain their individual variability as long as they are not combined into *composite samples* by placing two or more in a single bag. The choice of one or another kind of sample involves a paleontological decision, in that the purposes of the study dictate whether certain levels or kinds of variability are to be preserved in the sample or sacrificed by mixing the samples together.

INFLUENCE OF KINDS OF SAMPLES
ON STATISTICAL MODELS

As stated, the decision to take a given kind of sample is paleontological, but this decision influences what can be done statistically with the data. Consider the simple random samples in fig. 1,*a.* The paleontological problem, as before, is to estimate the mean size of adults in species I of genus A. The use of shale strips extending from top to bottom of the bed, plus the decision to make a single measurement of the attribute of interest on each fossil specimen (duplicate measurements are considered unnecessary by some paleontologists), gives rise to a statistical model of the form

$$X_i = \mu + e_i, \tag{1}$$

where $X_i$ is a single measurement on a single fossil. The statistical model is such that $X_i$ is composed of the subpopulation mean size, $\mu$, of the organisms, plus a random component, $e_i$, that represents the departure of any single measurement from the subpopulation mean. Thus, only one source of variability is included in the model, and if various assumptions are true (such as the overall homogeneity of the subpopulation and a negligible measurement error), the model is appropriate. If second thoughts arise regarding systematic size differences in the lower and upper halves of the shale, this model will not permit their estimation.

If the paleontologist wishes to take into account the possibility that differences in attributes may occur between the top and bottom of the shale, the same randomization procedure is used to locate sampling points, but now the shale strip is collected as two separate segments representing the upper and lower halves of the shale bed. The statistical model now becomes

$$X_{ij} = \mu + \alpha_i + e_{ij}, \tag{2}$$

where $X_{ij}$ is a single measurement on a single fossil from the $i$th segment $(i = 1,2)$ and the single fossil is the $j$th specimen in the $i$th segment $(j = 1,2, \ldots, n)$. The single measurement is now composed of the subpopulation mean size, $\mu$, plus a component, $\alpha_i$, which represents the departure of the $i$th channel segment mean from the overall subpopulation mean, and $e_{ij}$ is a random component that represents the departure of the $j$th specimen in the $i$th segment from its segment mean.

In this example the same measurements are made on the same fossils in the same shale strips, but the model in equation 2 permits separation of two sources of variability in the data, one of which ($\alpha_i$) permits evaluation of possible changes in size attributes in the upper and lower halves of the shale strips. The second model requires additional labor; and the paleontologist makes the decision whether the question of vertical change is worth examining or not. If $\alpha_i$ is zero, the shale bed is homogeneous, and by combining the measurements made in the two segments, the model reduces to that in equation 1.

## VERTICAL AND AREAL SAMPLING

Emphasis in fig. 1 was given to sampling along an outcrop. Exactly the same plans are applicable to sampling stratigraphically across an outcrop, and if fig. 1 is tipped on its side to represent a vertical section, the same rules hold. Stratified sampling, however, would normally be based on beds selected by the paleontologist, rather than on the arbitrary sampling strata in fig. 1. Again, decisions regarding the kinds of samples to be collected are paleontological in terms of the purposes of the study and of the statistical model to be used in the analysis.

Sampling over an area requires mainly a modification of the randomization procedure to permit location of points on a map or on an outcrop face. Thus, for simple random sampling, two random numbers are taken, one representing the horizontal distance from some origin, and the other representing the vertical distance from that origin. Space limitations prevent detailed discussion of areal sampling, especially inasmuch as the same kinds of randomization procedures are involved as in line sampling, giving rise to simple random samples, systematic (grid) samples, various kinds of stratified samples, and various kinds of nested samples. Some of the annotated references at the end of this paper refer to areal sampling.

Randomization of points on a map brings up a topic not yet touched upon. It is the restraint imposed upon statistical sampling by the absence of outcrops in positions that happen to be selected by randomization. These restraints give rise to the concept of a *target population* that is the object of interest, as against a *sampled population* that represents the accessible portion of the target population. These topics are considered in the section, *Target and Sampled Populations,* which summarizes the statistical procedures described in the examples of fig. 1.

## SUMMARY OF STATISTICAL SAMPLING

In the preceding discussion of randomization procedures, it was emphasized that the selection of a sampling plan depends on the objectives of the study. Table I lists five common objectives in statistical paleontological studies. These range from estimation of population means and variances to interpretation of areal patterns of variation in faunal assemblages. The second column of Table I lists some of the statistical models available for these categories of study. The third column of the table indicates the kinds of sampling plans that may be appropriate in each case.

It is difficult to assign a specific sampling plan uniquely to a particular objective, since more than one sampling plan may satisfy essentially the same model, and sometimes more than a single model may be applicable to a particular paleontological objective. This is particularly true in the last objective in Table I, that of detecting paleontologically important differences in population attributes. Here a large variety of analysis of variance models is available for analyzing such data. Virtually any of the four kinds of samples discussed in fig. 1 are appropriate, depending in part on the specific model used. Once a particular analysis of variance model is selected, the appropriate sampling plan is part of the statistical design, and can be discerned from the model by the manner in which the data are arranged in the analysis of variance table.

The most important point that emerges from Table I is that although there is a close relationship between paleontological objectives and the statistical model with its sampling plan, it is the paleontologist who decides what he wants to study. These decisions involve the substantive evaluation of sources of variability that may enter his data, and the choice of sources to be taken into account in reaching paleontological generalizations. Moreover, the pa-

**Table I.** *Statistical Models and Sampling Plans in Relation to*
*Paleontological Objectives*

| PALEONTOLOGICAL OBJECTIVES | STATISTICAL MODELS | SAMPLING PLANS |
|---|---|---|
| Mean values and degrees of variability of measured properties of paleontological populations. | Confidence intervals on sample statistics. | Simple random samples, stratified samples. |
| Degrees of variability associated with different "spacings" in paleontological populations. | Estimation of variance components associated with nested data. | Cluster samples; in general, multilevel samples. |
| Associations among measured properties of paleontological populations. | Linear correlation; R-factor analysis. | Simple random samples apparently are optimum. |
| Areal patterns of variation in mappable attributes of paleontological populations. | Various multiregression models for trends along outcrop lines and for polynomial trend surfaces on maps; Q-factor analysis. | Systematic samples along line or on a grid are optimum; in general, fairly evenly spaced samples. |
| Paleontologically important differences in measured properties of paleontological populations. | Various analyses of variance models; discriminant functions. | Sampling plan largely specified by particular model used. |

leontologist decides what is to be measured, and he is responsible for the accuracy and precision of his measurements.

As mentioned earlier, there is no guarantee that mistakes may not be made, but these are less likely if critical thought is given to paleontological objectives before samples are collected. It is not true in general that haphazard collection of a very large number of samples will furnish data for virtually any kind of statistical analysis. On the contrary, numerous samples collected without a clear idea of what is to be done with the data are commonly less useful than a moderate number of samples collected in accordance with a specific design.

## TARGET AND SAMPLED POPULATIONS

Discussion of statistical sampling was based on the use of a continuous shale outcrop as a subpopulation of some larger unspecified population. The subpopulation in fig. 1 was defined so that each individual shale strip was equally accessible and had an equal chance of being included in the sample.

When the shale body is considered as a whole, it is seen to be a three-dimensional rock body having areal extent and varying thickness from place to place. Thus, the individuals making up the total population comprise a much larger number of shale strips than occur along the face of the outcrop used in the example.

In the broadest paleontological sense the whole shale body is of interest; and hence, the *target population* comprises all possible shale channels 6 inches wide and 2 inches thick, extending from top to bottom of the shale over its whole areal extent. Commonly, the great bulk of any rock body is hidden from view by overburden or by covered intervals, so that the shale is accessible for sampling only in surface exposures. Boreholes are ignored in this discussion simply for expediency.

Suppose a map is made showing all outcrops and road cuts in the shale body. Then the individuals available for sampling consist of all shale channels of the form specified that occur in these exposures. These available individuals constitute the *sampled population*. If every outcrop is visited, and if randomization is used in sampling from the outcrops, then every individual in the sampled population has some chance of entering the final sample.

Because the paleontologist has no control over the location of the outcrops, but does have control over the collection of samples from an outcrop, the samples just described are called *semiprobability samples*. In these situations statistical inferences about the smaller scaled features observed on an outcrop may be very similar for the sampled and target populations. Some larger scaled features, however, which may in part control the location of the outcrops, may be quite different in the exposed and buried portions of the rock body.

Limitations on statistical sampling imposed by inaccessible parts of the target population add up to this: the paleontologist may derive valid statistical inferences about the sampled population from his samples, but any extension of these generalizations to the target population is substantive. That is, the paleontologist must draw upon geological and paleontological principles in evaluating similarities and differences in his target and sampled populations. There is no direct statistical method by which this comparison can be made, unless the entire target population ultimately becomes available for study.

In a way, the situation is analogous to a two-span bridge. One span is statistical, and carries the paleontologist from his samples to his sampled population by statistical inference. The second span carries him to his target population by substantive reasoning. The relative length of the two spans varies from problem to problem; if the geological evidence supports the decision that no important differences are present, the substantive span may be relatively short, and vice versa.

It is increasingly recognized that many decisions in a statistical paleontological study are in fact substantive and that the role of statistical inference varies widely from study to study. Visualized in this way, it is apparent that statistical analysis provides a safeguard at various stages of a study, by assuring the paleontologist that his samples are free of unintentional bias; and that his substantive assumptions, judgments, and decisions are supported by the objectively derived statistical inferences that arise from his sample data.

## CONCLUDING REMARKS

The contribution that statistical analysis can make in a paleontological study increases in the degree that the paleontologist recognizes those parts of his study that have statistical content, and designs his work so that the statistical part is adequately provided for by careful design. This design includes the selection of a statistical model appropriate to the purposes of his study, as well as a sampling plan that furnishes data appropriate to the model.

Although substantive generalizations regarding a target population derived from knowledge of the sampled population may at times pose difficult problems, these are no more difficult than the substantive problem of reconstructing original living populations from death populations of fossil organisms. The combination of statistical inference and substantive judgment is not new in paleontology; in the main, the new element is wider recognition of the advantages of formal statistical analysis as an operational procedure for allowing the data to speak for themselves.

A second new element that has entered much of paleontological analysis is the advent of the digital computer, which permits extension of commonly used univariate statistics to their truer multivariate dimension. As methods of analysis become more sophisticated, added premium accrues to formal design in the acquisition of data. Good sampling is obviously fundamental for obtaining reliable data in virtually all paleontological studies. It is perhaps appropriate to close by saying that the paleontologist can be greatly aided in his problems of sampling and statistical design by making the acquaintance of a professional statistician.

## REFERENCES

To my knowledge no complete bibliography on sampling in paleontology is available. The relatively few papers listed here have been selected, with paleontological guidance, to call attention to some generally available publications that explicitly treat sampling techniques. The first two are basic statistical references.

Cochran, W. G. (1963). Sampling techniques (2nd ed.). New York, Wiley. This is the standard reference on the subject, and contains chapters on each of the sampling techniques mentioned in this paper.

Cochran, W. G., F. Mosteller, and J. W. Tukey (1954). Principles of sampling. J. Am. Stat. Assoc., v. 49, p. 13–35. A very lucid expression of the concepts of target and sampled populations.

Collinson, C. (1963). Collection and preparation of conodonts through mass production techniques. Illinois Geol. Survey Circ. 343. Discusses reconnaissance, selective, and bulk collecting, and indicates the size of sample needed to produce a meaningful number of conodonts.

Fox, W. T. (1962). Stratigraphy and paleoecology of the Richmond Group in southeastern Indiana. Geol. Soc. America Bull., v. 73, p. 621–641. This paper describes a sampling plan for counting fossils on exposed bedding planes, using a cluster sample model. The plan is illustrated in Fox's fig. 8, p. 635.

Imbrie, J. (1955). Quantitative lithofacies and biofacies study of Florena Shale (Permian) of Kansas. Am. Assoc. Petrol. Geologists Bull., v. 39, p. 649–670. Use of fairly evenly spaced samples along an outcrop, with sampling unit a short channel adapted to lithologic character.

———— (1956). Biometrical methods in the study of invertebrate fossils. Am. Mus. Nat. History Bull., v. 108, p. 215–252. Clear definitions of paleontological populations, and a summary of basic statistical concepts.

Johnson, R. G. (1960). Models and methods for analysis of the mode of formation of fossil assemblages Geol. Soc. America Bull., v. 71, p. 1075–1086. Use of a line sampling technique for measuring distances between fossils on an outcrop.

Krumbein, W. C. (1960). The "geological population" as a framework for analyzing numerical data in geology. Liverpool and Manchester Geol. J., v. 2, p. 341–368. Discusses ways in which populations may be defined, with examples. Also discusses target and sampled populations.

Yochelson, E. L. (1957, 1960). Permian gastropods of the southwestern United States; Parts 1, 3. Am. Mus. Nat. History Bull., v. 110, art. 3, p. 179–275; v. 119, art. 4, p. 209–293. These compare percentages of various kinds of fossils in silicified and picked residues, and are thus an extension of field sampling to laboratory counterparts.

# Collecting in Sedimentary Rocks

DONALD W. FISHER

*New York State Museum and Science Service, Geological Survey*

Finding fossils is more luck than skill, but gathering them involves appreciably more skill, patience, and hard work than most of us are willing to admit. Where to look entails some geologic intuition.

Published by permission of the Assistant Commissioner, New York State Museum and Science Service.

## WHERE TO COLLECT

### NATURAL EXPOSURES

Among the best sites for fossil collecting are natural exposures, particularly ledges which have been subjected to prolonged weathering. Such weathering causes partial disintegration of the rock matrix, making it more susceptible to breakage and more likely to break around the fossil rather than across it. In addition, fossils commonly weather in relief, making them more obvious. River and stream cuts and ocean and lake shores are good collecting sites, but because rocks in such places are either constantly wet or alternately wet and dry, and commonly covered by algal scum, fossils are masked and the resulting slippery rock is dangerous.

### ARTIFICIAL EXPOSURES

Highway and railroad cuts offer excellent collecting opportunities. Quarries are also favorable, especially those that are inactive; the longer the inactivity the better. Noticeably good specimens are seldom seen in active quarries because the rock is too fresh, and organic markings are not readily seen. Nevertheless, more material is available for breaking. There is, however, the ever-present danger of loose rock, interference with normal quarrying operations, and potentially greater danger from moving vehicles. Building or bridge excavations, though temporary, are sometimes good, but here again, the same hazards may exist. Old stone fences have produced some exceptional weathered fossils, but permission from the property owner should, of course, be obtained before dismantling a stone wall!

## WHAT TO COLLECT (FOSSIL-BEARING ROCKS)

Fossils are most commonly found in sediments (see Sohl's paper in this section) or sedimentary rocks. Only rarely do they occur in igneous rocks (lava, volcanic ash) or metamorphic rocks (see Neuman's paper in this section). Some sedimentary rocks, because of their fertile sites of deposition or physical makeup, are more liable to hold and yield fossils than others. Determine the grain of the rock (direction of easiest breakage), and if this seems to parallel the bedding, try to split the rock this way.

*Conglomerates, breccias.* Owing to their origin, these coarse-textured rocks seldom contain abundant fossils. When they do, specimens are much fragmented and haphazardly arranged. If fossils occur in the pebbles or cobbles, this is a polymictic association of faunas of older age—possibly of differing ages.

*Sandstones, siltstones.* These medium-textured rocks often contain relatively large numbers of fossils, for they usually were deposited in environments where life was abundant. If the grains are well bonded it may take extra effort to extract the fossils. Sledges and crowbars are commonly employed.

*Shales*. These fine-textured rocks may or may not contain abundant fossils. Usually the remains are crushed parallel to the bedding. Often, the shale crumbles and special precautions must be employed to inhibit breakup; an application of shellac or transparent plastic spray (Krylon) from a pressurized can aids immeasurably.

*Limestones*. These are among the most fossiliferous of rocks. Their densities vary, and so does the ease with which fossils are extracted. If compositional differences between fossils and matrix are observed or suspected, bulk collecting is common and acid can be used to recover fossils.

*Dolomites*. Only rarely do fossils occur in dolomites, and then only in greatly limited numbers and in a relatively poor state of preservation. Either recrystallization during replacement of limestone by dolomite or an original hostile dolomitic environment may account for the scarcity of fossils in dolomites.

*Graywackes, akoses*. These are poorly sorted, rapidly deposited rocks that formed in environments that supported little life. Fossils are rare to absent.

*Evaporites*. Fossils are exceedingly rare; usually absent.

*Coal*. Exquisite plant fossils are often found associated with coal.

## HOW TO COLLECT

### TECHNIQUES

*Float versus in situ collecting*. If careful stratigraphic work is being done, float should be avoided. Ordinarily, fossils should not be collected from float unless the exact horizon from which is came is known or can be ascertained with assurance, and then only if representative material cannot be obtained from rock in situ.

*Bulk collecting versus specimen collecting*. If the compositions of fossil and matrix differ, fossils may be recovered by acid immersion. Since acid recovery work is done in the laboratory on bulk samples brought in from the field, the capacity of one's transportation should be kept in mind. Compositional differences are manifested by the varying depth to which weathering has proceeded. For example, if fossils stand out in relief, the chances are good that there are compositional differences. One need not be so careful about wrapping bulk samples to avoid marring specimens. Specimen collecting is pursued usually by specialists who are seeking some particular type of fossil.

*Kinds of data*. It is better to record more information in the field than will ever be used or else revisitation may be required. Items to note are date, precise locality, remarks on kind and thickness of rocks, position of fossils in sequence, relative abundance of types of fossils, attitude of fossils (in "nests," direction of orientation, upside down, and so on), top and bottom of beds, dip and strike, name of collector. Rough sketches and photographs are usually of aid for future reference.

## TOOLS AND EQUIPMENT

The choice of tools and equipment depend on personal habits and purpose of the collecting.

*Clothing.* Field clothing should be comfortable, durable, and functional. There should be ample pocket space. Shoes, especially, should be comfortable, durable, and preferably waterproofed. Hobnails are recommended for slippery shales; sponge rubber or ribbed cork for dry areas. A belt to accommodate hammer holder, compass, and notebook holder is desirable so that hands may be free for carrying the haul.

*Hammers.* There are many types of hammers. Usually, personal preference governs which will be used. There are some, however, that are more suitable for certain rocks and special kinds of collecting. Stonemason hammers with a chisel end are particularly good for splitting shales and thin-bedded limestones or siltstones. Pick-end hammers are good for prying rock where crowbars are not used. Small one-handed sledges or crack hammers (preferably with at least 18-inch handles and with 2 or 3 pound heads) are exceptionally good for breaking compact sandstones, limestones, and dolomites. Light-weight trimming hammers (less than $\frac{1}{2}$-pound heads) are suitable for rocks easily broken or severely weathered. Heavy sledges (5-pound heads and up) are mandatory for breaking slabs. It has been traditional to use hammers with wooden handles but hammers with metal shafts covered with leather washers or vinyl-nylon and hammers with fiberglass handles are also available. I prefer wooden handles, because most of the hammer's weight and striking force is in the head. Hammers with vinyl-nylon handles are a good second choice; they afford a good grip for moist hands. Care of hammers is important but pitifully neglected. Those with wooden handles should be occasionally soaked in water or oil to cause the handle to swell where fitted into the metal head. If wooden handles dry out, they are liable to deteriorate and split. Shrinkage may result in a "lost head" (that of your hammer, your colleague, or both!). Wrapping the shaft with friction tape or plastic tape for a few inches near the head will prolong the handle's life, as frequent misses and near-misses chafe the wood and weaken it. A common practice of holding a rock with one's foot while applying a resounding wallop to the rock with a hammer should be avoided, as a near-miss may result in an injured foot. Using one hammer as a chisel and hitting it with another hammer is to be discouraged. The hammer was not intended to be used in this fashion, and flying steel splinters will result.

*Chisels.* Rock chisels, because they receive unusual abuse, ought to be constructed of steel tempered for rock breaking. They are made in various sizes suited for different purposes. Short, stout ones are used for splitting; long, narrow ones for working in restricted crevices. Pointed ones are used for outlining specimens preparatory to further extraction. A recently marketed type has a vinyl-nylon grip which not only provides a firmer grasp on the chisel but inhibits spalling of metal slivers, which are painful if they penetrate the hand.

*Collecting bags.* An assortment of various sized bags of durable material is requisite. Canvas bags with sturdy drawstring (for closure) at the top are customary. Small well-sample bags are fine for small specimens; they save time and circumvent wrapping. If bags are brightly colored they are less likely to be lost in grass or leaves. A stout rucksack or backpack frees the hands upon return from the collecting jaunt. Cheap cotton or burlap bags are wholly unsatisfactory. When several persons are collecting, individually identified bags are an aid in preventing mix-up.

*Boxes, containers.* Fragile fossils require sturdy containers for transporting them. If placed in cardboard or wooden cigar boxes or plastic containers, and packed with cotton, they will be protected from shock. Small fossils, such as echinoderm calices, might be lost if wrapped and dumped into a larger bag. I have some flat wooden trays with covers which are excellent for small slabs or moderately fragile fossils. Crumpled newspaper or cotton packing prevents moving and jarring.

Wrapping should be done in the field with newspaper or with plastic or aluminum foil. This prevents marring and further breakage during transport.

Labels should be affixed to collecting bags, placed within each wrapped parcel, or tightly secured with a rubber band to the outside of wrapped parcels. It goes without saying that data should be complete as possible. It is often helpful to mark the top and the bottom of specimens with wax pencil.

*Maps.* Topographic maps or geologic maps (if available) are necessary for accurately locating the collecting site geographically and stratigraphically.

*Hand lens.* Without a hand lens, tiny fossils may escape detection, or delicate detail on larger fossils may be overlooked. Magnification of $10\times$ is adequate. Fastening the lens around the neck is good insurance against loss.

*Steel tape.* The common 6- or 8-foot retractable steel tape is convenient for recording the stratigraphic position of the fossil within the rock unit.

*Notebook, pencils.* A hard-cover (brightly colored) notebook and several pencils are, of course, mandatory items. A notebook case that can be fastened to the belt is handy for carrying notebook and pencils (and perhaps chisels) and frees hands. Some workers employ wax marking pencils to identify specimens.

*Camera.* A camera is not necessary but is helpful where a record of the appearance of the collecting site or position of the collection in sequence is required. Sometimes it is helpful to photograph the fossil in situ prior to extraction in the event of breakage during removal. Choice of camera depends largely on personal preference, although a heavy, bulky one is to be avoided. I prefer a 35-mm single-lens reflex camera capable of focusing to 7 inches.

This permits taking many pictures, close up if necessary, and with a minimum of extra weight. A small metric scale of good quality is needed for showing scale in closeups; the rock hammer can be used to show scale in photographs of the entire section.

*Hard hat.* Where falling rock is a menace, fiberglass or metal (aluminum) hats offer partial head protection against small blocks of rock.

*Eyeglasses.* Safety glasses or sunglasses afford protection against flying rock chips.

*Gloves.* Some rocks break with a hackly fracture (chert, cherty limestone, siliceous sandstone), producing knife-like edges which are hard on the skin. Durable deerskin or cowhide gloves offer good protection.

*Glue.* Duco cement or a similar quick-drying plastic cement are indispensable for repairing broken fossils. It is wise to do as much repair work as possible in the field to minimize loss of fragments.

Krylon or shellac is useful for coating fragile fossils prior to extraction; they are especially good for bryozoans, fish fragments, and fossil-bearing fissile shales.

# Collecting in Unconsolidated Sediments

NORMAN F. SOHL

*U. S. Geological Survey, Washington, D.C.*

The Upper Cretaceous outcrop belt of the Atlantic and Gulf Coastal Plains offers an almost unparalleled opportunity for collecting a wide variety of Mesozoic invertebrate fossils. Coastal plain fossils abound principally in chalks, marls, sands, sandstones, clays, and less commonly in limestones. Normal collecting procedures suffice for collecting the fossils from the lithified sediments. However, the greatest diversity of shells, and the best preserved, occur in the micaceous, glauconitic, clayey, or silty sands so commonly referred to as marls in the literature. Although the shells in these sands may be very well preserved, they are usually fragile, and recovery is generally difficult for all save the most stout-shelled individuals. Ignoring for the moment the factor of freshness of the exposure, the degree of fragility is commonly related to the percentage of clay and to some extent correlated with grain size of the sand. Poorly sorted sands with a large coarse fraction generally contain shells weathered to a flakey, chalky, or sometimes filmy consistency. The best preser-

Publication authorized by the Director, U. S. Geological Survey.

vation is exemplified by that found at the classic locality in the Ripley Formation on Coon Creek, McNairy County, Tennessee.

At Coon Creek there is little coarse sand, and the finer or clay-silt fractions of the blue-gray "marls" appear to afford a binder that is relatively impermeable to ground water. Hence the fossils are essentially "hermetically sealed" or protected from being dissolved or recrystallized by ground water.

In collecting from such argillaceous sands, results are almost always proportional to the freshness of the exposure. Fossils are best preserved when outcrops are fresh: Shells weather rapidly on exposure. For this reason, it is commonly necessary to dig well into the exposure to recover fresh material. The results are well worth the extra effort.

Collecting from road cuts or stream cuts in unconsolidated sediments is naturally time consuming, and care in extracting the fossils is important. Procedures will, of course, vary with each outcrop. I have generally followed the practice of first scanning the surface for loose specimens, and at the same time noting the obvious specimens that have partly weathered out, and flagging or marking their location for later removal.

The loose or weathered-out specimens gathered on the surface are carefully laid out on newspaper and sprayed with a coating of clear plastic spray or other hardening agent to facilitate handling. When dry, these specimens are placed on a bed of cotton in cigar boxes or other suitable containers. Several layers can be placed in each box, with each layer separated by cotton. Care in packing is essential: the specimens must be dry, or cotton may adhere to their surface; they must be separated and cushioned, or breakage will result; the boxes must not be overloaded, or delicate specimens may be crushed.

Specimens partly weathered out on the surface may be excavated individually with a stiff-bladed knife. A hunting knife or other noncollapsable blade is preferable to avoid accidents. Cuts should be made a sufficient distance from the specimen to prevent spalling of the surface. Always make cuts away from the fossil so that the specimen forms the apex of a truncate pyramid. Depth of cut is, of course, dependent on the specimen, but sufficient matrix should be taken to support the fossil, and will later aid in preserving it during shipment. The matrix can later be removed in the laboratory by conventional methods; usually other smaller fossils may be found in the washings. When such small blocks are removed, the matrix may be pared to save space in shipping, if desired. Various methods of additional hardening of the small blocks are available, and further insure safe arrival of the collections. L. W. Stephenson (1953, verbal communication) successfully collected very fragile specimens from the Snow Hill Marl member of the Black Creek Formation in North Carolina. He first dried the blocks as thoroughly as possible, then immersed them in a very thin solution of glue. This permeated the surface and upon drying formed a hard crust that later could be removed by soaking the blocks in water. Others have used solutions of gum tragacanth or Alvar for the same purpose. If Alvar is used, the blocks should be thoroughly dried, as a white film develops upon contact with water, and penetration of blocks and specimens is insufficient to provide enough hardening or support to justify the effort expended.

Especially rich or promising zones may be quarried and bulk samples taken. Generally, I have attempted to quarry rectangular blocks about 1 by 1 by $1\frac{1}{2}$ feet in size. Blocks of any dimension are best quarried with a large laborer's pick. The block is first outlined by digging with the pick and is then wedged out. A table knife makes an excellent wedge. A thicker blade or a chisel will cause spalling or cracking of the block. If the blocks are wrapped well with paper and packing material and then crated, they usually withstand the normal wear and tear of shipment. Alternatively, blocks may be encased in plaster and cloth. Such blocks aid in obtaining a good faunal representation and especially yield the smaller faunal elements. Laboratory procedures for treatment of such blocks have been roughly outlined by Sohl (1960, p. 50).

If time permits, a second close perusal of the surface will likely yield numerous less obvious, or smaller, specimens. In addition, the single and probably most useful tool for collecting in such sands—a pick-mattock—can be used to dig out smaller blocks. Such sampling turns up many fine specimens. If little or nothing appears on the surface of such blocks, breaking them down carefully by hand usually is rewarding.

Occasionally, sands that contain little clay bear a wealth of shell material. The loose sand and shells can be collected in bulk and sacked for shipment. It may be even more profitable to concentrate the sample by sieving. If water is available sieving can be tried and may work successfully with the argillaceous or compact sands. Sieves of almost any dimensions can be used, but one should not neglect the smaller fractions, as young growth stages can be recovered. Smaller fractions may also contain small pelecypods or opisthobranch gastropods as small as one millimeter in length.

In clays, or in sediments having a very high clay content, special problems arise. Even in the relatively undisturbed sequences of the Coastal Plain, the clays—perhaps owing to compaction or load—commonly develop a slight fissility, and whole specimens are difficult to recover. Moreover, with the exception of the massive ostreids (*Exogyra, Gryphaea*), shells are commonly thin and usually crushed. The best specimens are found on the flat bedding plane surfaces, but these thin, fragile, cracked shells usually spall off as the block dries. It is therefore necessary to coat the surface while still moist. Plastic spray has been used with considerable success for this purpose. Bulk samples of the clays should be taken and washed down in the laboratory, as the smaller gastropods are generally not distorted or cracked and are recovered with ease. Some samples can be prepared by first immersing them in hydrofluoric acid. Conversion of the shells to CaF from $CaCO_3$ occasionally appears to strengthen them.

## NOTES ON INDIVIDUAL GROUPS OF FOSSILS

The mollusks dominate the faunas of the unconsolidated sands of the Coastal Plains. Of these the thick-shelled forms such as the ostreids are probably the easiest to collect. They weather out easily and their hard calcitic shells remain even when the aragonitic shells of other mollusks have been leached away. Among the other pelecypods the greater problems in collecting are presented by the inoceramids, which have a large shell in proportion to their shell thickness. When encountered, great care must be taken in their recovery. Generally they are cracked and many are fragmental. Hand excavation is usually necessary for recovery. The shell surface should be cleaned and the specimen coated or cemented as needed before removal. Recovery of thin-shelled forms such as the larger limas, pectens, and razor clams is generally fortuitous.

Gastropods are perhaps even more difficult to recover than pelecypods. The less compact nature of the shell makes them more susceptible to breakage, especially in the area of the spire and the anterior canal. Thus, it is even more important to quarry sufficient adhering matrix to support the more delicate structures. A second difficulty is due to their great diversity of shape. Aberrant morphological forms, such as the winged aporrhoids and strombids, must be recognized when only partially exposed. If not, the chance of loosing the distinctive winged apertures is great. Thus, ample matrix must be taken to allow for size. The best preparation for collecting is to become well enough acquainted with the fauna such that the form is recognized before attempting to remove it.

Cephalopods are not generally abundant. In the unconsolidated sands they are among the more difficult species to recover intact, owing to their large size and thin shell. Commonly, the matrix does not fill all the chambers, and thus there is little internal support. Almost invariably, the body chamber is crushed or compressed. One surface of the larger cephalopods should be cleaned in place in order to strengthen and patch the surface before removal.

Any thorough collection of Recent faunas includes the less obvious elements such as wood, rock, or plant borers, parasites, and encrusting organisms. So should it be with fossil faunas. Wood and plant fragments, and even the occasional clay or siltstone pebble encountered, should be inspected carefully for boring pelecypods. The same holds true of the shells themselves. The oysters are commonly riddled by sponge, pelecypod, and barnacle borings. Surfaces of such shells should also be scanned for holdfasts of gorgonids and encrusting Bryozoa. The capulid snail *Thylacus cretacus* Conrad has been noted attached to the columella of a number of siphonate genera.

An additional source of information about the faunal content can be derived from the attachment scars of the ostreids. These are especially valuable where the aragonitic shells have been leached out. The staunch calcite-shelled ostreids faithfully retain the scar of the surface to which they were attached, and commonly provide a fine external mold of the shell which they overgrew.

No single formula can be applied to the collecting of fossils from unconsolidated sands. The methods outlined here are rather elementary and basic, but each locality and fossil presents its own problems. Care and time are the best tools for collecting, but care in packing and shipping, as well as the final preparation of the specimen, are as important as obtaining the material.

## REFERENCE

Sohl, N. F. (1960). Archeogastropoda, Mesogastropoda and Stratigraphy of the Ripley Owl Creek, and Prairie Bluff Formations. U. S. Geol. Survey Prof. Paper 331-A, 151 pp.

# Collecting in Metamorphic Rocks

ROBERT B. NEUMAN

*U. S. Geological Survey, Washington, D.C.*

> Since those who know where to find fossils are unwilling to look, and most of those who look at metamorphic rocks do not know what to look for and where, much valuable material must remain undiscovered.
>
> Bucher (1953, p. 293)

Postdepositional changes of many kinds commonly obscure or obliterate the fossil content of rocks. Such changes range in time and effect from diagenetic compaction to regional metamorphism. The collection, preparation, and identification of fossils thus obscured raise special problems that are seldom faced by geologists who normally work with rocks that are but little changed since they were deposited. Some of the more common problems of collecting from these altered rocks are discussed in the paragraphs that follow, and some suggestions are offered. No suggestions, however, can substitute for thorough observation by the geologist.

Facets of both the rewards and the problems that face the paleontologist who works in metamorphosed rocks were reviewed by Professor Walter Bucher in 1953. Professor Bucher's review is not as pessimistic as the sentence quoted from it might indicate; reading it is a must for those who would

Publication authorized by the Director, U. S. Geological Survey.

collect fossils from metamorphic rocks. Most of the information in the present paper was drawn from Bucher's review and from papers referred to by him. Some points are further emphasized here in the hope of encouraging both "those who know" and "those who look."

## DIAGENETIC METAMORPHISM

Diagenetic or postdiagenetic changes have altered the fossil content of many beds that appear otherwise unmetamorphosed and undeformed. Flattened and compressed fossils attest to the effects of compaction of shales, siltstones, and sandstones. In many places, however, concretions in such rocks contain uncompressed specimens of microfossils and megafossils, commonly in greater variety and abundance than might have been suspected from examination of the enclosing rock (Reeside and Cobban, 1960, p. 23–25).

Decalcification of sandstones by ancient as well as present-day water circulation can remove all shelly material. Thus, fossils in the Oriskany Sandstone (Devonian), which are locally abundant over wide areas of Pennsylvania, are preserved in places only as faithful molds of internal and external features of the shells that were dissolved.

Dolomitization of limestones can obliterate fossils. Some large, thick calcite shells may be preserved in dolomite beds, but in many limestones, massive or nodular chert formed prior to dolomitization preserves features of the limestone protolith that were obscured by dolomitization (Bucher, 1953, p. 292; Neuman, 1960). Opportunities for observation and recovery are increased where chert fragments are weathered free and are concentrated on the ground surface.

## CONTACT METAMORPHISM

The occurrence of trilobites with chiastolite, brachiopods with garnet, and corals with pyroxene were cited by Bucher (1953, p. 288–291) as examples of preservation of fossils in aureoles of contact metamorphism. Bucher pointed out that fossils preserved in these recrystallized rocks are larger than the average size of the new minerals of the altered zone. Thus, microfossils and thin-shelled organisms are unlikely to survive contact metamorphism, and microstructures are unlikely to be preserved. Nevertheless, the form of many megafossils has survived contact metamorphism. Because calc-silicate minerals may completely replace fossils or outline them, the collector should be alert for anomalous clusters of diopside, tremolite, and related minerals, as well as for calcite, as indications of fossils in areas of contact metamorphism.

Because pure carbonate rock crystallizes readily to coarse-grained marble on thermal metamorphism, it offers little promise to the collector. Nevertheless, some large, thick shells or massive forms such as tabulate corals may persist. Naturally weathered or water-worn surfaces that accentuate subtle textural differences are the most likely places to find fossils, although occasionally a fresh break may reveal shells.

## DEFORMED ROCKS

That fossils are distributed along bedding surfaces is a fundamental tenet of the collector. Where shear surfaces and slaty cleavage tend to mask bedding, fossils are hard to find. The first step in the search for fossils in such rocks is to distinguish between bedding and cleavage. In the well-stratified rocks, where the cleavage is relatively weak, this can be done readily, but where the original stratification was more massive, and with increasing development of cleavage, the distinctions are more difficult to make, and a painstaking search must be made for the more subtle variations that mark bedding. Fossils are most likely to be preserved where bedding and cleavage are parallel, or where they are nearly perpendicular to each other; they are less frequently preserved where cleavage cuts bedding at acute angles. Fossils are rare on cleavage surfaces and are more common in the less deformed rock between them, even where bedding and cleavage are parallel. Spacing between cleavage surfaces is commonly controlled by the grain size of the rock, the spacing being wider in coarser grained rocks. In slaty rocks, therefore, intercalated sandstones may preserve fossils that are small enough to lie between cleavage surfaces.

Differential movements involved in folding are not uniform; although they obliterate fossils in parts of a fold, they are minimal in other parts. A most remarkable example of those differences was recorded by Thompson (1956), who found well-preserved brachiopods and corals (Thompson and Boucot, 1958) in the axial parts of recumbent folds whose flanks are unfossiliferous schists, all in garnet, staurolite, and sillimanite grades.

## REGIONAL METAMORPHISM

In the course of regional metamorphism, both thermal alteration and deformation combine to obliterate fossils. Nevertheless, identifiable fossils of great importance to both the geologist and the paleontologist have been found in many such regions.

Discovery and identification of fossils from various places in New England (Boucot, et al., 1958; Hurley, et al., 1959; Cady, 1960), for example, have led to significant advances in the understanding of this regionally metamorphosed area. The fossils occur in rocks of many kinds that range in age from Early Cambrian to Early Devonian. Although the fossils there are most common in rocks of lower metamorphic grade, a few important finds have been made in middle- and high-grade rocks.

In areas of low-grade metamorphism, deformation has been more important than recrystallization in the obliteration of fossils; here they have been found in a wide variety of rocks, including slate, marble, quartzite, fine- and coarse-grained sandstone and conglomerate, and water-laid tuff. In areas of high-grade metamorphism, however, where argillaceous rocks have been altered to micaceous schists or, depending on rock composition and temperature, where other minerals have formed, quartzite and other rocks of stable composition are least altered, and offer the greatest promise of fossils.

In these rocks the most common indications of the presence of fossils are the voids left after the weathering of calcite. These are seen as scattered holes or rows of holes that follow the bedding on a weathered outcrop surface, or as porous leached zones that indicate the presence of calcareous shell beds.

## COLLECTING AND PREPARING

This account would be incomplete without an urgent plea that adequate collections be made. The fossils that come from metamorphic rocks are generally deformed, their structural details are obscured, and they are commonly incomplete. Many specimens may be needed to see all the critical features necessary for identification; samples weighing hundreds of pounds may yield only a few identifiable specimens. Therefore, blocks of the fossiliferous rock, rather than individual specimens, should be collected.

Preparation should be attempted only in the laboratory, and not in the field, where equipment is crude and conditions far from ideal. Loss of the best specimen in the underbrush may be avoided by patience in the field. Rock matrix is the best of packing materials, and freight rates for broken stone are low, considering the potential scientific value of a good collection.

## REFERENCES

Boucot, A. J., G. J. F. MacDonald, Charles Milton, and J. B. Thompson, Jr. (1958). Metamorphosed middle Paleozoic fossils from central Massachusetts, eastern Vermont, and western New Hampshire. Geol. Soc. America Bull., v. 69, p. 855–870.

Bucher, W. H. (1953). Fossils in metamorphic rocks, a review. Geol. Soc. America Bull., v. 64, p. 275–300.

Cady, W. M. (1960). Stratigraphic and geotectonic relationships in northern Vermont and southern Quebec. Geol. Soc. America Bull., v. 71, p. 531–576.

Hurley, P. M., A. J. Boucot, A. L. Albee, Henry Faul, W. H. Pinson, and H. W. Fairbairn (1959). Minimum age of the Lower Devonian slate near Jackman, Maine. Geol. Soc. America Bull., v. 70, p. 947–950.

Neuman, R. B. (1960). Geology of the Wildwood quadrangle, Tennessee. U. S. Geol. Survey, Geol. Quad. Map GQ 130.

Reeside, J. B., Jr., and W. A. Cobban (1960). Studies of the Maury Shale (Cretaceous) and contemporary formations in the United States and Canada. U. S. Geol. Survey Prof. Paper 355, 126 pp.

Thompson, J. B., Jr. (1956). Skitchewaug nappe, a major recumbent fold in the area near Claremont, New Hampshire (abs.). Geol. Soc. America Bull., v. 67, p. 1826–1827.

———, and A. J. Boucot (1958). Late Lower Silurian fossils from sillimanite zone near Claremont, New Hampshire. Science, v. 128, p. 362–363.

# Collecting Fossils on Tropical Pacific Islands

HARRY S. LADD

*U. S. Geological Survey, Washington, D.C.*

The hundreds of islands scattered over the tropical Pacific can be conveniently grouped into low islands and high islands. The low islands include existing atolls and slightly elevated atolls. They are composed almost exclusively of limestone. The high islands include volcanic islands, limestone islands, and islands composed partly of volcanic rock and partly of limestone. The limestones of most low islands are post-Tertiary in age. Outcrops that lie within a few feet of present-day sea level may be well lithified or case hardened with well-preserved fossils. They have been above the sea only a short time, and the original aragonite of shells and skeletons has not been leached or recrystallized to calcite. Mollusk shells, echinoid spines, pieces of the alcyonarian "blue coral," and red encrusting Foraminifera may retain at least traces of their original color. Species are identical with living forms and reveal but little about the geologic history of the islands.

Most of the limestones of the high islands are appreciably older, and have been above the sea so long that much if not all of the original aragonite has been removed by solution or recrystallized to calcite. The search for well-preserved fossils in such rocks is apt to be discouraging, though molds of corals and shells may be abundant. Conditions are more favorable on islands where volcanic rocks occur, particularly if some of the limestone beds contain tuffaceous material. On many islands limestone rests on a volcanic foundation, and the basal sediments contain reworked volcanic material. Perfect calcite molds, and even original shell material, may be found abundantly in such beds. Water-laid tuffs (sometimes called "wuffs"!) are found on some islands, and may contain well-preserved marine fossils. Tuffs and ash beds deposited on land have yielded plant remains.

Publication authorized by the Director, U. S. Geological Survey.

No fossils older than Tertiary have yet been found on islands of the open Pacific. Most of the rocks are reef and lagoon deposits, and the assemblages are similar to those found on existing reefs and in lagoons. Comments on the abundance and the value of the main organic groups are given below.

## CORALLINE ALGAE

Calcareous reef-building red algae are highly magnesian and many are preserved in elevated limestones where most other fossils have been removed by solution. Nonmagnesian algae (*Halimeda*) are widespread in existing lagoons, but are comparatively rare in elevated limestones. The identification of algal species calls for numerous thin sections, recognition of conceptacles (spore cases) and other structures, and detailed measuring and counting of cells. Until recently, the fossil algae of the Pacific islands were little known, but enough has now been done on Micronesian and Melanesian islands to show that the algae have real stratigraphic potentialities. Algae are commonly associated with larger Foraminifera and some of the species described to date are widely distributed. Known occurrences have been tied to various Tertiary units whose age has been determined primarily by larger Foraminifera.

## OTHER PLANTS

Aside from reef-building algae, plant fossils are rare in the islands. Marls have yielded plant stems, carbonized wood (probably mangrove), impressions of leaves and of tree fern bark. Lignite beds are rare, but have been found on such widely separated islands as Rapa and Babelthuap (Palau). Carbonaceous crusts from Tertiary beds beneath Eniwetok Atoll have been found to contain rich concentrations of spores and pollens that indicate the existence of a rich deciduous forest at a time when the atoll stood above the sea as a high island.

## FORAMINIFERA

Smaller benthonic Foraminifera are preserved in many elevated reef limestones, particularly those that contain some tuffaceous material. Planktonic globiginerids may be well preserved in off-reef limestones and in elevated *Globigerina* oozes. Dense *Globigerina* limestones that apparently are of shallow-water origin have been described, but the conditions under which they were deposited are not well understood.

At the present time larger Foraminifera appear to be the most valuable index fossils for recognizing Tertiary units in the islands. They are most easily used where they are weathered free, so that oriented thin sections can be prepared. Many dense crystalline limestones contain well-preserved larger Foraminifera and these usually can be identified from random thin sections.

## CORALS

On many reefs, corals are the most abundant of the larger invertebrates, and their remains are equally abundant in elevated limestones. Well-preserved corals, however, are exceedingly rare as fossils. Specific identification of most specimens depends on the preservation of surface details, and these are almost invariably destroyed if the coral head is eroded prior to deposition or if the original aragonite of the skeleton is dissolved away or replaced by calcite. Fossil corals that clearly are in position of growth are known from a number of islands, but in most occurrences of this sort, the fossils appear as unidentifiable molds. Some molds have been given specific names, but it may be difficult to distinguish such named species from better-preserved younger forms.

## BRYOZOA

Fossil bryozoans are strangely rare on Pacific islands. Large collections of fossils made in Fiji contained only scrappy remnants of five genera. Collections made in the Mirianas and Palau were equally poor in identifiable bryozoans. The rich and varied collections obtained by drilling in the Marshall Islands contained no specifically identifiable bryozoans, and less than half a dozen identifiable genera.

## BRACHIOPODS

Brachiopods are rare in the island seas of today, and they are equally rare as fossils. A few Tertiary species have been described, and one, at least, is known from two separate island groups. Minute forms that live today cemented to the undersides of slabs of coral in atoll lagoons have been recovered in drill cuttings from Funafuti and the Marshall Islands (Recent and Tertiary). An interesting form recently found in the elevated Tertiary limestones of Fiji has living relatives only in the deep sea.

## MOLLUSKS

Some mollusks, such as oysters and pectens, have shells composed mainly of calcite and are commonly well preserved in limestone where mollusks with aragonitic shells are found only as molds. Many gastropods that have an exterior protective layer of calcite, such as *Neritina,* show well-preserved color patterns.

Molds of both gastropods and pelecypods are specifically identifiable if both exterior and interior impressions are collected. On many islands clear calcite casts of mollusks are found, these being particularly abundant in impervious tuffaceous limestones near contacts with underlying volcanic rocks.

The original shells of aragonitic mollusks may be preserved in tuffaceous limestones and in marls. These, of course, are the most satisfactory molluscan fossils. Such preservation is widespread in zones that have never been above sea level for appreciable times, as, for example, in the Miocene beds drilled beneath the Marshall Islands.

Gastropods seem to be most abundant in reef limestones, and pelecypods are most common on islands where volcanic rocks have given rise to muds and tuffaceous sediments. Fossil chiton plates are known in island limestones, and terminal valves can be identified specifically.

## OSTRACODS

Very few fossil ostracods have been described from the islands, but at the present time, assemblages are being studied from the Tertiary and younger beds of Palau, Fiji, the Marshall Islands, and Funafuti.

## BARNACLES

Balanoids are rare and little known as fossils. A specialized type (*Pyrgoma*) that lives on reef corals is as widely distributed as the corals themselves, but the species have not yet been described. Because their shells are of calcite, they may be well preserved where the enclosing aragonitic corals occur only as molds.

## DECAPODS

Crab claws and finger segments are fairly common in island limestones but can rarely be identified specifically. Complete carapaces of crabs are rare, but a few have been named from Tertiary and younger beds. Fossil decapods have little stratigraphic value at present.

## ECHINOIDS

Tests of echinoids are fairly rare as fossils in most island limestone, but when found, they are well preserved and easily identifiable. Cidarid spines are widespread, but are of little use except where weathered free, as in tuffaceous limestone beds. Some spines of this type exhibit knobby protuberances of generic or even specific value.

## FISH REMAINS

To my knowledge, only one Tertiary fish skeleton has been recovered from island rocks; it was incomplete and could not be determined below the family level. Fish vertebrae and otoliths have been recovered from Tertiary marls and limestones, but none have been named. Sharks' teeth, including Tertiary index species, are rare, but are widely scattered and invariably well preserved.

## OTHER VERTEBRATES

These are exceedingly rare as fossils but should be looked for. Bones of an undescribed species of whale were collected on the island of Okinawa.

## SUGGESTIONS FOR COLLECTING

Localities where well-preserved fossils may be collected are uncommon on Pacific islands. This is particularly true of corals and mollusks. When, with good fortune, such a locality is found, an exhaustive collection should be made.

On islands made up of volcanic rocks and limestones, a search for contacts between the two should be made, and basal conglomerates or tuffaceous beds in the limestones should be carefully examined for fossils. If beds of this sort are weathered, bulk samples should be collected. These can be washed later for microfossils.

Hard crystalline limestones should be examined with a hand lens for larger Foraminifera. If such fossils appear to be well preserved, sizable pieces should be collected for random sectioning.

Molds of mollusks and other fossils should be collected, and care should be taken to collect both internal and external molds. All parts of the mold of a given specimen should be wrapped together. It is possible, of course, to carry rubber or other material in the field for the preparation of casts on the spot. This, however, is a time-consuming process, and after the cast has been prepared, both internal and external molds should be collected.

It may be desirable to collect molds even if they are not complete. Although the internal mold of a pelecypod or a gastropod may not be identifiable, even generically, a fragment of a mold showing unusual sculpture may be specifically identifiable. Even incomplete molds have some value in ecologic interpretation.

Mollusks, particularly some of those found in marl beds, may exhibit a chalky appearance and show a tendency to flake and otherwise disintegrate if handled roughly. Such fossils should be impregnated in the field with a solution of Alvar dissolved in acetone.

Finally, one should not be discouraged by failure to find identifiable fossils at the first few outcrops examined. I once worked for three weeks on a small limestone island before finding the first diagnostic Tertiary fossils. On Fiji, the largest island in the group, the Oligocene is known from but a single limestone outcrop, surrounded by volcanic rocks, near the top of one of the higher mountains. Volcanic rocks must not be completely overlooked in the search for fossils. In Palau the Eocene is known only from larger Foraminifera recovered from pieces of limestone in a volcanic agglomerate (breccia). In Fiji gastropod shells with delicate spiny processes perfectly preserved and other molluscan shells have been collected from the matrix of such breccia between blocks of rock as much as a foot in diameter.

# Underwater Paleontological Collecting Techniques

## H. K. BROOKS

*Department of Geology, University of Florida, Gainesville*

The philosopher Benoit de Maillet (1659–1738), first to argue convincingly that fossils are the remains of past life, emphasized the importance of underwater studies in the interpretation of geological phenomena. In his fascinating, heretical book, first published in 1748 under the anagram Telliamed, he described diving gear and techniques for underwater study. In a later work, de Maillet (1797, p. 38–45) discussed submarine observation of animals and sediments relative to the interpretation of fossils and sedimentary rocks. Only recently have geologists and paleontologists taken advantage of the incomparable opportunities offered by direct underwater studies realized by de Maillet more than two hundred years ago.

A vast realm covered by relatively shallow water became readily available for study with the perfection of the self-contained underwater breathing apparatus. Discussion of underwater research and collecting techniques, however, should not be limited to situations where diving gear can be employed. More than 72 percent of the earth's surface is covered by water, and fossiliferous outcrops exist even at great depths in the ocean (Furon, 1949). Abundant Pleistocene vertebrate remains have been obtained from the shallow springs and spring runs in Florida by swimmers without special gear. The other extreme in underwater paleontological collecting is represented by the rare fossiliferous rock specimens brought up in rock dredges from the depths of the ocean.

Gear and methods for underwater collection will be discussed in four categories: oceanographic collecting gear; devices of the civil engineer (i.e., cofferdams and caissons); swimming and diving; and robots.

## OCEANOGRAPHIC COLLECTING GEAR

Of the specialized oceanographic equipment used in collecting bottom samples, the rock dredge for consolidated rock and the piston corer for unconsolidated deposits are the most useful. All that is presently known about rock outcrops in the deep parts of the ocean has been learned through dredging. It has long been known that Pleistocene vertebrate fossils and fossiliferous rock samples are occasionally brought up in fishing trawls and dredges. Since Stetson (1936) and Stephenson (1936) first obtained Cretaceous fossils from outcrops on the walls of the Georges Bank Canyons, there has been increased use of the rock dredge. Many fossiliferous Mesozoic and Tertiary samples have been collected subsequently from along the outer edge of the continental shelf of Eastern North America (Heezen, 1959, p. 43–51). Sufficient samples were obtained from the San Pedro Shelf of California to enable Moore (1954) to do stratigraphic work and prepare a geological map.

The rock dredge should be used only when other methods of collecting are impracticable. The time, expense, fortuitousness of sampling, inaccuracy of site location, and inability to observe the occurrence of fossils obtained by this method greatly limit its use.

Deep penetration of the ocean floor by the piston coring device has been achieved. Samples containing fossils dating back to the Early Pleistocene have been obtained from oceanic ooze. Conversely, Heezen and his associates have successfully obtained short cores of semiconsolidated Tertiary deposits on the continental slopes. Northrop and Heezen (1951) adapted the Ewing underwater camera to automatic photography of the outcrop as it was being cored.

## DEVICES OF THE CIVIL ENGINEER

It is often easier to remove the water than to work under it. The cofferdam and the caisson can be used beneficially in deposits covered by shallow water. This is especially true if precise observations are required on the occurrence of the fossils or if it is necessary to excavate considerable amounts of material.

Cofferdams may vary from sediment thrown up to divert small streams to major engineering feats. I have successfully used small earthen cofferdams to divert water from fossiliferous deposits discovered by wading and swimming. Using a small gasoline-driven, centrifugal sump pump to remove water from within the dammed enclosure, it is possible to work a considerable area under reasonably water-free conditions. Use of the cofferdam depends on the depth of water, current, extent of excavation required, porosity of the deposit, and time and funds available for the collecting project.

In deeper water an air chamber (caisson) could be constructed above the fossiliferous deposit if the significance of the fauna merited the expense. So far, this method has not been used specifically for scientific studies. Scuba divers could easily convert some of the underwater caverns in Florida into caisson chambers so that the Pleistocene fossils therein could be excavated safely and efficiently. Except for materials needed to construct an air lock, and materials for caulking the cavern walls (heavy plastic sheeting could be used to prevent air leakage through the porous limestone walls), only a high-volume low-pressure air compressor for pressurizing the caisson would be needed. Air pressure of 43 pounds per square inch (psi) would keep a cavern dry to 100 feet below the water table. Workers in an air chamber should observe standard decompression procedure if air pressures greater than 20 psi are used.

## SWIMMING AND DIVING

It is a common pastime in Florida for swimmers equipped with face mask and swim fins to float down clear spring runs on an automobile inner tube. A snorkle enables the swimmer to keep his face submerged for viewing the bottom continuously. Fossils are retrieved by free diving. Without a face mask or goggles, it is impossible for humans to focus their vision underwater. The face mask with a glass plate gives best visibility. Even rubbing with a raw potato will not prevent fogging of a plastic face plate. Before the advent of the face mask, glass bottom buckets were used to scan the spring runs for bones that had washed out of the Pleistocene deposits. Large numbers of specimens have been obtained in this manner (Simpson, 1930) by both professional and amateur collectors.

Underwater scavenging is fun, but unscientific. Unfortunately this criticism is true of most underwater collecting. Without proper stratigraphic observation of the occurrence of the fossils, the full significance of the deposits cannot be determined.

A variety of diving gear is available that is designed to permit prolonged dives to greater depths. The diving suit, with its heavy weights, metal helmet, air hose, and a low-pressure compressor, is too cumbersome to use for paleontological collecting. The invention of the Aqua-lung regulator—essentially a reducing valve modified to supply breathing air on demand (at water pressure) from a high-pressure air cylinder carried on the diver's back—greatly stimulated interest in underwater exploration. The self-contained breathing apparatus consisting of regulator and air tank is known as scuba diving gear. Aqua-lung has become a trade name. The scuba regulator attached to a small hose supplying air at low pressure (about 100 psi) from a portable compressor is known as the hookah system. Scuba and hookah diving gear are dependable, easy to operate, relatively inexpensive, and allow the diver freedom of movement.

Professional scientists have been slow to take advantage of the research possibilities made possible by scuba diving equipment. In some parts of the country, Florida in particular, amateurs in great numbers have been attracted to the spectacular vertebrate accumulations in the sinkholes, deep springs, and underwater caverns. Many significant archaeological sites and vertebrate fossil sites have now been destroyed.

It is not difficult to become proficient in the use of scuba gear, but each person must learn his skin diving limitations through experience. If possible, the scientist should not depend on the collecting activities of amateurs. More scientific evidence is usually vandalized than is gained from specimens obtained. Generally the observations of amateur collectors are inaccurate or exaggerated.

It is so easy to use scuba gear that many inexperienced and unqualified divers acquire a false sense of security. Good physical condition, ability to swim well without gear, breath control, and calmness under conditions of overpowering emergency may determine survival. No deaths due to failures of scuba gear have been reported, but accidents due to human failure are much too common. Overconfidence and panic are the most frequent causes to which drownings can be attributed.

A large number of persons otherwise well qualified for underwater swimming are restricted by their inability to equalize pressures in the inner ear and sinus cavities. Though anahistimines and nasal sprays are useful for clearing sinus passages and eustachian tubes, some individuals can never dive deeper than 12 to 16 feet.

The principles and techniques of diving with scuba gear can be found in many available publications. Concise rules and discussion of diving principles adequate for beginners are to be found in manufacturers handbooks, such as U. S. Divers (1960). Most of these little handbooks tend to minimize the limitations and dangers of scuba diving. The popular books on the subject are padded with nonsense and sensationalism. The *Diving Manual* of the U. S. Navy (1952) and *Basic Scuba* by Roberts (1960) are recommended.

Though useful in abandoned quarries, in lakes and streams, and in the ocean, scuba diving for fossils finds its greatest use in the sinkholes, springs, and underwater caverns in limestone terrains. Precautions beyond the basic safety rules must be observed when going below ground. Practically all drownings underground are due to the inability of the divers to find their way back to the surface. The paleontologist working underwater must not become so engrossed in collecting that he loses his orientation through straying or because his activities have roiled the water.

The hazards of cave diving can be minimized for the experienced diver if alternative methods for breathing, unentanglement, lighting, and escape back to the surface are planned and provided for in advance of their need. The diver working in open water will critically need his life preserver usually only once in his lifetime—when he is not wearing it. Scientific work cannot be done by persons preoccupied with their survival. A dependable diving partner is a must. When working in sinkholes, springs, and caverns an unbreakable descent line firmly secured at or near the surface is the only reliable guide. There is no such thing as an infallible underwater light. Even if both divers carry two lights, they may find themselves in total darkness. A diving team standing by at the twilight zone of large underwater caverns is highly recommended as a safety precaution.

Inefficiency, time limitations, and the distractions of the strange working conditions have limited most underwater work to the collection of fossils that are already free of matrix. It is possible to excavate unconsolidated deposits and study their stratigraphy, but it requires a great deal of planning, effort, and patience.

Underwater excavation can be done by digging if a current exists to carry away the turbid water produced by the activity of the collectors. In springs, spring runs, and rivers, fine unconsolidated sediment can sometimes be removed by fanning the bottom with the hand or swim fin. Matrix is roiled into suspension, leaving behind the heavier fossils. Fanning is also useful in exploration of standing water where a thin film of fine sediment and organic detritus blankets the bottom.

The air lift has been used extensively by archaeologists. This simple device offers an efficient means of excavating unconsolidated deposits when the mode of occurrence of specimens is not important. Air under low pressure (40 to 100 cubic feet per second at 10 to 50 psi) is pumped through a small hose into the bottom of a metal pipe 6 to 8 inches in diameter. The air rising to the surface through the pipe drags water, sediment, archeological specimens, and even heavy cannon balls with it. A mesh basket at the surface is used to catch the larger pieces of debris and specimens. Strenuous effort by divers is necessary to control the suction end of the air lift pipe. Fossils obtained by this method have been the by-product of archaeological projects. The air lift will probably never find much use in paleontological studies.

I have used two methods of excavation for underwater studies in Florida. In Warm Mineral Springs, the deposit was zoned by digging with a trenching shovel to produce a vertical face. Layers of the deposit could then be distinguished, measured, and collected by zone. Large volumes of sediment from each zone were carried to the surface in buckets. It is possible to catch exhaled air from the scuba regulator in a suitable bag or balloon-like device to lift heavy loads to the surface. Materials from each zone were later washed on fine screens. This is undoubtedly the most reliable method of collecting from an unconsolidated stratified deposit.

The zonation of the deposit in Warm Mineral Springs was rechecked by coring with a light aluminum tube $2\frac{1}{2}$ inches in diameter equipped with a piston. The cores revealed details that could not be detected underwater. A chain fastened to an irregularity of the wall of the spring held the piston in a fixed position just above the deposit while the tube was forced downward.

An "underwater vacuum cleaner" was devised which has proven useful in collecting from sites requiring removal of large amounts of fine matrix. A gasoline-driven centrifugal sump pump with a capacity of about 5000 gallons per hour is used to suck water and sediment through a nozzle and hose to the surface, where it is discharged away from the sinkhole containing the deposit. The flared suction end of the nozzle must be covered by wire mesh to prevent entry of small bones and other particles that could damage the pump impellers. Large particles accumulate on the screen and frequently clog it. They fall away when suction is relieved in the system by opening a leather flap valve on the side of the nozzle. The diver operating the nozzle places the specimens and particle concentrate in a canvas bucket as they are freed from the matrix. A stratified deposit containing artifacts, human bones, and an extensive vertebrate fauna including several extinct species has been excavated by this method from a Florida cavern 35 feet below the surface. The cavern was surveyed and a grid laid out by tying lines to pegs on the floor. Collecting was done by quadrant and by stratigraphic zone.

Collection of specimens from consolidated and semiconsolidated submerged outcrops has been done with chisel, hammer, and crowbar. Although subaerial stratigraphic exposures are limited in Florida, there are marvelous underwater exposures of continuous sections more than 240 feet thick in some sinkholes. A descent line, collecting tools, specimen receptacles with premarked labels, good lights, and an accurate depth gauge are needed for the collection and measurement of the undisturbed rock sections exposed on the walls of sinkholes. Collection of fossils and lithologic samples can be done by zone or by fixed interval. A graduated rule is necessary to measure beds that are only a few inches thick. Many of the better depth gauges (e.g., U. S. Divers no. 7202) are accurate to within one-half foot. For measuring sampling intervals, thickness of zones, and total thickness of section, this instrument gives more accurate results than are usually achieved in measuring surface sections. Menard, et al. (1954) used scuba gear to do stratigraphic mapping of deformed strata cropping out on the sea floor off the coast of California. The geological techniques employed are described by Dill (1954).

The invertebrate paleontologist accustomed only to surface collecting will be amazed at the profusion of calcified fossils in the limestone walls of some of the sinkholes and springs in Florida. Subaquatic disintegration and solution of rock materials leaves calcified fossils etched in relief. Delicate fossils can be picked off walls that would be disintegrated under subaerial conditions of exposure. Calcified fossils that have been completely freed from the matrix are often concentrated in large numbers in solution pockets and on ledges. The surface features of crinoids, echinoids, and other fossils that have weathered from matrix under water are preserved in exquisite detail.

The depth to which divers can safely descend and work underwater is about 140 feet. For periods of a very few minutes it is possible to go deeper, but efficiency is greatly impaired by nitrogen narcosis unless special mixtures of gases are used for breathing.

## ROBOTS

The two-man submarine and television have enabled man to inspect the bottom beyond the reach of divers. The "Diving Saucer," for example, if equipped with a grappling system, could be used for collecting samples from fossiliferous outcrops at considerable depths in the ocean. A grappling system operated by remote control could be used to break off and store samples selected by the observers in the submarine. A device that in time will be used in submarine geological studies is the robot underwater television inspection and grappling system, controlled from a ship by cable.

## SUMMARY

We can look forward to more geological and paleontological studies of materials collected from underwater outcrops. The paleontologist should not be satisfied with underwater methods and collecting techniques which only yield specimens. It is now possible to perform reliable scientific studies on fossiliferous deposits occurring even at great depths.

## REFERENCES

Dill, R. T., and G. Shumway (1954). Geologic use of self-contained diving apparatus. Am. Assoc. Petrol. Geologists Bull., v. 38, p. 148–157.

Furon, R. (1949). Sur de trilobites dragues a 4255 m. de profondeur par le Talisman (1883). Acad. Sci. Paris, C. R. v. 228, p. 1509–1510.

Heezen, B. C. (1959). The floors of the oceans. Geol. Soc. America Special Paper 65, 122 pp.

Maillét, Benoit de, Telliamed; printed by J. A. G (Jean Antone Guer), Amsterdam, 1748.

Menard, H. W., R. F. Dill, E. L. Hamilton, D. G. Moore, Geo. Shumway, M. Silverman, and H. B. Stewart (1954). Underwater mapping by diving geologists (Calif.). Am. Assoc. Petrol. Geologist Bull., v. 38, p. 129–147.

Moore, D. G. (1954). Submarine geology of San Pedro Shelf (Calif.), J. Sed. Petrol., v. 24, p. 162–181.

Northrop, J., and B. C. Heezen (1951). An outcrop of Eocene sediment on the continental slope. J. Geology, v. 59, p. 369–399.

Roberts, F. M. (1960). Basic scuba. Princeton, D. Van Nostrand, 386 pp.

Simpson, G. G. (1930). Tertiary land mammals of Florida. Am. Mus. Nat. History Bull., v. 59, art. 11, p. 149–211.

Stephenson, L. W. (1936). Upper Cretaceous fossils from Georges Bank. Geol. Soc. America Bull., v. 47, p. 367–410.

Stetson, H. C. (1936). Geology and paleontology of the Georges Bank Canyons; Part 1, Geology. Geol. Soc. America Bull., v. 47, p. 339–366.

———— Telliamed; printed by W. Pechin for D. Porter, Baltimore, 1797.

U. S. Divers (1960). Aqua-lung diving. U. S. Divers, Santa Ana, Calif. 59 pp.
U. S. Navy (1952). Diving manual. Bureau of Ships, Navships, U. S. Printing
Office, 160 pp.

# Collecting in Concretions, Nodules, and Septaria

ERLE G. KAUFFMAN

*U. S. National Museum, Washington, D.C.*

Concretions and related structures are important sources of well-preserved fossils. They occur throughout the geologic column in nearly all types of sedimentary rocks, being particularly important in Mesozoic marine sediments. Accretionary structures commonly contain diverse and well-preserved faunas in otherwise unfossiliferous strata. Even in more fossiliferous deposits, they usually yield better-preserved and more diverse macrofossil assemblages than found in the host rocks, preserving delicate structures otherwise distorted or destroyed by prolonged compression or deformation of the enclosing sediment. The formation of many types of accretionary structures depends on the presence of an organically derived nucleus, which guarantees their consistent association with fossils.

In the past, the term "concretion" has been applied loosely to a variety of accretionary structures with different morphologies and modes of origin. Pettijohn (1949, p. 149, pl. 5, fig. 47) recognizes four major types of accretions, on the basis of structural and genetic differences: concretions, nodules, spherulites and rosettes, and forms having an interior cavity partially or wholly filled with secondary mineral deposits (septaria, geodes, and so on). Of these, concretions, nodules, and septaria commonly contain fossils, the first being of greatest importance.

Accretionary structures occur in all common types of sediments. They have been reported in beds of marine, brackish to fresh-water, and continental origin. Most commonly they are developed in fine-grained marine rocks; shale, chalk, and limestone. Locally, they are abundant in siltstone and sandstone. Concretions, nodules, and septaria typically occur in distinct zones, either as single beds or scattered throughout a thin sedimentary sequence.

Published by permission of the Secretary of the Smithsonian Institution.

Where common within any zone, they may coalesce into aggregates or grade laterally into lenticular beds of the same composition. Many accretionary zones persist laterally for considerable distances, forming excellent stratigraphic and paleontologic markers.

Some of the most famous fossil beds of the world produce from accretionary structures. In the United States, concretions in the Eagle Ford, Benton, Pierre, and Bearpaw shales, and in the Fox Hills, Codell, and Ripley sandstones yield some of the outstanding Cretaceous faunas known from the Western Hemisphere. Excellent Paleozoic faunas are obtained from accretions—for example, invertebrates from the Devonian concretions in the Antrim and Pomley shales, fish from the Devonian Kettle Point, Antrim, Marcellus and Cleveland shales and vertebrates, invertebrates, and plants from Pennsylvanian nodules at Mazon Creek, Illinois (see Collinson and Skartvedt, 1960). Mississippian concretions from numerous western localities yield well-preserved cephalopods.

Accretionary structures of various types are being formed today in many different environments. As in the past, modern concretions and nodules form predominantly around a nucleus of organic origin.


## STRUCTURE AND ORIGIN OF FOSSILIFEROUS ACCRETIONARY MASSES

The place and mode of origin of various accretionary types is still poorly known, despite the importance of this subject to the related fields of paleontology, stratigraphy, sedimentology, paleoecology, and oceanography. Any study dealing with these aspects of accretions would be complex; since different accretionary types have different origins, a single type can potentially form in a variety of environments, and multiple-stage concretions having a complex history are commonly encountered.

The collector should be aware, however, of one factor in the formation of concretions and nodules which stresses the importance of considering them in any collecting program. The majority of concretions, and many types of nodules, form around a nucleus. This nucleus is typically of organic origin, such as calcareous shell material, bone, teeth, chitinophosphatic structures, organic carbon, coprolites, and possibly even soft organic tissue. This is apparently not a chance association. The accretion of minerals about a nucleus seems to be controlled by the physical and chemical characteristics of the nucleus itself. Formation of many types of accretionary structures depends on the presence of some organically derived object in the sediment or at the sediment-water interface and on the chemical interaction between this object and the surrounding environment. This is the collector's guarantee of success in prospecting accretionary structures for fossils.

CONCRETIONS

Concretions are dense, resistant, spherical, discoidal, or irregular rock masses formed in a softer host rock (most commonly marine shale, chalk, siltstone, and sandstone) by concentric layering (accretion) of minerals around a nucleus. Concretions commonly form around nuclei isolated in the sediment as well as around local accumulations of shell or bone. The latter have been observed in all stages of formation, from a small limestone core near the center of the accumulation to concretions totally enclosing such accumulations. The principal identifying characteristic of concretions is concentric banding of the matrix. They range in size from a few inches to more than ten feet in diameter, and commonly occur in distinct, laterally persistent beds.

The mineralogic composition of concretions differs from that of the host rock either in the minerals involved or in the proportion of minerals. Commonly, concretions are composed of some cementing agent of the host rock. In addition, they may contain a diverse assortment of other minerals found in the surrounding sediment, such as clay, silt, or sand. The great majority of fossiliferous concretions are composed of limestone and siderite, containing various amounts of clay and coarser clastics. Phosphatic concretions are common in certain sediments, generally formed around arthropod exoskeletons, bones, teeth, and coprolites. These are commonly difficult to distinguish from phosphate nodules. Locally, more bizarre types of concretions contain fossils in abundance; among these are pyrite and marcasite concretions and coal balls (see Mamay and Yochelson, 1953, 1962). Occurrences of unusual concretionary types in abundance should be investigated as a possible source of fossils. Some types of limestone concretions are commonly associated with a peripheral ring of cone-in-cone structure which will rarely yield well-preserved fossils.

The relationship between concretion and host rock is variable, and depends upon the place and time of mineral accretion. Certain types of concretion apparently formed within the sediment at shallow depth during early diagenesis of the host rock. These typically contain uncrushed fossils, and show relict bedding or fossil layering continuous with that of the surrounding matrix; the host rock is not generally warped around the concretion, perhaps indicating a certain amount of cementation prior to formation of the concretion. Such concretions probably grow interstitially and/or by replacement of the host rock before or during lithification. Other concretions, thought to have formed at the sediment-water interface, show either a layered or random arrangement of fossils and show no relict bedding; laminae of the host rock are generally warped over them.

Different types of concretions show evidence of different origins. Limestone concretions apparently form either at the interface or at shallow depth within the sediment, both by interstitial growth, and by replacement of the host rock. They generally contain uncrushed fossils, many of them quite delicate or ornate. Siderite concretions predominantly form within the sediment, not deeply buried but probably deeper than limestone concretions, since contained shells and skeletons are typically crushed. Shells in siderite concretions generally are also fractured into small polygons of similar dimensions, possibly due to volume change during formation of the concretion. The fragments are not greatly separated or moved out of place. Two-stage concretions, having a limestone core and a thinner outer ring of siderite, are locally common and represent two phases of accretion, probably at different depths of burial or under different environmental conditions.

In restricted Atlantic Coast bays, recent phosphate concretions have been noted forming around bone and arthropod remains at the sediment-water interface, or just below it. It is assumed that ancient concretions of this kind formed in the same manner. This is perhaps borne out by the lack of relict bedding in phosphatic concretions and by the warping of the host rock around them in many instances.

### NODULES

Nodules are typically small, highly irregular, and composed of minerals distinct from those in the host rock, usually silica in the form of chert, flint, or chalcedony in a host rock of chalk, limestone, or dolomite. Some authors characterize their internal construction as featureless and homogeneous. Others have noted that they form around a nucleus (generally a fossil), and grow by holoperipheral replacement of the host rock, much like some concretions. The concentric arrangement of incompletely replaced carbonate grains in some chert nodules supports this interpretation. The accretionary material itself, however, does not show concentric banding in nodules as it does in concretions. This, perhaps, constitutes the only major internal morphologic difference between them.

Nodules characteristically occur in distinct zones, generally in great numbers, with adjacent nodules anastomizing along their margins. The location and form of the nodules is probably largely controlled by the physical and chemical characteristics of the sediment before lithification. Emery and Rittenberg (1952, p. 796) have shown that slightly lower than normal pH in a single bed of a growing sediment may cause selective precipitation of silica along that zone.

Nodules grow by replacement of the host rock. Some modern authors contend that this occurs during early diagenesis of the sediment, before consolidation; others claim that it occurs by ground-water action long after lithification. Nodular growth usually takes place around a nucleus, but an organically derived nucleus apparently is not necessary for their formation. Although many nodules contain fossils, many others are barren of recognizable organic detritus. The distribution of fossils in nodules, therefore, seems to be mostly a function of their original distribution and density in the replaced host rock. The geochemical role of organic remains in the formation of nodules around a fossil (as the nucleus) is not clearly understood.

The greatest advantages of collecting in nodules are that certain faunal elements are better preserved in them than in the host rock, the fossils are more likely to be uncrushed, and in dolomitic sections, they are likely to contain the only determinate fossils present.

SEPTARIA

Septarian "concretions" are similar to argillaceous limestone concretions in shape, size, and mineralogy, but differ in both internal structure and mode of origin. Septaria are characterized by a series of radiating shrinkage cracks, expanding toward the center of the mass, and filled with coarsely crystalline calcite (rarely with other minerals). They are commonly, though not exclusively, surrounded by a thin cone-in-cone layer. In addition to the shrinkage cracks, they differ from true concretions in lacking any internal concentric structure, and in having a higher alumina content at the center than at the outside.

Septaria apparently form at shallow depths within the sediment, before lithification, by the following process (Pettijohn, 1949, p. 154): formation of a body of aluminous gel, followed by case hardening of the exterior and dehydration of the interior. The latter causes volume loss and formation of shrinkage cracks. Secondary filling of the cracks is the final step in the process.

Septaria commonly contain fossils, although they do not depend on organically derived material for their formation. The fossils are generally poorly preserved, fractured, recrystallized, and irregularly distributed during formation of the septaria. They are more common near the periphery of the structure than at its center. Pieces of a single large fossil broken during formation of the septaria may be widely distributed throughout it, or spread out around its perimeter.

## COLLECTING FROM CONCRETIONS, NODULES, AND SEPTARIA

The importance of collecting from accretionary structures should be evident from a general understanding of their mode of origin and physical characteristics. The chances of finding fossils within any unit are greatly improved by the presence of concretions and nodules, since many depend on an organically derived nucleus in their formation. Accretions commonly contain more numerous, more diverse, and better-preserved faunas than the host rock because of their early diagenetic origin and association with shell and bone concentrations. They often contain the only fossils in a sedimentary unit. The early sedimentary origin of concretions is an important consideration, since it insures protection for enclosed fossils against crushing by subsequent compaction of the host rock. Dense accretionary matrix is often of low permeability and protects contained fossils from solution or alteration by percolating water. It also provides greater protection for fossils against weathering than do many other lithologies. Owing to their greater resistance to weathering, accretionary structures are more accessible for collecting over a greater area than the enclosing sediment, especially where the strata are deeply weathered or covered by a veneer of vegetation.

EQUIPMENT

In collecting from accretionary structures the equipment must be fitted to the condition of the fossils and the matrix and to the logistics of the transportation. If one can drive to the outcrop, there is no excuse for not being prepared for any type of collecting, but in inaccessible areas a great deal of planning should go into minimizing weight and bulk of collecting apparatus.

Equipment needed for collecting from large accretionary masses is bulky. A set of sledge hammers, 4, 6, and 10 pounds, preferably with one end blunt and the other wedge-shaped, are needed to break the accretions of various size and density normally encountered in a single section. Long handles are better than short ones because they give greater leverage. The standard rock pick is too light to break most accretions larger than a foot in diameter. Chisels and wedges are useful if concretions contain relict bedding and bedded fossils, or septaria are to be split along shrinkage cracks to isolate a fossiliferous portion. Many collectors carry pry bars to aid in getting concretions and septaria out of matrix in fresh exposures.

Those who prefer to do some cleaning in the field should bring a normal assortment of small picks and chisels and a light hammer. Quick-setting glue is an important accessory, so that broken fossils may be repaired on the spot, when all the pieces are at hand and their original relationship to one another is fresh in the collector's mind. To provide maximum protection for the fossils, packing material such as paper or cloth bags should be carried into the field and the specimens wrapped at the outcrop.

The heavy, angular blocks commonly obtained in breaking large accretionary structures demand a strong back pack, heavy canvas or burlap bags, or canvas slings for packing out material when the locality is inaccessible by car or truck. Small canvas bags for individual samples further aid in protecting the pack and packer from sharp rock edges, and the fossils from abrasion during transport. Bags and large blocks are best marked in the field with a felt-tipped marking pen.

Any collecting which involves breaking up hard, dense rocks so characteristic of accretionary structures must be done with great care. This is particularly true if sledge hammers and wedges are used, and the danger from flying metal chips is added to that from rock fragments. The lower parts of the body, and the hands, wrists, and eyes should be adequately protected.

Experience is the best teacher in any collecting. The actual mechanics of collecting—breaking up accretionary masses with an assortment of hammers —involves mostly hard physical labor, and merits no special verbiage here. There are, however, a few characteristics of accretionary structures which, if recognized, will aid the collector immeasurably. The tricks of the trade are in knowing how and where to find accretions, determining which ones to collect from, knowing what to consider before attempting to break them and to what degree they should be broken.

FINDING ACCRETIONS

Recognition of concretions, nodules, and septaria in the field is not difficult. They stand out on weathered slopes as resistant, rounded, lenticular or irregular masses that are distinct in color and generally arranged in linear belts. Limestone and siderite concretions are commonly iron-stained, orange, rusty, or reddish brown. Nonferruginous limestone concretions range from black and gray to brown and buff. Phosphatic concretions and nodules are characteristically black. Chert nodules are most often gray, brown, or tan. There is often a distinct color contrast between the host rock and the accretionary structures. Accretions commonly weather free and accumulate in great numbers at the base of the weathering slope, where they are easily accessible. Collections made from such accumulations are of greatest value if the collector can determine precisely from which part of the measured section the accretions came.

Dark marine shales are the primary source of concretions and septaria. These are common in other marine sediments as well—chalk, marl, siltstone, and sandstone. Marine dolomites and limestones contain the greatest abundance of nodules (predominantly siliceous), but rarely other accretions. Accretionary structures form in almost every type of sediment, however, and the collector should always be on the alert for them.

CHARACTERISTICS OF FOSSIL-BEARING ACCRETIONS
AND COLLECTING TECHNIQUES

The best vertebrate and calcareous macroinvertebrate fossils are found in limestone or argillaceous limestone concretions. Claystone and siliceous claystone concretions also yield good vertebrate remains. Siderite concretions and septaria often contain numerous fossils, but they are not as well preserved as those in limestone, being commonly crushed and fractured. Limestone-siderite, and claystone-siderite combinations locally yield good fossils of all types, including plants. Bones, teeth, and arthropod exoskeletons are well preserved in phosphatic concretions and nodules. Dense siliceous nodules are good sources of certain invertebrates that can be studied in thin section. They are worth collecting in dolomite, recrystallized limestone, and some chalks, where they may contain the only identifiable fossils in the sequence. In limestone, preservation is usually better in the host rock itself than in contained nodules. Weathered accretions of all types are easier to break, and yield more numerous well-preserved specimens than do fresh structures.

Macrofossils are generally better preserved in accretionary structures than in the host rock, but microfossils, unless they can be studied in thin section, are best collected from the softer surrounding sediments.

Concretions and related structures commonly occur at many levels in a single section, and some will be more fossiliferous than others. It is tempting to collect only from those that will yield a great amount of material, but the geologist interested in obtaining the greatest amount of information from his collection, and the most accurate correlations, will find it advantageous to sample all occurrences of accretionary structures in each measured section. Each band of concretions or nodules will probably yield a somewhat different fauna than found in adjacent bands, even within a single well-defined faunal zone. Vertically successive beds of concretions, nodules, or septaria may represent a number of distinct and well-established faunal zones. For this reason, it is important that collections from each zone of concretions or nodules be kept separate, no matter what their vertical separation or apparent similarity. A few feet of sediment with closely spaced concretion zones in one section may be equivalent to hundreds of feet of section elsewhere, and millions of years in time. If a relatively complete picture of the fauna is desired, it is equally important to sample each accretion zone laterally at several places along the strike. Although some well-known concretion zones (in particular those of the Upper Cretaceous Fox Hills Sandstone) contain only a single species or a restricted and uniform assemblage throughout their range, this is exceptional. Normally, different accretions within a zone contain different fossil assemblages, or different proportions and sizes of the common species, reflecting such phenomena as selective sorting, variation in ecology or environment from place to place, or gregarious habit of certain organisms.

The density of individuals within concretions also varies laterally within a single zone, and vertically through successive zones. It is wise to do preliminary prospecting within each zone of accretionary structures to find those which are most fossiliferous. In some zones, only a small percentage of the accretions will contain usable fossils. If the rest of the section is highly fossiliferous, these can be overlooked. However, it is worth much effort to obtain even scattered fossils from such zones if the section is relatively barren. The exact stratigraphic and geographic position of isolated fossiliferous concretions in otherwise barren zones should be accurately recorded.

The orientation of fossils in accretions varies from random to distinctly bedded, and should be studied in detail before the structures are broken. This can be determined by examining weathered surfaces of accretions, or fossil orientation in the host rock itself. If fossils within a concretion are bedded to any degree, the most complete and best-preserved specimens will be obtained by splitting the concretion along bedding planes. Even if the structure shows no evidence of fossils externally, or if the orientation of specimens appears random, it is best to split the structure parallel to the bedding plane in the host rock, or relict plane in the structure itself. This is easily done with a chisel or wedge or with a sharp upward swing of the hammer directed at the lateral edge of the accretion.

Fossils generally occur at the center of limestone, siderite, claystone, and phosphate concretions. If the concretions are sparsely fossiliferous, no evidence of their fossil content will be observed on the exterior surface. The collector should not be deterred from investigating these structures because they appear barren on the exterior. In septaria, the centers are commonly barren, the fossils being irregularly distributed around the periphery. The distribution of fossils in nodules, particularly in siliceous nodules, is more variable. Some nodules are barren; others contain fossils near their centers; still others have no organic nucleus, but contain fossils scattered throughout, much as they occur in the host rock. The distribution of fossils in all accretionary structures except septaria probably reflects their occurrence in the host rock.

In limestone concretions and septaria, a peripheral ring of crudely developed cone-in-cone is commonly present. This may weather much more than the accretionary material it surrounds, and fossils contained in it may actually weather free of the matrix. This is another feature which should be investigated before the structure is broken up.

Concretions and septaria more than 3 feet in diameter are difficult to break even with large hammers unless they are unusually soft or weathered. The collector should therefore concentrate on small structures, if possible, since they seem to contain the same quality and diversity of fossils as those of greater size. In the long run, more specimens and a greater diversity of animals will generally be obtained in the same amount of time by collecting from these smaller accretions. Weathered accretions yield better material than fresh structures.

The extent to which an accretionary structure should be broken in the field depends upon the amount and preservation of fossils it contains. Sparsely to moderately fossiliferous masses should be extensively broken to acquire the maximum number and diversity of individuals. Concretions and nodules containing an abundance of fossils can be transported in large blocks, and the fossils later segregated in the lab.

The degree to which fossils in accretionary structures can be cleaned in the field depends largely on the nature of the animal and where the rock splits relative to the fossil. No cleaning should be attempted on delicate specimens— thin or highly ornamented shells, or parts of vertebrate skeletons that have protruding bones, teeth, or spines. If the rock splits around the exterior surface of shells or bones that have smooth to planar surfaces, much preliminary cleaning can be done in the field, but if the rock splits at the shell-steinkern (internal mold) interface, attempts to clean fossils in the field will only cause destruction of many valuable specimens. Such fossils should be collected and returned to the laboratory in matrix, where they can be extracted with mechanical tools. The collector should be able to determine which way the accretion will break relative to the contained shell or bone with the first few fractures. All fossils should be wrapped and labeled (or assigned a field number) before they are removed from the collecting locality.

Concretions, nodules, and septaria are among the greatest potential sources of well-preserved fossils in most sedimentary sequences, and should receive careful consideration in any collecting program. However, even the most thorough knowledge of collecting techniques will be of little use unless the collector has patience and perseverance. Collecting from accretionary structures can be exciting or discouraging, and the collector should be prepared for either experience.

## REFERENCES

Collinson, C. W., and Romayne Skartvedt (1960). Field book of Pennsylvanian plant fossils of Illinois. Illinois State Geol. Survey Educ. Ser., no. 6.

Emery, K. O., and S. C. Rittenberg (1952). Early diagenesis of California basin sediments in relation to the origin of oil. Am. Assoc. Petrol. Geologists Bull., v. 36, p. 796.

Mamay, S. H., and E. L. Yochelson (1953). Floral-faunal associations in American coal balls. Science, v. 118, no. 3061, p. 240–241.

———— (1962). Occurrence and significance of marine animal remains in American coal balls. U. S. Geol. Survey Prof. Paper 354-I, p. 193–224.

Pettijohn, F. J. (1949). Sedimentary rocks. New York, Harper, p. 149, pl. 5, fig. 47.

# Collecting Amber

R. L. LANGENHEIM, JR.

*Department of Geology, University of Illinois, Urbana*

The widespread occurrence of amber in Cretaceous and Tertiary rocks has not received adequate attention from paleontologists and geologists, in spite of the well-known, extensive, and highly significant occurrences of fossil insects in amber from the Baltic region (Bachofen-Echt, 1949), Cedar Lake, Manitoba (Carpenter, et al., 1937), and Chiapas, Mexico (Hurd, Smith, and Durham, 1961). As a consequence, this paper is offered in the hope that more workers will either collect or report occurrences of fossil gums. At least one occurrence in the Dominican Republic is known to contain large numbers of unstudied fossil insects (Vaughan, et al., 1921, p. 244; Sanderson and Farr, 1960), and it is probable that many other such occurrences are scattered over the globe.

The name, "amber," is loosely applied to all forms of fossil tree gum, but is strictly applicable only to gums containing succinic acid. Succinite, the mineralogic name for true amber, is derived from *Pinites succinifer* Goeppert, the presumed coniferous source tree of the Baltic amber. Other amber "minerals" include bacaite, burmite, copalite, duxite, krantzite, rosthornite, rumanite, sieburgite, simetite, walchowite, and at least 29 additional varieties listed by Hintze (1933, p. 1375, 1397) in the succinite and retinite groups. Palct (1953), however, recognizes 52 named varieties and several unnamed varieties, which he classifies as follows: resins of coniferous origin (34 varieties); resins of angiospermous origin (4 varieties); and resins of unknown origin (14 varieties). All of these different ambers are distinguished from one another by slight differences in physical properties and greater or lesser differences in chemical composition. Although these differences may be paleontologically significant so far as they represent differences in the original gums, the name "amber" will be used here in a general sense to include all transparent to translucent fossil gums capable of preserving organic inclusions.

Color, luster, diaphaneity, fracture, and specific gravity are among the most useful properties for distinguishing amber from its natural surroundings. In addition, amber may be recognized by its electrical properties, flammability, odor, heat conductivity, hardness, and chemical composition. The latter properties are important in distinguishing amber from synthetic resins sold as amber. Amber ranges from black through brown and yellow to bluish and greenish tints. Most amber, however, is golden yellow or somewhat reddish-yellow. Weathered amber is generally brown or yellow, having the appearance of dried pine resin. Amber generally has a vitreous or resinous luster; but some fresh amber is greasy, and weathered amber has a dull luster. The conchoidal fracture surfaces of much amber are highly efficient reflectors; for this reason the collecting site should be approached so that sunlight will be reflected into your eyes by these surfaces. This means collecting with the sun in your face, which is contrary to best practice, but in this manner bits of amber as small as $\frac{1}{8}$ inch in diameter are easily seen at a distance of 10 feet or more.

Amber has very nearly the same specific gravity as water, ranging from 1 to 1.25, with most material in the 1.05 to 1.08 range. Thus some ambers float in salt water and all are readily moved by weak currents. In addition, the property of near-flotation tends to protect amber from abrasion and fracture. Thus, amber is readily transported and may occur in reworked deposits, remote both in age and locality from the original deposit. Much of the Baltic and Sicilian amber occurs on sea beaches (Bachofen-Echt, 1949; Farrington, 1923). At Cedar Lake, Manitoba (Carpenter, et. al., 1937) amber has traveled at least 150 miles by river to accumulate in a Recent lakeshore deposit. On the Arctic Coastal Plain of Alaska (Langenheim, Smiley, and Gray, 1960) amber has traveled at least 200 miles down the Kuk-Kaolak drainage to accumulate on Recent strands, bars, and sea beaches as well as in Pleistocene terrace deposits. Most of the amber collected in this area has come from the lines of wrack on bars and beaches and from accumulations of soggy driftwood at the sites of eddies and below channel obstructions (Langenheim, Smiley and Gray, 1960, p. 1350).

Amber is not only easily transported and protected from abrasion but is chemically inert. For these reasons, isolated, reworked fragments of amber occur in a wide variety of detrital rocks. An example of the problems which may arise is the occurrence of Eocene amber associated with reworked Miocene coal in a Pleistocene sand deposit involved in ice-shove thrusting on the coast of Usedom in East Germany (Schulz, 1960).

Although amber may occur in almost any sediment or sedimentary rock, it is most abundant in clay-sized to medium sand-sized detrital material. Most occurrences are associated with plant debris, but coals are not particularly notable sources of amber. In fact, many of the most famous and prolific source-beds are marine in origin. The Baltic amber source-beds (Bachofen-Echt, 1949; Farrington, 1923) include lignite layers, but most of the amber comes from "blue clay" layers that lack plant debris and are probably of marine origin (Durham, 1957; Kirchner, 1950). Some of the Alaskan amber occurs in coal beds, but most of it is in shale or siltstone and is accompanied by plant debris (Langenheim, Smiley, and Gray, 1960). Amber from Colorado occurs in "bluish-gray rock, full of plant remains, in the immediate vicinity of the coal" (Cockerell, 1909, p. 141). The widely distributed amber of the Atlantic Coastal Plain is apparently largely associated with lignite and plant fossils (Holick, 1905). Mexican amber, however, occurs within a marine sequence, but many of the richer, amber-bearing layers contain plant debris in addition to marine fossils (Hurd, Smith, and Durham, 1961). British Columbian amber (retinite) occurs in coal (Durham, 1957). The amber of the Dominican Republic occurs in "beds of sandy shale containing seams of lignite and lumps of amber" (Vaughan, et al., 1921, p. 244) at Tamboril and in sandstone at Palo Alto de la Cumbre (Sanderson and Farr, 1960).

Amber is known in relative abundance from Cretaceous, Eocene, Oligocene, Miocene, Pliocene, and Pleistocene rocks. The Baltic amber is of both Eocene and Oligocene age (Bachofen-Echt, 1949). The prolific deposits of Chiapas range from Oligocene to Miocene in definitely known autochthonous deposits, and there are also secondary deposits of Pliocene age. The rich deposits of the Dominican Republic are probably Oligocene (Sanderson and Farr, 1960). Cretaceous amber is abundant on the Atlantic Coastal Plain (Holick, 1905), in northern Alaska (Langenheim, Smiley, and Gray, 1960), and at Cedar Lake in Manitoba (Carpenter, et al., 1937). Cretaceous amber is also reported from Tennessee (Carpenter, et al., 1937, p. 12), Baja California (Hurd, Smith, and Durham, 1961), Moldavia (Haidinger, 1845; Palct, 1953; Schroeckinger, 1878), and New Mexico (Loew, 1874).

Although the Early Cretaceous has yielded the oldest insect-bearing amber of reliably known age (Langenheim, Smiley, and Gray, 1960), an intensive search should be made for older fossil resins. Palct (1953, p. 340) lists five different older Mesozoic or Permo-Carboniferous resins, and there is no reason to doubt that gum-producing plants capable of giving rise to fossil resins existed before the Cretaceous.

Many fossil species preserved in amber are exceedingly rare, and species represented by single specimens are not uncommon. Therefore, the usual arguments against using material not collected in place, may have to be ignored. Float, reworked material, or even purchased specimens may provide the basis for paleontologic publication. Amber collected in the field may have been reworked; in fact, any accumulation in which small amounts of amber are scattered throughout current-laid deposits should be suspected of having been reworked. Purchased specimens or those obtained from amateurs or persons having no paleontologic training not only pose problems of geographic and stratigraphic origin, but must be carefully tested to prove that they are, indeed, fossil resins and that the inclusions did, in fact, originate with the amber. My associates and I have frequently been fooled by Mexican amber salesmen, and Farrington (1923) mentions "salting" of Baltic amber with marine invertebrates. In addition, synthetic resins or modern gums such as copal have been widely sold as amber (Williamson, 1932) with or without fraudulent inclusions.

In testing a suspected gum the color, specific gravity, luster, diaphaneity, and fracture should be checked in the same manner as in dealing with field material. In addition, a suspected gum should be rubbed briskly to determine whether it generates static electricity; almost all amber becomes strongly negatively charged and readily attracts small pieces of paper. Most ambers are poor conductors of heat, and therefore feel warm to the touch in contrast to glass and some amber-like synthetic resins, which are notably cool to the touch. Ambers are all flammable and give off characteristic aromatic to irritating fumes. Although it is necessary to know the range of odors produced by amber to apply this test confidently, it can be stated that formaldehyde and acetone do not occur in natural resins or amber. Many synthetics are nonflammable, or nearly so. Although most synthetics may be eliminated through use of the preceding tests, some synthetics and many natural resins will "pass" as amber and must be more carefully analyzed. Careful determination of specific gravity, optical properties, and chemical composition is required for definite proof of identity in some instances.

Modern insects or other objects may be embedded in melted or pressed amber, "ambroid," or may be inserted in a prepared cavity in natural amber. Ambroid may be identified by a "cloudy, misty" appearance and by flow lines and layering that resembles cirrus clouds (Williamson, 1932, p. 237–

238). Inclusions in ambroid are not likely to be fossil. The cavity-filling which surrounds a fraudulent inclusion in natural amber must either be melted amber, synthetic resin or modern gum. Such fillings may be identified by recognizing the introduced resin as such or by noticing a well-marked contact between the filling and the amber.

## REFERENCES

Bachofen-Echt, A. (1949). Der Bernstein und seine Eischlüsse. Vienna, Springer, 240 pp., 188 figs.

Carpenter, F. M. (and others) (1937). Insects and arachnids from Canadian amber. Univ. Toronto Studies, Geol. Ser., no. 40, p. 7–62.

Cockerell, T. D. A. (1909). Amber in the Laramie Cretaceous. Torreya, v. 9, no. 7, p. 140–142.

Durham, J. W. (1957). Amber through the ages. Pacific Discovery, v. 10, no. 2, p. 3–5.

Farrington, O. C. (1923). Amber, its physical properties and geological occurrence. Field Mus. Nat. History, Geol. Leaflet no. 3, 7 pp., 3 pls., 1 fig.

Haidinger, W. K. (1845). Ubersichte der Resultate Mineralogischer Forschung im Jahre 1843. Erlangen, 150 pp.

Hintze, C. (1933). Handbuch der Mineralogie. Berlin and Leipzig, Walter de Gruyter & Co., v. 1, Abt. 4, Haelfte 2, p. 721–1454.

Holick, C. A. (1905). The occurrence and origin of amber in the eastern United States. Am. Naturalist, v. 39, no. 459, p. 137–145.

Hurd, P. D., R. F. Smith, and J. W. Durham (1961). The fossiliferous amber of Chiapas. Ciencia, v. 21, no. 3, p. 107–118, pls. 1–2.

Kirchner, G. 1950). Amber inclusions. Endeavour, v. 9, no. 34, p. 70–75, 3 pls., 1 fig.

Langenheim, R. L., Jr., C. J. Smiley, and Jane Gray (1960). Cretaceous amber from the Arctic Coastal Plain of Alaska. Geol. Soc. America Bull., v. 71, no. 9, p. 1345–1356, 2 figs.

Loew, O. (1874). On Wheelerite, a new fossil resin. Am. J. Sci., v. 107, p. 571–572.

Palct, J. (1953). A system of Caustolites. Tschermaks Geol. Petrog. Mitt., v. 3, no. 4, p. 332–347.

Sanderson, M. W., and T. H. Farr (1960). Amber with insect and plant inclusions from the Dominican Republic. Science, v. 131, no. 3409, p. 1313.

Schroeckinger, J. (1878). Zwei neue Harze aus Mahren. Verh. Geolog. Reichs., Jahrb. 1878, no. 17, p. 387–390.

Schulz, W. (1960). Die natürliche Verbreitung des Ostseebernsteins und das Bernsteinvorkommen von Stubbenfelde (Usedom). Zeitschr. Angewandte Geologie, no. 12, p. 610–614, 7 figs.

Vaughan, T. W., and others (1921). A geological reconnaissance of the Dominican Republic. Geol. Survey Dominican Republic Mem. 1, 268 pp.

Williamson, G. C. (1932). The book of amber. London, Ernest Benn, 268 pp., 4 tables, 6 figs.

# Collecting Molds of Fossils

R. M. LINSLEY

*Colgate University, Colgate, New York*

The greatest deterrents to the accumulation of a good collection of molds of fossils are laziness and lack of patience on the part of the collector. The epitome of laziness is exemplified by the collector who collects *only* steinkerns (internal molds) of fossils. Steinkerns should not be ignored, as they can be of inestimable value in determining internal shell structure of such organisms as brachiopods and pelecypods; for other groups, however, such as gastropods, scaphopods, and the living chambers of cephalopods, steinkerns have only limited value. In no group are steinkerns alone sufficient. Concerted efforts should always be made to obtain the external molds.

Molds contribute little, however, to the study of many groups of organisms, particularly those groups whose identification depends on internal structures and whose anatomical arrangements prevent molds of these structures from being formed. Included in this category are fusulinids, corals, bryozoans, and cephalopods. Most frequently, molds of these animals reveal only the external form of the fossil, and this rarely permits more than familial identification, though occasionally the generic rank may be ascertained. In other groups, such as gastropods, many echinoderms, and most arthropods, molds may be sufficient for most kinds of systematic work. In the pelecypods and brachiopods both the external and the internal molds are necessary for most systematic or detailed stratigraphic work.

It should be noted that though the steinkerns of gastropods are usually worthless, there are many species possessing columellar structures, the features of which can be ascertained from internal molds. Steinkerns of gastropods and other animals whose shells have an aperture through which sediments can enter are confluent with the surrounding matrix. It is best to leave the apertural portion of such steinkerns intact with the external mold. This can greatly aid the interpretation of many apertural features such as the presence or absence of parietal teeth, reflected lips, re-entrants, and, of course, the thickness of the shell near the aperture. Often the sediments will have only partly filled the empty shell, in which case all that will be present is an apertural steinkern. It may take some practice to recognize these nubs of rock—the apertural steinkerns—for they frequently look inconsequential or even unrelated to the specimens you are trying to collect, but they are worth watching for. Even after you have recognized one, it frequently takes patience and a great deal of luck to get it back to the laboratory intact.

It has been noted that though steinkerns are frequently of little consequence, they can be valuable when properly used relative to the external mold. It might also be noted, however, that steinkerns can be a serious problem. If they attain an appreciable size, they may occasionally slump against the side of the external mold; internal molds in limestones may become fused to the wall of the external mold. Needless to say, this makes it more difficult to clean the external mold and frequently ruins it completely.

In collecting external molds it is, of course, necessary to collect a good deal of worthless surrounding rock. It is here that laziness can lead to the destruction of good material. The temptation to trim off another pound of rock should be resisted. Because the mold generally creates an area of weakness, a fracture in the rock is more apt to take place through the mold than any other place. If the mold should be broken, it is most convenient to identify the adjoining pieces in some manner that will facilitate reassembly in the laboratory. If your collections are large, you will also find it convenient to wrap the broken pieces together and thus avoid accidental separation of the two pieces and all of the resultant confusion.

It is not unusual to find a desirable mold in a block of rock that is too large to be transported back to the laboratory and too tough to be broken with available equipment. Usually it would be sufficient to make a cast of the specimen in the field with one of the many substances used for this purpose. However, if it is anticipated that this particular specimen might be used as a type specimen, then a plastotype is no substitute for the original mold, and every effort should be made to take the block to the laboratory for proper treatment. Casts properly taken in the field may be adequate for almost all exploratory phases of geology and for many stratigraphic problems, but they are not sufficient for most systematic paleontological studies.

One of the biggest disadvantages of working with molds is that very frequently you can collect only one half of the specimen. Half a specimen is better than none, but a complete specimen is far more desirable than a fragment; thus every effort should be made to collect all pieces of a mold and to carefully label and wrap each piece for easy assembly in the lab.

If the rock is sufficiently replete with molds it is most practicable to bring back to the laboratory the largest manageable pieces, in the hope that they may contain complete specimens. These pieces may then be broken in the lab at your convenience and the labor involved in packing and unpacking avoided. This procedure frequently involves carrying many pounds of relatively worthless rock to the lab, but the completeness of the specimens obtained make it the most satisfactory method of collecting molds. Once the large pieces are in the lab they may readily be broken by a suitable rock crusher, and the pieces containing the two halves of a given mold may then be easily labeled and trayed for subsequent study. It is far better to reduce molds by means of a rock crusher rather than a saw, for the saw frequently cuts through the mold at an undesirable angle and, of course, removes a portion of the fossil merely by the cutting action of the saw.

Once the material has been adequately assembled in the laboratory the only steps that remain before it can be studied consist of cleaning the molds and preparing the casts. Unfortunately, many molds are lined with drusy accretions of various minerals, most commonly calcite or quartz. If these incrustations are excessively thick and well cemented to the rock, it is frequently best to disregard the molds and look for cleaner ones. Most often this type of occurrence is only local, and investigation of nearby outcrops will usually reveal clean molds. If clean molds are unattainable, then of course it becomes necessary to use most propitiously the available material. If the composition of the druse differs sufficiently from that of the rock, it may prove readily removable by solution. If the rock is even slightly soluble in the solvent used to remove the druse, this then means loss of small details of sculpturing (which so many molds exhibit so nicely). In this case it is usually preferable to try to remove the druse mechanically through careful use of Vibro-tools, dental picks, sonic vibrators, or whatever tool is most suitable. The use of the fossil is of considerable importance here. If the fossil has been collected for taxonomic purposes, all care must be taken to preserve all available details. In some stratigraphic problems and gross faunal studies, sculptural details may be of secondary importance, and the loss of some detail because of solution may be preferable to the more lengthy, individual mechanical treatment of the material.

Cleaning natural molds can lead to many mistakes even when the preparator is thoroughly familiar with the form of the organism he is working with. A negative impression frequently takes on a completely new appearance in contrast to the positive, and the preparator must be careful not to "create new species" by digging out spines where they don't exist or adding new "growth lines" through a slip of the pick, and so on. I have found it most helpful to make casts frequently during the cleaning processes to help guide my understanding of contours of the mold.

In conclusion it should be emphasized that the best molds can usually be gathered only by spending some effort. The best molds are complete molds, and you are most apt to get complete molds when you bring in large quantities of large blocks of rocks, trusting that some of these blocks contain complete specimens hidden in their interiors.

# Collecting Coal Balls

S. H. MAMAY

*U. S. Geological Survey, Washington, D.C.*

Although coal balls have interested only a relatively small group of paleo-botanists, the morphologic and anatomical information contained in coal balls is of sufficient significance to warrant a few remarks here. Coal balls are nodular masses of petrified plant debris that occur sporadically within some Pennsylvanian or upper Carboniferous coal seams. Occasionally, they also contain intermixed marine remains, and at one known locality their organic remains are almost exclusively of animal origin.

In the United States coal balls are abundant in the Midcontinent coal fields and rare in the southern Appalachians, being found only in Kentucky. They are unknown in the anthracite regions or in any of the post-Paleozoic coals. However, it is not impossible that they may occur in hitherto unproductive geographic areas or stratigraphic levels; the field collector is therefore encouraged to examine carefully any potential exposures. An important point to keep in mind is that wherever coal balls occur, the seam is invariably overlain by a marine rock unit.

Coal balls may be rounded, lenticular, or irregular in shape, and may be as small as a pecan or large enough to weigh several hundred pounds. Occasionally, they are found as large intergrown masses weighing a ton or more, and in some locations they constitute a major part of the waste mined with the coal.

Preservation of cellular details of the included plant parts is due to impregnation by various minerals. The impregnative matter is usually calcium carbonate, but dolomitic coal balls are common in the European occurrences, and at least one occurrence of silicified coal balls is known in the United States. Pyrite in varying amounts occurs in nearly all coal balls, and where it is a major mineral constituent, preservation of plant matter is usually poor.

Coal balls are easily recognized when found intact in coal seams; owing to their shape and mineralization, they stand out as irregularities within the seam. They may be dug out of the seam if necessary, but where they occur in commercially mined coal they are generally found in waste heaps at the tipple. At some mines they are set aside in large heaps as future sources of road ballast, and are generally identifiable by the thin layers of coal that usually adhere as they are separated from the coal.

Publication authorized by the Director, U. S. Geological Survey.

Collecting coal balls is a haphazard process unless one can identify desirable plant specimens in the field, on broken and weathered surfaces. This is sometimes possible, but more often the nature and quality of the included fossils cannot be determined until the coal balls are sliced and etched in the laboratory. In occurrences where there is a significant variation in amounts of pyrite, those with large amounts may be discarded as undesirable simply by judging their weight relative to volume and by observing excessive amounts of pyrite on broken surfaces. Some collectors prefer to select rounded specimens, and others prefer lenticular specimens, but it has not been demonstrated that shape is an infallible clue to good specimens.

Shipment of coal balls is a simple matter, as their durability obviates the necessity for careful packing. They may be shipped by railroad freight in ordinary burlap feed sacks which easily handle 40 to 80 pounds each. Although the sacks are usually cut and torn to some extent, in the shipping process, damage to the sacks is rarely extensive enough to cause loss of specimens.

# Collecting Microvertebrate Fossils by Washing and Screening

MALCOLM C. McKENNA

*American Museum of Natural History, New York*

Most museums cannot afford to collect large samples of large-sized fossil vertebrates because of collection costs, preparation and storage problems, or all three of these reasons. The most efficient way to collect a large number of small bones and teeth from some fossiliferous sites consists in digging up, transporting, and screening large quantities of sediment in water and sorting the dried concentrate—a process that has come to be called "washing." The process is especially useful in recovering fossils of very small vertebrates, such as shrews and various rodents. The idea is, of course, an old one, derived from the most elementary principles of mining and milling. Micropaleontology makes use of the same principles to recover tiny Foraminifera in the laboratory. The washing process discussed here is merely an extension to a

An abridgment of the author's article in the July 1962 issue of *Curator*.

larger size range of the principles employed to concentrate invertebrate microfossils in the laboratory. Since somewhat larger fossils are involved, the various operations employed must be transferred from the laboratory to the field, where water and equipment can be made available on a suitably extensive scale. Because water is used, the screening of consolidated sediments is frequently possible—an improvement over dry-screening techniques such as have been used for years by archeologists in search of artifacts. Clays and semi-indurated *sands and silts* are immune to dry-screening but can often be processed by washing.

The recovery of molluscan and small fossil vertebrate remains by screening either consolidated or unconsolidated sediments in water on a large scale apparently dates from the work of Charles Moore, an amateur geologist of Bath, who washed and sieved three tons of clay to obtain thirty *Haramiya* teeth from a Rhaeto-Liassic fissure infilling (Savage, 1960) more than 100 years ago. In 1891 J. L. Wortman (see part VI of Osborn and Wortman, 1892) sacked and transported to water by horseback and by wagon a quantity of matrix from several sites in the early Eocene of the Bighorn basin, Wyoming. The matrix was washed, and valuable specimens of several genera of carnivorous mammals were obtained when the recovered bone fragments were cemented together. Wortman's work was done primarily with the aim of collecting all available fragments of single specimens after the fragments had become separated at the outcrop. The employment of large-scale washing, year after year, as the primary means of obtaining large samples of various kinds of small fossil vertebrate remains, dates from 1936. In that year, C. W. Hibbard began a remarkable series of expeditions to southwestern Kansas which resulted in a flood of specimens of late Cenozoic small vertebrates and mollusks from many sites. Hibbard (1949) published a valuable exposition of his techniques, a publication out of print by 1950 and now much sought after. Hibbard's method has since been extended by others to Mesozoic and early Cenozoic deposits with considerable success.

The washing process is ideally suited to the gathering of large numbers of small specimens from fossiliferous sites. Large specimens may, of course, be collected by other means at the time the matrix is collected. Some isolated parts of large animals will, however, appear only after the matrix has been washed. Very few surface indications are needed for fossil mammals. If a few small specimens are found on the surface, it is almost always possible to recover many hundreds, or even thousands, underground. The quantity recovered is usually as much a function of the willingness of the collector to process sediment as it is of the actual richness of the deposit. Statistically significant samples of at least the more common groups of organisms at a site can frequently be obtained after processing only a few tons of sediment, but the amount, of course, varies widely. Therefore, it is possible to develop a site which would be considered poor by a surface collector. However, it is also possible to a considerable extent to choose where one wishes to collect fossils and then to set about recovering them. One can thus gain a certain degree of freedom from the essentially random distribution of rich surface concentrations to which the "surface collector" of small fossils is bound if he wishes to collect a large number of specimens. This increased degree of freedom is especially valuable if such fossils are rare in a certain part of the stratigraphic section, or in a particular area, or if a supposedly barren unit is being prospected. If the age of a stratigraphic unit is unknown, washing is frequently the most rapid and economical way to obtain enough fossils to date the unit. Small fossils are as valuable stratigraphically as large ones, but are usually much less expensive to obtain.

Should this site be washed? That is the question facing the discoverer of a fossiliferous site. There are few general rules other than the following, which are offered as provisional guideposts. There should be at least *some* surface indication of the type of fossil wanted before matrix is sacked for washing; only in desperation should matrix be washed if none are seen on the surface. Such action is sometimes called for in undated sediments or when no fauna of a certain age has previously been recovered. The fossils must be reasonably durable. If broken, the fragments should at least have sharp enough breaks to permit recognition of fits and subsequent repair. If the fossils are in clay, it should be kept in mind that clays swell when placed in water and that extensive damage or total destruction of powdery or brittle bone may result if the deposit is washed. If fossils are common enough at a site, there may be no need to wash them. They can then be obtained by the usual quarrying techniques, without running the risk of damage or dissociation inherent in washing. Such techniques will have to be employed anyway if the matrix is indurated. The commoner the fossils, the greater the loss of association if washing is employed. Breaks can be repaired easily when fossils are rare, because only one or a few specimens are likely to be found in any particular washing box (see below), and there is thus a minimum of specimens of which any given fragment might be a part. Suites of isolated teeth from irreparably damaged jaws of fossil mammals frequently can be fitted together if fossils are rare, because most of the boxes will contain no other fragments belonging to the same species, and there will be no duplicates or missing parts of the specimen.

The best way to screen sediment from a fossiliferous site is to use a large number of washing boxes. Efficient washing boxes can be constructed of wood and galvanized window screen at relatively low cost. When more than fifty boxes are needed, it is not generally economical to build all-metal boxes or to devise complicated collapsible or nesting designs. An inexpensive yet strong type of construction suitable for mass production is almost always called for, because it is generally not efficient to attempt to operate with fewer than fifty boxes, no matter how small the available crew. A box about 18 inches on a

**Fig. 1.** *At the washing site. Boxes in the water contain matrix set out to soak. Those on the bank have been washed and are drying. The crew sorts concentrate from rewashing trays drying out of view. [Photo by M. F. Skinner.]*

side and 12 inches deep, with a screened bottom and two sides constructed partly of screen, has been found to be most convenient, as this construction will permit the stream current to wash away much of the fine matrix.

The question most frequently asked about the washing operation concerns the loss of tiny specimens through the screens. Specimens do go through the screens, sometimes in large numbers. A balance must be achieved between the rate of recovery of all specimens and the rate of loss of tiny specimens. Both rates are related to screen mesh size. Frequently it is possible to estimate the number of tiny teeth which are passing through the screens by comparing the number actually recovered to the number that might be expected, judging from the number of jaws collected. The loss is generally not serious. A mesh finer than that of window screen (eighteen wires per inch) is unnecessary for the recovery of virtually all vertebrate and molluscan fossils. Finer mesh is necessary for the consistent recovery of ostracods, charophyte zygospores, snail eggs, and the smallest isolated vertebrate teeth, but the use of finer mesh generally results in an unacceptable reduction in the amount of matrix that can be processed in the field. A fine strainer downstream is sometimes necessary to catch small floating shells which have passed through the screens of the washing boxes. If 100 percent of the fossils contained in a small amount of matrix must be recovered, it is best to process the matrix in the laboratory. Other details of washing-box construction are subject to wide variation, but a design that has proved to work well is described at the end of this paper. If carefully constructed, washing equipment will last for at least three or four field seasons—that is, for about six to eight months of continuous operation. The major kinds of damage to the boxes are two: torn screens and split side boards. Wide runners will prevent tears at the edges of the screen bottoms, but sharp rocks on the bottom of the stream frequently puncture the screens if the boxes are loaded heavily, especially if the screens are old. Breakage to the side boards results from a natural tendency to split, coupled with excessive horizontal stress. Such breakage can be reduced by treating the wood with clear wood preservative. The side boards can be cleated when they split, or cleats can be nailed vertically across the grain of the boards at the time of original construction. When a large number of boxes of varying ages are in operation, about one percent of them will need repairs each day. Repairs should be made within a reasonable time in order to return broken boxes to useful work, but it is advisable to schedule repairs for a time when other work is light, such as immediately after afternoon thunder showers.

Enough washing equipment should be on hand so that lack of equipment never becomes the reason for temporary halts. The amount of equipment necessary for this varies with the number of crew members available, the type of matrix being washed, the distance between the quarry and the washing site, the quantity of overburden to be removed at the collecting site, the field funds available, and so forth. Equipment is less expensive than manpower, however, and a small crew working with a large amount of equipment is much to be preferred over a large crew without enough. If all concentrates are to be sorted in the field, the ratio of the number of boxes to the number of crew members should be kept at about twenty-five to one. If little or no sorting is planned beyond that necessary to check on productivity, the ratio should be approximately fifty to one.

A large number of burlap sacks should be on hand so that the collection and storage of matrix can be done at any time. Matrix should be placed in burlap sacks at the site, to be carried by hand to a vehicle, but collectors should keep in mind that placing more than 50 or 60 pounds of matrix in one sack may result in serious back injuries. At a large collecting site it may be desirable to tag certain sacks, giving detailed locality information. The contents can then be kept segregated, and a close check on productivity of various parts of the quarry can be maintained. If fossils are so abundant that checking of this sort is unnecessary, it may be questionable whether washing itself is necessary. Only a small part of a site should be excavated at any one time.

The matrix should be collected in large chunks, unless it needs to be dried prior to washing, to help the preservation of material that is associated. When the matrix is placed in a washing box in the water, it should be allowed to soak before it is agitated. The period of time necessary varies: large chunks take longer than small ones, and clays take longer than sands or silts. Massaging clay lumps or scrubbing matrix against screens can cause irreparable damage to the contained fossils.

Some fossiliferous sites are water-saturated, either because of recent rains or a high water table. In some humid areas night dews produce as much moisture as a light shower. Wet matrix has already expanded and will therefore not expand much more when placed again in water. It is therefore necessary to process dry matrix only.

Generally one is forced to use the stream closest to the source of fossils in order to minimize the time necessary to transport matrix, but if there is a choice, a permanent, small stream is preferable to a river or an intermittent stream. A small stream will have a local drainage which can be kept in view, thus reducing the chances of an unexpected flood which might carry away valuable fossils and equipment. It is advisable to determine whether there is a dam upstream. Water from small dams is frequently released for irrigation purposes downstream, and resulting floods have carried away equipment and fossils in the driest of weather! If a large quantity of matrix is to be washed, it is necessary to determine whether muddy water downstream will do any damage. Rapid flow or varying water level is to be avoided. If there is no flow at all, the boxes may be washed in pools, but the stream bottom will become muddy at the washing site, and the screens will become fouled unless racks are used to hold them off the bottom. Racks are not practical as a rule, especially in a large operation. Intermittent streams can be dammed with burlap sacks filled with clay, sand, and rocks. When the bottom of the resulting pool is fouled with mud, the dam can be moved to allow the current to remove accumulated mud, thus providing a renewed rocky or sandy surface for the boxes to rest upon.

As soon as a box has been agitated and no more material will pass through the screen, it should be removed from the water and the contents dried. If immediate reuse of the box is necessary, the wet contents may be dumped onto absorbent canvas drying tables, but in most cases it is preferable to dry the concentrate in the same box in which it was washed. Breakage and drying time are thereby diminished. If wet burlap sacks are placed on the stream bank, and boxes temporarily placed there when processed, the screens will not be fouled with mud before the boxes are stacked for drying. Fouled screens will prevent free air circulation and will therefore delay drying of the concentrate. Boxes set out to dry may be arranged in a series of rows facing the sun, each leaning on the row behind it and each row containing one more box than the previous one, so that a triangular array results. The whole array should be directed towards the point where the sun will be at midway. The number of boxes in such an array should be kept to less than about fifty. If the number is larger, access to dry boxes will be difficult and the available space for drying will be used inefficiently.

Manipulation of clay-bearing concentrates while they are drying will result in "balling" and will therefore obscure or damage valuable fossils and delay completion of drying. Most fossils are easily damaged when wet, but become markedly more durable when dry.

Drying time varies with humidity, air temperature, availability of direct sunlight, matrix type, and the amount of concentrate remaining in each box. The last of these variables is subject to control at the time the box is loaded. Optimum results are obtained when the amount of concentrate remaining in a box is a layer one-quarter of an inch thick or less. If the concentrate consists mainly of nodules, the layer may be somewhat thicker. If drying time is thus minimized, two complete cycles of washing and drying can be accomplished with the same equipment each day. More matrix can be processed in this way than by overloading boxes and processing them only once a day.

When completely dry, the concentrate can be sorted, stored for future sorting, or washed a second time. With certain deposits considerable residue remains in each box even after agitation. Vigorous agitation may damage any fossils contained. For this reason it is frequently preferable to dry the residue in the box in which it was washed and then, when it is thoroughly dry, either recycle the box or dump the contents into a special large tray for rewashing. Before any box is dumped its contents should be carefully inspected for associated material, because associations may be lost when the contents of two or more boxes are dumped into a single rewashing tray. Generally rewashing involves little extra effort, but it substantially reduces the amount of concentrate to be sorted by hand. The ratio of rewashing trays to washing boxes may be as high as 1:10, depending on the nature of the matrix being processed. A shallow box 24 by 36 by 6 inches, with wooden sides, a screen bottom, and runners will serve adequately as a rewashing tray. Two short handles diagonally placed across opposite corners are generally better than a single long diagonal handle. The mesh of the screen should be the same as that of the washing boxes.

It is desirable to keep equipment in use at all times, even at night. It is usually not safe to do so at night, however, unless the crew camps at the washing site, which may be uncomfortable because of mosquitos. But if camp can be made at the washing site, the daily schedule should be arranged, if possible, so that matrix soaks in the washing boxes at night and dries in daylight. Drying at night is generally a waste of time. The level of small streams usually rises to a more useful level at night because of decreased evaporation upstream, permitting slightly more efficient soaking. While the boxes are drying in the morning, the crew can obtain more matrix. The number of persons processing matrix can be adjusted so that those remaining at the washing site will run out of work at about the time that the others return with more matrix. It may also be desirable to keep approximately half of the boxes in the water while the rest are drying. Dry boxes may be dumped and reloaded when the wet boxes are removed from the water to dry, which is quivalent to running two washing operations at once and has the advantage of minimizing work stoppages. If the weather is hot and the humidity low it is sometimes possible to run the equipment through two complete washing cycles in one day.

A table should be constructed which will serve as a protection from rain for stored sacks of unsorted concentrate, a buffet when guests come to camp, and a sorting table. The best sorting table is about ten feet long, four feet wide, and has a white canvas top over wood. The canvas should be absorbent, not waterproof, and should be stretched tightly over the flat top and stapled to the sides so that it will not flap up and down in high winds. A tarpaulin should be available to cover the table and any concentrate being sorted on top, in case of sudden rain showers.

Dried concentrate from the rewashing trays or washing boxes can be sorted at any time, but in fair weather at least some of it should be sorted every day as a check on the productivity of the collecting site. No more than one experienced member of the crew need sort, unless the concentrate is very rich or a limited time is available to obtain a fully curated collection. For morale purposes, it is best to rotate personnel at sorting if possible. Unsorted concentrate should be sacked in burlap bags of the highest quality and tagged with the necessary locality data. Sacks of concentrate being stored for future sorting should be kept in a dry place out of the reach of rodents and rainwater. If concentrate is to be stored for more than a week or two or shipped, the sacks should be placed in clean metal 110-pound lard canisters (available at most bakeries) or the equivalent. The canisters should then be marked with the same data that appear on the sack tags.

The best method of sorting is to sit facing the bright sun. In this way it is easy to see the light reflect from enamel and bone surfaces. A minimum of fancy gadgetry should be used while sorting. Anti-sunburn preparations are advisable because sorting personnel are subjected to both direct and reflected sunlight. Dark glasses may be necessary, and some people find magnifying equipment useful. Concentrate should never be sorted in the shade, especially under trees in mottled light. Sorting when the sun is within about fifteen degrees of the horizon is also to be avoided. The most successful way to sort is to spread the concentrate out in a layer one particle thick over a wide area and then sweep the eyes back and forth over it in a definite pattern which covers the area. Then the examined concentrate should be swept off the table, either with the hands or a whisk broom. Experienced crew members can sort rapidly and efficiently in much the same way as a rapid reader scans a page. For a few days inexperienced crew members should save the examined concentrate and have an experienced crew member go through it again. Some inexperienced crew members can learn to sort efficiently in one day; others, never.

## MATERIALS FOR ONE WASHING BOX

*Lumber.* One piece, 1 by 2 by 62 inches, will make two runners, 1 by 2 by 18 inches, and the handle, 1 by 2 by 26 inches.

One piece, 1 by 12 by 33 inches, will make the two sides, 1 by 12 by 16½ inches.

One piece, 1 by 8 by 36 inches, will make the two ends, 1 by 8 by 18 inches.

*Screen.* Galvanized window screen, 28 by 18 inches. Plastic window screen should not be used under any conditions whatever.

*Nails.* Twenty-six resin-coated nails, 2½ or 3 inches long (no. 4 or no. 6 box nails).

*Staples.* Fifty-two short staples. A staple gun usually can be borrowed or rented, but for a large washing operation it is advisable to own one because of the frequent box repairs that become necessary. Staples can usually be purchased in boxes of 5000.

The cost of boxes is constantly increasing, but in 1961 materials purchased to construct a large number of boxes cost approximately $1.30 per box. Lumber costs vary greatly, depending on the location. If enough lumber is purchased at one time, the lumber salesman is usually agreeable to cutting it into the appropriate lengths. Cut lumber for 100 boxes approximately fills a half-ton hauling trailer. Finished lumber is worth the extra cost over unfinished in that there will be fewer splinters and the boxes can be slid past one another more easily during packing for transport.

### CONSTRUCTION OF WASHING BOXES, 18 BY 18 INCHES

1. Cut a roll of galvanized window screen (28 inches wide) into pieces 18 by 28 inches, with a sharp knife against a board. For best results scissors or tin snips should not be used.

2. Overlap about two inches of eighteen-inch screen onto the inside surface of an end board, 1 by 8 by 18 inches, and staple it into place with about six staples, so that the screen will be tight against the end board during later stages of construction. A staple gun and gloves are essential if many boxes are to be made.

3. Nail the end board with screen to the edges of the two side boards, 1 by 12 by 16½, in such a way that the screen is flush with the outside edges of the side boards but does not project farther. Make sure that no knots are present in the lower part of any side board, as they eventually fall out. Use resin-coated nails, driven in at various angles to increase strength. Three nails, one low enough to pass through the screen, will efficiently attach an end board to the upper part of each side board. The handle will prevent the end boards from pulling free.

4. Staple the screen to the edges of each side board, spacing the staples at about 1-inch intervals. Use plenty of staples. The most troublesome damage to boxes during use consists of torn or separated screens. The use of sufficient staples in the original construction will prevent a great deal of grief later on and will prolong the useful life of the box. Cracked wood can be repaired easily, but the repair of torn screens takes a lot of manpower. Do not allow the screen to project beyond the edges of the side board, or personnel will be constantly scratched and cut by the rough edges.

5. Nail on the second end board, completing the frame of the box. Make sure

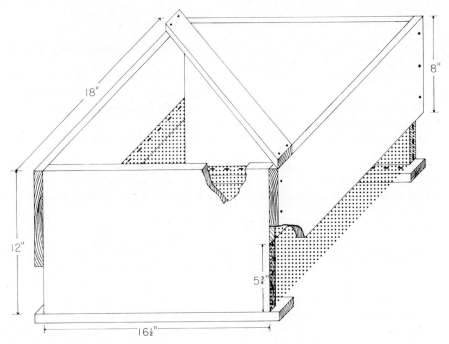

**Fig. 2.** *Design of a washing box.*

that the two side boards are widely separated and the screen is tightly stretched. If it is not tight, matrix will be caught between the top of the screen and the end board.

6. Staple the screen to the inside of the second end board close to the top of the screen. Use plenty of staples.

7. Nail a runner, 1 by 2 by 18 inches, to the bottom of each side board, overlapping each end and making the outside edges flush. This use of an extra-wide runner will result in enough space to staple the bottom of the screen to the top of the runner on the inside of the box. Use lumber with knots for runners, saving the knot-free lumber for handles.

8. Staple the screen to the top part of the runner exposed inside the bottom of the box. This is additional insurance against the tearing of screens from hard use.

9. Nail knot-free handles, 1 by 2 by 26 inches, diagonally across the box from end board to end board. Two nails driven at different angles will suffice. The main purpose of the handles is to hold the box rigidly together.

10. Inspect boxes for projecting nail points and screen edges, slivers, knot holes, split wood, screen not stapled, and staples not driven in all the way.

## REFERENCES

Hibbard, C. W. (1949). Techniques of collecting microvertebrate fossils. Contrib. Mus. Paleont. Univ. Michigan, v. 8, no. 2, p. 7–19, pls. 1–4.

McKenna, M. C. (1960). Fossil Mammalia from the early Wasatchian Four Mile fauna, Eocene of northwest Colorado. Univ. Calif. Publ. Geol. Sci., v. 37, no. 1, p. 1–130, 64 figs.

——— (1962). Collecting small fossils by washing and screening. Curator, v. 5, no. 3, p. 221–235, 6 figs.

Osborn, H. F., and J. L. Wortman (1892). Fossil mammals of the Wasatch and Wind River beds. Collection of 1891. Am. Mus. Nat. History Bull., v. 4, no. 1, art. 11, p. 81–147, 19 figs., 1 pl.

Savage, R. J. G. (1960). Cenozoic mammals in North America. Nature, v. 188, p. 200.

# Problems of Collecting from Fissures

K. A. KERMACK

*University College, London*

Caves and fissures are well known as a source of Pleistocene fossils. Much of our knowledge of post-Tertiary mammals is due to the discovery of animals preserved in them. The Triassic mammals and reptiles found in Great Britain by Dr. W. G. Kühne and his successors have stimulated interest in the possibilities of pre-Pleistocene fissures.

It is not generally realized, perhaps, that remains from such caves and fissures had already made a major contribution to our understanding of the early Tertiary vertebrate faunas of Europe. The famous phosphorites of Quercy, discovered in 1865, are an example of just such a fissure and cave deposit. These fissures formed in the massive Jurassic limestone and were of great extent, individual fissures often being more than thirty yards in length and several yards in breadth. So abundant were the deposits that, at one time, they were worked commercially as a source of phosphatic rock. Their ages range from Upper Eocene to Middle Oligocene.

Excellent examples of older fissures are those of the Mesozoic of the West of England and South Wales. These are Upper Triassic in age and were formed in the Carboniferous Limestone. Like those at Quercy, their ages vary considerably. There are indications of two faunal assemblages of different date. The earlier fauna seems to be coeval with the upper part of the local Keuper Marl; the later fauna seems to be of Lower Rhaetic age. The earlier deposits have yielded a rich fauna of archosaurs and lepidosaurs; the later deposits have yielded squamates and the earliest known mammals. Both are of fresh-water origin like those of Quercy. A third type of fissure deposit occurs in the same area, at Windsor Hill. This formed as a neptunian dyke close offshore and was filled with marine sediments. The invertebrate fauna show the deposit to be Liassic in age. It is from this deposit that Kühne obtained the advanced mammal-like reptile *Oligokyphus*. This type of fissure is uncommon and will not be discussed further.

The Permian infillings at Fort Sill, Oklahoma, are, to my knowledge, the only fissures that have yielded Paleozoic bones. These infillings, of freshwater origin, formed in Ordovician limestone and have yielded a rich fauna of small amphibians and reptiles.

Fissure systems are formed by solution. Thus for them to form at all the country rock must be soluble—that is, it must be a limestone or a dolomite. Furthermore, the rock must be sufficiently mechanically strong to prevent the fissures once formed from collapsing under the weight of the overlying rock. In Britain the rock in which most fissure systems form is the Carboniferous Limestone. This is a hard limestone, often dolomitic, mechanically strong, and well bedded. Extensive cave systems are not, for example, generally found in chalk, which would be too weak to support them.

The detailed mechanism of the formation of caves and fissures is obscure. It seems, however, that they are generally formed *below* the water table, but that they do not become filled with sediments until, for some reason, the water table has fallen below their level (or they have been raised above it). The direction of flow of the water through them may often be determined by examining the fluting and scalloping of their walls. These flutes are generally assymetric in section, the steeper slope facing upstream.

The bones found in the fissure systems often show signs of being rolled, indicating that they have been transported by the stream which flowed through the fissures and filled them with sediment. However, the way in which the bones got into the system in the first place remains rather a mystery. Some of the Welsh fissures from which the mammals have come contain the remains of many thousands of individuals. Here, as may also have been true of the Windsor Hill deposit, the primary deposit was perhaps made by a predator. A similar accumulation of remains of an enormous number of small animals occurs in the Pleistocene caves of Makapan, in the Transvaal. Here it is certain that we are dealing with a predator deposit made by owls.

In deposits where complete articulated skeletons are found, the action of predators seems unlikely. Such remains may be those of cave-dwelling animals or, perhaps more likely, animals washed in by a flood or trapped by falling down a swallet hole. There is so little evidence for all pre-Pleistocene fissures, however, that speculation on this theme has never proved particularly profitable.

All such fissure systems must necessarily have been filled fairly close to the surface. If this surface has been subjected to much subsequent erosion any fissures originally present will have been destroyed. Thus fissure systems containing bone will only be found where an old landscape is being eroded, and the probability of finding them will be greatest close to the edge of the cover which is being removed. This shows up strikingly in the British Mesozoic fissures. Here the Carboniferous Limestone forms just such a fossil landscape, and it is notable how close the bone-bearing fissures lie to the edge of the Mesozoic cover.

The infillings are almost always softer than the surrounding limestone, and hence weather away more rapidly. Thus, in Britain at any rate, only artificial exposures formed by commercial quarrying are worth investigation. In natural exposures either the fissures rapidly become completely cleaned out, forming open caves, or the surface of the fissure-filling breaks down and becomes covered with vegetation. In either event they are no longer accessible to the palaeontologist.

An active quarry, however, is cut back so fast that fissures can appear and vanish in a few days. To make matters worse, the vertebrate fossils may be concentrated—in all probability, in small pockets within the fissure. Thus, the quarries which seem promising must be visited at frequent intervals; occasional visits at long intervals will be much less profitable.

It is also worth emphasizing that a large modern quarry is a dangerous place, and due regard must be taken of this. It should only be entered with the knowledge and consent of the management, and their advice should be sought on the safety precautions necessary.

It is often fairly difficult to find fossils in fissures. Although fissures often contain valuable samples of the small animals that are rarely preserved in conventional deposits, the size of these fossils—often tiny—makes them hard to find. Every year large parties of students study the geology of the classic areas where Mesozoic fissure deposits occur in the Carboniferous Limestone. Not a single piece of bone, however, has ever been discovered by these groups; all finds have been made by vertebrate paleontologists visiting these areas for the specific purpose of searching for fossils in the fissure infillings.

Since the surrounding rock was already consolidated before the fissures were formed, the fossils found within them have been protected from the crushing and distortion which usually affect specimens preserved in bedded deposits. In addition, their degree of mineralization tends to be low. Thus, although the individual specimens are often exquisitely preserved due to the absence of any distortion, the bone itself is generally rather soft.

The preparation of such fragile material involves difficulties. This is the field for chemical methods. The water that percolated through infillings was inevitably highly charged with calcium carbonate, so that the cement of the matrix is almost always calcareous. This breaks down under the action of dilute (10 percent) formic or acetic acid. Formic acid is the more active and is in other ways preferable, but it will sometimes attack the bone or break up fragile bone as a result of the vigorous effervescence. In either case, acetic acid must be used.

Finally it must be emphasized that if an area is suspected to contain fossiliferous fissures they must be searched for—preferably with as few preconceptions as possible. Both the color of the fissure-fillings and of the bone are quite variable. In the Welsh mammal-bearing fissures, adjacent fissures in the same quarry and yielding the same fauna have contained, in one fissure, white bone in a red matrix, and in the other, black bone in a gray matrix. The size of the fissure also fails as a guide. In the same fissure system one finds joints less than a foot wide and caves containing many thousands of tons of filling.

It is not profitable to spend too much time considering geological data and theories which may not be really relevant. The only thing to do is to look for the bone. Nothing else really matters.

# A Biofacies Approach to Collecting Nonmarine Fossils

PAUL TASCH

*Department of Geology, University of Wichita, Wichita, Kansas*

Of all possible living invertebrates that inhabit nonmarine environments, only two large groups are frequently found as fossils: the Mollusca and the Arthropoda. Among the mollusks are clams and snails; among the arthropods are the branchiopod crustaceans (anostracans, conchostracans, notostracans, and cladocerans), ostracods, xiphosurans, eurypterids, and insects. Vertebrates, chiefly fish and reptiles, are also frequently reported in nonmarine facies (Jones, 1862; Dunbar, 1923, 1924; Henderson, 1935; Scott, 1944; Bradley, 1946; Palmer and Bassett, 1954; Frey, 1960; Beerbower, 1961; Tasch, 1961, 1962a, 1962b, 1962c).

Many of these arthropods and mollusks are encountered in conchostracan-bearing beds. In searching for such beds in Kansas and Oklahoma, a biofacies approach was developed. To illustrate collecting methods using this approach, the Branchiopoda will be referred to as a primary example, although a close study of the available literature indicates that what holds true for Permian branchiopod crustaceans has parallel applications to most of the nonmarine deposits in the rock column.

## A BIOLOGICAL-ECOLOGICAL APPROACH

Nonmarine fossils are found in two ways. The usual way is fortuitous discovery. A more rewarding, if more exacting, way is *deliberate* search at specific localities in certain beds for a particular fossil—for example, a clam shrimp. The first way involves pure chance and rarely permits prediction of where equivalent beds might be located. By contrast, purposeful exploration for nonmarine fossils requires planning and a kind of preview or blueprint of where to look and what to look for.

A planned search for specific nonmarine fossils can be a frustrating task if the collector does not use a biological-ecological approach. A series of questions must be raised and answered *prior* to any successful exploration. What kinds of animals were these? In what habitats did they live? With what floral and faunal associates might one expect to find them? How did they reproduce, molt, and so on?

Fortunately, most fossil mollusks and arthropods found in nonmarine facies have living equivalents. It is therefore possible to derive first-hand biological-ecological data (Ward and Whipple, 1959; Popham, 1961; Reid, 1961).

## CRITICAL LITHOLOGIES AND OTHER LITHIC FEATURES

Fossil conchostracans and other crustaceans, fresh-brackish-water ostracods, and mollusks have frequently been reported from beds of the following lithologies: fine-textured, argillaceous, thin limestones; nodular and lenticular limestones; red, green, gray, and black argillites, including massive, platy, blocky, banded, spotted, laminated, paper-thin, organic, and carbonaceous shales and slates; ferruginous clay; clay-ironstone concretions; evaporitic shales; marls; peat, cannel, and lignite coals.

The occurrence of certain types of beds or characteristics of beds have been found to be good indications of the possible presence of a fresh-brackish-water biofacies, including fossil conchostracans, xiphosurans, ostracods, mollusks, and insects. That is, some of these forms may be found interbedded with, above or below, or contained within, any of the following.

### EVAPORITES

Fossil conchostracans and xiphosurans have been found interbedded with gypsum or on the same bedding planes with salt casts, hopper and gypsum crystals (Tasch, 1961). Fossil anostracans have been reported in association with borate deposits (Palmer, 1954) or may be represented by fecal pellets occurring in the halite facies of ancient lacustrine sediments (Tasch, 1962a).

### CARBONIZED MATERIAL

Fresh-water ostracods occur in Pleistocene peats (Hornibrook, 1955) as well as in shales associated with Permo-Carboniferous and Mesozoic coals (Jones, 1862). Fossil conchostracans are commonly found in the fresh-water facies of Permo-Carboniferous cyclothems (Beerbower, 1961). Permo-Carboniferous carbonized wood zones or beds bearing carbonized leaves, seedcoats, and so on, often contain fossil conchostracans, insects, and other crustaceans, and less frequently, fresh-water mollusks (Tasch, 1962b).

ALGAL REEFS

Permian nonmarine shales occurring above or below algal reefs were found to contain fossil conchostracans. These reefs are restricted and local and indicate either a brackish-water environment or a temporary invasion of a sea over ponds on a coastal swamp. Fresh- to brackish-water ostracods that apparently lived in patches of freshening water on the surface of exposed algal reefs may be found fossilized and incorporated in the sedimentary infilling of the reef rock (Tasch, unpublished data).

INSECT BEDS

Since certain insects frequent the same ponds inhabited by conchostracans, one might expect to find fossil conchostracans in, above, or below insect beds. This is true of Permo-Carboniferous and some Mesozoic fresh-water deposits (Dunbar, 1924; Tasch, 1962a, 1962c). Conversely, fossil conchostracans are often an excellent indication of the presence of fossil insects in the same horizon, or above or below it.

MUDCRACK BEDS

Fossil conchostracans inhabited the marginal areas of temporary ponds, as do their living equivalents. Today such ponds dry up at the end of the season or go through several dry-wet cycles in a single season. The desiccation involved leads to shrinkage along the strandline. Such events are represented in the rock column as argillaceous mudcrack beds. Fossil conchostracans and other fresh-water forms have been found to occur in such beds. In a thickness of one foot, it is possible to identify as many as ten distinct events of desiccation and four to five generations of conchostracans.

SNAIL-OSTRACOD COQUINAS AND CLADOCERAN WINDROWS

Coquinoid assemblages of living mollusks (clams and snails) and ostracods are not uncommon in modern streams or in the marginal areas of ponds and the shallows of lakes. The equivalent assemblages occur in the rock column. Weathered hematitic zones of argillaceous limestones may contain molluscan-ostracod assemblages (Tasch, 1962b). Cladoceran ephippia often pile up along the shores of modern lakes. Equivalent events occurred in the geologic past (Tertiary-Pleistocene) (Frey, 1960; Tasch, 1926b).

CONCRETIONS AND NODULES

Fossil branchiopods and insects are found in lenticular and nodular limestones and clay-ironstone concretions in beds varying in age from Permo-Carboniferous to Tertiary.

COPROLITES AND ORGANIC CHERTS

Fossil conchostracans are known from Mesozoic coelocanth coprolites; other branchiopods as well as fossil arachnids are found in carboniferous cherts of Devonian age. Such cherts will generally occur in a shale sequence with interbedded sandstones; coprolites are usually found in Mesozoic slates.

### FISH AND CLAM BEDS

Fresh-water fish and/or clams are frequent associates of conchostracans in beds of the coal measures (Jones, 1862). Finding fossils of one or the other of these and/or carbonized material should lead one to search on the same horizon for other fresh-water invertebrates.

## MICROSTRATIGRAPHY

The biological-ecological orientation noted earlier aids directly in the field search for fresh-water biofacies. For example, instead of measuring and sampling sections in feet, measurement, and often sampling, is made in inches or millimeters. This is necessary because many fresh-water bodies are of temporary duration, and as a result, many of the inhabitants are *seasonal*. On any given bedding plane, their fossil remains can easily be bypassed by crude sampling. The collector should bear in mind that the search for fresh-water biofacies in any given exposure consists in finding bedding planes that represent *seasons* of time estimated in months, and not millenia (Tasch, 1960; Tasch and Zimmerman, 1961).

## BIOFACIES

No matter what the horizontal extent of an outcrop happens to be, it is essential to study multiple sections or to trace and sample beds laterally. The reason is that many fresh- and brackish-water arthropods (branchiopods, insects, and xiphosurans), as well as mollusks, live in marginal puddles or in the peripheral zone of ponds and lakes. A single columnar section may fail to reveal any fresh-water fossils, no matter how carefully the sampling is carried out. The collector might, for example, be sampling the deeper basin sediments (pond, lake, or river). Only lateral tracing and sampling will disclose marginal biofacies. Two general characteristics of such litho-biofacies must be kept in mind: they are usually very thin units, and they are exceptionally restricted in horizontal extent.

## BULK COLLECTING AND PROCESSING OF SAMPLES

In the search for fresh-water biofacies, one cannot rely on field evidence alone. Failure to locate fresh-water fossils in the field does not signify their absence in all rocks of a given outcrop. Fossil fresh-water mollusks, for example, are often extremely small, and some may be detected only by microscopic examination. It follows that sizable samples from *every* bed in the section should be collected. So-called nonfossiliferous beds, such as massive red shales and evaporites, are not exceptions.

The bulk samples cannot be processed in the usual manner. Acid digestion is not indicated initially. All surfaces of any given sample should be checked *before* the sample is broken down into multiple slices. This initial step often reveals such indications as salt casts, carbonized fragments, fish scales, concretions, and fecal pellets. Successively smaller slices should then be prepared. At each stage, *each* slice should be studied by examining *all* faces, first with a hand lens and then with a binocular microscope, proceeding from low to high power.

When the smallest meaningful slice has been studied without success, then *all* examined slices should be processed by acid treatment. At this stage, one cannot expect to find macrofossils. However, a silicified molluscan fauna and various palynomorphs may be recovered from the residues.

## REFERENCES

Beerbower, J. R. (1961). Origin of cyclothems of the Dunkard Group (Upper Pennsylvanian-Lower Permian) in Pennsylvania, West Virginia, and Ohio. Geol. Soc. America Bull., v. 72, p. 1029–1053, 1 fig.

Bradley, W. H. (1946). Coprolites from the Bridger Formation of Wyoming, their composition and microörganisms. Am. J. Sci., v. 244, p. 215–231.

Dunbar, C. O. (1923). Kansas Permian insects, Part I; The geologic occurrence and the environment of the insects. Am. J. Sci., ser. 5, v. 7, no. 39, p. 171–208.

———— (1924). Part II; *Paleolimulus,* a new genus of Paleozoic Xiphosura with notes on other genera. Am. J. Sci., v. 5, no. 30, p. 443–454.

Frey, D. G. (1960). On the occurrence of cladoceran remains in lake sediment. Natl. Acad. Sci. Proc., v. 46, no. 6, p. 917–920.

Henderson, J. (1935). Fossil non-marine Mollusca of North America. Geol. Soc. America Spec. Paper 3, 268 pp.

Hornibrook, N. de B. (1955). Ostracoda in the deposits of the Pyramid Valley Swamp. Records of the Canterbury Mus., v. 6, p. 267–276.

Jones, T. R. (1862). A monograph on fossil Estheriae. Paleontogr. Soc. (London), 114 pp., pls. 1–5.

Palmer, A. R., and A. M. Bassett (1954). Non-marine Miocene arthropods from California. Science, v. 120, p. 228–229.

Popham, E. J. (1961). Some aspects of life in fresh water. Harvard Univ. Press, 119 pp.

Reid, G. K. (1961). Ecology of inland waters and estuaries. New York, Reinhold, 340 pp.

Scott, H. W. (1944). Permian and Pennsylvanian fresh water ostracods. J. Paleontology, v. 18, no. 2, p. 141–147, pls. 23–24.

Tasch, P. (1960). Microstratigraphy and the search for Permian fresh water biofacies. SEPM-AAPG Program (Atlantic City, N. J.) (abs.) p. 83.

———— (1961). Paleolimnology, Part II: Harvey and Sedgwick Counties, Kansas: stratigraphy and biota. J. Paleontology, v. 35, p. 836–865, pls. 97–98, 6 text-figs.

———— (1962a). Branchiopoda, *in* R. C. Moore (ed.), Treatise on invertebrate paleontology. Kansas Univ. Press. In Press.

——— (1962b). Paleolimnology, Part III: Marion and Dickinson Counties, Kansas: with additional sections in Harvey and Sedgwick Counties: Stratigraphy and Biota. J. Paleontology, v. 37, p. 1233–1251, pls. 172–174, 5 text-figs.

——— (1962c). Vertical extension of midcontinent Leonardian insect occurrences. Science, v. 135, no. 3501, p. 378–379, table 1.

———, and J. R. Zimmerman (1961). Comparative ecology of living and fossil conchostracans in a seven-county area of Kansas and Oklahoma. Univ. of Wichita Bull., Univ. Studies 47, p. 1–14, fig. 1.

Ward, H. B., and G. C. Whipple (1959). Freshwater biology (2nd ed.), W. T. Edmondson (ed.), 1202 pp.

## MECHANICAL METHODS OF PREPARATION

---

*Coordinator:* R. L. LANGENHEIM, JR.

# Serial Grinding Techniques

---

## D. V. AGER

*Imperial College, London*

The techniques described below were developed particularly for the study of the internal structures of brachiopods, and have become more or less standard, especially among European workers on Mesozoic forms. They are equally applicable, however, to many other groups of fossils such as plants, corals, and forams. Almost independently, similar techniques have been used for a long time in the study of vertebrate remains.

The object of the fossil serial grinding techniques is to study internal structures not otherwise visible. Structural characteristics such as the sequence of septal insertion in corals can be studied only by grinding or allied techniques. In the Brachiopoda and some other groups, grinding provides the researcher with a method for studying internal structures of almost any specimen, instead of having to rely on rare miracles of preservation or on the often vain hope of finding silicified examples of the species in which he is interested. In many years of work on British Lower Jurassic brachiopods, I have found few specimens in which it was possible to expose the brachidia by excavating the infilling sediment. Although I found no silicified specimens, the vast majority of the thousands of specimens collected proved completely suitable for serial grinding.

As I have written elsewhere (Ager, 1956a): "Ideally . . . the best technique is the careful exposure of the internal structures by removal of the matrix. This is only occasionally possible . . . due to the nature of the

sediments. Even so, there are limitations, especially in the way of reproduction, and serial sections usually show the structures much more clearly than
do photographs of excavated specimens. In certain structures—notably the
articulation of the valves—sectioning is the only technique possible, as the
valves cannot be separated without breaking the teeth." Some brachiopod
structures that are visible only in transverse section are shown in fig. 1.

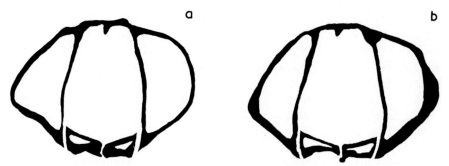

**Fig. 1.** *Transverse sections of the Jurassic rhynchonelloid brachiopod* Cirpa langi
*Ager, showing the structure of the deltidial plates, which could be revealed
only by serial grinding.*

In many ways the serial grinding technique is superior to any other
method in its ease of application, in the information it yields, and in its simple
presentation of the facts. Even the most painstaking and time-consuming
needle dissections do not provide the same sort of information.

It is unfortunate that the specimen (or the greater part of it) is destroyed
in the process of grinding, but the same may be said of most biological
dissections. The destruction is of no practical disadvantage, provided that a
careful record is kept of the original appearance of the specimen (preferably
a plaster cast) and that judgment is used with respect to rare material. In
fact, it is often advantageous; since most museum curators do not like their
specimens destroyed, the investigator is forced to collect his own—to his
greater good as a paleontologist!

It should be noted here that, though these techniques are commonly called
"serial sectioning," they are more correctly called "serial grinding," since the
sections are only the records of successive ground surfaces. True sectioning—
cutting successive thin slices of a specimen—is not usually feasible with
small fossils, since too much is lost in the cutting process. Sectioning may be
effected in a sense, however, by taking cellulose peels more or less continuously throughout a small specimen, in the manner of a biological microtome.

## SELECTION OF SPECIMENS

When selecting specimens for sectioning it is, of course, desirable to find
uncrushed and well-preserved specimens. It is equally important to find speci-

mens filled with a suitable matrix. The most suitable are fine-grained sediments which contrast (after treatment) with the shelly structures. Usually burning is sufficient to bring out this contrast, but fine-grained white limestones (such as chalk) present a special problem (see below). Coarser matrices, such as calcarenite, are less suitable, because delicate internal structures are more likely to be broken, and the lack of uniformity obscures the details, especially photographic reproduction.

The least suitable matrix, though a common one in certain sedimentary environments, is crystalline calcite. It is usually almost impossible to distinguish this from the fossil itself on ground surfaces. Cavities can be filled with plaster or other suitable medium, but when the specimen is completely hollow, the important structures are usually lined with and obscured by calcite crystals. Other mineral fillings are comparatively rare, but may present special problems in connection with heating the specimen (see below) and in grinding (due to their relative hardness).

Ideally, several specimens should be selected, as nearly alike as possible. These may then be sectioned in different directions to permit the removal of the shell by burning, for the study of muscle scars and other features. At least one specimen should be preserved untouched, to be used as a future standard of reference.

## BURNING

The burning technique for studying internal structures in brachiopods was discovered accidentally by an old Burmese roadmender. La Touche (1913), an Indian Geological Survey geologist then working in the North Shan States of Burma, described how he found a "navvy" breaking up blocks of limestone which had been burnt in a kiln, and noted "the fossils falling out of it like kernels of nuts." La Touche then extracted many brachiopods from this very hard limestone by dropping blocks into a fire. Subsequently, these specimens were sent to S. S. Buckman in England for identification. Buckman found that, owing to their harsh treatment, the brachiopods had lost most of their shells and were, in fact, internal molds, though they still retained internal plates, such as dorsal median septa and dental lamellae. These showed clearly because of the calcining of the shelly material, and muscle scars were also often clearly visible as elevated or rough patches on the sediment molds. Buckman was very excited by this discovery and, rather in the manner of Charles Lamb's Chinese discoverer of roast pork, burned much of his own collection of brachiopods to obtain the same effect. Buckman published his results in one of the most important works on Mesozoic Brachiopoda (1918).

As a laboratory technique, simply holding the specimen with tongs in a bunsen flame is usually sufficient. The beak area should be made white hot and the specimen then allowed to cool slowly. Plunging the specimen into cold water is often effective in removing the shell, but this may be disastrous.

It is usually better to remove the calcined shell gently (after cooling) with a stiff brush.

For specimens which are to be serially ground the burning technique is also used, but the shell is not removed. The object here is to provide a contrast between the whitened shell structures and the darkened sediments inside. If this is not done, it is often difficult to distinguish two, or to see the more delicate structures at all.

Care should be taken when burning specimens in this way, since certain infillings (notably iron pyrites) tend to burst violently on heating. Moreover, the specimens often retain heat longer than expected and should not be mounted in plaster blocks or other media until completely cool.

In certain sediments, such as the white chalk of the European Cretaceous, it is almost impossible to distinguish shell from infilling, even after burning. A technique discovered by E. F. Owen (1955) is fairly successful with such matrices. He suggested boiling the specimen in a 40 percent sugar solution before burning. The sediment takes up the solution more readily than the fossil, and so blackens to a greater extent. The success of this technique depends on the permeability of the sediment, and I have found that repeated treatment is often necessary.

## PREPARING THE SPECIMEN FOR GRINDING

Before grinding any specimen, it is vitally important to make a plaster cast as a permanent record of its external appearance. Alternatively, or in addition, photographs should be taken of it from several directions.

If the ground surfaces are to be drawn or photographed directly, and the specimen is suitably preserved, it should be burned and allowed to cool slowly, so that shell does not flake away.

When completely cool, the specimen should be mounted in a plaster block. This is best done by mounting the specimen on a small cone of Plasticine, surrounded by "walls" of plasticine or other material, and then gently pouring in plaster of paris. The plaster should only just cover the top of the specimen. Great care must be taken with the orientation of the fossil, since this will very much affect the subsequent appearance of the ground surfaces.

With brachiopods many misleading and apparently contradictory sections have been published because of slight differences in original orientation. I have argued elsewhere (Ager, 1956a) that the most logical and satisfactory orientation for a brachiopod is with the posterior part of the lateral commissure vertical (see fig. 2).

It is useful to color the plaster of paris by mixing in a small blob of poster paint. This provides a clear contrast with the shell for drawing or photographing. Red seems to be the most satisfactory color.

Instead of plaster, some paleontologists use a transparent resin mount (such as Marco Resin). This is advantageous when the specimen is distorted or obscured with sediment, since the orientation can be changed during the grinding. The disadvantages are the longer time required for mixing and setting, and the much slower grinding due to the relative hardness of the resin.

The block is mounted on a metal disk, which forms part of all the apparatuses described, by means of ceresine wax or other suitable adhesive. If the investigator marks the block to show the orientation of the specimen inside, he will know what to expect when the fossil begins to appear.

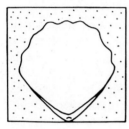 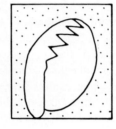

**Fig. 2**

*Standard orientation used for brachiopods when mounted in a plaster block for serial grinding. The posterior part of the lateral commissure is vertical.*

## GRINDING

The serial grinding technique appears to have been introduced independently, and at different times, to the specialists in different groups of fossils. Sollas and Sollas (1913) applied it to the study of fossil vertebrate skulls, and it has since been used with very great success by Stensiø (1927) in his classic work on the skull of *Cephalaspis*.

Its most famous application to invertebrate groups has perhaps been in Kozlowski's study of early graptolites. It was under his direction that Wisniewska (1932) first applied serial grinding as a standard method in the study of fossil brachiopods. This was then introduced to the English-language literature by Muir-Wood (1934), and since then it has become a standard technique in the study of Mesozoic brachiopods, though it has only more recently been used on Paleozoic forms.

Several different apparatuses have been designed for serial grinding, the chief problem being the preservation of a constant orientation throughout, but there is little point in describing them all in detail.

The apparatus that I use most is the Croft Parallel Grinder, designed by the late W. N. Croft of the British Museum (Natural History) and described by him (1950). It consists essentially of a cylindrical micrometer mounted on a triangular platform (fig. 3). This is rotated by means of ball bearings on the grinding surface. The specimen on its metal disc is mounted on the underside of the micrometer and arranged so that the top of the plaster block is just in contact with the grinding paste below. Fine-grained emery powder is mixed into a soft paste with water and placed on a thin plate made of zinc, or other metal, below the grinder; this in turn is secured by adhesive tape to a sheet of plate glass mounted in a block of concrete for rigidity. The grinding

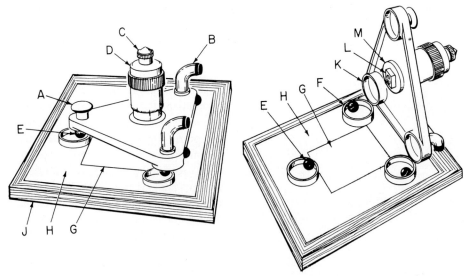

**Fig. 3.** *Croft parallel grinder. Left: in the grinding position; right: when raised to examine the specimen. A: lifting knob. B: bracket supports. C: milled-headed rod screwed into specimen disk. D: micrometer. E: steel balls. F: aluminum rings. G: metal sheet. H: plate glass. J: solid base. K: cups. L: specimen. M: specimen disk. [Reproduced with permission of the manu-facturers, Cutrock Engineering Company of Plowman's Yard, 35 Ballards Lane, London, N. 3.]*

paste is best confined by means of a low Plasticine wall to prevent it from spreading into the cups and wearing away the ball bearings.

The ground surface is examined at short intervals (0.1 mm is suitable for average-size brachiopods) and is drawn or photographed if it shows some significant difference from the previous record. There is no point in recording the surface at regular intervals, since much more detail is required at some levels (e.g., passing through the cardinal process) than at others (e.g., passing through long brachidia).

## OTHER SERIAL GRINDING INSTRUMENTS

Several other apparatuses have been described for this purpose, but only three need be mentioned here. (See the references at the end of this section.) Croft (1953) described a simplified version of his own instrument, which dispensed with the expensive micrometer and replaced it with a pile of plastic washers located between the weighted specimen holder and the base plate (see fig. 4). The washers are removed one at a time as grinding proceeds, and the thickness of specimen ground away is determined simply by measuring the thickness of the washers.

Keyes (1962) described a new instrument for serial grinding which incorporated a micrometer but dispensed with the base plate. In his first description of his parallel grinding instrument, Croft (1950) showed how the instrument could be mechanized by attaching it to an electric motor. In practice, the labor of grinding is so small compared with that of photographing or drawing the sections that mechanization is hardly worthwhile. Recently, however, Jefferies, Adams, and Miller (1962) briefly described an ingenious new machine which not only grinds specimens mechanically, but also automatically photographs the ground surface at fixed intervals. The grinding is done on a revolving plate glass wheel, and the photographs are taken through this wheel with a 35-mm cinecamera set at single exposures. A thin film of water on the surface of the wheel counteracts the frosting effect of the abrasive. The mechanism is too complicated to explain here in detail (besides, the present model is only a prototype), but the sequence of events is as follows:

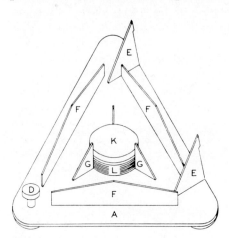

**Fig. 4**

*Croft parallel grinder (simplified version). A: base plate. D: lifting knob. E: bracket supports. F: stiffeners. G: stops. K: lead weight. L: pile of annular shim washers. [Reproduced with permission from the* Annals and Magazine of Natural History.]

1. The motor starts and the wheel rotates a few times to remove surplus water.
2. The micrometer winds on.
3. The specimen is ground down $100\mu$.
4. A jet of water washes the surface of the wheel.
5. The motor stops, the wheel stops, the water stops.
6. The camera operates and the film is wound on another frame.

Then the motor starts again and the cycle is repeated. As a result of this completely automatic procedure, a specimen may be ground away in a matter of minutes instead of the hours taken by the normal methods. The only apparent drawback is that, because the machine is automatic, one cannot stop it to examine critical structures when they appear, nor can one take cellulose peels. With the ordinary method it is often necessary to examine particular features with a binocular microscope, especially when one is looking for boundaries between structures in recrystallized specimens.

## CELLULOSE PEELS

Cellulose peels are being used more and more in certain branches of paleontology, especially in paleobotany, and in that connection they are discussed elsewhere in this handbook. It is desirable, however, to say something here about their use as an intrinsic part of the serial grinding technique.

One of the most frequently heard criticisms of serial grinding is that it involves the destruction of the specimen. This is not the case if thin peels of the actual fossil are taken at every significant stage, and it is therefore particularly desirable to take them when rare material is involved. The other great advantage of cellulose peels is that fine structures are preserved and may be studied by transmitted light, as are thin sections. Cellulose peels of well-preserved brachiopod specimens may reveal details of shell growth which are impossible to study by any other method (fig. 5).

The procedure to be followed when peels are to be taken is exactly as outlined above except that the specimen must not be burnt, since this prevents good peels from being taken and obliterates any microscopic structures which might have been preserved. The consequent lack of contrast makes it much

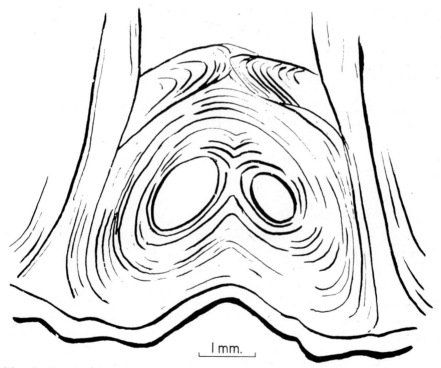

**Fig. 5.** *Drawing from a cellulose peel of part of the beak region of the Devonian spiriferoid brachiopod* Spinocyrtia iowensis (*Owen*) *from Vinton, Iowa, showing growth lines within the shell.*

more difficult to observe changes during grinding, and it is usually necessary to record the appearance of the fossil more frequently.

When the specimen is removed from the grinder it is plunged into dilute hydrochloric acid for about 10 seconds, gently washed, and allowed to dry. This etches the ground surface of the fossil, bringing it into low relief.

In my work, I put a few drops of acetone on the etched surface and allow it to spread out evenly over the exposed part of the fossil. A piece of cellulose acetate sheet, just larger than the fossil, is then applied gently to the surface. One edge should be brought into contact first and then the rest lowered gently but firmly, excluding air bubbles. It should then be pressed down firmly without any lateral movement.

Various materials are used, and have been used, for making peels, but I have found that thin cellulose sheeting, such as that used as a transparent wrapping or as a lining for specimen trays is particularly suitable. Thin sheets are desirable (although liable to cockle), because the thicker varieties show dark parallel lines under the microscope. Thicknesses of 0.005 to 0.01 inch are commonly used.

After the cellulose has been in contact with the fossil for about 5 to 10 minutes it is peeled off carefully from one corner and should take with it a perfect record of the fossil surface. Peels are fragile and will soon curl up; it is desirable to mount them as soon as possible between glass and to indicate on a label the precise serial section from which each was taken.

## METHODS FOR RECORDING SERIAL SECTIONS

Generally speaking, drawn outlines of internal structures are preferable to photographs, since they omit irrelevant details such as fortuitous cracks and variations in matrix. Moreover, it is rarely possible or desirable to publish large numbers of photographs of ground surfaces, and the drawings might as well be made sooner rather than later. Four principal methods have been used:

### DIRECT PHOTOGRAPHY

The ground surface, with suitably contrasting matrix and mounting medium, can be photographed in the ordinary way with a vertical camera. As an economy measure, in view of the large number of photographs required, direct prints may be made on sensitized paper to dispense with the need for negatives. The substitution of white for black and vice versa is of no importance (and is, in fact, the normal method of representation); for most groups, the reversal of the image, left for right, is of no importance.

### THE PARKES-LAPWORTH MICROSCOPE

This was designed for drawing graptolites; an illustration by Lapworth appeared in Elles and Wood's "Monograph of British Graptolites" (Elles and

Wood, 1901, p. 3). It consists of a horizontal low-power microscope with a camera lucida attachment. The specimen is held on a mechanical stage which can readily be adjusted when the whole specimen cannot be contained in a single field of view. The mechanical stage is mounted on a universal joint which can be adjusted to bring the surface of irregularly shaped specimens normal to the microscope.

This instrument has proved very convenient to use with the parallel grinder, since the specimen, on its mounting disk, can be clipped directly onto the stage. With the usual 3-inch objective, a magnification of about 14× is obtained, which is suitable for small- to average-size brachiopods. For larger specimens the barrel of the microscope is refitted farther back and a 4-inch objective used, giving a magnification of about 7×. With larger specimens, however, changing the field of view tends to introduce slight errors (as well as optical distortion), in which case the apparatus discussed below is more convenient to use.

### SIMPLE IMAGE-PROJECTOR

This was designed primarily to deal with large specimens and for rapid recording. An early simple version was illustrated in Ager (1956a, p. vi), and an improved version has since been developed. The specimen on its disk is attached to a wing bolt at the top of the apparatus and illuminated from below. A picture of the ground surface is projected through a lens into a light-proof box equipped with a black cloth hood, where it can be drawn or recorded directly on sensitized paper. The box is also equipped with a shutter and a safety light. The picture is focused by means of an adjustable counterweight attached to the specimen (see fig. 6). This apparatus was designed to give a lower magnification than the Parker-Lapworth microscope.

Muir-Wood (1953) described a similar apparatus for this purpose, but in this the specimen was mounted on a horizontal screw shaft for focusing, and the light system incorporated a prism to project the picture downward for drawing.

### CELLULOSE PEELS AS NEGATIVES

When cellulose peels are taken of ground surfaces, these may be placed between sheets of glass in an ordinary photographic enlarger, either to make direct prints or for drawing.

## RECONSTRUCTIONS FROM SERIAL SECTIONS

Many brachiopod specialists feel that serial grinding should be used only as a means to an end, the end being to reconstruct the original appearance of the shell. In my opinion this is rarely necessary or even desirable, since the objective record of the sections is far preferable to the subjectivity of the reconstruction. Furthermore, the reconstruction is often just as inadequate

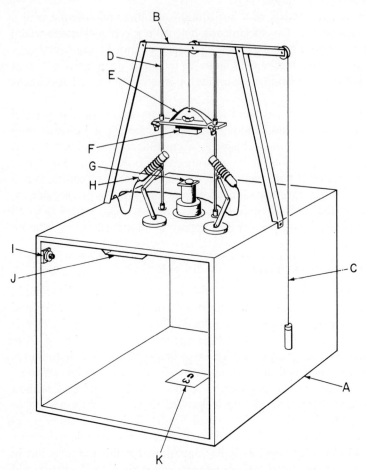

**Fig. 6.** *Simple drawing/photographic apparatus for recording serial sections. A: light-proof box (sides 20 inches long). B: frame with pulleys. C: cord with counterweight. D: guide rods. E: movable carriage with locking nuts. F: specimen on specimen disc attached by wing nut. G: adjustable lens. H: spotlight (controls not shown). I: switch for safety light in far corner. J: slide shutter. K: image. The black cloth hood, which covers the front of the box (and the operator), is omitted for clarity.*

for the presentation of certain salient features as the photograph of the dissected specimen.

The chief value of reconstruction is as a simplification for general use (especially for teaching) and as a personal discipline of mental clarification about the structures studied. This is particularly desirable when complex structures are involved.

When the fossil studied is large or considerably magnified, great use can be made of the technique of cutting out and putting together sheets of plastic or wax in the form of the successive sections, or tracing these sections on transparent sheets of appropriate thickness. This was done very effectively, for example, by Sollas and Sollas (1913) in reconstructing a reptile skull, and by St. Joseph (1937) in reconstructing brachiopods.

Alternatively, graphic reconstructions can be produced simply (Muir-Wood, 1934). A reconstruction of the interior of the dorsal valve of a long-looped terebratuloid was produced by redrawing the sections on a skewed grid (Ager, 1956b) (fig. 7). The brachiopod was viewed, as it were, turned slightly sideways and downward, the same as a clinographic projection of a crystal model! The amount of skew must, of course, vary according to the structures it is required to present. The successive skew sections are superimposed on each other at the correct intervals—that is, the interval between the sections multiplied by the magnification.

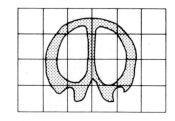

a

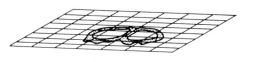

b

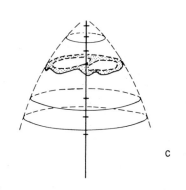

c

**Fig. 7**

*Method for reconstructing clinographic projections of a brachiopod from serial sections. (Top) Serial section with superimposed transparent grid. (Middle) Serial section transferred to tracing paper placed over a skew grid. (Bottom) Successive skew sections superimposed by means of a central guide line on which the midpoints are spaced according to the grinding intervals.*

## REFERENCES

Ager, D. V. (1956a). A monograph of the British Liassic Rhynchonellidae, Part 1. Palaeontogr. Soc. Mon., p. 1–50, pls. I–IV.

———— (1956b). Some new Liassic Terebratuloids. Proc. Geol. Assoc., v. 67, p. 1–14, pl. 1.

Buckman, S. S. (1918). The Brachiopoda of the Namyau beds, Northern Shan States, Burma. Palaeont. Indica, N.S., v. 3, no. 2, 299 pp., 21 pls.

Croft, W. N. (1950). A parallel grinding instrument for the investigation of fossils by serial sections. J. Paleont., v. 24, p. 693–698.

———— (1953). A simplified parallel grinding instrument. Ann. Mag. Nat. History, ser. 12, v. 6, p. 915–918.

Elles, G. L., and E. M. R. Wood (1901). A monograph of British graptolites, Part I. Paleontogr. Soc. Mon., p. 1–54, pls. I–IV.

Jefferies, R. P. S., J. B. Adams, and R. C. Miller (1962). Automatic serial sectioning machine for fossils. Nature, v. 193, no. 4821, p. 1166–1167.

Keyes, I. W. (1962). A new instrument for the serial grinding of invertebrate fossils. New Zealand J. Geol. Geophys., v. 5, p. 46–54.

La Touche, T. H. De (1913). Geology of the Northern Shan States, Part 2. Geol. Survey India Mem., v. 39, p. 1–379.

Muir-Wood, H. M. (1934). On the internal structure of some Mesozoic Brachiopoda. Roy. Soc. (London) Phil. Trans., v. 505, p. 511–567, pls. 62–63.

———— (1953). Techniques employed in grinding and illustrating serial transverse sections of fossil brachiopods. Ann. Mag. Nat. History, ser. 12, v. 6, p. 919–922.

Owen, E. F. (1955). The use of sugar solution in the differentiation of the internal structures of Upper Chalk brachiopods. Proc. Geol. Assoc., v. 66, p. 369–370.

St. Joseph, J. K. (1937). On *Camarotoechia borealis* (von Buch 1834, ex. Schlotheim 1832). Geol. Mag., v. 74, p. 33–48.

Sollas, I. B. J., and Sollas, W. J. (1913). A study of the skull of a *Dicynodon* by means of serial sections. Roy. Soc. (London) Phil. Trans. v. 204, p. 201–225, pl. 17–18.

Stensiø, E. A. (1927). The Downtonian and Devonian vertebrates of Spitsbergen. Skrift, Svalbard Nordishavet, v. 12, p. 1–391, 112 pls.

Wisniewska, M. (1932). Les Rhynchonellidés du Jurassique sup. de Pologne. Palaeont. Polonica, v. 2, p. 1–71, pl. I–VI.

# The Peel Technique

WILSON N. STEWART, THOMAS N. TAYLOR

*Botany Department, University of Illinois, Urbana*

The innovation of the peel technique has had a profound effect on at least one branch of paleontology—in paleobotany, where calcified or dolomitic petrifactions called coal balls are used as the principal materials. Although not as extensively used, modifications of the peel technique have also been employed by Appel (1933), Fenton (1935), and others in sedimentology, for paleontological studies of corals (fig. 1,*a*), brachiopods, and vertebrate fossils.

No matter whether the material is coal ball or coral the basic steps of the

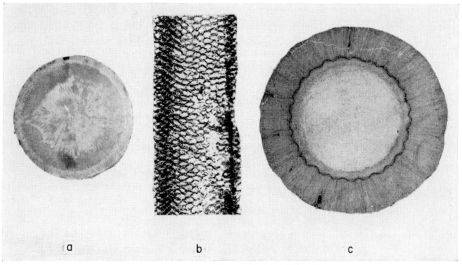

**Fig. 1.** (*a*) *Transverse section of a coral, showing internal structure.* (*b*) *Longitudinal section through a tracheid in the vascular system of a large Paleozoic tree fern.* (*c*) *Transverse section, showing wood and pith of the arborescent lycopod* Sigillaria.

technique are the same. The technique involves treating a prepared surface with acid, applying a thin coat of plastic in a liquid form or as a sheet of cellulose acetate, allowing the film of plastic material to dry, then removing the film, or peel, from the acid-treated surface.

## THE DEVELOPMENT OF THE TECHNIQUE

The use of a plastic material (collodion) seems to have been suggested as early as 1906, but the first information on its use was published in a paper by Nathorst (1908), who described how collodion films could be used to obtain epidermal structures from compression fossils of leaves. Twenty years later great improvements in the technique were made by Walton (1928), Walton and Koopmans (1928), and Koopmans (1929), who introduced the idea of etching the prepared surface of the fossil before applying the liquid plastic (a nitrocellulose compound). The fossils they used were dolomitic coal balls containing petrified plant fossils. The technique was soon adopted by other paleobotanists (Leclerq, 1928; Noé, 1930; and Krick, 1932), all of whom used it to study the internal structure of plants preserved in calcified and dolomitic coal balls (fig. 1,*b,c*).

The principle of the technique is beautifully simple and is a tremendous improvement over the tedious, material-wasting, time-consuming technique of making hand-ground thin sections. A coal ball has two components, a matrix of inorganic mineral [generally $CaCO_3$, $CaMg(CO_3)_2$, $FeS_2$] and embedded organic plant remains. The prepared surface of the coal ball is treated with weak hydrochloric acid. This dissolves a small amount of the inorganic material, but does not affect the organic plant remains. After removal of the matrix—a matter of seconds—the plant material stands in relief on the acid-treated (etched) surface. A liquid plastic is applied to the treated surface and allowed to dry. While liquid, the plastic spreads over the surface, embedding the organic material from which the rock matrix has been removed. As the plastic hardens into a film (peel) the organic material becomes firmly embedded in it. After hardening, the peel and the included plant material are pulled from the rock surface (fig. 2, bottom). In essence, the plant material has been transferred from rock to a transparent plastic film, and in this form it can be studied in the same way as are sections of modern plant materials cut from paraffin blocks.

**Fig. 2**

*Steps involved in making peels. (Top) Preparing to make a poured peel. (Middle) Placing sheet of cellulose acetate film in acetone on inclined surface of coal ball. (Bottom) Removing a peel.*

The early investigators encountered difficulties in the peel technique, especially with the liquid plastics they used. The plastics would wrinkle upon drying, there would be bubbles in the finished peels. Walton (1930) overcame both of these difficulties by substituting gelatin for nitrocellulose. Gelatin, however, has other disadvantages; it is brittle and less permanent. What was needed was a "plasticizer" and a solvent for the more permanent nitrocellulose plastic that would allow bubbles to break on the surface of the peel before drying into the film. Graham (1933) provided the solution to both of these difficulties by adding castor oil as a plasticizer and butyl acetate as the solvent. Final modifications in the preparation of a liquid plastic for making peels were made by Darrah (1936). His formula, which is still widely used in making poured peels is:

| | |
|---|---|
| Parlodion (Mallinckrodt) | 28 grams |
| Butyl acetate (commercial) | 250 cc |
| Amyl alcohol | 30 cc |
| Xylol | 10 cc |
| Castor oil | 3 cc |
| Ether | 3 cc |

It will take at least a week for the parlodion to dissolve and for a usable solution to be produced. The most recent improvement in the peel technique, as it is used in most paleobotanical laboratories, was introduced by Lacey (1953). It is known as the cellulose acetate sheet technique, in which sheets of acetate are substituted for the liquid plastic. The chief advantage in using sheets of cellulose is the great amount of time saved. If the poured liquid plastic is used, at least 6 hours are required for the films to dry. A peel can be made in 20 minutes with a sheet of cellulose acetate. When a number of serial sections must be produced in a limited time, the cellulose sheet technique is obviously preferred. If fine details of cell structure (pits in tracheids, cell contents, wall structure, and so on) are desired, use the poured liquid plastic.

## MAKING POURED OR LIQUID PEELS

The basic equipment and materials required for this technique are:

Cut-off saw with diamond or Carborundum blade.
Lapidary wheel.
Plate glass, 18 by 24 inches.
Hard-rubber developing tray, 18 by 24 inches.
Wooden box or tray at least 24 by 30 by 3 inches.
Coarse white sand or washed gravel to fill box with a layer 2 inches deep.
Small carpenters' string level, 2 to 3 inches long with an aluminum case.
Carborundum (100- and 600-mesh).
Liquid plastic (see formula above).
Acetone in a squeeze bottle.
HCl (5 percent).

The equipment needed to make peels from cut specimens is shown in fig. 3.

### GRINDING AND POLISHING

After the specimen has been cut the saw marks are removed on the lapidary wheel using 100-mesh Carborundum. To finish the cut surface to a satin smoothness the specimen is hand polished on the glass plate. The 600

Carborundum is used for this. It is desirable to get as flat a surface as possible. If the same glass plate is used too long for polishing, or if a groove is worn in the lapidary wheel, the surface of the specimen will be slightly rounded. This will result in a peel with thick edges and a thin center that will tear when the peel is removed.

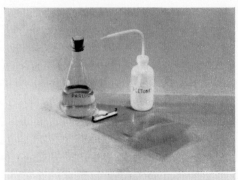

**Fig. 3**

*General view of equipment and materials needed to make peels. (Top) Acetone, liquid parlodion, string level, and cellulose acetate sheet. (Bottom) Glass plate, etching tray, 100- and 600-mesh Carborundum, and 5 percent hydrochloric acid.*

ETCHING

If the specimens are calcified or dolomitized 5 percent HCl is used to treat the surface; silicified specimens require concentrated HF. The use of this corrosive acid requires plastic dishes, a fume hood, and great care in handling, to avoid contact with the skin.

When 5 percent HCl is used it is placed in the rubberized developing trays to a depth of $\frac{1}{4}$ inch. A few grains of coarse white sand or small pebbles are placed in the bottom of the tray to hold the specimen off the bottom while the prepared surface is etched.

Etching time will vary considerably, depending on the material. Some dolomitic specimens from England and Europe may require as much as 2 or 3 minutes. Calcified specimens from Illinois can be etched in 20 to 30 seconds, whereas silicified specimens in HCl may take several minutes. In any event, the investigator will have to do a little experimenting to find the correct etching time for his material. *Never smear an etched surface with your finger or any other object that will smudge the prepared surface.*

WASHING

As soon as the etching is complete the acid must be washed from the treated surface. This can be done by running a stream of water over the surface. A gentle stream should be used so that the organic material is not washed from the surface.

### DRYING

Acetone from a plastic squeeze bottle can be sprayed on the etched surface to hasten drying. If available, compressed air can be used as long as the air stream is not too strong. Air-drying, without trying to speed up the process, is probably best.

### POURING

The specimen is placed in the sand or gravel box. The prepared surface must be made perfectly level. This is done with the aid of the string level, which, because it is light, can be placed directly on the etched surface. Care must be taken not to drag the level over the etched surface.

The parlodion mixture is poured directly on the leveled, etched surface (fig. 2, top). After a little practice the technician will soon learn the right amount to pour on the surface. There should be just enough to cover the surface, so that it forms a meniscus at the edge of the specimen and does not run over the edges.

### DRYING THE PEEL

To reduce shrinkage of the peel to a minimum it should be allowed to dry on the surface of the specimen for at least 12 hours. Peels may appear to be dry long before this time is up, but they will show as much as 10 percent shrinkage if they are removed too soon.

### REMOVING THE PEEL

The peel will have to be loosened at the edges with a single-edged razor blade or scalpel. Then the peel can be pulled off with the fingers (fig. 2, bottom). If a tear develops run a razor blade beneath the peel to loosen it beyond the point of the tear. Some peels stick to the specimen so tightly that they have to be removed with a razor blade. This is especially true if specimens contain much pyrite.

When the peel has been removed the specimen can be polished lightly once again and prepared for another section. Thus, it is possible to prepare serial sections at intervals as small as $40\mu$. This allows one to study the finest detail and reconstruct the fossilized structure with great accuracy.

### CARE OF PEELS

With ordinary treatment a peel is almost indestructible. It can be bent, folded, washed in water, and cut with scissors to remove any desired parts. Numbers or notes can be written directly on them, and interesting specimens can be circled with colored pencil. Peels are generally stored in envelopes with the investigators notes written on the front. It is easy to file envelopes and build a collection of peel specimens. I have peels in my collection, made according to this technique, that are 25 years old. They show no sign of deterioration.

## MAKING CELLULOSE ACETATE SHEET PEELS

All of the materials listed for making poured or liquid peels are required except for the liquid plastic and carpenter's level. Cellulose acetate sheet is used in place of the liquid. As reported by Taylor (1962) the most suitable film is 0.003 inch in thickness. It can be obtained in any quantity and in a great range of sizes from the following companies:

Colonial Kolonite Co., 2232 West Armitage, Chicago 47, Illinois.
Transilwrap Co., 4427 N. Clark Ave., Chicago, Illinois.
Bee Paper Co. Inc., 1–9 Joralemon Street, Brooklyn, New York.

The steps involved in making peels with cellulose acetate sheet are the same as those already outlined—grinding and polishing, etching, washing, and drying.

When placing the specimen in the gravel box the technician should incline the prepared surface slightly away from him. Do not try to level the specimen, as is done when making liquid peels.

### CARE OF CELLULOSE ACETATE SHEETS

Under certain conditions cellulose acetate sheets accumulate much static electricity, which in turn attracts dust particles. This can be avoided to a degree by cutting the film into various usable sizes on hot, humid days when the film will not become statically charged and then storing the film in dust-free drawers or boxes.

### MAKING THE PEEL

Have at hand a piece of acetate film that will cover the specimen, so that it can be reached quickly and placed on the specimen when the time comes.

Using the squeeze bottle filled with acetone, wet the *entire* inclined surface of the specimen, so that there is an *accumulation* of acetone on the lower edge of the specimen. Quickly place the piece of acetate film in the acetone on the lower edge of the specimen, gradually letting the film down onto the etched surface of the specimen in a way that will push the acetone up the inclined surface of the specimen (fig. 3, middle). This will make an even layer of acetone that will wet the side of the acetate film next to the specimen. If there is too little acetone the acetate film will not be completely wet with acetone and a peel with air spaces will result. If there is too much acetone the acetate film will wrinkle excessively and lines of air bubbles will form.

Again, it is up to the technician to determine, from experience, the proper amount of acetone to use and the speed he must acquire to make a good peel.

Generally, acetate-film peels are easier to take off than poured peels and can be pulled without loosening the edges, with a razor or scalpel. They should be allowed to dry for an hour, but they can be pulled within 20 minutes after they are made.

## MAKING SLIDES

If slides are to be made of specimens in peels by either method described above, the specimens are cut out of the peel with ordinary scissors. When this is done use the following procedure:

1. Place specimens in a dish containing 5 percent HCl for 2 minutes. Using tweezers remove the specimen and place it in water.

2. Place the specimen in a dish containing 95 percent alcohol.

3. Remove and blot the specimen dry on a paper towel. Be sure the specimen is absolutely dry before taking the next step.

4. Place the dried specimen in clearing reagent, either Eycleshymer's or Terpinol. Eycleshymer's is made of equal parts of bergamot oil, cedar oil, and carbolic acid. This clearing agent has a very pleasant odor, one that is characteristic of many paleobotany laboratories.

5. Blot off excess clearing reagent on a paper towel, and dip specimen into a mounting medium, either canada balsam or one of the many synthetic resins now available.

6. Place the specimen on a slide with sufficient mounting medium to fill the space between cover glass and slide.

7. Place the completed slide on a warming table. If the peel shows a tendency to curl under the cover slip, this can be corrected by placing a small weight on the cover slip.

## CONCLUDING REMARKS

The techniques outlined above have made it possible to turn out a large number of sections of fossilized materials in a relatively short time. Where it once took an experienced technician an hour to grind one thin section by hand with questionable results, as well as wasting great quantities of material, it is now possible to obtain a series of 8 to 10 serial sections in the course of a day with little loss of material. Improvements in the peel technique during the past 10 years have had a profound effect on the increased quantity as well as the improved quality of paleontological research.

## REFERENCES

Appel, J. E. (1933). A film method for studying textures. Econ. Geology, v. 28, p. 383–388.

Darrah, W. C. (1936). The peel method in paleobotany. Harvard Univ. Bot. Mus., Leaflets, v. 4, p. 69–83.

Fenton, Mildred Adams (1935). Nitrocellulose sections of fossils and rocks. Am. Midl. Naturalist, v. 16, p. 410–412.

Graham, R. (1933). Preparation of paleontological sections by the peel method. Stain Tech., v. 8, p. 65–68.

Koopmans, R. G. (1929). Celluloid preparat anstatt Dünnschliff. Jaarverslag over 1928, Geol. Bur. Nederl., Neerlen., p. 131–132.

Krick, Henrietta V. (1932). Structure of seed-like fructifications found in coal balls from Harrisburg, Illinois. Bot. Gaz., v. 93, p. 153–154.

Lacey, W. S. (1953). Methods in paleobotany. N. Western Natur., Abroath, Wales, v. 24, p. 234–249.

Leclerq, Suzanne (1928). La Méthode J. Walton pour la Preparation des Lames Mince. Ann. Soc. Geol. Belg., v. 52, p. B24–B27.

Nathorst, A. G. (1908). Über die Anwendung von Kollodiumabdrucken bei der Untersuchung fossiler Pflanzen. Arkiv. For. Botanik, v. 7, p. 1–7.

Noé, A. C. (1930). Celluloid films from coal balls. Bot. Gaz., v. 89, p. 318–319.

Taylor, T. N. (1962). The coal ball peel technique. Fast Journal, April–May, p. 5–6.

Walton, J. (1928). A method of preparing fossil plants. Nature, v. 122, p. 571.

———— (1930). Improvements in the peel-method of preparing sections of fossil plants. Nature, v. 125, p. 413.

————, and R. G. Koopmans (1928). Preparation of cellulose films and their use in making serial sections of coal ball plants. Rept. British Assn. at Glasgow, p. 615, 688.

# An Improved Instrument for Sectioning Microfossils

ZACH M. ARNOLD

*Museum of Paleontology, University of California, Berkeley*

Since its first description (Arnold, 1958), several improvements have been made not only in the design and construction of the precision sectioning instrument but also in the techniques of using it to prepare microfossils for study. Major structural improvements (see fig. 1,*a*) include:

1. Addition of built-in facilities for transmitted illumination and for carefully balancing reflected and transmitted illumination whenever their joint or complementary use is desirable.

2. Addition of a built-in heating element atop the specimen carrier.

3. Addition of micromanipulatory controls to the specimen carrier to facilitate precise orientation of the specimen.

4. Development of a process for preparing custom-made grinding wheels.

5. Development of a simple but effective means of viewing the ground surface without interruption throughout the grinding operation.

6. Increased power and variable speed for the grinding wheel.

7. Simplification of the cooling system.

Improvements in the techniques of using the instrument have centered on the preparation of thin sections, although as a result of basic structural changes, the instrument's efficiency, versatility, and precision in the preparation of both dissections and polished sections have also been enhanced.

Although reflected light from an external source is often adequate during the preparation of dissections or relatively thick sections, the attainment of a high degree of precision in the preparation of thin sections requires that fine structural features and morphological details be illuminated in good contrast. Usually these are revealed only through the use of transmitted light. The insertion of a minute cystoscopic bulb beneath the stage of the specimen carrier (fig. 1,*b*), together with an electrical circuit for controlling its intensity, has made possible the efficient use of transmitted light alone or in properly balanced conjunction with reflected light. A variety of miniature bulbs of the type employed in surgical instruments have dimensions and intensity ranges that render them suitable for use in this instrument, but a Neico 589 cystoscopic bulb, rated at 2.5 volts and measuring 9 mm in length and 2.7 mm in diameter has proved highly satisfactory over a three-year period. In order to eliminate the filament image and to provide a broad, even field of illumination with this bulb, its lens should be ground flat with 600-mesh Carborundum and left frosted. A thin layer of air between the ground surface and the glass base of the specimen stage insures the preservation of the diffusing effect of the frosted surface; this would be lost if the mounting resin were allowed, when molten, to come into contact with the frosted surface of the lens.

The stage of the specimen carrier, shown in fig. 1,*b,* contains a heating element by means of which one can readily melt the thermoplastic cement that holds the specimen in place. This feature is most valuable during removal of the exceedingly delicate finished section and its glass support from the stage. The problem at this point is to loosen the section-bearing cover glass from the specimen carrier without overheating it and producing bubbles in the cement. One bubble exploding in or near a section can badly damage or totally destroy an otherwise perfect preparation. By designing the stage so that the heating element lies below the specimen and its glass support, softening of the thermoplastic cement will first take place below the cover glass and gradually move upward toward the specimen. The operator controls

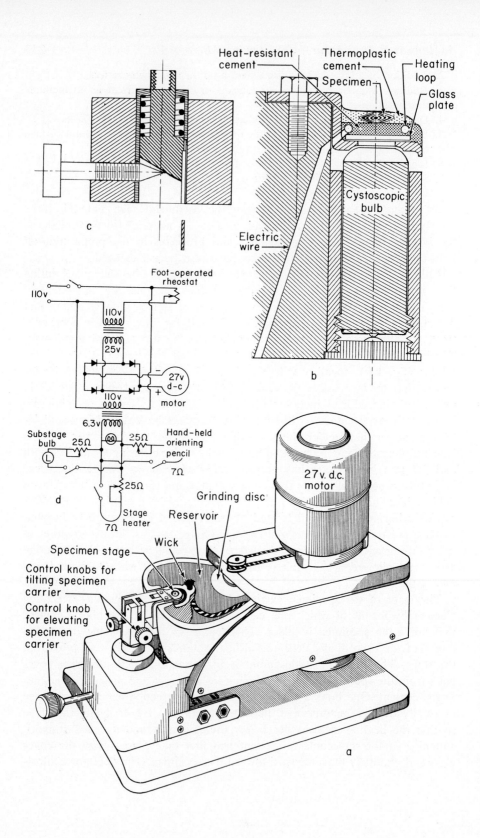

c

Heat-resistant cement

Thermoplastic cement

Heating loop

Specimen

Glass plate

Cystoscopic bulb

Electric wire

b

Foot-operated rheostat

110v

110v

25v

27v d-c motor

110v

6.3v

Substage bulb

25Ω

25Ω

Hand-held orienting pencil

7Ω

25Ω

7Ω

Stage heater

d

27 v. d.c. motor

Grinding disc

Reservoir

Wick

Specimen stage

Control knobs for tilting specimen carrier

Control knob for elevating specimen carrier

a

the degree and areal extent of softening by means of a potentiometer, while watching the entire operation through the microscope. Thus, the hazards of overheating or misdirecting the heat—major difficulties when the heat is applied from above by means of a handheld electric loop—may easily be eliminated altogether. As can be seen in fig. 1,*b*, the metal base of the stage is overlain by a glass plate cut to the same shape and notched to permit the entrance of the leads to which the resistance loop is attached. The plate can be easily and rapidly shaped through the use of a high-speed grinder (equipped with a thin Carborundum wheel) if the glass from which it is to be cut (a No. 0 cover glass) is first attached to a glass microscope slide or a strip of metal with molten wax to prevent destructive vibrations during cutting.

A second important improvement in the specimen carrier is the addition of micromanipulatory controls for tilting it about two horizontal axes, one parallel to the line along which the grinder's carriage moves, the other perpendicular to it. These two additional controls (fig. 1,*c*), designed as an integral part of the specimen carrier, permit the operator to reorient the specimen by remote control instead of by direct contact with a needle, which, no matter how fine and how skillfully handled, could easily inflict irreparable damage upon a delicate section if control over it were lost for a fraction of a second. The basic design of the micromanipulatory element is illustrated elsewhere in this manual by Wornardt. Dimensional reductions necessary for its use with the grinder, however, have created at least one constructional difficulty, that of producing minute springs having sufficient resiliency and power to return the displaced elements to their compressed position as the screws are loosened. An effective, though simple and inelegant, solution was found by substituting rubber bands for springs; the bands simply slip over the counteracting elements of the micromanipulator, forcing their occlusion as the control screws are withdrawn.

The construction of abrasive discs suitable for use on the grinder is described in a later section of this article. Since the diameter, thickness, flexibility, and grit-size of homemade discs may readily be modified to suit the particular needs of the operator, a knowledge of the technique of preparing them is helpful for those planning to use the apparatus. By mounting the discs eccentrically, or by cutting peripheral notches in them, it is possible to obtain a continual image of the specimen during the grinding process without removing the grinder from the field of vision, just as one might when

**Fig. 1.** *Precision section grinder for microfossils. (a) Complete grinder showing motor-driven grinding disc, specimen carrier, cooling system, and control knobs for positioning specimen in path of grinder. (b) Details of specimen carrier showing heated stage and substage illuminator (length of bulb: ⅝ inch). (c) Detail of specimen carrier, showing spring-loaded elevating mechanism and control knob. (d) Wiring diagram for section grinder.*

reading a newspaper through an electric fan. This simple artifice markedly increases control over the grinding process.

A 27-volt D.C. motor, adapted for use on a 110-volt A.C. line by the addition of a 25-volt transformer and four selenium rectifiers, has proved adequate in the rapid preparation of tests as much as 1.5 mm in diameter if the motor is run at top speed driving a one-inch disc formed of 320-mesh Carborundum; a more powerful motor should be employed if larger specimens are to be cut efficiently. By incorporating a foot-operated rheostat in the circuit, grinding may be more carefully regulated. An electrical diagram of the circuits required for the grinder and its accessories is shown in fig. 1,*d*.

The design of the cooling system has been improved and its construction simplified through use of a polyvinyl chloride plastigel that can be molded to shape within the ways of the machine and hardened in place by heating at 350°F for 15 minutes. The splash tray and reservoir thus formed are a single unit of enhanced capacity and stability.

## PROCEDURE

The first step in preparing to section a specimen is to cover the stage of the specimen carrier with Lakeside 70 cement. I prepare pellets for this purpose by heating a stick of cement above a beaker of water into which the molten drops fall and immediately solidify; they are then separated into various sizes by sieving and are stored in separate compartments for future use. After placing upon the stage a pellet whose volume exceeds that of the specimen to be ground, the heating unit is energized sufficiently to melt the plastic; bubbles of entrapped air are removed with the manually controlled electric loop described earlier (Arnold, 1958). The specimen is then placed upon the molten drop of plastic in approximately correct orientation; as soon as the stage heater is turned off the plastic hardens, but the control screws of the specimen carrier can be used to bring the specimen into precise orientation for exposing the desired section. If the electric pencil is used during grinding, exposed cavities within the test may readily be filled with molten cement, thereby affording support of internal structures; this not only enables one to avoid their destruction during sectioning but also gives additional insight into the internal morphology and general test organization, since, of course, a direct cause-effect relationship exists between the morphological characteristics and the mechanical behavior of structural elements under the strain of grinding.

As soon as the desired plane of section is reached, the stage heater is energized and the specimen moved to one side of the stage. A small cover glass is pressed into the fluid plastic, and the specimen, its ground surface lowermost, is centered upon the cover glass directly over the substage illuminator. The stage is then allowed to cool. (Cover glasses for this purpose, measuring only 1 or 2 mm on a side, may be cut from standard cover glasses with a diamond-tipped scriber. These are handled with a fine brush, the tip of which has first been moistened slightly.) After proper orientation has been achieved by means of the micromanipulatory controls of the specimen carrier, the critical steps of the final grinding operation may be completed. It is at this point that the illuminator beneath the specimen proves its worth. If one carefully balances the light falling onto the specimen from an external illuminator against that being transmitted through the specimen, optimum conditions may readily be established for successful sectioning; but even though this design provides precise mechanical control of many of the variables involved, the perception and sensitivity of the operator are still decisive in determining the quality of the completed section.

After the section has been ground to the desired plane, the substage heating element is carefully warmed just enough to permit sliding the cover glass and section as a unit from the softened surface of the plastic cement. Care must be taken to avoid overheating and formation of bubbles, a chore greatly simplified by the substage position of the heat source. A fine cold needle readily adheres to the excess cement on the cover glass as cooling occurs; this permits one to transfer the glass to the first of three reagents used to prepare the section for final mounting. A small, shallow cup, made of aluminum foil and attached by a slot to the tip of an applicator stick, forms a handy container for transferring the cover glass preparation from one reagent to the next.

The first reagent, Glyptal thinner (available from the General Electric Co.), effectively and rapidly removes the Lakeside 70 without leaving a residue. It is superior to other solvents I have used. Since the bond between needle and cover glass is quickly dissolved, the aluminum cup should be kept just under the cover glass to catch it as it falls from the needle. As soon as the last remnants of plastic have been dissolved from the preparation (several seconds or more, depending on the amount of cement present), it should be transferred to absolute ethyl alcohol for a few seconds. This removes the Glyptal solvent, dehydrates the section, and prepares it for the final reagent, xylene, to which the specimen is transferred until clearing is complete (a few seconds). Special care must be taken in placing the preparation in the xylene, lest violent convection currents dislodge the cover glass or the section from the cup. It is practically impossible to pick up unsupported thin sections of certain types of structurally weak tests without breaking them, hence the need to keep the section safely aboard its supporting cover glass throughout the sequence of fluid changes. The specimen should not be permitted to dry out at any stage following the removal of the Lakeside 70. After clearing has been completed, the section and cover glass must be transferred as a unit to a small drop of mounting medium (balsam, piccolyte, clarite, H.S.R., or other suitable synthetic resin) on the glass slide to which they will be permanently attached. The transfer to this final medium is best effected by sliding the cover glass onto a small thin strip of glass which can subsequently be inverted over the drop of mounting medium and carefully manipulated until the specimen and cover glass settle into the viscous medium, after which the strip of glass is withdrawn. The transparent strip permits the operator to observe the section throughout the transfer operation. After the mount has been allowed to harden for a few hours, the surface of the cover glass may be lightly brushed with xylene and excess resin removed to leave the preparation ready for study.

**REFERENCE**

Arnold, Z. M. (1958). A precision sectioning instrument for microfossils. Micropaleontology, v. 4, no. 1, p. 103–112.

# Preparing Paired Thin Sections from Single Larger Foraminifera

K. N. SACHS, JR.

*U. S. National Museum, Washington, D.C.*

Specific identification of certain larger Foraminifera, particularly of the genera *Lepidocyclina* and *Discocyclina* is based on the appearance of internal features, mainly the shape and arrangement of the embryonic apparatus, equatorial chambers, lateral chambers and pillars, and wall structure. External appearance of the test is of no value when attempting to distinguish between closely related species.

Since two differently oriented thin sections, equatorial and vertical, are required for adequate examination of the internal features of any one species, a dilemma immediately arises. It is possible to make but a single section from any given specimen by the technique of grinding away all but the desired section of test material. If two sections are necessary, one must have a second specimen of the same species: but how can this second specimen be identified with certainty as being the same as the first, especially since the determination must be made on the basis of external features already noted to be invalid?

One technique which will overcome the problem is to grind a specimen to the equatorial layer on one side only. The arrangement of the embryonic apparatus and equatorial chambers can then be observed and photographed by reflected light. The remaining part of the test is then made into a vertical thin section. This vertical section will contain lateral chambers on only one side of the equatorial layer, but this is sufficient, owing to the symmetry of the test. Cole (1952, pl. 17, figs. 5, 14; pl. 19 fig. 11) has illustrated several

such vertical half-sections. Although this method assures that both sections were derived from the same species, the only permanent record of the equatorial section can be a photograph taken by reflected light, Such photographs may be of value in determining such gross features as chamber arrangement, shape, and size, but are worthless for such fine details as wall structure, canal systems, and stolons. Good thin sections which can be examined by transmitted light are absolutely necessary to bring out these features.

Shortly after I began a study of the American species of *Lepidocyclina* in 1957 it became evident that a method of producing sections in both the equatorial and vertical planes from a single specimen would be desirable. After some experimentation, I devised an apparatus which made it possible to obtain such a pair of sections.

The apparatus (fig. 1) consists of a thin-bladed motor-driven circular saw mounted vertically above a carrier (A) designed to hold a microscope slide on which the specimen to be cut is mounted. The specimen on the slide can

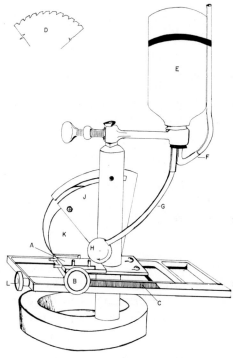

**Fig. 1**

*Device for sawing Foraminifera. A: carrier for holding petrographic slide with mounted specimen. B: lateral adjusting screw knob. C: feed screw. D: detail of edge of saw blade. E: bottle containing abrasive and water. F: air vent for bottle. G: tube for feeding slurry to saw (stopcock omitted from drawing). H: saw blade showing direction of rotation. J: adjustable motor mount to allow vertical adjustment of saw blade. K: motor. L: feed screw knob.*

be accurately positioned under the saw by means of a lateral adjusting screw (B). The specimen is fed by means of a slow-motion feed screw (C) into the saw, which rotates just above the slide.

Several materials were tried for use as a saw blade with varying success. Currently a hard steel jewelers' saw with a diameter of 22 mm and thickness of 0.08 mm is being used. The teeth of this blade were removed by grinding until the circumference showed only fine notches between broad smooth portions (D). These small notches were left to aid in clearing the cut during operation. The cutting operation is aided by a slurry of fine (600×) alundum abrasive and water carried from an overhead mixing bottle (E) to the saw by a flexible tube with an adjustable stopcock that regulates flow. Very little slurry is necessary, so that with proper adjustment, spatter can be nearly eliminated, thus obviating the necessity of a hood. The blade is coupled directly to a 1/30 hp electric motor rated at 1530 rpm. Under normal operation this speed is reduced to approximately 1200 rpm.

The procedure for obtaining paired sections from a single specimen can be divided into three operations: (1) initial preparation, (2) cutting, (3) final grinding of thin sections.

## INITIAL PREPARATION

The specimen to be sectioned is first ground parallel to the equatorial plane until the outline of the embryonic chambers is visible. The specimen is then mounted on a slide with the ground surface up and examined under a microscope. A line is drawn across the ground surface with a fine-pointed pencil to indicate the location of the cut which will be made normal to the equatorial plane. If necessary, the specimen can then be reoriented on the slide so that the line of the cut will be parallel to one of the long edges of the microscope slide and therefore parallel to the direction of feed. Care must be used to keep the equatorial layer of the specimen parallel to the surface of the slide.

## CUTTING

The slide with its specimen is placed in the carrier and adjusted by means of the lateral adjusting screw until the saw blade and cutting line are aligned. The specimen is then fed into the saw and cut.

## FINAL GRINDING OF THIN SECTIONS

The cut surface of one of the two fragments resulting from the cutting operation is ground to remove irregularities. The fragment is then mounted on a slide and ground to a vertical thin section. The other fragment is further ground on the initially ground surface to the equatorial plane, mounted, and finished as an equatorial section.

Although one of the objectives of this technique is to obtain the narrowest possible kerf, some of the test will be lost during sawing. With the apparatus described here, cuts are consistently made with a kerf of less than $100\mu$. Thus, the cut can be located so that at least half of the embryonic apparatus will remain intact within the fragment that is to be made into an equatorial section. As a result, the fragment to be made into a vertical section will be somewhat off center, and will not show the true height of the embryonic chambers. Where the embryonic chambers are small, this section may be tangent to the embryonic chambers. However, the shape of the embryonic chambers as seen in vertical section is not considered significant in studies involving this technique. The features of primary interest in vertical section are the equatorial layer, lateral chambers, and pillars. The appearance of these features will not significantly be changed if the cut is kept as close as possible to the center of the test. Only a few light turns on a grinding plate should be necessary to polish the cut surface before it is mounted for final grinding to thin section.

It is important that the line of the cut be oriented approximately parallel to a line passing through the centers of the first and second embryonic chambers and normal to the partition separating these chambers. The arrangement of periembryonic chambers which are in contact with the first embryonic chamber may differ from the arrangement of those around the second. By aligning the cut as suggested above, this arrangement around each embryonic chamber can be determined in the final equatorial section.

## REFERENCE

Cole, W. Storrs (1952). Eocene and Oligocene larger Foraminifera from the Panama Canal Zone and vicinity. U. S. Geol. Survey Prof. Paper 244, 41 pp., 28 pls., 2 figs.

# Thin Sections and Peels for High-magnification Study and Phase-contrast Microscopy

SUSUMU HONJO, ALFRED G. FISCHER

*Princeton University, Princeton, New Jersey*

Traditionally the earth sciences have approached microscopy through classical petrography, via the "standard" $30\mu$ thin section and the petrographic microscope. These serve well in the identification of comparatively coarse mineral grains, and in determining their orientation, by means of their optical properties. They also provide good optical images at low magnifications. But in the range from 150× to 1000× the image becomes progressively worse. The optical quality of the petrographic microscope may be improved by substituting more highly corrected lenses for the achromatic ones normally used (taking care to select comparatively strain-free objectives in order to maintain good extinction between crossed nicols). But the main limitations lie in the standard thin section.

The $30\mu$ thin section (here called T-section) is, for purposes of high-power magnification, a "thick section." At low powers it lies within the focal-depth range of the objectives, and no importance attaches to the resolution of grains much smaller than section thickness. Hence the image is satisfactory. At higher magnifications, designed to explore the finer features of the fabric, the image is disturbed by the overlap and superposition of grains, and blurred because the focal depth of the optical system is less than the thickness of the section: the crisp images of the grains within the focal range are superimposed on the blurred images of grains outside this focal range. In birefringent minerals this is not only a disturbance by simple refraction but by double refraction and polarization. When teamed with a 10× periplan ocular a 25× apochromat (NA 0.65) with a resolving power of about $0.8\mu$ has a focal range of about $5\mu$, or one-sixth of a T-section; a 90× oil-immersion objective (NA 1.32) with a resolving power of about $0.4\mu$ has a focal range of about $0.5\mu$, or one-sixtieth of a T-section.

The microscopic study of rocks and skeletal materials at higher magnifications therefore requires differently prepared objects: *polished surfaces* (as in ore microscopy); *peel replicas* of polished and etched surfaces; or thin sections with a thickness of $0.5\mu$ to $5\mu$, here termed ultra-thin sections, or U-sections. Polished surfaces are most useful in the study of opaque materials, but will not be discussed here. Although somewhat tedious to prepare, U-sections have two main advantages: they provide the actual material for study, and the more highly birefringent materials, such as the carbonate minerals, can be examined to advantage under cross-polarized light. Peels are mainly imprints of the etched surface, though they may carry with them etch-resistant grains. They are more quickly prepared, may be duplicated by taking several replicas off the same surface, and lend themselves to three-dimensional studies by means of closely spaced serial sequences.

## PREPARATION OF U-SECTIONS

*Materials.* High-quality slides and cover glasses of standard thickness (cover slips 0.17 mm). Mounting medium: A mixture of the two Union Carbide resins, UNOX epoxide 206 and ERL-2774, with hardeners, HET anhydride and ZZL0814. Impregnating medium for porous rocks: UNOX epoxide 206 and HET anhydride. Abrasives: 1-F, No. 600, No. 800, No. 1200, No. 3200. Other equipment: Oven, two grinding laps, glass plates, methylene glycol, synthetic immersion oil; a vacuum dessicator for porous specimens.

*Stage 1, Cutting.* Rectangular plates of desired size are cut by means of a saw. Plates of even thickness are required.

*Stage 2, Impregnation.* Porous materials must be impregnated with a highly fluid resin. Specimens are immersed in acetone (for a number of days if necessary) and are then transferred to vials filled with the resin mix. To prepare this dissolve the HET anhydrided hardener in UNOX 206 epoxide resin in the ratio 14:30, taking care to avoid entrapment of bubbles (a magnetic stirrer is useful). This mix is unstable in batches greater than about 50 cc: at 20°C a 40-cc batch has a pot-life of about 80 minutes; a batch of a few cc, a pot-life of about 8 hours. Before the resin sets, the samples are exposed to a vacuum in a vacuum dessicator attached to a water aspirator, and are brought back to atmospheric pressure; this procedure may have to be repeated several times to insure deep penetration of the resin.

If only U-sections are required, then other highly fluid resins, such as the methyl methacrylate resins used in impregnating tissues for biological sectioning, may prove equally satisfactory, and perhaps advantageous. But if peels are to be prepared from the specimens, it is necessary to use resins which are not attacked by acetone, such as the one here employed.

*Stage 3, Grinding. Step a:* Grind on a coarse lap with 1-F until the saw marks have vanished. *Step b:* Grind on a second lap with No. 600 for 10 to 60 seconds, using ample powder and pressure, moving and rotating the specimen freely and evenly over the lap; lightly bevel the edges. *Step c:* Hand-grind on a glass plate with tap water and No. 800, exerting moderate pressure with one or two finger tips and sweeping a large H-pattern over the plate; after 3 minutes wash, dry, and examine for scratches; if none, proceed to *d. Step d:* Hand-grind on another glass plate with tap water and No. 1200, using a moderate amount of abrasive and pressure, for 2 to 3 minutes. Dry and check for scratches. *Step e:* Hand-grind on another glass plate with No. 3200, using a mixture of 90 percent distilled water and 10 percent methylene glycol (to inhibit evaporation), with a light touch, for 2 to 3 minutes. Dry and check under a microscope.

*Stage 4, Mounting.* In place of the conventional canada balsam or Lakeside 70 cement, we use epoxy resin because of its greater bonding strength, essential to such thin sections. Furthermore, epoxy-mounted sections may be boiled or treated with solvents.

Wash the specimen with detergent, dry, and cool. Prepare the mounting medium by thoroughly mixing and dissolving in each other 30 grams of UNOX epoxide 206, 12 grams of HET anhydride, 10 cc of ERL-2774, and 2.5 to 3 cc of ERL-0814. Avoid entrapment of air bubbles by very cautious stirring or use of a magnetic stirrer. Mount the specimen with a drop of resin on an acetone-cleaned slide, work out any entrapped air bubbles, and remove

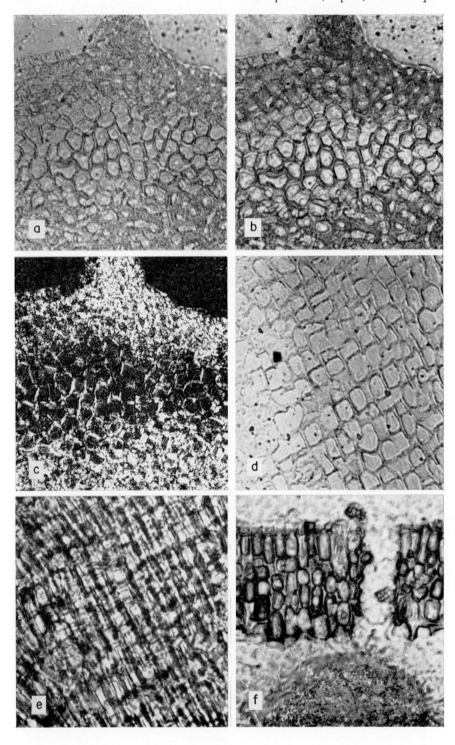

the excess epoxy. Cure glass-down for 4 to 5 hours at 90°C. Cool and label with a diamond pencil.

*Stage 5, Grinding. Step a:* Reduce the section to 50$\mu$ in thickness. Some of this may be done with a diamond cutoff saw or with coarse abrasives. The last stages are done with 1-F and No. 600 Carborundum (we have found a boron carbide slide holder useful). *Step b:* Hand-grind with No. 800 to about 30$\mu$. *Step c:* Hand-grind with No. 1200. *Step d:* Hand-grind with No. 3200 to about 10$\mu$, where calcite begins to show bright low-order colors, using a light touch and an evenly spread film of abrasive in a mixture of distilled water and ethylene glycol. An even film can be obtained by spreading the mixture with a sponge. *Step e:* Continue grinding, applying light pressure to one end of slide. This produces a wedge-shaped section with one very thin edge. Stop when the edge begins to vanish. Wash with detergent, dry, and label.

*Covering.* We do not cover our sections permanently, but mount cover glasses with immersion oil.

## PREPARATION OF PEEL REPLICAS

Preparation of peels for intermediate magnifications and the preparation of serial peels are discussed by Honjo (1963). Peels for high-magnification studies must have low relief but great detail. These can be obtained only at the expense of contrast, hence such peels are best studied under the phase-contrast microscope.

*Materials.* Polishing lap, polishing silk, 15$\mu$ gamma alumina suspension, ammonium chloride, ethyl acetate, Bioden acetyl cellulose film.

*Stages 1 to 3.* Preparation of specimens follows the U-section procedure through stage 3.

*Stage 4.* The specimen is then polished on a silk-covered high-speed lap with a suspension of 0.1$\mu$ gamma alumina. The specimen should be applied with moderate pressure for intervals of about 3 seconds, repeated 15 or 20

**Fig. 1.** *(a–e) A specimen of a branching* Lithothamnium *sp., picked up dead on a Hawaiian beach. (f) A fresh* Melobesia *from Zumaya, Spain. (a–c) Section of surficial portion, including part of a conceptacle (upper right), 400×. (a) plane-polarized light; (b) positive phase contrast; (c) cross-polarized light. The skeleton in the mid-part of the field has remained intact. Around the conceptacle (upper right) and at bottom of field the cells have become partly to completely permineralized with carbonate, and many cell walls have become obliterated. (d,e) Interior, unpermineralized parts of* Lithothamnium *section, 500× in plane polarized light. (e) T-section (20–30$\mu$), showing confused image of overlapping elements within and outside of focal range. (d) The same field, cut to extreme thinness (est. 2$\mu$). (f) Peel of the roof of a conceptacle, 400×, in phase contrast. A tetraspore (bottom) is shown within the conceptacle; above it, a pore piercing the cellular roof. This peel shows greater than normal relief, owing to incomplete impregnation of the cells and entry of plastic into these cavities.*

times. The amount of alumina suspension on the silk should be such that specimen dries within about 5 seconds after removal from the lap.

*Stage 5, Etching.* Carbonate specimens are etched by immersing, face-up and horizontal, in an acidic salt solution such as ammonium chloride (pH about 5.6) for a period of several minutes or longer. This provides a more even and controlled etching than do acids. Rinse very gently, without touching surface. Dry with heat or acetone.

*Stage 6, Peel application.* Cover surface with a thin layer of solvent (anhydrous ethyl acetate) and gently lay on, from one end, a strip of the Bioden film. Allow to dry at room temperature, for several minutes or longer. Then bake in oven, or peel with sharp forceps, clamp between glass slides, and bake to flatten.

*Stage 7, Mounting.* Attach to glass slide, face down, by acetate cement applied to corners, and add cover glass.

## STUDY OF U-SECTIONS AND PEELS

Figure 1 shows a series of sections and peels made of the skeletons of Recent calcareous (melobesiid) red algae, having rather small cells.

A T-section (*e*) some $20\mu$ to $30\mu$ thick shows the confusing effect of overlapping cells and out-of-focus images. The same field of the same section, cut to a thickness of about $2\mu$, is illustrated in *d*. The cells are here clearly defined, but contrast in normal or plane-polarized light is low.

Another, somewhat thicker part of the same U-section is shown in *a, b,* and *c*. The field in normal (plane-polarized) light is shown in *a*. The field is somewhat improved in positive phase contrast (*b*); cross-polarized light brings out the areas which have been diagenetically permineralized, and in which there has been partial destruction of the skeleton (*c*).

Peels made for high-magnification study are normally so low in relief that phase-contrast microscopy is essential for their study. A peel of fresh *Melobesia* is illustrated in *f*.

## ACKNOWLEDGMENT

Acknowledgment is made to the donors of The Petroleum Research Fund, administered by the American Chemical Society, for support of this research.

## REFERENCES

Bennett, A. H., H. Osterberg, H. Jupnik, and O. W. Richards (1951). Phase microscopy, principles and applications. New York, John Wiley, 320 pp.

Croft, W. N. (1950). A parallel grinding instrument for the investigation of fossils by serial sections. J. Paleontology, v. 24, no. 6, p. 693–698.

Darrah, W. C. (1936). The peel method in paleobotany. Bot. Mus. Leaflets, Harvard Univ., v. 4, no. 5, p. 69–83.

Finck, Henry (1960). Epoxy resins in electron microscopy. J. Biophys. and Biochem. Cytology, v. 1, 7, no. 1, p. 27–30.

Fukami, Akira (1955). Experiment concerning replica preparation method (II); On a new rapid and reliable positive replica process (filmy replica system). J. Electron Microscopy, v. 4, no. 1, p. 274–278. (Japanese with English résumé.)

Honjo, S. (1960). A study of some primitive *Neoschwagerina* by a new serial section technique. J. Fac. Sci. Hokkaido Univ., ser. 4, v. 10, no. 3, p. 457–470.

———— (1963). New serial micropeel technique. Kansas Geol. Survey Bull., no. 165, pt. 6, 16 pp.

Kesling, Robert V. (1957). A peel technique for ostracod carapaces and structures revealed therewith in *Hibbardia lacrimosa* (Swartz and Oriel). Nat. Hist. Mus. Univ. Michigan Bull., v. 14, no. 4, p. 27–40.

Rohm and Hass Company, Special Products Department (1960). Embedding specimens in methacrylate resins. Rohm and Hass Company Technical Series SP-46, p. 1–10.

# Preparation of Individual Microfossils on Cellulose Acetate Films

ANDERS MARTINSSON

*University of Uppsala, Sweden*

The mechanical-chemical methods generally used for disintegration of clayey or sandy microfossil samples have some obvious disadvantages. For example, in many Palaeozoic samples, most of the microfossils are split along the fine cracks in their shells, and it is often better to pick out with a needle single, undamaged specimens that are largely buried in matrix than it is to clean and concentrate samples by chemical or mechanical methods, especially as neither method can be used on an individual specimen without damaging it.

Even very small calcareous fossils can be prepared by the proper use of an ordinary sewing needle. This preparation is considerably facilitated if the fossil is immersed in water. The specimen must be firmly fixed on a temporary mount with a substance from which it may be rapidly detached without leaving adhering traces, which complicate coating and photography. A convenient substance is a cement of the cellulose acetate type. Such glues, with slightly different solvents, are sold in most countries. A cement made by Klärre and Co. A.B., Box 9119, Stockholm 9, and exported under the name of *KK-33* (in Scandinavia called *Karlsons Klister*) has proved to be suitable for preparations of the kind dealt with here.

The bottom of an embryo dish, of the "salt tray" type, preferably made of black glass, is covered with a thin film of glue. Even if the glue is of the type recommended for cementing glass, a thin film on a smooth glass surface generally tends to break away when immersed in water. In order to avoid this, the glue should be smeared with the finger against the glass until it becomes tough. Another small drop of the same glue is placed on this film and smoothed out to a convenient thickness. If the specimen is immediately placed in the liquid cement before its surface begins to dry, then at least a minute is available for orienting the specimen.

The preparation is left to dry for at least ten minutes. Various arrangements may then be made in order to strengthen the attachment of the specimen—for example, building up walls or folds of glue around it or drawing threads of glue, attached to the film by means of a small drop of acetone, across such parts of the specimen as are not to be touched during the preparation.

The specimen is then covered with water. The finest sewing needle available is ground to a very sharp point and mounted in a convenient handle.

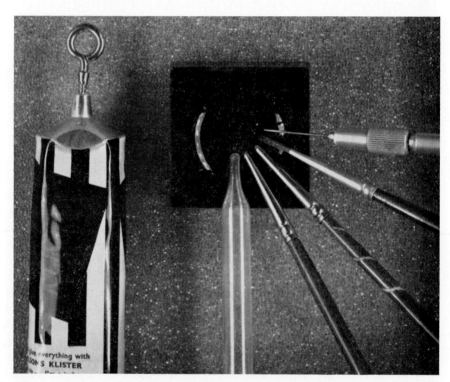

**Fig. 1.** *Equipment for preparing microfossils on cellulose acetate films. Resting on embryo dish, made of thick, black glass, are, from left to right: an eyedropper, two camel's-hair brushes with shortened hairs, an ordinary camel's-hair brush, and a hypodermic needle in holder.*

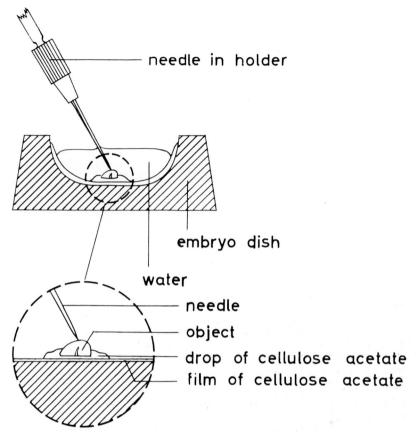

needle in holder

embryo dish

water

needle

object

drop of cellulose acetate

film of cellulose acetate

**Fig. 2.** *Mounting a specimen in an embryo dish. This type of dish is heavy enough to keep the specimen firmly in place during preparation.*

With this tool it is comparatively easy to remove marl particles from the specimen, not by digging or scratching, but by repeated delicate touches. It is recommended that the needle be kept in steady motion, so that it touches the specimen only at the extreme turning point of the movement; it is risky to let the needle rest on a thin shell, a thin spine, or other brittle structures.

Fossils without brittle processes may be cleaned with fine sable brushes during preparation; some can even be brushed with brushes whose hairs have been shortened to a length of a few millimeters. The fine detached particles, which tend to cover the specimen and complicate further preparation, are easily moved aside by a jet of water from an eye dropper or a syringe.

After preparation, which may require remounting the specimen several times in order to clean it on different sides, the cellulose acetate is dissolved and thoroughly washed away with acetone. The fossil may then be mounted with the same cement on a glass slide to be coated and photographed (simple

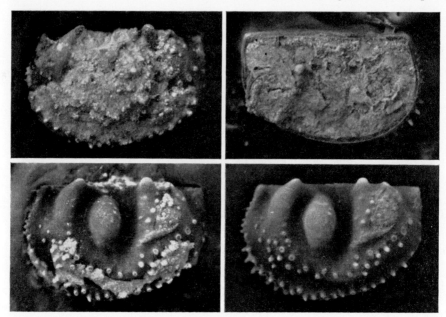

**Fig. 3.** *Stages in preparing a male left valve of the ostracod* Beyrichia (Beyrichia)
dactyloscopica *Martinsson, from the Silurian Mulde Beds at Mulde, Gotland.* (Upper left) *Specimen covered with marl and small fossil fragments.* (Lower left) *Same specimen after removal of the looser material.
The inner marl particles are more firmly cemented than the surficial material, especially those situated between the valve and a covering fossil
fragment.* (Upper right) *Same specimen turned over and remounted for
removal of particles protruding from the interior of the valve.* (Lower
right) *The specimen after preparation, coated with ammonium chloride.
The coating also covers the background, a thin film of cellulose acetate on
a glass slide, not artificially blackened on this photograph. Unretouched.
20×.*

preparations may be made directly on a slide immersed in a convenient
vessel).

However, if a specimen without cracks cannot be found, the fossil is likely
to break into pieces when it has been cleaned on all sides and is no longer
held together by the matrix. To repair the specimen it is necessary to use two
different glues—one, the cement used in preparation; the other, a glue that is
soluble in water, such as gum tragacanth. Before the specimen is removed
from the acetate film, its upper side is covered with a thin film of tragacanth.
It can then be removed from the cement with acetone, be handled as an
intact specimen, and the lower side photographed after it is mounted on a
slide with the cellulose acetate cement. If the specimen was not photographed from the other side before it fell apart, the procedure can be repeated,
though with less elegance, in the opposite direction. After the fossil has been

removed from the slide by means of acetone, the parts of the valves not covered with tragacanth are covered with a thin coating of cellulose cement diluted in acetone. When this coating is dry, the specimen is placed in water; this dissolves the tragacanth film, which should be thoroughly washed away. The specimen can then be mounted once again on a slide, using gum tragacanth. Both kinds of glue are slowly dissolved or weakened by alcohol, but for a rapid wash before coating, alcohol may be used.

The methods described here have been applied to Palaeozoic calcareous microfossils, particularly ostracods, as small as $350\mu$ in size, though most of those prepared were between 1 and 2 mm long. The equipment used is shown in fig. 1. Figure 2 is a schematic drawing of a microfossil specimen mounted in the embryo dish. Figure 3 shows the results of cleaning by the method described.

This method was originally described by Martinsson (1962, p. 40–42). To avoid damage due to shakiness during the free hand preparation, a manipulator of the pantograph type described by Kesling (1954, p. 193–199) can probably be used on the immersed specimen.

### REFERENCES

Kesling, R. V. (1954). An instrument for cleaning small fossils. Contr. Mus. Paleontology, University of Michigan, v. 11, no. 10, p. 193–199, 2 pls.
Martinsson, A. (1962). Ostracods of the family Beyrichiidae from the Silurian of Gotland. Publ. Paleont. Inst. Univ. Uppsala, no. 41, Geol. Inst. Univ. Uppsala Bull., v. 41, p. 1–369, 203 figs.

# Methods for Study and Preparation of Foraminifera

JAN HOFKER

*The Hague, Netherlands*

The study of dry tests is rather unsatisfactory. Finer structures such as pores and apertural lips can be analyzed successfully only in a fluid clarifier. Hofker

(1951, p. 13; 1956, p. 17; 1957, p. 9) found castor oil (oil of *Rhicinus*) a good medium for this purpose. It quickly penetrates into all air-filled holes and interior hollows, and on longer contact absorbs air bubbles. Its refractive index is low enough so that finer structures remain easily visible, yet it clarifies the test sufficiently to facilitate the study of internal structures. Castor oil dissolves readily in xylol, so that after treatment the tests can be mounted on dry slides. Moreover, since castor oil is miscible in canada balsam, tests first treated with castor oil can afterwards be mounted on glass slides for storage or for section grinding. Castor oil does not evaporate, and remains fluid for at least 20 years. Thus, tests mounted in it (without cover glass!) can be restudied later if stored in a dust-free place.

Because the viscosity of castor oil is low, immersed tests often cannot be kept in a desired position for study and drawing. Thus, the following method is required. A small drop of dissolved canada balsam is placed in castor oil. Since the castor oil withdraws the dissolving fluid from the balsam, the drop of balsam hardens within ten minutes. This is sufficient time to mount small tests in any desired position on the canada balsam. The balsam eventually dissolves in the oil.

## SECTIONING SMALL FORAMINIFERA

No new species of Foraminifera should be based on external characters alone. Many examples are known in which species were assigned to the wrong genus because the author describing the species did not study the inner structure of the test. Yet making sections of small Foraminifera is easy (Hofker, 1951, p. 13).

Two sections usually suffice, one horizontal and one transverse. The transverse section should go through the proloculus. The specimen is heated on glass together with a small piece of dry canada balsam. For this purpose, the balsam is put in an open bottle until it has hardened. Small pieces are extracted from the bottle with a blunt knife. The heating is best done on an electric heater at about 150°C. As soon as the slide begins to boil, it is put under a microscope. A wooden support is used so that the balsam does not harden too rapidly. The test is then oriented in the desired position and the canada balsam allowed to cool.

For grinding small tests, the author uses a small piece of fine Solenhofen chalk lubricated with castor oil (Hofker, 1957, p. 7), which does not easily dissolve the hard canada balsam. Using water instead of oil would make the grinding motion too jerky. The test is ground down by hand to the desired plane, and the slide is then dried thoroughly with a soft rag. The balsam is heated again (it must not be allowed to boil) and then, under the microscope, the test is turned over in the balsam so that the ground side is down. After the balsam is cool, the test is ground until a thin section is produced. The oil used in grinding must be removed or else it will dissolve the balsam within several days. Gentle heating of the slide removes scratches on the surface of the balsam. Finally, the section is drenched in fluid balsam and covered with a cover glass.

## MAKING SLIDES OF LARGER FORAMINIFERA

When transverse sections through the proloculus must be obtained, the center of the test is marked by a spot of India ink. The test is ground down nearly to the plane of the ink spot. During grinding, the test is held between the fingers in the desired position and pressed against a rotating fine-grained Carborundum stone. The ground surface is then provisionally finished on a flat, very fine-grained Carborundum stone. Calcareous as well as agglutinated tests may be treated in this way. The test is fastened to a glass slide as described in the preceding section, and the other side is ground down close to the ink spot. The test is next ground by hand on a fine-grained Carborundum stone (lubricated with castor oil) until the ink spot appears in the section. The slide is then dried with a soft rag until the test can be turned over and the first side ground until the ink spot appears. The slide may now be inspected in transmitted light under a microscope. Often the proloculus can already be observed through the section. Grinding is continued until the proloculus is cut transversely. Once again the section is turned over in heated canada balsam, using a wooden slide as a support, and grinding is continued on the other side until the section is thin enough. Care must be taken to press the turned section gently on the glass so that bubbles do not spoil the result. If it is necessary to turn a slide which already is too thin to turn with a needle, the slide is heated (after first drying off the oil) along with another slide bearing a small piece of balsam. As soon as this piece of balsam begins to boil, the glass containing the section is held upside down in an inclined position above the new slide, and the section will glide down onto the new slide without breaking (Hofker, 1949, p. 3).

## MAKING DRAWINGS OF A SERIES OF SECTIONS

Internal structures which are too complicated to be unraveled through study of a single thin section may be analyzed by the following procedure. Grinding is done as usual, but at each stage a drawing is made of the section. The drawings are made on paper at higher magnification using a microscope and transmitted light (Hofker, 1951, p. 13). Only the surface of the section is drawn, each drawing being located with reference to some plainly marked visible object in the canada balsam. Successive grindings may involve the whole test or only part of it. The completed drawings, carefully numbered, are then redrawn on glass plates, which have been prepared as follows. First they are cleaned with alcohol and dried. A very thin solution of canada balsam in xylol is then painted on one side of each plate, using a clean paint brush. After the plate has dried, it is easy to draw on it with India ink. The final result is a set of sections on glass plates which, when placed in correct order and oriented with respect to the reference object, show the internal structure of the test (Hofker, 1957, p. 9). Glass plates can be removed in order to look into the interior of any particular chamber of the test. The method gives excellent results (see Hofker, 1956, p. 126, pl. XVII; p. 129, pl. XVIII; p. 145, pl. XXII).

## THE STUDY OF CANAL SYSTEMS IN FORAMINIFERAL TESTS

In many rotaliids, especially *Elphidium, Streblus, Calcarina,* and *Siderolites,* and camarinids, such as *Operculina* and *Heterostegina* there are canals between the double walls of the septa. Moreover, the inner structure of complicated chambers, the orientation of foramina, and the direction of stolons within the test and between the chambers are difficult to observe and analyze. I have developed a handy method for use on air-filled tests (including fossil as well as Recent specimens) (Hofker, 1927, p. 2, p. 58, fig. 9, pl. II, fig. 10, pl. IV, fig. 1; 1930, pl. 62). This so-called canada balsam method has also been used with good results by many other workers, including Umbgrove and Vaughan.

Small tests can be treated as a whole, but larger tests are better ground down until a relatively thin section is obtained, but not too thin. The test or section is laid on hardened canada balsam and gently cooked. It is then placed on a glass slide and ground (using water as a lubricant) until a sufficiently large part of the calcareous test wall is laid open. The slide is next submerged in a petri dish filled with a 5 percent solution of acetic acid for about 24 hours or until all of the shell material has dissolved. The slide can then be observed at high magnification in water or glycerin. All pores, stolons, and chambers are clearly visible. Some balsams are stained (e.g. with dark brown bone oil), but I prefer clear balsam.

Instead of canada balsam, paraffin with a melting point of about 80°C may be employed with good results. The paraffin is, however, somewhat more brittle than balsam and less transparent (Hofker, 1949, p. 3).

## EXTRACTION OF FORAMINIFERA FROM SAMPLES BY DECANTING

Sandy, marly, and soft calcareous samples often contain many Foraminifera belonging to planktonic groups. With normal methods of washing in sieves, most of these specimens, particularly when air-filled, are crushed and washed away. Fifty to ninety percent of the entire foraminiferal fauna of samples from the type Danian of Denmark were shown to consist of smaller plank-tonic Foraminifera, whereas previous workers had considered this material to contain very few planktonic tests.

The following method of extracting most of the thin-shelled forms from a sample has been used (Hofker, 1960, p. 73). Water-wetted samples are crushed in a stone basin with a wooden rolling pin. The crushed mass is then immersed in water in a flat decanting pan and gently shaken. The milky water is decanted into the finest-mesh bronze sieve and sieved gently (in an excess of water) until all the finest particles have disappeared. Care must be taken not to decant material which has sunk to the bottom of the pan. The shaking and decanting process is repeated several times. One is astonished at the large number of thin-shelled forms found on the sieve upon drying. The material which remains at the bottom of the pan contains the larger and thicker shelled forms. The sieved material, when dry, can be further sorted with a set of dry sieves.

In some cases, a large amount of nonforaminiferal material remains in the decanted material. The Foraminifera can be separated in the following way. A glass cylinder about 40 cm high is filled with cold water, and the dried material from the sieve is thrust quickly into the water. After 2 or 3 seconds the floating material should be decanted into an aluminum pan. When this has sunk to the bottom of the pan, the water is gently poured off. The entire process may then be repeated with this material by filling the cylinder once again with water, introducing the material, and again decanting the portion which floats. The material thus obtained will consist mainly of air-filled tests of small, thin-shelled Foraminifera (as well as closed tests of ostracods, which may easily be opened later in castor oil). The residue in the decanting pan consists mainly of sand grains and chalky particles of no importance.

By this method the normally time-consuming task of separating Fora-minifera can be completed within half an hour. Moreover, samples which would otherwise be considered poor in Foraminifera may prove to contain a large and varied fauna. Small planktonic Foraminifera, small Buliminidae, Polymorphinidae (with the important fistulose chambers preserved), and thin-shelled Nonionidae are often present in large quantities, whereas the same samples treated in the normal way show none of these fossils. More-over, forms which were originally deposited in the bed from which the sample was taken can be separated from those which have been reworked. The autochthonous specimens are often air-filled, and float, whereas the re-worked specimens are generally filled with chalk or glauconite and remain at the bottom of the decanting pan or cylinder.

This method has proved especially useful in the study of glauconitic and quartzose sands containing a sparse fauna. The method also has distinct advantages over the heavy-liquid method, which is both expensive and time consuming.

## REFERENCES

Hofker, J. (1927). The Foraminifera of the Siboga Expedition, Part I, Tinoporidae, Rotaliidae, Nummulitidae, Amphestiginidae. Monograph IV, Uitkomsten op Zoologisch, Botanisch, Oceanographisch en Geologisch Gebied, verz. in Ned. Oost-Indie 1899–1900, H. M. Siboga, Lt. G. F. Tydeman, Max Weber Lieder der Expeditie, p. 1–78, pls. 1–38.

———— (1930). The Foraminifera of the Siboga Expedition, Part II, Families Astrorhizidae, Rhizamminidae, Rheophacidae, Anomalinidae, Peneroplidae with an introduction to the life-cycle of the foraminifera. Monograph IVa, Uitkomsten op Zoologisch, Botanisch, Oceanographisch en Geologisch Gebied, verz. in Ned. Oost-Indie 1899–1900, H. M. Siboga, Lt. G. F. Tydeman, Max Weber Lieder der Expeditie, p. 78–170, pls. 38–64.

———— (1949). On Foraminifera from the Upper Senonian of South Limburg (Maestrichtian). Inst. Royal Sci. Nat. Belgique, Mem. 112, 69 pp., 23 figs.

———— (1951). The Foraminifera of the Siboga Expedition, Part III, Ordo Dentata, Sub-ordines Protoforaminata, Biforaminata, Deuteroforaminata. Monograph IVa, Uikomsten on Zoologische, Botanisch, Oceanographisch en Geologisch Gebied, verz. in Ned. Oost-Indie 1899–1900, H. M. Siboga, Lt. G. F. Tydeman, Max Weber Lieder der Expeditie, *xii* + 513 pp., 348 figs.

———— (1956). Foraminifera Dentata, Foraminifera of Santa Cruz and Thatch-Islands Virginia-Archipelago West-Indies. Univ. Zool. Mus., Copenhagen, Skr., v. 15, 237 pp., 21 diagrams, 35 pls.

———— (1957). Foraminiferan der Oberkreide von Nordwestdeutschland und Holland. Geol. Landesant., Geihefte Geol. Jahrb., no. 27, 464 pp., 495 figs.

———— (1960). Planktonic foraminifera in the Danian of Denmark. Contrib. Cushman Found. Foram. Res. Contr., v. 11, pt. 3, p. 73–86, 5 tables, 38 figs.

# Blade Mounting

RAYMOND A. LEWANDOWSKI

*U. S. Geological Survey, Washington, D.C.*

Mounting an abrasive blade on a rock cutoff saw is a simple process, but a good many expensive blades have been ruined by improper mounting on the spindle shaft (arbor). The blade must fit precisely on a firm true-running spindle in which end play is reduced to a minimum.

Always be sure that the diameter of the arbor hole in the blade corresponds to the diameter of the spindle shaft. Never force a wheel onto the arbor, as

Publication authorized by the Director, U. S. Geological Survey.

this will cause a diamond blade to wobble laterally and can permanently damage its trueness. If forced onto the shaft, a Carborundum blade will break into several pieces the moment pressure is applied. Mounting an abrasive blade with an oversize arbor hole on an undersize spindle is equally disastrous, as the blade will rotate eccentrically and shatter the moment it touches the rock. An eccentrically turning diamond wheel will dig into the rock, crimp, twist, tear, or stop, and may even seize the rock and throw it out of the holding vise.

To prevent abrasive wheels from breaking or distorting, two suitable metal disk collars of equal diameter must be used, one on each side of the blade. These collars must be parallel and run true when mounted on the spindle arbor. For thin Carborundum blades the collars should be approximately one-third of the wheel diameter; for diamond blades, about one-fourth of the diameter.

Before mounting a blade, it should be examined for manufacturer's markings that may indicate which side belongs next to the outside collar and locking nut. On some wheels a printed arrow indicates the direction of rotation. Unless there are indications to the contrary, the manufacturer's trademark commonly is on the outside face. Orientation of the wheel may not be as important for Carborundum blades, but it is essential for the diamond wheels. The method used by the manufacturer to embed the diamond dust into the blade grooves affects the design of the blade periphery and determines the cutting efficiency and the length of service to be expected. If the blade is mounted inversely, the wheel edge becomes belled and cutting is laborious. If the outside face is not indicated, it should be determined and marked with paint or scratched on with a diamond pencil so that the same mounting is used each time.

Finally, when the cutoff wheel is correctly in place, the locking nut is tightened with a wrench. If it is not tightened sufficiently, the blade may fly off during sawing and possibly injure the operator. If tightened too much, Carborundum blades may crack under the strain, and diamond wheels may warp so that the cutting edge wobbles laterally while in operation. Holding the blade with one hand and the wrench with the other while unlocking the nut is not recommended; a diamond blade may bend or a Carborundum wheel break because of the coupling force.

Examine the threads on the shaft and locking nut to be sure that they are free from grit, rust, and water. The threads should be lubricated occasionally with light oil.

# The Centrifuge as a Tool in Foraminiferal Preparation

ZACK M. ARNOLD

*Museum of Paleontology, University of California, Berkeley*

The difference between success and failure in the study of Foraminifera, particularly in biological areas or those paleontological areas having strong biological overtones, often lies in the application of efficient and effective techniques in conjunction with apparatus that has been designed specifically for the problem and materials at hand. Because of their peculiar natural attributes, including cytologically refractory tests, preference for marine environments, and relatively long life spans, Foraminifera have been less frequent subjects of biological inquiry than have more amenable types of protozoa; hence progress in their study has lagged seriously. Moreover, the biologist or the paleontologist wishing to investigate living Foraminifera often discovers that the technical procedures needed for a profitable study are best developed under the combined inspiration of biologically and paleontologically disciplined imaginations. The technical developments herein discussed are the outgrowth of such a confluence of disciplines. Although principally micropaleontological in origin, some should be useful in other types of paleontological inquiry as well.

## CONCENTRATING SPECIMENS

Paleontologists in general, and certainly those wishing to study living Foraminifera, would do well to acquaint themselves with the role of the centrifuge in many of the biologist's routine laboratory procedures, especially those of the protozoologist and microbiologist. The problem of changing fluids in which Foraminifera are immersed without losing any specimens is one that must frequently be faced. A centrifuge is the logical tool for the job, but centrifuges generally available in paleontological or biological laboratories are not specifically designed for the efficient performance of the specialized chores with which the foraminiferologist is concerned. Most are too large for effective treatment of the small quantities of material with which the foraminiferan biologist must often work; furthermore, it is often impossible to avoid losing some specimens unless special precautions are taken against the normal hazards attendant upon the application of standard protozoological or micro-

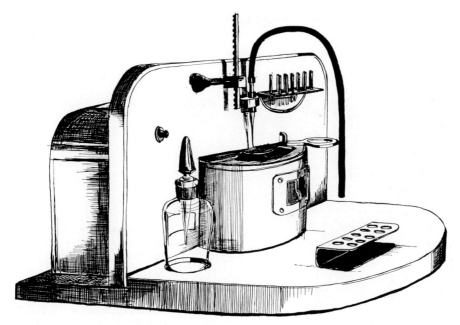

**Fig. 1**

*Centrifuge and fluid-changing apparatus.*

paleontological technique. The apparatus and methods here described have been developed to permit handling any quantity of specimens—from one to thousands of individuals—with speed and efficiency and without the loss of a single specimen if, as in my research on controlled lineages of culture populations, it is essential to retain every microscopic specimen throughout a complicated sequence of fluid changes. Because of their size and specific gravity, most Foraminifera settle relatively rapidly in the fluids normally employed by the biologist; for this reason, the motive force required to drive a foraminiferan centrifuge need not be great. The two small centrifuges described below effectively and inexpensively complement the standard laboratory machines (for 15-ml tubes) and actually supplant them for more demanding operations.

The first of these (fig. 1) is driven by a 1/20 hp motor equipped with a 10-tube plastic head, the whole housed in a one-pound coffee tin. Glass centrifuge tubes, easily formed in the laboratory and having a capacity of 0.2 ml, are held in place by brass trunnion rings from which they need not be removed until the end of the entire fluid-changing sequence, since fluids are evacuated from them by means of a vacuum pipette which can be lowered mechanically and with precision through a port in the top of the centrifuge housing and observed through a plastic window that affords an unrestricted view of the centrifuge's electrically illuminated interior. This

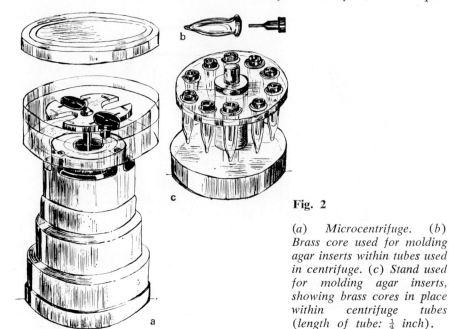

**Fig. 2**

(*a*) *Microcentrifuge.* (*b*) *Brass core used for molding agar inserts within tubes used in centrifuge.* (*c*) *Stand used for molding agar inserts, showing brass cores in place within centrifuge tubes (length of tube: ¼ inch).*

design permits safe removal of fluids from small quantities of concentrate after centrifugation. For still greater precision and safety in changing fluids without losing a single specimen from a small batch of valuable research materials, two additional refinements have been devised: the first, a centrifuge for use under the microscope; the second, a removable lining (for the specimen container of either centrifuge) which can itself become a permanent envelope or container for the Foraminifera and be subjected to the same preparatory precedures (e.g., serial sectioning) as the Foraminifera.

The small centrifuge illustrated in fig. 2,*a,* also powered by a 27-volt D.C. motor is designed to fit between the metal castings of the stage of a stereoscopic microscope after the glass plate has been removed from the stage. Essential features of the device are: (1) a heavy base for stability; (2) a low-power motor with variable speed control; (3) a plastic head, bearing four suitably pivoted cups; (4) plastic disks in which are molded conical depressions having a capacity of 0.1 ml to 0.01 ml or less; (5) a metal or plastic housing which serves as a combined dust cover and safety shield; and (6) a foot-operated rheostat for controlling the motor's speed.

The base is a simple brass turning into which the lower half of the motor can be snugly inserted. An A.C. motor could just as well be used, as several of these having suitable dimensions and adequate power are commercially available. The brass cups that hold the plastic disks and specimens have a heavy elongate base which effectively shifts their center of gravity well below the pivot point and assures their proper behavior during centrifugation; if these extensions were omitted, the plastic disks would be thrown from the cups. The disks, molded from black opaque polyethylene, must be carefully designed if they are to perform their intended task effectively. In designing the mold, consideration should be given to the size of the specimens with which you will be working, the volume of specimens that will be treated in each operation, and the volume of fluid that will be required during preparation. The simple expedient of preparing several crude mockups of the disk from modeling clay can save valuable and often expensive shop time, for by this means the suitability of a given set of dimensions for the depression can easily be tested and altered until optimum volumetric relationships are obtained for translation into a mold.

The mold is best constructed of brass, since this metal effectively retains the heat required during the molding process. A polished brass disk with a short shaft that can be chucked in the drill press is used to close the mold, the press itself forming a convenient source of pressure during the compression-molding operation. Any one of a variety of thermoplastic materials would be suitable for molding the disks, but polyethylene is probably the most readily available of those which are relatively inert, chemically and biologically. Discarded articles of neutral polyethylene, easily obtained around the home or laboratory, may be melted with a blowtorch and pigmented by adding powdered charcoal, after which they may be pressed into thick sheets between heated plates of metal. From these sheets, one then cuts disks whose diameter and thickness slightly exceed those of the disks to be molded. These preformed disks are inserted into the mold, the assembly is heated to melt the plastic, and pressure is applied to fill and close the mold. After cooling in air or water, the mold is opened and the disk is ready for use.

An important adjunct to either of the centrifuges described above is a special agar insert or lining for the centrifuge tubes or disks. The inserts for the tubes (fig. 2,*b*) are molded in place about metal cores, a molding stand (fig. 2,*c*) facilitating the operation; the inserts for the disks are formed by allowing a drop of molten agar to harden in the depressions of the disk and then molding a cavity in the agar blank by means of a heated glass rod with a tip of appropriate shape.

With the inserts in place, specimens pipetted into them may be carried through a complex sequence of fluids but ultimately compressed into a small volume and, if desired, sealed within a solid block of agar which can subsequently be subjected to serial sectioning or other special treatment with far greater mechanical ease than if one were dealing with free specimens.

# The Vacuum Oven
# for Impregnating Microfossils

ZACK M. ARNOLD

*Museum of Paleontology, University of California, Berkeley*

A vacuum oven for use in infiltrating the tests of foraminifera or other micro-fossils with synthetic resins prior to sectioning is illustrated in fig 1. This oven, sufficiently small to permit efficient manipulation and observation of its contents under the stereoscopic microscope, has a variety of uses in the laboratory, such as heating small quantities of fluids and boiling small sam-ples containing pollen, diatoms, or other microfossils; moreover, its construc-tion and operating costs are insignificant.

The body of the oven is a 1-inch cube of brass, bored to produce a central cavity $\frac{3}{4}$ inch deep and $\frac{3}{4}$ inch in diameter. Two holes tapped for $\frac{3}{8}$-inch pipe are drilled on adjacent faces, one to receive a 1-inch nipple to which a vacuum line may be attached, the other to receive a 5-inch length of pipe that houses the heating element. The heating unit consists of a length of 0.75-mm nichrome wire bent to form a $\frac{1}{2}$-inch loop which is energized by

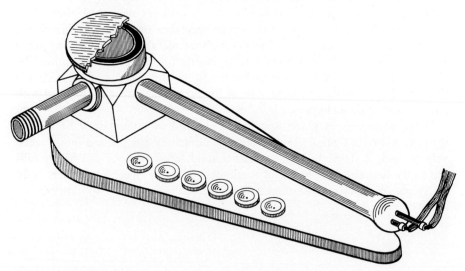

**Fig. 1.** *Vacuum oven for impregnating microfossils (extra specimen cups stored on base plate of oven).*

the current from a variable transformer (1 to 3 volts). This resistance wire is attached by setscrews to sockets formed at the ends of two brass leads, the whole being readily removed from the oven block for servicing by simply unscrewing the tube through which the leads pass. The rods may be insulated with electrical cement (Sauereisen's Insalute Cement) or by means of a specially formed ceramic insulator turned on a lathe from leather-hard ceramic clay and fired. A satisfactory vacuum seal at the outer end of the tube may be effected with a high-temperature sealing wax or with a thick layer of electrical cement. The top of the heating chamber is sealed by a thick glass disk centered over an O-ring which fits snugly into the channel turned for it around the orifice.

Crucibles of turned brass, fitting loosely into the resistance loop of the oven, form effective containers for tests of foraminifera or other organisms that must be impregnated with a thermoplastic resin under vacuum. But if corrosive fluids are to be heated in the oven small glass flasks blown from soft or pyrex tubing should be substituted.

# Magnetic Separation of Conodonts

VERNE E. DOW

*Geologist, Martin Marietta Corporation, Topeka, Kansas*

Substances vary in their response to magnetic fields. The type of magnetism exhibited by any particular material depends on its permeability (magnetic permeability = ratio of magnetic induction to the magnetizing force). For most materials, the permeability differs only slightly from the value 1. On the basis of permeability, three major groups have been generally recognized; *ferromagnetics,* with large permeabilities; *diamagnetics,* with permeabilities slightly less than 1; and *paramagnetics,* with permeabilities slightly greater than 1. Ferromagnetic and paramagnetic materials placed in a magnetic field will move from the weaker to the stronger part of the field; diamagnetic minerals will move from the stronger to the weaker part of the field.

A variety of minerals occurs in sedimentary rocks, and each mineral has its range of magnetic susceptibility. In practice the problem of working out a separation involves determining this range of susceptibility for the principal constituents of any particular residue.

The Frantz Isodynamic Magnetic Separator which has been used successfully in the separation of conodonts consists of a powerful electromagnet with a rheostat for adjusting the field strength; a vibrating chute of nonmagnetic material through which the minerals to be separated are moved; an adjustable vibrator to control the vibration chute; a feed funnel with adjustable rate; two nonmagnetic collecting cans; and a precise calibration for adjusting forward and side inclinations of the magnet.

Samples fed onto the chute are acted upon by the magnetic field, which is strongest on the left side of the chute and weakest on the right side. As the particles move down slope, they are forced to take paths that depend on their susceptibility. A "splitter" at the center of the chute guides the separated materials into the outer and inner collectors. The outer, left side of the two collectors receives the more magnetic fraction of any particular run.

## METHOD

Reduce the residue as far as possible using standard acid-solution and "washing" techniques. Boiling and washing with a chemial deflocculant, such as sal soda, will remove much of the troublesome fine clay that may be present; dust-size particles impair a good separation. Since the best results are obtained from residues of uniform particle size, the sample should be carefully screened.

After the residue has been washed and dried, it should be examined with a microscope to determine the dominant mineralogy, which in turn determines the various settings for the first run through the separator. The magnetic and nonmagnetic fractions should be examined again with a microscope after the sample has been passed through the separator to check the effectiveness of the separation.

Residue which contains appreciable amounts of limonite should be run through the separator at forward slopes of 20 to 25°, side slopes of 10 to 15°, 1.0 to 1.3 amperes, vibrator setting 4.0, and medium-fast feed (fig. 1). When

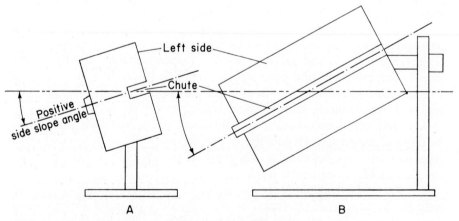

**Fig. 1.** (*A*) *Positive side slope.* (*B*) *Forward slope.*

there is an extremely large percentage of limonite it is best to run the sample one time at 1.0 ampere and then rerun the nonmagnetic portion at 1.3 amperes. This prevents aggregation and clogging of the chute during separation. The above separation results in a barren magnetic portion and a concentration of conodonts in the nonmagnetic side. The concentration of conodonts in the nonmagnetic side determines whether further separation is necessary. Since most of the nonmagnetic residues at this stage contain dominantly quartz and/or dolomite, the separation of this fraction will be discussed in detail later on.

If the residue is mainly clay-shale in shades of red or green, the initial run should be at a 10 to 15° forward slope and a 5 to 15° side slope, with a maximum amperage, medium fast feed, and the vibrator set at about 4.0. If the sample is run through at one of the higher side slopes (10 to 15°) and some of the material goes to the nonmagnetic side, that portion should be rerun at a lower side slope setting (2 to 5°).

After the initial one or two passes, the nonmagnetic fraction should be passed through at a different setting to further concentrate the conodonts. If the nonmagnetic fraction is principally dolomite, use the following settings: forward slope 10°, side slope −2°, 0.9 ampere, vibrator at 2.5 to 3.0, and slow feed. Conodonts will remain on the magnetic side, as they are not as diamagnetic as quartz. When very small amounts of iron stain are present on the surface of the quartz, it is often necessary to pass the magnetic portion through several times to insure separation. It often helps to pass the sample through the separator at 25° forward slope, 10° side slope, maximum amperage, vibrator setting 4.0, and fast feed to remove the more magnetic material.

Samples consisting mainly of dolomite should be passed through the separator at 10° forward slope, −2° side slope, vibrator setting 2.5 to 3.0, maximum amperage, and very slow feed. Since most dolomites contain a large volume of residue in proportion to the number of conodonts, it is often desirable to rerun magnetic and nonmagnetic fractions.

The initial pass will often remove most of the more magnetic material without removing any conodonts. If conodonts do occur in the magnetic side on the first run, probably the material was being fed too rapidly or the forward slope was too steep. If the current to the coils is decreased or shut off before the entire run is completed, conodonts will also accumulate in the magnetic side on the first run. Magnetic materials which should be removed in the first run may be incorporated in the nonmagnetic fraction if the amperage is too high and the feeding too rapid. High amperage may attract an aggregate of highly magnetic materials and clog the chute on the magnetic side, causing both magnetics and nonmagnetics to go down the nonmagnetic slot.

To further concentrate the conodonts after the initial run, the portion of the sample in the nonmagnetic side is passed through the instrument at prescribed settings, depending on the type of mineralogy. Some samples need to be passed through only once; others may take several passes. The number of runs depends only on the lithology of the residue and the degree of separation desired by the operator. Many times a fine powder accumulates with the separated fractions. This may be removed by dry screening.

It should be noted here that discussion of *magnetic* fractions refers to material which is removed at any particular setting and moves to the outer (left) slot of the instrument. In general, there will be a magnetic and a nonmagnetic fraction for each setting of the instrument. In the early stages of the separation, the nonmagnetic fractions may contain paramagnetics and diamagnetics but probably no ferromagnetics. As the degree of separation is increased, the fraction referred to as *nonmagnetic* is primarily, if not completely, diamagnetic.

After running a few samples, the operator should be able to concentrate most of the conodonts in the nonmagnetic side after one or two runs. Quartz and dolomite are usually the most common minerals present in the conodont-bearing fraction. In some fractions, conodonts are so abundant that no further reduction is necessary after the first run.

## RANGE OF SUSCEPTIBILITY OF QUARTZ, DOLOMITE, AND CONODONTS

In a test made to determine the amperage and slope needed to give optimum separation of conodonts, several grams of conodonts were first concentrated and put through the separator. After a number of runs it was determined that nearly all the conodonts came out as paramagnetics in one pass with a forward slope of $10°$, a side slope of $-2°$, an amperage setting of 1.5, a vibrator setting of 2.5, and slow feed. However, conodonts appeared on the nonmagnetic side at an amperage of 1.0.

Dolomite will be held on the magnetic side at the same setting as that used for maximum conodont separation. This relationship is quite reasonable, for in petrographic examination of dolomites there seems to be a characteristic banding of iron in the dolomite rhombohedrons. Both the iron content and magnetic susceptibility of dolomites vary. The settings mentioned above, however, have worked quite well for the samples I have studied. Maximum available amperage should be used when separating dolomite residue, but if the instrument is operated at maximum amperage for extended periods, the coils become warm and amperage drops. Therefore, if the machine is to be used for considerable lengths of time it should be put in a cool place, or a fan used to cool the coils. A small transformer can be secured to boost the output.

Quartz overlaps the lower range of conodont separation. At a $10°$ forward slope, a $-2°$ side slope, a vibrator setting of 2.5, and slow feed, conodonts will start to move to the nonmagnetic side at 1.0 ampere. Quartz begins to move to this side at 0.75 ampere, but it does not move in a significant amount until 0.9 ampere is reached. At 0.9 ampere most of the quartz moves to the nonmagnetic side. Any increase above 0.9 ampere will cause conodonts to move over with the quartz. Therefore, it is desirable to run the conodont-bearing fraction through more than once, removing part of the quartz with each pass. The presence of limonite on quartz grains also complicates separation. If there is sufficient limonite on the surface of the grains, much of this material can be attracted to the magnetic side by using a forward slope of 10 to 15°, a *positive* side slope of 1 to 2°, maximum amperage, a vibrator setting of 2.5, and slow feed.

I have used this separation technique on only a few lithologies. The settings described above will probably have to be modified somewhat for other lithologies during the initial stages of separation. However, the settings described for the separation of dolomite, quartz, and conodonts should be reliable.

In modifying the settings for the initial separation, keep in mind that by decreasing the forward slope, rate of feed, and vibrator settings, you increase the amount of time the magnetic field will act on a particle, therefore allowing a more complete separation, particularly of the weakly magnetic materials. The vibrator should be set so that the particles bounce down the chute. It seems that a better separation can be made if the particles bounce (but not too fast) rather than slide down the chute. Another factor to consider is that as the side slope is decreased the particles having the least paramagnetism will be attracted to the magnetic side.

# Use of the Vibro-tool for Mechanical Preparation of Fossils

RICHARD A. ROBISON

*University of Utah, Salt Lake City*

The Burgess Vibro-tool [1] is an instrument that operates by vibration of one of a variety of cutting or chipping attachments. A Vibro-tool is illustrated in fig. 1,*A*.

## OPERATION OF THE VIBRO-TOOL

Adjustments are few and simple. The following instructions are taken from the manufacturer's brochure.

---

[1] Sold by Burgess Vibrocrafters, Inc., Grayslake, Illinois.

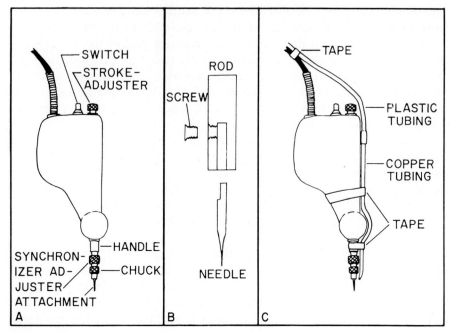

**Fig. 1.** *Vibro-tool and adaptations for the mechanical preparation of fossils. (A)*
*Parts of the Vibro-tool. (B) Cutaway view of special attachment to hold*
*a sharpened dental burr or phonograph needle. (C) Airhose attached to*
*Vibro-tool.*

The length of stroke is determined by the Stroke-Adjuster (fig. 1,*A*). Tightening
the Stroke-Adjuster reduces the stroke length and loosening the Stroke-Adjuster
increases the stroke (to a maximum of $\frac{3}{16}$-inch). As a general rule, a long
stroke adjustment is most efficient for coarse preparation of large fossils, whereas
a short stroke adjustment is necessary for preparation of small or delicate fossils.

Smoothness of vibration is determined by the Synchronizer-Adjuster (fig. 1,*A*).
It should be opened or closed until the tool has a smooth, constant hum.

To place an attachment in the Vibro-tool, slip the shank of the attachment into
the chuck, and then tighten the chuck.

## SPECIAL ADAPTATIONS

A variety of attachments is available from the manufacturer, but most of them
do not have points sharp enough for efficient preparation of fossils. For mechanical preparation of many kinds of macrofossils a needle attachment has
been found to be particularly efficient. This attachment (fig. 1,*B*) can be
made from a solid steel or brass rod and a sharpened dental burr or phono-
graph needle. The metal rod should be $\frac{7}{32}$ inch in diameter and $\frac{3}{4}$ inch long.
In one end of the rod, drill a hole $\frac{3}{8}$ inch deep with a diameter large enough
to accommodate the dental burr or phonograph needle. Drill another hole in

one side of the rod about $\frac{5}{16}$ inch from the end. Thread this hole so that a setscrew can be used to hold the burr or needle.

Another convenient adaptation is to attach an air hose to the Vibro-tool to keep the specimen free of dust and small rock particles during preparation. A cheap and efficient source of compressed air can be improvised from a small aquarium aerator, a length of flexible plastic tubing, and a nozzle made from a 6-inch piece of copper or aluminum tubing. The nozzle is bent to fit the upper contour of the Vibro-tool (fig. 1,C), attached to the tool with adhesive tape, and connected to the aerator by the plastic tubing. An alternative but less convenient method is to blow into the plastic tubing.

## USE OF ACCESSORY TOOLS

Before using the Vibro-tool it is sometimes desirable to use other tools for preliminary steps in preparation. The rock-trimmer may be used to break the fossil-bearing rock into pieces of convenient size and to remove large amounts of matrix. A rotary grinder with flexible shaft and Carborundum or diamond blade may then be used to cut away much of the remaining matrix immediately above the surface that is to be exposed with the Vibro-tool. Additional preliminary or final removal of matrix may be made with a rock-saw or with hammers, chisels, and needles of various sizes. Uses of some of these tools are discussed elsewhere in this book.

## USE OF THE VIBRO-TOOL

After most of the matrix has been removed the specimen is placed under a low-powered microscope and the remaining matrix removed with the Vibro-tool. For best results the tool should generally be held so that the vibrating needle is perpendicular to the surface to be cleaned. Starting at the edge of an exposed surface of the specimen, the matrix is gradually flaked away until the entire surface is exposed. Abrupt changes in the configuration of the surface may cause the preparator to accidentally chip or break off pieces of the specimen. These misfortunes can usually be overcome with patience, experience, and knowledge of the morphology of the particular object that is being excavated.

A few simple techniques increase speed, precision, and convenience in the preparation of fossils with a Vibro-tool. The importance of maintaining a sharp point should be stressed because of the faster cutting speed that is available and the greater precision that is possible in excavating delicate or minute structures. The point may easily be sharpened with a rotary grinder or a whetstone. Additional precision and stability may be obtained by resting the side of the vibrating needle against the tip of an extended finger of the hand used to hold the Vibro-tool, and by resting this finger against a firm base.

Considerable noise is usually generated when the Vibro-tool is used on a rock resting on a metal microscope stand or on a table. Much of this noise may be muffled by placing the specimen on a small sand-filled cloth bag.

If the shell or carapace of a fossil has been weathered, or if it is otherwise loosely attached to the internal mold, it may tend to exfoliate when subjected to vibration. This can sometimes be prevented by allowing a drop of Alvar dissolved in acetone or benzol to penetrate between the shell and the internal mold. The acetone or benzol will evaporate and the Alvar will cement the shell to the internal mold. Care must be taken, however, to prevent the solution from penetrating between the shell and the external mold, as this will make excavation of the external surface difficult.

It is difficult, if not impossible, to clean the surface of some ornamented specimens without damaging the ornamentation. Good results sometimes have been obtained by cleaning out the external mold with a sharp needle mounted in a Vibro-tool and then making a positive cast with latex or plastic.

The Vibro-tool can be used with variable degrees of success on fossils preserved in most rock types, except those with a siliceous matrix or strong siliceous cement. Often only trial will determine whether a certain matrix is amenable to satisfactory removal by the Vibro-tool.

# Rock Trimmers

HARLAN H. ROEPKE

*Department of Geology, University of Texas, Austin*

The two types of rock trimmers in widespread use today differ principally in the mechanism by which pressure is exerted. Those that exert pressure by means of a screw are probably the most common, having been available through geological supply firms for many years. The more recently available hydraulic jack-operated trimmers have proved advantageous in dealing with especially tough rock. Both types exert downward pressure on a horizontal bar that is guided by a pair of upright columns and to which a wedge-shaped tooth is fixed, edge down. Directly beneath this tooth is a similar tooth secured edge up in the base of the trimmer. By exerting downward pressure on the upper tooth, a rock specimen placed between the teeth may be readily broken along a plane roughly parallel to the aligned edges of the teeth.

As many trimmers have been manufactured by local tool companies to individual specifications, both types are susceptible to considerable variation in size, pressure capacity, and ease of use. Limiting factors inherent in the two types are:

| SCREW-OPERATED | HYDRAULIC JACK-OPERATED |
|---|---|
| *Vertical capacity.* Limited by length of uprights and screw; commonly 4 to 7 inches. (Screw diameter must increase with length.) | *Vertical capacity.* Limited by length of uprights and piston travel, commonly 4 to 5 inches. (Hydraulic piston devices other than hydraulic truck jacks may provide a greater vertical range of travel.) |
| *Horizontal capacity.* Limited by separation of uprights and strength of the frame; commonly about 1 foot. | *Horizontal capacity.* Same as for screw-operated trimmer. |
| *Pressure capacity.* Severely limited by screw thread design and strength of the thread box through which the wheel or lever is attached to the screw, and by the strength of the operator. | *Pressure capacity.* Limited by capacity of hydraulic jack and strength of materials. Jacks of 8- and 12-ton capacity are most common. Hydraulic piston devices having greater capacity may be incorporated. |
| *Ease of use.* Permits fine control and a "feeling" for the nature of the rock; preferred for close and delicate work. | *Ease of use.* Requires less strength to operate and is capable of greater pressure. It may be modified to permit application of electric motors to a rack and pinion gear device for coarse vertical adjustment and/or to the hydraulic pump, thus providing rapid vertical movement. |

With a few trials the operator should be able to trim specimens of most sedimentary rocks with ease. Soft mudstones and arenaceous rocks are readily broken with little, if any, tendency to shatter. However, tough, dense rocks, such as metasediments, silicified and cherty sediments, and dense, brittle carbonates, as well as most igneous rocks, require considerable pressure to break. When such rocks yield, a spray of rock fragments and chips generally results. The operator should protect his eyes by wearing safety glasses, goggles, or a face shield when handling samples of this kind. Adjustable plastic goggles or slip-on plastic face shields kept in the immediate vicinity of the trimmer will encourage their use.

Some operators, handling large and/or unusually tough specimens, have attempted to use crow bars or extended handles to apply increased pressure to the sample. Since properly designed trimmers provide enough leverage to create pressures approaching the safe limit of the equipment, the use of additional levers to increase pressure is discouraged. Improperly tempered or unskillfully retempered trimmer teeth may wear excessively or may be dangerously brittle and likely to add bits of steel to the spray of chips when used on hard rocks. Teeth should be inspected regularly for excessive wear and chipping and, when necessary, either be replaced or retempered by a skilled mechanic.

Samples of metasediments that are sheared or cleaved may present faces at an acute angle to the plane along which the rock is to be broken, and it may be necessary to make several parallel breaks at right angles to the desired breakage plane to provide bearing surfaces against which the teeth may press without sliding. Where this is not possible, bearing surfaces may be trimmed square with a hammer or the rock may be split with a hammer and chisel. A grinding wheel may be used to notch acutely cleaved surfaces to provide a bearing surface for the trimmer teeth. A small, flat-topped iron anvil designed to straddle the lower tooth is handy to use when a rock specimen offers only one face perpendicular to the breakage plane. A tempered steel triangular prism placed on the anvil provides a lower cutting edge that may be placed in any desired position with respect to the upper tooth.

In dealing with large or especially tough samples the plastic properties of the rock may be used to advantage. By increasing the pressure slowly, or step-by-step, pausing after each increase, the rock may yield somewhat plastically due to fatigue before breaking at a pressure lower than its shear strength. Large blocks under sustained high pressure have been known to break after several minutes.

Trimmer teeth should be kept as sharp as is practical. Frequent sharpening on a grinding wheel precludes prolonged grinding, which leads to overheating of the edge and loss of temper. Sharp teeth provide greater control over the location of the breakage plane, give a better purchase on subparallel faces of the sample, and require less pressure to break the rock. Some operators use an extra, especially sharp set of teeth just for fine work.

Screw-type trimmers should be oiled occasionally and threads cleared of adhering grit. Sliding surfaces on both types should be lightly greased when necessary and hydraulic jacks refilled and oil seals checked when the teeth no longer meet.

# Removing Matrix from Fossils by Miniature Sandblasting

G. F. STUCKER, M. J. GALUSHA, M. C. McKENNA

*American Museum of Natural History, New York*

A method of fossil preparation has come into use recently which employs small-scale sandblasting to remove refractory matrix from small specimens (Stucker, 1961). The S. S. White Company produces an industrial airbrasive unit which is as useful in the preparation of fossils as it is in etching steel, glass, and hard plastics. Briefly, the machine is a device for suspending minute abrasive particles in a stream of rapidly moving gas. The abrasive-laden gas is then expelled through a nozzle towards a target with enough force to erode the target surface. In the hands of a skilled operator this machine permits the preparation of specimens previously considered either impractical or impossible to prepare. The airbrasive machine has become one of the most valued tools of the paleontological laboratory.

The proper choice of abrasive is essential. The size depends on the nature of the work to be performed: removing matrix, delineating delicate anatomical features, roughing out areas to be treated with acid, and so forth. The hardness of both matrix and specimen must also be taken into account. The coarsest grade of abrasive employed is aluminum oxide milled to a particle size $50\mu$ in diameter. It is the manufacturer's No. 3 compound, used for bulk removal of rock and very fast cutting in hard matrix. The No. 1 powder ($27\mu$ aluminum oxide) allows greater latitude of application and is especially effective on matrix of moderate hardness. Work on delicate areas, such as the removal of matrix or preservative films from teeth, or work on paper-thin bones or shells, requires the manufacturer's No. 2 powder (calcium magnesium carbonate). Tissue-thin bone can be prepared with No. 4 powder (sodium bicarbonate).

Storage hoppers containing the abrasive are mounted over vibrators which keep the abrasive powder in constant agitation during operation; the particles sift through the perforated base into a mixing compartment below. Adjusting the vibration regulates the flow of abrasive into the lower chamber, where the particles are combined with dry compressed carbon dioxide gas or carefully dried air fed into the machine under controlled pressure. This mixture is then conducted in elastic tubing to a tungsten carbide nozzle and ejected at about 1100 feet per second toward the specimen. There are two main types of nozzle tips: one with a round hole 0.018 inch in diameter, used for most work; and one with a rectangular 0.006 by 0.060 inch opening, used for special work, including precision cutting. Each type of nozzle is attached to a hand piece by a ball and socket joint, permitting free rotation of the nozzle for greater usefulness. The quantity of abrasive used and the force with which it is expelled should be regulated according to the material being prepared. Too much abrasive or too much pressure can destroy a specimen in seconds. The force with which the abrasive strikes the specimen is determined by the gas pressure, usually about 100 psi, but this can be reduced to about 30 psi for extremely delicate work. The stream of particles leaving the nozzle is activated by a foot control. During normal operation about ten grams of abrasive pass through the line per minute.

No written description of techniques can be definitive, for each specimen presents its own problem of preparation, but hard matrices usually show greater abrasion than elastic materials, which tend to absorb the forces of impact. The machine works best with the very matrices that defy other methods of attack. However, the machine works poorly on matrix of varying density. Pits and undercuts form in this type of matrix, and particles of abrasive may pass through small crevices to damage the specimen.

For making incisions or deep cuts the nozzle tip is held close to the specimen and moved back and forth. The closer the tip, the deeper the cut. Holding the tip at a distance and moving it with a sweeping motion over an area results in a spray technique useful in exploring for buried parts of a specimen, for removing very thin layers of matrix, and for cleaning smooth surfaces.

If the work is done in an air-tight working chamber incorporating an exhaust system, spent abrasive and debris can be removed efficiently. A chamber approximately two feet on a side and one foot deep is convenient. The specimens are inserted through a side door and manipulated through two arm holes. A removable glass window seals off the entire top and permits the operator to view his work. A solid top with a small window constructed from a standard lantern slide cover glass may be substituted in order to reduce the expense of replacing glass when it becomes frosted. A cycloptic microscope, such as one of American Optical Company's Spencer cycloptic series number 59, with a long working distance $0.5\times$ apochromatic objective, will permit microscopic vision of specimens through the glass window at a distance of approximately eight inches from the microscope objective.

The airbrasive unit has various disadvantages, the main one being that parts coming into contact with the abrasive are worn down, resulting in frequent need for maintenance, but this feature is entirely offset by the efficiency with which delicate fossils are extracted from the most stubborn matrix. In general, this machine considerably reduces preparation time, freeing laboratory technicians for other tasks.

**REFERENCE**

Stucker, G. F. (1961). Salvaging fossils by jet. Curator, v. 4, no. 4, p. 332–340, figs. 1–6.

# The Ro-Tap as an Aid in Sample Preparation

JOHN W. KOENIG

*Missouri Geological Survey, Rolla*

Microcrinoids are rarely visible in the field. Therefore, patience is required because each sample must be completely processed and carefully picked before the collector can tell whether it will yield specimens. The size of samples to be collected depends on the time available and on the kind of study. A large grocery sack full of material takes a lot of processing, and the amount of work involved to process such a large sample may not be worth the number or variety of specimens obtained. Usually a large sample is reserved for complete, detailed faunal studies from a bed which is known to be productive. For reconnaissance, a small driller's sample sack is ample, and this amount of material takes much less processing time.

The sample is first washed and decanted in plain water until most of the debris, clay, and silt are removed. Then a generous amount of potassium hydroxide is added to the water and the sample is soaked for several hours, either at room temperature or simmering on a hot plate. The sample is again thoroughly washed and decanted and is then dried on a hot plate. I have found that the pot or pan in which the sample is dried should not be in direct contact with the hot plate when drying because the sample will pop and scatter all over the laboratory. Because this kind of treatment takes too long for reconnaissance work, I have developed a more rapid method which I find very satisfactory for processing small samples. I give the sample a perfunctory washing to eliminate such debris as twigs, grass, and lichen, and then I place it in a sieve pan and add a fair amount of potassium hydroxide and just enough water to cover the sample. Then I place the pan on the oscillating part of a Ro-Tap sieve shaker, deactivate the Ro-Tap hammer, and turn on the machine. About two hours of oscillation is sufficient to clean most samples. There is little danger of abrasion, because the sample very soon becomes a thick sludge of flocculated clay, which apparently cushions the specimens. Washing, of course, is necessary after this shaking process, but the flocculated clay washes very quickly, and most samples come out good and clean.

After a sample is dry it is sieved through a nest of sieves. In my own work I use five mesh sizes (10, 18, 35, 60, and 120) and a pan. Although all fractions should be examined for specimens, by far the greatest number of microcrinoids will concentrate on the 35- and 60-mesh screens. The average specimen size is about 1 mm in diameter. After the sample is sieved, the fractions can be stored in small glass vials or in manila sample bags.

Procedure in sample picking is largely a matter of preference. For my own work, I use a tray about 2 by 3 inches, floored with a piece of dark blue glass. I shake a small portion of the sample onto the tray and spread it out to a thickness of one grain. Then I arrange the grains into a number of rows, using a little, hoe-shaped tool made out of a small sheet of plastic clamped into the end of a metal Exacto knife handle. The grains move smoothly on the glass and do not stick to the plastic "hoe," which makes row-splitting a simple matter. Then I put the tray under a binocular microscope and pick one row after another. In this way, I am not likely to overlook a part of the sample, and my picking time is considerably reduced. Picking yields will, of course, vary widely. The yield may be as high as several specimens an hour or as low as one specimen per sample, or, often, nothing.

This type of sample collecting and processing will yield, of course, most types of microfossils such as conodonts, holothurian sclerites, bryozoans, corals, fish teeth, foraminifera, ostracods, and immature brachiopods and gastropods.

# Microfossil Vacuum-needle Segregating Pick

E. H. STINEMEYER

*Shell Oil Company, Bakersfield, California*

The vacuum-needle pick is used to rapidly remove microfossils or small objects from disaggregated samples. It is usually faster to vacuum the fossils out of the washed sample material than it is to pick them out individually with a dissecting needle or a fine camel's-hair brush. Other small objects such as mineral grains can also be segregated.

## CONSTRUCTION

Figures 1 and 2 illustrate the vacuum pump, suction tube, and needle used in making this instrument. Instructions for constructing the instrument follow.

### NEEDLE ASSEMBLY

Grind the socket flange of the hypodermic needle flush with the hub of the socket. Grind off the flange that secures the needle in its socket attachment, using a $\frac{1}{15}$-inch drill. Remove the needle and ream out the hole that it occupied to $\frac{1}{16}$ inch. Then reinsert the needle into the socket and force it $\frac{1}{4}$ inch above the top of the socket hub. Fill the socket with solder, cut the needle to a length of $1\frac{3}{8}$ inches, and file the needle point to a 40° angle.

### VALVE AND TRAP CHAMBER

The valve and trap chamber is made of $\frac{1}{4}$-inch aluminum tubing $1\frac{1}{2}$ inches long, with a $\frac{7}{32}$-inch inside diameter. Bore a $\frac{3}{32}$-inch hole at a distance of $\frac{3}{4}$ inch from one end of the tube. Fit an aluminum eyelet snugly into this hole. The needle shank fits into the lower end of the tube to form the needle-valve trap assembly.

### HANDLE WITH SCREEN INSERT

A piece of $\frac{7}{32}$ O.D. aluminum tubing $3\frac{1}{4}$ inches long with a $\frac{3}{16}$-inch inside diameter receives the screen insert assembly, which consists of a 200-mesh stainless steel screen cut to shape so that it can be placed over a $\frac{1}{4}$-inch segment of $\frac{1}{16}$-inch tubing. Telescope a segment $\frac{1}{8}$ inch in diameter over this combination to stretch the screen tightly over one end. Stretch a $\frac{1}{4}$-inch O.D. piece of rubber hose 2 inches long over the other end of the tubing to serve as a connector to $\frac{3}{16}$-inch plastic tubing, which in turn connects the vacuum pump to the hypodermic-needle pick assembly. The needle-valve-trap chamber telescopes over the handle-screen unit. Fit the two units snugly by compressing the outer tubing with pliers and rotating the tube.

### VACUUM PUMP

The vacuum pumps I use are modified Tropic and Topper aquarium aerator pumps manufactured by Buchanan Products Co. of Long Beach, California. The pumps operate on 115 volts and 60 cycles. They run quietly and may be operated over long periods of time without overheating. The amount of vacuum may be changed by turning a knurled screw on the bottom of the pump. The upright Tropic pump is shown in fig. 1. It has been converted to a vacuum pump by removing the flat air-intake filter pad and inserting a plastic nipple into the recess. The fitting is made air-tight with plastic cement. A $\frac{1}{4}$-inch O.D. segment of rubber tubing 2 inches long connects the

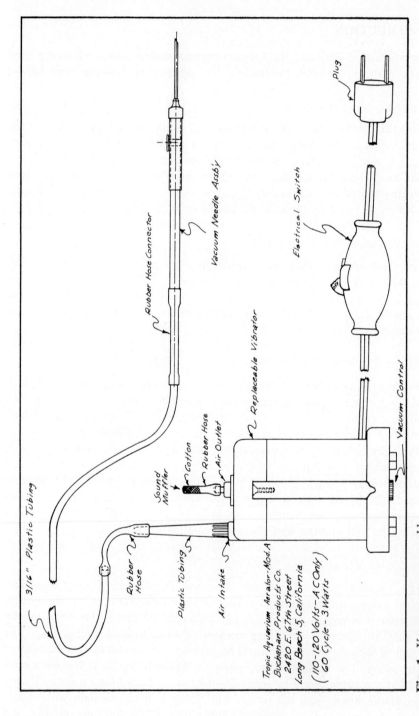

**Fig. 1.** *Vacuum pump assembly.*

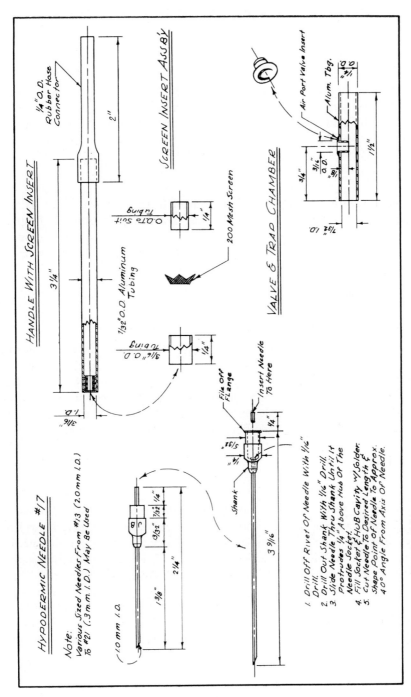

**Fig. 2.** *Vacuum needle assembly.*

nipple to the $\frac{3}{16}$-inch plastic tubing. An electrical switch is connected to the pump's electrical lead-in wires for convenience.

### HYPODERMIC NEEDLES

Hypodermic needles manufactured by Bishop and Company of Malvern, Pennsylvania varying in inside diameter from 2 mm (JB 13) to 0.3 mm (JB 21) have been used. A JB 17, with a 1-mm inside diameter, is the most useful, as all fossils that pass through a 40-mesh screen can be segregated with this needle. The final shaping can be done with whetstone and fine emery paper.

### MATERIALS

Suitable aquarium pumps can be obtained from most pet stores. Hypodermic needles, rubber and plastic tubing, are available from all hospital supply companies. The aluminum tubing and valve inserts are stocked at hobby shops and auto supply stores. Cost of construction, including labor, amounted to between $8.00 and $10.00 in 1960.

## EMPLOYMENT

### SAMPLE LAYOUT

One method is to screen the sample through the 40- and 100-mesh screens. Place the minus 40-plus 100 fraction in an elongate pile at the top of the sorting or examination plate or tray. Take off a thin line $\frac{1}{8}$ inch wide or less with a razor blade, and move it to the center of the plate. Tap the edge of the plate to obtain a layer of sample material one grain thick. Another method is to arrange the sample in several thin lines with sufficient working space between them. It is not necessary to screen the samples, but a judicious use of screens is advised.

### FOSSIL SEGREGATION

Turn on the pump, and see that the air-volume screw is adjusted to about three-quarter capacity. If the vacuum is too great, unwanted material will be sucked into the needle, even with the valve open. Hold the vacuum-needle as you would a pencil or dissecting needle (fig. 3). Sort through the sample by pushing the fossils out from the material with the end of the needle. When it is desired to pick up a fossil, place the forefinger over the valve hole on the lower portion of the handle. This will establish a vacuum, and the fossil will be sucked through the hypodermic needle, the solder-filled socket of the needle, and the inside of the aluminum tubing. The 200-mesh screen backed with a cotton filter prevents any of the fossils or small particles from going into the vacuum pump.

It is important to move the fossils into a clear space to avoid picking up undesired sample material. Each screen size may be picked in a like manner.

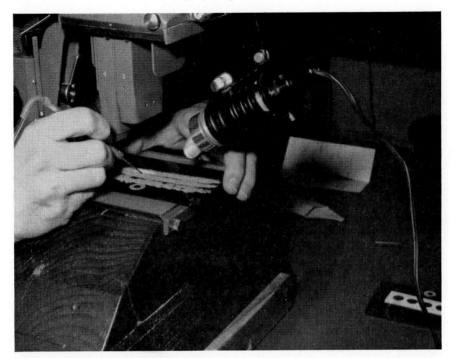

**Fig. 3.** *Close-up of sorting.*

If it is desired to pick the +40-mesh material with this method, a JB 13 needle should be used. A JB 19 or 21 needle may be used for picking the minus 100-plus 200 sizes. The needles are interchangeable. Alternatively, complete needle-trap-valve assemblies may be interchanged on the hand-screen unit.

TRANSFER FROM THE FOSSIL TRAP TO SLIDES

When it is desired to transfer the picked fossils to a slide, pull the trap section off of the handle section and invert it over an open paleontological slide (fig. 4). Then tap the socket of the needle sharply with a screen brush to dislodge all of the fossils. To insure that no fossils are lost in the transfer, place the slide on a small piece of paper to catch those that miss the slide opening.

ADDITIONAL SORTING

Until dexterity is acquired, some detritus will also be picked up. It can be quickly removed by sorting through the vacuumed material and removing unwanted objects. Where large samples are picked and there are a considerable number of specimens of each species these may also be segregated by means of the vacuum needle. If it is desired to segregate the species of a fauna, the

**Fig. 4.** *Emptying fossil trap.*

first-picked assortment may be dumped onto the bottom of a slide, and mounting can be started at the top of the slide using a camel's-hair brush and gum tragacanth.

CLEANING THE VACUUM NEEDLE

The fossil trap and interior of the holder can be cleaned with a blast of air from a squeeze-bulb aerator. A No. 21 wire can be used to clean the needles. The 200-mesh screen can be cleaned by stroking it lightly with a brush.

## SUMMARY

When large numbers of microfossils must be separated from unwanted material, much time can be saved by using the microfossil vacuum-needle. This tool is easy to operate and clean. It costs little and is easy to make. The advantages of the vacuum-needle pick are that (1) it is not necessary to shift focus each time a specimen is vacuumed into the fossil trap, thus saving much eyestrain and time; (2) it eliminates the need for vertical or lateral transfer of individual specimens, which, multiplied many times, requires much time; (3) it generally requires only one fossil transfer operation per sample; (4) it has a secure fossil trap; and (5) it does not require wetting or waxing.

**ACKNOWLEDGMENT**

I wish to thank Lee Holcomb, William Polski, Martin Reiter, Robert Boon, Robert Steinert, and Ralph Bigham for suggestions which contributed to the development of this tool.

# Mechanical Finger for Preparation of Diatom Slides

W. W. WORNARDT

*California Academy of Sciences, San Francisco*

The mechanical finger in use at the California Academy of Sciences for mounting individual diatoms was originally designed by Dr. G. Dallas Hanna in 1916, when he was stationed on St. Paul Island in the Bering Sea, Alaska. He used the instrument to prepare slides of diatoms from a local deposit of Pliocene age. Many different models of mechanical fingers have been made, some of which have been produced commercially, but this is the only one I know of that clamps onto the microscope stage. Although it is a mechanical manipulator in simplified form, it is not intended in any way to substitute for the elaborate apparatus designed for microdissection and injection in biology.

Many diatomists adhere to the practice of selecting individual diatoms for description, illustration, and museum preparation. This practice seems especially important in selecting holotypes and paratypes of new species, because it enables later workers to find these particular specimens with ease and dispatch. It is usually desirable to mount only one specimen on a slide if it is a type specimen; in other cases a group of specimens may be lined up on the slide to show variation.

Others work entirely from "strewn slides," without endeavoring to select individual specimens. On strewn slides there will nearly always be individuals of many species, fragmentary diatoms, and some detrital material in random positions. In such cases it is desirable to indicate individual diatoms to which attention is directed by a system of coordinates derived from the graduations of a mechanical stage or a separate graduated slide. If the system used is lost— and it may be through the passage of years—the designated specimens may be difficult to find on a slide.

Still other workers who make strewn slides use a commercially available device called an "object marker." It is the same size as a standard objective and screws into the nosepiece of the microscope. A diamond chip is used for scribing a small circle around the specific diatom to which attention is directed. The diamond is mounted in a vertical rod, adjustable sideways with a screw, and works up and down against a weak coil spring in the body of the device.

However, for permanent museum preservation and cataloguing, mounting an individual specimen on a slide has many desirable features. Therefore, the mechanical finger will be described here in some detail, and directions for use given. Attention is called to two other forms of mechanical finger which have been recently described and with which many thousands of beautiful slides have been made.

It is assumed that material to be picked over has been properly cleaned and concentrated. The compound microscope will have been adjusted optically and mechanically in accordance with directions such as those given by Shillaber (1944, p. 4). The selection of most specimens will be done with a 16-mm objective and 5× to 15× oculars. For very minute species an 8-mm objective may be employed.

Preliminary preparation of slides, cover slips, and at least one picking slide is necessary. Approximately 100 slides and cover slips should be thoroughly cleaned and kept as free of dust as possible. The California Academy of Sciences uses standard cover slips 10 mm in diameter, which generally must be between 0.17 and 0.19 mm thick. A minute drop of liquid canada balsam is placed in the center of each slide and a cover slip is placed over this. A thin layer of a dilute solution of gum tragacanth is spread over the top of the center of the cover by means of a dissecting needle and allowed to dry. The slide is then placed on a turntable and a ring about 3 mm in diameter drawn on it in India ink. The diatoms will subsequently be placed in the center of these rings.

Using a compound microscope with 16-, 8-, and 4-mm apochromatic objectives and 5×, 10×, and 15× Hugyens oculars, adjust the illuminating microscope according to Shillaber's directions (1944, p. 4). Set in place the 16-mm objective and the 15× ocular (this, of course, depends on the size of the object to be picked).

Step-by-step instructions for use of the mechanical finger (fig. 1) follow:

1. Attach mechanical finger to microscope stage at about one or two o'clock using screw A.

2. Insert the glass rod and tighten it in place with screw B. To make this glass rod correctly, bend a piece of 3-mm (diameter) glass tubing about 3½ inches long into shape (see side view), round off one end, and draw out the other end (curved portion) to a fine, slender point. The point should not be too stiff or too resilient.

3. Focus the microscope, and position the glass point in the center of the microscope field (optical axis), with the point almost touching the glass slide.

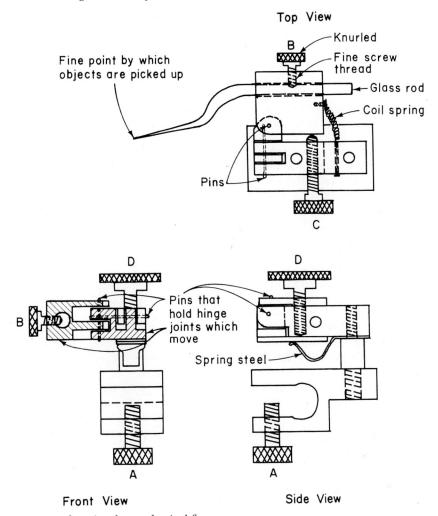

**Fig. 1.** *Plans for the mechanical finger.*

Movement of the fine glass point is controlled by two screws with positive controlled movement. Horizontal movement is controlled by screw C (this screw works against a coil spring); vertical movement is controlled by screw D (this screw works against a piece of spring steel). Screws C and D have fine threads and large, knurled turning heads. Thus, large movements of the knurled head result in small horizontal or vertical movement of the point. Hinge joints should work freely yet have little lost motion.

4. Raise the glass point slightly out of focus by turning screw D clockwise.

5. Place the strewn picking slide on the stage, within the microscope field. A picking slide is one that has been ruled horizontally with numbered lines 1 mm apart and about 25 mm long. To make a picking slide, warm a 3 by 1 inch microscope slide (convex side up if it is not flat), and cover its surface with a thin layer

of beeswax. Place the slide firmly on a mechanical stage of the microscope. A special tool is used to cut the lines through the beeswax. This may be made by attaching a small piece of round steel, with a sharp point at one end, to the side of an objective with tape or a rubber band. It does not have to be held truly normal to the stage. The slide is worked back and forth under the point to scribe the lines.

Use a fine needle to scribe small numbers at the ends of the line, preferably with the aid of a dissecting microscope. Pour a small quantity of hydrofluoric acid over the surface of the slide and allow it to remain for about 3 seconds. Rinse the slide with water, then remove the beeswax. A drop of thoroughly washed and cleaned material is placed on this ruled area and allowed to dry in a dust-free container, either naturally or with gentle heat. Be sure that the water does not boil. Picking is done without a mechanical stage.

6. Hold the left edge of the strewn picking slide with the left index finger on one corner and the left thumb on the other corner; hold the right edge of the slide with the right middle finger on one corner and the right thumb on the other corner. This leaves the right index finger free to operate screws C and D.

7. Locate the desired individual specimen.

8. Place the specimen in the center of the microscope field.

9. Pick up the specimen by turning screw D very slowly in a counterclockwise direction, until the fine glass point just touches one edge of the diatom valve. If the diatom will not adhere readily to the point, move the picking slide very slightly to one side or the other, and at the same time manipulate screw D.

For large individuals, place the glass point far under the diatom valve. To turn the diatom over, merely place the point under one edge of the diatom valve and very slowly move the picking slide toward the point of the rod, while manipulating screw D. Dust may be easily picked off the surface of the diatom valve with just a fine manipulation of the glass point. When the diatom adheres to the glass point, turn screw D in a clockwise direction so that the diatom and point are completely out of focus.

10. Remove the picking slide from the stage.

11. Place one of the specially prepared slides under the microscope, and focus on the black ring.

12. Turn screw D in a counterclockwise direction until the diatom and glass point begin to come into focus.

13. Place the diatom inside the black ring on a small cover slip as follows. As the diatom and glass point come into focus, move the glass slide very slightly and at the same time bring the diatom into contact with the surface of the small cover slip. Extreme care should be taken at this point, especially in the very slow manipulation of the mechanical finger and the slide, because the slightest jerk or jar will either break the glass point, cause loss of the diatom, or both. Orient the diatom for study, with the surface to be studied placed downward.

14. Turn screw D clockwise to lift the glass point out of focus.

15. Carefully remove the slide along with the cover slip. Hold the slide horizontally and breathe gently on the slide and on the cover slip. Moisture from the breath will soften the gum tragacanth; when it dries, the diatom will be firmly fixed in place. To complete the slide, place a small drop of hyrax on a clean microscope slide, and place the slide on a hot plate (about 300°F). At the same

time gently heat the slide that has the cover slip with the diatom on it. With forceps pick up the cover slip with the diatom on it, turn it over, and place it on the hot hyrax. The surface to be studied is now facing upward. Boil for a second or two, then remove and cool. Label the slide.

## REFERENCE

Shillaber, C. P. (1944). Photomicrography in theory and practice. New York, Wiley, 773 pp.

# Preparing Fossils in Amber

ROBERT L. LANGSTON

*Department of Entomology and Parasitology, University of California, Berkeley*

Insects, spiders, plant materials, and other fossils preserved as inclusions in amber (fossil resin) are, as a rule, only sparsely distributed. Therefore, the first step in working with such material is to locate the inclusions. Usually the smaller inclusions can be seen only through a microscope. An ordinary dissecting microscope used with transmitted light is adequate when working with the original raw material. Pieces of amber containing inclusions small enough to require use of the compound microscope have to be prepared before higher magnification can be used effectively. Light transmitted through the amber permits detection of small inclusions that would be missed by viewing the amber with only one overhead light source. Quite often the surface of the raw amber is encrusted with matrix (sand, grit or shale), and it is necessary to remove this before a clear view of the amber itself can be had. For large quantities of material these encrusted surfaces can be removed by tumbling.

## TUMBLING

In this process the raw material is revolved for several weeks in drums containing an abrasive. Commercial tumbling machines are available at lapidary supply houses. A similar apparatus may be improvised for particular needs. The apparatus I use consists of a pair of rollers attached by a belt to a $\frac{1}{3}$-hp electric motor. A large pulley attached to the end of one roller reduces the speed from 1725 rpm for the motor to 26 rpm for the drum. The raw amber is placed in hexagonal drums with a rubber inner liner. The hexagonal shape forces the material to tumble from one surface to the next rather than staying on the bottom. Various sizes of jars or tin cans with ribs soldered on the inside accomplish the same purpose. For the first tumbling, a mixture of abrasive powder and water is used. The abrasive may range from coarse to medium or fine grit, depending on the size of the pieces of amber and how badly their surfaces are encrusted. If relatively small lots of amber are to be tumbled, a filler such as coarse sawdust is added for bulk. The grit, sawdust, and water are mixed into a slurry about the consistency of pancake batter. Sufficient slurry should be made to fill each drum about three-quarters full. The slurry and amber are then sealed in the drum by bolting on a tight-fitting lid. A screw-cap cover suffices if jars or cans are used.

The drums are then placed horizontally on the rollers and are left to revolve continuously night and day for several weeks. Periodically a few pieces of amber are examined to check their condition. After being tumbled in the abrasive grit for a sufficient time, the amber is then removed for examination and/or polishing. The grit removes the surface encrustations, but it may leave the amber rough, with numerous small scratches. If adequate visibility has not been attained, the amber is tumbled again with a finer abrasive agent.

For final polishing, the amber is tumbled in a slurry of tin oxide (or levigated alumina), sawdust, and water and is examined after one or two weeks. After this additional tumbling the amber pieces have polished surfaces, and many of the clearer pieces possess a gem-like quality as if ground and polished individually. The pieces containing inclusions are ready for cutting.

## CUTTING

Cutting involves sawing larger pieces of amber into smaller pieces of convenient size and shape and trimming away excess material. Some of the larger pieces of amber may contain many inclusions, and it is desirable to separate them if possible.

For the larger pieces of amber a trim saw is used. This is a regular rock-cutting saw with a diamond blade. In our laboratory a 6-inch blade is used. Like larger saws, these trim saws must run in a coolant especially when working with amber. A large amount of heat is generated, which not only will cause the blade to become red hot and lose diamonds but will also cause expansion fractures in the amber. Smaller fractures may merely cloud up the inclusion and impair visibility, but major fractures may enlarge until the amber crumbles into small pieces. The use of an adequate coolant will prevent this. The coolant used in our laboratory is a mixture of kerosene and light motor oil. The kerosene keeps the saw blade cool and tends to flush out the cut; the oil lubricates the blade while it is embedded in deep cuts. The coolant is supplied by a splash feed system located where the coolant is picked up by the lower edge of the blade.

For smaller pieces of amber a dental saw is used. Powered by a small electric motor, this apparatus is controlled by a foot treadle. The treadle permits quick starts and stops and allows both hands to be free. The shaft is fitted with a dental cutting disk. These disks are $\frac{7}{8}$ inch in diameter, and come with coarse, medium, or fine abrasive on one surface. For cutting amber, the coarse grade is used almost exclusively, although occasionally the fine grade is used for delicate work. The dental disks are sold by the dozen and are considered expendable.

The actual cutting process is strictly a hand operation. The amber is held in one hand and the dental saw in the other. Most of the inclusions in amber are relatively small, ranging from barely visible spores and pollen grains to objects as large as one centimeter in diameter. Therefore, it is usually necessary to hold the amber under a microscope while cutting, or at least for the beginning of the cut, until the position and the direction of the cut are determined. If the amber is of poor quality with fissures, the cutting must be done slowly to keep heat at a minimum and prevent widening of fissures and the eventual crumbling of the entire piece. Some amber pieces are rich in inclusions; several pieces worked on in our laboratory contained 20 to 40 inclusions, one piece containing a record number of 66 inclusions. In such pieces the fossils are quite densely packed together. To separate one from the other and permit observation of concealed specimens requires patience and skill. The inclusions closest to the surface are naturally removed first. Sometimes, however, only partial cuts can be made, because if the cut is carried too far the specimens behind may be sliced in half. Contrary to the normal gem-cutting procedure partial cuts may be made from the other side. In these rich pieces the fossils are often so close together and interwoven that they cannot be separated, in which case they are left together in large polished pieces. If it is at all possible to separate the specimens, especially if they are of different kinds, every effort is made to do this without damaging them. If the specimens are closer together than the thickness of the dental disk this is impossible, but if only one part comes close—e.g., if the legs of one insect almost touch the extreme end of the wing of another (fig. 1,*a*)—they can be separated by making partial cuts from both sides, almost to the point of contact, and gently breaking the amber across the unsawed portion. If the amber does not break with very gentle finger pressure, the cuts should be made a little deeper until the separation can be accomplished. After the inclusions are sawed out of the larger blocks or separated from each other, the pieces are ready for sanding and shaping.

## EMBEDDING

Some specimens are originally in very small pieces, or pieces so fragile that they would break with handling. Occasionally a specimen becomes broken either in cutting or during subsequent sanding and shaping. These poor and broken specimens may be embedded in plastic. It is usually necessary first to

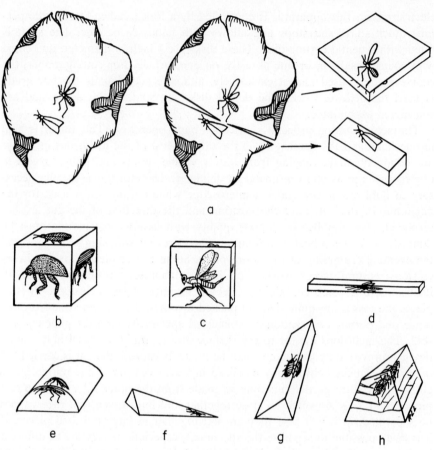

**Fig. 1.** (*a*) *Separating two specimens in close proximity.* (*b–d*) *Fossil specimens in amber blocks of desirable shapes.* (*e–h*) *Amber pieces in which the position of the fossil determines the shape.*

dehydrate the amber, either by using the common dehydrating chemicals or a vacuum pump. The smaller pieces may be placed in shell vials and oriented in the desired position. Depending on the quality of the amber and its size, various plastics may be used: acrylic or one of several polyesters. The plastic should be relatively warm, but not hot enough to melt the amber. To obtain good penetration into cracks and fusion with the surfaces, a vacuum pump is used. After the plastic has hardened, the shell vial is broken away and the specimens are ready for sanding and shaping.

## SANDING AND SHAPING

This work is done on a lapidary wheel powered by a $\frac{1}{4}$-hp electric motor. The sanding is done with silicon carbide cloth glued to a plastic disk which is bolted to the master lapidary wheel. In our laboratory 8-inch silicon carbide disks are glued to the plastic with "Peel 'em off Cement." This substance is a nondrying cement which is applied to the sanding and polishing wheels and permits quick interchange of the sanding cloth and polishing leather or buff. For sanding and shaping, four grades of silicon carbide are used: 220, 320, 400 and 600. For very large pieces, and especially those in which no inclusions are immediately visible, the coarsest grade (220) is used. This provides quick sanding of large surfaces, but generally leaves surfaces too rough for polishing. Therefore, they are again sanded with increasingly finer disks. For very small precut pieces the finest grade (600) can be used immediately after cutting. Many of the cut pieces are very small, and it is important not to sand into the inclusions while shaping the pieces. For some of these an almost worn-out 600 disk may be the most efficient. The sanding may take a little longer, but the results justify the extra time spent.

Since sanding and polishing generate considerable heat, the disks are run wet. One end of a piece of tubing is connected to a water faucet and the other end clamped in position so that water drips slowly onto the wheel. For smoother and quicker sanding before polishing, tin oxide is applied to the turning disks with a small paint brush.

The amber is shaped entirely by hand. No jigs, holders, or faceting devices are used. The fewer the surfaces and corners that the observer has to look through, the better. Assuming the original piece of amber is clear (without fissures, bubbles, or opaque debris surrounding the fossil), and is large enough, the optimum shape is either a regular cube (fig. 1,*b*) or a flattened cube (fig. 1,*c*), depending on the shape and orientation of the fossil. For a very small insect (e.g., a mite), this flattened cube is made very thin (from 1.0 mm to sometimes less than 0.5 mm thick) to permit viewing under a compound microscope. If the inclusion is in a piece of amber that (a) was originally very small, (b) has numerous cracks, or (c) contains considerable debris that obscures the inclusion, or if the inclusion is close to the surface, only an approximation of the desired shape can be obtained.

If the inclusion is in clear amber between two layers of opaque material, a long, thin block may be shaped (fig. 1,*d*), in which case additional amber is left at both ends purely for ease in handling. The smaller the piece, the easier it is to lose or break. If the inclusion is close to the surface it may be necessary to curve that surface (fig. 1,*e*). This is not desirable, as distortion occurs through a curved surface. If it is possible to shape the ends and the bottom as flat surfaces, the fossil can be viewed through any of these three surfaces without distortion. Often the fossil inclusion is embedded in such an undesirable position that the piece must be shaped in such a way that opposite sides are not parallel to each other (figs. 1,*f,g,h*). In a highly polished piece of amber this may produce a prism effect, and often a double or triple image may occur. This may be corrected by immersing the specimen in a liquid having about the same refractive index as the amber. Use of a high grade mineral oil, such as Nujol, will not harm the amber, but alcohols, glycerin, and other solvents are to be avoided. The polished piece may be immersed in mineral oil, syrup, kerosene, or turpentine, the choice depending on which of them shows the details of structure better. According to Petrunkevitch (1964), immersion in xylene should never be prolonged beyond a few minutes, as otherwise it ruins the high polish of the amber.

In our laboratory, amber has been experimentally stored in Nujol for as long as five years. Although no harm is discernible after this period to some ambers, caution should be exercised with poorer material. Specifically, amber blocks with cracks or with considerable surface debris should not be kept in oil, except briefly during observation. The oil gradually works into cracks, giving the amber a tendency to crumble. In other pieces, foreign material may dissolve, making the surfaces gummy. This may ruin the surface by making it more opaque, or the foreign material may actually diffuse into the specimen.

## POLISHING

After cutting, shaping, and sanding, the amber is ready for final polishing. The most important factor in obtaining a highly polished product is to be sure that the previous steps have been carried out completely. The piece must already be in the desired shape and size before it is polished. All surfaces should be relatively smooth and have no high spots or ragged edges.

The polishing is very similar to sanding, except that a disk of leather is used—a relatively soft grade of cowhide, such as Canadian Kip. The leather is run wet, as in the sanding operation, and tin oxide is applied with a small paint brush. In our laboratory a double lap is used, the polishing wheel being powered by a second motor. This speeds the operation, as a sanding disk can be mounted on one wheel and the leather buffer on the other. Without changing disks, the operator can go directly from sanding to polishing. In polishing it is quite important to hold the leading edge of the piece up at a slight angle, polishing the trailing edge first. The piece is then turned 180 degrees and the remainder of the surface polished. If the piece is held completely flat against the buffer, the sharp corners will dig into the leather. This may cause the piece to flip out of the fingers with considerable force. A corner digging in will also cause gouges and rough spots in the buff, thereby shortening its useful life considerably. During polishing, each surface is examined under the microscope for removal of all scratches. If deep scratches are still present on a surface after 5 or 10 seconds on the polishing wheel, it may be necessary to touch it to the fine-grade sander again for a few seconds.

In soft amber, the polishing may slightly round off corners or sharp edges of the shaped piece. This may be done either accidentally or intentionally. If the inclusion is very close to the surface, the polishing may take off just enough opaque material for better visibility of the inclusion, whereas additional sanding may penetrate to the inclusion, thereby ruining the specimen.

## CLASSIFYING

When polishing is completed the fossil specimens are considered finished products available for scientific description. Occasionally a specialist may not be able to see the definitive characters in a particular finished block. A taxonomist of mites, for example, may want the piece thinner to enable it to be viewed under very high magnification. A systematist of beetles may require a flat surface parallel to the plane of the venter to enable better description of coxae, sutures, and other parts. Therefore, some of the finished pieces may have to be reworked. If it is necessary for a piece of amber to be reworked, the risk goes up considerably. As the piece gets smaller, with further sanding and polishing, any fissure or imperfection becomes effectively larger, increasing the probability of partial or complete breakage of the fossil specimen.

## CONCLUSIONS

The preparation of fossil specimens in amber requires the various steps of tumbling, cutting, sanding, shaping, and polishing. Except for the tumbling, none of the steps can be performed by a mass-production method. Of course, in the initial searching procedure, much raw material can be eliminated from further consideration if no inclusions are present. However, all pieces that contain fossil inclusions must be treated individually.

It should be emphasized that each piece of raw amber presents its own challenge. If an inclusion is present, the resultant size, shape, and quality of the finished product will have been determined, within limits, several million years back in geologic time.

## ACKNOWLEDGMENT

Many of the techniques in the preparation of fossil specimens in amber were developed during studies carried out under National Science Foundation Grant no. G-10705.

## REFERENCE

Petrunkevitch, Alexander (1964). Fossiliferous amber arthropods from Chiapas, Mexico. Univ. of California Publ. Entomology, v. 31, no. 1, 60 pp.

# CHEMICAL METHODS OF PREPARATION

*Coordinator:* H. B. WHITTINGTON

# Use of Acids in Preparation of Fossils

## G. ARTHUR COOPER

*U. S. National Museum, Washington, D.C.*

## H. B. WHITTINGTON

*Museum of Comparative Zoology, Harvard University, Cambridge, Massachusetts*

The object in any preparation is to free the fossil as completely as possible from the enclosing matrix; if there is a difference in chemical composition between fossil and matrix, acid may be used to facilitate or completely effect the separation. This technique is not new, for it was in use before Holm performed his remarkable work on graptolites (1890) and on *Eurypterus* (1898). When the fossils, because of original composition (chitin) or replacement (e.g., silicification) are unaffected by certain acids, but are in a matrix that can be completely broken down or dissolved by these acids, the advantages of the technique may be fully realized, and all the unaffected fossils in the sample freed. Not only may large numbers of fossils of a wide range of size be obtained, but the inner and outer surfaces of shells are freed, and may exhibit minute details of morphology. Furthermore, kinds of fossils not observed on weathered or broken surfaces may be revealed. The large-scale program of etching Permian limestones of West Texas (Cooper and

Knight, 1946; Yochelson, 1956, 1960; Batten, 1958; Finks, 1960) has yielded a wealth of superbly preserved silicified invertebrates. The Ordovician limestones of Virginia (Whittington and Evitt, 1954; Cooper, 1956a; Whittington, 1959, and references; Kraft, 1962) have also yielded well-preserved invertebrates. The Miocene arthropod fauna described by Palmer (1957) was also preserved by silicification and prepared with acid.

Precautions should be taken in the storage and use of acids. Acid baths should be placed under a ventilated hood, and heavy rubber gloves and a face mask should be worn when handling hydrofluoric acid.

## FOSSILS REPLACED BY QUARTZ, OPALINE SILICA, OR ANHYDRITE

A cheap and effective acid to use for extracting silicified fossils is commercial hydrochloric acid (approximately 10 percent). Glass or plastic tanks must be used, of a size to hold the block of limestone and twice or more its volume of acid. Dissolution may have several days or two or three weeks. When effervescence ceases, much of the liquid should be siphoned off to remove the dead brine of calcium chloride, taking care not to let the siphon take up any insoluble residue. Fresh acid should then be added. Acetic or formic acid (Palmer, 1957) may be used instead of hydrochloric, but both are expensive and acetic acid is slower in action. Their only advantage is that they do not dissolve skeletons composed of calcium phosphate (e.g., inarticulate brachiopods or conodonts). If such fossils are not present, muriatic acid is preferred.

To decrease the possibility of damage to the fossils by collapse of the partly dissolved block, the base of the block may be coated with a cellulose or latex film, so that the acid works from the sides and top only. To facilitate handling of the residue, a screen may be hung across the tank near the bottom, and the block placed on it. To prevent corrosion, the screen must be made of monel, plastic, or iron wire coated with latex. If the matrix contains little mud or sand, and the fossils are relatively large, such a relatively coarse-mesh screen can be lifted from the tank when all action ceases, and will have all the specimens on it. The screen and contents should then be washed for several hours in a tank of slowly flowing water and dried in air. The Middle Ordovician limestones from Virginia were muddy, and the insoluble residue consisted of this mud and the fossils it contained, many of which were less than 1 mm in maximum dimension. A screen was not used in the tank, but the residue was carefully washed by siphoning off part of the solution, replacing it with fresh water, and allowing it to settle; the process was repeated several times. The residue was then decanted under water, first into a coarse sieve, and then a fine one (opening less than 1 mm in maximum dimension), the coarse sieve serving to catch larger fossils and lumps of mud. The residual mud passed through the fine sieve, particularly after slight agitation. (An alternative procedure is to remove the fine mud particles by agitation and decantation.) Sieves and contents were washed in a tank of flowing water, and finally lifted out of the water to dry in air. Extremely tiny and delicate fossils survived this washing and sieving when it was all performed under water, and the washed sieves lifted carefully from the water.

Fossils can be removed from the insoluble residue with a fine camel's-hair brush, or with tweezers whose tips have been extended with fine wire or watch spring to give a delicate but firm hold (Evitt, 1951). Hardening the larger fossils with a solution of a resin such as Alvar in acetone may be desirable. The fossil may be dipped in a thin solution and placed on absorbent paper to dry in air. In storing fossils, cotton should not be used, because individual strands get tangled in the specimen and are difficult to remove. Plastic boxes, and for tiny fossils, cardboard or plastic 3 by 1 inch microscope slides of various depths and size of cavity and with a removable glass or celluloid cover, are suitable.

In this work, the desirable size of blocks to be collected depends on the size of the fossils. Some of the Permian invertebrate specimens from West Texas were more than six inches long. The etching of blocks one to two cubic feet in volume and weighing up to 300 pounds proved well worthwhile: Cooper recovered 10,000 brachiopods from a single block weighing 180 pounds. In Virginia, blocks more than one foot long and four inches thick could rarely be obtained, because the limestones were thin-bedded and nodular. Such blocks were adequate, however, since few specimens were more than an inch long, and most were less than a tenth that size.

Mister J. C. Walter, of the University of Texas, in working on the Rustler Formation, found that fossils replaced by anhydrite could be removed from dolomites with hydrochloric acid. The shells extracted were hardened in a solution of acetone and Alvar.

Doctor R. H. Flower, of the New Mexico State Bureau of Mines, reports that:

Silicified cephalopods are unsatisfactory to deal with, as either they are silicified internal molds, as is true of much of the Canadian material, or silicification of the shell spreads to include added silica which obsures deposits, and commonly structure of the siphuncle wall is lost or so altered as to be difficult of interpretation. An exception is found in the endoceroids, commonly represented by isolated endosiphuncles, the part of the siphuncle filled in by endocones, and consisting of relatively solid calcareous material. Commonly silicification of such specimens is imperfect, and silicious replacement affects the outer surface and the anterior end of the endosiphuncle; with more advanced silicification tubes and blades may be replaced, but if silicification is much more advanced, or if secondary late silicification follows early silicification, chance structures, in which these varying stages cannot commonly be distinguished prior to etching or cutting, is quite unsatisfactory, and the silicified parts which remain are most difficult of interpretation in the majority of specimens. Removal of partly silicified siphuncles from the limestone matrix has been done by masking the exposed parts of the siphuncle with paraffin wax. As etching proceeds, further applications of wax are desirable, as imperfections are common in the silicified crusts, and if they are not masked in this way, the acid will penetrate and remove internal calcareous material. After removal of the siphuncle, the wax can be removed under hot water, or by solution in xylol. Such etching was found particularly useful in studying piloceroids, where the shape of the siphuncle is variable and diagnostic. Removal of the entire specimen is desirable, while at the same time, it is necessary to investigate the pattern of cones, tubes, blades and possible diaphragms by means of sections.

## CHITINOUS FOSSILS

Acids—hydrochloric, acetic, or if necessary to dissolve chert, hydrofluoric—have long been used in the extraction of eurypterids (Holm, 1898) and graptolites (Holm, 1890; Bulman, 1944, 1955; Kozlowski, 1948). Remarkable preparations of Carboniferous "scorpions" from ironstone nodules have been made by Wills (1959, 1960), who describes his technique in detail. He found that a heated 10 percent solution of hydrochloric acid would dissolve the ironstone, and also took advantage of transparent synthetic resin as a mounting medium in a variation of the "transfer method" (Toombs and Rixon, 1950). The nodule is trimmed to a rectangle, and with the exposed specimen face up, the lower part of the ironstone is embedded in wax in a dish. The resin is then poured over wax and specimen until the specimen is covered by a layer 2 to 3 mm thick. After polymerization of the resin and removal of the wax, etching is carried on in stages from the back of the block. Eventually the specimen, completely exposed, lies in a well in the resin. This well is filled with resin and the specimen thus preserved in a transparent block.

## FOSSILS COMPOSED OF CALCIUM PHOSPHATE

Inarticulate brachiopods (Bell, 1948; Cooper, 1956a) and conodonts (Collinson, 1963) can be extracted in the same manner as silicified fossils, by using 10 to 15 percent solutions of acetic or formic acid. It is essential that the rock sample be in a vessel of adequate size—that is, surrounded by two or three times its volume of dilute acid—otherwise, concentration and subsequent crystallization of salts will take place rapidly and inhibit the dissolution. Doctor Walter C. Sweet, of the Ohio State University, states that in his laboratory:

Bulk samples of limestone, dolomite, or clastic rocks with calcareous cement, are crushed to fragments about 0.5 inches in diameter and screened to remove small chips and fine powder. Crushed fragments are then placed in porous aluminum baskets and suspended in pyrex or polyethylene containers about two-thirds full of a 10 to 15 percent solution of commercial grade acetic or formic acid. The suspended baskets, containing the crushed rocks, are periodically agitated in the container to dislodge silt and clay particles that tend to mask surfaces of the fragments and inhibit further acid digestion. With agitation, these wash loose from the fragments and settle to the bottom of the container. After the acid is spent, the fluid is decanted and both the residue on the container floor and the fragments remaining in the basket are washed in a gentle stream of water. The container is then refilled with a fresh solution of acid. This procedure is repeated until all fragments in the basket have been digested.

With especially argillaceous rocks, it is desirable to screen the mud from the residue each time the acid is changed and to return to the container only the fraction coarser than 100 mesh. Microfossils in the latter are then further "cleaned" in subsequent acid baths. The muddy fraction of the residue is carefully washed to remove the acid and transferred to a storage vessel until the entire sample has been disaggregated. With use of formic acid, it is especially important to remove and wash the complete residue from the container bottom at each acid change, for prolonged exposure to this reagent etches conodonts or produces a disagreeable white surface coating that cannot be removed.

Rolfe (1962), in his investigation of the microstructure of the cuticle of Silurian crustaceans, preserved in collophane partially replaced by calcite, successfully used acetic acid treatment to recover fragments of cuticle.

The preparation of vertebrate fossils using a 15 to 20 percent solution of acetic acid or a 10 percent solution of formic acid has been described by Toombs (1948), Rixon (1949), and Toombs and Rixon (1959). Embedding in resin has also been employed to advantage (Toombs and Rixon, 1950). A special technique for dealing with vertebrate bones coated with iron oxide and enclosed in a siliceous matrix has been developed in the Preparation Department, Museum of Comparative Zoology, Harvard University as a result of research by Miss Gail McGeevy, under the direction of Prof. Eugene G. Rochow of the Chemistry Department, Harvard University. The specimens are placed in a solution of 6 to 12 percent HF diluted with $1N$ HCl (made from 1cc 31 percent HCl in 9cc of water). The HCl dissolves the iron oxide, and the HF attacks the siliceous component of the rock. The bone is somewhat affected, but good preparations have been obtained. The HCl-HF solution has proved more effective than the HCl solution, which damages the bone. The bony material may turn white in color, presumably through deposition of calcium fluoride, but this process appears to be helpful in holding the specimen together. Polyethylene containers are used for the solutions, and heavy rubber gloves worn. Thorough washing of the specimen in running water is necessary after removal from the solution and before handling without gloves. To facilitate handling, the middle portion (smaller in dimensions than the bottom of the vessel) of a length of plastic screening is encased in a block of paraffin wax. This block may then be suspended in the vessel, near the bottom, by attaching the free ends of the screening to wooden rods. The specimen, resting on the wax block, may then readily be lifted in and out of the solution. Holes for drainage may be cut through the wax block. In some specimens the matrix is loosened but not removed by the acid, so that removal, washing, and brushing helps the process.

## PRODUCTION OF ARTIFICIAL MOLDS

In graywacke, quartzite, sandstone, siltstone, and tuffs, natural molds may be present on the weathered surfaces, but in the fresh rock the shells may be composed of calcium carbonate. Such shells are notoriously difficult to extract. Large blocks should be collected and soaked in dilute hydrochloric acid. This procedure will decalcify the outer skin of the block and produce in this region artificial molds of the calcareous fossils. Portions of the block containing these molds are split off, and the remainder placed in acid. Alternate splitting and soaking in acid is continued until the block is reduced. Portions containing fossils must be washed and may require hardening in a solution of Alvar and acetone. The molds may then be cast in latex. Cooper (1956b) used acid to remove calcareous shells from dolomite to produce molds.

## ARTIFICIAL REPLACEMENT

The transformation of calcium carbonate shells to calcium fluoride can be accomplished by immersing them in dilute hydrofluoric acid (Wetzel, 1953; Sohn, 1956, and references). The shells may thus be rendered translucent when wet, and in this way internal structures such as muscle scars may be visible inside Foraminifera, small Brachiopoda, Bryozoa, and Ostracoda.

## REFERENCES

Batten, R. L. (1958). Permian Gastropoda of the southwestern United States. Am. Mus. Nat. History Bull., v. 114, no. 2, p. 157–246, pls. 32–42.

Bell, W. C. (1948). Acetic acid etching technique applied to Cambrian brachiopods. J. Paleontology, v. 22, p. 101–102.

Bulman, O. M. B. (1944). A Monograph of the Caradoc (Balclatchie) graptolites from limestones in Laggan Burn, Ayrshire, Part 1. Palaeontogr. Soc., London.

——— (1955). Graptolithina; Treatise on invertebrate palaeontology (volume V). Geol. Soc. Am. and U. of Kansas Press, p. 1–101.

Collinson, C. (1963). Collection and preparation of conodonts through mass production techniques. Illinois Geol. Survey, Circ. 343, 16 pp., 6 figs.

Cooper, G. A. (1956a). Chazyan and related brachiopods. Smithsonian Misc. Coll., v. 127, 1245 pp., 269 pls.

——— (1956b). A new upper Canadian fauna from a deep well in Tennessee. J. Paleontology, v. 30, p. 29–34, pl. 5.

———, and J. Brooks Knight (1946). Permian studies at the Smithsonian Institution. J. Paleontology, v. 20, p. 625–626.

Evitt, W. R. (1951). Paleontologic techniques. J. Paleontology, v. 25, p. 693–695.

Finks, R. M. (1960). Later Paleozoic sponge faunas of the Texas region. Am. Mus. Nat. History Bull., v. 120, p. 1–160.

Holm, G. (1890). Gotlands Graptoliter. Bih. K. Svenska Vet.-Akad. Handl., v. 16, pt. 4, no. 7, p. 1–34, pls. 1, 2.

———— (1898). Über die organisation des *Eurypterus fischeri:* Eichw. Mém. l'Acad. Imp. Sci. St. Pétersburg, ser. 8, v. 3, no. 2, p. 1–57, pls. 1–10.

Kozlowski, R. (1948). Les Graptolithes et quelques nouveaux groupes d'animaux du Tremadoc de la Pologne. Palaeont. Polonica, v. 3, p. 1–235, pls. 1–42.

Kraft, J. C. (1962). Morphologic and systematic relationships of some Middle Ordovician Ostracoda. Geol. Soc. America Mem. 86, *viii* + 104 pp., pls. 1–19.

Palmer, A. R. (1957). Miocene Arthropods from the Mojave Desert, California. U. S. Geol. Survey Prof. Paper 294-G, p. 237–280, pls. 30–34.

Rixon, A. E. (1949). The use of acetic and formic acids in the preparation of fossil vertebrates. Mus. J. London, v. 49, p. 116.

Rolfe, W. D. I. (1962). The cuticle of some Middle Silurian ceratiocaridid crustacea from Scotland. Paleontology, v. 5, p. 30–51, pls. 7, 8.

Sohn, I. G. (1956). The transformation of opaque calcium carbonate to translucent calcium fluoride in fossil Ostracoda. J. Paleontology, v. 30, p. 113–114.

Toombs, H. A. (1948). The use of acetic acid in the development of vertebrate fossils. Mus. J., London, v. 48, p. 54–55, pl. 7.

————, and A. E. Rixon (1950). The use of plastics in the "transfer method" of preparing fossils. Mus. J., London, v. 50, p. 105–107.

————, (1959). The use of acids in the preparation of vertebrate fossils. Curator, v. 2, p. 304–312, 4 figs.

Wetzel, W. (1953). Die Mikroskopierung der kalkigen fossileinschlüsse der Feuersteine. Mikroskopie, v. 8, p. 173–179.

Whittington, H. B. (1959). Silicified Middle Ordovician trilobites. Harvard Mus. Comp. Zoology Bull., v. 121, no. 8, p. 371–496, pls. 1–36.

————, and W. R. Evitt (1954). Silicified Middle Ordovician trilobites. Geol. Soc. America Mem. 59, p. 1–137, pls. 1–33.

Wills, L. J. (1959). The external anatomy of some Carboniferous 'scorpions,' Part 1. Palaeontology, v. 1, p. 261–282, pls. 49–50.

———— (1960). The external anatomy of some Carboniferous 'scorpions,' Part 2. Different Journal Palaeontology, v. 3, p. 276–332, pls. 46–47.

Yochelson, E. L. (1956). Permian Gastropoda of the southwestern United States, Part 1. Am. Mus. Nat. History Bull., v. 110, no. 3, p. 179–275, pls. 9–24.

———— (1960). Permian Gastropoda of the southwestern United States, Part 3. Am. Mus. Nat. History, Bull., v. 119, no. 4, p. 209–293, pls. 46–57.

# A Method for Obtaining
# Small Acid-resistant Fossils
# from Ordinary Solution Residues

JAMES M. SCHOPF

*U. S. Geological Survey, Columbus, Ohio*

Palynologic studies of sedimentary rocks and studies of invertebrate mega- and microfossils in the same material are usually conducted independently of one another, although preparation techniques that depend on differential solution characteristics of fossils and matrix are used in both. This paper presents a practical preparation schedule that will permit the recovery of acid-resistant microfossils in the course of applying any of the various rock-solution procedures, and eliminate the uneconomic and illogical practice of pouring a potential source of important paleontologic information down the laboratory drain. Only a minimum of extra effort is needed to indicate the presence of the smaller microfossils in solution residues, and at least a cursory examination should always be made. Even if it is impractical to study the smaller acid-resistant fossils in detail, a simple statement of their occurrence has geologic value. Observations of occurrences of good material will, of course, probably lead to further studies.

Usually, solution residues are prepared in large containers, with or without a tray to facilitate removal of large insoluble fragments. The solution residue, usually a fine insoluble clayey sludge, is removed by decantation or washing. If the quantity of insolubles is a significant feature of the study, spent acid containing fine material in suspension may be filtered. The easily suspended sludge or "clay" that results from any of the solution techniques is likely to consist, in part, of small acid-resistant microfossils. The organic acid-resistant microfossils tend to be associated with clayey sediments because their lower average density results in a similar settling rate.

This fine material is usually collected as a filtrate on ordinary filter paper, and as the fossils we are concerned with are considerably larger than clay particles (nearly all $> 10\mu$), they are more easily retained on filters. Open-texture filter paper (Whatman No. 4), or even some kinds of paper toweling is sufficient. However, a filter paper of finer texture is generally used in pre-

Publication authorized by the Director, U. S. Geological Survey.

paring insoluble residues in order to retain the clay. If the filter papers and fine residue are dried for weighing, the filter papers can simply be marked and laid aside for further examination. Although drying is not wholly desirable, a great many of the smaller acid-resistant fossil forms are not perceptibly damaged by it, and can be prepared satisfactorily from dried filtered residues for any desired future study.

The sludge from paleontologic solution techniques is an even more promising material because it can be easily concentrated and examined immediately for the presence of any smaller forms. All that is required is a container large enough to hold the spent acid and wash water. Although the organic acid-resistant fossils are small (many in the 20 to 100$\mu$ size range) and of low density (about 1.2 sp gr) they have a positive settling rate in water: those that float usually contain bubbles of gas. Some may be held at the surface by surface tension, but this can be minimized by using an antifoam spray or detergent. Only a few of the fossils will be lost if, after the sludge has settled, the supernatant water is poured off carefully. An overnight settling period is more than adequate. After water is decanted, the fine residual sludge (with microfossils) can be poured into a smaller container for further concentration or preparation, or for temporary storage. A suitable decantation sequence is suggested in fig. 1.

The presence of small fossils can be detected by examining a small quantity of the fine sludge in aqueous suspension in a watch glass, half of a petri dish, or the smaller Syracuse watch-glass type of staining dish. At 60$\times$ or 70$\times$ magnification, pollen grains and spores, hystrichosphaerids, chitinozoa, rhizopod remains, and similar fossils can easily be seen. Greater microscopic resolution is needed for actual taxonomic study, but even a student unfamiliar with these fossils can tell whether or not they are present. They consist of altered waxy or chitinous, carbonaceous material, usually yellowish or brownish in color.

Of course, much amorphous nonfossil material is commonly mixed with the small fossils in the sludge from a raw solution. Much of palynological preparation consists of concentrating the fossils and separating them from nonfossil contaminant particles of approximately the same density and size. A centrifuge and other laboratory equipment are needed for this work. But all that is needed to determine the *presence* of the fossils is an extra container for the residue.

The simplest way to obtain individual fossils is to pick them from the sludge with a flattened needle. Satisfactory observations can then be made from spores under a cover glass in a drop of water on a slide, using a microscope with 400$\times$ or 500$\times$ magnification. The greatest disadvantage of this technique is the time it takes to pick out enough of the small spores or other fossils individually in order to represent the fossil assemblage adequately. It is not impractical, however, to pick out enough examples to determine the nature of the most abundant fossils.

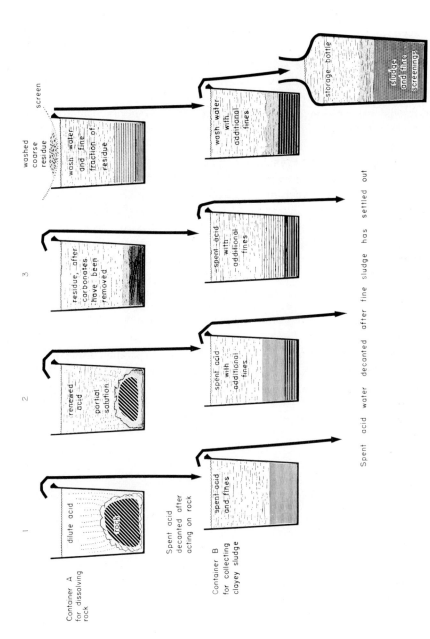

**Fig. 1.** *Decantation sequence.*

Further processing of the sludge should follow the usual methods of palyno-logical preparation as described by Funkhouser and Evitt (1959), Staplin, et al. (1960), Schopf (1960), and others. If carbonates and ferrous iron have been thoroughly removed by the initial treatment, the next step is usually removal of silicates by treatment with HF. Differential oxidation of the organic residue may be subsequently used to increase fossil concentra-tion. Permanent slides should be prepared if there is a chance the fossils will be used for any taxonomic research.

Additional preparation and special studies may be impractical for those who are principally concerned with the amount of insoluble residue, or in-terested only in the larger invertebrate microfossils and megafossils. However, raw sludge residues can be examined quickly and stored conveniently for reference without interfering with the simpler solution techniques. The mere determination of the presence or absence of organic acid-resistant fossils in the unprepared sludge is important enough to justify the small additional effort that it takes. Furthermore, if the rock samples are weighed before preparation and the complete sludge is saved, it is easy to quantify the fre-quency of occurrence of any fossil form. The number of land-plant spores per unit of rock, for example, may be used as an indication of the comparative efficiency of transport at the time sediments were deposited.

## REFERENCES

Funkhouser, John W. and William R. Evitt (1959). Preparation techniques for acid-insoluble microfossils. Micropaleontology, v. 5, no. 3, p. 369–375, text-figs. 1, 2.

Schopf, J. M. (1960). Double cover-glass slides for plant microfossils. Micro-paleontology, v. 6, no. 2, p. 237–240, text-figs. 1–6.

Staplin, F. L., S. J. Pocock, J. Jansonius, and E. M. Oliphant (1960). Palynological techniques for sediments. Micropaleontology, v. 6, no. 3, p. 329–331.

# RADIATION AND RELATED TECHNIQUES

*Coordinator:* DAVID M. RAUP

# Radiographic Techniques

RAINER ZANGERL

*Chicago Natural History Museum*

Soon after the discovery of X-rays by Wilhelm Konrad Roentgen in 1895, experiments to test their possible usefulness in paleontology were made by Brühl (1896), who reported his results in generally optimistic terms. A number of papers have since been written on the usefulness of radiographic techniques, many of them, regrettably, without illustrations, or with inadequate illustrations. The most important of these contributions, most of which are well illustrated, are Branco (1906), Hartmann-Weinberg and Reinberg (1925), Lehmann (1938), Peyer (1934), Roger (1947), and most recently, Schmidt (1948 and 1952). These papers contain most of the literature on the subject, but various other paleontologists have reported use of the technique in connection with the study of specific materials.

Although the general usefulness of radiographic methods in paleontology has been amply and repeatedly documented, surprisingly few paleontologists have adopted the method as a standard tool for preparation, study, and illustration of fossils; foremost among those who have is B. Peyer, who has used X-ray routinely for these purposes since 1929. I became acquainted with radiographic methods as a student of Prof. Peyer in Zürich, and have used the tool whenever its use was warranted, but have used it most extensively since 1954 in connection with a paleoecological study (together with Eugene S. Richardson, Jr.) of a Pennsylvanian carbonaceous shale from Parke County, Indiana. This study could not have been undertaken without the use of radiographic methods, which permit almost immediate routine examination of the fossil content of many hundreds of slabs of black shale.

There are several reasons why this method has failed to become widely, not to say generally, used by paleontologists (and neozoologists). Relatively few paleontological laboratories have X-ray equipment, so that the tool is not readily available at all times. Today, however, X-ray units are almost everywhere available in clinics and hospitals, physics laboratories, and in many industrial laboratories. Perhaps the most important reason is that many investigators seem unwilling to acquaint themselves with the nature of radiographs as shadow pictures. Admittedly, some experience is necessary to "read" an X-ray picture. Finally, many paleontologists may have disregarded the method because of the difficulties in preparing acceptable paper prints for purposes of illustration. This justified objection has recently been overcome by the use of logEtronic printing devices (see p. 313).

## RADIOGRAPHIC PRINCIPLES

A radiogram is a shadow picture on a photographic film or plate produced by X-rays or gamma rays as they are passed through an object. If the object is of uniform substance, density, and thickness throughout, the resulting shadow on the photographic emulsion is a uniform area of gray. If the specimen examined consists of materials of different chemical (especially elemental) composition, or density or thickness, the penetration by the X-rays is no longer the same over the entire area of the specimen. On the photographic emulsion, a shadow picture is produced that reflects the differential absorption of the X-rays by the object.

X-ray absorption is primarily a characteristic of the material. It increases to about the fourth power of the atomic number of the particular material. It increases proportionally with the density and thickness of the object. X-ray absorption capability is approximately proportional to the third power of the wavelength used.

These factors determine the type of equipment best suited to a given purpose, exposure, and quality of the radiograph. In practice, the problem is not as formidable as it may seem, because what ultimately matters is the *difference* between the penetrability of the matrix and that of the fossil. Figure 1 shows the relationships between material (atomic number), thickness and density of the fossil and the enclosing matrix, and the chance of obtaining a good radiograph.

The kilovoltage applied to the X-ray tube determines the penetration of the X-rays through the object. Thus, an object of high atomic weight requires a higher kilovoltage setting than one of low atomic weight, and a thick object requires a higher kilovoltage than a thin object of the same material. Because fossils may be enclosed in sediments consisting of, or containing, a wide

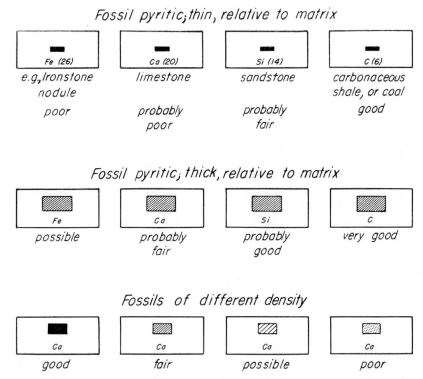

**Fig. 1.** *Chart showing relationship of material to thickness and density of fossils and enclosing matrix for optimum radiography of fossils.*

variety of materials, it is desirable (but not absolutely necessary) that the equipment permit the use of a wide range of kilovoltage settings.

## X-RAY EQUIPMENT

A great variety of equipment may be used for the purpose of X-raying fossils. Medical and dental diagnostic machines are the most widely available and are quite satisfactory for most purposes. For those who plan to purchase equipment for their laboratories, however, these are not the best choice. Medical equipment is designed specifically for human radiography, which requires but a limited range of penetration, short exposure times, and maximum safety to the patient. For fossil work a notably greater range of penetration and long exposure times are a distinct advantage, but require more elaborate safeguards for the operator (see below). At the present time there are on the market industrial units rated at 0 to 150 kilovolts (kv) that are designed for continuous operation at 6 milliamperes (150 kv setting or lower). These are water-cooled units, and should be well suited for paleontological purposes. Old medical machines, however, especially those designed for therapeutic purposes, using air-cooled tubes, perform excellently, but they should be operated with the greatest of caution because of the exposed electrical system and the minimal shielding of the X-ray tube. Units of this sort are still occasionally available, may be obtained at a minimal cost, but require special rooms that are totally lead-lined, and the controls must be located on the outside to insure the protection of the operator. I have used such a unit (now about 35 years old) for the past 15 years with complete satisfaction. The range of this machine is about 30 to 125 kv; at 5 milliamperes it may be operated at the 125 kv peak for at least 30 seconds. This may not give enough penetration or enough time for thick (4 inches or more) blocks of limestone, but it has been my experience (admittedly not wholly representative) that in most paleontological work it rarely seems advisable to X-ray a thick block of limestone. The acquisition of an X-ray unit is, of course, a major investment for any paleontological laboratory, but since adequate protection of the operator is mandatory even with the most modern machines, the purchase of old units seems reasonable, even granting that modern equipment is better.

## EXPOSURE TECHNIQUE

The kilovoltage applied to the tube is determined by the atomic weight of the principal elements in the material and by the thickness and the density of the specimen. Settings of 20 to 140 kv have been used by various authors for a great variety of rocks and specimens. The current, expressed in milliamperes, reflects the radiation density; it is inversely proportional to the exposure time, usually expressed in seconds. If medical diagnostic machines are to be used, relatively high milliamperages and short exposure times are required because of the design of the equipment. Peyer (1934), who X-rayed his materials with medical diagnostic units, cites the following settings for bituminous shales of various quality and thickness (2 mm to 10 mm): 40 to 50 kv, 60 milliamperes, 3 to $5\frac{1}{2}$ seconds at a target-to-object distance of 1 meter. Other authors have used notably lower milliamperage settings (5 to 10) and exposure times of several seconds to 20 minutes. My own experience indicates optimal results with low milliamperages ($\pm5$) and long exposure times, 30 seconds to 1 minute.

Because radiation density and exposure time are inversely proportional, a setting of 5 milliamperes at 30 seconds produces the same amount of exposure as a setting of 10 milliamperes at 15 seconds, since the product, milliampere-seconds, is 150 in both examples. The picture quality, however, will not be quite the same in both examples, since the photographic emulsion reacts differently to the two exposure settings. The differences are slight though notable to the experienced eye.

The target distance is the distance between the photographic film and the target within the tube, from which the X-rays are emitted. The target distance depends somewhat on the size of the object; increase in target distance requires an increase in exposure time, but a long target distance (about 36 inches) is generally an advantage because it decreases distortion in the picture. With equipment that permits long exposure times the target distance may be left at 36 inches for nearly all work. A compromise is necessary with units in which exposure times are limited.

### FILM

A number of film types are available. They vary in contrast, speed, and emulsion grain size. X-ray film is coated with photographic emulsion on both sides, which is an advantage in subjective viewing of the picture, but a disadvantage if the picture is to be printed on paper. Regular photographic films (coated on one side only) having characteristics similar to those of standard X-ray films may be used when very fine detail is desired. Simple cardboard film holders with lead backing are inexpensive and readily available. They are designed for the use of non-screen film, and are most satisfactory for paleontological purposes.

As in ordinary photography, the choice of film depends on the nature of the work and possibly on the limitations of the X-ray equipment. Eastman Type M industrial film (or equivalents of other manufacturers) is an extremely fine-grained, high-contrast material, but it is very slow and requires long exposures. Medical non-screen film is much faster, but its grain size makes it undesirable for very small, delicate materials. Nevertheless, I have found it satisfactory for nearly all routine work; if very fine detail is desired, and if the picture is to be enlarged and printed, a fine-grained film is strongly recommended. Medical X-ray film is used routinely in hospitals and is thus readily available. Since most paleontologists will have to depend on medical equipment and medical non-screen film, I purposely chose to use this type of negative material in preparing figs. 3 to 8.

### PROCESSING FILMS

Since X-ray film is coated on both sides, it should be processed in tanks rather than in trays. Metal hangers are used to hold the film. Special X-ray developer and fixer should be purchased, as they may be kept in the tanks for extended periods of time. Since X-ray units in paleontological laboratories are used only intermittently, the processing liquids rarely become exhausted; more often the developer gradually oxidizes and becomes spoiled. To retard this process it is advisable to cover the developing tank with an air-tight lid.[1]

For those unfamiliar with photographic processing techniques it is best to follow the recommendations furnished by the manufacturer of the developer

---

[1] No satisfactory covers are on the market at the present time; homemade covers of the internal dimensions of the tank, coated with paraffin or beeswax (but not grease) and permitted to float on the developer, appear to be the most efficient.

and fixer. The experienced technician, however, may vary developing time and film agitation and even design the original exposure setting for a particular manipulation in the processing procedure.

Since there is often but a slight difference between the absorptive qualities of matrix and fossil, it is desirable to use the lowest possible kilovolt setting and achieve a relatively high contrast by overdeveloping the film.

SCATTERED RADIATION

When an X-ray exposure is made, most of the rays in the beam pass through the object and expose the film. Many rays, however, are scattered in all directions, presenting a safety hazard if the operator is located in the same room as the tube. Furthermore, scattered rays may fog the film, thus reducing the contrast and obscuring fine detail.

For these reasons it is imperative that the walls, ceiling, and floor of the room in which the tube is located be lined with lead foil of appropriate thickness. The room should be kept as free of dust as possible. The operator must be located outside the X-ray room, well shielded from direct and indirect radiation.

To reduce the danger of fogging the film a number of techniques have been suggested (Schmidt, 1948). The most important of these is to line the table on which film and specimens are to be positioned with a sheet of lead, and to use a cone at the tube head. Beyond these simple measures additional shields (such as cutout masks around the objects) may be necessary, but these vary greatly with the nature of the work. No special shielding was used in taking the X-rays shown here.

## RADIOGRAPHS FOR EXPLORATORY PURPOSES

Many vertebrates and invertebrates are enclosed in the rock matrix in such a way that it is uncertain to what extent, or in what state of articulation, they are preserved. If a radiograph promises an answer it is generally advisable to first reduce the matrix by mechanical means (splitting or grinding) as much as possible in order to obtain a satisfactory thickness ratio between fossil and rock. This is especially necessary if the sediment is a limestone. Even for carbonaceous or rich bituminous shales such preparation is still advisable in view of the resulting superior quality of the radiographs. Such exploratory pictures may be used as a guide during the mechanical preparation of the fossils. When the fossil is entirely removed from the sediment the exploratory X-ray picture is the only record of the burial position of the fossil.

In paleoecological work involving finely bedded sediments, radiographs of this sort provide accurate records of the horizontal distribution of fossils or fossil debris and permit the study of particle orientation within the sediment.

## RADIOGRAPHS FOR THE STUDY OF INTERNAL STRUCTURES

The demonstration of internal structures of invertebrates and vertebrates in specimens that have been freed from the matrix is often desirable if the specimens are not to be injured or if mechanical or chemical preparation seems inadvisable. If the internal structures are relatively simple, straight radiograms may be satisfactory. More often, however, three-dimensional, complex structures such as vertebrate skulls, brachiopods, or cephalopods produce shadow pictures of such complexity that their interpretation is often very difficult. In such cases stereoscopic pictures are called for.

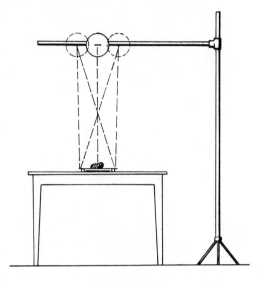

A set of stereoscopic pictures is made by first centering the specimen and film directly beneath the tube target (fig. 2). The tube is then moved a short distance to one side of center and an exposure is made. Then the film holder must be removed from beneath the specimen and a new film holder placed below the specimen. Care must be taken during this operation to avoid moving the specimen. The tube head is then moved an

**Fig. 2**

*Setup for stereoscopic radiography.*

equal distance from the center position to the opposite side and a second exposure is made using the same exposure settings as for the first picture. The two films should be processed together to insure equal emulsion density. The pair of radiographs can then be studied with the aid of a stereoscopic viewer.

At a target distance of 36 inches, the tube head is moved about 2 inches to either side of center, amounting to a total tube shift of 4 inches. When working with crushed materials, however, it may be advantageous to increase the depth perception by distorting the visual image in the direction in which the fossil is crushed. This may be done by reducing the target distance and increasing the tube shift (fig. 7).

A particular set of stereoscopic radiographs can be used for visualizing the

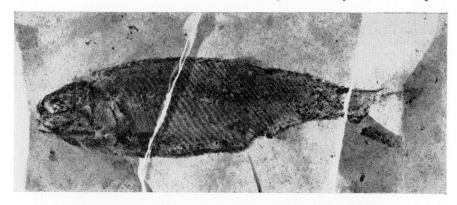

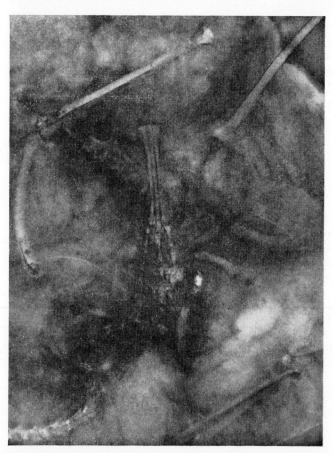

**Fig. 3.** (*Top*) *Palaeoniscoid fish from the Logan quarry shale, Chicago Natural History Museum's Logan quarry, Parke County, Indiana. The specimen is entirely enclosed in a black, highly carbonaceous, sheety shale, and is visible only along the broken edges of the shale pieces. It is entirely intact,*

specimen not only from the front but from the back, depending on which way the films are viewed (figs. 5 and 6).

## THE PRINTING OF RADIOGRAPHS

Perhaps the most outstanding features of any X-ray negative is its great overall contrast, and generally low detail contrast. By overall contrast is meant the great difference in the gray tone values in different areas of the negative. Some areas are virtually black (background and thin areas of the object); others, nearly transparent (dense or thick areas of the object). The detail contrast, the differences in the gray tone values from one point to the next, is low both in the dark and in the light areas of the negative.

For these reasons it is virtually impossible to print X-ray pictures on paper without elaborate dodging of the light areas. With conventional printing equipment this is virtually impossible for negatives in which light and dark areas are intermingled. Until recently, complicated photographic manipulation was required to produce acceptable paper prints, but even so, the results were never quite perfect. The statement has been made, repeatedly, that the fine detail visible on a transparent film cannot be reproduced on an opaque paper and that it is impossible to perceive on photographic paper an equal number gradational steps of the gray tone scale. These statements appear to be no longer valid since the introduction of LogEtronic contact printers and enlargers,[2] which make it possible to reduce the great overall contrast of the negative while the detail contrast is very strikingly increased. Good logEtronic prints not only reproduce the very finest shadow detail visible on the original radiogram, but actually show shadow details so minute that they are invisible to the human eye on the original radiogram. The reason for this lies in the "edge enhancement effect" produced as the scanning beam (which exposes the print) traverses shadow boundaries in the negative (for further detail see: St. John and Craig, 1957).

[2] Produced by LogEtronics, Inc., 500 East Monroe Avenue, Alexandria, Virginia.

*except for an injury to the tail fin. Technical data: Specimen PF2275, XR-Logan 179; 1 mm thick at break behind head; shale 9 mm thick. Target distance 41 inches; 53 kilovolt peak; 5 milliamperes, 30 seconds. Medical non-screen film. LogEtronic print directly from original negative. About 0.25 natural size. (Bottom) A portion of the third known skeleton of* Archaeopteryx lithographica. *The thickness of the limestone slab was reduced to 13 mm; the bones are delicate. The original negative was kindly provided by Dr. W. Stürmer of Erlangen, Germany. Technical data from Stürmer (1960): 80 kv; about 200 mas; Schleussner Mikrotest-Film. The portion of the specimen reproduced here shows the proximally fused metatarsal bones. Demonstration of the presence of a primitive tarsometatarsus in* Archaeopteryx *was possible primarily with radiographic methods. About 0.33 natural size.*

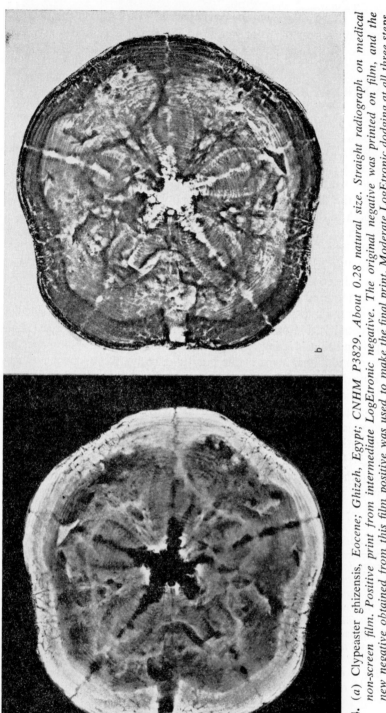

**Fig. 4.** (a) *Clypeaster ghizensis, Eocene; Ghizeh, Egypt; CNHM P3829. About 0.28 natural size. Straight radiograph on medical non-screen film. Positive print from intermediate LogEtronic negative. The original negative was printed on film, and the new negative obtained from this film positive was used to make the final print. Moderate LogEtronic dodging at all three steps. Technical data: specimen about 1.25 inches thick in the middle, calcareous, but interior not filled with matrix. Lantern of Aristoteles disarticulated and component parts loose on the inside. Target distance 36 inches; 66 kv peak; 5 ma; 30 seconds. (b) Same specimen and radiogram as in (a), but negative print, obtained from film positive. LogEtronic dodging at both steps.*

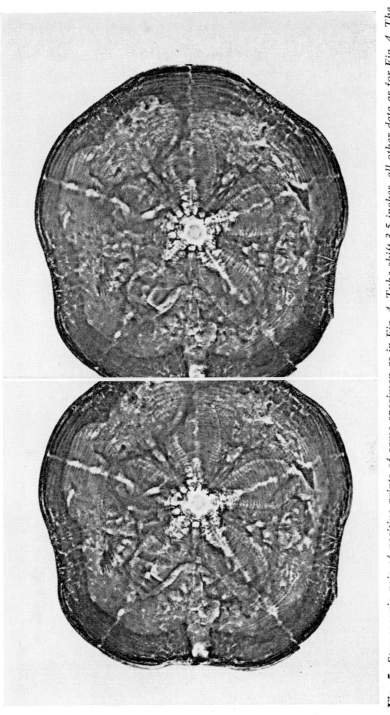

**Fig. 5.** *Stereoscopic pair of positive prints of same specimen as in Fig. 4. Tube shift 3.5 inches, all other data as for Fig. 4. The specimen is seen from the upper, convex side. Note vertical shadow distribution when visualized with stereoscope, which greatly simplifies the "reading" of the radiograph.*

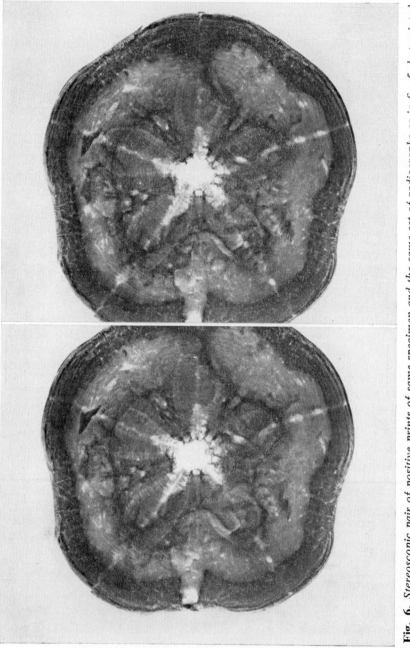

**Fig. 6.** *Stereoscopic pair of positive prints of same specimen and the same set of radiographs as in fig. 5, but printed directly from the reverse sides of the original negatives (with full LogEtronic dodging), which produces a reversed stereoscopic effect. The specimen is seen from the flat, lower side.*

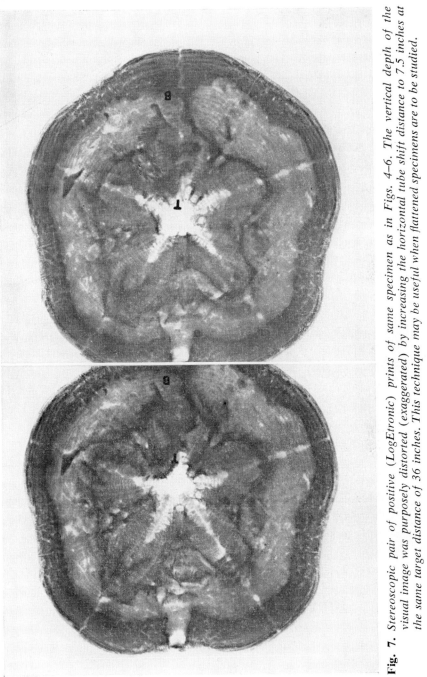

**Fig. 7.** Stereoscopic pair of positive (LogEtronic) prints of same specimen as in Figs. 4-6. The vertical depth of the visual image was purposely distorted (exaggerated) by increasing the horizontal tube shift distance to 7.5 inches at the same target distance of 36 inches. This technique may be useful when flattened specimens are to be studied.

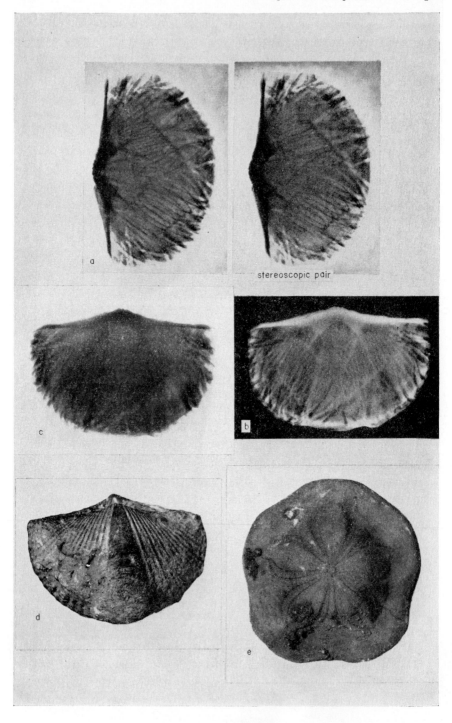

stereoscopic pair

The cost of this equipment justifies its acquisition only where large numbers of radiograph and other difficult negatives have to be printed. There are, however, a number of commercial photo processers that make LogEtronic prints on commission. Information about this service may be obtained from the manufacturer.

Radiographs may be printed in two ways: as positives or as negatives. In a negative print the background is black, and the structure of the specimen appears in various shades of gray (as in the original radiograph) (fig. 4). In a positive print all shadow values are reversed, the structure of the specimen appears dark against a white background (fig. 4a). The choice between them is largely a matter of preference; some persons, however, seem to have less difficulty reading a positive print, either on film or on paper.


## READING X-RAY PICTURES


Personal observations over the years have convinced me that perhaps the most important reason why X-ray techniques have not become a standard tool in neozoological and paleontological work lies in the unwillingness of most investigators to learn to read radiographs. Radiographs *are* used fairly commonly where reading the shadow picture requires neither effort nor experience, as for example, in the determination of the number of multiple structures (vertebral counts in fishes, snakes, and so forth).

X-ray pictures, being pictures of shadows of various intensity, have to be interpreted. If the viewer is entirely unfamiliar with the construction of a given object, its radiograph is no more than a meaningless pattern of emulsion densities. For this reason it is strongly recommended that a person willing to learn to read radiographs should start with objects of relatively simple construction, with which he is perfectly familiar. Stereoscopic pictures, furthermore, are very helpful to a beginner. Beyond this, the interpretation of X-ray pictures is a matter of experience.

---

**Fig. 8.** (*a*) *Stereoscopic pair of positive prints (made from intermediate negatives; LogEtronic dodging at all three steps) of* Spinocyrtia euruteines *from the Middle Devonian, Hamilton, of Lucas County, Ohio; CNHM PE5573. About 0.5 natural size. Technical data: The specimen is entirely filled with limestone matrix; maximum thickness 32 mm; target distance 36 inches; 91 kv peak; 5 ma; 35 seconds, medical non-screen film.* (*b*) *Negative LogEtronic print of same specimen as in a.* (*c*) *Positive print from same negative as was used for b, but printed by conventional means with heavy dodging. This illustrates the great difference in quality between ordinary and LogEtronic printing of radiographs.* (*d*) *Photograph of same specimen as in a, b, c.* (*e*) *Photograph of* Clypeaster ghizensis, *CNHM P3829, shown in figs. 4–7. About 0.18 natural size.*

**A NOTE ABOUT THE ILLUSTRATIONS**

The wide range of usefulness of X-ray methods in paleontology has been amply documented in the literature. With the development of LogEtronic printing techniques a revolutionary change has come about in the practical value of X-ray pictures both for study and documentation. I have, therefore, attempted to demonstrate several techniques of illustration of the same specimen, including stereoscopic techniques that may prove to be most helpful in the study of paleontological materials. The stereoscopic pictures may be visualized with simple lens, prism, or mirror stereoscopes.

**REFERENCES**

Branco, W. (1906). Die Anwendung der Röntgenstrahlen in der Palaeontologie. Abh. Preuss. Akad. Wiss. Berlin, p. 1–55, 4 pls.
Brühl (1896). Über Verwendung von Röntgenschen X-Strahlen zu palaeontologisch-diagnostischen Zwecken. Verh. Berliner Physiol. Gesell., Arch. Anat. Physiol., Abt. Jahrg. 1896, p. 547–550.
Hartmann-Weinberg, A., and S. A. Reinberg (1925). Die fossilhaltigen Gesteinsformationen im Röntgenbilde. Akad. Nauk, Izvestia, v. 19, p. 279–292, 2 pls.
Lehmann, W. M. (1938). Die Anwendung der Röntgenstrahlen in der Paläontologie. Jahresber. Oberrhein, geol. Ver., Mitt., N.F., v. 27, p. 16–24, 6 pls.
Peyer, B. (1934). Ueber die Röntgenuntersuchung von Fossilien, hauptsächlich von Vertebraten. Acta Radiologica, v. 15 (5-5), p. 363–379, 2 pls., 2 text-figs.
Roger, J. (1947). Sur l'application des rayons X aux études paleontologiques. Bull. Mus. Natl. d'Hist. Nat., v. 19, no. 1, p. 118–120; no. 2, p. 224–229.
St. John, E. G., and D. R. Craig (1957). LogEtronography. Am. J. Roentgenology, Radium Therapy and Nucl. Med., v. 78, no. 1, p. 124–133, 13 figs.
Schmidt, R. A. M. (1948). Radiographic methods in paleontology. Am. J. Sci., v. 246, p. 615–627, 6 pls.
——— (1952). Microradiography of microfossils with x-ray diffraction equipment. Science, v. 115, no. 2978, p. 94, 3 figs.

# X-ray Microscopy in Morphological Studies of Microfossils

KENNETH HOOPER

*Carleton University, Ottawa, Canada*

The extension of microscopy from visible light into X-ray wavelengths results in increased penetration and higher resolving power. In optics resolving power is directly proportional to the wavelength of illumination. The wavelengths of visible light are on the order of $0.5\mu$ ($1\mu = 10^{-4}$ cm), whereas the wavelengths of X-rays are on the order of angstrom units (1 Å $= 10^{-8}$ cm). The resolving power of X-rays is thus four orders of magnitude greater than light. Theoretically, the ultimate resolution of X-ray microscopy is in the electron microscope range, although this has not yet been realized in practice.

Examination of extremely small opaque objects is possible in X-ray microscopy because of the great resolving and penetrating power of X-rays. Stereo X-ray microscopy is readily possible due to the great depth of focus attainable. Microchemical analysis may be combined with microscopy because the absorption of X-rays depends on atomic number, so that differential absorption measurements will give the nature and concentration of the elements present (Long, 1957; Long and Cosslett, 1957; Ong, 1961). Crystalline substances may be identified by microdiffraction (Nixon, 1957). Microfluorescence analysis and microemission analysis are also possible (Duncumb, 1957).

From the earliest days of X-radiography attempts have been made to obtain radiographs of minute structures; but the large X-ray source area and the comparatively low resolution of photographic plates used for recording the image gave disappointing results. In the last decade, however, ways have been found to reduce the X-ray source area (i.e., the focal spot) and to produce ultra-fine-grained photographic emulsions. Consequently, X-ray micrographs of minute structures are now obtainable in practice.

In micropaleontology some advantages of using X-ray techniques include (1) detailed information of the internal morphology of opaque microfossils, (2) high-accuracy measurement of internal structures, (3) rapid derivation of information, and (4) nondestruction of microfossils. As a result, X-ray methods are particularly useful in studies where biometrical and statistical analyses are contemplated.

## METHODS

There are three main methods of X-ray microscopy and microradiography: (1) reflection X-ray microscopy, (2) contact microradiography, and (3) point projection X-ray microscopy.

### REFLECTION X-RAY MICROSCOPY

In this method X-rays are totally reflected from a mirror at a very small angle (fig. 1,*a*). Then they are focused by a curved mirror system to give the angle. There are considerable technical difficulties to be overcome in the preparation and alignment of mirrors, and these have retarded the development of this method (Nixon and Baez, 1956; Kirkpatrick, 1957).

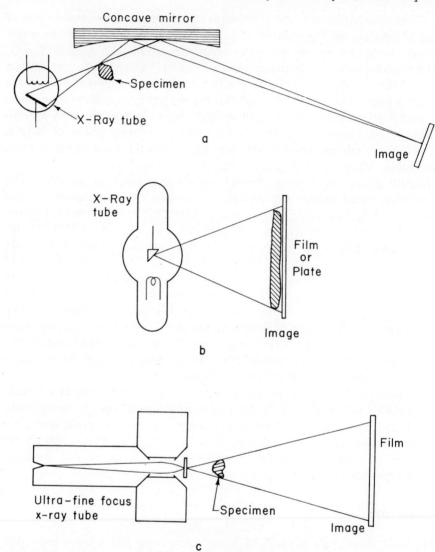

**Fig. 1.** (*a*) *Reflection microscopy;* (*b*) *Contact microradiography.* (*c*) *Projection microscopy.*

CONTACT MICRORADIOGRAPHY (C.M.R.)

This method has been used to obtain microradiographs of foraminifera (Schmidt, 1952; Hedley, 1957; Hooper, 1959). It has the advantage that ordinary X-ray diffraction apparatus may be used. Such equipment is commonly available these days.

The specimens are placed very close to a photographic plate (Kodak maximum-resolution emulsion) in a brass camera of special, but simple, design (fig. 1,*b*). The camera is set up in the path of the X-ray beam so that the target-to-plate distance is great enough to permit utilization of nearly parallel rays at the plate, but not so far that exposure time is inordinately long. After exposure to X-rays the plate is developed. In practice the processed plate is likely to show considerable density variation over its area, and it is usually necessary to photocopy the image of each specimen separately. Photocopying of an enlarged image upon roll film is recommended. Subsequently the film strip is projected and further enlargement of image obtained, from which measurements of internal structures are made. This technique has been described in detail in the literature (Hooper, 1959).

### POINT-PROJECTION X-RAY MICROSCOPY, OR PROJECTION MICRORADIOGRAPHY (P.M.R.)

The principle of the point-projection microscope is illustrated in fig. 1,*c*. An electron gun produces an electron beam which is focused by an electromagnetic lens system to a point upon a target. The target used to produce the X-rays may be copper, tungsten, gold, silver, or some other element, each of which produces its own characteristic X-rays. For the tests of calcareous foraminifers, copper has been found most satisfactory. The X-rays are emitted from the target in a conical beam. The specimen is placed in the path of the beam, between the target and the photographic plate or film. A magnified image is recorded, the degree of magnification depending on the target-to-specimen and specimen-to-film distances. By using a camera to hold both the specimens and the film, a number of foraminifers can be microradiographed simultaneously. As in C.M.R. the image is enlarged by projection, and internal structures are measured. In P.M.R., emulsions giving lower resolution may be used; the image is recorded directly on the film, with a consequent economy of time and materials.

The principle and development of point-projection X-ray microscopy have been described by Cosslett and Nixon (1953), Cosslett, Nixon, and Pearson (1957), and Ong (1959). The application of the point-projection X-ray microscope to micropaleontology was described in Hooper (1959).

Rovinsky, Latsau, and Avdeyenko (1957) described a new kind of electron gun incorporated in a variant of the point-projection X-ray microscope, named the X-ray microprojector. They claim a resolving power of less than 1 micron. I have had no experience with this apparatus, but it ought to have applications in microfossil morphology studies.

### CONCLUSIONS

#### POINT-PROJECTION X-RAY MICROSCOPE

Important features of the point-projection X-ray microscope are its great depth of focus and great penetrating power. Resolution is approximately equal to the source diameter (about $0.1\mu$). The great depth of focus is useful for stereomicroradiography, as all parts of a three-dimensional object show sharply on a plane, and the image is in correct perspective. However, the magnification for different parts of a thick object varies for different points on the object. A method for dealing with this difficulty has been discussed by Ong (1959).

For biological materials soft X-rays are required, and the specimen must be in vacuo during irradiation. This is not necessary when dealing with the calcareous tests of fossil foraminifera, which can be irradiated in air, allowing more space for the specimen holder. In practice, the physical arrangement of pole pieces and target determine the limit of the X-ray beam angle, and the design of the specimen holder determines the maximum size of specimen. I have obtained satisfactory microradiographs of foraminifera ranging from 1 cm to $60\mu$ in diameter, using the point-projection X-ray microscope built by Cosslett and Nixon. It is important to check the specifications of commercially produced X-ray microscopes to ensure that there is sufficient space between the specimen holder and the target for large specimens.

Resolution is limited by the accuracy of focusing, but even so, a point-projection X-ray microscope requiring an elaborate, inconvenient and time-consuming focusing procedure is unsuitable for routine work. This difficulty may be overcome by using a binocular accessory for observation of the focusing screen (Ong, 1959).

### CONTACT MICRORADIOGRAPHY

The advantage in C.M.R. is that the ordinary diffraction apparatus used is available in many laboratories. Moreover, a large number of foraminifers (sometimes many hundreds) can be handled per exposure. The disadvantages are that resolution and depth of focus are less than for P.M.R. Thus, C.M.R. is not recommended where stereomicroradiography is required and P.M.R. is available.

### OVERLAPPING DETAILS

X-ray micrographs of some microfossils present a confused mass of detail which is difficult to interpret and impossible to measure. This is due to the complexity and overlapping of numerous internal structures. Not all microfossils are ideally suited to X-ray methods of morphological study. Such microfossils are best handled by a combination of sectioning and X-ray techniques.

### AVAILABILITY OF COMMERCIAL APPARATUS

All commercial point-projection X-ray microscopes currently produced are essentially modified electron microscopes. An R.C.A. electron microscope modified for P.M.R. has been described by Siegel and Knowlton (1957). Phillips (Norelco) supplies accessories for conversion of the E.M. 75 to a point-projection X-ray microscopy. The Hitachi H.U. 11 is also convertible to P.M.R. Siemens does not supply accessories for conversion of their electron microscopes to P.M.R. and are not proposing to do so at present (personal communication).

In this paper I have skimmed lightly over the field to indicate the potential of X-ray microscopy and microradiography in morphological studies of microfossils, particularly foraminifera. It is well to remember, however, that morphological characters are not the only criteria of classification even for fossils. Microchemical composition may also be investigated using the point-projection X-ray microscope, as has been indicated by Nixon (1957) and Ong (1961); but a discussion of these methods is beyond the scope of this paper.

## REFERENCES

Cosslett, V. E., and W. C. Nixon (1953). The x-ray Shadow microscope: J. Appl. Phys., v. 24, p. 616.

————, and H. E. Pearson (1957). Improvements in the point projection x-ray microscope, *in* V. C. Cosslett (ed.), Proc. Symp. X-Ray Microscopy and Microradiography, Cambridge, 1956. New York, Academic, p. 96.

Duncumb, P. (1957). Microanalysis with a scanning x-ray microscope, *in* V. E. Cosslett (ed.), Proc. Symp. X-ray Microscopy and Microradiography, Cambridge, 1956, New York, Academic, p. 617.

Hedley, R. H. (1957). Microradiography applied to the study of Foraminifera. Micropaleontology, v. 3, no. 1, p. 19.

Hooper, K. (1959). X-ray absorption techniques applied to statistical studies of Foraminifera populations. J. Paleontology, v. 33, no. 4, p. 631.

Kirkpatrick, P. (1957). The problem of reflection microscopy, *in* V. E. Cosslett (ed.), Proc. Symp. X-Ray Microscopy and Microradiography, Cambridge, 1956. New York, Academic, p. 17.

Long, J. V. P. (1957). Applications of and some sources of error in x-ray microchemical analysis, *in* V. E. Cosslett (ed.), Proc. Symp. X-Ray Microscopy and Microradiography, Cambridge, 1956, New York, Academic, p. 628.

————, and V. E. Cosslett (1957). Some methods of x-ray microchemical analysis, *in* V. E. Cosslett (ed.), Proc. Symp. X-Ray Microscopy and Microradiography, Cambridge, 1956, New York, Academic, p. 435.

Nixon, W. C. (1957). The point projection x-ray microscope as a point source for microbeam x-ray diffraction, *in* V. E. Cosslett (ed.), Proc. Symp. X-Ray Microscopy and Microradiography, Cambridge, 1956, New York, Academic, p. 336.

————, and A. V. Baez (1956). Lectures on the x-ray microscope. University of Redlands, California.

Ong, Sing Poen (1959). Microprojection with x-rays. The Hague, Nijhoff, 131 pp.

———— (1961). Isolation of selected elements with an x-ray projection microscope. Norelco Reporter, v. 8, no. 1, p. 2.

Rovinsky, B. M., V. G. Lutsau, and A. I. Avdeyenko (1957). X-ray microprojector, *in* V. E. Cosslett (ed.), Proc. Symp. X-Ray Microscopy and Microradiography, Cambridge, 1956, New York, Academic, p. 269.

Schmidt, R. A. M. (1952). Microradiography of microfossils. Science, v. 115, no. 2978, p. 91.

Siegel, B. M., and K. C. Knowlton (1957). The conversion of an electron microscope to point projection x-ray microscopy, *in* V. E. Cosslett (ed.), Proc. Symp. X-Ray Microscopy and Microradiography, Cambridge, 1956, New York, Academic, p. 106.

**FURTHER READING**

Proc., 2nd Internat. Symp. X-Ray Microscopy and X-Ray Microanalysis. Stockholm, 1959. Amsterdam, Elsevier, 1960.

# Paleontological Investigation of Limestones by Electron Microscope

SUSUMU HONJO, ALFRED G. FISCHER

*Princeton University, Princeton, New Jersey*

The electron microscope provides a means for extending paleontological investigations into the ultramicroscopic realm. It can add much to our knowledge of optically recognizable fossils, as exemplified by recent advances in our knowledge of coccoliths (Black and Barnes, 1959, 1961; Hay and Towe, 1962). It can also reveal the presence of minute fossils where optical methods fail, as shall be shown here.

To date, electron microscopy in paleontology has dealt mainly with microfossils in unconsolidated sediment (chalk, soft marl, and so on), separated from the matrix. Exceptions are the studies of Grunau and Studer (1956) and Grunau (1959) on *Nannoconus*-bearing limestones from the Alpine Mesozoic, and the studies of Grégoire and Monty (1963) on stromatolites from the Belgian Carboniferous.

We have begun a survey of fine-grained limestones by optical and electron microscopy. Our optical work, even with very thin sections (Honjo and Fischer, Part II, Section B) suggested to us that in fine-grained limestones, such as those from the Cretaceous-Eocene flysch of Spain and from the Late Jurassic *Aptychus* beds of the Alps, most or all fossil material smaller than 10 to 15$\mu$ in size had been lost by recrystallization, a view previously advanced by Bramlette (1958). Electron microscopy provided a delightful surprise: These rocks do contain abundant small coccoliths and coccolith-like fossils, in the size range from 2 to 15$\mu$, and in varying states of preservation, as shown in figs. 1 and 2. All of these fossils are large enough to be seen in ultra-thin sections at high optical powers—but they are generally not recognizable as fossils, owing to the undistinctive nature of their outlines, to internal recrystallization, and to the fineness of their distinctive internal structure, which is not resolved by optical means.

The conclusion is that consolidated fine-grained limestones may contain vast numbers of fossils that are unrecognizable by optical study but are revealed by electron microscopy of the rock as a whole. From the recognition of these small fossils in such sections, it may be a long step to their identification with genera and species recognized on the basis of three-dimensional data, but the limited work which we have done has shown striking differences between samples. We here present the techniques utilized.

## ELECTRON MICROSCOPY OF LIMESTONES

To date it has not been possible to prepare sections of limestones which are thin enough to allow penetration of the electron beam and to withstand the temperatures produced by such bombardment. Electron microscopy of bulk limestone therefore depends on replicas of surface topography prepared either from freshly fractured surfaces or from polished and etched surfaces.

Described here are (1) a technique for obtaining a polished surface of limestone with minimal disturbance of fabric, (2) a method of finely etching this polished surface to bring the limestone fabric into delicate relief, and (3) a procedure for preparing two-stage replicas.

### REPLICAS

Basically, the preparation of a replica revolves around two requirements: (1) a faithful image (positive or negative) of the surface to be depicted must be obtained in the form of a film—commonly a carbon film—that can be penetrated by the electron beam, and (2) the hills and valleys of the topography must be brought out in some way. This is generally done by "shadowing" the replica—evaporating heavy metal onto the topography at a low angle, to produce a film of varying thickness and varying opacity to the electron beam. There are two main methods of obtaining such replicas: the "pre-shadow method" and the "two-stage method."

In the pre-shadow method, an acid-resistant metal is evaporated onto the surface to be replicated to form the shadows, and is then coated with an even layer of carbon or silicon monoxide; alternatively, the carbon or silicon monoxide layer may be applied first, and the shadowing second (with some loss of resolution). The original sample is then dissolved away by acid, leaving the replica. This is the technique which has been used in the study of free coccoliths (Deflandre and Durrieu, 1957; Black and Barnes, 1959, 1961; Hay and Towe, 1962). Great resolution may be obtained in this manner, but the

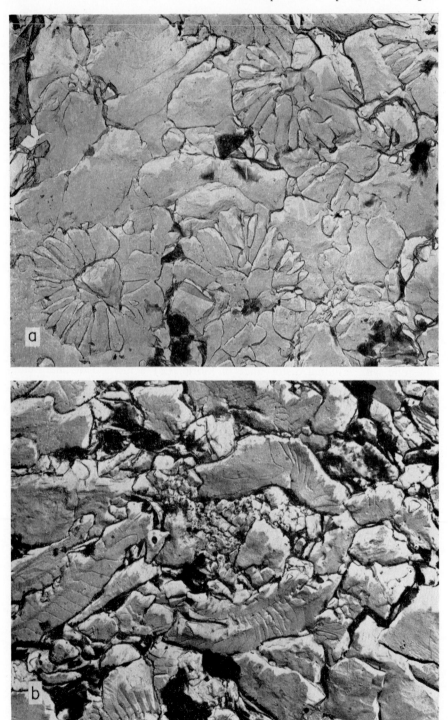

technique has two disadvantages for the study of limestone surfaces. One is that replicas retain a heavy coating of insoluble materials (called pseudo-replicas or extractions), which interfere with the normal replica image and may cause trouble in the microscope (although for mineralogical-petrological studies they may be desirable). Such materials can be removed only by further treatment of the replica. The second disadvantage is that the process destroys the specimen; no duplicate replicas can be prepared.

In the two-stage method, the limestone surface is first replicated negatively on a film or plate of plastic. This first replica is then shadowed obliquely with metal, and an even layer of carbon is applied. These two layers constitute the second (positive) replica. The first replica is then removed by solution, leaving the carbon-metal replica for study. In this method less insoluble material is retained, and a given surface can be replicated over and over, which is particularly advantageous—type material can be preserved, polish and etch can be modified if unsatisfactory, and the specimen is not lost if the first replica is poor or becomes damaged in the course of observation. For a more elaborate discussion of replicating techniques, see Bradley (1961).

SURFACE

Replicas may be made from fracture surfaces or from polished and etched surfaces. Fracture surfaces are more easily prepared, and there is no danger of producing a so-called Beilby layer—a surface layer of spurious fabrics, developed during grinding and polishing. Their disadvantage is that fracturing of rocks develops a rather high and irregular relief, in which the structure of small objects is more difficult to interpret than in polished and lightly etched sections. Most work on limestones, including that here reported, has been done on polished-and-etched surfaces.

IMAGE

The image which is produced by these replica methods is merely an image of the topographic relief of the sample (except for such extractions as may be present). It is therefore not directly comparable with the images provided by thin-sections under the optical microscope—quite aside from the differences in scale. Another problem—one that is much greater in electron microscopy than in optical work—concerns the introduction of contaminant particles and

**Fig. 1.** *Electron photomicrographs of limestones. 7500×. (a) Late Jurassic (Tithonian) Aptychus (or Oberalm) limestone, Unken Valley, Salzburg, Austria. Rosettes are nannoplanktonic fossils, possibly coccolithophorid remains, surrounded and partly engulfed by calcite crystals of matrix. Thin sections fail to reveal fossils at this order of magnitude. Compare Fig. 2,a. (b) Late Cretaceous (Maestrichtian) or Paleocene limestone in flysch at Zumaya, Spain. Whereas thin sections reveal only few and large coccoliths, the electron microscope shows that at least 30 percent of the rock is composed of fragmented coccoliths. Compare Fig. 2,b.*

artifacts into the replicas. Great pains must be taken to avoid them, for they are not easily distinguished as such.

The resolution provided by replicas made by the two-stage process is limited by a number of factors, among them the topography of the etched surface, the thickness and background effect of the evaporated metals, and the shadowing angle. However, the most important factor appears to be the precision with which the first, plastic replica duplicates the original surface. We have not attempted to measure the correspondence of the carbon replicas to the etched rock surface, but according to Fukami, et al. (1961) the limit of resolution of the two-stage method may, in general, be expected to lie between 50 and 100 Å.

In our work we have used a Kinney SC-3 High Vacuum Evaporator and a Hitachi HS-6 electron microscope.

## PROCEDURE

*Stage 1, Embedding.* Cut a cube of the rock to be studied, about 7 mm thick. Grind off the saw marks with medium abrasive, wash thoroughly, and dry in an oven for a few hours at 45°C, then cool to room temperature and affix a pressure-sensitive paper label to one side for identification.

Place the cube, labeled side up, in the middle of a polyethylene vial approximately 20 mm in inside diameter, and pour mounting resin over the cube to make a plug about 16 mm high. Let stand at room temperature for at least 10 hours to complete polymerization.

To prepare the mounting resin, mix 14 grams of HET anhydride, as a hardener, into 30 grams of "Unox" epoxide 206 monomer with a magnetic stirrer until the resin is totally dissolved. Mixed monomer is unstable in batches of more than 50 grams and may not set in very small batches. The pot-life of the monomer mix is approximately 80 minutes at 20°C for a 40- to 45-gram batch.

The monomer mix has the advantages of low viscosity (about 8 cps), and there is little chance that air bubbles will be entrapped in the plug. Since the vapor pressure of the mix is very low (0.1 mm Hg at 20°C), vacuum impregnation can be used for porous specimens. The polymer is straw-colored, translucent, highly resistant to organic solvents, and has great hardness (about 60 Barcol hardness) and impact strength.

*Stage 2, Grinding.* Step a: Cut the plug out of the vial, and grind it on the

---

**Fig. 2.** *Electron photomicrographs of coccoliths in limestones. 10,000×. (a) Coccolith in Late Jurassic (Tithonian) Aptychus (or Oberalm) limestone, Unken Valley, Salzburg, Austria. Coccolith appears somewhat deformed. Failure to recognize a normal coccolith "swastica" extinction pattern in thin section suggests that initial orientation of calcite in the individual plates has been altered. Compare fig. 1,a. (b) Coccolith in limestone from the flysch at Zumaya, Spain, revealing complex microstructure.*

bottom to expose a face of sample cube. Bevel the edges of the plug. *Step b:* Grind with Buehler's no. 600 grinding compound on a slow-speed lap, using water and 10 percent ethylene glycol. *Step c:* Grind manually for several minutes on a ground glass plate, using a thin film of no. 800 grinding compound in a mixture of distilled water and 10 percent ethylene glycol. *Step d:* Grind similarly, first with no. 1200 and then with no. 3200 compound and similar lubricant on separate plates. After this step, the surface should not be touched by bare fingers.

It is important to avoid straining the surface, especially during the later steps: heavy pressure and prolonged grinding should be avoided for this reason. Adding ethylene glycol to the grinding water moderates the strain by decreasing the intense impact of abrasive grains on the surface. The presence of some pits and scratches which would spoil a light microscopic image is immaterial, since the field of view in the electron microscope is very small.

*Stage 3, Polishing.* Polish on the high-speed lap, with $0.1\mu$ *gamma* alumina suspended in distilled water. We have used pellon synthetic fabric, 0.5 mm in thickness, for a polishing cloth. The specimen should be applied with moderate pressure for intervals of a few seconds, repeated 15 or 20 times. The surface of the specimen should have a mirror-like luster after this treatment. Flowage and recrystallization in the surface to be studied may be induced by too much pressure or polishing.

A specimen should be thoroughly cleaned between and after each grinding and polishing procedures. The ultrasonic vibrator and dilute detergent solution may be used for highly consolidated rocks.

*Stage 4, Etching.* Immerse the specimen, face up and horizontal, in 0.1 $N$ HCl deionized water solution. For most limestones, 40 to 100 seconds of etching at 20°C is sufficient, but the precise interval may have to be determined by trial and error. Rinse the specimen repeatedly in deionized water, and then dry it in an oven for a few hours at 45°C.

*Stage 5, Replication. Step a:* The first-stage replica. Place a few drops of replicating solution on the polished surface, and then cover it with a piece of acetate replicating tape large enough to project beyond the edges of the sample. Hold the tape against the sample with your forefinger for several seconds, then rub the back of the tape firmly with lens tissue. After 10 minutes, peel off the replica with forceps, and mount it face-up on a glass slide with a bit of cellophane tape. We have been preparing several successive peels of the polished surface, discarding the first ones because they tend to extract most of the insoluble material. *Step b:* Shadowing. Place the slide with the replica into a bell jar or vacuum evaporator, and a chip of chromium into a tungsten basket. Evacuate to $10^{-4}$ mm Hg, and apply current to the tungsten basket until the Chromium chip is evaporated, hopefully depositing a layer some 20 Å thick on the facing parts of the replica. We use a 32° shadowing angle. For the quantity of metal necessary to form this thickness of shadow, see Bradley (1961). *Step c:* Carbon replica. A carbon arc inside the vacuum evaporator is used to apply carbon to the replica. We use an angle of 90° to produce a 200 Å layer which, together with the metal shadow, forms a positive replica of the polished and etched rock surface. *Step d:* Remove the slide from the evaporator, and score the surface of the replica sandwich with a razor blade to obtain a 1.5 to 3 mm grid. Remove the sandwich from the slide, and trim the excess with clean scissors.

*Stage 6, Grid preparation.* Utmost care must be taken during removal of the negative replica to avoid contamination. Place three petri dishes full of acetone side by side on a white-topped table under sufficient illumination. We have found that a big magnifier with built-in illumination is useful for preparation. Swiftly immerse the replica sandwich in the first bath, carbon surface up. After a minute or two the carbon film begins to separate from the negative acetate replica, and will begin to break up along the scored lines. This may be aided by gently rocking the dish. Let the squares of replica stand for a few minutes, and then scoop them up with an electron microscope grid. Bathe them for a few minutes in the second petri dish and then in the third. If the carbon squares curl, they can be straightened by a method described by Fukami (1955), by successively transferring them into 3:1, 1:1, and 1:3 mixtures of acetone and double distilled water, in which the film is suddenly stretched flat on the surface by differential surface tension. Finally, place the individual squares on separate grids with 75 by 300$\mu$ slot perforation, and hold them in the air with forceps until dry. They are now ready for study.

*Stage 7, Observation and photography.* This can proceed along standard lines. We scan and photograph the replicas at a magnification of 3000×, using a 30$\mu$ objective aperture and an accelerating voltage of 50 kv. Develop the plates in a fine-grained, high-demarkation developer, and print at a convenient enlargement scale, normally 10,000×.

## ACKNOWLEDGMENTS

Our ultramicroscopic study of limestones is supported by a grant from the Petroleum Research Fund of the American Chemical Society. The study of Mesozoic facies in the Alps has been carried out with the help of the National Science Foundation. We are greatly indebted to the Department of Biology, Princeton University, and especially to Dr. L. I. Rebhun and to Mr. W. C. Gorthy, Jr., for the use of the electron microscope and accessory facilities and for technical advice. For collection and preparation of samples we are indebted to Mr. R. E. Garrison, Jr., Mr. P. G. Temple, and Mr. F. M. Floyd.

## REFERENCES

Beilby, G. (1921). Aggregation and flow of solids. London, Macmillan, 274 pp.
Black, M., and B. Barnes (1959). The structure of coccoliths from the English Chalk. Geol. Mag., v. 96, p. 321–328.

———— (1961). Coccoliths and discoasters from the floor of the South Atlantic Ocean. J. R. Micros. Soc. v. 80, pt. 2, p. 137–147.

Bradley, D. E. (1961). Replica and shadowing techniques, *in* D. Kay (ed.), Techniques for electron microscopy. Springfield, Charles Thomas, p. 82–137.

Bramlette, M. N. (1958). Significance of coccolithophorids in calcium carbonate deposition. Geol. Soc. America Bull., v. 69, p. 121–126.

Deflandre, G., and Durrieu (1957). Application de la technique d'empreintes de carbone a la systématique des coccolithophorides fossiles. C.R. Acad. Sci., v. 244, p. 2948–2951.

Fukami, A. (1955). Experiment concerning replica preparation method (II). On a new rapid and reliable positive replica process (filmy replica system). J. Electron Microscopy, v. 4, no. 1, p. 274–278.

————, H. Kushida, and A. Suzuki (eds.) (1961). Saikinno Denshi-Kenbikyo Shiryo-seisakuho (Recent Development of Sample Preparation Techniques for Electron Microscopy). Tokyo, Denshi-Kenbikyogakkai Kanto shibu, 155 pp.

Grégoire, C., and C. Monty (1963). Observation au microscope électronique sur le calcaire à pâte fine entrant dans la constitution de structures stromatolithiques du Viséen Moyen de la Belgique. Géol. Soc. Belgique, Ann., no. 10, p. 389–397.

Grunau, H. R. (1959). Mikrofazies und Schichtung ansgewählter, jungmesozoischer, radiolarit-führender Sedimentserien der Zentral-Alpen. Int. Sed. Petrog., ser. 4, p. 179.

————, and H. Studer (1956). Elektronenmikroskopische Untersuchungen an Bianconekalken des Südtessins. Experientia, v. 12, p. 141–150.

Hall, C. E. (1957). Introduction to electron microscopy. New York, McGraw-Hill, 451 pp.

Hay, W. W. and K. M. Towe (1962). Electromicroscopic examination of some coccoliths from Donzacq (France). Eclogae Geol. Helv., v. 55, no. 2, p. 497–517.

Union Carbide Chemical Company (1960). "Unox" Epoxide 206. New York, Union Carbide Chemical Company, adv. tech. rep., 4 pp.

# Electron Microscopy of Internal Structures of Foraminifera

DAVID KRINSLEY

*Department of Geology and Geography, Queens College
of the City University of New York
Lamont Geological Observatory of Columbia University,
Palisades, New York*

ALLAN W. H. BÉ

*Lamont Geological Observatory of Columbia University,
Palisades, New York*

The present classification of microfossils is based almost entirely upon gross test morphology. Although such recognition is highly useful and often tenable, it is not always sufficient for a natural classification of such a diverse and variable group of microorganisms as the Foraminifera. Examples of artificial generic lumping of Foraminifera have been pointed out by Nørvang (1958) and Reiss (1957), and examples of artificial splitting of species and genera appear to be even more numerous, as indicated by the studies of Nyholm (1961), Boltovskoy (1958), and Resig (1962). Additional data on their laboratory culturing, ecological adaptations, biographic zonations, infraspecific and interspecific variability of living species, chemical-mineral composition, and microstructural details of their tests are essential considerations in a taxonomic scheme. These criteria have not been used extensively by paleontologists and neontologists.

Investigations of the internal morphology and wall structure of Foraminifera by light microscopy have been made by Wood (1948), Reiss (1958, 1959), Blackmon and Todd (1959), and Hedley (1957). We know of only two electron microscopic studies of Foraminifera, those of Jahn (1953) and Hay, et al. (1963).

Some work with the electron microscope has been done on fossil spores, coccolithophorids (Braarud, 1962; Hay, 1962), and diatoms (Helmcke and Krieger, 1952, 1953–54; Okuno, 1954, 1955, 1959; Cassie and Bertaud, 1960), but considerably more work has been done on molluscan shell structure (Gregoire, et al., 1955; Gregoire, 1957; Watabe and Wada, 1956; Watabe, et al., 1958; Wada, 1957, 1961).

We wish to present here a method for light and electron microscopic

Lamont Geological Observatory Contribution No. 748.

examination of the internal morphology and wall structure of Foraminifera and other calcareous microfossils. The reader is also referred to the works of Rochow et al. (1960) and Zworykin, et al. (1945) for general methods and publications in electron microscopy.

## OBTAINING REPLICAS BY THE ACETATE PEEL METHOD

### CLEANING

Foraminiferal specimens collected from core samples often contain extraneous particles which should be removed. These tests may be cleaned by placing them in an ultrasonic vibrator. If specimens collected from plankton tows are used, their protoplasm can be removed by soaking in a hydrogen peroxide solution.

### EMBEDDING

The clean specimens should be dry before they are embedded. Flexible polyethylene vial caps (15 mm diameter and 4 mm high) or rigid metal containers with a removable base are suitable molds for specimen embedding. The metal containers permit easy removal of the plastic casts.

The fossils are attached to the bottom of the mold with Duco cement and oriented in the desired position. Care should be taken not to cover the entire specimen with glue, as this will prevent the embedding medium from penetrating the interior of the tests. Our experience indicates that optimum conditions obtain when about twenty-five specimens are spaced roughly one millimeter apart in a square pattern.

A thin layer of embedding plastic[1] diluted with liquid styrene[2] is then poured over the specimens; the embedding plastic may have to be diluted as much as 50 percent with liquid styrene. A small amount of catalyst (tertiary butyl hydroperoxide) is added. It is important that the embedding material be very fluid to allow penetration into all interstices of the specimens; penetration may be aided by placing the mold in a bell jar vacuum chamber. After several minutes of evacuation, air bubbles from the interior of the tests are forced to the surface.

The specimens are then cured in an oven between 70 and 100°C for 15 to 30 minutes, depending on the amount of catalyst used. The plastic can be removed from the mold when the surface becomes rigid.

### SECTIONING AND POLISHING

Removal of the excess plastic around the specimens will yield a block of small surface area which may be attached to a microscope slide with Lakeside 70 cement. The specimens are then ground with No. $303\frac{1}{2}$ ($11\mu$) grinding

---

[1] Methacrylate, clear, transparent, fast-curing thermosetting resin of the Copolymer type, obtained from N. Y. Scientific Supply Co. 28 W. 30th Street, New York 1, N. Y.
[2] Ward's Natural History Establishment, Inc., P. O. Box 1712, Rochester, N. Y.

powder[3] on a glass plate until the desired level is reached. Then they are ground with No. 305 (5μ) grinding powder[4] and polished to a very smooth surface with No. 309W powder (White polishing compound)[5] on a velvet surface. The slide can be effectively cleaned between each of these operations by placing it in an ultrasonic vibrator for a few seconds.

### REPLICATING

The surface of the polished calcareous specimens is etched in an EDTA solution. The slide is agitated in the solution for 30-second intervals, removed, washed, and examined under a microscope. The degree of surface relief depends on the etching time, the most satisfactory replicas being obtained at etching times between 60 and 120 seconds.

A replica of the etched foraminiferal surface is made by putting a drop or two of replicating solution on the surface to be replicated and then placing an acetate film (Faxfilm)[6] over it. The film should be somewhat larger than the specimen surface. Pressure is applied by means of a small vise to press the acetate film firmly against the etched specimen. The replicating solution serves as a solvent and permits the acetate to reproduce the differentially etched specimen surface. After 1 to 5 minutes the film should be thoroughly dry and ready to be stripped. The resulting impression, here called an acetate peel, gives an accurate mirror-image reproduction of the original surface. In order to obtain the original view, the replica is placed on a microscope slide with the impression side down.

## OBTAINING ELECTRON PHOTOMICROGRAPHS

### SHADOWING

Since the acetate film is too thick to be viewed directly through the electron microscope, a much thinner film (less than 200 Å thick) must be prepared for successful penetration of electrons at 75 to 100 kv (fig. 1).

The process of preparing such a thin film is known as shadowing. It is accomplished by evaporating a metal onto the acetate replica at an angle of about 45°. A smaller angle (about 30°) may be used if the specimen shows little relief. A platinum-palladium alloy is used as the shadowing agent because of its high scattering power for electrons, its ready evaporation under vacuum, its lack of granulation under the electron beam, its relatively low melting temperature, and its lack of reaction with the tungsten filament used to carry heat to the platinum-palladium metal.

The shadowing process is carried out in a bell jar evaporator, where a

---

[3] American Optical Co., Southbridge, Mass.
[4] American Optical Co., Southbridge, Mass.
[5] American Optical Co., Southbridge, Mass.
[6] Replicating fluid and acetate film can be obtained from Ladd Research Industries, Inc.. P. O. Box 901, Burlington, Vermont.

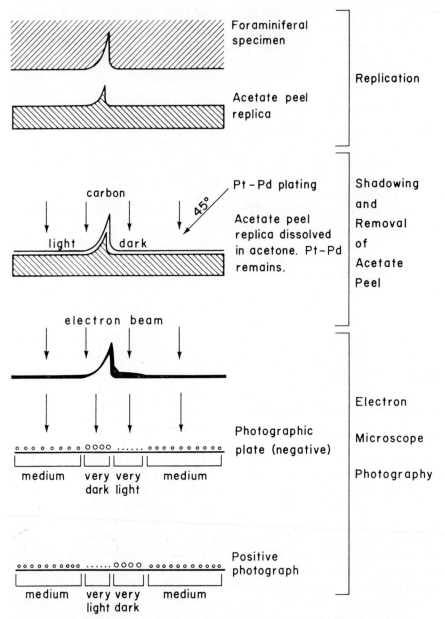

**Fig. 1.** *Diagrammatic representation of the peel and replicating process neces-*
*sary for electron microscopy.*

vacuum of about $5 \times 10^{-6}$ mm Hg may be attained. The specimen is placed
below the tungsten filament, from which platinum-palladium metal is suspended. A low-voltage, high-current, power supply of roughly 10 volts and
50 amperes is then applied to the filament. It is suggested that cellophane

tape be used to fasten the specimens to the glass slide, as this material requires less degassing time than other kinds of tape.

The evaporator is evacuated and a current sent through the tungsten wire,
vaporizing the platinum-palladium metal onto the specimen. Next, a support
film of carbon must be evaporated directly down onto the specimen. Carbon

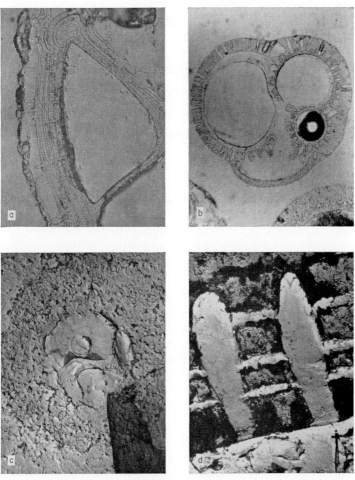

**Fig. 2.** (*a*) *Acetate peel replica of* Globorotalia menardii (*d'Orbigny*). *290×.* (*b*) *Acetate peel replica of* Sphaeroidinella
dehiscens (*Parker and Jones*). *100×.* (*c*) *Electron microphotograph of a pore on the surface of* Globorotalia menardii (*d'Orbigny*). *About 4900×. The central object is
probably a coccolith which had fallen into the pore opening.* (*d*) *Electron microphotograph of cross section of two
pores in* Globorotalia menardii (*d'Orbigny*). *About 1800×.
The bottom of the photograph, where the pores narrow,
represents the test surface. The parallel structures are test
layers.*

is used because it is chemically inert, amorphous, and highly transparent to electrons. To judge whether the correct amounts of both metal and carbon have been deposited on the acetate film, a sheet of white paper, which the operator can examine after shadowing, is placed beside the specimen. As little paper as possible should be used as it must be degassed during the process of pumping down to a usable vacuum; paper usually tends to trap air, and this increases the pumping time. The amount of carbon deposited and the voltage used are critical: either too little or too much carbon will cause the film to break up when the plastic is subsequently dissolved, whereas too high a voltage will cause the film to burn so that breakage occurs.

### REMOVAL OF THE ACETATE PEEL

The acetate peel containing the thin, shadowed film is cut and placed (shadowed side down) on a round, fine (about 200-mesh) screen which can be inserted in the electron microscope. The acetate peel is now ready to be separated from the platinum-palladium-carbon film. Most techniques for removing the acetate peel involve the insertion of the screen and acetate into an acetone bath; frequently the metal film will float off the screen in the bath, curl up, and become useless. A more efficient method is the use of a reflux unit (Ladd Research Industries), in which acetone is heated and vaporized, cooled by running water, and condensed on the acetate peel. This process does not involve moving the screen or immersing the specimen, and thus is safer than other methods.

A method of eliminating the acetate peel has been used by a number of workers, among them Hay and Wright (1963). The metal and carbon are evaporated directly down onto the specimen, which is then dissolved in acid, replicated, and viewed directly, without an acetate-peel intermediary. However, the metal-carbon replica must be considerably stronger than in the techniques described above; the specimen is, of course, lost.

### VIEWING

After the acetate peel has been removed, the copper specimen screen with the platinum-palladium-carbon film is placed in the electron microscope. At magnifications of 5000×, or even less, only very small portions of the final film can be observed; all electron microscopes are equipped with a mechanical drive which enables the operator to scan the entire film and select the portion desired for photography. The specimen is viewed on a fluorescent screen; in many instruments the image can be magnified several times by using a binocular microscope.

---

**Fig. 3.** (*A*) *Horizontal section through* Globorotalia truncatulinoides (*d'Orbigny*). *Acetate peel replica. 207×.* (*B*) *Electron microphotographs of* (*a*) *wall lamellae of inner chambers, 555×;* (*b*) *wall lamellae, pores, and calcite crust of outer chambers, 555×;* (*c*) *outer wall, showing relatively thin original lamellae and very thick calcite crust, 555×.*

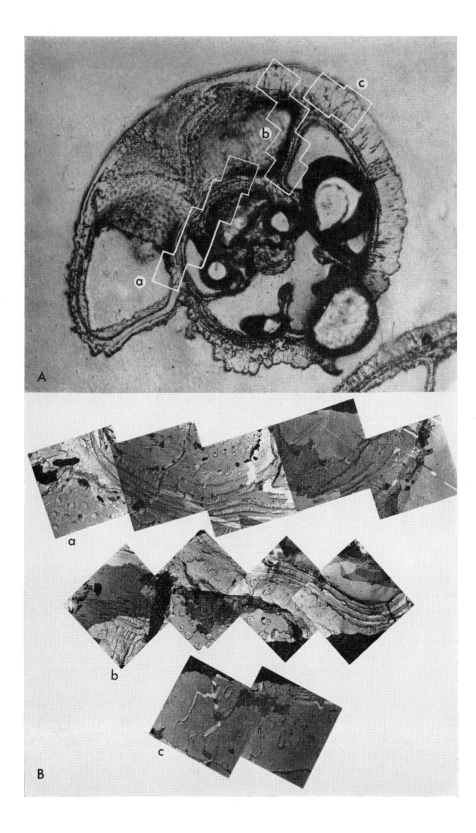

A

B

a

b

c

PHOTOGRAPHY

Photography is simple with the electron microscope; a plate camera is usually placed near the fluorescent screen, and the shutter opened when a photograph is desired. Most photographs are taken either on Kodak lantern-slide plates or on 35 mm film. Depending on the resolution of the electron microscope, the negatives may be enlarged as much as 10×.

Photographs of foraminiferal shells have been taken at magnifications of up to 1000× with the light microscope (figs. 2,*a,b* and 3), but resolution is rather poor. Even with the smaller electron microscopes, however, resolution averages about 30 Å (figs. 2,*c,d* and 3,*c,d,e*). Thus, electron microphotographs taken at 1000× usually can be enlarged ten times; this is sufficient for all practical purposes.

Stereophotographs may be prepared by rotating the specimen a few degrees from its original position and taking an additional picture. This can be easily controlled from outside the microscope without breaking vacuum. A light meter is usually built into the more expensive electron microscopes; in addition, they are commonly equipped with devices which prevent double exposures.

The entire technique, starting with the original specimens and ending with photographs of the shell structures of foraminifera, may be accomplished in about twelve hours if the equipment is available and in working condition.

## ACKNOWLEDGMENTS

The authors are grateful to Mr. Leroy Lott for his laboratory assistance. We wish to acknowledge the support of the National Science Foundation (Grants GB-155 and G-24472) and the Petroleum Research Fund of the American Chemical Society.

## REFERENCES

Blackmon, P. D., and R. Todd (1959). Mineralogy of some Foraminifera as related to their classification and ecology. J. Paleontology, v. 33, p. 1–15.

Boltovskoy, E. (1958). Problems in taxonomy and nomenclature exemplified by *Nonion affine* (Reuss). Micropaleontology, v. 4, p. 193–200.

Braarud, T. (1962). Electron microscope studies of coccoliths in oceanic deposits. Nature, v. 193, p. 1035–1036.

Cassie, V., and W. S. Bertaud (1960). Electron microscope studies of New Zealand marine plankton diatoms. J. Roy. Micros. Soc., v. 79, p. 89–94.

Gregoire, C. (1957). Topography of the organic components of mother-of-pearl. J. Biophys. Biochem. Cytol., v. 3, p. 797.

————, G. Duchateau, and M. Florkin (1955). La trame protidique des nacres et des perles. Ann. Inst. Oceanog., v. 31, p. 1.

Hay, W. W., and K. M. Towe (1962). Electron-microscopic studies of *Braarudosphaera bigelowi* and some related coccolithophorids. Science, v. 137, p. 426–428.

————, and R. C. Wright (1963). Some ultra structures of some selected foraminiferal tests. Micropaleontology, v. 9, no. 2, p. 171–195.

Hedley, R. H. (1957). Microradiography applied to the study of foraminifera. Micropaleontology, v. 3, p. 19–28.

Helmcke, J. G. von, and W. Krieger (1952). Feinbau der diatomeenschalen in einzeldarstellungen. Instit fur Mikromorphologie der Deutschen Forschungshochschule, v. 61, n. 2, p. 83–92.

———— (1953–54). Atlas der diatomeenschalen im elektronmikroskopischen Bild. Berlin-Ulmersdorf, p. 1–2.

Jahn, B. (1953). Elektronenmikroskopische Untersuchungen an Foraminiferenschalen. Zeitschr. Wiss. Mikroskopie, v. 61, p. 294–297.

Nørvang, A. (1958). *Islandiella* and *Cassidulina* d'Orbigny. Vidensk. Medd. fra Dansk Natur. Foren., v. 120, p. 25–41.

Nyholm, K. R. (1961). Morphogenesis and biology of the foraminifer *Cibicides lobatus*. Zoologiska bidrag Från Uppsala, v. 33, p. 157–196.

Okuno, H. (1954). Electron-microscopical study on fine structures of diatom frustules, XII. Bot. Mag., v. 67, p. 172–177.

———— (1955). Electron-microscopical study on fine structures of diatom frustules, XIII. Bot. Mag., v. 68, p. 125–128.

———— (1959). Electron-microscopical study on fine structures of diatom frustules, XVII. Bot. Mag., v. 72, p. 62–67.

Reiss, Z. (1957). The Bilamellidea, Nov. Superfamily and remarks on Cretaceous Globorotalids. Contr. Cushman Found. Foram. Res., v. 8, pt. 4, p. 127–145.

———— (1958). Classification of lamellar foraminifera. Micropaleontology, v. 4, p. 51–70.

———— (1959). The wall structure of *Cibicides, Planulina, Gyrodinoides* and *Globorotalites*. Micropaleontology, v. 5, p. 355–357.

Resig, J. M. (1962). The morphological development of *Eponides repandus* (Fichtel and Noll), 1798. Contr. Cushman Found. Foram. Res., v. 13, pt. 2, p. 55–57.

Rochow, T. G., A. M. Thomas, and M. C. Botty (1960). Electron microscopy. Anal. Chem., v. 32, p. 92R–103R.

Wada, K. (1957). Electron-microscopic observations on the shell structure of the pearl oyster (*Pinctada martensii*) II. Observations of the aragonite crystals on the surface of nacreous layers. Natl. Pearl Res. Lab. Bull., v. 2, p. 74.

———— (1961). Crystal growth in molluscan shells. Nat. Pearl Res. Lab. Bull., no. 7, p. 703–783.

Watabe, N., and K. Wada (1956). On the shell structure of the Japanese pearl oyster, *Pinctada martensii*. I. Prismatic layer I. Rept. Fac. Fish. Pref. Univ. Mie, v. 2, p. 227.

————, D. G. Sharp, and K. M. Wilbur (1958). Studies on shell formation, VIII. Electron microscopy of crystal growth of the nacreous layer of the oyster *Crassostrea virginica*. J. Biophys. Biochem. Cytol., v. 4, p. 281.

Wood, A. (1948). The structure of the wall of the test in Foraminifera; its value and classification. Quart. J. Geol. Soc. London, v. 104, p. 229–255.

Zworykin, V. K., G. A. Morton, E. G. Ramberg, J. Hillier, and A. W. Vance (1945). Electron optics and the electron microscope. New York, Wiley, 766 pp.

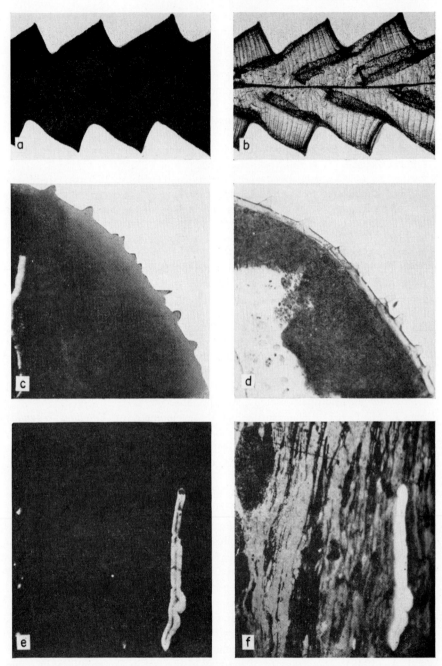

**Fig. 1.** *Photographs illustrating the transparency of some fossils to infrared radiation. Photographs on the left were taken in normal light with orthochromatic emulsions and a yellow filter; those on the right were taken in infrared with the appropriate emulsion and filter. (a,b)* Diplograptus gracilis

# Uses of Infrared Rays

W. D. IAN ROLFE

*Hunterian Museum, Glasgow, Scotland*

Infrared rays have wavelengths from 7600 Å to one million Å, but only the near region of this spectrum is of practical use (out to about 13,500 Å). The value of infrared radiation lies in the fact that some substances absorb it, some reflect and scatter it, and others allow it to pass through them. Thus, "the appearance of an object under infrared radiation often bears small resemblance to its appearance in visual light" (Moss, 1954, p. 14). Many fossils that are of the same color as the matrix or are dark or even opaque may, when examined by infrared, show contrast with their matrix or may become transparent enough to permit the elucidation of structural details.

Studies have recently been made of the infrared luminescence emitted by fossils when excited by blue-green light (Gibson, 1962, 1963). This new technique needs to be developed further before its value in paleontology will become apparent, and hence it will not be further discussed here.

The best-known use of infrared in paleontology is probably in paleobotany. Thin sections and transfer preparations of carbonized plant tissues may be dark or opaque under visible light yet translucent to infrared (figs. 1,c–f). Photographs illustrating this application are given in Clark (1946), Eggert (1935b, 1936), Fröhlich and Luft (1934), Leclerq (1933), Radforth (1939), Walker and Slater, in Wandless and Macrae (1934), and Walton (1935). Walker and Slater (1935) point out that infrared photographs of coal sections give more realistic contrast between the yellows of spores and cuticle and the reds and dark colors of the coaly matrix than can be obtained with normal light, and, furthermore, that the field is flatter.

Kraft obtained good results with such dark objects as isolated graptolites (figs. 1,a,b), fish scales, and the hair of fossil mammals. Recent insect cuticles also show greatly increased transparency with infrared, so that by analogy this procedure should be useful in the study of fossil arthropod cuticles. Bones of fossil frogs preserved in the Geiseltal lignite yielded details under infrared radiation which were invisible with ordinary illumination (Eggert, 1936, Fröhlich and Luft, 1934) (figs. 2,a,b).

F. Roemer. 20×. [*From Kraft, 1932a.*] (*c,d*) *Macrospore of Bothrodendron. 115×.* [*From Leclerq, 1933.*] (*e,f*) *Vertical section of steam coal. 115×.* [*From Leclerq, 1933.*]

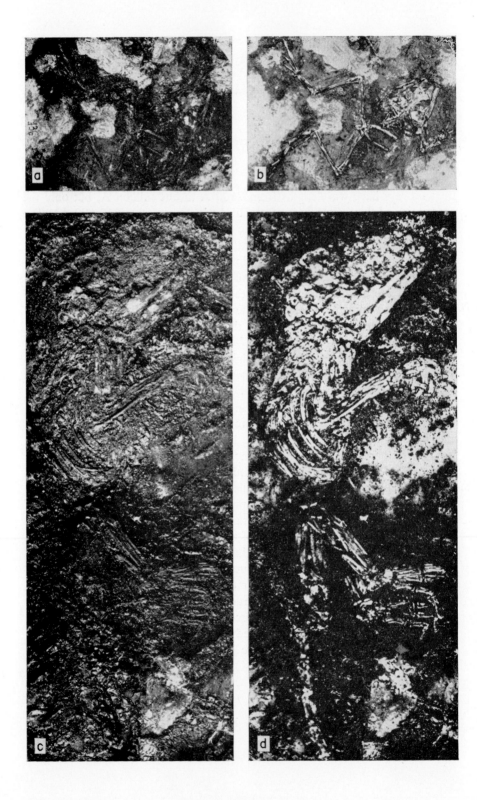

Fossils that show little or no color contrast with the matrix may differ in their capacity to absorb or reflect infrared, thus enabling contrasty photographs to be prepared of otherwise "flat" subjects, with consequent gain in detail. Eggert (1935b, 1936) first used this technique to increase the contrast between leaves and matrix in the Geiseltal lignite. Spectacular use was made of this technique by Harris in 1936–1937 (Harris and Latham, 1951) to record details of *Palaeospondylus*. Richardson has been able to distinguish shiny black crustacean carapaces from the equally black bituminous matrix in this way, the fossil then appearing light on a dark ground. Similarly, Bachmayer (1960) was able to emphasize the pyritized regions of the body of a minute Callovian cumacean.

An incidental use of infrared which may be mentioned is in the decipherment of faded, obliterated, erased, or dirty writing on specimen labels and the restoration of writing on charred documents.

## METHODS

Since infrared rays are invisible the above advantages cannot be enjoyed visually unless an "image converter" is employed. This device consists of a tube equipped with a photocathode at one end which converts the infrared image into a stream of electrons. This stream is focused by high-voltage electronic lenses onto a fluorescent screen and produces a visual image. Such electronic image converters are ideal for viewing and focusing preparatory to photomicrography (Bailly and Holke, 1949; Maresh, 1953) or for large specimen inspection (see Maresh, 1953 and Moss, 1954 for details). Several commercial models are available (e.g., RCA 1P25, British Service Tube CV 144, Mullard ME 1201). If such a converter is not available photography must be used to record the specimen's "appearance" by infrared radiation.

Any tungsten-filament bulb is an excellent source of infrared radiation, since in all such lamps the maximum spectral energy is emitted in the infrared and not the visible region. Photofloods and Pointolites are particularly suitable for macroscopic and microscopic work respectively.

Specially sensitized plates and films are available for wavelengths up to 13,000 Å, but those sensitive to waves longer than 8600 Å require special storage and to be most effective need longer wavelength bulbs. Infrared emulsions are hypersensitive to shorter wavelengths, however, and if a purely infrared photograph is to be taken these visible wavelengths must be filtered off by such filters as the Kodak Wratten 25 (A) or 87, Agfa 85, Ilford 207, or Corning 254. Red filters are also suitable for most work, although the

**Fig. 2.** *Middle Eocene frog and insectivore from the Geiseltal, showing improved contrast obtainable with infrared radiation (photographs on right). (a,b)* Archaeopelobates? eusculptus *Kuhn. 0.39×. [From Fröhlich and Luft, 1934.] (c,d)* Ceciliolemur delasaucei *Weigelt. 2.1×.*

resultant image will not then be strictly an infrared photograph unless the emulsion used is insensitive to red.

One important point to check before using a camera for infrared photography is the opacity to infrared of the bellows, shutter, dark slide, and plate holders. This is especially important for wooden parts of the camera. Moss suggests the following convenient test for infrared "light tightness." The camera is set up as usual, loaded with infrared film or plate, and the draw slide removed; then, with the shutter closed or with the cap over the lens, the lamps are turned on for three or four times the period needed for a normal exposure (i.e., three or four minutes). If on development the emulsion is found to be unfogged, the camera is satisfactory, otherwise infrared leaks must be repaired with metal or metal foil.

Another thing to remember is that unless specially corrected lenses are used, all camera lenses will focus infrared rays at a different point from that at which they focus visible light. This is because such lenses are corrected so that most (apochromatic) or much (achromatic-anastigmats) of the visible spectrum comes to focus in one plane. Therefore, after focusing the subject visually, a correction must be applied (unless the smallest aperture is used, in which case the depth of field will usually cover such a difference). A useful rule of thumb is to extend the lens (or rack back of the plate holder) by 0.03 to 0.05 of the focal length. The lens may also be calibrated by taking a series of photographs at and beyond the visual focal point (preferably determined under green light), and applying the correction thus obtained to future exposures. This problem becomes more acute in photomicrography. With apochromatic lenses the visual focal point determined with a dark red filter in position will usually suffice when the infrared filter is substituted. With achromatic lenses, however, a correction must be determined either photographically, as outlined above, or by Naumann's method (Clark, 1946, p. 280–281). In this method the microscope is focused by using green light of about 5400 Å centroid wavelength, and is then refocused in dark red light of about 6800 Å wavelength. The difference between the settings of the fine-adjustment knob in these positions is noted, and the knob is turned in the same direction by an amount equal to twice this difference, at which position the infrared rays should be in focus.

Harris and Latham (1951) point out that attention must be paid to the heating effect of high-intensity lamps, since heat may alter the camera-to-object distance. It is therefore advisable to allow the apparatus to warm up for an hour before making the exposure.

Photography is then carried out as for visible light, exposures being determined by trial, guided by the manufacturers' instruction leaflets supplied with filters and plate or film. Darkroom practice is the same as for normal materials except that the safelight must be suitable for infrared work (e.g., Wratten 7), or else work must be done in total darkness.

Harris and Latham (1951) and Mutschke (1953) have independently suggested a refinement of the infrared technique for increasing contrast between fossil and matrix by photographing the specimen when immersed in water. To eliminate the mottled appearance resulting from reflections from a micaceous matrix the specimen is immersed in a liquid of refractive index closer to that of mica, such as monobromine naphthalene. Reflections from the surface of the immersion liquid are cut out by a polarizing filter over the camera lens (in addition to the infrared filter). Exposure times are very long with this method—1 to 2 hours at f 4.5, or if an additional polarizing filter is used over the light source, 10- to 30-hour exposures are required.

## ACKNOWLEDGMENTS

The writer is indebted to Professor Dr. H. W. Matthes and Dr. G. Krumbiegel of the Martin-Luther-Universität for the photographs used in figs. 2,c,d. Doctor W. Clark of Kodak Research Laboratories, Rochester, N. Y., Dr. T. Edinger, Professor B. Kummel, and Professor H. B. Whittington have given much assistance in the preparation of this account.

## REFERENCES

Bachmayer, Friedrich (1960). Eine fossile Cumaceenart (Crustacea, Malacostraca) aus dem Callovien von La Voulte-sur-Rhone (Ardèche). Eclog. Geol. Helvetiae, v. 53, p. 422–426, 2 pls., 2 figs.

Bailly, R. J., and K. A. Holke (1949). Microscope and refractometer for infrared light (abs.). Geol. Soc. America Bull. 60, p. 1871–1872.

Clark, Walter (1946). Photography by infrared, its principles and applications (2nd ed.). New York, Wiley, *xvii* + 472 pp., 93 figs.

Eggert, John (1935a). Die Photographie im Dienste der paläontologischen Wissenschaft (abs.). Die Naturwiss., v. 23, p. 168.

———— (1935b). Einige neue Anwendungen der Infrarot photographie. Die Naturwiss., v. 23, p. 281–286, 7 figs.

———— (1936). La photographie au service de la paléontologie. International Congress of Photography, 9, Paris, 1935, Procès-verbaux, rapports et mémoires, p. 737–741, 6 figs.

Fröhlich, Alfred, and Fritz Luft (1934). Photographie von Geiseltalfunden. Die Umschau, v. 38, p. 534–535, 5 figs.

Gibson, H. L. (1962). The photography of infra-red luminescence; Part 1, General considerations. Medical and Biol. Illus., v. 12, p. 155–166, 10 figs.

———— (1963). Photographing ultraviolet and infrared luminescence. Dental Radiography and Photography, v. 36, p. 34–39, 4 figs.

Harris, J. E., and E. Latham (1951). Infra-red photography of fossils. Med. and Biol. Illus., v. 1, p. 130–135, 8 figs.

Kraft, Paul (1932a). Die Mikrophotographie mit infraroten Strahlen. International Congress of Photography, 8, Dresden, 1931, Berichte, p. 341–345, 4 figs.

———— (1932b). Neue optische Wege in der Mikrophotographie und Mikroskopie im Dienste der Geologie und Paläontologie. Deutsche geol. Gesell. Zeitschr., v. 84, p. 651–652.

Leclerq, Suzanne (1933). Application de la lumière infra-rouge à l'étude microscopique des végétaux fossiles. Ann. Soc. Géol. Belgique Bull., v. 56, p. 351–356, 3 pls., 1 fig.

Maresh, Charles (1953). Infrared photomicrography with the electron image converter tube. J. Biol. Photog. Assoc., v. 21, no. 3, p. 14–23, 20 figs.

Moss, A. A. (1954). The application of x-rays, gamma rays, ultraviolet and infrared rays to the study of antiquities. London, Mus. Assoc., Handbook for Museum Curators, Part B, sec. 4, 16 pp., 8 pls., 1 fig.

Mutschke, F. (1953). Infrarot-Aufnahmen von Fossilien. Naturwiss. Rundschau, v. 6, no. 2, p. 74–75, 4 figs.

Pax, F. (1934). Die Untersuchung von Korallenskeletten im infraroten Licht. Zool. Anzeig., v. 106, p. 15–17, 1 fig.

Radforth, N. W. (1939). Further contributions to our knowledge of the fossil Schizaeaceae; genus *Senftenbergia*. Roy. Soc. Edinburgh Trans., v. 59, p. 745–761, 1 pl., 3 figs.

Walker, J. J., and L. Slater (1935). Infra-red photography of coal. Nature, v. 135, p. 623.

Walton, John (1935). An application of infra-red photography to palaeobotanical research. Nature, v. 135, p. 265, 3 figs.

Wandless, A. M., and J. C. Macrae (1934). The banded constituents of coal. Interrelationships deduced from analytical data. Fuel in Science and Practice, London, v. 13, p. 4–15, 8 figs.

# Uses of Ultraviolet Rays

W. D. IAN ROLFE

*Hunterian Museum, Glasgow, Scotland*

Ultraviolet rays can be used in two different ways in paleontology: (1) to improve photographic resolution when photographing small specimens, and (2) in fluorescence studies.

## IMPROVEMENT OF PHOTOGRAPHIC RESOLUTION

Colbert and Tarka (1960) published excellent photographs of small vertebrate fossils demonstrating this technique, and I can do no better than quote their succinct account of the principle and method involved.

Very small specimens that are strongly three-dimensional pose special problems in photography. Under these conditions it is the effect of diffraction inherent in the wave nature of the light that most seriously deteriorates the quality of the image, rather than other lens aberrations usually considered at length in discussions of optical performance. The theoretical limit of resolution with any lens is fixed by the relationship of the relative aperture to the wavelength of the light used. Thus, for any given aperture, resolution can be improved only by the use of a shorter wavelength. Ultraviolet radiation at 3650 Å, readily obtained from high pressure mercury vapour lamps with suitable filtration or, from black light fluorescent lamps, has a notable advantage over white light in reducing the effects of diffraction. Although still shorter wavelengths, in the middle and far ultraviolet range, would be even more desirable, most glasses become opaque to ultraviolet at about 3000 Å, and only quartz and reflection optics can then be used.

The 3650 Å wavelength radiation strongly affects photographic emulsions and it is possible to use printing films (positive emulsions) which are sensitive only to blue and ultraviolet. Although ultraviolet does not render tones as the eye sees them, this is rarely of importance in dealing with fossil material. Some adjustment of the white light focus is usually necessary and will vary for lenses of different design. The gain in resolving power can be employed either to increase the size of a sharp image or to increase the depth of field for any given size of image, by permitting an equivalent resolution at relatively smaller apertures.

This method may also be used to increase resolution in photomicroscopy (Maier and Wetzel, 1958, p. 129). Roselt (1962, p. 321) states that photographs of Ludlovian plants taken by ultraviolet with the specimens immersed in xylol were better than those taken in air.

## FLUORESCENCE

When excited by ultraviolet rays (electromagnetic radiation having a wavelength from 136 Å to 4000 Å) some substances have the ability to act as "transformers" by converting the invisible, or black, light to different wavelengths (usually longer, and therefore visible), giving rise to the phenomenon of luminescence. Luminescence which ceases when the exciting stimulus is removed is known as fluorescence, whereas that which persists for any time is termed phosphorescence.

The discovery that some fossils fluoresce was made independently by Miethe (1927a,b), Simpson (1926), and Wagner (1928). Many paleontologists have assumed that organic residues in the fossil are responsible for such fluorescence, but it must be emphasized that no such generalization is possible. The causes of fluorescence are usually complex; some organic chemicals do indeed fluoresce, and hydrocarbons may form activation centers in minerals, but the fluorescence of most fossils probably is of inorganic origin. The variable performance of fossils in this respect is "due to minute traces of impurities (such as rare earth metals and manganese), which are not intrinsic constituents of the mineral (or minerals comprising the fossil) and

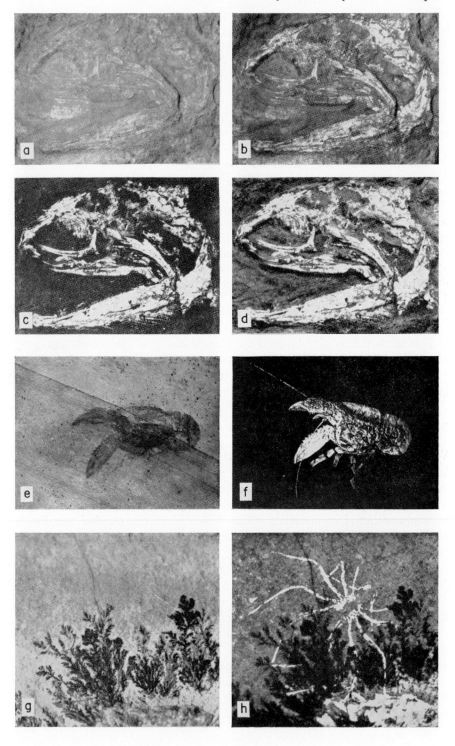

which sometimes can be identified but more frequently are unknown" (Pringsheim, 1949, p. 646). In addition, the position of such impurities in the crystal lattice, the thermal pretreatment of the specimen, and long-lasting exposure to radioactive radiation will affect the nature of the fluorescence. It is therefore not surprising that no general rule can be formulated that will predict which fossils are most likely to fluoresce. Rapid inspection of all fossils by ultraviolet light should be regarded as a routine paleontological test.

USES

Perhaps the most spectacular success achieved with ultraviolet was Léon's discovery, in the Solnhofen Limestone, of crustacean larvae which were invisible, or practically so, in ordinary light (figs. 1,*e–f*). I have repeated Léon's technique and found numerous previously unsuspected specimens on slabs of Solnhofen material in the Museum of Comparative Zoology. Specimens of the same color as the matrix in normal light may fluoresce a different color, thus enabling the recognition of morphological detail and the preparation of contrasty photographs (figs. 1,*e–h*). In this way De Beer was able to reveal the sternum of *Archaeopteryx* (1954, p. 20) and Lambrecht (1928a,b) bundles of elastic fibers in the wing of *Pterodactylus*. Tarka has prepared reverse photographic prints via an intermediate positive transparency so that the fluorescing specimen appears dark on a light ground. This provides a more suitable background for detailed labeling, as Hecht's (1960, figs. 4 and 6) illustrations of an Eocene frog show (figs. 2,*a–c*). Boni first observed that the muscle scars and pallial line of pelecypods may fluoresce brightly and that the color patterns of gastropod shells may be enhanced (see also Sacchi Vialli, 1962b). Doctor H. E. Vokes has revealed fluorescent radial color patterns on the Tertiary bivalve *Macrocallista poulsoni?* and in conjunction with D. Wilson has discovered a new species of *Cancellaria* in the Caloosahatchie Marl having a different color pattern from that of the typical *C. reticulata* (personal com-

**Fig. 1.** *Illustrations of the use of fluorescence in paleontology. All about 1.25×. (a–d) Upper Triassic fish skull from Colorado. (a) Photographed in visible light. (b) Ultraviolet-stimulated fluorescence combined with blue and visible violet light. (c) All radiation except fluorescence filtered off, giving maximum contrast between fluorescent bone and nonfluorescent matrix. (d) A low-angle, white-light exposure added to the exposure in (c) to restore topography. [From Colbert and Tarka, 1960.] (e–h) Decapod crustaceans from the Upper Jurassic Plattenkalk of the Solnhofen district. (e,f) Left lateral views of the "lobster" Eryma fuciformis (Schlotheim). (e) In visible light, showing the iron-staining obscuring detail on photograph. (f) Only fluorescence recorded, revealing detail of spines and warts on chelae, of walking legs, and the otherwise unnoticeable antennae. [From Miethe, 1927b; Miethe and Born, 1928.] (g,h) Palinurid larva Phyllosoma priscum (Münster). (g) In visible light, showing dendrites but with larva invisible. (h) Fluorescence photograph discloses larva. [From Leon, 1933, 1934.]*

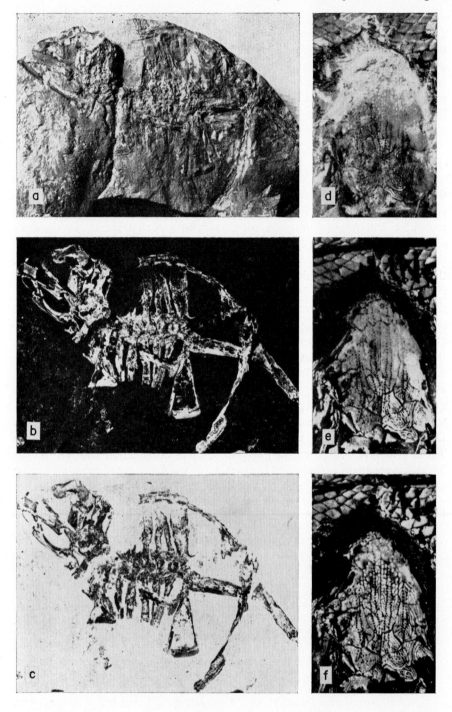

munication). Boni lists fluorescence colors of fossils of the different animal groups and notes that fluorescence in fossil plants is rare, but not absent (1938, p. 20; cf. Maier, 1959), and Portratz and Ziegenspeck (1932) have tabulated the fluorescence colors of plant microfossils from fossil peat. The conotheca of belemnites may fluoresce in contrast to the guard, although Wetzel has recorded strong fluorescence from the concentric lines of *Belemnitella* (1959, p. 267, figs. 10 and 11). Trusheim has obtained fluorescence from notostracan branchiopods of Triassic and Recent age.

Rapid rough-sorting of fossils from unfossiliferous debris should be possible using ultraviolet light, if the fossils are fluorescent, in much the same way as ultraviolet is employed commercially for separating the fluorescent pieces of cuticle from lobster and crab meat. In this connection mention should be made of the use of ultraviolet in preparing small specimens that are otherwise difficult to differentiate from their matrix. In this technique—brought to my attention by Chester Tarka—a sealed-beam, 100-watt mercury-vapor spotlight with filter is used with a stereomicroscope at magnifications up to 20 diameters. Even when the fossil fluoresces weakly or not at all, good matrix differentiation is usually possible.

The extension of fluorescence microscopy to paleozoology was made only recently by Maier and Wetzel (1958), although Portratz and Ziegenspeck obtained valuable paleobotanical data with this method in 1932. Using this technique Wetzel (1959) revealed borings in Foraminifera and belemnites, eggs of Upper Lias marine invertebrates, fragments of fish bone, the siphuncle of ammonoids, Radiolaria, diatoms, the cell structure of pyritized wood fragments, and what Wetzel interprets as the egg membrane ("Eihaut") of Upper Lias ammonites. He has also been able to obtain good reactions from Foraminifera in Upper Chalk flints. Although the calcareous tests of these Foraminifera have been dissolved away, the resulting "nucleus" gives a strong white fluorescence. Maier found that hystricospherids from the Cenozoic of Germany fluoresced but that dinoflagellates and pollen from the same deposit did not. She used this to argue that hystricospheres were of animal origin, and that the dinoflagellates were phytoplankton. As Evitt (1961, p. 386) has pointed out, however, and as discussed above, several other explanations are possible for these phenomena. Organic particles in carbonaceous chondrites have different fluorescence colors from those of the mineral matrix and by

---

**Fig. 2.** *(a–c) Eocene frog,* Eorubeta nevadensis *Hecht, showing improved contrast between fossil and matrix, and reversed-tone print. Natural size. (a) Photographed in visible light on panchromatic film. (b) In ultraviolet with K2 filter on lens. (c) Tones reversed via intermediate positive transparency [From Hecht, 1960.] (d–f) Undescribed fish from the Chinle Formation, Upper Triassic, illustrating use of ultraviolet-absorbing dyes. (d) Photographed in visible light on panchromatic film. (e) In ultraviolet with K2 filter on lens. (f) As in (e), but fluorescence balanced by painting areas with ultraviolet- absorbing dye.*

using suitable color filters Nagy, Claus, and Hennessy (1962) have been able to produce contrasty microphotographs of these objects.

These examples illustrate the use of fluorescence in what Wetzel (1959, p. 263) has termed "Strukturverdeutlichung" (structure elucidation). A quite different use of fluorescence is made in Stanciu's technique (1937) for sorting out lithologically similar specimens which have become misplaced in collections. Here, the characteristic fluorescence color of fossil and matrix may give an indication of the locality from which the specimen derives. I have used fluorescence color to distinguish between poorly preserved penaeid decapod crustaceans from the Middle Eocene of Monte Bolca, Italy, and Upper Cretaceous species from Syria, since the former fluoresced apple-green and the latter a dull red. Of course, great care must be taken to have ample control specimens when using this technique, since a wide range of fluorescence colors may be produced by specimens from one locality.

Sacchi Vialli (1962a,b) has recently obtained quantitative intensity and wavelength data of emitted luminosity by using a fluorescence microscope as it is used in histophotometry—that is, fitted with a photomultiplier and a monochromator. This novel quantitative approach has revealed similarities in the enamel of the teeth of nine fossil vertebrates from different geological periods. This apparatus can be used to measure accurately the phosphorescence period of fossils as well as the response of fluorescence to different physicochemical conditions, enabling deductions to be made about the geochemistry of the fossil under consideration.

Other applications of fluorescence, which may be of use in paleontology, are more familiar to archeologists and criminologists. These include the detection of repairs to fossils—plasters, glues, varnishes, and most plastics fluoresce vividly—and the improvement in legibility of faded writing on labels.

METHODS

A large number of commercial ultraviolet lamps are available which are suitable for paleontological work. Simple inspection by eye is best carried out in a dark room; several minutes should always be allowed for the eye to adapt itself to the dark in order that the weaker fluorescence colors may be appreciated. Both short-wave (maximum emission at 2537 Å) and long-wave (maxima 3650 to 3660 Å) sources are available, but goggles must be worn when using lamps that emit wavelength shorter than 3050 Å to avoid damage to the eyes. High-pressure mercury-vapor lamps (available from Hanovia Chemical and Manufacturing Co., Newark 5, N. J. and General Electric Co., Lamp Division, Cleveland 12, Ohio) used in conjunction with a Wood's glass filter to remove visible light are necessary for long periods of continuous use. For most purposes, however, the inexpensive "black bulbs" are adequate, and operate from standard 110-volt A.C. sockets. These lamps generate considerable heat, hence one bulb should be used intermittently, or two bulbs alternately.

It should be borne in mind that any fluorescence visible to the eye will usually be enhanced on a photograph because of the masking effect of reflected ultraviolet light. Since photographic emulsions are more sensitive to ultraviolet than to the visible light emitted during fluorescence, great care must be taken to ensure that no rays *reflected* by the specimen are allowed to reach the camera. This is done by placing a suitable filter in front of the camera lens. Miethe produced the first fluorescence photographs of fossils using a liquid filter in a glass cell, but nowadays glass filters such as the Corning Noviol C, Ilford Q, or Kodak Wratten 2A, 2B, and K2 are more convenient and reliable. A normal photographic setup is used, with the ultraviolet source substituted for normal illumination. Fast panchromatic films or plates should be used to minimize the exposure times, which are typically long (about 30 minutes) even at large apertures, and depend chiefly on the intensity of the ultraviolet and thus the intensity of the fluorescence emitted.

Photographs of fluorescing specimens may be improved by painting ultraviolet-absorbing dyes on the specimens themselves in order to balance the fluorescence, so that all parts fluoresce uniformly. This method, recently developed by Chester Tarka, makes possible a balanced negative, in which further contrasts can be achieved during processing. The camera used is a single-lens reflex with an image-erecting viewer having a clear glass instead of the conventional ground glass. The specimen is then observed under ultraviolet illumination through the objective lens of the camera with the appropriate filter in position. Dyes are applied with a brush to the parts of the specimen that are fluorescing too brightly to be printable in relation to weakly fluorescing adjacent areas (figs. 2,*d–f*).

Fluorescence microscopes are available commercially (e.g., Zeiss) but a normal microscope may be adapted by replacing the substage filters, lenses, and mirror by quartz optics and silver reflectors and employing high-intensity illumination. The specimen slide must also be of quartz if transmitted light is used. Such mountants as canada balsam, gelatin, glycerin jelly, gum arabic, Hoyer's solution, and agar-agar have fluorescence colors which may obscure those of the specimen. Wetzel (1959, 1960) suggests creosote or the epoxy cement Araldite as a mountant, whereas for peat preparation Portratz and Ziegenspeck used glycerine, after normal treatment with alkali or hydrochloric acid. Thin sections can be made by cementing a polished surface down with hard paraffin wax, and then grinding in the usual way; the slice is removed by dissolving out the wax with benzol or other solvent and is then mounted.

Daylight color-reversal films may be used to record fluorescence; Maier and Wetzel (1958, 1959) have recently given excellent color plates of microfossils.

## ACKNOWLEDGMENTS

I wish to thank Dr. Tilly Edinger for drawing my attention to the use of ultraviolet light when I was curating the Solnhofen Crustacea in the Museum of Comparative Zoology, and for providing me with references. Chester Tarka kindly criticized the manuscript, provided the accompanying photographs, and granted permission to quote techniques developed by him at the American Museum of Natural History.

## REFERENCES

CITED IN TEXT

Boni, Alfredo (1938). Osservazioni preliminari su alcuni fossile alla luce de Wood. Rivista Ital. Paleont., v. 44, p. 13–45.

——— (1940). Florescenze di fossili eccitate con luce visibile. Rivista Ital. Paleont., v. 46, p. 61–72, pl. 2.

Colbert, E. H., and Chester Tarka (1960). Illustration of fossil vertebrates. Medical and Biol. Illus., v. 10, p. 237–246, 9 figs.

De Beer, Gavin (1954). *Archaeopteryx lithographica*. London, British Museum, *xi* + 68 pp., 16 pls., 9 figs.

Evitt, W. R. (1961). Observations on the morphology of fossil dinoflagellates. Micropaleontology, v. 7, p. 385–420, 9 pls., 8 figs.

Fischer, P. H., and Jean Saddy (1948). Examen des nacres actuelles et fossiles en-lumière de Wood. C. R. Acad. Sci. Paris, v. 227, p. 218–219.

Hecht, M. K. (1960). A new frog from an Eocene oil-well core in Nevada. Am. Mus. Nov. no. 2096, 14 pp., 6 figs.

Lambrecht, Kalman (1928a). Die Verwendung der Fluorographie in der paläontologischen Forschung. Zool.-bot. Gesell. Wien, Verhandl., v. 78, p. 62–70, 3 figs.

——— (1928b). Fluorographische Beobachtungen an den "elastischen Fasern" des Pterosaurier-Patagiums. Arch. Mus. Teyler, ser. 3, v. 6, p. 40–50, 2 pls.

Leon, Robert (1933). Ultraviolettes Licht entdeckt Versteinerungen auf "leeren" Platten. Ein Pantopod im Jura-Kalk. Senckenberg. Naturf. Gesell., Natur Mus., v. 63, p. 361–364, 2 figs.

——— (1934). Über *Phalangites priscus* Mstr. und *Palpipes cursor* Roth (Noch keine Pantopoden im Jura). Senckenbergiana, v. 16, p. 24–29, 4 figs.

Maier, Dorothea (1959). Planktonuntersuchungen in tertiaren und quartaren marinen Sedimenten. Neues Jahrb. Geol. Paläont., Abh., v. 107, p. 278–340, pls. 27–33, 4 text-figs.

———, and Walter Wetzel (1948). Fluoreszenzmikroskopie geologischer und paläontologischer Objekte. Zeiss-Mitt. Fortschr. technisch. Optik, v. 1, p. 127–131, 6 figs. (in color).

Miethe, A. (1927a). Über die Photographie von Fossilien bei ihrem eigenen Fluoreszenzlicht. Photogr. Korrespondenz, v. 63, p. 69–70.

——— (1927b). Fossilien-Photographie; Koralle. Magazin alle Freunde von Natur Technik, v. 3, p. 145–147, 6 figs.

————, and Axel Born (1928). Die Fluorographie von Fossilien. Paläont, Zeitschr., v. 9, p. 343–356, 6 figs.

Nagy, Bartholomew, George Claus, and D. J. Hennessy (1962). Organic particles embedded in minerals in the Orgueil and Iruna chondrites. Nature, v. 193, no. 4821, p. 1129–1133, 5 figs.

Portratz, K., and H. Ziegenspeck (1932). Fluoreszensuntersuchungen an Torfpräparaten. Blätter für Untersuchungs-und Forschungs-Instrumente (Emil Busch A. G.), Rathenow, v. 6, p. 6–8, 1 fig.

Pringsheim, Peter (1949). Fluorescence and phosphorescence. New York, Interscience, *xvi* + 794 pp., 219 figs.

Roselt, Gerhard (1962). Über die ältesten Landpflanzen und eine mögliche Landpflanze aus dem Ludlow Sachsens. Geologie, v. 11, p. 320–333, 4 pls.

Sacchi Vialli, G. (1962a). Ricerche sulla fluorescenza dei fossili; I. Osservazioni sullo smalto dei denti di alcuni vertebrati. Atti dell'Istituto geol. Univ. Pavia, v. 13, p. 23–53, pl. 3 (in color), 4 figs.

———— (1962b). Ricerche sulla fluorescenza dei fossili; II. Disegno cromatico e fluorescenza in *Neritina mutinenses* d'Anc. Atti dell'Istituto geol. Univ. Pavia, v. 13, p. 55–64, 1 fig.

Simpson, G. G. (1926). Are *Dromatherium* and *Microoconodon* mammals? Science, v. 63, p. 548–549.

Stanciu, Victor (1937). Die Bestimmung des Fundortes der Gesteine und Mineralien durch UV-Strahlen. Cluj Univ., Mus. Geol.-Miner., Revista, v. 6, p. 321–327.

Wagner, Ernst (1928). Zur Fluorographie von Fossilien; Ein neues und einwandfreies Glasfilter. Paläont. Zeitschr., v. 10, p. 298.

Wetzel, Walter (1959). Das lumineszenzmikroskopische Verhalten von Sedimenten. Neues Jahrb. Geol. Paläont., Abh., v. 107, p. 261–277, pls. 24–26 (5 figs. in color).

———— (1960). Die Anwendung der lumineszenzmikroskopischen Sediment-Analyse in der erdölgeologischen Grundlagen-Forschung. Erdöl Kohle, Erdgas, Petrochemie, v. 13, p. 541–544, 1 fig.

NOT CITED IN TEXT

Dake, H. C., and Jack De Ment (1941). Fluorescent light and its applications. New York, Chemical Publishing Co., Inc., *xi* + 256 pp.

Déribéré, Maurice (1938). Les applications pratiques de la luminescence. Paris, Dunod.

Drevermann, Fritz (1927). Versteinerungen in ultraviolettem Licht. Senckenberg. Naturf. Gesell., Natur und Museum, v. 57, p. 193–201, 6 figs.

Eastman Kodak Co. (1961). Infrared and ultraviolet photography (7th ed.; reprint). Kodak Advanced Data Book No. M-3, Rochester, New York, 48 pp.

Fischer, P. H. (1954). Examen en lumiere de Wood du test de quelques cephalopodes fossiles. J. Conchyliologie, v. 94, p. 49–53.

Furreg, Erich, and F. R. von Querner (1929). Über eigenartige Fluoreszenzerscheinungen an Gastropoden-Schalen (Fam. Trochidae, Fam. Turbinidae). Akad. Wiss. Wien, Math. Nat. Kl., Anz., v. 66, p. 96–98.

———— (1930). Über Fluoreszenzerscheinungen an Gastropodenschalen. Zeitschr. Wiss. Zool., v. 136, p. 355–375, pls. 5, 6, 13 figs.

Hanzawa, Shoshiro (1935). Study of fossils in ultra-violet ray [in Japanese]. J. Geol. Soc. Japan, v. 42, p. 733–735, 1 fig.

Lambrecht, Kalman (1933). Handbuch der Palaeornithologie. Berlin, Gebruder Borntraeger, *xix* + 1022 pp., 4 pls., 209 figs.

Möskes, Adolf (1931). Über die Fluoreszenz und Phosphoreszenz der Fossilien. Berichte über eigene Untersuchungen. Naturw. Mh. Biol., Chem., Geog. unterricht., v. 11, p. 167–170.

Moss, A. A. (1954). The application of x-rays, gamma rays, ultra-violet and infra-red rays to the study of antiquities. London, Mus. Assoc., Handbook for Museum Curators, pt. B, sec. 4, 16 p., 8 pls., 1 fig.

Radley, J. A., and Julius Grant (1959). Fluorescence analysis in ultra-violet light (4th ed.; reprint). London, Chapman and Hall Ltd., *xvi* + 560 pp., 46 pls., 27 figs.

Seegert, Bruno (1928). Fluoreszenzphotographie von Fossilien. Die Umschau, v. 32, p. 134–136, 6 figs.

Trusheim, F. (1937). Triopsiden (Crust. Phyll.) aus dem Keuper Frankens. Paläont. Zeitschr., v. 19, p. 198–216, pls. 13, 14, 10 figs.

Wagner, Ernst, and A. Born (1928). Zur Priorität der UV-Untersuchung von Fossilien. Paläont. Zeitschr., v. 10, p. 215–216.

Wetzel, Walter (1939). Lumineszenzanalyse und Sedimentpetrographie. Zentralbl. Miner. Geol. u. Paläont., ser. A, p. 225–247, 6 figs.

——— (1962). Lumineszenzmikroskopische Studien an chilenischen Sedimenten. Neues Jahrb. Paläont. Mh., 6, p. 303–308.

Young, M. R. (1961). Principles and techniques of fluorescence microscopy. Quart. J. Micros. Sci., v. 102, p. 419–449, 4 pls., 3 figs.

# Analytical Techniques Applied to Fossils and Shells

KENNETH HOOPER

*Carleton University, Ottawa, Canada*

Significant advances in science frequently derive from the introduction of new techniques resulting from technological development. Often an innovation in a specific field is found much later to be applicable in another field, or may even affect every branch of science. A prime example of this is the invention of the optical microscope by Van Leeuwenhoek, circa 1670. As paleontologists, we are aware that much of our knowledge of the microstructure and mineralogical composition of fossils is obtained from optical microscopic studies, supplemented in earlier days by wet and dry chemical analyses. Since

World War II, however, the rapid rate of technological development has brought about a host of new analytical techniques which are capable of advancing our knowledge of Recent and fossil skeletal materials to an astonishing degree, widening the scope of paleontological inquiry from the strictly morphological, to include physiological, paleoecological, and biochemical evolutionary concepts as well.

The purpose of this essay is to review some of these modern analytical techniques and methods in very general terms, with a minimum of technical detail, but stressing for each method such factors as discrimination of elements, sensitivity, limitations, and suitability for macro- or microorganisms. For detailed descriptions of the methods, reference should be made to appropriate literature as indicated.

## GRAVIMETRIC AND VOLUMETRIC METHODS

Chemical analyses of rocks and minerals by the classical methods of gravimetric and volumetric analysis have been practiced by chemists and geologists for many years. The reader is referred to the work of Washington (1930), Kolthoff and Sandell (1950), Groves (1951), and Hillebrand, et al. (1953). Some aspects of these methods are applicable to the analysis of fossils and shells, but achievement of high standards of precision and accuracy in classical analysis depends mainly upon the personal skill of the analyst, and detailed comparison and correlation of analyses for petrological and mineralogical ends is highly suspect.

An introduction to the analyses of silicon, aluminum, magnesium, iron, titanium, manganese, phosphorus, sodium, and potassium is given by Vincent (1960).

The inorganic constituents of marine invertebrates have been described by Clarke and Wheeler (1922). In their paper they give analyses of Foraminifera, sponges, madreporanian and alcyonarian corals, hydroids, annelids, crinoids, echinoids, asteroids, ophiuroids, holothurians, Bryozoa, Brachiopoda, Pelecypoda, Scaphopoda, Gastropoda, Cephalopoda, Crustacea and calcareous algae. In a comprehensive survey of the elementary composition of marine organisms, Vinogradov (1953) referred to the work of numerous workers using many analytical techniques, including classical methods. This monumental work is the most complete compendium of information on the subject yet available. A wide range of elements and organisms is described.

## MICROCHEMICAL TESTS FOR SPECIFIC ELEMENTS
## FOR QUALITATIVE ANALYSIS OF MINERALS

Pioneer work by Bořický; Behrens and Kley; Chamot and Mason; and others has been comprehensively summarized by Short (1940). A useful concise account is given by Cameron (1961). Elements commonly found in shells which are particularly amenable to the method are copper, iron, lead, manganese, nickel, silver, sulfur, tin, titanium, and zinc.

A small amount of the material to be analyzed is picked out with a needle and transferred to a glass slide. A drop of an appropriate acid is applied and the slide is gently heated until the drop is dry. The residue is leached, covered with a drop of an appropriate liquid, and transferred to a clean part of the slide. The reagent is then placed beside the test drop and the two are merged by drawing a platinum wire across one drop and into the other. The drop is now viewed under a microscope as characteristic precipitates form. Oxides require fusion with fluxes.

Many tests for elements are very satisfactory. Some tests are subject to interference from associated elements. Some are time consuming and tedious, and require experience. Although they are only qualitative, they are highly sensitive.

A special method of qualitative microchemical analysis is known as contact printing (Hiller, 1937; Gutzeit, 1942). A sheet of gelatin-coated photographic paper is impregnated with a selective attacking reagent and placed on the polished surface in contact with the specimen. Ions from the element enter the gelatin. The paper is removed and placed in a specific reagent. The resulting print shows the distribution of the element on the polished surface and, when color intensity is compared with intensities of prints of known minerals, indicates relative amounts of the element and its distribution on the surface of the specimen. This method is described by Cameron (1961, p. 220).

## MINERALOGICAL STAINING

Staining methods for carbonate minerals have a long history; the most recent comprehensive account of these methods is by Friedman (1959). Routine identification of carbonate minerals is by alizarin red S and Harris' hematoxylin, both of which are fast, efficient, and dependable. For dolomite twenty organic dyes are available, providing a wide color range of staining. For differentiating dolomite, calcite, aragonite, high-magnesian calcite, gypsum, and anhydrite, a combination of two different stains, alizarin red S and Feigl's solution, can be used. The organic dyes stain calcite in acid solution and dolomite and magnesite in basic solution. The composition, porosity, and grain size of the specimen determine the choice of immersion time, pH, and temperature of solution. Friedman (1959) gives staining procedures, methods of preparing stains, and names of some suppliers.

## COLORIMETRIC METHODS

Colorimetric methods of analysis depend on the conversion of an element to a more or less strongly colored compound in solution, or colloidal suspension, and are in principle applicable to a wide range of elements. A colored solution absorbs light of different wavelengths differentially, the amount of each wavelength that is absorbed being related to the concentration of the solution.

Sometimes, because of interference of other elements, it is necessary to isolate the particular substance to be analyzed before its determination. Where this is not necessary rapid analysis is possible, as with Si, Al, Fe, Mn, Ti, and P.

The optical density or transmittancy is usually measured with a spectrophotometer. A precision of 0.2 percent in transmittancy is claimed by some specialists. Improved precision may be obtained by the technique of high-precision differential absorptiometry, as described by Hiskey (1949). A precision equal or better to that obtained by spectrographic methods has been claimed, especially in the determination of Be, Cd, Co, Cr, Ga, Ge, Mo, Ni, Pb, Zn.

Among the elements of interest in shells and fossils the method is most useful for Ti, Mn, Cu, Pb, and Zn, but is also applicable to Al, Fe, F, P, and S. The subject has been thoroughly investigated by Sandell (1950).

## FLAME PHOTOMETRY

A solution of the sample to be analyzed is sprayed under controlled conditions into a flame of sufficient energy to excite the elements to emit radiation. The light from the flame passes into a narrow entrance slit of a monochromator. The intensity of the isolated radiation is measured by a photosensitive detector and some type of meter or electronic amplifier. The flame photometer is calibrated with solutions of known composition and concentration, so that it is possible to correlate the intensity of emission of a given spectral line of the unknown element with that of the same element in a standard solution.

A high degree of constancy, reproducibility, and precision is attainable. The spectrum is simple, consisting of a few lines, and spectral interference is less frequent. Qualitative and quantitative analyses are possible. Details are given by Dean (1960), who discusses the application of the method to many elements. Flame photometry is especially suited to the alkali metals, but difficulties arise in the analysis of magnesium and the alkaline earth metals. A useful introduction to the subject has been given by Vincent (1960), and Thompson and Chow (1955) have applied the method to strontium-calcium atom ratios in carbonate-secreting marine organisms—Algae, Foraminifera, Porifera, Coelenterata, Annelida, Cirrepedia, Decapoda, Mollusca, Bryozoa, Brachiopoda, and Echinoderma.

Sensitivity varies with the element but better than $10^{-5}$ is usually obtainable.

## ATOMIC ABSORPTION SPECTROPHOTOMETRY

This technique is likely to become important in the next decade or so. It resembles flame photometry but is simpler and more efficient. Energy of the wavelength absorbed by the element to be analyzed is provided by a source lamp whose emitting cathode is made of that element. The energy is passed through a flame in which the sample is vaporized, then passed on through a grating monochromator for isolation of the desired wavelength. The intensity is compared with that of the source as standard, so that a direct measure of concentration is obtained. The following elements of fossils and shells can be detected in parts per million or parts per billion: Ca, Ba, Cu, Fe, Pb, Mg, Mn, Ni, K, Sr, Sn, and Zn.

## THERMOLUMINESCENCE

Thermoluminescence is an exoenergetic radiation phenomenon exhibited by certain materials during thermal stimulation. It is a temperature-dependent form of phosphorescence that requires excited electrons. The thermoluminescent potential of calcareous fossils has been considered by Johnson (1960), who qualitatively defined it as the visible band from 3000 to 6000 Å.

The equipment used to measure thermoluminescence consists of an electric-electronic device which detects, measures, and records luminescent emission from a heated sample. Luminescent intensity is plotted against temperature of emission. This glow curve is characteristic of the sample. Comparison of glow curves permits identification of samples.

In order to reinforce the natural luminescence and energize to a practical level of saturation, it may be advisable to expose the sample to gamma irradiation. After irradiation and before determining its glow curve, the sample may be kept at the temperature of dry ice ($-79°C$) and in a dark container to prevent inadvertent thermal or photo stimulation (Johnson, 1960). Johnson has also shown that the radio-thermoluminescent potential of calcareous shell material is a function of $CaCO_3$ polymorphism. Shells belonging to a given taxonomic category tend to have similar and sometimes diagnostic thermoluminescent properties.

## OPTICAL EMISSION SPECTROGRAPHY

Spectrochemical analysis is widely used in geochemical studies, but its use on paleontological materials is somewhat limited. A high degree of sensitivity is possible, better than .001 percent (10 ppm) of metallic ions and Pb, Si, As, C, and B in samples of a few milligrams. An accuracy exceeding 5 percent can be attained for most elements. This method of analysis also offers the advantage of considerable speed.

When a sample is heated to a high temperature it is vaporized and the atoms of the elements become excited, emitting radiant energy of many discrete and distinct wavelengths. There are three kinds of emission spectra: (1) continuous, emitted by incandescent solids and characterized by the absence of any sharply defined lines; (2) the band spectra, which consist of groups of lines that come closer as they approach a limit at the head of the band, and are caused by excited molecules; and (3) line spectra, consisting of definite, usually widely spaced, lines. Line spectra are characteristic of atoms or atomic ions which have been excited and are emitting their extra energy as light of definite wavelengths.

On addition of thermal or electrical energy to the atom, one or more electrons may be removed to a higher state (shell) farther from the nucleus. These excited electrons tend to return to the ground state, emitting extra energy as photons. For a particular transition from high to low energy levels, radiation of fixed wavelength is emitted. Many different transitions are possible. Some are more probable than others, so that each element emits a characteristic set of lines of different wavelength and different intensity.

Excitation methods include flame, D.C. arc, A.C. arc, high-voltage A.C. arc, and high-voltage spark. The flame is a low-energy source, producing spectra of a few metals, primarily the alkali metals and alkaline earths. The D.C. arc (50 to 250 volts) excites all metals. The lines produced are mainly due to neutral atoms. It is sensitive and useful for low concentrations of elements. The high voltage A.C. arc (1000 volts or more) provides a steadier source and leads to more reproducible results. The high-voltage spark is more reproducible and stable than the arcs, and is free of cyanogen bands. The electrodes may be made of carbon, graphite, or copper. A small cone in the end of the electrode holds the sample.

Spectrographs consist of a dispersing medium (either a grating or a prism), a slit, and a camera or other recording device. The spectral lines are replicas of the slit recorded on a photographic film strip.

Qualitative identification of elements present in a sample can be determined by comparing the spectrum of the unknown with spectra of pure samples of the elements or by measuring wavelengths of the lines and looking up corresponding elements in tables.

Quantitative identification is accomplished by measuring the intensity (density) of an unknown line relative to that of an internal standard. Alternatively, electronic recording devices may be used instead of photographic film. A review of equipment currently available is given by Harley and Wiberley (1954).

It is possible to analyze for a wide range of elements by spectrochemical analysis, including many which are found in fossils and shells, as indicated in table I (p. 366).

In studies of the composition of skeletal materials of fossil and living organisms, spectrochemical analysis has been used to investigate rare alkali elements in the Trilobita (McKerrow, et al., 1956). Chave (1954a,b) has used

**Table I.** *Spectrochemical Analysis of Some Elements and Their Limit of Detectability*

| ELEMENT | LIMIT (ppm) | ELEMENT | LIMIT (ppm) |
|---------|-------------|---------|-------------|
| Al | 2 | Pb | 2 |
| Ba | 3 | P | 100 |
| Ca | 1 | Si | 10 |
| Cu | 0.5 | Sn | 10 |
| F | 100 | Sr | 5 |
| Fe | 5 | Ti | 10 |
| K | 2 | V | 5 |
| Mg | 1 | Zn | 100 |
| Mn | 5 | | |

spectrochemical techniques in conjunction with X-ray methods in his studies of magnesium content in modern and fossil calcareous skeleton organisms of the Algae, Mollusca, Foraminifera, Ostracoda, Bryozoa, Echinoidea, Crinoidea, and Serpulidae. Emiliani (1955) conducted spectrochemical analyses of Ti, Al, Fe, Mn, Mg, and Sr of Recent and Pleistocene pelagic Foraminifera from the Caribbean, Atlantic, and Pacific. Kulp, et al. (1952) studied the strontium content of fossil brachiopods (Paleozoic and Triassic), crinoids (Silurian, Mississippian, and Pennsylvanian), corals (Devonian and Pennsylvanian), gastropods (Pennsylvanian and Mississippian), pelecypods (Upper Miocene, Eocene), belemnites (Jurassic and Cretaceous), Algae (Proterozoic), echinoderms (Pliocene), scaphopods (Miocene), and pelecypods (Recent). Krinsley (1959, 1960) investigated manganese in modern and fossil gastropod shells and magnesium, strontium, and aragonite in shells of certain littoral gastropods. Krinsley and Bieri (1959) described changes in the chemical composition of pteropod shells after deposition on the sea floor. Paleoecological implications are the subject of a paper by Lowenstam (1961), in which the results of spectrochemical and other analyses are reviewed.

Turekian and Armstrong (1961) studied the chemical and mineralogical composition of molluscs from the Fox Hills Formation of South Dakota, using emission spectrography for analyses of Ba, Mg, Sr, Mn, and Fe with a precision estimated at 10 percent.

Optical emission spectrography is well suited to integration with other means of analysis such as (1) flame photometry for the alkali metals, (2) volumetric or colorimetric methods, using Fe as a useful internal standard for volatile elements, (3) X-ray fluorescence, and (4) laser as excitation source.

## LASER (MASER) AS AN ALTERNATIVE OPTICAL EMISSION SPECTROGRAPH SOURCE

The laser (light amplification by stimulated emission of radiation) is a special case of the maser (microwave amplification by stimulated emission of radiation). Basic principles have been elucidated by Schawlow and Townes (1958) and Schawlow (1961).

An intense burst of incoherent light from an electrical discharge is made to impinge upon a special ruby rod. An optical cavity is set up along the long axis of the ruby, and certain ions are stimulated to emit electromagnetic radiation of a single frequency and with a planar wave front. Oscillation is set up along the ruby rod, resulting in further stimulation at increasing intensity. Finally, it emerges as a monochromatic and directional beam of red light. Because it is parallel and coherent it can be focused with accuracy.

The equipment as modified for geological, mineralogical, or paleontological studies essentially consists of a ruby rod, a helical xenon flashlamp and cooling device, a shutter, a microscope fitted with cross-excitation electrodes suspended between the objective lens and the surface of the sample resting on the stage, and a spherical lens which focuses the light on the slit of a spectrograph.

In operation the specimen is placed on the microscope stage, and the cross hairs are focused on the area of interest. The electrodes are inserted, the capacitors charged to 4200 volts, and the firing switch thrown. The laser pulse produces a 50 to $100\mu$ hemispherical pit. The spectra of the vaporized material may be recorded on film in the spectrograph. The lower limit of sensitivity is said to be 0.001 percent, although by superimposing ten successive shots on one exposure it may be possible to increase the sensitivity to detect a few parts per million. A reproducibility of $\pm 5$ percent is claimed by some specialists. The elements Fe, Cu, Zn, Si, Pb, Mg, Mn, Ca, Al, Ni, Ti, and others have been detected in minerals by Maxwell (1963), who has described the method in some detail as applied to geological materials. The method is in the exploratory stage at present, and is mainly qualitative, but with experience and refinement quantitative analysis should be possible.

## X-RAY DIFFRACTION

This is the most important method for the identification of crystalline substances, and in view of the crystalline nature of much shell material, is very relevant to fossil and shell studies. X-ray patterns are characteristic of the crystal form and spacing, and thus of chemical compounds rather than of elements or chemical groups.

When a beam of monochromatic X-rays strikes the planes of atoms in a crystal, interference phenomena occur, and the reinforced beams are diffracted from the crystal according to Bragg's Law,

$$n\lambda = 2d \sin \theta,$$

where $n =$ the order of the diffraction, $\lambda =$ the wavelength of the X-rays, $\theta =$ the incident angle or one-half the angle of scattering, and $d =$ the distance (in angstroms) between atomic planes in the crystal.

For a single crystal, the diffracted X-rays consist of a few specific beams which when recorded on photographic film show up as spots. For a powder composed of randomly oriented small crystals the diffracted radiation will consist of a series of concentric cones which are recorded on film as arcs of circles. The diameters of these circles are measured, and $2\theta$ values are obtained from a table of trigonometric functions. The $d$ values of the interplanar spacings are then calculated from the Bragg equation. The crystal is identified according to its $d$ spacings. The most useful camera for working with either powders or single crystals is the Debye-Scherrer type with a revolving spindle. The sample is mounted on the revolving spindle so that preferred-orientation effects are counteracted. Details of the method are given by Azároff and Buerger (1958).

Lowenstam (1954) used a quantitative X-ray method for determining aragonite:calcite ratios in calcium carbonate specimens on the basis of relative intensities of X-ray reflections characteristic of each mineral, assuming no preferred orientation or self-absorption. His equipment consisted of an X-ray diffraction unit, a goniometer spectrometer, a Geiger counter, and a Brown recoder. Lowenstam was able to determine to within $\pm10$ percent the concentration of aragonite (or calcite) in a wide range of marine invertebrates (including Algae, Anthozoa, Bryozoa, Annelida, and Mollusca). Chave (1954a,b) used similar equipment in a study of factors controlling the distribution of magnesium in the calcareous skeletons of marine organisms.

Emiliani (1955) applied the powder diffraction method, as described by Goldsmith, Graf, and Joensuu (1955), in his study of the mineralogical and chemical composition of the tests of certain pelagic Foraminifera. Switzer and Boucot (1955) pointed out that many microfossils do not need to be crushed in the X-ray powder method. The crystals composing the tests of Foraminifera and Ostracoda are so small that the specimen may be regarded as a powder sample. Thus, individual specimens may be investigated. Blackmon and Todd (1959) used X-ray diffraction to study the mineralogy of the tests of Foraminifera as related to their classification. Using both powdered and individual specimens they showed the importance of magnesium as an aid to classification of this order.

Krinsley and Bieri (1959) studied the changes in the chemical composition of pteropod shells after deposition on the sea floor using X-ray diffraction methods (in part), for which they claim an accuracy of $\pm5$ percent. Krinsley (1959) also studied manganese in modern and fossil gastropod shells, aragonite percentages being determined by Chave's X-ray powder method. Later,

Krinsley (1960) investigated the content of magnesium, strontium, and aragonite in shells of certain littoral gastropods. He obtained calcite:aragonite ratios using X-ray diffraction techniques, with an estimated error of ±5 percent. Turekian and Armstrong (1961) used X-ray diffraction techniques to obtain calcite:aragonite ratios in a study of the chemical and mineralogical composition of fossil molluscan shells from the Fox Hills Formation, South Dakota, with an estimated error of 5 to 10 percent. Siegel (1960) used this method to obtain aragonite:calcite ratios in a study of the effect of strontium on these ratios in Pleistocene corals.

## X-RAY ABSORPTION METHODS

X-ray absorption methods of analysis have been reviewed by Liebhafsky (1953) and by Cosslett and Nixon (1960). Little use has been made of absorption as an analytical method in macroscopic work. In microanalysis the methods have been very thoroughly developed, especially by Engstrom, Lindstrom, and co-workers.

A high sensitivity is obtainable, $10^{-12}$ to $10^{-14}$ gram of element being detectable in a volume as small as 1 to $10\mu^3$. Absorption techniques have developed hand in hand with microradiography and projection X-ray microscopy, which are discussed elsewhere in this volume.

Analysis for elements by absorption depends on mass absorption coefficients that vary with atomic number—approximately proportional to $Z^3$ at X-ray wavelengths in the range 1 to 10 Å. Absorption edges at particular wavelengths increase the differential effect. Elementary composition can be found locally by measuring the absorption of X-rays and comparing it with that of the pure element or of standard reference material. The measurements may be made photometrically on film or with Geiger or proportional counters. Line radiation giving well-defined absorption coefficients should be used. The appropriate wavelength is isolated by reflection in a crystal spectrometer or by selective recording with a proportional counter and pulse analyzer. Quantitative microanalysis requires observations at two or more wavelengths on each side of the absorption edge of the element in question and is best carried out with a projection microscope, although Engstrom has used the contact method with considerable success. Lindstrom has made estimates of oxygen content, but measurement of nitrogen and carbon content has proved difficult. Engstrom has calculated the detection limit for different elements and has shown that it is less than $1\mu g/mm^2$ ($10^{-4}g/cm^2$) for elements below manganese in the periodic table. He reports an overall experimental error of about ±3 percent. Details of X-ray absorption microanalysis (including a comprehensive bibliography) are given by Cosslett and Nixon (1960). The method has not yet been used in the analysis of fossils and shells, although it has been used on bone and teeth by Engstrom and others.

## FLUORESCENT X-RAY SPECTROGRAPHY

If a beam of primary X-rays is made to impinge upon a sample, secondary X-rays are emitted which are characteristic of the elements present. These secondary X-rays are analyzed on film, or with Geiger, proportional, or scintillation counters. Plane or curved crystal spectrometers have sometimes been used to analyze the X-ray spectra.

The method is reproducible, rapid, nondestructive, and independent of the physical state of the sample. X-ray spectra have fewer lines than those of optical emission, so that analysis of results is easier. Unfortunately, it is limited to elements heavier than 16, but this limitation should be removed as techniques improve. An introductory account of fluorescent X-ray analysis is given by Shalgosky (1960). The method has been applied to petrological and mineralogical specimens and will doubtless be applied to fossils and shells. Accuracy of the method is about 1 percent for major constituents. For minor constituents, in amounts as low as parts per 10,000, accuracies of approximately 5 percent are quoted by Birks, et al. (1953).

## ELECTRON-PROBE X-RAY MICROANALYSIS

In the last decade interest in the chemical composition of the foraminiferal test has been stimulated as a result of studies in radiocarbon dating and isotope ratio, and trace element analysis. Moreover, certain elements appear to have classificatory importance, whilst others may have environmental significance (Blackmon and Todd, 1959).

In the Metazoa the secretion of the calcareous shell in layers is well known, and variation in composition between layers is established. However, there are no tissues in the unicellular (noncellular) Protozoa, in which the order Foraminifera is placed, and it may be speculated that the calcite secretion process is different from that in the Metazoa. X-ray diffraction studies made with the Debye-Scherrer camera show that some elements, such as magnesium, are substituted in solid solution for calcium in the calcite crystals of the test. Unfortunately, the results are generalized for the entire specimen. It is not known how these elements vary from crystal to crystal or from layer to layer or even if layering exists. If such variation exists its relation to such microstructures as pores, foramina, and canals might provide valuable clues of physiological significance. The development of electron-probe X-ray microanalysis has made it possible to determine the distribution of elements on a micro scale ($1\mu^2$).

An exploratory study of the application of the electron-probe technique to Foraminifera has been made by Hooper (1964). At present, the method is not applicable to elements lighter than number 12 (Mg).

An electron beam focused to a $1\mu$ spot scans over a specimen area $\frac{1}{2}$ mm square or less. Some electrons are back-scattered upon striking the specimen.

They are detected by a scintillation counter, and the resultant signal is amplified and used to modulate the brightness of the beam on a cathode ray display tube.

Meanwhile other electrons from the beam enter the specimen and excite X-rays. Emitted X-rays are collected by a crystal spectrometer which can select the characteristic emission from an element in the surface of the specimen. This is detected by a proportional counter, and the resultant signal is amplified and used to modulate the brightness of a cathode ray display tube. The X-ray image shows the distribution and concentration of the selected element.

Electron-probe X-ray microanalysis may be preceded by qualitative optical spectroscopic analyses of species, the results of which are used as a guide to the elementary composition of specimens.

Polystyrene is used as an embedding medium for Foraminifera, polished sections of which are placed under the electron probe. The composition of the equatorial section is assumed to be representative of the entire specimen.

The following forms have been investigated in an exploratory way. *Elphidium* cf. *excavatum* (Terquem): Ca, Si detected. *E. bartletti* (Cushman): Ca, Si, S, Fe detected. *Quinqueloculina* cf. *seminulum* (Linné): Ca detected. *Operculina* cf. *victoriensis* (Chapman and Parr): Ca, Fe, Si, Mn, Mg, Cu detected. *O.* cf. *complanata* (Defrance): Ca, Mg, Si, Fe detected.

Interpretation of electron and X-ray images is complicated by topographic and microstructural effects which reduce their usefulness. Before beginning quantitative studies, magnesium detection must be improved by modifying the embedding technique and the microanalyzers employed. The modifications include (1) a removable spectrometer window, (2) a fully focusing spectrometer, and (3) an X-ray take off angle higher than 20°. Some instruments now incorporate these modifications.

The applications of the electron probe are not confined to microfossils. Wells (1963) points out that some corals show daily variations in the rate of calcium carbonate secretion in the form of growth lines, and that these variations may be a source of information on the length of the year in past geological times. However, counting these daily growth-lines is difficult, owing to their minute size. The electron probe should prove useful if applied to this problem, for the variations in calcium concentration should be easy to detect.

## MASS SPECTROMETRIC ANALYSIS

Mass spectrometric analysis has only recently come widely into favor as a routine analytical method, although the mass spectrometer has been known for some time. It was described by Smith in 1931 and by Mattauch and Hertzog in 1934.

The mass spectrometer sorts ions according to their ratio of mass to charge. This is brought about by passing them through a combination of electrical and magnetic fields. The radius of curvature of an ion in the magnetic field depends on the accelerating potential, the strength of the magnetic field, and the ratio of mass to charge. Where the radius of curvature of the ion is fixed (as it is in some mass spectrometers), then for given values of accelerating potential and field strength only ions of a certain mass to charge ratio impinge upon the collector. By varying the accelerating voltage, ions of each specific mass to charge ratio are successively made to strike the collector. The intensities of the ionic species are then measured electronically and their relative abundance recorded.

When the sample is large, it may be evaporated from an oven and the vapor ionized by electron bombardment. When the sample is small, surface ionization is used, positive ions being emitted either directly from the surface of a salt heated on a filament or from neutral atoms impinging on a hot surface.

Mass spectrometric methods have been used in studies of radioactive isotope and stable isotope ratios, the former chiefly in geochronometry. A wide range of elements has been studied, including those most commonly found in fossil and shell material; for example, carbon, nitrogen, potassium, strontium, sulfur, calcium, aluminum, and lead. Magnesium has been determined by Daughtry, et al. (1962), although reproducibility of results seems to be difficult to attain. Sensitivity varies with the element and with experimental conditions, but detection limits better than $10^{-5}$ are normal.

So far as studies involving fossils and shells are concerned the $C^{13}$ and $O^{18}$ isotopic compositions have been studied by several workers—Recent calcareous algae by Craig (1953), and Lowenstam and Epstein (1957); serpulid worms by Lowenstam and Epstein (1957); molluscs by Craig (1953, 1954); and brachiopods by Epstein, quoted by Compston (1960). Fossil material studied includes Permian brachiopods and crinoids and Devonian brachiopods (Compston, 1960) and Cretaceous brachiopods and molluscs (Urey, et al. 1951).

A relationship between temperature and relative $O^{18}$ abundance in calcium carbonate of marine shells (brachiopods, pelecypods, and gastropods) was determined by Epstein, et al. (1951). Emiliani and Epstein (1953) studied $O^{18}:O^{16}$ ratios of the $CaCO_3$ in fossil Foraminifera from the lower Pleistocene Lomita Marl and used these ratios to determine paleotemperature variations that prevailed during deposition of that bed. The relationship between temperature and $O^{18}$ content relative to that for a Cretaceous belemnite was reported by Epstein, et al. (1953).

Emiliani (1954a) reported on the depth habitats of some species of pelagic Foraminifera as indicated by oxygen isotope ratios. In the same year (1954b) he also reported on oxygen isotope ratios in Tertiary Foraminifera from the Pacific Ocean and the polar oceans. Epstein and Lowenstam (1953) studied the temperature-shell-growth relations of Recent and interglacial Pleistocene shoal-water biota from Bermuda, using oxygen isotope ratios mainly from pelecypods. Pleistocene paleotemperatures were also investigated by Emiliani

(1955), using oxygen isotope ratios determined from the tests of Foraminifera.

Lowenstam and Epstein (1954) determined paleotemperatures of the post-Aptian Cretaceous by using oxygen isotope ratios of belemnite guards, brachiopods, and *Inoceramus* fragments. The same authors later (1957) reported on the origin of sedimentary aragonite needles of the Great Bahama Bank using $O^{18}:O^{16}$ and $C^{13}:C^{12}$ ratios, showing that the needles may be derived from certain algal carbonates.

Thode, et al. (1953) studied sulfur isotope fractionation in Recent and fossil organisms, concluding that autotrophic organisms which oxidize $H_2S$ were not significant until about 700 to 800 million years ago.

## RADIOACTIVATION ANALYSIS

This method of elementary analysis does not appear to have been used for fossils, but it has been used for some living representatives of the Mollusca and Crustacea (Fukai, 1959; Fukai and Meinke, 1959). Because of its extreme sensitivity, it is of great importance in trace element analysis.

In this method the sample is irradiated with nuclear particles, the intensity of the radioactivity induced in the element(s) is measured, and because the intensity of the induced radioactivity is directly proportional to the amount of the element(s), a quantitative analysis of the sample is obtained.

Protons, deuterons, and neutrons have been used as bombarding particles, but the most generally available and useful particles are the slow or thermal neutrons produced in nuclear reactors (neutron activation analysis). Some neutron sources are given in table II.

**Table II.** *Neutron Sources*

| NEUTRON SOURCE | NEUTRON FLUX ($n$/cm²/sec) |
|---|---|
| X10 reactor, Oak Ridge, U.S.A. | $5 \times 10^{11}$ |
| LITR reactor, Oak Ridge, U.S.A. | $1 \times 10^{13}$ |
| BEPO reactor, Hanwell, U.K. | $2 \times 10^{12}$ |
| NRX reactor, Chalk River, Canada | $7 \times 10^{13}$ |
| CP-5 reactor, Argonne, U.S.A. | $2 \times 10^{13}$ |
| MTR reactor, Idaho, U.S.A. | $5 \times 10^{14}$ |
| Cyclotron | $10^8$–$10^9$ |
| Van de Graaff generator | $10^6$–$10^8$ |
| Ra-Be, 1 g | $10^4$–$10^5$ |
| Sb-Be, 1 g | $10^3$–$10^4$ |
| Ra-Be, 25 mg | $10^2$ |

During irradiation, the rate of increase in the amount of radioactivity in the stable isotope of the element being determined is proportional to (1) the number of atoms of the target nuclide in the sample; (2) the neutron flux; (3) the activation cross section for the nuclear reaction—that is, the measure of the probability that a neutron will strike and interact with the nucleus (Mapper, 1960); (4) the half life of the radionuclide produced and, (5) the duration of irradiation.

After irradiation all elements of the sample are radioactive. The half-lives of the elements vary from a few minutes ($Mg = 9.6$, $Al = 2.3$) to many days ($Ca = 164$, $Zn = 245$, $S = 87$, $Sr = 50$, $Fe = 45$). It is necessary to discriminate between various activities. Beta emitters can be measured with a Geiger counter, but the most suitable apparatus is the gamma ray scintillation spectrometer. Characteristic gamma ray energies can be recognized and quantitative estimates can be made (Salmon, 1959). Unfortunately, it is not always possible to use these nondestructive methods; techniques of chemical separation sometimes have to be used, and in these cases the specimen is destroyed (Cook, 1959). A procedure for radioactivation analysis is shown in the flow diagram on p. 375 (Leddicotte, 1959).

Radioactivation analysis is highly sensitive. In table III sensitivities determined by neutron activation analyses are compared with those determined by other methods of analysis for some of the elements which commonly occur in fossils and shells. Sensitivities of parts per million and even parts per billion have been obtained (Meinke, 1955).

Radioactivation analysis is highly specific, for radionuclides disintegrate in a unique manner, and detection and identification is not too difficult. Moreover, the method is free from spurious contamination unless the contaminant is introduced before irradiation.

The size of the specimen which may be analyzed depends on the particular neutron source to be used. Generally, specimens larger than 1 inch may be difficult to accommodate. Microfossils and microshells would seem to be ideally suited to activation analysis. There are two main nuclear limitations to the method:

1. Some specimens contain a large amount of material of high activation cross section which can result in lower production of radioactivity than would otherwise be expected. However, techniques exist for compensating for this (Leddicotte, 1959, p. 64).

2. Secondary nuclear particle reactions sometimes interfere with the primary reaction. This may be overcome by pre-irradiation separation (Leddicotte, 1959, p. 65).

Few laboratories have suitable irradiation facilities. Consequently, for most workers, the use of the method is restricted to the longer lived isotopes unless special arrangements can be made.

The method is not suitable for oxygen, carbon, nitrogen, and fluorine, all of which may be present in fossil and shell material. Basile, however, has in-

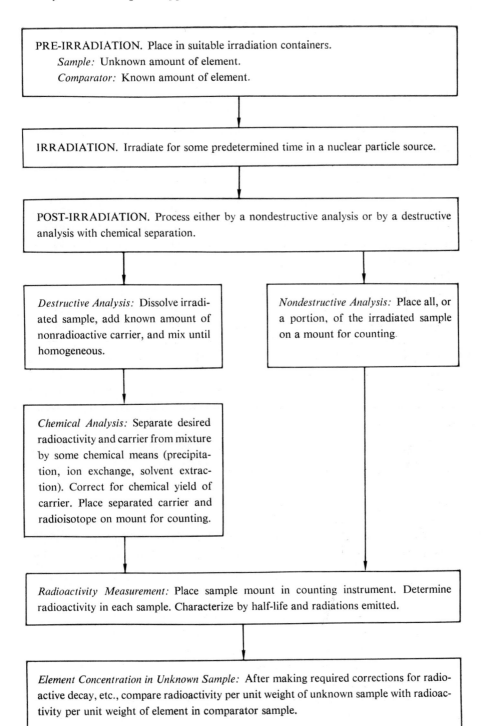

PRE-IRRADIATION. Place in suitable irradiation containers.
*Sample:* Unknown amount of element.
*Comparator:* Known amount of element.

IRRADIATION. Irradiate for some predetermined time in a nuclear particle source.

POST-IRRADIATION. Process either by a nondestructive analysis or by a destructive analysis with chemical separation.

*Destructive Analysis:* Dissolve irradiated sample, add known amount of nonradioactive carrier, and mix until homogeneous.

*Nondestructive Analysis:* Place all, or a portion, of the irradiated sample on a mount for counting.

*Chemical Analysis:* Separate desired radioactivity and carrier from mixture by some chemical means (precipitation, ion exchange, solvent extraction). Correct for chemical yield of carrier. Place separated carrier and radioisotope on mount for counting.

*Radioactivity Measurement:* Place sample mount in counting instrument. Determine radioactivity in each sample. Characterize by half-life and radiations emitted.

*Element Concentration in Unknown Sample:* After making required corrections for radioactive decay, etc., compare radioactivity per unit weight of unknown sample with radioactivity per unit weight of element in comparator sample.

**Table III.** *Sensitivity Comparisons ($\mu g/ml$)*

| ELEMENT | REACTOR | | COPPER SPARK | GRAPHITE D.C. ARC | FLAME SPECTRO-PHOTOMETRY | SENSITIVE COLOR REACTION | AMPERO-METRIC TITRATION |
|---|---|---|---|---|---|---|---|
| | X10 | LITR | | | | | |
| Na | 0.007 | 0.00035 | 0.1 | 20 | 0.002 | — | — |
| Mg | 0.6 | 0.03 | 0.01 | 0.1 | 1 | 0.06 | — |
| Al | 0.001 | 0.00005 | 0.1 | 0.2 | 20 | 0.002 | 300 |
| Si | 1 | 0.05 | 0.1 | 2 | — | 0.1 | — |
| P | 0.02 | 0.001 | 20 | 50 | — | 0.01 | 15 |
| S | 4 | 0.2 | — | — | — | — | 5 |
| K | 0.08 | 0.004 | 0.1 | — | 0.01 | — | 100 |
| Ca | 3.8 | 0.19 | 0.1 | — | 0.03 | — | 100 |
| Ti | — | — | 0.1 | — | 2 | 0.03 | ~10 |
| V | 0.001 | 0.00005 | 0.05 | — | 2 | 0.2 | 3 |
| Mn | 0.0006 | 0.00003 | 0.02 | 0.2 | 0.1 | 0.001 | 0.0003 |
| Fe | 9 | 0.45 | 0.5 | 0.2 | 2 | 0.05 | 2 |
| Cu | 0.007 | 0.00035 | — | 0.2 | 0.1 | 0.03 | 10 |
| Zn | 0.04 | 0.002 | 2 | 20 | 2000 | 0.016 | 10 |
| Sr | 0.6 | 0.03 | 0.5 | — | 0.1 | — | — |
| Sn | 0.2 | 0.01 | — | 0.2 | 10 | — | 2 |
| Ba | 0.05 | 0.0025 | 0.1 | — | 3 | — | 25 |
| Pb | 2 | 0.1 | 0.05 | 0.2 | 20 | 0.03 | 3 |

Source: Meinke (1955).

dicated the possibility of extending the method to carbon and nitrogen (Jenkins and Smales, 1956).

## CONCLUSION

A comparative table of detection limits of some of the main analytical methods is given below.

| METHOD | DETECTION LIMIT |
|---|---|
| Gravimetric | $10^{-2}$ |
| Volumetric | $10^{-2}$ |
| Colorimetric | $10^{-5}$ |
| Spectrographic | $10^{-5}$ |
| Mass spectrometric | $10^{-6}$ |
| Radioactivation | $10^{-8}$ to $10^{-10}$ |

Actual limits, however, often depend on the element sought and the matrix material, as well as other factors affected by experimental conditions. The wide range of analytical techniques now available, their refinement, and the fact that some do not require the destruction of the sample, should result in significant advances in our knowledge of macro- and microskeletal composition in the near future.

## REFERENCES

*Starred references not cited in text.*

GRAVIMETRIC AND VOLUMETRIC METHODS

*Bøggild, O. B. (1930). The shell structure of the mollusks. Danske Vidensk Selsk. Skr., v. 9, pt. 2, p. 235–326.

*Butschli, O. (1908). Untersuchen über organische Kalkgebilde. Kgl. Gesell. Wiss. Göttingen Abh., new ser., v. 6, no. 3, p. 1–164.

Clarke, F. W. and Wheeler, W. C. (1922). The inorganic constituents of Marine Invertebrates: U. S. Geol. Survey Prof. paper 124, p. 1–62.

*Damour, A. (1852). Note sur la composition des millepores et de quelques corallinées. Acad. Sci. Paris, Comptes rendus, v. 32, p. 253–255.

*Forchammer, G. (1852). Beiträger zur Bildungsgeschichte des Dolomits. Neues Jahrbuch für Mineralogie, Jahrb. 1852, p. 854–858.

Groves, A. W. (1951). Silicate analysis (2nd ed.). London, Allen and Unwin.

Hillebrand, W. F., G. E. F. Lindell, H. A. Bright, and J. I. Hoffman (1953). Applied inorganic analysis (2nd ed.). New York, Wiley.

Kolthoff, I. M., and E. B. Sandell (1950). Textbook of quantitative inorganic analysis. London, Macmillan.

*Nichols, H. W. (1906). New forms of concretions. Field Columbian Mus. Pub. 111, geol. ser., v. 3, no. 3, p. 25–54.

Smales, A. A., and L. R. Wager (1960). Methods in geochemistry. New York, Interscience.

Vinogradov, A. P (1953). The elementary chemical composition of marine organisms. Memoir 11, Sears Foundation for Marine Research, Yale Univ. 646 pp.

Washington, H. S. (1930). The chemical analysis of rocks (4th ed.). New York, Wiley.

MICROCHEMICAL TESTS FOR SPECIFIC ELEMENTS

Cameron, E. N. (1961). Ore microscopy. New York, Wiley.

*Guillemin, C. (1953). Microanalyse qualitative appliquée à la détermination d'espêces minerales. France, Bureau Recherches geologiques, geophysique, et mineralogique, Pub. 13, 31 pp.

Gutzeit, G. (1942). Determination and localization of metallic minerals by the contact print method. A.I.M.E. Tech. Pub. 1457, 1942, 13 pp.

Hiller, Th. (1937). Sur l'application de la méthode des empreintes à la détermination des minéraux opaques en section polie. Schweiz. Mineralog. Petrog. Mitt. v. 17, p. 88–145.

*Parker, R. L. (1941). Systematische Übersicht mineraldiagnostisch wichtiger Mikroreaktionen. Schweiz. Mineral. Petrog. Mitt., vol. 21, p. 139–160.

Short, M. N. (1940). Microscopic determination of the ore minerals. U. S. Geol. Survey Bull. 914, 1940, 314 pp.

*Staples, L. W. (1936). Mineral determination by microchemical methods. Am. Mineralogist, v. 21, pp. 613–634.

### MINERALOGICAL STAINING

Friedman, G. M. (1959). Identification of carbonate minerals by staining methods. J. Sed. Petrology, v. 29, no. 1, p. 87–97.

### COLORIMETRIC AND FLAME PHOTOMETRIC METHODS

Hiskey, C. F. (1949). Principles of precision colorimetry. Anal. Chem. 21, p. 1440–1446.

Sandell, E. B. (1950). Colorimetric determination of traces of metals (2nd ed.). New York, Interscience.

*Chow, T. J., and T. G. Thompson (1955). Flame photometric determination of calcium in sea water and marine organisms. Anal. Chem., v. 27, p. 910–913.

*———— (1955). Strontium in sea water. Anal. Chem., v. 27, p. 18–21.

Dean, J. A. (1960). Flame photometry. New York, McGraw-Hill, 354 pp.

Thompson, T. G., and T. J. Chow (1955). Strontium-calcium atom ratio in carbonate secreting marine organisms. Deep Sea Research, Papers in Marine Biology and Oceanography, suppl. to v. 3, pp. 20–39.

Vincent, V. E. (1960). Analysis by gravimetric and volumetric methods, flame photometry, colorimetry and related techniques, *in* A. A. Smales and L. R. Wager (eds.), Methods in geochemistry, 1960, pp. 52–55.

### THERMOLUMINESCENCE

Johnson, N. M. (1960). Thermoluminescence in biogenic calcium carbonate. J. Sed. Petrology, v. 30, no. 2, p. 305–313.

### OPTICAL EMISSION SPECTROGRAPHY

*Ahrens, L. H. (1954). Quantitative spectrochemical analysis of silicates. Oxford, Pergamon Press.

Chave, K. E. (1954a). Aspects of the biogeochemistry of magnesium: 1. Calcareous marine organisms. J. Geology, v. 62, no. 3, p. 266–283.

———— (1954b). Aspects of the biochemistry of magnesium: 2. Calcareous sediments and rocks. J. Geology, v. 62, no. 6, p. 587–599.

Emiliani, C. (1955). Mineralogical and chemical composition of tests of certain pelagic Foraminifera. Micropaleontology, v. 1, no. 4.

Harley, J. A., and S. E. Wiberley (1954). Instrumental analysis. New York, Wiley.

*Hower, J. (1959). Matrix corrections in the X-ray spectrographic trace element analysis of rocks and minerals. Am. Mineralogist, v. 44, p. 19–32.

Krinsley, D. (1959). Manganese in modern and fossil gastropod shells. Nature, v. 183, p. 770–771.

———— (1960). Magnesium, strontium and aragonite in shells of certain littoral gastropods. J. Paleontology, v. 34, no. 4, p. 744–755.

———, and R. Bieri (1959). Changes in chemical composition of pteropod shells after deposition on the sea floor. J. Paleontology, v. 33, no. 4, p. 682–684.

Kulp, J., K. Turekian, and D. W. Boyd (1952). Strontium content of limestone and fossils. Geol. Soc. America Bull., v. 63, 7, p. 701–716.

Lowenstam, H. W. (1961). Isotopes and trace elements in paleoecology. Geol. Soc. America Program, Ann. Meeting, 1961, p. 96A.

McKerrow, W. S., S. R. Taylor, A. L. Blackburn, and L. H. Ahrens (1956). Rare alkali elements in trilobites. Geol. Mag., v. 93, p. 504.

Turekian, K., and R. L. Armstrong (1961). Chemical and mineralogical composition of fossil molluscan shells from the Fox Hills Formation, South Dakota. Geol. Soc. America Bull., v. 72, no. 12, p. 1817–1828.

*Vincent, V. E. (1960). Analysis by gravimetric, flame photometry, colorimetry and related techniques, *in* A. A. Smales and L. R. Wager (eds.). Methods in geochemistry, New York, Interscience, p. 52–55.

*Willard, H. H., L. L. Merritt, and J. A. Dean (1960). Instrumental methods of analysis. New York, Van Nostrand, p. 218–257.

## LASER (MASER) AS AN ALTERNATIVE OPTICAL EMISSION SPECTROGRAPH SOURCE

Maxwell, J. A. (1963). The use of the optical maser (laser) as a tool in the study of geological materials. Ottawa, Canada Dept. Mines Tech. Surveys, Geological Survey Topical Report 74.

Schawlow, A. L. (1961). Optical masers. Scientific American, v. 204, p. 52–61.

———, and C. H. Townes (1958). Infrared and optical masers. Phys. Rev., v. 112, p. 1940–1949.

## X-RAY DIFFRACTION

Azároff, L. V., and M. J. Buerger (1958). The powder method in X-ray crystallography. New York, McGraw-Hill, 342 pp.

Blackmon, P., and R. Todd (1959). Mineralogy of some Foraminifera as related to their classification and ecology. J. Paleontology, v. 33, no. 1, pp. 1–15.

Chave, K. E. (1954a). Aspects of the biochemistry of magnesium; 1. Calcareous marine organisms. J. Geology, v. 62, no. 3, p. 266–283.

——— (1954b). Aspects of the biochemistry of magnesium; 2. Calcareous sediments and rocks. J. Geology, v. 62, no. 6, p. 587–599.

Emiliani, C. (1955). Mineralogical and chemical composition of tests of certain pelagic foraminifers. Micropaleontology, v. 1, no. 4.

*——— (1952). A solid solution between calcite and dolomite. J. Geology, v. 60, p. 190–192.

Goldsmith, J. R., D. L. Graf, and O. Joensuu (1955). The occurrence of magnesian calcites in nature. Geochim. Cosmochim. Acta, v. 7, p. 212–230.

*Hower, J. (1959). Matrix corrections in the X-ray spectrographic trace element analysis of rocks and minerals. Am. Mineralogist, v. 44, p. 19–32.

Krinsley, D. (1959). Manganese in modern and fossil gastropod shells. Nature, v. 183, p. 770–771.

———, 1960, Magnesium, strontium and aragonite in shells of certain littoral gastropods. J. Paleontology, v. 34, no. 4, p. 744–755.

————, and R. Bieri (1959). Changes in chemical composition of pteropod shells after deposition on the sea floor. J. Paleontology, v. 33, no. 4, p. 682–684.

*Kulp, J., K. Turekian, and D. W. Boyd (1952). Strontium content of limestone and fossils. Geol. Soc. America Bull., v. 63, p. 701–716.

Lowenstam, H. A. (1954). Factors affecting the aragonite: calcite ratios in carbonate secreting marine organisms. J. Geology, v. 62, p. 284–322.

*———— (1961). Isotopes and trace elements in paleontology. Geol. Soc. America Program, Ann. Meeting, 1961, p. 96A.

*Mayer, F. K. (1932). Uber die Modifikation des Kalzium-karbonats in Schalen und Skeleton rezenter und fossiler Organism. Chemie der Erde, v. 7, p. 346–350.

*Pilkey, O. H., and J. Hower (1960). Effect of environment on the concentration of skeletal magnesium and strontium in Dendraster. J. Geology, v. 68, no. 2.

Siegel, F. R. (1960). The effect of strontium on the aragonite-calcite ratios of Pleistocene corals. J. Sed. Petrology, v. 30, no. 2, p. 297–304.

Switzer, G. and A. J. Boucot (1955). Mineral composition of some microfossils. J. Paleontology, v. 29, no. 3, p. 525–533.

Turekian, K., and R. L. Armstrong (1961). Chemical and mineralogical composition of fossil molluscan shells from the Fox Hills Formation, South Dakota. Geol. Soc. America Bull., v. 72, no. 12, p. 1817–1828.

*Wray, J. L., and F. Daniels (1957). Precipitation of calcite and aragonite. J. Am. Chem. Soc., v. 79, p. 2031–2034.

*Zeller, E. J., and J. L. Wray (1956). Factors influencing precipitation of calcium carbonate. Am. Assoc. Petroleum Geologists Bull., v. 40, p. 140–152.

### X-RAY ABSORPTION

Cosslet, V. E., and W. C. Nixon (1960). X-ray microscopy. Cambridge University Press, 406 pp.

Liebhafsky, H. A. (1953). Analytical methods based upon X-ray absorption. Anal. Chem., v. 25, no. 5, p. 689–692.

*Ong, S. P. (1961). Projection microscopy and microanalysis. Advances in X-ray analysis, v. 5, p. 324–334.

*———— (1961). Isolation of selected elements with an X-ray projection microscope. Norelco Rept., v. 8, no. 1, p. 3–9.

### FLUORESCENT X-RAY SPECTROGRAPHY

Birks, L. S., E. J. Brooks, and H. Friedman (1953). Fluorescent X-ray spectroscopy. Anal. Chem., v. 25, no. 5, p. 692–697.

Shalgosky, H. I. (1960). Fluorescent X-ray spectroscopy, A. A. Smales and L. R. Wager (eds.), Methods in geochemistry. p. 111–147.

### ELECTRON PROBE X-RAY MICROANALYSIS

*Agrell, S. O., and J. V. P. Long (1959). The applications of the scanning X-ray microanalyser to mineralogy, *in* Second International Symposium on X-ray microscopy and X-ray microanalysis, Amsterdam, Elsevier, p. 391–400, 1960.

Blackmon, P. D., and R. Todd (1959). Mineralogy of some Foraminifera as related to their classification and ecology. J. Paleontology, v. 33, no. 1, p. 1–15.

*Castaing, R. (1951). Application of electron probes to a method of chemical and crystallographic point analysis. Thesis, Univ. of Paris.

*Cosslett, V. E. (1962). Scanning electron and X-ray microscopy. Ann. New York Acad. Sci., v. 97, no. 2, p. 464–481.

*——, V. E., and P. Duncumb (1956). Microanalysis by a flying spot method. Nature, v. 177, p. 1172.

*——, V. E., and W. C. Nixon (1960). X-ray microscopy. Cambridge Univ. Press, 406 pp.

*Duncumb, P. (1957). Microanalysis with an X-ray scanning microscope. Thesis, Cambridge Univ.

Hooper, K., Electron probe microanalysis of Foraminifera; an exploratory study. J. Paleontology, p. 1082–1092.

*Long, J. V. P. (1959). Microchemical analysis with X-rays. Thesis, Cambridge Univ.

*—— (1960). Some factors affecting the range and accuracy of the point-projection method of X-ray absorption microscopy, *in* Second International Symposium on X-ray Microscopy and Microanalysis, Amsterdam, Elsevier, p. 98.

*——, and V. E. Cosslett (1957). Some methods of X-ray microchemical analysis, *in* First International Symposium on X-ray microscopy and microradiography. New York, Academic, p. 435.

*Reed, S. J. B., and J. V. P. Long (1962). Electron probe measurements near grain boundaries, *in* Third International Symposium on X-ray Optics and X-ray Microanalysis. Stanford University, California, August 1962.

*Springer, G., and J. V. P. Long (1962). Electron probe analysis of minerals in the system $FeS_2$-$CoS_2$-$NiS_2$, *in* Third International Symposium on X-ray Optics and X-ray Microanalysis, Stanford University, California, August 1962.

Wells, J. W. (1963). Coral growth and geochronometry. Nature, v. 197, no. 4871, p. 948–950.

MASS SPECTROMETRIC ANALYSIS

*Baertschi, P. (1950). Isotopic composition of the oxygen in silicate rocks. Nature, v. 166, p. 112–113.

*Ballario, C., *et al.* (1955). Apparatus for $C^{14}$ dating. Science, v. 121, p. 409–412.

Craig, H. (1953). Geochemistry of the stable carbon isotopes. Geochim. Cosmochim. Acta, v. 3, p. 53.

—— (1954). Carbon 13 in plants and the relationships between Carbon 13 and Carbon 14 variation in Nature. J. Geology, v. 62, p. 115.

Compston, W. (1960). The carbon isotopic compositions of certain marine invertebrates and coals from the Australian Permian. Geochim. Cosmochim. Acta, v. 18, no. 1 & 2, pp. 1–22.

*Dansgaard, W. (1954). The $O^{18}$ abundance in fresh water. Geochim. Cosmochim. Acta, v. 6, p. 241–260.

Daughtry, A. C., D. Perry, and M. Williams (1962). Magnesium isotope distribution in dolomite. Geochim. Cosmochim. Acta, v. 26, p. 857.

Emiliani, C. (1954a). Depth habitats of some species of pelagic foraminifera as indicated by the oxygen isotope ratios. Am. J. Sci., v. 252, p. 149–158.

—— (1954b). Temperatures of Pacific bottom waters and Polar superficial waters during the Tertiary. Science, v. 119, p. 853.

—— (1955). Pleistocene temperatures. J. Geology, v. 63, no. 6, p. 538–580.

————, and S. Epstein (1953). Temperature variations in the lower Pleistocene of Southern California. J. Geology, v. 61, p. 171.

Epstein, S., R. Buchsbaum, H. Lowenstam, and H. C. Urey (1951). Carbonate water isotopic temperature scale. Geol. Soc. America Bull., v. 62, p. 417.

———— (1953). Revised carbonate-water isotopic temperature scale. Geol. Soc. America Bull., v. 64, p. 1315.

Epstein, S., and H. A. Lowenstam (1953). Temperature-shell-growth relations of recent and interglacial Pleistocene shoal-water biota from Bermuda. J. Geology, v. 61, p. 424–428.

*Epstein, S., and T. Mayeda (1953). Variation of $O^{18}$ content of waters from natural sources. Geochim. Cosmochim. Acta, v. 4, p. 213–224.

*Flint, R. F., and M. Rubin (1955). Radiocarbon dates of pre-Mankato events in Eastern and Central North America. Science, v. 121, p. 649–658.

*Libby, W. F. (1952). Radiocarbon dating. Univ. of Chicago Press.

*Lowenstam, H. A. (1948). Paleobiologic implications of the measurement of paleotemperatures (abs.). Geol. Soc. Americo Bull., v. 59, p. 1337.

————, and S. Epstein (1954). Paleotemperatures of the post-Aptian Cretaceous as determined by oxygen isotope method. J. Geology, v. 62, no. 3, p. 207.

———— (1957). Origin of sedimentary aragonite needles of the great Bahama Bank. J. Geology, v. 65, no. 4, p. 364.

*Mayne, K. I. (1960). Stable isotope geochemistry and mass spectrometric analysis, *in* A. A. Smales and L. R. Wager (eds.), Methods in geochemistry. New York, Interscience, p. 148–201.

*McCrea, J. (1950). On the isotope chemistry of carbonates and a paleotemperature scale. J. Chem. Phys., v. 18, p. 849.

*McKinney, C. R., J. M. McCrea, S. Epstein, H. A. Allen, and H. C. Urey (1950). Improvements in mass spectrometers for the measurement of small differences in isotope abundance ratios. Rev. Sci. Instruments, v. 21, p. 724–730.

*Nier, A. O. (1940). A mass spectrometer for routine isotope abundance measurements. Rev. Sci. Instruments, v. 11, p. 212–216.

*———— (1947). A mass spectrometer for isotope and gas analysis. *Ibid.*, v. 18, p. 398–411.

*———— (1955). Determination of isotopic masses and abundances by mass spectrometry. Science, v. 121, p. 737–744.

*Rubin, M., and H. E. Suess (1955). U.S.G.S. radiocarbon dates; II. Science, v. 121, p. 481–488.

*Silverman, S. R. (1951). The isotope geology of oxygen. Geochim. Cosmochim. Acta, v. 2, p. 26–42.

Thode, H. G., J. MacNamara, and W. H. Fleming (1953). Sulphur isotope fractionation in nature and geological and biological time scales. Geochim. Cosmochim. Acta, v. 3, p. 235–243.

*Urey, H. C. (1947). The thermodynamic properties of isotopic substances. Chem. Soc. J., p. 562–581.

*———— (1948). Oxygen isotopes in nature and in the laboratory. Science, new series, v. 108, p. 489–496.

Urey, H. C., H. A. Lowenstam, S. Epstein, and C. R. McKinney (1951). Measurement of paleotemperature and temperatures of the Upper Cretaceous of

England, Denmark and southeastern U. S. Geol. Soc. America Bull., v. 62, p. 399–416.

RADIOACTIVATION ANALYSIS

Cook, G. B. (1959). Radioactivation analysis in a nuclear reactor, *in* Proc. Radioactivation Analysis Symposium, Vienna. London, Butterworth, p. 15–31, 1960.

Fukai, R. (1959). Trace analyses in seaweed, molluscs, crustacea, fish and sea water. Limnology and Oceanography, v. 4, no. 4, p. 398.

———, and W. W. Meinke (1959). On trace analyses of seaweeds, crustacea, seawater—summary. Nature, v. 184, p. 815.

*Herr, W. (1959). Neutron activation applied to geochemistry. Proc. Radioactivation Analysis Symposium, Vienna. London, Butterworth, p. 35–52, 1960.

*Hughes, D. J., and J. A. Harvey (1958). Neutron cross sections. BNL-325 (1955); revised, July 1958. Washington, D.C.; U. S. Govt. Printing Office.

Jenkins, E. N., and A. A. Smales (1956). Radioactivation analysis. Quarterly Reviews, v. 10, no. 1, p. 83–107.

*Kemp, D. M., and A. A. Smales (1960). Neutron activation results for vanadium and scandium in G-1 and W-1. Geochim. Cosmochim. Acta, v. 18, no. 1 & 2, p. 149.

Leddicotte, G. W. (1959). Experience in the U.S.A. on the use of radioactivation analysis. Proc. Radioactivation Analysis Symposium, Vienna. London, Butterworth, p. 61–79, 1960.

*———, and S. A. Reynolds (1954). Determination of the alkali metals by neutron activation analysis. Oak Ridge Natl. Lab. Pub. 1623, p. 14.

*———, and R. C. Plumb (1956). Activation analysis. Nucleonics, v. 14, no. 5, p. 46–50.

*Mapper, D. (1960). Radioactivation analysis, *in* A. A. Smales and L. R. Wager (eds.), Methods in geochemistry. New York, Interscience, p. 297–357.

Meinke, W. W. (1955). Trace-element sensitivity: Comparison of activation analysis with other methods. Science, v. 121, p. 177–184.

*——— (1959). Sensitivity charts for neutron activation analysis. Anal. Chem., v. 31, no. 5, p. 792–795.

*———, and R. E. Anderson (1953). Activation analysis using low level neutron source. Anal. Chem., v. 25, no. 5, p. 778–783.

Salmon, L. (1959). Gamma-ray spectroscopy applied to radioactivation analysis. Part 1, A.E.R.E. C/R. 2377(1), H.M.S.O. London.

*Savchuk, W. B. (1959). A comparison of bone growth in normal and strontium-treated rats. J. Dental Res., v. 38, no. 1, p. 49–59.

*Smales, A. A. (1955). Some trace-element determinations in G.1. and W.1. by neutron activation. Geochim. Cosmochim. Acta, v. 8, nos. 5 and 6, p. 300.

# Preparing Fossils and Shells for Chemical Analysis

JAMES R. DODD

*Texaco, Inc., Bellaire, Texas*

Although chemical analysis of fossils and modern shells has become more common in recent years, it is not a new development. Vinogradov (1953) discusses some of these early works in his review of the chemical composition of marine organisms. The first systematic work on skeletal chemical composition covering several groups of organisms (both fossil and modern) was that of Clarke and Wheeler (1922). Vinogradov (1953) tabulated all chemical analyses of shells available in the published literature at that time and included some new analyses. The development of improved analytical techniques has made chemical analyses of fossils and shells more readily available to the paleontologist in recent years. The potential usefulness of such data in making paleoecologic and taxonomic interpretations has been an added incentive for work toward a better understanding of the factors affecting chemical composition of fossils.

## GENERAL SAMPLE PREPARATION PROCEDURES

The first step in preparing fossils for chemical analysis is the selection of the specimens to be analyzed. Many fossils have been chemically and mineralogically altered since they were formed (Bøggild, 1930; Chave, 1954a,b; Stehli, 1956; Odum, 1957; and Lowenstam, 1961). The chemical mineralogical stability of skeletal material is variable, being dependent on original composition (Lowenstam, 1961; Stehli and Hower, 1961; and Chave, 1961). Preservation of original internal skeletal microstructure is an indication that the original chemistry and mineralogy may also be at least in part preserved (Bøggild, 1930; Kulp, et al., 1952; Compston, 1960; and Lowenstam, 1961). Replacement of the original microstructure by an irregular, blocky mosaic of secondary calcite crystals is an indication that skeletal chemistry has been altered (Kulp, et al., 1952; and Compston, 1960). Skeletal chemistry may, however, be altered with no apparent microstructural alteration (Urey, et al., 1951; Compston, 1960; Lowenstam, 1961; and Turekian and Armstrong, 1961). Fossils from fine-grained sediments are likely to be less altered than those from limestones and coarser clastics (Bøggild, 1930). Some of the best examples of preservation have come from asphalt-impregnated sediments, which are effectively sealed against ground water migration (Stehli, 1956). In general, the older the fossil, the more likely it is to be altered (Bøggild, 1930; Stehli, 1956; and Lowenstam, 1961).

Adhering sediment must be removed from the fossil. If the sediment is not firmly cemented, it can usually be removed with a dissecting needle or dental scraper. A dentist's drill can be used to remove particles of sediment which are more firmly attached. Hollow shells such as those of gastropods may have to be broken or cut to remove internal sediment. At least the final stages of this cleaning should be done with the aid of a binocular microscope. Ultrasonic vibration is excellent for removing fine sediment which is not cemented to the fossil (Stevens, et al., 1960). It is particularly useful in cleaning irregular surfaces and in removing clay material which is too fine to be effectively removed with a dissecting needle. Removal of encrusting organisms, such as bryozoans, serpulid worms, calcareous algae, and barnacles, presents a special problem. They can sometimes be removed with a dissecting needle, but often require the use of a dentist drill. More detailed discussions of the surficial cleaning of various types of fossils are found elsewhere in this volume.

Removal of the organic fraction of the shell is necessary for some types of analysis. The organic content of fossils is usually low (Abelson, 1954), but may be significant in modern shells. Complete removal of the organic fraction is often difficult, especially in molluscs, in which crystals are surrounded by a protein matrix (Abelson, 1954). Soaking in a commercial sodium hypochlorite solution (Clorox) effectively oxidizes much of the organic material. Ultrasonic vibration of the specimen in the solution (suggested by M. Dekkers) makes this technique even more effective. Shells can be left in Clorox for several days with no apparent alteration of shell chemistry. Longer treatment may result in gradual alteration (H. A. Lowenstam, personal communication).

Heating is also effective in removing organic material. For some samples, however, high temperatures should be avoided. Aragonite is metastable at room temperature and atmospheric pressure, and is rapidly converted to calcite at temperatures above approximately 400°C (Pruna, et al., 1948). Some exchange of atmospheric oxygen with the carbonate oxygen of shells was noted by Epstein, et al. (1953). They developed a technique of heating the sample in a purified helium atmosphere to avoid this difficulty. At relatively low temperatures and with poor oxygen circulation, samples often develop a brownish color, indicating that some organic material remains, products of decomposition still being present.

For some purposes (e.g., determining aragonite : calcite ratios) samples prepared from the total shell are desirable. In preparing samples of this type, special care is necessary to select unworn shells and to avoid removing significant amounts of the shell during the cleaning process. If the sample can be prepared from a portion of a single shell, the cleaning process is simplified: the sample can be taken from the interior of the shell, which is likely to be less weathered than the surface. These samples can be taken by careful use of a dentist's drill or a dissecting needle if the shell is not too compact. For many purposes, all of the sample should come from the same structural unit of the shell. Different structural units may not have the same chemistry, particularly when they have different mineral compositions (Clarke and Wheeler, 1922; Chave, 1954a; and Odum, 1957).

For some purposes, a study of the chemistry of successive growth increments of shells is of interest (Urey, et al., 1951; Kulp, et al., 1952; Epstein and Lowenstam, 1953; and Bowen, 1961). Samples of this type can be ground from the shell with a dentist's drill. Sampling of this kind should be preceded by a careful study of the structure of the shell to determine the growth directions (see fig. 1). Many shells grow by thickening on the inside

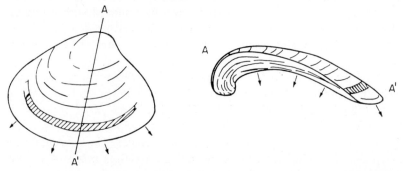

**Fig. 1.** *Pelecypod shell showing shell structure and growth directions. (Left) The exterior surface of the shell. (Right) A longitudinal section through the shell along line A-A'. The arrows show direction of growth. The cross-hatched areas are growth increments which could be used as samples.*

as well as lengthening at the margin. Thus, indiscriminate grinding of samples back from the margin will not necessarily yield true growth increments.

Samples will usually have to be ground. For trace element studies, this can best be done with a scrupulously cleaned agate mortar and pestle. If this mortar and pestle is used only for carbonate samples, careful cleaning with acid between samples should suffice. Prolonged grinding may alter the sample (Jamieson and Goldsmith, 1960). Burns and Bredig (1956) demonstrated that calcite may begin to convert to aragonite after as little as one-half hour of grinding in a laboratory power mortar. Jamieson and Goldsmith (1960) detected aragonite in originally pure calcite samples after grinding for 24 hours. Some samples will need to be sieved (particularly for X-ray diffraction studies). This can be accomplished by brushing the samples through nylon bolting cloth or using standard brass sieves. Samples for trace element analysis should not be passed through brass sieves. Sieves and bolting cloth should be carefully cleaned with compressed air between samples.

## ACKNOWLEDGMENTS

I wish to express my gratitude to H. A. Lowenstam of the California Institute of Technology, who originally suggested many of the techniques of sample preparation discussed here, and to his laboratory assistant, Mrs. Margaret Dekkers, who made additional helpful suggestions.

## REFERENCES

Abelson, P. H. (1954). Paleobiochemistry. Carnegie Inst. of Washington Year Book, no. 53, p. 97–101.

Bøggild, O. B. (1930). The shell structure of the mollusks. Kgl. Danske Vidensk. kgl. Skrifter Naturridensk. kgl. Math. Afdel., v. 2, p. 232–326.

Bowen, R. (1961). Paleotemperature analyses of Belemnoidea and Jurassic paleoclimatology. J. Geology, v. 69, p. 309–320.

Burns, J. H., and M. A. Bredig (1956). Transformation of calcite to aragonite by grinding. J. Chem. Phys., v. 25, p. 1281.

Chave, K. E. (1954a). Aspects of the biogeochemistry of magnesium. 1. Calcareous marine organisms. J. Geology, v. 62, p. 266–283.

———— (1954b). Aspects of the biogeochemistry of magnesium: 2. Calcareous sediments and rocks. J. Geology, v. 62, p. 587–599.

———— (1961). Skeletal durability and preservation (abs.). Geol. Soc. America Program, 1961 Ann. Meeting, p. 22A–23A.

Clarke, F. W., and W. C. Wheeler (1922). The inorganic constituents of marine invertebrates. U. S. Geol. Survey Prof. Paper 124, 62 pp.

Compston, W. (1960). The carbon isotopic composition of certain marine invertebrates and coals from the Australian Permian. Geochim. Cosmochim. Acta, v. 18, p. 1–22.

Epstein, S., R. Buchsbaum, H. A. Lowenstam, and H. C. Urey (1953). Revised carbonate-water isotopic temperature scale. Geol. Soc. America Bull., v. 64, p. 1315–1326.

Epstein, S., and H. A. Lowenstam (1953). Temperature-shell growth relations of Recent and interglacial Pleistocene shoal-water biota from Bermuda. J. Geology, v. 61, p. 424–438.

Jamieson, J. C., and J. R. Goldsmith (1960). Some reactions produced in carbonates by grinding. Am. Mineralogist, v. 45, p. 818–827.

Kulp, J. L., K. Turekian, and D. W. Boyd (1952). Strontium content of limestone and fossils. Geol. Soc. America Bull., v. 63, p. 701–716.

Lowenstam, H. A. (1961). Mineralogy, $O^{18}/O^{16}$ ratios, and strontium and magnesium contents of Recent and fossil brachiopods and their bearing on the history of the oceans. J. Geology, v. 69, p. 241–260.

Odum, H. T. (1957). Biogeochemical deposition of strontium. Inst. Marine. Sci. Publ., v. 4, no. 2, p. 38–114.

Pruna, M., R. Faivre, and G. Chaudron (1948). Etude cinetique par dilatometrie isotherme de la transformation de l'aragonite en calcite. Acad. Sci. Comptes rendus, Paris, v. 227, p. 390–391.

Stehli, F. G. (1956). Shell mineralogy in paleozoic invertebrates. Science, v. 123, p. 1031–1032.

———, and J. Hower (1961). Mineralogy and early diagenesis of carbonate sediments. J. Sed. Petrology, v. 31, p. 358–371.

Stevens, C. H., D. H. Jones, and R. G. Todd (1960). Ultrasonic vibration as a cleaning agent for fossils. J. Paleontology, v. 34, p. 727–730.

Turekian, K. K., and R. L. Armstrong (1960). Magnesium, strontium and barium concentrations and calcite-aragonite ratios of some Recent molluscan shells. J. Marine Res., v. 18, p. 133–151.

Urey, H. C., H. A. Lowenstam, S. Epstein, and C. R. McKinney (1951). Measurement of paleotemperatures of the Upper Cretaceous of England, Denmark and the southeastern United States. Geol. Soc. America Bull., v. 247, p. 257–275.

Vinogradov, A. P. (1953). The elementary chemical composition of marine organisms. Sears Foundation for Marine Research, Memoir 2, 647 pp.

# SECTION E

## CASTING AND MOLDING

---

*Coordinator:* J. KEITH RIGBY

# Casting and Molding

---

J. KEITH RIGBY

*Brigham Young University, Provo, Utah*

DAVID L. CLARK

*University of Wisconsin, Madison*

There are few paleontologists who, at some time, do not find it necessary to prepare casts or molds. The various techniques are perhaps most commonly used for duplicating type material or for making casts of study specimens in laboratories or exhibits. The following brief discussion is intended for those who have not prepared molds or casts, and also for those paleontologists who may desire to experiment with different techniques. Some hints are given for general preparation of specimens for molding, as well as for the selection of materials for the particular problem. The main body of the paper is devoted to a discussion of materials commonly used in molding and casting. Widely used and simple techniques are discussed first, with a discussion of the more complex methods following; a short discussion of impregnation and embedding techniques completes the paper.

There are many "brand name" materials that are not discussed here, but we feel that most of the usable kinds are included. Adequate summaries are available in standard reference works such as Clarke (1940, 1948) and Rich (1956).

## PREPARATION OF SPECIMENS FOR MOLDING

Proper preparation of specimens prior to molding will do much to ensure creditable results. In general, specimens should be clean of loose matrix, dirt, or oil. Cleaning solutions, acetone, alcohol, soap and water, or paint removers may be applied to ensure a cleaned surface. In some instances weak hydrochloric or acetic acid may be brushed over the specimens to remove extraneous matrix or adherent debris.

Porous specimens should first be impregnated with a hardener or sealer. If a nonthermal molding material is used, a thin solution of shellac—approximately 20 to 30 parts per 100 parts alcohol—will penetrate the pores and seal the surface. The specimens may be either brushed with the hardener or soaked in it. Alvar in acetone, again in a dilute solution, will also serve as a sealer, as will thinned varnish. Hot paraffin may also be employed if detail is not critical.

If a thermal-setting material is used, thicker layers of sealers are necessary to prevent the air still retained in the specimen from breaking through the surface and ruining the mold. Soaking in the sealer or hardener is recommended, for this treatment forms a more secure barrier. After impregnation, the specimen should be dried for at least 24 hours and then cleaned with the solvent. Warming in an oven (up to 80°C) will accelerate drying.

Manufacturers of some thermoplastic materials suggest use of an additional sealing oil, applied after the initial treatment with shellac, varnish, or Alvar. The specimen should be immersed in the sealing oil for 30 minutes for small specimens and 2 or 3 hours for larger ones. After removal from the bath and the specimen has completely drained, the excess oil should be wiped from the surface.

After hardening and sealing, and immediately prior to molding, the specimen may be coated with a suitable separator, if one is necessary.

## SELECTION OF MOLDING MATERIALS

The molding compound and the techniques to be used will be determined by the composition of the original specimens, their size and complexity of shape, by whether a temporary or permanent record is desired, and by the availability of supplies.

Fossils which heat might destroy, such as pyritized shells, must be treated with nonthermal molding materials. Molds of simple objects may be obtained with modeling clay, beeswax, paraffin, paper mache, or plaster of paris; more complex objects may be molded with latex, silicone rubber, polyvinyl chloride compounds, or other more complicated materials.

Materials that require elevated temperatures may be used for reproductions of most fossils. Thermal-plastic or thermal-setting plastics, type metals, solder, polyvinyl chloride, or bakelite are useful for various results. Each of these materials has its advantages and limitations, as the details of the following sections will show.

## MOLDING MATERIALS AND TECHNIQUES

### BEESWAX AND PARAFFIN

Both beeswax and paraffin are temporary molding or casting materials. Beeswax has the advantage of being soft and pliable at room temperatures and can thus be pressed directly onto the specimen for a mold. Either wax may be used without a separating medium; however, if hot sealing wax is used, superior results are obtained if the specimen is coated with glycerine.

Liquid wax is useful for obtaining natural casts of complexly structured fossils preserved as natural molds in acid-soluble matrixes. The wax is melted in a double boiler, using either a water or an oil bath. Direct flame should be avoided, for the paraffin is flammable. The melt is poured directly into the natural molds, preferably with the specimen warmed to prevent sudden cooling of the wax. Care should also be taken to avoid trapping air. Once the melt has set, the matrix may be dissolved, leaving the wax cast free.

### MODELING CLAY AND POTTER'S CLAY

Plastic clays are easy to use in making temporary molds of many fossils, particularly if the specimens are not complex. Clays mixed with oils are available from art supply houses, either as modeling clay or—mixed with water—as potter's clay. Powdered clay is also available where large quantities are desired. Some chemically self-hardening clays are now available which may be of use for more permanent molds or casts. Potter's clay may be fired for permanent record, as may some of the clays designed for firing in domestic ovens at lower temperatures.

Molds may be made with plastic clay by pressing the material around the specimen or by forcing the clay onto the surface by hand. Release of the mold will be facilitated if the specimen is slightly damp (for oil-base clays) or slightly oily (for water-base clays). Plaster of paris casts are easily made in the molds.

Casts of natural molds can also easily be made with plastic clay, merely by forcing the clay into the mold. Only molds without undercuts may be used, however; otherwise the clay will not release from the undercuts. Successful casts of conodonts have been made from molds etched in siliceous shales. Clay casts have retained enough surface features to enable specific identifications. Larger features, such as those of trilobites or gastropods, model well in the plastic clays.

NATURAL MOLDS

Calcareous or phosphatic specimens embedded in a matrix not suitable for easy or satisfactory preparation may be dissolved with suitable acids—usually weak hydrochloric, acetic, or formic acid—leaving a natural mold.

Badly decayed small bones in a hard matrix may be removed mechanically and then cast for study. To facilitate study, the bone cavities may be filled with latex (or other suitable flexible molding compound) of one color, and the "background" with latex of another color.

LATEX

Latex is one of the most suitable and easily used of the flexible molding compounds. It is relatively inexpensive, readily available, and requires little specialized equipment. The simple techniques of molding are easily mastered. Molds made with latex can be stretched or distorted during and after removal of the specimens without loss of the original shape or detail. The greatest disadvantage of latex is shrinkage and hence loss of the original dimensions. Drying time between successive coats also limits the employment of latex where speed is necessary. Latex molds tend to decompose with time, but— under ideal conditions—may be used for many years.

Latex is not restricted to large-scale molding. Baird (1955) has described specialized techniques for micromolding where great detail is necessary. Garner (1953) utilized a diluted latex mixture for casting animal excavations in the field, in a manner adaptable to some paleontologic problems.

Latex molds can produce some of the best high-fidelity casts if care is taken in preparation of the specimen (outlined earlier) and the mold. On most fossils no separating medium is necessary, particularly if the pores have been sealed. If latex is to be molded over wax models, they should be coated with plastic spray or shellac.

Molds of latex are built up by the gradual addition of a number of coats, beginning with thinned latex for the initial coats and using thicker material for later ones. The first coat should be applied with a soft brush, with the latex thinned to a cream-like consistency. Air bubbles should be broken by pricking or blowing before the initial coat has set. Care should also be taken to apply the coats uniformly, for thickened areas will remain soft and will deform upon demolding.

Additional coats may be applied when the surface is tacky. After the second coat, fillers may be used to add rigidity to the mold, if necessary, and to add some dimensional stability. Open-weave fabric of any kind may be used by shaping to the mold surface in thin strips, then covering with subsequent layers of latex. Bubbles between layers should be guarded against when fillers are used, for these will destroy the usefulness of the mold.

Deep undercuts may be filled with mixtures of latex and any inert material such as cork fragments or sawdust. An instantly setting filler of plaster mixed with latex is useful for deep undercuts where flexibility is important: quickly mix in the palm of the hand about 1 part plaster to 8 parts latex, in small amounts, and apply to the mold where necessary. Small batches may be added until the fill is complete. Some experimentation may be necessary to adapt the mixture to individual needs.

Once the thickness of the mold has been judged sufficient and the last added coat is set, the mold may be stripped from the specimen. It should be dusted with a thin coat of talcum powder and labeled. It is then ready for casting.

Latex molds may also be constructed in pieces if the specimen has a complex structure that makes single molds impossible. These piece molds should be flanged or keyed for ready assembly. Such molds are usually backed by a shell of rigid material, such as plaster of paris. A discussion of piece molds is given on subsequent pages.

For maximum length of life, latex molds should be stored in a dark place, away from circulating air. Under ideal circumstances of humidity and light, a mold may last for several years, but since there is some deterioration, casts should be made during the first six months of the life of the mold.

Micromolding in latex is similar to the technique described above except that wetting agents are added to the latex, which has been deaerated by boiling (Baird, 1955, p. 202). The specimen may be wetted as well, to ensure even greater fidelity. Successive coats of the thinned latex are built up as described above.

Casting with latex is difficult, unless absorbent molds and slip-casting techniques are used. Since latex sets mainly by evaporation, water-proof molds cannot be used. A discussion of slip-casting is given in most reference works on sculpture or casting; for example, see Rich (1956, p. 40–44). The technique of latex slip-casting is similar to that of clay slip-casting.

Casts and molds of latex may be enlarged by soaking in light oil or kerosene. This will increase the size up to 50 percent without material distortion.

PLASTER OF PARIS

Plaster of paris can be used for casting and molding where rigid molds and casts are desired. It is one of the most extensively used compounds for reproduction, since it is inexpensive, quick-setting, easy to use, dimensionally stable, and does not deteriorate with long storage. The main disadvantages of plaster are that reproductions are relatively easily broken, bulky to store, and, since it is rigid, it will not tolerate undercuts in removal. It is, however, an excellent medium for rigid piece molds.

Specimens to be molded with plaster of paris should be cleaned and sealed, as discussed earlier. In some instances separators—such as a 1 to 9 mixture of beeswax in carbon tetrachloride or a 3 to 1 mixture of banana oil and acetone—may be useful. The beeswax preparation should dry on the specimen for at least one or two days, but the banana oil and acetone mixture prepares the specimen for pouring within minutes.

Plaster of paris is mixed with water in a ratio of 1 part plaster to $2\frac{1}{2}$ parts of water. Use an amount of water equal to the volume of the mix desired, and sift handfuls of the plaster of paris into it. The sifted plaster settles to the bottom until eventually the surface, when sufficient plaster has been added, appears like dried mud in a river bed. The mixture should be stirred gently to remove lumps, but care should be taken to avoid introducing air. Vibration of the mixture will free some of the air; this may be done by gently thumping the bottom of the container against the table or floor. Once the mixture is made, it should be used immediately, for setting commences within minutes. Vibration after pouring will free additional trapped air and make the mold denser. In some instances it is advantageous to speed or retard the setting time of plaster. Clarke (1940, p. 22–23) gives details for both. For hastening the setting he recommends the addition of $\frac{1}{2}$ teaspoon salt to each pint of water used in mixing the plaster, or of 1 part of saturated solution of potassium sulphate to 10 parts of mixing water. To retard setting, common carpenter's glue, a 7 percent solution of acetic acid, or burnt lime may be added. The amount added should be determined by experimentation.

After the plaster has set, it should be removed from the specimen and dried until the mold is at room temperature, not cooler. When dry, it should be painted with two coats of water-thin shellac and then given a finish coat of a mixture of shellac and alcohol in equal parts. Once this is dry, the mold is ready for use.

The mixture of plaster for casting is the same as that for molding. It may be poured into a prepared mold, vibrated, and let set. If plaster casts are to be made from a plaster mold, banana oil, beeswax, or some other separator must be used. In some instances a thin mixture of potter's clay in water will suffice; if a waxy surface is necessary, use a mixture of 5 parts carbon tetrachloride to 1 part paraffin. If the plaster is to be cast in a rubber mold, the mold should be painted with liquid soap, a glycerine and water mixture, or a zinc stearate and alcohol mixture. If plaster is to be poured into a glue or agar mold, it should be removed before the heat of crystallization destroys the mold (see p. 400).

POLYVINYL CHLORIDE COMPOUNDS

Polyvinyl chloride molding compounds are thermal plastic, flexible materials with broad application (Clarke, 1940, 1948; Rich, 1956; Vernon, 1957; Keyes, 1959). These compounds are marketed as Plastiflex by Calresin Corporation, as Korogel by B. F. Goodrich Company, and as Vinamold by Vinatex, Ltd.

These compounds, developed especially for high-quality molding, might be described as "plastic rubbers"; they turn fluid when heated and are tough flexible substances when cool. Molds prepared of these compounds will not shrink or distort from continued use, and, for nearly all fossil material or casting compounds, they require no parting or separating compounds. They are resistant to water, oil, and grease, and they remain firm at temperatures well over 200°F. Although the initial cost is relatively high, the long-term cost is low because of complete reusability of the molding compound.

Nonporous materials need little preparation, other than the general cleaning described earlier, although Clarke (1948, p. 15) recommends light oiling with mineral oil. Bulky samples, or materials which might break from sudden contact with the hot compound, should be warmed before molding.

Porous materials, particularly those containing water, present more problems. Since the molding compound is poured at a temperature considerably above the boiling point of water, unless the water is driven off prior to molding or is allowed to vent as steam following pouring, bubbles will form at the mold surface. In most instances, warming the specimen for some time will drive off sufficient water to allow molding without trouble. Where this will not suffice, the sample may be sealed by soaking in a thinned solution of shellac. After impregnation, the surface should be cleaned and the specimen dried for at least 24 hours (or a shorter time if the specimen can be warmed). If some unfilled pores are still present, they can be filled with sealing oils recommended by the various manufacturers. After soaking in sealing oil for at least half an hour, the sample should be drained free of excess oil and wiped clean. The specimen is now ready for molding. If a warming oven is available, the specimen may be warmed prior to molding. This may cause some of the sealing oil to exude, so that the surface must be wiped clean again, immediately prior to molding.

Molding of models made of "plasticene" or similar modeling clays can be accomplished if the temperature of the compound is near the melting temperature, usually 120 to 130°C.

A retaining wall should be built around the specimen, making certain that it clears by at least half an inch—or a greater distance if the mold is of a comparatively large specimen. A simple retaining wall can be constructed of rolled lead flashing or cardboard, fastened so that it will not unroll, and secured at the base by clay or tape to prevent leaking of the molding compound beneath (fig. 1). Small cardboard boxes may be constructed by folding and stapling, to function as retaining walls, particularly if the specimens are wide and thin. The retaining wall should be sufficiently high to allow at least a quarter of an inch of molding material to cover the specimen, since shrinkage during setting forms a slightly concave upper surface of the mold.

Painted labels on specimens may be destroyed in molding with the hot polyvinyl chloride. For this reason care should be taken that no critical data are lost.

The specimen should be positioned within the retaining wall on an unimportant surface such as embedding matrix. If molding of the specimen "in the round" is desired, it may be positioned on supporting pins jutting from

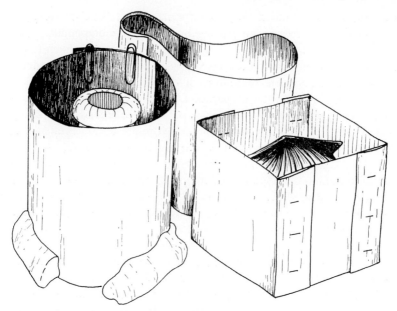

**Fig. 1.** *Retaining walls for poured molds made of metal flashing (rear), rolled cardboard cylinder with a clay base (left), and a stapled cardboard box (right). An infinite variety of simple retainers can be made from these materials and from modeling clay or plaster.*

either the base or sides of the retainer. In some instances small bits of plasticene may be used to support the specimen or to support the pins themselves. Irregular specimens may be positioned with modeling clay, but not with water-tempered potter's clay or waxes.

An electric hotplate and a covered sauce pan is the simplest equipment for melting the compound, but it is not the best, for the intense heat at the base may burn the material if not stirred constantly. The best melting equipment is a double boiler, which may be used as a simple "air bath" or as an oil bath. This will supply more even heat and prevent possible burning of the compound, which darkens and decomposes with too much heat. Even with an oil bath, the contents of the upper pan should be stirred frequently. If smoking starts, indicating that the compound is too hot, reduce the heat immediately; excess heat will burn the compound and not materially hasten melting. It may take from 30 to 40 minutes to melt a one-pound batch, and up to two hours for amounts as large as 6 pounds.

Large batches can be easily made in enameled portable electric roasters. These roasters may also function well as melting pots for smaller batches, if limited containers are placed inside. Secondary heating coils or infrared bulbs from above will hasten melting from the top.

For small batches (up to 5 pounds), overhead heating with an infrared lamp directed into the top of an uncovered stainless steel pan serves as an efficient melter. The bottom of the pan should be insulated to prevent heat loss.

Place a small amount of the molding compound in a metal container— preferably stainless steel, aluminum, or enamelware—and melt, stirring frequently. Wait until the lumps have melted, then add more compound. Do not increase the heat, but add small amounts until the desired amount is melted. Since the material is reclaimable, melt a little more than necessary for the molding contemplated. The temperature at which the entire mass becomes fluid will vary from approximately 120 to 135°C, depending upon the brand and grade purchased. At a temperature of approximately 135 to 140°C, the molding material should be fluid enough to pour. Temperatures should be constantly checked with a thermometer and should not exceed 180°C under any circumstances, for at this temperature the compounds begin to decompose.

Once fluid, and once the specimen is prepared, pour the melt into a corner of the retaining wall, at some distance from the fossil, in a steady stream, to allow the molding compound to rise gently, avoiding trapping air bubbles on the surface of the specimen. Avoid pauses, which leave layering effects in the mold.

After pouring, the mold is set aside to cool, preferably overnight or for several hours. The time of cooling will depend upon the quantity and thickness of molding material. Attempts to remove the specimen before the mold has completely set will often result in distortion of the cavity. There seems little advantage to forced cooling with water or refrigeration, although it has been done when rapid results were essential. Slow cooling seems to produce the best results, for it allows the compound to gel directionally away from the surfaces being molded.

Removal of the specimen is easily accomplished if it has been set on plasticene or wooden plugs, or flat on the base of the retainer, by gently stretching and loosening the specimen. With complex surfaces, the mold can be loosened with jets of compressed air. If the specimen has been cast in the round, the mold must be cut to remove the specimen. Care should be taken to cut the mold along the least critical lines. The best are at planes of juncture of valves, in regions of matrix, or along any natural breaks.

After removal of the specimen, the mold should be checked for the detail retained and for flaws. It should be washed with water, using detergents if desired. The mold is then ready for casting.

In some instances, where the models or specimens molded are large or where the molding material appears too weak to support casting without distortion, it may be wise to cast a supporting shell of plaster of paris before the specimen is removed. Or the original retainer for the mold may serve well as the supporting shell.

Once a mold has served its purpose, it may be cut into small pieces (less than one-inch cubes) and returned to the stock. These materials are totally reclaimable, unless burned by heating to too high a temperature.

### POLYVINYL CHLORIDE–DIBUTYLPHTHALATE

Polyvinyl chloride and dibutylphthalate can be employed to make flexible molds of relatively complex features, following a method described by Stahl (1956, p. 285–295). Finely ground polyvinyl chloride is intimately mixed into dibutylphthalate until the mixture is a white, creamy, smooth fluid. Once mixed, it is ready to be poured, like the melted prepared polyvinyl chloride compounds, either into the space between a specimen and an outer shell, as in glue molding, or as a flexible primary mold inside a retaining wall. The compound may be forced into small crevices with a vacuum system or with small wood splinters or brushes.

After pouring, the mold and specimen is baked for 2 to $2\frac{1}{2}$ hours at 120°C. This turns the fluid mixture to a tough, rubbery, elastic mass. Longer baking times may be required for molds more than 3 or 4 cm thick.

Demolding may be done by distortion of the mold. In some instances submersion in water during demolding helps, as does separation with a gentle air stream.

The mold, in addition to being elastic, is unshrinkable and inert to most solvents, yields fine detail without dimensional distortion, and has a long storage life.

### SILICONE RUBBER

Silicone rubbers are semifluid material which, when catalyzed, vulcanize at room temperature to form flexible, rubbery solids. These compounds are useful for rapid mold making and are functional at temperatures from −70 to 500°F. The completed molds have a long shelf life without hardening or distortion. These compounds are particularly suitable for molds requiring some flexibility, yet not the elasticity of latex, and for molding heat-sensitive materials. The molds are unaffected by water and most solvents and remain stable in form over a long time. The silicone rubbers release easily from most materials; for exceptional specimens, household detergent in water is an effective separator.

The chief drawbacks of these products are the short shelf life of the uncombined materials—approximately 4 months at 70°F—and limited elasticity. The major advantages are ease of preparation and speed of molding.

The only preparation necessary for nearly all fossil material is that of general cleaning. If the material is very porous, some impregnation may be advisable, for the rubber will penetrate the pores and make release difficult. Retaining walls should be built to pool the compound over the desired areas; if objects are to be cast in the round, some type of deep retainer must be used. At least $\frac{1}{4}$ inch should be allowed for major specimens, but $\frac{1}{8}$ inch is sufficient for smaller items. Thick molds will set more slowly than thin ones.

Silicone rubber material is mixed with the catalyst for preparation, the amount varying according to the grade or system used, as directed by the manufacturer. This proportion ranges from 0.5 parts per 100 to 4.0 parts per 100, by weight. Silastic RTV 502, manufactured by Dow Corning Corporation, is the system found most satisfactory for paleontologic use. With the addition of 0.5 parts catalyst to 100 of the matrix, this system sets to a rubbery solid in 30 minutes. By varying the amount of catalyst added, working times as short as 2 minutes and as long as 1 hour are possible. For consistent results, mixing with the catalyst must be thorough. It seems false economy, therefore, to shorten the working time much below 10 or 15 minutes, for it takes some time to make certain that the mixture is uniform. Since the amount of catalyst added is small in this mixture, dilution with xylene or silicone fluid increases accuracy.

Viscosity of the compound may be lowered by addition of not more than 10 percent thinner, usually silicone oil. Thinning must be done before the catalyst is added. Too much thinner will result in a softer mold, greatly extending vulcanizing time without marked change in viscosity.

Once mixed, the compound may be poured onto the specimen or poured to the side, allowing gradual engulfment. Trapped air bubbles, if such are present, may be released with a vacuum system.

After vulcanization has taken place, distortion of the mold will release the specimen. Even after becoming firm, vulcanization will continue for several days. Acceleration in set-up time may be accomplished by warming in some systems, but in Silastic RTV 502 there seems little advantage to this.

Little needs to be done with the mold prior to casting, except to make certain that it is clean. Plaster, metals of low melting point, latex, wax, resins—in short, most casting materials—may be used in silicone rubber molds. If it is desirable to cast a silicone rubber positive from the mold, a 3 to 5 percent solution of household detergent in water serves as a good separator.

POLYSULFIDE RUBBER

Polysulfide rubber is an artificial rubber, which vulcanizes at room temperature when the polymer and curative are mixed. This produces a tough, flexible, relatively inert molding compound well suited for use on heat-sensitive materials.

Advantages of the compound are principally those of a flexible, easily prepared mixture, while the main disadvantages are the ultimate shrinking (usually after about 6 months) and the cost (currently about $6.00 per quart and $22.00 per gallon).

Specimens should be prepared as for polyvinyl chloride or latex molding. Porous specimens should be sealed and then brushed with a releasing agent, such as "Sonite," or a thin (1 to 1) mixture of vaseline and kerosene. After excess of sealer and releasing agent are wiped off, the specimen is ready for molding.

Store the unmixed components at room temperatures, for lowering will retard setting and heat will speed it. Stir both components until they are of even consistency before mixing, for certain ingredients may have settled during storage. Estimate the volume needed and weigh the components.

Mix the curative into the polymer slowly, according to the manufacturer's recommendation—commonly 5 or 6 parts of curative per 100 by weight— and stir well. Amounts of curative material above that recommended will speed the curing but at a loss of strength. The polymer will not harden unless the mixing is thorough. Care should be taken to prevent stirring air into the mixture. Once mixed, the compound is ready for pouring. Working life of the mixture will depend upon the system used.

Use an open mold with a retaining wall, and pour the mixture slowly and in a thin stream, to allow breaking of bubbles. Pour into a corner and let the compound rise around the specimen, to prevent trapping air. In intricate models the mixture may be painted on the surface to assure filling corners and fine detail, but the backing must be poured before the skin coat has set. After pouring is complete, a gentle stream of water on the surface will hasten the rise of bubbles to the surface. Once poured, the mold should be set aside to cure for at least 16 hours. Curing may be accelerated by heating at 100°F, and not above 110°F, until firm. In certain systems, fast-acting curatives may produce molds which can be handled in 2 or 3 hours.

Demolding can be done by gentle distortion and removal of the specimen. Intricate specimens may be released more easily with a fine jet of air at the parting line as a separating tool.

Most cold-setting compounds may be readily cast without separators in the mold. Plaster and gypsum cements work well, particularly when the mold has been wetted with a dilute detergent solution. Thermal-setting plastics may be cast in molds of certain grades and systems of the rubber, but not in others. The manufacturer's recommendations should be followed.

### GLUE, GELATIN, AND AGAR

Flexible gelatin, glue, or agar have been used in casting for a considerable time. These substances produce molds which are flexible and will tolerate deep undercuts. They are relatively delicate to cast and time-consuming to construct, but the materials are inexpensive and little equipment is necessary for their construction. Since the advent of latex and flexible, plastic molding compounds, gelatin, glue, and agar have been less frequently used. Detailed discussion of these materials are presented in Rich (1956), Clarke (1940, 1948), Butler (1934), and others.

Clean the specimen of loose matrix, oil, and grease; seal, if porous, by soaking or painting with thinned shellac. Dry the specimen and coat with a separator. Equal parts of lard and tallow, melted together and applied with a hot brush, or a mixture of 1 part stearic acid and 3 parts benzene serve as good separators (Clarke, 1940, p. 230). Light oil may also be used where detail is more critical. The specimen is next coated with a layer of clay, from $\frac{1}{4}$ to $\frac{1}{2}$ inch thick, depending upon the thickness of the glue or agar mold desired. Cylindrical or conical masses of clay should be used to form the pouring spouts and vents through the outer protective shell. After the clay layer is shaped, a protective shell of plaster of paris is applied and allowed to harden. After the plaster has set, the specimen and the clay layer are removed, and the clay stripped from the specimen, leaving a space the thickness of the layer between the protective shell and the specimen. This space is filled with warm glue or agar once it is properly prepared.

The following, from Clarke (1948, p. 7), is considered superior for the glue preparation (amounts in parts by weight):

| | |
|---|---|
| Glue (dry) | 33.6 |
| Sorbitol (Arlex) | 25.2 |
| Glycerin | 25.2 |
| Water | 16.0 |

The sorbitol and glycerin are mixed with water. The dry glue is added and the mixture allowed to stand overnight. It is then heated until melted. The use of a candy thermometer will enable the worker to hold the temperature down to 72°C (160°F).

The glue or gelatin may be used alone, without adding any ingredients other than water, but this produces a less flexible, more fragile mold. Simply let the glue soak in water for about 12 hours, pour off the excess water, and heat the glue in a double boiler until melted. It is then ready for pouring.

Clarke (1940, p. 226) reports that a good elastic mold may be made with gelatin (amounts in parts by weight):

| | |
|---|---|
| Gelatin | 6 |
| Laundry soap | 1 |
| Glycerin | 1 |

The glue is soaked in water for about 12 hours, after which the excess water is poured off. The mixture is heated until melted and glycerin and soap are added, with constant stirring, until the soap is melted and thoroughly mixed in the composition. . . . It is advisable to test a small amount of the glue during heating process by pouring it on a cold surface, allowing it to cool, then pressing and stretching it to determine its hardness and elasticity.

Rich (1956, p. 99) outlines an improved agar formula for molding at low temperatures:

| | |
|---|---|
| Agar | 4 ounces |
| Water | 100 ounces |
| Zinc oxide | 1 ounce |
| Oxyquinoline sulphate | 10 grains |
| Cellucotton | $\frac{1}{2}$ ounce |
| Cotton | 15 grains |

Place the agar in most of the water and stir. If the agar is powdered it will absorb all the water, if shredded it will not absorb the water until heated. Place in a double boiler and stir until the mass goes into solution. Put the remainder of the water and the other ingredients in a bottle and stir, or shake, until thoroughly mixed. After the agar is dissolved and the temperature is at 100°C, pour the second mixture into the agar solution with constant stirring, and heat again to 100°C. The mass should then be poured into an enameled tray and let cool and set. Grind this cooled mass in a food chopper and let stand until the water has evaporated and none can be squeezed from a ball by hand. The material is then ready for melting and pouring.

The various mixtures, glue, gelatin, or agar, are heated for use until melted, and then cooled until near body temperature, at which time they may be poured into the space between the specimen and the protective shell to make a flexible mold of the specimen. The molding material should be allowed to cool completely, and can then be demolded.

Prior to casting, the mold should be painted with a saturated water solution of alum to harden the containing surfaces of the impression. When this is dry, a thin oil separator is brushed on the inner surface of the mold. It is then ready for casting.

Most casting compounds which can be poured at room temperatures are suitable for use in molds of gelatin, glue, or agar. Plaster of paris, since it produces heat of crystallization, requires special care to prevent damaging the molds. The plaster positive should be removed from the mold during the time between initial setting and hardening, before the heat of crystallization is produced. Heat will soften the molding compound. Thermal-setting plastics, waxes, or other casting materials which are poured warm or which generate heat during casting should be avoided on glue, gelatin, or agar molds.

POLYURETHANE FOAMING RESINS

Jensen (1961) described the use of a foaming plastic compound for casting light-weight, rigid vertebrate material. The technique has considerable advantage where light weight and durability are critical.

The material, called "rigid-foam," is produced by a combination of a liquid prepolymer and a catalyst. The resulting reaction, if properly mixed, produces an expanding mass of foam which becomes rigid in a matter of minutes. The resultant foam reproduces detail of the mold surface and has amazing strength, can be worked easily, and is not softened by benzene, acetone, alcohol, lacquer thinner, turpentine, or water. It can be painted or dyed. It can be cast in rigid molds and also in flexible molds if they are adequately treated and supported by protective shells.

It is available in several densities, from 2 pounds to 20 pounds per cubic foot. Jensen (1961, p. 77) suggests the intermediate densities because the lighter ones are not durable and the heavier mixtures yield less detail.

The Du Pont Company produces the base material for all trade-marked rigid-foams. Information on local suppliers can be obtained from their regional offices.

Plaster molds may be used for casting rigid-foam if there are no undercuts and if they are sufficiently vented. As the foam does not shrink, removal of the cast from an undercut mold is difficult without risking damage. The mold should be clean, dry, and in good repair, for considerable pressure may be exerted by the foaming.

Plaster molds should be coated with a thin layer of liquid floor wax and then thoroughly dried and coated with a suitable separator. Liquid floor wax is a poor separator when used alone. Jensen (1961, p. 85–86) suggests stearine (a solution of stearic acid in kerosene) applied to a perfectly dry mold or Selectron (an alcohol-base, water-soluble release compound marketed by Pittsburgh Plate Glass). Separators must be applied to all surfaces which might contact the foam, including joints and vents of the mold. Wax applied to the vents, pour spouts, and exterior will keep the surfaces from being fouled. Once treated—and tightly bound, if a piece mold—the mold is ready for pouring.

Rubber molds should be clean and free of moisture and should be supported by sturdy rigid supporting shells to prevent swelling and distortion when the foaming takes place. Jensen (1961, p. 83) suggests that the mother mold should be at least 1 inch thick per foot of mold. After being cleaned and dried, the mold, and any other surface likely to contact the foam, should be painted with a separator, such as Selectron 5937, or a coating of paste wax if fine detail is not desired. Pieces of the supporting mold should be firmly lashed together with rubber tubing or with sash cord. When firmly secured, the mold is ready for pouring.

Metal or plastic molds need not be waxed, but should be coated with Selectron or a suitable separator. If the molds are flexible, like polyvinyl chloride molds, they should have supporting rigid mother molds. After cleaning, these molds may be poured in the same manner as plaster molds.

Preparation of the casting rigid-foam may be done leisurely up to the time of mixing the prepolymer and the catalyst; after that, only about two minutes remain for completing the mixing and pouring before foaming begins. When the foaming begins, the mixture cannot be poured and is waste.

Care should be taken to weigh accurately both components of the mixture to assure good results. The weight of the mixed components should equal one-third the weight of a dry plaster cast of the mold. Once weighed, as per manufacturer's directions, the components are combined in a throw-away container and intimately mixed. Small batches may be mixed by hand with wooden spatulas or tongue depressors, but larger batches may be mixed advantageously with a rod in a drill press. The mixture is about the viscosity of Karo syrup and should be poured immediately. The mold should be tilted back and forth to distribute the liquid throughout, leaving slightly more liquid in thicker parts of the mold. Excess liquid in thinner parts may build up damaging pressures.

Foaming should be done in a well-ventilated area or under a fume hood, for the resulting gases have irritating effects on eyes and lungs. The foaming begins slowly and lasts for several minutes. In about 5 minutes the foam ceases to be tacky, and simple objects can be demolded in about 30 minutes. More complex casts, or thin casts, should be allowed to cure for 24 hours. Curing may be accelerated by heating to 180 to 200°F for 1 to 2 hours.

Excess foam produced during casting should be allowed to spill on loose sand or sawdust for easy cleaning. Alcohol or acetone will aid in cleaning if used immediately. Uncombined liquids may be washed off with alcohol and then flushed with water.

Finishing the foam cast may be done with ordinary woodworking tools immediately after demolding. Where the open cellular structure of the interior is exposed during trimming, plaster of paris or paper mache may be used to smooth the surface or to join segments together. Elmer's glue or Duco Cement may also be used, but because the foam is an efficient vapor seal, these glues reach their maximum strength only after several days of drying.

The cast may be colored with ordinary preparations or dyed. Jensen (1961, p. 77) used a mixture of shellac and pigment with success.

PAPER MACHE

One of the oldest molding and casting mediums is paper mache. It is particularly useful in casting large fossils such as vertebrate remains, but can also be used for smaller objects where gross features rather than minute structure is desired.

There are various formulas which can be used in molding, but the one given by Clarke (1940, p. 282) is useful and will dry in 3 to 4 hours (amounts in parts by weight):

| | |
|---|---|
| Wet paper pulp | 1 |
| Water | 3 |
| Plaster of paris | 8 |
| Hot glue | 1 |

Any light paper, such as tissue or newsprint, is soaked or boiled in water; the paper may be in strips or may be macerated by prolonged boiling. The mixture (above) is made and should be used as soon as possible after making. The specimen to be molded should be prepared by coating with shellac or spraying with plastic to fill the pores. A light oil separator may be used. Paper thoroughly soaked in water, which has not yet been mixed with the glue, can be applied for the first several coats to keep the paper mache from sticking to the specimen. The mixture is then applied with the hand, slowly building up the mold by successive application of layers until the desired thickness and shape is reached. The mass of paper strips should be firmly pressed onto the object in order to remove lumps and bubbles.

If macerated paper mixtures are used, an occasional layer of thoroughly soaked paper strips may be added as reinforcing agents. Greater detail is acquired by the mold if the pulp mixture is used at all stages.

Waterproof paper mache may be made by adding egg white or calcium oxide (lime) to the formula. The finished and dried work can be oiled or sprayed with plastic to aid in preservation.

Another formula, used by the American Museum of Natural History, is given by Clarke (1940, p. 283). Felt building paper is torn into shreds and macerated in water. Dextrine is mixed in cold water to the consistency of thin syrup. Equal parts of dry plaster and dry whiting are mixed together. To equal parts of damp paper and plaster-whiting mixture, dextrine syrup is added to the desired consistency. This mixture is applied as a thick paste, and should set in less than 1 hour. To prolong setting, add more dextrine syrup and whiting. To hasten setting, add more plaster and dextrine. (Paper mache is made less combustible by the addition of borax and phosphate of soda to the pulp mixture.)

EPOXY RESINS

Recent work in epoxy resins has produced combinations which are useful for casting and molding to the paleontologist, although they are still expensive. Epocast systems, produced by Furane Products, Los Angeles, are typical of the range of products available. Two of their systems are of particular interest: Epocast 4 and Epocast 11. The former is for room-temperature epoxies, which are seldom poured in thick sections; the latter is designed for mass casting, when thick pours are wanted without danger of excessive heating.

In each system, the hardener is intimately mixed with the resin and then poured. The pot life of the mixture will vary with the hardener and with the particular type of system, usually from a few minutes to a few hours. The systems employing shorter times are usually of most interest, unless complicated specimens are to be prepared.

Contact with either the resin or the hardener should be avoided by using rubber gloves and disposable containers. Equipment may be cleaned by washing with acetone or methyl ethyl ketone before the compound hardens. A barrier cream of a 1 to 1 mixture of toluene and isopropyl alcohol, or soap and water, are useful in cleaning.

The two resin systems above cure at room temperature within 24 hours, but faster curing may be accomplished by warming the cast to 130°F. There is an exothermic reaction following mixing, with increases of temperature up to 90°F resulting. Because of this, care should be taken to select proper molding compounds to withstand the heat generated.

Colored hardeners are available for the most common systems of epoxies, to allow assurance of thorough mixing and for colored specimens.

### METALS WITH LOW MELTING POINT

Wood's metal and related alloys of lead, bismuth, tin, and cadmium may be used in casting because of the low melting points of the mixtures. Solder (a mixture of lead and tin) and pewter (a mixture of lead and tin with minor amounts of copper, antimony, and zinc) may be similarly employed. The following table summarizes various alloys and their melting points (Clarke, 1948, p. 131):

| ANTIMONY | LEAD | TIN | CADMIUM | BISMUTH | MELTING POINTS | | NAME |
|---|---|---|---|---|---|---|---|
| | | (Parts by weight) | | | (°F) | (°C) | |
| 0 | 20 | 40 | 26 | 96 | 135 | 57 | Wood's |
| 0 | 3 | 2 | 2 | 5 | 140 | 60 | Molyneau's |
| 0 | 2 | 1 | 1 | 4 | 155 | 68 | Wood's |
| 0 | 5 | 5 | 4 | 11 | 162 | 72 | Merck's |
| 0 | 4 | 4 | 1 | 7 | 180 | 82 | Marber's |
| 0 | 5 | 5 | 1 | 8 | 190 | 88 | Crouse's |
| 0 | 1 | 1 | 0 | 2 | 199 | 93 | Erman's |
| 0 | 5 | 3 | 0 | 8 | 202 | 94 | Richman's |
| 0 | 1 | 1 | 0 | 2 | 203 | 95 | Rose's |
| 0 | 3 | 5 | 0 | 8 | 205 | 96 | Melotte's |
| 0 | 2 | 3 | 0 | 5 | 212 | 100 | Neuton's |
| 0 | 5 | 5 | 0 | 3 | 212 | 100 | |
| 0 | 11 | 10 | 0 | 12 | 240 | 116 | Brophy's |
| 2 | 5 | 3 | 0 | 8 | 244 | 118 | Hidgen's |
| 0 | 1 | 1 | 0 | 1 | 257 | 125 | |
| 0 | 2 | 2 | 0 | 1 | 288 | 142 | |
| 0 | 28 | 30 | 0 | 5 | 311 | 155 | |
| 0 | 20 | 24 | 0 | 5 | 335 | 168 | |
| 0 | 6 | 4 | 0 | 1 | 347 | 175 | Solder 60–40 |
| 0 | 1 | 1 | 0 | 0 | 370 | 188 | Solder 50–50 |

The metals should be melted in the order of their individual melting points, the highest first, to prevent volatilization of the metals with low melting points. Antimony should be melted first, then lead, tin, cadmium, and finally bismuth. The heat should be particularly low when bismuth is added to a mixture.

Most of these alloys expand when cooling and fill out the detail of the mold. Demolding is relatively simple with flexible molds, but sectional molds should be prepared with the expansion of the metal in mind. No undercuts should exist in rigid molds.

In casting alloys whose melting points are above the boiling point of water, molds should be completely dry. Plaster molds should be dried to make certain that all possible water is driven off, including some of the water of crystallization, if the temperature of the melt is high. Failure to drive off excess water, or completely dry a mold, may result in violent explosion of the produced steam and the molten metal.

### ACETATE FILM MICROMOLDS

Molds of organisms with little relief or molds of etched ground surfaces can be made with acetate film, acetone, or a peel solution. These techniques are useful only for limited areas and on relatively smooth surfaces where the relief is less than the thickness of the film.

The surface to be molded is ground with 400- or 600-mesh Carborundum and then etched for 1 to 2 minutes in very dilute hydrochloric acid. It is dried, then wet with acetone, placed upon a sheet of acetate film, and weighted, until the acetone has softened the surface of the film and made an impression. After the film is dried, it may be peeled from the surface.

The following solution may be also used for making peels and micromolds (Darrah, 1936):

| | |
|---|---|
| Parlodion | 28 grams (1 ounce) |
| Butyl acetate | 250 cc |
| Amyl alcohol | 10 cc |
| Ether | 3 cc |
| Castor oil | 3 cc |

To the above may be added an additional 20 cc of amyl alcohol and 10 cc of xylol if more flexible and easier peeling molds are desirable. If the parlodion is in strips, considerable time is necessary to prepare the solution, for the solid materials dissolve slowly.

The solution, once mixed, is poured on the surface to be molded, allowing it to flow gently from one side to the other to eliminate air bubbles. The specimen should then be mounted level, to pool the solution; the film is left to dry, usually taking several hours. It may be loosened around the edges and peeled as an acetate film, then trimmed and labeled. The peels may be mounted on cardboard or in glass sandwiches.

### CONSTRUCTION OF PIECE MOLDS

Piece molds allow casting of complex specimens with rigid material and allow greater flexibility in casting even the more elastic compounds. A piece

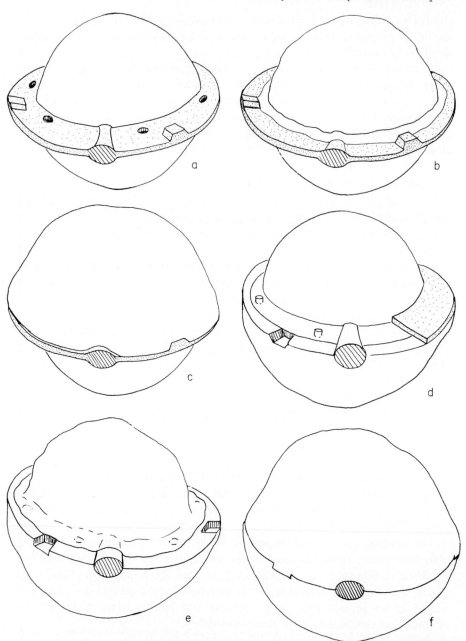

**Fig. 2.** *Steps in construction of a composite latex and plaster piece mold. (a) Construction of clay wall to separate two pieces of mold. Keys are carved into the margin of the wall for registration of the plaster supporting mold and small cylindrical depressions for registration of the latex primary mold. The diagonally ruled part of the wall will become the opening.*

mold is a negative mold that has been constructed of several sections or pieces, so fashioned as to be easily removed and reassembled without injury to the original or the cast. The number of pieces in the mold is dictated by the complexity of the subject and the elasticity of the molding compound.

The specimen should be studied to determine the lines and planes along which the specimen might be divided to eliminate undercut areas within a single piece. Pencil lines should be drawn along the lines of separation of the various pieces. The specimen should be sealed or painted with a suitable separator, if not already done.

A clay wall is built around the first section, complete with keys for registration (fig. 2a). Usually one of the easiest pieces to remove is selected, and the wall is built to the height of the desired thickness of plaster or other molding compound. The piece is then poured, brushed, or shaped with a spatula, with plaster thin enough to reproduce detail, yet thick enough to stay on the spatula. After the plaster is set, the clay walls are removed (fig. 2,d) and the surfaces trimmed. The piece should be removed from the specimen if trimming in place will endanger the original. After the piece is smoothed, it should be painted with shellac and hardened, to allow separation from subsequently cast pieces.

Each additional piece is poured against the treated earlier pieces or the clay walls. Registration grooves or keys should be cut or prepared in the clay walls so that each adjacent piece will interlock firmly. Small mounds of plaster shaped on the exterior of the mold will allow tight cords to hold the mold together without slipping.

Piece molds of glue, gelatin, or agar may be constructed, as well as plaster forms, but in each case individual pieces of the mold must be made separately, making a complex procedure.

Piece molds of latex or polyvinyl chloride compounds may be advisable under certain circumstances, particularly when large specimens are to be cast. Division of the specimen into pieces is done, as in plaster of paris molding, with clay walls. Painting with latex is done one piece at a time (fig. 2,a-f), making certain that the rubber mold overlaps onto the clay walls far enough

---

*through which the mold is filled. (b) Painting the model with the first layers of latex, to which successive layers are gradually added until the first piece of the mold is of the desired thickness. (c) Covering the primary mold with a thick supporting shell of plaster of paris for the first piece. (d) Removal of the clay wall, except for the plug which will form the pouring spout, and exposing the flange of both the latex and plaster of the first piece. This exposed surface should be treated with a separator to make certain that the second piece will not stick. Notice the registration devices for both latex and plaster. (e) Painting the surface of the model with latex for the second piece of the mold, after the separators are dry. (f) Covering the second latex primary mold with a supporting shell of plaster to complete the two-piece mold.*

that registration depressions can be made when adjacent pieces are prepared. Once the first piece has set, separators are painted on the surfaces and adjacent pieces are made.

Mother molds or protective shells should be made of each piece as it is finished, complete with registration keys, before additional pieces are made. Because of the flexibility of latex and other rubbery molding compounds, the protective shell and piece molds may often be made in two sections only.

## IMPREGNATION

Fossils occasionally occur in a matrix too friable for safe transport or preparation or too soft to be prepared properly. In such cases it is useful—often necessary—to impregnate or harden the material.

The main requisites of an impregnating material are that it should have low viscosity and surface tension, allowing easy penetration into porous media. It should be stable at somewhat elevated temperatures, firm at ordinary room temperatures, and—where grinding is necessary—brittle enough to grind but firm enough not to pick up abrasive grains; in some instances it should have a degree of transparency where thin sections are planned. Deeper penetration of any medium is almost always accelerated by impregnation in a vacuum system.

Impregnation or hardening in the field is accomplished by using a variety of materials. Water-thin solutions of shellac in alcohol, Alvar in acetone, or other vinyl acetates in acetone may be brushed onto fragments of fossils too large to be removed and soaked in the solution. Since the greatest evaporation is at the surface, when the solution is brushed, soaking in a covered container is necessary when deeper penetration is desired.

Commercial aerosol plastic spray has been used by many and has proven particularly useful in preserving graptolites and leaf impressions in soft shales. Although somewhat more expensive than the shellac or Alvar solutions, the compactness of the spray container and the ease of application make this material ideal for use in the field and laboratory when only limited hardening of small areas is desired.

Small fragments of fossiliferous material may be impregnated by soaking in a thinned solution of canada balsam for from a few hours to a few days. The balsam is then cooked, as in preparation of a thin section, to a tough but not brittle condition. Impregnation may also be accomplished by soaking the specimen in melted Lakeside 70, a precooked balsam preparation, but since heat is necessary to keep the preparation fluid and the viscosity is relatively high, the material is limited to either very porous material or small specimens.

Bakelite varnish dissolved in alcohol has also been used for impregnation (Ross, 1924). After soaking, the fragment is heated—first to drive off the solvent and then to cause fixation of the varnish into bakelite.

## BAKELITE

Embedding small paleontologic specimens in bakelite is accomplished by utilizing the same technique described by Short (1940, p. 11–12) for mounting metallographic and ore specimens. High pressure and temperature are necessary and the size of most hydraulic presses is such to restrict this technique to mounting microfossils or small megafossils.

Necessary equipment includes a hydraulic press and powdered bakelite, both commonly used in metallographic or ore specimen laboratories. The specimen is placed on the basal plate and the matching hollow cylinder is dropped over it. The powdered bakelite is poured through the hollow top to cover the specimen. Short suggests that the combined volume of specimen and bakelite be 28 cc, but in practice a quantity is added to the level desired. The solid matching cylinder, which acts as a piston and compresses the bakelite, is then inserted through the upper end of the hollow cylinder. These three parts thus assembled are placed in the press, the temperature probe and heater are lowered into position, and the assemblage is ready. The temperature is raised at the same time as the pressure is elevated to about 1000 psi. Between 50 and 100°C, the bakelite melts. This is detected by a drop in pressure. At this point the pressure is elevated to about 2500 psi and maintained there until no lowering of pressure is noted; this means that the melting is complete. The pressure is then elevated to about 3500 psi and maintained until the temperature reaches about 135°C. At this point the cylinder assemblage is removed and emersed in water for cooling or—on newer presses—the heater element is removed and cooling jackets are applied around the cylinder. On these presses the cylinder assemblage can be removed from the jacket at about 90°C. The embedded specimen is ready for polishing, sectioning, and so on. About 20 minutes is the maximum time required for the entire process on a good press.

## VINYLITE RESINS

Bioplastic, Castolite, and related plastics are useful in paleontology for embedding, impregnation, and casting. Of these uses, certainly the most common in paleontology is that of embedding. Bioplastic, supplied by Ward's Natural Science Establishment, is typical of the group. These plastics are colorless, rigid, tough, inert substances resulting from reaction of a syrupy polymer with a catalyst. Colors may be added, as well as materials to produce an opaque substance.

Cleaned specimens, washed in ether or carbon tetrachloride if the specimen is oily, should be dried. The dried specimen is placed in a small quantity of the uncatalyzed plastic (enough to cover the specimen) and soaked until the trapped air bubbles are released, usually taking overnight. Evacuation with a vacuum system will accelerate release of air and assure uniform results. When completely wet by the plastic, the material is ready to embed.

Almost any container will serve as a retaining mold for the plastic. Tapered glass containers are among the best, for these generally have smooth walls that allow easy demolding of the plastics, once cured. Aluminum foil, prepared metal containers, or boxes made of formica-lined wood (Harden, 1963, p. 15–19) are all equally usable. For ease of removal a separator or mold release compound should be used.

The desired amount of plastic—enough to form a layer up to $\frac{1}{4}$ inch thick over the bottom of the mold—and sufficient hardener are stirred to form an intimate mixture. Stirring should be gentle to avoid beating air into the mixture, although bubbles can be removed from the mixture with a vacuum assembly. The mixture is poured into the mold and allowed to gel in a dust-free area until the layer will support the object. After the supporting layer has gelled, the specimen is removed from the unhardened plastic bath and drained, and then placed on top of the first layer, and set aside for an additional 6-hour period. The specimen should adhere to the hardened lower layer. Plastic for the covering layer is then mixed with hardener and poured over the adhering specimen. The composite is then set aside for several hours, until the covering layer has gelled. Gelling, in most instances, can be accelerated by gently warming the mixture to 120°F until set. Care should be exercised not to overheat.

Once the covering has gelled, a cellophane vapor shield is placed over the mixture and gently smoothed to make a firm contact with the gel, making certain that all air bubbles are excluded. The composite is then cured by heating to 140°F for 3 to 4 hours. (With Castolite the curing is at 200°F for a 30-minute period.) Slower curing will produce a harder plastic. Allow the mold and plastic to cool to room temperature slowly, preferably in a warming oven, and then remove from the mold and finish with grinding powders and polishing powders.

Ordinary woodworking tools may be used for finishing. Grinding laps and buffing wheels may be similarly used for more rapid polishing.

Casting of transparent objects may be made with the same material, but the molding compounds must be suitable for the long heating demanded by the curing. In open molds air should be excluded by a vapor shield to ensure even hardening during curing. In closed molds little is necessary other than making certain that the mold is dry, clean, and painted with a suitable separator.

**REFERENCES**

Baird, Donald (1955). Latex micro-molding and latex-plaster molding. Science, v. 122, no. 3161, p. 202.
Butler, A. E. (1934). Building the museum group. Guide Leaflet Series No. 82, New York, Am. Mus. Nat. History.

Clarke, C. D. (1940). Molding and casting, its technique and application. Baltimore, Maryland, The John D. Lucas Company, 308 pp., 69 text-figs.

————, (1948). Metal casting of sculpture. Butler, Maryland, The Standard Arts Press, 170 pp., 77 text-figs.

Darrah, W. C. (1936). The peel method in paleobotany. Harvard Univ. Bot. Mus. Leaflets No. 4, 8 pp.

Garner, M. R. (1953). The preparation of latex casts of soil cavities for the study of tunneling activities of animals. Science, v. 118, no. 3066, p. 380–381.

Harden, C. E. (1963). How to preserve animal and other specimens in clear plastic. Healdsburg, California, Naturegraph Company, 64 pp., 23 figs.

Jensen, J. A. (1961). A new casting medium for use in flexible and rigid molds. Curator, v. 4, no. 1, p. 76–90, 12 figs.

Keyes, I. W. (1959). Paleontological casting and moulding techniques. New Zealand J. Geology and Geophysics, v. 2, no. 1, p. 56–65, 10 text-figs.

Rich, J. C. (1956). The materials and methods of sculpture. New York, Oxford Univ. Press, 416 pp. 62 pls., 17 text-figs.

Ross, C. S. (1924). A method of preparing thin sections of friable rocks. Am. J. Sci., v. 7, p. 483–485.

Short, M. N. (1940). Microscopic determination of the ore minerals. U. S. Geol. Survey Bull. 914, 311 pp. 14 plates, 33 figs.

Stahl, E. (1956). A casting method for paleontological purposes. Geol. Inst., Univ. Uppsala Bull., v. 36, pt. 4, p. 285–295.

Vernon, R. O. (1957). New techniques for casting fossils and forming molds. J. Paleontology, v. 31, no. 2, p. 461–463.

# Galvanoplastic Reproduction of Fossils

RAINER ZANGERL

*Chicago Natural History Museum*

The reproduction of fossils by the process known in the trade as electroforming (galvanoplastic reproduction) has, admittedly, limited usefulness in paleontology, but where it is applicable, it is far superior to other good techniques such as casting in rubber, plastics, agar-agar, and plaster of paris because (1) the material (metal, usually copper) is durable, (2) fine detail is obtained, and (3) such reproductions often photograph much better than the originals (figs. 1 and 2).

A good general account of the electroforming process, its triumphs, and its limitations is given by Read (1960). It is sufficient here to outline the technique as it is applied to paleontological work. Electroforming is one of the

**Fig. 1.** (*Left*) Glarichelys knorri (*Gray*), type specimen (Zoological Museum, University of Zürich), an early Oligocene sea turtle from Glarus, Switzerland. About 0.34 natural size. Photograph of galvanoplastic reproduction which was made in Zürich. The highly reflective metallic surface preserves shadow detail even when relatively contrasty negative and print materials are used. The result is a brilliant print with excellent detail. (*Right*) Photograph of the original specimen (courtesy Zoological Museum, University of Zürich). There is no difference in color between matrix and skeleton, and very oblique lighting is required to bring out relief. Since the shale absorbs light, detail tends to disappear in shadow areas unless a very low-contrast negative and print are used. Details are difficult to see.

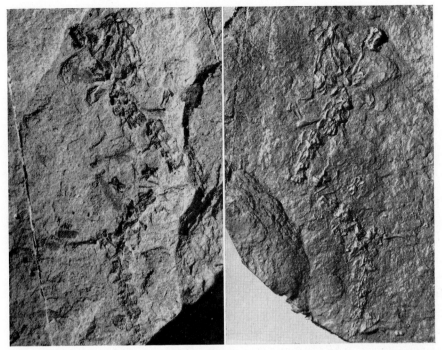

**Fig. 2.** (*Left*) *An Oligocene salamander skeleton (CNHM PR-411) preserved as negative on the bedding plane of a light brown shale. About 0.75 natural size. (Right) The same specimen, but positive galvanoplastic reproduction.*

electrometallurgical processes. The principle consists in building up a body of metal at the cathode in a container filled with a suitable electrolyte. The anode usually supplies the metal used to form the replica, and provides the cations for continued deposition of metal at the cathode.

## APPLICABILITY TO PALEONTOLOGICAL MATERIALS

Electroforming is particularly recommended for specimens that are spread out parallel to the bedding planes of well-bedded sediments or along the split faces of concretions. The technique is especially useful if there is very little difference in color between fossils and matrix, as in many black shales.

Fossils that are freed of the matrix and those that have very irregular surfaces, especially those having deep re-entrant angles and crevices, are generally unsuitable for reproduction by electroforming.

## EQUIPMENT

The equipment required for this technique depends on the uses to which it is put. Standard electroforming units are fairly expensive, and their acquisition for paleontological laboratories is justified only where this method is particularly suitable to the material being studied. For example, at the Chicago Natural History Museum, work is being done on large collections of vertebrates and invertebrates from a highly carbonaceous Pennsylvanian shale from Indiana, as well as on the large nodule flora and fauna from the Mazon Creek area of Illinois. For much of this material the electroforming process not only permits accurate reproduction of the specimens, but serves as a tool in the preparation of the material for study and for photographic illustration.

The equipment used at the Chicago Natural History Museum (fig. 3) has the following specifications:

1. Steel tank. Walls $\frac{1}{8}$ inch thick, double welded, with a 3/32-inch thick lining of Koroseal. Size: 18 by 12 inches, and 12 inches deep.
2. Clinton selenium-type rectifier. Input: single phase, 60-cycle, 110-volt. Output: 100 amperes, 0 to 6 volts D.C.
3. Miscellaneous items. Cables, connections, anodes.

The size of the tank limits the unit to specimens no larger than about 10 by 16 inches, which is adequate for most of our work. Electroforming of very large specimens not only requires regular production equipment, but is probably too expensive to be considered, except in very special cases.

## PREPARATION OF A MOLD

Although it is theoretically possible, it seems rarely, if ever, advisable to use the original fossil as the cathode on which the metal is being deposited. The usual procedure involves preparing a cast or mold and covering it with a thin layer of an electrical conductor. The casting material must be resistant to the electrolyte in the tank, must give very fine surface detail, must be relatively free of bubbles, and must not adhere to the fossil specimen.

Although we have experimented with a number of substances to see whether they meet these requirements, our survey has by no means exhausted the possibilities. Liquid latex, applied in thin layers (each coat being permitted to set before the succeeding one is applied) and reinforced by strips of cheesecloth, has proved fairly successful. Latex, however, may stick to the specimen: to overcome this difficulty a silicon separator may be applied to the specimen; this must be done carefully so that none of the surface detail is obliterated. Furthermore, latex may produce bubbles at the casting surface, but if great care is exercised in applying the first coat, bubble-free molds with exceedingly fine surface detail can be obtained.

Our experiences with other casting materials have been less successful, but continued experimentation will probably result in the discovery of a material notably superior to latex as the casting medium.

Once a good mold is obtained, it is covered with an electrical conductor. In

**Fig. 3.** *Electroforming equipment at Chicago Natural History Museum.*

industry, extremely thin films of silver can be chemically precipitated on molds. Our experiences with this method have not been satisfactory: for reasons unknown, we have been unable to precipitate a good silver film on a latex mold; further experimentation is needed. In the meantime, the classic standby, graphite, gives satisfactory results.

Finely powered graphite is strewn on the mold and worked over the surface with a fairly stiff paintbrush. This must be done very carefully to make sure that the entire surface is covered but that no excess graphite powder remains in crevices or anywhere else on the surface.

## ELECTROFORMING IN COPPER

For several reasons, not the least of which is cost, electroforming with copper is recommended. Copper anodes—thick rectangular pieces of copper plate—may be purchased from electrometallurgical suppliers. These copper plates are supplied with copper hooks that permit them to be hung vertically in the tank and connected to the anode cable from the rectifier.

The tank bath for this process consists of a solution of cupric sulfate and sulfuric acid made according to the following formula:

$CuSO_4$, tech., 32 oz/gal water;
$H_2SO_4$, 66°Bé, 8 oz avd/gal water;
molasses, Bre'r Rabbit, 4 oz/100 gal of above solution.

The last item is an additive (chosen from among a variety of recommended substances) whose function is to equalize deposition of copper over the surface of the mold. With the molasses added, the solution should look green (after standing), rather than blue, and it should froth slightly when shaken in a bottle. With use, more molasses has to be added, and the solution loses acid due to chemical reaction with the anode. It eventually becomes necessary to test the solution with a combination of specific gravity determination and acid-base titration to determine the amount of acid required to restore the solution to proper composition.

## OPERATING NOTES

After the mold has been covered with an electrical conductor, a copper wire is securely fastened to it along the margin, care being taken that the wire is in firm contact with the electrical conductor. The mold is now ready to be hung in the bath and connected with the cathode cable from the rectifier. Cathode and anode should be placed opposite one another in the bath, and as far apart as possible.

If the electrolyte is not agitated and if the bath is operated at room temperature, it is advantageous to start the electroforming process at a current density of about 5 amperes per square foot of mold surface for about $\frac{1}{2}$ hour. The current is then increased to about 20 amperes per square foot. At this current density, copper is deposited at a rate of about 0.001 inch/hour. The finished cast should have an average thickness of about 0.015 inch.

At a given amperage the voltage depends on the anode-cathode spacing; at a given spacing, a given voltage determines the amperage. Once an electroforming unit is set up, the anode-cathode spacing may remain constant. In the first experiment the area of the mold must be determined and the proper current (20 amperes per square foot) applied. The operating voltage may then be read off the voltage dial on the rectifier. Thus, by using standard spacing, the operator can apply the proper amperage per square foot without measuring the area of each mold simply by setting the determined operating voltage.

## SURFACE TREATMENT OF THE COPPER CAST

When the thickness of the copper deposit on the mold is adequate, mold and cast may be carefully separated. The cast surface is a bright, fresh color which will change upon contact with the air. It is best to color (the process is called "oxydizing" in the trade) the cast immediately, and for this purpose innumerable recipes have been recommended. The simplest way is to use a chemical dip. The cast is immersed at room temperature in a solution of $\frac{1}{4}$ ounce of liver of sulfur or liquid polysulfide per gallon of water. Coloring will progress from yellow to purple to black. The concentration of the solution should be such that black color develops in approximately one minute.

After rinsing and drying the cast, it may be brushed with a firm but not hard toothbrush in order to produce highlights in the copper sulfide film.

## PROBLEMS IN ELECTROFORMING

Irregular deposition of copper on the mold is perhaps the chief difficulty in electroforming. Since we are primarily interested in a good surface against the mold the roughness that develops on the backside of the cast is of no consequence, except possibly in case of extremely streaky (linear) deposition, which tends to weaken the cast. Even streaky deposition, however, is no serious difficulty because it is a simple matter to back the cast with a low-melting-point metal, or better yet, with an epoxy resin; for example, Resiweld No. 603 (parts A and B).[1] Proper electrolyte composition, periodic filtration of the solution, and reasonable cleanliness should minimize the deposition difficulties.

Irregular coverage of the mold (areas on the mold on which no copper is being deposited, regardless of how long the process is permitted to proceed) indicates that the mold was not properly covered by the electrical conductor (graphite or silver). Application of graphite to the mold renders it black even if the powder is not adequately rubbed onto the mold surface; hence it is somewhat difficult to judge whether the mold is properly covered. A check under a binocular microscope usually reveals areas that are not adequately covered with graphite.

---

[1] H. B. Fuller Company, St. Paul 2, Minnesota.

## REFERENCES

Bloom, W., and G. Hogaboom (1930). Principles of electroplating and electro-forming. New York, McGraw-Hill.

Metal Finishing Guidebook—Directory 1960. Metals and Plastics Publications, Inc., 381 Broadway, Westwood, N. J.

Read, H. J. (1960). Electroforming. Mineral Industries, Penn. State Univ., v. 29, no. 6.

# The Use of Plastics in Paleontology

ZACH M. ARNOLD

*Museum of Paleontology, University of California, Berkeley*

Paleontologists could profitably pay more attention to the applications of plastics in solving numerous technical problems related to research and teaching. These materials are relatively easy to work, and the many different types that are available cover a wide range of applications.

I have found that the problem of explaining the notoriously troublesome three-dimensional complexities that result from the rotation of the growth and coiling axes during the development of the tests of milioline foraminifera can be greatly simplified through the use of demountable models fashioned from a polyvinyl chloride plastigel—a substance of modelling-clay consistency which, when cured at 350°F for a few minutes, becomes tough and rigid.

The ease with which the techniques of compression, injection, and extrusion molding can be successfully applied in the fabrication of laboratory materials is not generally appreciated. Complex machines of the type used in commercial production are by no means essential for small-scale laboratory operations. A metallurgist's laboratory press can readily be adapted to perform these operations if one is available, but a satisfactory substitute for this is a bench vise or drill press (a source of pressure) and a bunsen burner or blowtorch (a source of heat). Compression molding can be accomplished successfully in a vise by closing a heated mold upon a piece of heat-labile plastic whose dimensions are slightly larger than those of the piece to be formed in the mold. A simple technique for fabricating multihole slides for microfossils has been described previously (Arnold, 1955). By inserting a brass plunger into its chuck, the drill press can be used to close a mold during a compression molding operation in which heavy pressure is required. By adding a heating chamber equipped with nozzle and piston, injection or extrusion molding can be accomplished (fig. 1); by chucking the piston rod in the drill press and resting the attached mold upon the table of the press, a blowtorch can be played on the cylinder as it is manually rotated in the press; within minutes the plastic pellets inside the chamber are fused into a syrupy mass that is easily forced into the mold and there quickly cooled when the surrounding tray is flooded with water.

Using these simple techniques and primitive equipment I have formed: (1) polyethylene disks (7/16 inch in diameter, $\frac{1}{16}$ inch thick) that serve as specimen holders for a microcentrifuge; (2) transparent and opaque compartmented slides (1 by 3 inches) for storing microfossils either in air or immersed in various fluids; (3) multicompartment dishes (1 inch in diameter) for isolation cultures of living foraminifera; and (4) small, covered vessels for making chemical and biological analyses of foraminiferan tests while viewing them under the microscope. The most exacting phase of the entire molding operation, of course, is the preparation of the mold itself. A simple mold may be turned on a lathe in 15 minutes, but one that I have used successfully with the apparatus described above consisted of 36 pieces and took me 25 hours to make. The largest piece of polyethylene apparatus yet produced by this equipment weighed 2.64 ounces, was $4\frac{1}{4}$ inches in diameter and $\frac{1}{2}$ inch thick, and was formed from a mold having 20 extractable cores.

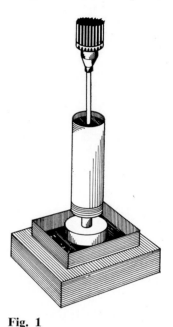

**Fig. 1**

*Simple apparatus for shaping thermoplastics by the injection-molding technique, showing injection cylinder, mold, and cooling tray mounted on drill press.*

A final example of the uses to which plastic may be put in a paleontological laboratory is the custom preparation of grinding disks to be used with the precision grinder described elsewhere in this manual (p. 217). Disks of suitable specifications were fabricated by suspending Carborundum powder in catalyzed epoxy or polyester resin, letting the mixture set to a leathery consistency between glass plates, cutting disks from the resulting sheet, lettting the disks harden completely, and finishing their edges by light grinding while they were rotated by a mandrel held in a lathe or drill press. Sturdy, metal-backed disks were subsequently prepared by coating the surface of steel disks with a paste-like cement of epoxy resin and pressing into this a heavy layer of Carborundum powder. When the cement was completely hard, the disks were lightly tapped on a frosted glass plate to remove all loose grains of Carborundum and were then ready for use.

## REFERENCE

Arnold, Z. M. (1955). The construction and use of a simple die for plastic micropaleontological slides. Micropaleontology, v. 1, no. 4, p. 365–367.

*Coordinator:* FRANCO RASETTI

# Photography of Fossils

FRANCO RASETTI

*Department of Physics, The Johns Hopkins University,
Baltimore, Maryland*

This article deals with some general principles of image formation by optical instruments of interest to the fossil photographer, and with practical details about photography by means of ordinary camera lenses. Photomicrography of microfossils will be treated elsewhere in this volume (p. 433). Some of the considerations developed here have been treated in greater detail elsewhere (Rasetti, 1946). Whittington (1956) and Gutschick (1960) are among the recent authors who contributed valuable suggestions on photographic techniques.

## DEPTH OF FIELD AND RESOLUTION
## OF OPTICAL SYSTEMS

The most important problem confronting the fossil photographer is obtaining sufficient sharpness of detail in all parts of the photograph. This may be critical, because fossils are usually small and three-dimensional. The results are determined by factors that are usually unimportant in the photography of flat objects or large, distant, three-dimensional objects. For example, the nature of light and its relation to the sharpness of the optical image impose severe limitations on the photography of small fossils that have high relief.

Here we are considering exclusively those limitations that are due to the nature of light, not those caused by imperfections (aberrations) of the optical system employed. Almost any reasonably good photographic lens can produce results close to the optimum allowed by the laws of physics. It follows that no conceivable advance in technique will ever lead to better results than we can obtain now.

One measure of the quality of a photograph is the *resolution* of detail. Optical resolution is measured in terms of the smallest distance between two object points that produce separate images. One aim of fossil photography is to obtain the best resolution possible in all parts of the photograph. In order to have all parts of a fossil of a certain depth reasonably in focus, we focus on a median plane. A point in this plane will be sharply imaged on the photographic plate; a point either above or below this plane will not be imaged into a point, but rather into a circle—a *circle of confusion,* which increases in diameter away from the median plane. It is clear that for geometric reasons the circle of confusion becomes smaller if we *decrease* the angle of the cone of light that issues from an object point and is accepted by the optical system. Thus, by reducing the diaphragm aperture we obtain greater depth of field. This does not mean, however, that unlimited improvement of the image can be achieved by decreasing the angle of the cone of light; *diffraction,* which depends on the wavelength of light used, causes another circle of confusion, superimposed upon the one due to defocusing. The diameter of this circle *increases* with decreasing angle of the cone. The optimum conditions are realized when the sum of the diameters of the two circles of confusion is a minimum.

The conditions that yield the highest resolution for object points situated in the uppermost and lowermost planes may be stated in extremely simple form, since the effects of defocusing and diffraction on resolution depend exclusively (for a given wavelength of light) on the angle of the cone accepted by the instrument. Other optical factors are immaterial. It also makes no difference whether the final magnification is obtained on the negative or whether the negative is subsequently enlarged. The choice between these possibilities may be dictated by convenience, but has no effect on the resolution attainable.

Optimum resolution is achieved when the ratio of the object-to-lens distance $L$ to the diameter of the lens aperture $d$ (the ratio which determines the angle of the light cone) equals the square root of the object depth $t$ divided by twice the wavelength of light $\lambda$. In formula:

$$L/d = \sqrt{t/2\lambda}.$$

We have little control over the wavelength. A slight improvement will result from employing slow, unsensitized emulsions affected only by the shorter waves of visible light (blue and violet). For a wavelength of $4 \times 10^{-6}$ cm and for a series of object depths, table I gives the optimum value of $L/d$ and the *numerical* aperture which is usually indicated for microscope objectives, and, when not too large, is just the reciprocal of $L/d$.

It is not necessary to measure the ratio $L/d$, since this quantity can be related to the f-number, which is marked on the diaphragm setting of most photographic lenses. If the photograph is obtained under fairly high magnifica-

**Table I.** *Optimum Aperture Versus Object Depth*

| OBJECT DEPTH (mm) | OPTIMUM VALUE OF $L/d$ | OPTIMUM NUMERICAL APERTURE |
|---|---|---|
| 0.01 | 3.54 | 0.28 |
| 0.02 | 5.00 | 0.20 |
| 0.04 | 7.08 | 0.14 |
| 0.08 | 10.0 | 0.10 |
| 0.16 | 14.1 | 0.07 |
| 0.32 | 20.0 | 0.05 |
| 0.64 | 28.3 | — |
| 1.28 | 40.0 | — |
| 2.56 | 56.6 | — |
| 5.12 | 80.0 | — |
| 10.24 | 113 | — |
| 20.48 | 160 | — |
| 40.96 | 226 | — |
| 81.92 | 320 | — |

tion (say 5× or greater), then $L/d$ may be taken equal to the f-number (it becomes exactly equal for infinite magnification). For a 1× photograph, $L/d$ is twice the f-number. Since the resolution obtained is not critically affected by small errors in $L/d$ (within ±30 percent), the f-number can be estimated.

It will be seen that the numerical aperture of most microscope objectives, even those of relatively low magnification, is too large for the photography of any but the thinnest of the objects considered. Some special microscope objectives have an adjustable diaphragm and these may be used perhaps up to object depths of 0.3 mm. In general, an object depth of 0.1 mm represents the limit beyond which a photographic objective will produce results that are as good as or better than results obtained with a microscope objective.

For very deep objects, even photographic lenses seldom have a diaphragm that can be stopped down to a sufficiently high f-number. For example, a fossil 80 mm deep would require, for a 1× picture, a lens setting of f/160. For such large fossils it is convenient to demagnify on the negative and subsequently magnify in printing, in order to increase the object-to-lens distance, thus increasing $L/d$ while the f-number remains the same.

## LENSES AND CAMERAS

We are concerned here with photography by means of camera lenses rather than microscope objectives. Expensive camera lenses are wholly unnecessary in fossil photography. A lens designed for ordinary photography is expensive because of two requirements: (1) a large numerical aperture (small f-number); (2) a wide angular field. Neither of these features is necessary for the present purpose. As shown in the preceding section, depth of field requires a high f-number (f/10 or greater). Fossils must be photographed at small apertures to avoid a distorted perspective (see later discussion). The only conceivable use of a fast lens is to obtain a sufficiently luminous image for good focusing on the ground glass. Lenses whose widest apertures are between f/4.5 and f/6.3 are usually sufficient for this purpose. Such lenses often give sharper images than faster lenses stopped down to the same aperture. It should be noticed that many unsymmetrical objectives, such as the Tessar type, are meant for one-sided use—that is, for photographing distant objects. When used to produce an enlarged image of a small object—that is, when the object-to-lens distance is smaller than the lens-to-film distance—such lenses have to be mounted in reverse position, with the front of the lens facing the film rather than the object. With symmetrical lenses, the type used in enlargers, this is not necessary.

It is possible, but hardly convenient, to photograph all fossils with one lens. At least 2 or 3 lenses of different focal lengths should be available. We advise the use of 3 lenses, having focal lengths of about 35, 80, and 150 mm. The quality requirements for a lens having a focal length of 35 mm are somewhat more stringent; it should be a good anastigmatic objective (f/3.5 to f/4.5) provided with a diaphragm that can be stopped down to f/22. A microscope objective may be substituted, provided that it has an iris diaphragm. For the longer focal lengths, almost any photographic lens will do, as long as it can be stopped down to a small enough aperture—at least f/32 but preferably f/64. A lens shutter is unnecessary, as exposures are usually taken by turning the lights on and off.

If the object is too close to the lens, distortion will result, the nearer parts of the object being imaged under greater magnification than the distant parts. Distortion should not exceed 10 percent, which means that the lens-to-object distance should be at least ten times the object depth. With a 150-mm lens fossils as much as 30 mm in depth can be photographed at a magnification of 10× with less than 10 percent distortion. Larger fossils should be demagnified on the negative.

The abovementioned lenses may be made interchangeable on the same camera, especially if it has an extendible bellows. Even a simple box camera, with a lens adapter at one end and a film or plate holder at the other, may be conveniently used for two lenses, say of 35- and 80-mm focal length. The length of the box and the lens adapters may be chosen to give convenient magnifications with the two lenses, say $2\times$ and $8\times$. If a camera with an extendible bellows is used, it is inadvisable to focus by adjusting the bellows, as each photograph will then have a different magnification. Instead, the camera should be set at any one of a few marked lengths chosen to give magnifications of, say $2\times$, $3\times$, $5\times$, and focused by moving the fossil. The rack and pinion adjustment from an old microscope or other instrument can be conveniently used to move a small platform built to hold the specimens.

An enlarger allows greater control over final magnification. Contact printing obliges the photographer to decide on the final magnification when taking the negative.

## NEGATIVE MATERIALS

Good arguments may be brought in favor of both films and plates. The former are light and unbreakable, and large numbers of pictures can be developed at once. On the other hand, slow emulsions with desirable qualities are more easily available on plates.

For most fossil photography, the slower and the less sensitized the emulsion, the better the results. Sensitivity to the green, yellow, and red portions of the spectrum is only a nuisance, since fossils have no color. Unfortunately, emulsions unsensitized with organic dyes, and hence affected only by blue and violet light, are now hardly available on film. They are, however, readily available on plates (lantern slide plates). These have a number of advantages: extremely fine grain, clear unexposed areas, possibility of developing under bright red light, and long storage without deterioration. The high gamma (contrast index) is no objection to their use. Contrast can always be decreased to the desired value by overexposure and underdevelopment. Speed of processing is another advantage (about 40 seconds each for developing and fixing).

In some laboratories extensive use is made of the Polaroid process, which yields a positive print within one minute after exposure. The Polaroid film holder may be adapted to whatever camera is being used to photograph fossils. A disadvantage of the method is that only one print is obtained, hence separate photographs must be taken when more copies are desired.

## MOUNTING AND LIGHTING FOSSILS FOR PHOTOGRAPHY

The coated fossils should be mounted in the desired orientation. This is conveniently obtained for most specimens by mounting in Plasticine or a similar material [1] on a flat, smooth, black surface that will provide a dark background for the positive. A glass plate painted black on the back side serves this purpose. The background is important, especially for fossils separated from the

---

[1] A product particularly suited for this purpose is marketed by Eberhard Faber under the name *Holdit*. It is strongly adhesive and does not stain the specimens.

matrix. Small and delicate specimens, such as silicified trilobites, should be attached with cement (soluble in some medium that will later be used to remove it) to the head of an insect pin or some other support that will not appear on the photograph.

Since shadows on coated specimens are already provided to a large extent by the more dense coating of prominent parts, lighting should be almost uniform rather than highly directional. I use two desk lamps with 100-watt frosted bulbs, one providing light from above, the other from below. A slight difference in distance provides the conventional stronger light from the upper left. Such diffuse light sources, when placed close to the object, avoid undesirable sharp shadows.

Fossils coated for photography do not have a glossy surface, but if for any reason it is necessary to photograph a fossil whose surface gives unwanted reflections, these may be eliminated by polarizing the light. Light is polarized by passing it through a Polaroid sheet. To avoid reflection from a surface, the plane of polarization must be in the proper direction (this may readily be found by rotating the Polaroid sheet in its own plane until reflection is minimized), and the angle of incidence of the light on the surface must have a certain value (Brewster angle) dependent on the refractive index of the material. Since the angle of reflection equals the angle of incidence, the angle by which the light is deviated in going from the source to the object and from this to the camera lens, must be twice the Brewster angle. In practice, it is easier to find the proper angle by trial and error.

Focusing is done by means of a fine-grained ground glass screen, using the widest lens opening. The lens is then stopped down to the optimum value discussed earlier. Unless one uses 35 mm film, it is convenient to take several, generally 4, photographs on the same film or plate. For this purpose, a mask that covers three quarters of the field is placed in front of the plate or film holder. The fossil image is centered on the ground glass in the uncovered quarter. The mask is turned around after each exposure until all quarters have been exposed.

## STEREOPHOTOGRAPHY

Stereophotographs have gained acceptance in many paleontological publications. It requires a little more time and care than ordinary photography but presents no special difficulties. Two pictures are taken of each specimen at slightly different angles. The prints are later mounted parallel to each other, at a distance of about $2\frac{1}{2}$ inches, which is about the average distance between pupils. The stereogram can be viewed either through a pair of lenses mounted at the same distance, or with the unaided eye.

Several methods may be used to photograph the two views of the specimen. The specimen may be either rotated or translated, or it may be kept fixed while the camera is rotated. Gott (1945) describes in considerable detail a camera that is used for the last-mentioned method. Evitt (1949) discusses various advantages of stereophotography and makes useful suggestions about the arrangement of stereograms on plates for publication. Lehmann (1956) describes the technique used in making stereograms of microfossils.

If the two pictures are obtained by rotating the specimen or the camera, the angle between the two positions should range from 8 to 10° to produce the appearance of the original relief. If the angle is too small, the specimen will appear flatter than in reality, whereas a larger angle gives the appearance of excessive relief. I have successfully used translation of specimens mounted on a sliding carriage. The distance between the two positions should range from 14 to 17 percent of the object-to-lens distance (measured from the lens diaphragm), to yield the angles mentioned above. If the specimen is moved between exposures while the camera is kept fixed, one should see to it that the illumination is almost identical in the two positions, since even small differences in the shadows produce a poor stereogram. If the light sources are diffuse and relatively distant, the difference in illumination will be negligible. It is also important that the exposure times be equal, and both pictures should be taken on the same plate or film to ensure identical processing.

## IMMERSION IN LIQUIDS

Fossils may be photographed when immersed in an appropriate liquid in order to (1) increase the contrast between fossil and matrix, (2) eliminate unwanted reflections from shiny surfaces, (3) render the surface of the fossil more uniformly dark when it is covered with irregular deposits of powdery calcite, iron oxide, etc., and (4) render the fossil transparent so that internal details may be observed and photographed.

All these effects of immersion depend on the refractive index of the medium being close to that of the fossil, so that reflection and refraction at the surface are minimized. A variety of liquids lend themselves to use as immersion media. An immersion liquid must not react with the fossil, must be transparent, must not be highly volatile, and, especially for rendering fossils transparent, must have a refractive index close to that of the fossil material, usually calcite or quartz. Water, ethyl alcohol, colorless mineral oil, glycerin, xylene, and many other organic solvents have been used. Xylene has an index of refraction that is close to quartz and calcite and is an excellent medium for immersion of most fossils when internal structures of translucent specimens must be observed and photographed. With most organic solvents it shares the advantage of readily penetrating porous materials.

Photography and observation of immersed specimens seldom offer any advantage if the fossils stand out from the matrix because of their form and/or surface ornamentation. For such specimens, coating with ammonium chloride or magnesium oxide generally best fulfills the first three purposes mentioned above. Immersion in liquids is useful when the fossil is distinguished from the matrix by its color or texture rather than relief. It is difficult to specify in greater detail just when immersion will yield the best results. However, one may readily experiment and observe whether the desired features appear more distinctly when the fossil is immersed.

Photography of a specimen immersed in a liquid offers another advantage which, although it is usually of no great significance, may be offset by other inconveniences. It is commonly known that an immersed object appears shallower than it really is, due to the refraction of the light rays. The apparent thickness $t'$ is $t/n$, where $n$ is the refractive index of the medium. Consequently, the resolution is increased by a factor equal to the square root of $n$. In practice, this means an increase in depth of focus of about 20 to 30 percent. Only where the best results must be achieved in photographing convex microfossils, is the improvement worth considering. Of course, coating with ammonium chloride or magnesium oxide cannot be used in this case.

## REFERENCES

Evitt, W. R. (1949). Stereophotography as a tool of the paleontologist. J. Paleontology, v. 23, p. 566–570, pl. 88.

Gott, P. F. (1945). Procedure of simplified stereophotography of fossils. J. Paleontology, v. 19, p. 390–395, pl. 59, 9 text-figs.

Gutschick, R. C. (1960). Photography of Paleozoic arenaceous Foraminifera. J. Paleontology, v. 34, p. 756–762, 2 text-figs.

Lehmann, E. P. (1956). A technique of stereophotomicrography for illustrations in micropaleontology. J. Paleontology, v. 30, p. 757–759, 1 text-fig.

Rasetti, Franco (1946). Optimum conditions for the photography of fossils. J. Paleontology, v. 20, p. 514–516, 1 text-fig.

Whittington, H. B. (1956). Photographing small fossils. J. Paleontology, v. 30, p. 756–757. 1 text-fig.

# Photography of Small Fossils

## H. B. WHITTINGTON

*Museum of Comparative Zoology, Harvard University*

The technique described here was developed in the course of trying to obtain the best possible photographs of trilobites in their early growth stages. The maximum dimension of these fossils may be less than 1 mm, their shape

An earlier version of this paper appeared in the *Journal of Paleontology,* v. 30, no. 3, May, 1956.

hemispherical or even subspherical, and their external surface granulate or spinose. My aim was to produce pictures at magnifications of 30 to 50 diameters. To photograph these fossils directly at this magnification with a vertical camera is almost impossible because of the great bellows extension demanded with a lens having a focal length of 50 mm or longer, and the small diaphragm aperture required to give the necessary depth of focus. I therefore made negatives at 10 diameters and enlarged them—a procedure that requires a sharp, blemish-free, fine-grained negative. To avoid dark shadows the surface to be photographed must be evenly lit, and a moderate northwest highlight provided. The focus is critical—it must be as near as possible to the median plane of the object, so that when the diaphragm aperture is reduced the increased depth of focus may be used to best advantage.

A fluorescent ring light (A in the figure) provides an ideal source of even illumination over the whole surface, and two small fluorescent tubes (B in the figure) give the required northwest highlight. Fluorescent light has two great advantages: (1) it is clear and crisp and allows precise focusing on the right point on the specimen, and (2) the tubes do not emit heat, so that they are not only more comfortable to work with, but do not soften the Plasticine which may be used to support the specimen. Tungsten lamps or other sources of illumination may soften the Plasticine and cause the specimen to move during a long exposure.

I prefer the apparatus shown in the figure, but different types of cameras and other sizes of ring lights can be used. The camera I use is a Leica, mounted on Leitz Aristophot equipment, which incorporates an adequate bellows extension and a reflex mirror with a clear glass focusing screen. It is mounted on a heavy, vibration-free, vertical post and base. The 35-mm frame is large enough for small fossils, and roll-film cartridges are vastly more convenient than cut film, which must be loaded into film holders. A clear glass focusing screen with a magnifying viewer is essential for critical focus. The ring light (A) is a domestic ceiling fixture commonly carried by electrical supply and hardware stores, the ring 12 inches in diameter, 32 watts, and described as "standard cool white." An opening approximately 7 inches in diameter was made in the center of the convex metal disc (C) on which the ring is mounted, and this disc supported on a $\frac{1}{4}$-inch mild-steel-wire frame (D). The frame and disc are braced against the vertical support of the Aristophot to eliminate movement from side to side. If it is desired to have the height of the ring adjustable, it may be attached to sleeve clamps which run up and down vertical posts set in a horizontal base. I prefer to have the height of the ring fixed, and to move the camera. When a lens of about 5-inch focal length is used for magnifications of 1 to 3 diameters, the camera is placed about as shown in the figure; a 50-mm lens, for magnifications up to 10 diameters should be mounted in an extension tube and placed below the ring (A). A lens hood should be used to exclude all but the light coming

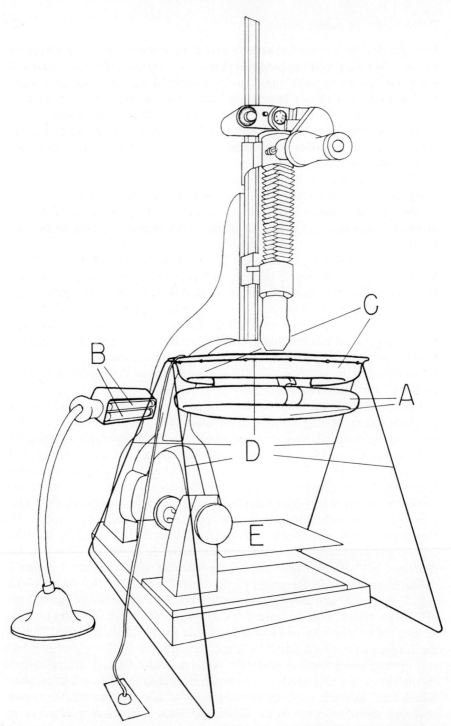

**Fig. 1.** *Use of fluorescent tubes (A: ring; B: two short tubes) to provide light for photography of specimens on the adjustable table (E). C: metal disk on which ring light is mounted. D: frame that supports ring light.*

from the specimen. The extension of the camera bellows is set to determine the particular magnification, and focusing is accomplished by raising and lowering the specimen table (E): a good quality rack and pinion will allow the necessary small adjustments. The two 4-watt fluorescent tubes forming the highlight are of the kind that can be screwed into an ordinary lamp socket (this Lite-Mite Bulb is manufactured by Stocker and Yale, Marblehead, Mass.). A goose-neck lamp affords a suitable socket, and can be adjusted conveniently.

Any of several films now on the market are suitable for use with this type of lighting, which does not demand over-long exposures. I prefer Adox, in 35-mm cartridges, manufactured by the Schleussner Company of Frankfurt am Main, Germany, and readily available in this country. The emulsion layer of this film is extremely thin, giving it a greater resolving power than any other film. A discussion of the merits of Adox film, and of how it should be developed, will be found in *Leica Photography,* issues for Summer and Fall, 1955 (vol. 8, nos. 2 and 3). I have found that Adox film, type KB-14, developed in the liquid formula X-22, made by the FR Corporation, New York City, will give negatives of exceptional resolution. Enlargements made from them show as much detail as can be reproduced by the prevailing collotype method—sometimes even more.

# Photography of Microfossils

RICHARD H. BENSON

*Department of Geology, University of Kansas, Lawrence*

Illustrations in paleontological papers are commonly used to supplement diagnoses and descriptions of fossils, enabling an author to express his concept of the variability, exclusiveness, and ideal morphological expression of the taxa treated and to furnish evidence of significant features of individual specimens. A good description of a species must be sufficiently comprehensive to permit understanding of various parts of its morphology and their relative importance. A good illustration must do the same.

A drawing represents a taxonomic decision. Someone must decide which morphological aspects of one or several specimens need to be emphasized, subdued, or combined. The author of the drawing seeks by means of it to depict his impressions and judgment of form as accurately as possible.

A drawing is subjective, in that it reflects the paleontologist's understanding (or that of the artist guided by him) of the morphology of a taxon. A photograph is objective, in that it portrays the actual form and surface sculpture of a microfossil.

To argue about the relative merits of photomicrography and drawing to illustrate microfossils is ridiculous today. The substitution of drawings for photographs in older micropaleontologic literature was as much a product of the technical difficulties characteristic of reflected light photomicrography as it was the result of any concerted philosophy. The role of photomicrography is to show objectively the morphology of specimens. It does this rather well, allowing the taxonomist to broaden the range of use of his drawings for diagnosing or synthesizing the characteristics of a species.

The purpose of this essay is to examine some of the more successful methods of photographing microfossils in the size range of most foraminifers, ostracods, and conodonts. Most of the difficulties encountered in using conventional apparatus are discussed. Particular attention is paid to obtaining adequate depth of field, preparing the fossil to reveal the surface morphology, and lighting the specimen for photography in reflected light. Practical procedures are stressed. The reader is referred to Rasetti's article on photography of fossils in this Handbook for a discussion of optical principles and theory.

## THE CAMERA

A few years ago the 35-mm camera housing, used in conjunction with the lens system of a compound monocular microscope, was considered to be basic equipment. The economy of fine-grained, slow-speed, panchromatic, 35-mm film and the large number of exposures that could be taken at one time seemed desirable. Extreme enlargement was necessary, but with continual improvement in films and developers this step in processing became less of an obstacle to obtaining quality prints. The final size of the print could be planned at a late stage in the process. There is a limit, however, to the quality that can be obtained in prints enlarged 5 to 10 times from the negative. Sheet film ($2\frac{1}{4}$ by $3\frac{1}{4}$ inches or 4 by 5 inches), which gives a larger negative image, has yielded better results, and by using a series of masks as many as four exposures can be made on one film sheet. Enlargement ($2\times$ to $3\times$) may still be necessary, but graininess does not obscure the finer details of the image. With increasing attention being paid to the lighting and composition of each exposure, the convenience of being able to develop a few exposures at a time provides a continuous quality check not possible with long film strips.

As photography of microfossils became more sophisticated, it progressed from the use of the 35-mm camera to the use of larger cameras and films. The basic lens system of a compound monocular microscope is still employed. The present art is analogous in many ways to portrait photography. Interest has shifted from problems of magnification to the improvement of lighting techniques and specimen preparation.

One of the most interesting improvements in photography was the development of the Polaroid Land film, which was used to photograph the microfossils (shown in fig. 1). These photographs were made in 10 seconds from

**Fig. 1.** *Photomicrographs of specimens of Foraminifera (20×) and ostracods (40×) coated with silver nitrate. Photos taken with Leitz Aristophot II camera; 32-mm B. & L. achromatic objective (4×, N. A. 0.10); 15× Huygenian eyepiece; Polaroid Land film, Type 42; lighting stage used with 3 A O microscope lights; immersion oil with refractive index 1.51; exposure time from 3 to 8 seconds.*

time of exposure to the finished print with Type 42 film, without use of a darkroom. Grain is almost nonexistent; contrast is high but can be compensated for by a fill-in light; range of light sensitivity is broad. Use of this kind of film may eventually replace that of conventional types for photographing fossils.

With regard to assembling the necessary component parts required for a suitable photomicrographic camera (fig. 2), I would recommend (1) a sheet film holder with extension bellows and viewing screen of finely ground frosted glass, and (2) a monocular microscope with Huygenian eyepieces (6× to 15×) and achromatic objectives (16-mm to at least 40-mm focal lengths). Addition to and modification of this basic equipment will be discussed later. The camera will need to be mounted on a vibration-free base, which can be constructed with tennis balls, bed coasters, and a steel plate. Commercial equipment is superior to homemade apparatus, because the

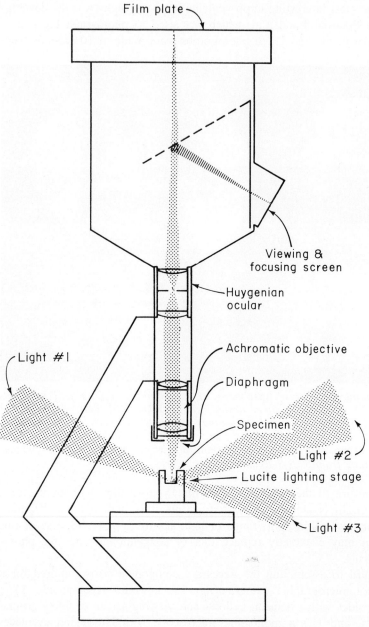

**Fig. 2.** *A functional diagram of the lighting and optical systems of a typical photomicrographic camera using sheet film and the lucite lighting stage. The shaded areas represent the paths of light from the three light sources to the film, and to the mirror and the operator.*

alignment and working tolerances of machined parts and the stability of the stand are better than can be turned out by most small machine shops.

## THE LENS SYSTEM

Magnifications of 30× to 100× are required to illustrate most microfossils. The objective is the most critical component of the lens system. It forms and magnifies the image (2× to 10×), which is further enlarged by the ocular (10× to 40×). Monocular compound microscopes equipped with the conventional set of medium- to high-powered objectives are designed for use with thin sections viewed under high magnification with transmitted light. Additional low-power objectives will be needed for use with three-dimensional, opaque objects observed by reflected light.

Because of geometric relations in the lens system (see Rasetti), the greater the magnification of the objective, the shallower is its depth of field. The relief of specimens is seldom more than 0.5 mm and usually less than 0.3 mm. It is therefore necessary to employ low-power objectives in combination with a higher powered ocular to achieve sufficient depth of field (with a diaphragm, as explained later). Achromatic objectives (16-mm, 10× to 48-mm, 2×) are used for microfossil photography, because apochromatic objectives are rare in focal lengths greater than 16 mm. Achromatic objectives are color corrected (preferred color usually yellow-green) for spherical aberration, giving good results when used with Huygenian oculars (compensating oculars give color fringes). The objectives most commonly used are the 22.7-mm (6×) and the 32-mm (4×) sizes in combination with 10× to 15× oculars (Leitz Periplan and Bausch and Lomb Hyperplan oculars can be used).

The usable depth of field of a medium- to low-power objective (25-30 mm) without a diaphragm is about 0.1 mm. The depth of field of an objective can be increased to about 0.3 mm by placing a diaphragm (5.5-mm diam. aperture with 4× objective; 3.2-mm diam. aperture with 6× objective) over the lower end of the objective. Other workers have had equally good results by fitting the diaphragm behind the objective. A friction-fit sleeve (fig. 3) is used to hold the diaphragm in front of the objective (Fournier, 1957). The aperture of the diaphragm allows use of only the axial resolution of the objective. Use of a smaller aperture decreases the circle of confusion and increases the depth of field until diffraction becomes significant in decreasing the total resolution of the objective.

As the aperture is decreased in size, the numerical aperture of the lens is decreased; consequently, the amount of light transmitted to the ocular is decreased, the contrast is increased, the field of view becomes flattened, and the peripheral distortion is lessened. Compensation for these factors is achieved by increasing exposure time, adding fill-in lighting, and decreasing the angle of incidence of the major lights. Fournier (1956, 1957) described

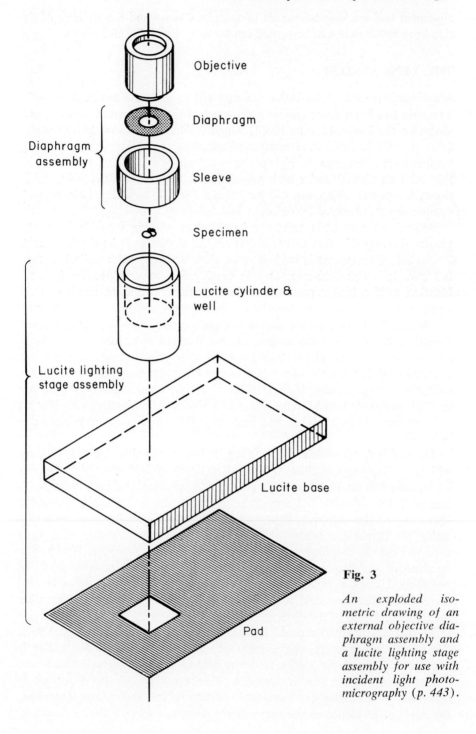

Objective

Diaphragm

Diaphragm assembly

Sleeve

Specimen

Lucite cylinder & well

Lucite lighting stage assembly

Lucite base

Pad

**Fig. 3**

*An exploded isometric drawing of an external objective diaphragm assembly and a lucite lighting stage assembly for use with incident light photomicrography (p. 443).*

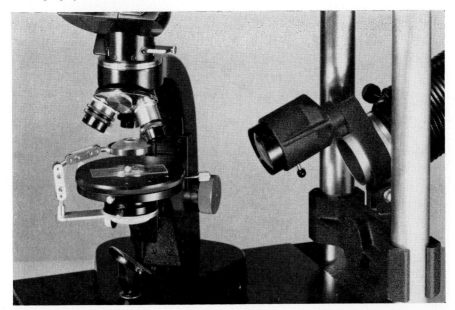

**Fig. 4.** *Lower part of Leitz photomicrographic apparatus showing Mikrophotar objectives with iris diaphragms and use of the Lieberkühn mirror system for incident light photography. [Courtesy of Leitz Wetzlar.]*

the use of pinhole diaphragms ($650\mu$) with the more powerful objectives, principally the $10\times$ objective. I have found that slightly larger apertures used on weaker objectives in conjunction with stronger eyepieces or longer bellows yield better results. Microtessar lenses and other similar low-power photomacrographic lenses are not designed to be used with oculars. They cannot equal the magnification and resolution given by objectives used with an aperture and eyepiece. Triebel (1947) has used the Leitz Minro-photar objectives (fig. 4), which have built-in adjustable diaphragms. These objectives have the advantage of ease of adjustment of the aperture to fit the relief of the specimen. They are more convenient to use than is a series of discontinuous diaphragm stops.

In addition to the use of a diaphragm to increase the depth of field, immersion of the specimen in a liquid with a high refractive index not only increases the range in size of specimens which can be photographed but also aids in lighting the specimen. Glycerol is inexpensive and easily obtainable. It is nontoxic and does not react chemically with specimens. It has a low rate of evaporation, an index of refraction of about 1.47, a high viscosity, and a high solubility in water or alcohol. Other values of an immersion liquid will be mentioned under the section on lighting.

The photography of microfossils that are very convex or have high surface relief and spinosity is still not possible without blurring some parts of the

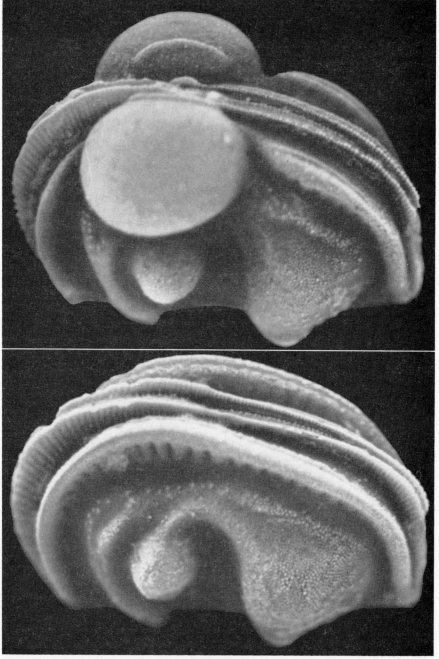

**Fig. 5.** *Two oblique views of the ventral and lateral regions of* Craspedobolbina (Mitrobeyrichia) clavata (*Kolmodin*), *a Silurian ostracod from Gotland. 39.5×. Specimen attached to glass slide with cellulose acetate cement; coated*

image. The lateral views of the flatter forms photograph easily. Peripheral, dorsal, and end views need to be taken with very low-power objectives (40-mm) and enlarged. It may be necessary to retouch the photo of the specimen to sharpen a region that had to be blurred in order to focus sharply on more important areas.

## COATING THE SPECIMEN

Most specimens of ostracods, foraminifers, and conodonts are partly transparent to opaque, mottled, and somewhat glossy. A very fine-grained coating of uniform color, texture, and thickness applied to the surface of the specimen will reveal its external sculpture and morphology under reflected light. The coating, properly applied, will hide the irregularity of shell-wall composition and color, and will provide a suitable reflecting surface.

Several coating substances have been used with varying degrees of satisfaction. Ammonium chloride can be applied either as a fine spray in liquid form or as the vapor from sublimation of crystals through heating (Cooper, 1935; Martinsson, 1962). (See fig. 5.) Unfortunately, excess moisture in the air combines with the ammonium chloride and forms hydrochloric acid, which noticeably etches or dissolves the surface of small specimens. Furthermore, it is very difficult to get a fine, even coating on the surface of morphologically complicated forms. However, ammonium chloride does have the advantage that it can be used and easily removed without permanent alteration of the specimen. If the crystals are fine and the coating even, it gives a dead-white appearance and can yield a very satisfactory reflecting surface for photography.

Magnesium oxide, another substance used for coating, is applied by briefly exposing the specimen to the smoke emitted by a burning magnesium ribbon. The ribbon burns very quickly, so that this procedure requires a deft hand and some directional control of the magnesium vapors. The quantity of magnesium oxide generated is difficult to control. Humidity does not affect this coating. It can be left on the specimen for a long period without harming its surface and can be removed with a dry brush. Magnesium oxide has not been widely used for coating microfossils, primarily because it is hard to keep the finer ornament of the surface from being obscured by a thick deposit.

Vegetable dyes of the type used in food coloring are also used in coating fossils. They can be applied with a brush, and the density of the coating can

*with ammonium chloride. Photographed with modified Leitz Aristophot II camera; 42-mm Leitz Summar objective, f/11, 5 seconds, Adox KB14 film (24 by 36 mm, 14 DIN = 20 ASA); Bromide WSG, 3S (hard) paper; negative magnified 10×; lighting by two Sylvania 5-inch 4W Daylight tubes (5 cm to upper left) and small paper reflector (7 mm to lower right). No retouching, background darkened. [Photomicrographs and information courtesy of Anders Martinsson, University of Uppsala.]*

be built up as desired. Red or green dye can be used. Red dye will appear black on orthochromatic film; green dye can be used with achromatic objectives, which are color-corrected for this part of the spectrum. Vegetable dye is difficult to apply evenly. It tends to concentrate in the crevices and pores and to thin out over the smooth areas of the specimen. It can be removed easily from most of the surface of the specimen with water and a brush, but some tends to remain in the crevices. The most unsatisfactory aspect of this method of coating is the tendency of the dye to stain organic residue or unclean areas preferentially. Its usefulness is confined primarily to very clean, bleached specimens.

Another coating method, similar to the use of food coloring, consists in using brown ink (Fournier, 1956) or malachite green (Triebel, 1947) on preheated specimens. For specimens with crevices, sutures, or depressions partly filled with matrix this stain, which concentrates in low or porous areas, can be very useful.

Triebel (1947) introduced a very satisfactory method of coating which consists in soaking a cleaned and heated specimen in a 3 to 5 percent solution of silver nitrate, then reheating the specimen to reduce the silver, leaving the specimen uniformly dark brown or black. With the application of additional silver nitrate and further heating the specimen will gradually develop a metallic luster. On intense reheating the reduced silver will become oxidized, changing the metallic luster to a dull gray. This method is used widely by European workers but is not as widely employed in America.

The details of this coating procedure are as follows: A representative specimen is selected and thoroughly cleaned. It is heated to bleach the surface and remove the excess moisture so that the solution will be readily absorbed. The specimen is then placed on an absorbent material, such as a cardboard microslide or a piece of filter paper, and a 3 to 5 percent solution of silver nitrate is applied with a brush. The solution can be painted on the specimen or it can be allowed to soak momentarily in a drop of solution until the excess liquid is absorbed by the underlying material or evaporates under the heat of the microscope lamp. The surface of the specimen will begin to turn brown as the silver is reduced. Some workers use a stronger solution (10 percent or more), but the uniform buildup of the coating is more difficult to control. Additional solution is added as needed until the specimen turns dark brown or black. It may be necessary to gently heat the specimen with the microscope lamp or expose it on an aluminum microslide holder over a hot plate to thoroughly reduce the silver. The surface eventually takes on a metallic luster. The process should be continued until the specimen is entirely silver-plated. Sometimes it is desirable to interrupt the process in the early stages, when the stain begins to turn light to medium brown, to emphasize the surface depressions. However, the best results can be obtained by using the silver as a uniform coating over the entire surface. As the coating process progresses many surface features become clear that were previously obscured by glare or transparency. Once the specimen is silvered, a dull gray color can be obtained by reheating the specimen over a hot plate on an aluminum microslide holder or a piece of aluminum foil. For this final step very high temperatures are required, and the specimen may need to be turned several times on the aluminum to obtain uniform oxidation. Reheating gives a fine-grained gray coating which will photograph easily.

Several problems may be encountered in using the silver nitrate method of coating. If the solution is too strong, crystals may form rapidly, obscuring details. A hyaline specimen may not receive the coating readily unless it is bleached by preheating. If the chitinous exterior is thick and dense, the reduced silver will not build evenly unless the chitin is transformed to cellulose by previous heating. Increasing the strength of the solution may also help if the speed of reduction of the silver can be controlled under the heat of a microscope lamp. These difficult chitinous specimens usually receive the best coating, but patience is required to get it applied. Sometimes intermediate washing of the surface with chlorinated tap water will tarnish the accumulating silver coating sufficiently to accelerate the application. A preheated or naturally bleached specimen may be easier to coat, but the chitin-covered form may receive a more photographable stain.

I have used a hot plate for heating specimens, but Triebel (1958) has described and illustrated an electric heater developed by Beckmann which can be inserted under a piece of mica contained in a specially constructed microslide. This apparatus has the convenience of heating the specimen under the microscope. Levinson (1951) described the use of a platinum dish and a bunsen burner to heat the specimen.

The major disadvantage of using silver nitrate is the permanence of the coating. Cummings (1956) has suggested removal of the silver from foraminifers by vigorous washing with warm water and brush, but this treatment is not recommended. Specimens of microfossils are usually sufficiently abundant to allow sacrifice of a few.

## LIGHTING THE SPECIMEN

Photography in reflected light is employed to show the external morphology of the specimen; transmitted light is used to display internal structures or structures in thin sections.

### REFLECTED LIGHT PHOTOGRAPHY

Most microfossil photography utilizes dark-field illumination. That is to say, the light is played on the upper surface of the specimen; and the excess light not used to illuminate the specimen then passes on through the background out of the lens field. Reflection from surfaces other than those of the specimen is not only aesthetically undesirable, but also causes uncontrolled lighting of the specimen.

The coated specimen should be mounted high above the stage of the microscope where several lights can be directed on it from any angle. The light must be able to pass on through the surface supporting the specimen to provide dark-field illumination and thus an extended black background. Glare from the specimen must be reduced to a minimum, and glare from surrounding objects must be eliminated. The specimen may be held in place with glue as long as the adhesive surface does not reflect light into the camera. The light must be concentrated with high intensity on the desired side or parts of the specimen without eliminating needed shadows in other areas of the specimen.

These prerequisites and a great deal of maneuverability in the working space beneath the objective can be provided by a lucite lighting stage (fig. 2), which consists of a vertically mounted, 1-inch long, solid cylinder of lucite with a well ($\frac{3}{8}$ inch in diam. by $\frac{3}{8}$ inch deep) in the upper end, bonded to a lucite base (2 by 3 by $\frac{1}{4}$ inches); the outside diameter of the lucite cylinder can range from $\frac{1}{2}$ to $1\frac{1}{2}$ inches. The specimen is placed in the well, which is filled with glycerol. The index of refraction of the lucite and the glycerol are close enough so that the specimen has the appearance of being embedded in the lucite. A set of such stages with cylinders of different sizes can provide flexibility in concentrating the light rays on specimens of different sizes. The wall of the lucite cylinder acts as a lens to refract and converge the light on the specimen. Overhead lighting is not usually needed, but if desired can be directed down through the well.

The refractive fluid, glycerol, has the effect of eliminating glare and also apparently flattening the specimen. It is also sufficiently viscous to hold most specimens upright. Gum tragacanth, a lucite chip, or a glass sliver can be used if necessary. Convection currents from the heat of the lights are generally not a problem. Dust can be a nuisance, and the glycerol must be kept clean. The specimen is placed in the glycerol with a small brush. Both the brush and the specimen must be wetted with water first to prevent air bubbles from forming on the surface of the specimen when it is placed in the glycerol.

With this lighting stage I use three American Optical Universal Microscope Illuminators (6.5 volt, 2.75 ampere) which have a three-element condensing system, spiral focusing, and are operated from rheostat-controlled transformers. These lights have stands that are adapted to movable mounts on a horizontal ring that surrounds the whole lower part of the camera and microscope base. Clear (unfrosted) 6-volt bulbs are needed, which permit pinpoint focusing of the light rays on the specimen. One light is used as the primary source, the second for balance, and the third for fill-in, usually from the lower side. For photographing ostracods all three lamps are used; for foraminifera only two lights are used.

The lights must be directed toward the specimen from a low angle to emphasize its surface relief. The use of glycerol, a diaphragm on the objective, and Polaroid Land film will tend to increase the contrast. A fill-in light is required for specimens with considerable surface relief.

Two commercial incident lighting systems are available. The Leitz Ultropak is a series of lenses that surround the objective and direct the light from a single source to envelop the specimen. This instrument was designed to work with the Leitz Laborlux microscope. It does not have the universality of an independent light system, but it is extremely convenient. Another lighting device, used by Triebel (1958), is a curved mirror with a hole in the center (Lieberkühn mirror), which is mounted over the specimen near the objective to receive light from the substage mirror (fig. 4). This apparatus also receives light from a single source but can be tilted on a universal mount to direct light from a particular quadrant.

Fournier (1956) and others have discussed the use of polarized light, monochromatic light, and high intensity light from a carbon arc, which, respectively, offer the advantages of eliminating reflections, reducing lens aberration, and increasing the quantity of light. For most microfossil photography the bulk of such equipment and the inherent lack of maneuverability of the light sources tend to outweigh the slight advantage they provide.

TRANSMITTED LIGHT PHOTOGRAPHY

It is difficult to summarize the problems and techniques of transmitted light photography in a brief discussion in a way that would do justice to the subject. Shillaber (1944) has written an excellent book on the subject which presents ample information about procedures.

Specialists in fusilinids have devised a method of photographing thin sections that eliminates use of the camera entirely. The thin section is placed in an enlarger and its image is projected on sheet film to produce a negative, which is then contact printed.

CONTROL OF EXPOSURE TIME

Besides the quality of light and the way it is directed toward the specimen, the quantity of light that reaches the film must be controlled. Photomicrographs, particularly those taken with reflected light, need long exposures. The length of the exposure depends on the size of the aperture, the speed of the film, and the intensity of the light. The exposures usually are longer than a second but should be kept shorter than a minute. To eliminate transmission of extraneous vibrations in the refractive fluid and in the camera system, the timing of the exposure can be best controlled by turning the lights on and off rather than using the camera shutter. A standard electric darkroom timer serves very well for this purpose.

**REFERENCES**

Cooper, C. L. (1935). Ammonium chloride sublimate apparatus. J. Paleontology, v. 9, p. 357–359.

Cummings, R. H. (1956). Preparation of microfossils for photography. Micropaleontology, v. 2, no. 4, p. 402.

Fournier, G. (1956). New methods and techniques in the photography of microfossils. Micropaleontology, v. 2, p. 37–56.

—— (1957). Construction of pinhole diaphragms for use in photomicrography. Micropaleontology, v. 3, p. 85–87.

Levinson, S. A. (1951). The Triebel technique for staining ostracods. The Micropaleontologist, v. 5, no. 2, p. 27.

Martinsson, A. (1962). Ostracods of the family Beyrichiidae from the Silurian of Gotland. Geol. Inst., Univ. Uppsala, v. 41, p. 1–369.

Shillaber, C. P. (1944). Photomicrography in theory and practice. New York, Wiley, 773 pp.

Triebel, E. (1947). Methodische und technische Fragen der Micropaläontologie. Senkenberg-Buch 19, Frankfurt, Verlag Waldemar Kramer, 47 pp.

——, and H. Freund (1958). Die Photographie im Dienste der Mikropaläontologie. Handbuch der Mikroskopie in der Technik, v. 2, Mikroskopie der Bodenschätze; part 3, Mikroskopie in der Geologie sedimentärer Lagerstätten (Mikropaläontologie), p. 83–144.

# Photomicrography of Thin Sections

## RAYMOND C. DOUGLASS

*U. S. Geological Survey, Washington, D.C.*

The photography of thin sections requires an adequate source of light, a satisfactory method of focusing, lenses capable of providing the desired magnification, and a holder for the sensitized material. The equipment used ranges from the simplest makeshift arrangement to elaborate commercial equipment. The design or selection of an outfit for photographing thin sections should take each of the essential elements into consideration.

### LIGHTING

Illumination of thin sections for photography is similar to that used for viewing slides through a microscope. The requirement is a source of light which will illuminate the entire field evenly and with an intensity sufficient to allow the details being studied to be viewed or photographed. For small areas of thin sections this is no great problem. A standard microscope lamp can be

Publication authorized by the Director, U. S. Geological Survey.

used to light the section directly or by reflection from a plane mirror. Most of the available illuminators will not light a large area evenly. The placement of a plano-convex condenser lens between the illuminator and the section, with the plane side toward the section, tends to even out the light. The larger the diameter of the condenser lens, the larger the area of even illumination. Ideally, a condenser matched to each objective lens should be used to distribute light evenly over the area covered by the objective lens. A double-condenser system of the type used in many projectors and enlargers may be quite adequate as a source of illumination and may be used by adapting the projector or enlarger.

Many photographs of thin sections have been made by placing the section in the negative carrier of an enlarger and the sensitized material on the easel. A double-condenser enlarger is most satisfactory for this purpose, whereas a diffusion enlarger is generally inadequate.

When illumination extends beyond the area to be photographed, the stray light may affect the sensitized material. It is therefore a good idea to mask the area to be photographed. This may be done by placing a diaphragm at the position of the thin section, by cutting out masks to the approximate dimensions of specimens, or by opaqueing around the specimen on the thin section. A set of masks with cutouts of approximate fields is handy. The appropriate mask can be laid on or under the section before making the exposure.

The use of a colored filter is recommended if the lenses used are not corrected for chromatic aberrations. A light-green or light-blue filter can be used with most films without affecting the exposure time too greatly, and will allow the use of the less expensive lenses. The intensity of the light should be controlled with neutral density filters rather than by changing voltage on adjustable transformers.

## OPTICS

The lenses used for photographing thin sections are no different from those used for other types of photography, and the same rules apply. Every lens will give a 1:1 ratio of reproduction on a film plane placed twice the focal length behind the lens or, as it is said, at double bellows extension. If the bellows extension (the distance from lens to film plane) is increased, magnification is produced; if the bellows extension is reduced, a reduction in image size occurs. Any lens, then, can be used for either magnification or reduction, the controlling factor being the distance from the lens to the film plane: the shorter the focal length, the shorter the bellows extension necessary to produce a given magnification. It is generally impractical to use lenses of long focal length for high magnification because of the excessive bellows lengths required.

The problems of depth of field are minimized in the photography of thin sections, so the use of lenses having short focal lengths does not seriously affect the results (see Rasetti, p. 423).

## LOW-MAGNIFICATION OPTICS

Lenses designed for general photographic use can be used for low magnification, as can lenses having shorter focal lengths, such as the 50 mm and 35 mm lenses used on 35 mm cameras; in addition, special lenses for closeup work are obtainable. Magnifications of 20 diameters or less can be attained without necessitating too great a bellows extension. The final image size can be obtained by original magnification or by a combination of magnification and enlargement of the negative. Enlarging a negative does not add any detail; in fact, some of the detail present in a negative may appear to be lost during enlargement, owing to magnification of the grain size. If the negative is made on a fine-grained film, some enlargement is possible without noticeable loss of detail. Enlargements of 5 to 7 diameters can be made without objectionable loss of detail.

The film size may determine the amount of original magnification used. An object magnified $5\times$ may not fit on a 35 mm negative; to obtain a final magnification of $5\times$ the object may have to be photographed at $2.5\times$ and enlarged $2\times$, or the original negative made on a larger film at $5\times$ directly.

## HIGH-MAGNIFICATION OPTICS

For magnifications greater than 20 diameters it is generally necessary to use a compound microscope. In such a system an objective is combined with an ocular to produce double magnification. In a sense this is really magnification and enlargement in one operation. The objective lens is the magnifier. The ocular enlarges the image produced by the objective and cannot add any details not resolved by the objective. An ocular is required, however, to reduce distortion. A low-power ocular of good quality gives all the detail available from the objective; high-powered oculars produce a larger image but produce no more detail. As no film is involved, the enlargement of grain is eliminated, but otherwise the problems are the same as in low-power photography. For higher magnifications, objectives with short focal lengths are used in combination with a negative photographic eyepiece. Depth of focus decreases with increase in magnification and, at high magnifications, may be less than the thickness of the thin section. Some objectives have diaphragms which may be closed down to increase depth of field, but ordinarily the only way to get good depth of field is to photograph at a lower initial magnification with an objective of longer focal length. The choice of ocular to be used should take into account both the power and the design. Some oculars are specially ground to produce a flat field; these are best suited for photography. Either stereoscopic or biologic-type binocular microscopes can be used for photography, but the monocular types generally can be adapted more easily because of their vertical ocular tube. Some microscopes have both inclined binoculars and a vertical tube especially for photography.

## SHUTTERS AND LIGHT CONTROLS

The duration of an exposure may be controlled in several ways. In many setups, a mechanical shutter is necessary; in others, the lights may be turned on and off, a lens cap simply removed and replaced, or a dark card placed in front of the lens may be removed for the exposure and then replaced. The method of control depends on the intensity of the light source and the speed of the emulsion on the sensitized material. If a fast film is being used, instantaneous speeds may be required, and these can only be timed accurately with a mechanical shutter. If a slower sensitized film or paper is being used, a timed light source or a hand switch may be sufficient, or the lens cap method may be satisfactory.

In general, focal-plane shutters tend to set up more of a vibration than between-the-lens shutters and should only be used if all the vibration occurs after the exposure is made. Between-the-lens shutters also vary in their action and should be checked as possible sources of vibration. Some behind-the-lens shutters are also available. These should also be checked for vibration.

A variety of light controls are available. The simplest is an on-off switch for the entire light system. In using this the lights are turned off when everything is set up for the exposure; the protective cover for the film is removed (this may be the dark-slide of a film holder or the equivalent); the lights are switched on for the prescribed time and switched off again; the protective cover is replaced and the lights switched back on. In some setups the room lights will not affect the exposure, and may be left on while the dark-slide is removed and the exposure made. Mechanically timed light controls are available for timing the exposure. Several kinds of these are made to control printers or enlargers. Some automatically turn out the room lights during the exposure. Some light sources tend to surge when the power is first turned on and cannot be used for constant on-off operation, in which case one of the other methods of exposure control must be used.

Some commercial photomicrography equipment now comes with an integrated lighting and light-control system which is electronically timed. A wide range of exposure times is available and no mechanical shutter is used, so the problem of shutter vibration, even at slow speeds, is eliminated.

## SENSITIZED MATERIALS

The purpose for which photomicrographs are taken should determine the kind of sensitized material that will be used. A wide range of materials is available, from glass plates through a variety of films to Polaroid[1] and

---

[1] Registered trade name.

various papers. When the image is going to be recorded only for study, regular printing papers, projection papers, or rapid printing papers should be used. These provide a direct negative print which is satisfactory for many study purposes. One type of polaroid film provides direct positive prints, another type provides a negative in addition to a positive print. Films are available in a wide variety of emulsions and sizes. The large films tend to buckle somewhat, which throws part of the picture out of focus. This buckling is minimized in the smaller sheet films and in many of the roll films, which are held under tension from the roll and pressure from a pressure plate in the camera back. Glass plates do not buckle but are fragile and more difficult to work with.

Sensitized materials come in a wide range of emulsion speeds. The slow-speed emulsions generally have a finer grained texture and are therefore capable of recording finer detail than the high-speed films. If any enlargement is to be made from the negative, the grain size of the sensitized emulsion should be taken into consideration. For contact printing, the grain size is seldom a problem.

## THE STAND

A good stand for photomicrography should be rigid, versatile, and equipped with a satisfactory means of focusing. It should be sufficiently large and heavy to hold the camera equipment in a steady, balanced position with a minimum of vibration. The upright on a light-weight stand may vibrate independently of the base when a heavy camera is mounted on it. Any such vibration will blur the negatives. On a horizontal mount all elements from light source to film plane should have internal rigidity so that no part moves independently of the rest when locked in position. Many enlarger stands can be adapted for photography either by converting the enlarger head itself (usually by removal of the lamp housing) or by mounting a camera in place of the enlarger head. Other ready-made stands include copy stands and complete photomicrography outfits.

Versatility is an important feature in a stand. If possible, a stand should be adaptable to large or small cameras with or without long bellows extension. The camera mount should be adjustable for height or distance from the object stage. The ideal adjustment is a smoothly operating rack and pinion which can be locked at any desired position. There should be room for a light source and stage, or for a microscope and light source.

Focusing methods in photomicrography vary from moving the camera or moving the object in relation to the camera, to moving the lens in relation to the film plane or the film plane in relation to the lens. Any time the lens-to-film distance is changed, the magnification ratio is changed. If pictures are to be made at a constant magnification, only movement of the object relative to the entire camera or vice versa can be used for focusing. Movement of the object by any large distance requires comparable movement of the lighting system if optimum lighting is to be maintained. With thin sections the plane of focus varies so little that once a setup at a given magnification has been completed, the distance the thin sections would be moved to bring each into focus would be of no consequence in relation to the lighting. Focusing by moving the entire camera is practical and easy with small or light cameras, but with large cameras or long bellows extensions it is much easier to leave the camera fixed and move the object. A focusing stage can be made or adapted from a microscope base with rack.

The rack should move as smoothly as possible without backlash. It is often difficult to reach the focusing knob for the stage while viewing the image in the ground glass. A prism or mirror can be useful near the ground glass, but if a remote focusing device can be installed near the ground glass, focusing is made faster and more accurate. A geared rod extension or a pulley and belt can sometimes be adapted to operate the focusing stage.

## OPERATION

The photography of thin sections is relatively simple because one does not have to balance several lights to obtain or eliminate shadows, and one does not have to worry about depth of field. Several factors are important, however, for obtaining photographs which will be of good enough quality for reproduction. Alignment of all elements in the photographic setup, whether vertical or horizontal, is of importance in minimizing distortion. Distortion cannot be eliminated completely, but it should be reduced to a minimum. The planes of the sensitized material and of the object should be parallel, and the optical axis of the lens should be at right angles to these planes. Focusing should be done by moving the object or camera along the axis of the lens. The beam of light from the illuminator should strike the thin section at right angles—that is, along the axis of the lens. The light should also be centered on the area of the thin section to be photographed.

The magnification can be determined by placing a stage micrometer in the position of the thin section and measuring its image at the film plane, usually on the ground glass. When this cannot be done, it is necessary to photograph the micrometer or scale and then measure it on the processed negative. When photographs are to be enlarged from the original negative size, it is convenient to photograph the micrometer or scale along with the object. The final magnification of the positive can then be checked directly by measuring the enlarged image of the scale, making it unnecessary to know the exact magnification on the negative.

Focusing is best accomplished on a ground glass screen. Some reflex cameras have a through-the-lens viewing system either with or without ground-glass screen, and no additional equipment is needed for focusing the object. With other types of cameras, a focusing magnifier is useful for inspecting the image on the ground glass. Many ground glass screens have a clear spot for use with a focusing magnifier. The magnifier must be focused first on the ground glass or on a cross hair provided and then moved over the clear spot to view the air image of the object for fine focusing. If the magnifier is not focused on the film plane first, an object in focus in the clear spot may not be in focus on the film. Focusing should always be done with the diaphragm (if any) wide open.

Proper exposure can be determined in several ways, depending on the equipment available. If a sensitive light meter is available it can be used at the film position; otherwise a series of test shots will have to be made to determine optimum exposure time. Whatever system is used, it will be profitable to keep records which will allow duplication of both setup and exposure. For each magnification and lighting intensity an approximate exposure can be determined for an average thin section. Then modifications can be determined for darker or thicker sections and for lighter or thinner sections.

The records should include magnification, light setting, lens and diaphragm setting, film type, exposure used, and number or description of the object. Familiarity with the equipment and appearance of the image on the ground glass will help in estimating approximate exposures. If a Polaroid camera or back can be adapted to the setup, exposures can be determined rapidly and adjustment made for the difference in film speed when shooting with regular film. One frame of Polaroid film can be used as a test strip by pulling the dark slide out a certain distance at a time to make a sequence of exposures differing by a chosen unit of time. If the proper exposure falls within the range of the test it can be determined quickly and easily.

A check list for making exposures is often a time saver. It should include such items as:

1. Light source of right intensity and centered.
2. Image centered and in focus with the diaphragm open.
3. Image masked to edge of picture area.
4. Lens clean and diaphragm closed to proper setting.
5. Shutter (if any) set to proper position and checked for action.
6. Unexposed film in position.
7. Reflex mirror (if any) swung out of light path.
8. Dark-slide (if any) pulled on film holder.
9. Shutter activated or lights switched for exposure.
10. Dark slide replaced.
11. Film advanced or removed.
12. Record made of exposure and subject.

Dust is an endless problem in photomicrography. Every precaution should be taken to eliminate sources of dust around the equipment. It helps to keep dust covers of plastic or other material over all equipment not in use. Dust-proof containers for the light source and lenses save time and trouble, and cleaning of each section just before photographing is often necessary. The delicate adjustment of the light source and the alignment of the optical system should be protected from jarring. Equipment should be kept out of normal circulation paths. It is sometimes necessary to reserve a space specifically for photomicrography.

# Whitening Fossils

PORTER M. KIER

*U. S. National Museum, Washington, D.C.*

RICHARD E. GRANT, ELLIS L. YOCHELSON

*U. S. Geological Survey, Washington, D.C.*

Surface detail may be brought out by coating fossils lightly with a white powder. When powder is blown across a fossil, it tends to cling to protuberances without settling in hollows, thus accentuating surface characteristics. Several different whitening techniques have been used for many years; they are most commonly employed in the United States, but recently many photographs in foreign publications show whitened specimens. Not only are whitened specimens superior in detail, but their uniformity of tone and texture produces a better-looking plate.

For good detail the whitening should be thin and light. It should be gray rather than chalk white. Too heavy a coat defeats the purpose of the whitening because it fills in the surface hollows and obscures rather than increases detail. The coat should be extremely fine grained; coarse grains of whitening material obscure true detail or may add spurious detail.

The specimen should be clean and dry to insure uniform adherence of the whitening agent. Oils from modeling clays and from hands inhibit clinging of the powder; they may be removed with any common organic solvent (acetone, carbon tetrachloride). Unless the surface of the fossil and matrix is already of fairly uniform color, for best results it should be inked to give it a homogeneous dark tone. Ordinary fountain-pen ink may be used for this purpose, as it can be readily bleached with a mixture of ammonia

Published by permission of the Secretary of the Smithsonian Institution and the Director, U. S. Geological Survey.

and hydrogen peroxide solutions to restore the original color of the specimen. India ink should not be used, as it is almost impossible to remove from a porous matrix. Dark latex molds need no treatment and produce excellent photographs when coated.

Coating specimens is best done in an area free from drafts. It is advisable to remove the coating as soon as the specimen has been examined or photographed. Specimens are occasionally damaged by ammonium chloride; this chemical is particularly bad for rubber casts and will cause them to rot and swell. Ammonium chloride is soluble in water. Other common whitening agents are insoluble and must be brushed or blown off.

Ammonium chloride is one of the most commonly used whiteners (Bassler, 1953). One method generates ammonium chloride smoke by the reaction of hydrochloric acid (HCl) with ammonium hydroxide ($NH_4OH$) in a simple but ingenious apparatus. Separate vials of HCl and $NH_4OH$ are corked with two-hole stoppers. A piece of glass tubing, bent to a right angle, is run through each stopper nearly to the bottom of each vial. A shorter tube extends just through the second hole in each stopper and leads forward to terminate in a tapered tip. The vials are filled so that the ends of the long tubes are below the surfaces of the two chemicals. The operator blows through the free ends of the longer tubes which forces fumes from the chemicals out through the shorter tubes at the tops of the vials. These fumes unite as they leave the tapered tips, and form a smoky sublimate of ammonium chloride ($NH_4Cl$), which is blown at the specimen to be coated. The specimen should be held away from the tips of the glass tubes so that the smoke is not too thick and the amount of coating can be controlled.

Once the glassware has been set up, this wet method is easy to use and will produce much sublimate with little effort. The coating is deliquescent, however, and becomes wet and uneven in high humidity. On extremely humid days this method is almost useless, unless specimens are heated before coating. As water tends to inhibit the formation of the sublimate, the apparatus should always be dry before use. Only chemically pure reagents should be used, and these should be changed at frequent intervals so that they do not collect moisture. Whitening should not be done in the vicinity of optical equipment; the fumes may damage lenses.

An alternate method (Cooper, 1935; Teichert, 1948; Sass, 1962) is to heat powdered $NH_4Cl$ until it sublimes and then blow the powder across a specimen. A simple and useful device for this process is a Pyrex glass tube, one end of which is blown into a sphere with an opening at one side. This may be loaded by pushing the sphere end into a jar of powdered $NH_4Cl$; the powder should be below the level of the tube and the hole at the far side of the sphere. (The sphere should be heated over a gas burner or a forced-draft alcohol lamp. A small alcohol lamp may be used, but only with some difficulty.) Once a sublimate is formed, it is blown out of the sphere onto a specimen. No extra glass tubing should be attached to the far side of the sphere, as the efficiency drops markedly as the sublimate cools.

This dry method has the advantage of using powder rather than corrosive liquids. It is not as limited by humidity and seems to supply a finer grained coat, but it does have the disadvantage of requiring an open flame. More sophisticated devices can be made by wrapping the tubing with Nichrome wire and heating it electrically. A pressure bulb can be used at the end of the tube to blow the sublimate outward.

Another fairly common whitening method (Rasetti, 1947) consists in burning magnesium ribbon to produce a smoke of magnesium oxide. Magnesium ribbon may be lit with difficulty by an ordinary match; a small alcohol or gas flame readily ignites it. The specimen to be coated is held above the flame in the path of the rising magnesium oxide. The advantages of this method lie in the availability of materials used, the exceedingly fine grain produced, and the coating's resistance to humidity.

Magnesium burns with an intense, bright flame. To avoid being burned, the operator should handle the specimen with tweezers and should hold the specimen at least a few inches from the burning ribbon. To limit the fire hazard, only short strips of ribbon should be used. A simple way to channel the magnesium oxide fumes is to burn the ribbon under an inverted funnel that rests on a chemist's tripod. The fumes come out the small end of the funnel, and the specimen is held above. Density of the coating can be controlled fairly well by adjusting the distance from the top of the funnel to the specimen and the duration of the exposure.

There are slight differences in the type of coating obtained with the ammonium chloride or magnesium oxide methods. The ammonium chloride procedure is definitely superior for uniformly coating large specimens (say more than one inch across) and especially those possessing deep concavities, in which magnesium oxide is deposited only with difficulty. Magnesium oxide, however, is preferable when the purpose is to bring out exceedingly shallow furrows or similar surface features, as it is more selective in its preferential deposition on the prominent parts of the specimen.

Antimony tetroxide has also been used for whitening fossils (Poulsen, 1957). The white smoke is obtained by passing an air current through a quartz bulb containing heated metallic antimony. Care must be exercised, as the fumes are poisonous.

Jeffords and Miller (1960) suggested the use of an air brush to spread a suspension of a fine white powder in a fast-drying liquid. One part magnesium oxide in 20 parts of alcohol is reported to produce good results. The method should combine some of the advantages of those previously described. Directing the jet obliquely onto the specimen allows selective coating of one side of the depressions, thus producing the appearance of shadows even under uniform lighting.

## REFERENCES

Bassler, R. S. (1953). Bryozoa, *in* R. C. Moore (ed.), Treatise on invertebrate paleontology, pt. G, Univ. Kansas Press and Geol. Soc. America.

Cooper, C. L. (1935). Ammonium chloride sublimate apparatus. J. Paleontology, v. 9, p. 357–359.

Jeffords, R. M., and T. H. Miller (1960). Air brush for whitening fossils and notes on photography. J. Paleontology, v. 34, p. 275–276, pl. 39.

Poulsen, Christian (1957). Improved method for whitening fossils for study. J. Paleontology, v. 31, p. 1029.

Rasetti, Franco (1947). Notes on techniques in invertebrate paleontology. J. Paleontology, v. 21, p. 397–399.

Sass, D. B. (1962). Improved techniques for the photographing of fossils. J. Paleontology, v. 36, p. 170–176, 1 text-fig.

Teichert, Curt (1948). A simple device for coating fossils with ammonium chloride. J. Paleontology, v. 22, p. 102–104, 1 text-fig.

# Preparation of Plates for Paleontologic Publication

ALLISON R. PALMER

*U. S. Geological Survey, Washington, D.C.*

Adequate illustration is almost as important as accurate description in a paleontological publication; the value of many an otherwise excellent paleontological report has been severely limited by poor illustration. Thoughtful preparation of plates will not only add to the polish of a paper, but will also eliminate many technical problems in reproduction and publication.

Before preparing plates for publication, the author should determine the dimensions of plates printed by the journal to which the paper will be submitted, and also the kind of reproduction available—that is, half-tone (including screen size) or collotype. Many paleontological journals state the plate dimensions on the inside of the cover. The dimensions can also be obtained by measuring published plates. Both the plate dimensions and the kind of reproduction can always be determined by writing to the editor. The kind of reproduction may influence the choice of journal, and it has an im-

Publication authorized by the Director, U. S. Geological Survey.

portant bearing on the character of the photographic prints used on the plates.

A plate is only as good as the photographs that make it up. Not only must the quality of the prints be good, but thought must be given to whether the characters being illustrated and described are adequately shown. For best published results, prints for half-tone publication should generally have slightly more contrast than desired, and prints for collotype reproduction should have slightly less contrast than desired, because contrast is reduced slightly in the half-tone printing process and heightened slightly in the collotype printing process. If resolution of surface detail or small structures is important for illustration of a species, be sure the magnification is sufficient to show this without causing eyestrain. Enlargement of critical parts of a specimen is often the most efficient way to do this. Degree of magnification can be given in the plate description or, preferably, can be shown graphically by attaching a similarly enlarged photograph of a millimeter scale or some other suitable scale to a margin of the photograph. If geometry of the species is important, as it is for many trilobites and for internal structures of many brachiopods and pelecypods, stereophotographs should be considered (see Rasetti's paper in this volume). Complete stereophotography of all specimens is generally not necessary and may result in additional expense for the author because of the increased number of plates. Judicious use of stereophotographs can, however, greatly enhance the value of illustrations of some specimens.

Adequate illustration also refers to the quantity of photographs used for a species. Characteristic specimens, examples of limits in structural variability, and views of all critical surfaces should be shown. But in these days of high cost of illustration, the question should always be asked: Is this picture really necessary? Photographs showing characters duplicated on other illustrated specimens should be avoided.

Completed photographs can be treated in several ways to facilitate plate composition or to emphasize illustrated features. Photographs of free specimens prepared against a black background (see Rasetti's paper) can be left on a black rectangle and mounted on a white background, or they can be trimmed about $\frac{1}{8}$ inch beyond the fossil outline and mounted on a black background. If a black background is used, the trimmed edges of each photograph should be painted black after mounting so that they will not show in the reproduction of the plate. If details of outline are not critical for comparison or identification, opaqueing around the margin of the fossil on the negative will result in a print of the specimen against a white background. Opaqueing, however, should be done sparingly. The image of a specimen should never be cut from a photograph. Specimens photographed in a natural matrix should generally be left on a rectangle that shows contact with the matrix. If the photograph does not show the features desired it is better to try another picture than to retouch. Sometimes not all details of small specimens can be shown in focus by a single photograph. Although several photographs showing different parts in focus can be used, a composite picture can be prepared, using only parts of each of several prints that are in focus. This is particularly helpful when space is at a premium.

Once the proper number of photographs of good quality is ready for mounting, consideration should be given to the materials used in mounting. The background material should be stiff enough to withstand rough handling and mailing without bending or folding. It should have a margin of at least $1\frac{1}{2}$ inches, to protect the area to be reproduced. Either a black or a white background can be used. White backgrounds are generally recommended; black backgrounds are occasionally used with striking effect to illustrate free specimens having irregular or ornamented margins, but plates with black backgrounds are difficult to reproduce with good contrast on the photographs.

Photographs can be attached to the background material by a variety of both wet and dry media. Wet media such as paste or glue have distinct disadvantages if photographs have to be rearranged after they have been mounted. Rubber cement is more effective as a wet mounting medium, but it can discolor a print and will deteriorate with time. Dry media such as mounting tissues applied with a warm iron or special double-surfaced wax paper applied by pressure have the advantage of permanence plus general ease of removal for rearrangement without damage to the mounting surface.

Logic of arrangement of photographs and their subsequent numbering on each plate deserves careful thought. Poor arrangement or random numbering of even the best photographs detracts from their usefulness and from the quality of a paper. Generally all specimens of a species should be grouped together on the same plate. In monographs that emphasize systematics and in which several plates are needed, photographs of related species should be grouped conveniently for comparative purposes. When faunal differences and stratigraphic paleontology are being emphasized, groups of photographs of associated species may be preferred. If possible, larger pictures should be placed toward the bottom or left margin of the plate, but logic should not be sacrificed to balance. Adequate space should be left for the placement of numbers so that they can be clearly associated with the proper picture. If stereophotographs are used, only the left member of a stereopair needs to be numbered. Numbers should usually be consecutive from left to right, beginning at the top of the plate. A random arrangement of numbers may be symptomatic of illogical arrangement of the photographs on the plate. When many photographs of several similar species are to be shown on the same plate, inked lines surrounding the group of photographs of each species often improve the usability of the plate. Designation of each outlined area with a letter will further increase the usefulness of this device

When all photographs have been mounted, a final touch of quality can be added to rectangular photographs of specimens in matrix by squaring up each picture with the plate margins and adjacent photographs by using a razor blade and a T-square. The surface of the finished plate should be protected by a clean sheet of paper attached to the upper edge of the background material.

The finished plate should be accompanied by a description providing name; figure number; brief description of the view, including comments on specific features (e.g., interior, left valve, note characteristic form of duplicature); magnification, locality collection number, and museum catalog number for each specimen. All holotypes, lectotypes, or neotypes should be specifically indicated.

As a general rule, drawings should not be included on plates with photographs. These can be reproduced at much less expense as text figures, but plates composed only of drawings are used, particularly for illustrating Foraminifera. Good plates of drawings are subject to the same recommendations for logical arrangement, balance, and numbering as are good plates of photographs.

# Preparation of Drawings for Paleontologic Publication

LAWRENCE B. ISHAM

*U. S. National Museum, Washington, D.C.*

A technical illustration is an attempt to reduce a three-dimensional object to an accurate, two-dimensional image which can be reproduced by current printing methods. The illustrator is primarily concerned with outline and shadow, and a good illustration is one in which these two items are correctly located and properly rendered. The outline and shading of an illustration should be regarded as separate steps, referred to as preliminary drawing and rendering.

## PRELIMINARY DRAWING

The preliminary drawing is a refined, unshaded sketch of the desired aspect of the object to be illustrated. The initial rough sketch may be obtained by several methods. In drawing by observation alone, without the aid of mechanical or optical devices, a rough general outline is first put down, omitting details. This will serve as a guide, and may be merely a square, an oval, or

Published by permission of the Secretary of the Smithsonian Institution.

some other simple shape to represent an outer limit within which the drawing will be made. This helps to center the sketch on the paper, and confine it to a desired size. The outline of the subject would come into contact with this outer limit at several points, where the specimen has its extremes of length and width or where it bears projections. Establishing these points and gradually revising the lines connecting them will produce the outline. Once any two points are fixed on the sketch, all further sketching of lines should be done by comparison with the distance between those two points. In laying out any distance on the sketch, it must be considered in terms of multiples or fractions of the first distance decided upon, thus keeping the whole sketch in scale. By comparing relative distances and angles between points on the specimen, the sketch is refined until an acceptable likeness is produced.

There are several devices which may be used to produce a preliminary drawing with greater speed and accuracy. Dividers or proportional dividers permit direct comparison between measurements on the specimen and lines drawn on the sketch. Proportional dividers also lend size control to the drawing so that it may be of a desired magnification. A camera lucida sketch or a tracing from a photograph allows immediate delineation of the outline and main features of the specimen, and can easily be refined to produce a preliminary drawing.

To conserve the surface quality of the drawing paper on which the illustration will be completed, it is advisable to carry out these preliminary steps on separate paper. Tracing paper is best for this purpose, since the progressive accumulation of extraneous lines and erasures will probably necessitate several separate stages. Each successive stage is begun by tracing only the most accurate lines of the preceding one. This will eventually produce an acceptable preliminary drawing on tracing paper.

Before transferring the sketch to drawing paper, it may be necessary to change the drawing to a desired size. The limitations of page size of the published copy, the desired magnification, and the possible deleterious effects of excessive reduction are factors to be considered. In general, it is wise to decide first what size the printed illustration should be, then make the drawing one and one-half times this size, with instructions to the printer to reduce it one-third. This amount of reduction will usually improve the appearance of the illustration.

The size of the drawing may be changed by the use of a projector or proportional dividers, or by placing the tracing paper sketch over a grid such as graph paper, and using a larger or smaller grid to scale the drawing.

To transfer this corrected sketch to drawing paper, the reverse side of the tracing paper is coated with graphite by means of a B or HB pencil, and any loose graphite is removed by shaking or blowing it from the paper. The graphite coating need not be particularly heavy or uniform. The sketch is then placed, face up, in the desired position on the drawing paper and taped down to prevent shifting. A sharply pointed hard pencil is then used to trace over the sketch, transferring the lines to the drawing paper by means of the graphite coating. Frequently these transferred lines must be refined by carefully going over them with a B or HB pencil. Smudges of graphite may best be removed with a pliable eraser of the kneaded-rubber type. The preliminary drawing, ready for rendering, should consist of fine, light lines, with the main outlines free of interruptions, vague areas, or other ambiguities.

## SHADING; GENERAL

The first and most important consideration in shading the preliminary drawing is observation of the specimen. Superficial details and perhaps taxonomic characteristics must be disregarded in favor of viewing the general shape of the object and the manner in which the light falls upon it. Customarily the specimen is illuminated from the upper left. It is better to draw the general form of the specimen and use this as a foundation upon which to build up details than to shade the details and later attempt to depict the overall shape.

A shaded rendering of the preliminary drawing should not be attempted before making one or more rough sketches which show the location and values of the shadows. This may be done by placing a piece of tracing paper over the preliminary drawing and quickly filling in the shadow masses by holding a soft pencil at a low angle, so that each pencil stroke leaves a wide mark on the paper. The values, or relative densities of the shadows should be decided upon in this stage, especially if the final rendering is to be in ink. The best of these shaded sketches is retained as a guide to follow in the final rendering.

In working on the final drawing a wrapping-paper mask should be taped to the illustration, leaving uncovered only that portion being worked upon, thus keeping the margins clean and allowing more freedom in handling the drawing as it is being shaded.

## STIPPLE DRAWINGS

A sphere may be used to show the various steps in completing a stipple drawing. When the preliminary pencil drawing has been made, the outline is inked (fig. 1,*a*), and the pencil-shaded rough tracing (fig.1,*b*) is referred to for locating the highlights and shadows. These may be lightly outlined in pencil on the inked drawing (fig. 1,*c*). Since the paper will be left blank where brightly lighted areas are depicted, all other parts of the object should be shaded to some degree. Working inward, a closely spaced single line of stipples is placed along the edge, touching the circumference (fig. 1,*d*). Another line, with dots alternating with those of the outer row, is inked along the edge (fig. 1,*d*), and further stippling is inked in, gradually increasing the distance between individual dots until a graded band of shading extends around the drawing. The area of darkest shadow is densely stippled (fig. 1,*e*),

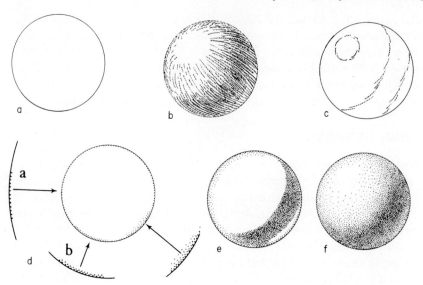

**Fig. 1.** *Successive steps used in making a stipple drawing of a spherical object.*

and then the areas of intermediate shading are filled in, starting with closely spaced stippling adjacent to the band of darkest shadow, and gradually making the dots more dispersed toward the highlight (fig. 1,*f*), thus completing the drawing.

Minor errors, such as misplaced stipples or slight detours of the pen in following a line, may be corrected when the ink is completely dry by carefully scraping the ink away with a sharp razor blade, taking care not to damage the paper too severely. After removing most of the ink in this fashion, the area is cleaned with an abrasive typing eraser. If heavy drawing paper of good quality has been used, a final rubbing with a soft eraser will smooth the area enough to allow corrections to be drawn in. It is possible to purchase opaque, white, correcting fluids which are brushed on, dry almost immediately, and take ink very well. The printed linecut will not show clean erasures or correcting fluid, nor will it show where a change has been made by pasting a piece of drawing paper over part of the drawing and inking the changes on a new surface.

### LINE SHADING

Line shading may be substituted for stippling. In one of these techniques, lines of uniform width are drawn with a stiff pen. The spacing may be varied, and the lines broken to produce varying degrees of contrast (fig. 2,*b*). In another technique, shown in fig. 2,*c,* a flexible pen is used to change the width of the lines. Line shading takes less time than stippling, but requires

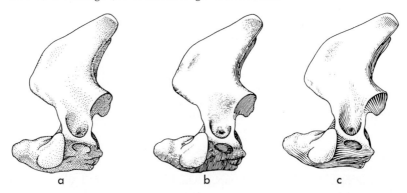

**Fig. 2.** *Examples of different shading methods using pen and ink.*

more practice, since the length, thickness, curve, and direction of each line may affect the illustration. A stipple drawing (fig. 2,*a*) is included for comparison.

## SCRATCHBOARD

Scratchboard is a drawing paper which has a surface of smooth chalk on one side. When this surface has been inked and allowed to dry, fine white lines may be scratched on the inked area, using any sharp instrument such as a pointed knife blade. Scratchboard knives are sold which resemble those with disposable blades used in model making. Scratchboard will not withstand careless handling because of its fragile drawing surface, and should be mounted on a heavy backing. Although the chalk surface takes ink very well, more time must be allowed for drying than on ordinary paper.

The outline of the drawing is inked on the scratchboard (fig. 3,*a*) and two coats of India ink are applied to the areas of dense shadow (fig. 3,*b*) with a small sable brush. When the ink is thoroughly dry, white lines are

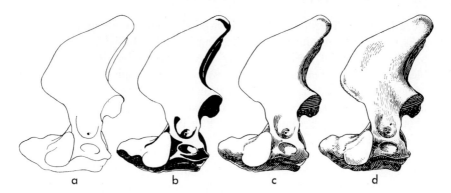

**Fig. 3.** *Successive steps used in an illustration done on scratchboard.*

scratched through it (fig. 3,*c*), generally following the form of the subject, in this case the axis vertebra of a wild pig. The spacing and width of these white lines may be varied to obtain different values in the dark areas. The edges of the shaded areas are softened by extending them with dots or lines drawn with a pen. Areas of lighter shadow may also be done in this manner (fig. 3,*d*). This method can be a fast, effective means of producing text figures, avoiding the time-consuming task of densely stippling large areas.

## STIPPLE BOARD

Stipple board is a drawing paper which has a textured surface composed of small, closely spaced, raised dots. When a line is drawn upon it with a lithographic crayon or a black china-marking pencil, close inspection shows the line to be made up of minute dark dots where the black wax of the crayon has adhered to the raised pattern of the paper surface.

The outline and important details are drawn with India ink, using a fine pen; the drawing is then shaded by varying pressure on the crayon to achieve several degrees of density. Large areas may be shaded quickly, and the technique is less confining and tedious than hand stippling. The drawing may be printed by linecut and will closely resemble a stippled ink drawing. Stipple board having a chalk surface is available, and as with scratchboard, white lines may be scratched into it after the drawing is shaded. This quality makes it especially effective where it is desirable to show sutures, surface spines, or other details in the darker portions of the drawing. In shading the drawing, the darkest parts may be painted over with ink and lightened, after drying, by scraping the surface to remove the ink from the raised dots. This produces an area of white stipples on a black background, and offers a tone intermediate between an area solidly inked in black, and one having black stipples produced by the wax crayon.

## BLEACHING INKED PHOTOGRAPHS

Occasionally a linecut text figure is needed when a photograph is available. It is possible to produce a line drawing by using India ink directly on the photographic print, later removing the photographic image by chemical bleaching. The photograph is inked with a stiff mapping pen for uniformity of line. Three solutions are necessary for the bleaching process, two of which are stock solutions to be diluted and mixed for use. The third solution is a photographic fixative, diluted according to the manufacturer's instructions for fixing print papers.

The first stock solution is made by adding 1¾ ounces of potassium permanganate to 32 ounces of water. The second is made by diluting 1 ounce of sulfuric acid with 32 ounces of water. The photograph is bleached in a dilute mixture made by combining 1 ounce of potassium permanganate stock solution with 2 ounces of the acid stock solution, and diluting this with 64 ounces of water. The separate stock solutions may be stored indefinitely, but when they are mixed and diluted, the resulting bleaching solution should be used immediately. When the print is placed in the bleaching solution the photographic image will disappear and the print paper will become yellow. It is then transferred to the fixative to remove the yellow color. The print is left in each solution only long enough to achieve the desired effect. When the print is completely white except for the inked lines, it is placed in running water to remove the excess fixative. After being thoroughly rinsed, the print is dried and mounted.

Although there are several methods involving different combinations of chemicals which will produce the same result, this method is rapid, and the chemicals are easily obtained. For technical advice concerning this method of bleaching photographs, the writer is indebted to Mr. Jack Scott of the Photographic Laboratory, United States National Museum.

The techniques mentioned thus far are intended for linecut reproduction. Other techniques are reproduced by halftone engravings, and two of these, pencil drawings and retouched photographs, will be considered here.

## PENCIL SHADING

In discussing pencil drawings the materials used must be given some consideration. The paper should be two or three-ply drawing paper or illustration board, and should be fairly smooth but not glossy. Although there is available a wide variety of pencils, it is suggested that those harder than 2H or softer than 4B would be of little use in the methods set forth here. It would be best to start with a selection of four grades of pencils—2H, B, 2B, and 4B. The softer pencils (2B and 4B) are used up more quickly, and pencils should be obtained in quantities proportional to the degree of softness. To facilitate effective pencil shading it will be necessary to acquire some paper tortillon stumps. These are small cylinders of fibrous paper made by rolling up a strip of coarse paper at a slight angle so that one end is pointed. A kneaded-rubber eraser will also be necessary. This is a soft, nonabrasive eraser which may be manipulated into any desired shape for erasing fine lines or cleaning large areas.

The first step in shading by this method is to block in the shaded areas on the drawing by means of a stump, using a paper stump coated with graphite. The stump is coated by smearing heavy 4B pencil lines drawn on scrap paper. If a new stump is employed it may be too hard to pick up graphite, in which case a razor blade is used to shape the point, exposing cut fibers of the paper and creating a surface to which graphite will adhere readily. The shaded areas are indicated quickly and smoothly by this indirect transfer of graphite to the drawing, and since graphite applied by this method is readily removed with the eraser, corrections and refinements are facilitated.

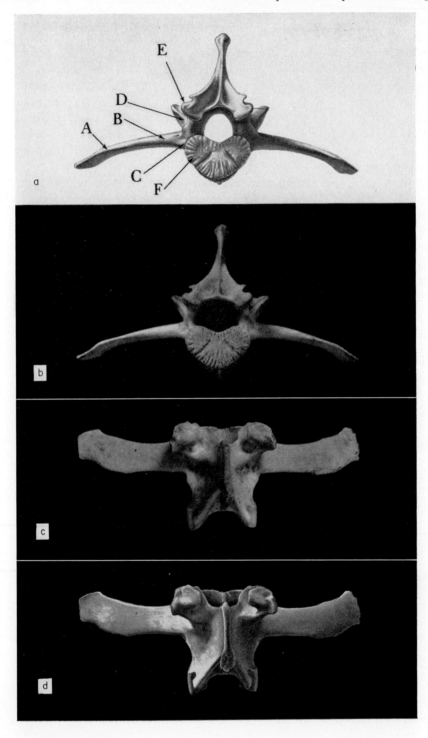

The soft pencils are used to darken the stumped areas for the stronger shadows. The areas so darkened should be slightly smaller than is ultimately intended since they will be spread slightly in using a stump to blur the edges. The stump is used again to smooth groups of pencil strokes so that they do not appear as striations on the finished drawing. As with other techniques, it is necessary to minimize in this way the natural texture of the medium being employed. The intent of the drawing is primarily representational rather than artistic, and the texture of the medium might be interpreted to be the surface texture of the specimen being illustrated.

In fig. 4,*a* it will be noted that abrupt changes in contour result in hard-edged shadows as at A, whereas at B, the surface of the specimen is gradually rounded and the shadow edge is indistinct. It is apparent from the photograph (fig. 4,*b*) that some of the shading contrast on the pencil drawing is intensified to achieve a particular result, rather than to depict natural shading. This is true at C, where the shading is darker than normal, and at D, where the shading is deliberately light. In both places these adjustments allow more contrast to be used to indicate that the overlying structures at E and F project somewhat toward the viewer and are in different planes than C and D. Silhouetting one part against the other in this manner helps to portray depth.

On the lighter side of the drawing, the harder pencils are used for details and more delicate shading. On the darker side, details must be shown by using the softer pencils and assuming a secondary light source at the lower right. If it is necessary to drastically lighten a small area already darkly shaded, in order to insert some important feature, a hard typewriter eraser of the kind which may be sharpened in a pencil-sharpener is a useful instrument. These contain an abrasive and should be used sparingly. Details on the dark side of the specimen should be less evident. The eye "expects" fine detail to be lost in shadow, and too much detail in the shadows will detract from their effectiveness in showing the general shape and will tend to make the illustration appear "flat."

## RETOUCHING PHOTOGRAPHS

When photographs are to be used for illustrations it is sometimes necessary to retouch the prints to emphasize details or alter the shading. Some authors view retouched photographs with suspicion and are reluctant to use this illustrating technique, although this reluctance apparently does not extend to the use of descriptive text to describe what would be presented graphically by a retouched photograph. In many cases unretouched photographs contribute

**Fig. 4.** (*A*) *Pencil drawing of wild pig vertebra.* (*B*) *Photograph of same view as in A.* (*C*) *Photograph before retouching.* (*D*) *Retouched photograph.*

little to a publication; with a little effort, the photographs could be a useful supplement to the text.

It is best if the print is on paper with a document finish or other dull finish. If it is a glossy print, it should be dulled by rubbing with a fine abrasive. Commercial powders are sold for this purpose, but the same effect can be achieved by rubbing the print with a coarse eraser or a pad impregnated with ordinary household cleanser to remove the gloss without leaving heavy scratches.

Figures 4,c and 4,d, an extreme example, show a photograph before and after retouching, and depict a dorsal view of the bone shown in fig. 4,b. The unretouched photograph (fig. 4,c) shows the subject slightly out of focus, and because of faulty illumination the ridges and projecting processes of the specimen are understated. If the specimen is observed lighted from the upper left, the shadows and highlights are arranged as in fig. 4,d, the retouched copy.

The lighter areas are painted on the photograph using a very small sable brush and chinese-white water color. Using water color in the paste form, either from tubes or jars, a small quantity is diluted with a few drops of water. The brush is not used directly to paint large areas, but is first stroked across a piece of paper to remove most of the paint and spread the brush point. Then, with a sort of dry-brush technique, each brush stroke leaves several fine, broken lines of color on the print. Only a small area can be covered at a time, and some parts must be gone over several times to arrive at the desired tone. Areas on the photograph which are too light are darkened using soft pencils and paper stumps. As in pencil rendering, these areas are first gone over with a graphite-coated stump, then darkened selectively with a pencil.

Many other techniques and media are used in technical illustration, but they require more experience or considerable natural dexterity to ensure satisfactory results. Most, if not all, of the ordinary illustration requirements for papers in paleontology can be met with the methods discussed here.

# Part III

---

## TECHNIQUES IN PALYNOLOGY

---

*Coordinator:* JANE GRAY

# Palynological Techniques

JANE GRAY

*Paleoecology Laboratory, Museum of Natural History,*
*University of Oregon, Eugene*

The past few decades have witnessed a rapid development of palynology from beginnings that were confined largely to study of pollen from Pleistocene peats and lacustrine sediments. At present the field encompasses the study of pollen and a varied group of acid-insoluble microorganisms found in sediments and sedimentary rocks of all geologic periods and representing diverse depositional environments: brackish water sediments; lacustrine and paludal muds, including playa deposits; water-laid volcanic ash; fine-grained alluvium; buried soils; cave deposits, including coprolites; midden deposits; barrow and ancient room fill; glacial ice; glacial till; salt deposits, including cap rock; amber; oil shales; asphalts and other bituminous deposits.

Palynological techniques have been developed primarily for the study of pollen and spores—the dispersed, usually microscopic, reproductive structures of plants. The durable outer wall of these structures seldom undergoes replacement or chemical alteration and is resistant to most forms of biological and chemical degradation in nature and in the laboratory. Most of the techniques applicable to recovery and study of microspores are, however, equally applicable to the investigation of acid-resistant microorganisms of similar size and density. In general, the techniques considered in the following papers are the routine procedures of palynology. Some specialized techniques are also considered (for example, making thin sections of microorganisms and certain statistical problems).

Field collection of samples by the palynologist ranges from the simple, direct securing of isolated spot samples (hand specimens or smaller samples) at surface outcrops or exposed profiles of consolidated or unconsolidated sediments, to use of various kinds of elaborate boring or core-drilling equipment (see the papers by Faegri and Iversen and by Wright, Livingstone, and Cushing in this volume). General field sampling theory and methods, reviewed by Krumbein and Pettijohn (1938, Chapter 2), will provide a foundation of principles that should govern the collecting of samples for palynological investigation. Some theoretical aspects of sampling of rock bodies are discussed by Whitten (1961); Whitten's study concerns a granitic complex, but his conclusions are of general importance. It is obvious that poor field practices may bias the analysis through contamination of samples and that the selection of matrix according to lithology and grain size may influence the nature and abundance of microfossils recovered. Few palynologists, however, have considered problems and objectives of adequate field sampling, even though inadequate sampling may give a microflora that does not indicate the average quantitative composition of microspores in the sedimentation unit. In particular, the adequacy of a few grab samples (the prevalent sampling method of many palynologists working with pre-Quaternary materials) to provide an accurate picture of microspore composition should be thoroughly and carefully tested by detailed sampling procedures.

Sediments exposed in road cuts, in railroad cuts, or in naturally trenched stream walls provide some of the more accessible sources of spot samples. Where outcrops permit, the common practice is to collect spot samples at more or less uniform intervals vertically throughout the deposit; the interval is chosen according to the thickness and the lithology of the outcrop, the rate of sedimentation, the compaction, and so on. Such samples usually include material of only one sedimentation unit or of one lithologic type; each sample is, of course, extracted separately. For deposits of heterogeneous lithology, some test of the various rock types exposed may be necessary before the most productive horizons are found. A fresh, unweathered surface must be exposed before the sediments are collected, especially where slopes are eroding slowly, and every care must be taken to ensure against contamination by fresh pollen at the time of collecting and during transport of the samples to the laboratory. Norem (personal communication, June 28, 1962) suggests that stream beds often provide good, unweathered samples, especially when samples are taken from under water. Some such samples may, however, prove to be contaminated from water-borne pollen.

A common method applied by palynologists to sampling coal beds, but useful as well for other sediments of homogeneous lithology, is so-called channel sampling. The channel sample is procured by removing, in its entirety, a single sample normal to the bedding through the vertical thickness of a seam. A single sample for extraction of microspores is taken from the homogenized matrix of this strip of material. Modified types of channel samples, intermediate between the true channel sample and the spot sample, are discussed by Krumbein and Pettijohn (1938; see also Tokunaga, 1958, fig. 2). Channel samples may provide palynological information useful for stratigraphic correlation by giving some idea of the average composition of the microflora in a homogeneous lithologic unit; such samples are of limited value, however, for detailed environmental or evolutionary studies. Modified channel samples may show up variations in microfossil assemblages that are not readily determinable in the standard channel sample.

In sampling coals, as well as other sediments whose lithologic characteristics might provide a less obvious example, one should be aware of the possibilities of microfloras with facies-dependent distribution—that is, floras that are associated with a single environment that might occur repeatedly (see

Kuyl, Muller, and Waterbolk, 1955). In the example given by Kuyl, et al. of repeating mangrove (swamp) floras, the facies-dependent assemblage was readily determinable because the pollen could be identified with modern genera. Where the identification of pollen types is in doubt, however, the problem of determining a facies-dependent microflora is more difficult. As pointed out by Hart (1962), European palynologists have long been aware of this type of problem with coal sampling, because they have found distinct microfossil assemblages associated with distinctive petrographic compositions of coal.

Peats in bogs and certain lake sediments are most commonly collected by hand-operated boring devices designed to penetrate sediment without compressing or destroying its sequence or allowing contamination. The use of such equipment is fully discussed in the papers by Faegri and Iversen and by Wright, Livingstone, and Cushing. Deeply buried consolidated sediments can be taken by well-drilling (diamond-core-drilling) equipment, which yields a core that is often hundreds of feet long. Long cores are sometimes taken in unconsolidated or semiconsolidated sediments by penetration corers.

Unconsolidated or semiconsolidated sediments and rock specimens which might disintegrate during transport may be protected by polyethylene sample bags and aluminum foil. Glass shell vials are useful if only a small sample is necessary. Cloth sample bags or paper bags are adequate for hard rock specimens that can be thoroughly cleaned in the laboratory.

Information to be collected for each sample should include an exact map reference, including township, range, and section, if available; a locality description with photographs or sketches; geologic features such as stratigraphic unit or level of sample, structure of deposit, lithology of matrix, and associated fossils (or archaeological remains); a check list of the local vegetation and a sample for analysis of the modern pollen rain, as a check in case of suspected contamination of the sample.

Acid-insoluble microfossils are liberated from sedimentary matrices and concentrated by chemical and nonchemical means; see the paper by Gray. The objective is to rid the sample of minerals and of organic detritus that would conceal the microfossils and make their quantitative study difficult. Poor extraction methods may bias the analysis by introducing contaminants, by causing destruction or loss of certain of the microspores, or by changing the size and appearance of the microfossils. Whether some sediments and sedimentary rocks yield microfossils at all may depend on how they are handled in the extraction laboratory.

Chemical extraction involves demineralization by acids, and the digestion of organic compounds by acetylation or oxidation. Nonchemical separation methods make use of heavy liquids, controlled centrifugation, and other simple techniques which depend on differences in the density of organic and inorganic components of the matrix.

Extraction should be carried out in a special laboratory, separate from the room housing optical equipment. Rigorous cleanliness must be maintained in the extraction laboratory; an air filter to prevent contamination of samples from fresh air-borne pollen is helpful. Standard equipment in an extraction laboratory includes a fume hood with an acid-proof ventilator, an electrical centrifuge with a 4- to 8-place head and with capacity for 15-ml and 50-ml centrifuge tubes, an acid-proof sink, gas and water outlets, and a source of distilled water. A list of apparatus and chemical reagents used in pollen laboratories is given in the Laboratory Equipment at the end of this paper.

Once extraction is completed, the polleniferous residue is mounted on a microscope slide. Andersen, in his paper, discusses methods of mounting residues and the importance of the mounting medium to the results of the analysis. The medium used is important also for the preservation of specimens. For example, over long periods of time the mounting medium may affect the appearance and size of microspores. Many mounting media, moreover, are impermanent and will eventually disintegrate on the slide and destroy valuable specimens; yet there are difficulties in examining microspores once they are embedded in a permanent, solid-drying medium that permits no rotation of the specimens.

Palynologists whose work is confined mainly to rocks of Cretaceous and Cenozoic age are often able to assign microspores to modern families, modern genera, and sometimes to modern species of plants. Taxonomic identification is one of the most important phases of pollen work for the paleoecologist. A collection of pollen from living plants for comparison with fossil pollen is a necessity for some palynologists, and for others it may be helpful in understanding the morphology of specimens which cannot be assigned to living taxa. To facilitate the comparison, fresh microspores are, in effect, fossilized by the methods described in the paper by Traverse, who also tells how and where to get pollen and spores of modern plants for comparison.

Many palynologists, especially those working with Cenozoic microfloras, find it instructive to compare fossil-pollen spectra with pollen rains from similar modern communities of plants. Such comparisons aid in interpreting the results of the analysis by providing some basis for understanding what the relative frequencies of fossil pollen mean in terms of the abundance of parent plants. Various methods of sampling modern pollen rains are described by Lewis and Ogden in their paper.

Good illustrations of spores and pollen are fundamental to descriptive work in palynology. Accurate and detailed drawings are very difficult and time-consuming to make, and most palynologists illustrate their specimens by photomicrographs. Methods of preparing good photomicrographs of microspores are discussed in the paper by Samuelsson.

Spores and pollen grains are commonly photographed a number of times at different focal planes so that all the details of exine structure and sculpture are illustrated (see Iversen and Troels-Smith, 1950, Pl. X). Sometimes, with modern material and with unflattened fossil specimens, eight or more photographs may be necessary to illustrate all morphological details. Phase-contrast and ultraviolet photography may help to bring out obscure morphological details of pollen and spores better than the conventional methods of photomicrography.

Photomicrographs of plant microfossils are often reproduced at a magnification of 1000×, but this practice is not universally followed. A micron scale introduced on the photomicrograph is helpful in assessing the size of the grains.

Although there are various types of equipment for securing photomicrographs, perhaps the most general in use is an expandable bellows system, which can be mounted over a monocular tube of the microscope and which is adaptable to a 35-mm camera back and to plate holders of various sizes ($3\frac{1}{4}$ by $4\frac{1}{4}$ and 4 by 5 are in most general use). A back for Polaroid roll film and a holder for Polaroid plate film (which provides a negative) are also available and can be adapted for use with most photomicrographic outfits. The photographic equipment need not be elaborate to give excellent pictures, but for best results the optical equipment should be of the highest caliber.

Few pollen workers have taken advantage of Polaroid film. The rapid production of good pictures makes Polaroid photomicrography especially valuable in the early stages of palynological research, particularly in new geographic areas or for samples where unfamiliar pollen and spore types may be abundant. My impression after several years of careful testing is that with careful work and good equipment the results obtained through the use of Polaroid film are completely adequate for illustrating details of exine morphology.

In addition to the routine palynological techniques, a few others of a more specialized nature are considered in this volume. Dettman discusses techniques especially applicable to the study of megaspores. Both Evitt and Praglowski discuss thin-section techniques for microspores and other microorganisms. Davis considers a method of determining absolute pollen frequency, and Mosimann discusses several statistical problems related to the interpretation of pollen diagrams.

Not considered, but deserving mention, is the use of size-frequency analysis in the study of both modern and fossil pollen grains and spores. There are a number of obstacles to meaningful size-frequency work with plant microspores (see Kurtz and Liverman, 1958). Size variations may be due to genetic, ecological, and physiological factors and may cause, as Martin (1959) found for *Podocarpus,* considerable variability in pollen size and in pollen proportions, both within and between populations of single species. Size variations may be artifacts of fossilization and of methods of extraction or preparation (Christensen, 1946; Faegri and Iversen, 1950; Butterworth and Williams, 1954; Faegri and Deuse, 1960; Pant and Srivastava, 1961). Variability resulting from extraction may even be differential when the composition of the matrix changes in a single sequence or when different chemicals are used to recover microspores. Variability in size is influenced also by the mounting media (see Andersen, this volume; Pant and Srivastava, 1961) and even by the amount of cover-slip compression (Cushing, 1961).

Although the use of size statistics in palynology needs thorough systematic investigation, the quantitative expression of morphological attributes, including size, is becoming more widely used in the description of fossil species. Size statistics does, moreover, seem to provide the main hope for differentiating microspores indistinguishable by qualitative morphology (for example, *Pinus, Betula,* Gramineae) and thus for enabling comparison between fossil and fresh pollen. A few examples of size-frequency analysis in palynology are provided by Cain (1940, 1944, 1948), Cain and Cain (1944), Eneroth (1951, 1953), Leopold (1956), Martin (1959), Axelrod and Ting (1960, 1961), Aytug (1960, 1962), Kurtz, et al. (1960), Ting (1960), Beug (1961), and Martin, et al. (1961).

## LABORATORY EQUIPMENT

The following annotated list of equipment and chemical reagents is intended as a guide in setting up a palynological laboratory. Not all of the items and chemicals are necessarily found in one pollen laboratory, nor will they necessarily be used by all palynologists. Some of the permanent equipment (marked with an asterisk) is considered to be essential for routine pollen work. For some items, specific sources are given, although there may be other equally good sources.

### PERMANENT EQUIPMENT

Camera lucida equipment.
*Chemical balance, 0.1–500 g, for weighing reagents and balancing centrifuge specimen loads.
*Computing machine, for statistical analyses (Monroe Calculating Machine Co., Inc., Orange, N. J.).
*Electric centrifuge, minimum 4-tube capacity with interchangeable heads (or reducing caps) for use with 15-ml, 50-ml, 100-ml centrifuge tubes. A centrifuge with a trunnion-type head is preferable to one with the tubes held permanently at an angle, which may cause some material to stick to the outside part of the tube.
*Electric hot plate with thermostatic control.
Flat-filing microslide cabinet (The Technicon Company, 215 E. 149th Street, New York 51, N. Y.).
*Fume hood with acid-proof ventilator, acid-proof sink, water and gas outlets, light.
*Microscope, binocular, compound, with graduated mechanical stage (or mechanical stage attached to rotating stage) and with quadruple revolving nosepiece, two-diaphragm condenser, and regulating transformer. For photomicrography, a binocular-photo-tube combination is available. A built-in light source is convenient, but not necessary. Choice of optics is arbitrary. Oculars used by palynologists include 8×, 10×, 12.5×, 15× (wide field). Objectives

include 3.5× achromatic, 10× achromatic, 20–25× achromatic, 40–45× apochromatic. Oil-immersion objectives used include 50× fluorite, 90× fluorite and apochromatic, 100× apochromatic. The numerical aperture (N.A.) of the high-power oil-immersion objective should be 1.3, 1.32, or for the very best results 1.4, in order to resolve the finest surface details of microspores. In general, for oil-immersion objectives, the magnification is of less importance than the aperture size. As compared with apochromatic objectives, fluorite objectives usually provide for somewhat greater contrast but less resolution and less color correction. Fluorite objectives do, however, approach apochromats in image quality and are much superior to achromatic objectives. Microscope equipment should include a stage micrometer and an ocular micrometer. Phase-contrast equipment is optional.

Microslide warming or drying table or drying oven with thermostatic control.

*Photomicrographic equipment: Camera bellows and base plate with camera carrier; 35-mm camera back; plate holders (3¼ by 4¼, 4 by 5); Polaroid Land Attachment for roll and sheet film; photographic filters; photoelectric light-measuring device (photometer).

*Pycnometer and/or heavy-liquid hydrometer.

*Still for distilled water, or diatomaceous filter for use with tap water.

*Thermometer, centrigrade.

Ultrasonic generator (Dynasonics Corporation, 200 Michael Drive, Syosset, N. Y.; Acoustica Associates, Inc., 10400 Aviation Boulevard, Los Angeles 45, California; Branson Instruments, Inc., 37 Brown House Road, Stamford, Connecticut; Bendix Sonic Energy Products, Davenport, Iowa).

U. S. standard sieves, diameter 3 inches, various mesh sizes.

Veeder-Root Counter (Veeder-Root "Vary Tally" Counter. Veeder-Root Incorporated, Hartford 2, Connecticut).

Vortex Jr. Mixer (Dynalab Corp., Rochester, N. Y.).

*Water or wax bath, electrical control optional.

GLASSWARE AND HARDWARE

Alcohol lamp.

Beakers, assorted sizes, glass, polyethylene.

Bunsen burners.

Centrifuge tubes, Pyrex glass, polyethylene, or polypropylene, 15-ml, 50-ml, 100-ml with closures (polypropylene tubes will withstand temperatures up to 320°F).

Crucibles, flat-bottomed, copper, nickel, or platinum for acid work, with covers.

Dispensing bottles: 5-gallon for distilled water, spigot; 1-gallon for storage of reagents; 8–16 ounce polyethylene with tubing from shoulder; 30-ml dropping bottles with dust cap.

Evaporating dishes, various diameters.

Funnels, various diameters, glass or polyethylene.

Glass file.

Glass shell vials, screw cap, or cork, ½, 1, 2 dram.

Glassware draining racks.

Graduated cylinders, assorted sizes up to 1000 ml.

Microscope cover glasses, No. 0, No. 1, square and circular, 18 and 22 mm.

Microscope slides, 3 by 1 inches.
Mortar and pestle, porcelain, agate, or metal.
Pencil, glass marking, tungsten carbide, or diamond point.
Pinch-clamps.
Pipettes, 10 cc, 20 cc.
Stirring rods, various sizes, stainless steel, glass, nickel or polyethylene.
Test (centrifuge) tube holder, 15 and 50 ml.
Tongs.
Tripod stand.
Watch-glasses, various diameters.
Wire gauze, with asbestos center, or asbestos shield.

### MISCELLANEOUS

Abrasive cleanser (Ajax, Babo, etc.).
Aluminum foil.
Collecting bags, cloth, polyethylene, various sizes.
Face shield, or eye protector (plastic bubble-goggle or equivalent).
Filter paper.
Kerodex barrier cream (hand cream) for wet work (Ayerst Laboratories Inc., New York 16, N. Y.).
Laboratory apron or laboratory coat.
Laboratory detergent, Haemo-Sol (Meinecke & Company, Inc., 225 Varick Street, New York 14, N. Y.).
Lens paper
Matches.
Microscope slide labels, assorted sizes.
pH test paper.
Plasti-phane plastic sheets (Acri-Lux Dental Mfg. Co., Inc., Long Island City 1, N. Y.).
Rubber and plastic tubing, assorted sizes.
Slide boxes.
Test-tube and centrifuge tube brushes, assorted sizes.

## CHEMICAL REAGENTS AND SUPPLIES

Chemical reagents come in different commercial grades. The purest is "analytical" or "reagent grade"; the second is C.P. (Chemically Pure); the third is technical or U.S.P. grade. Technical grade reagents may contain plant tissue, diatoms, and pollen and spores in the sludge present in the bottom of the reagent bottle (Fisher, 1962). Such material provides a possible source of contamination when technical grade reagents are used in chemical extraction.

### DISAGGREGATION AND DISPERSAL

Ammonium hydroxide
Darvan No. 4 (R. T. Vanderbilt Co., 230 Park Avenue, New York 17, N. Y.)

Ethyl alcohol
Gasoline
Kerosene
Lithium chloride

Lithium hydroxide
Nacconol (National Aniline Co.)
Polytergent J-400 (Mathieson Chemical Corp., New York, N. Y.)
Potassium hydroxide
Sodium carbonate
Sodium hexametaphosphate

Sodium hydroxide
Sodium oxalate
Sodium pyrophosphate
Soltrol C
Stoddards Solvent
Trisodium phosphate
Varsol (Standard Oil, N. J.)

## CHEMICAL EXTRACTION

Acetic anhydride
Acetone
Ammonium hydroxide
Ammonium sulfate
Ammonium vanadate
Benzene
Bromine
Chlorine solution
Chromium trioxide
Clorox (sodium hypochlorite)
Dichromic acid
Ethyl alcohol
Ethylenediaminetetraacetate (EDTA) (Dow Chemical Corporation, Midland, Michigan)
Formic acid
Glacial acetic acid
Hydrochloric acid
Hydrofluoric acid
Hydrogen peroxide
Monochloroacetic acid
Nitric acid (concentrated and fuming)

N, N-dimethyl formamide
Oxalic acid
Perchloric acid
Periodic acid
Phosphoric (orthophosphoric) acid
Potassium carbonate
Potassium chlorate
Potassium dichromate
Potassium hydroxide
Potassium permanganate
Pyridine
Sodium chlorate
Sodium chloride
Sodium chlorite
Sodium hydroxide
Sodium hypochlorite
Sodium perborate
Sodium sulfite
Sodium thiosulfate
Sulfuric acid
Vanadium pentoxide
Xylene

## NONCHEMICAL SEPARATION

Acetone
Acetylene tetrabromide (tetrabromoethane)
Benzene
Bromoform (tribromomethane)
Carbon tetrachloride
Ethyl alcohol
Hydriodic acid

Potassium cadmium iodide solution
Potassium mercuric iodide solution
Pine oil
Quebracho (American Cyanimide Co.)
Sulfuric acid (sp. gr. 1.84)
Zinc bromide solution
Zinc chloride solution

## SLIDE PREPARATION

*Common stains*

Bismarck brown
Fuchsin (acid, basic)
Gentian violet

Methyl green
Neutral red
Safranin Y or O

Common mounting media

Clearcol (*n* 1.40)
Silicone oil (*n* 1.40) (Dow Corning
   Corporation, Midland, Michigan)[1]
Glycerin (*n* 1.47)

Glycerin jelly (*n* 1.47)
Tanglefoot medium (*n* 1.49)
Canada balsam (*n* 1.53)

*Immersion oils*

Anisol (methyl phenylether)
Cedar wood oil

## REFERENCES

Axelrod, D. I., and W. S. Ting (1960). Late Pliocene floras east of the Sierra
Nevada. Publ. Geol. Sciences, Univ. Calif., v. 39, no. 1, 118 pp.
———— (1961). Early Pleistocene floras from the Chagoopa surface, southern
Sierra Nevada. Publ. Geol. Sciences, Univ. of Calif., v. 39, no. 2, p. 119–194.
Aytug, Burhan (1960). Quelques mensurations des pollens de *Pinus silvestris* L.
Pollen et Spores, v. 2, no. 2, p. 305–309.
———— (1962). Diagnose des pollens de *Pinus silvestris* et *Pinus uncinata* des
Pyrénées. Pollen et Spores, v. 4, no. 2, p. 283–296.
Beug, H.-J. (1961). Leitfaden der Pollen bestimmung. Stuttgart, Gustav Fischer,
63 pp.
Butterworth, M. A., and R. W. Williams (1954). Descriptions of nine species of
small spores from the British coal measures. Ann. Mag. Nat. History, v. 7, no.
82, p. 753–764.
Cain, S. A. (1940). The identification of species in fossil pollen of *Pinus* by size
frequency determinations. Am. J. Bot., v. 27, p. 301.
———— (1944). Size frequency characteristics of *Abies Fraseri* pollen as determined by different methods of preparation. Am. Midl. Naturalist, v. 31, p. 232.
———— (1948). Palynological studies at Sodon Lake, I. Size frequency study of
spruce pollen. Science, v. 108, p. 115.
————, and L. G. Cain (1944). Size frequency studies of *Pinus palustris* pollen.
Ecol., v. 25, p. 229.
Christensen, B. B. (1946). Measurement as a means of identifying fossil pollen.
Danm. Geol. Undersøg., ser. 4, v. 3, no. 2, 22 pp.
Cushing, E. J. (1961). Size increase in pollen grains mounted in thin slides.
Pollen et Spores, v. 3, no. 2, p. 265–274.
Eneroth O. (1951). Undersökning rörande möjlighetarna att i fossilt material
urskilja de olika Betula-arternas pollen. Geol. Fören. Stockholm Förh., v. 73,
p. 343–405.
————, *in* Wenner, C.-G. (1953). Investigation into the possibilities of dis-
tinguishing the pollen of the various species of *Betula* in fossil material. Geol.
Fören. Stockholm Förh., v. 75, p. 367–380.

[1] The Standard Dow Corning 200 fluid (industrial grade oil) is available in viscosities
from 0.65 to 2,500,000 centistokes. A 360 fluid, with identical properties is, however,
chemically pure. It is available in viscosities up to 12,500 centistokes.

Faegri, K., and P. Deuse (1960). Size variations in pollen grains with different treatments. Pollen et Spores, v. 2, no. 2, p. 293–298.

————, and J. Iversen (1950). Textbook of modern pollen analysis. Copenhagen, E. Munksgaard, 168 pp.

Fisher, J. C. (1962). Laboratory reagents as a possible source of microfossil contamination. Micropaleontology, v. 8, no. 4, p. 508.

Hart, G. F. (1962). Palynology—the key to stratigraphy? South African J. Sci., v. 58, no. 12, p. 365–374.

Iversen, J., and J. Troels-Smith (1950). Pollen morphologische Definitionen und Typen. Danm. Geol. Undersøg., ser. 4, v. 3, no. 8, 52 pp.

Krumbein, W. C., and F. J. Pettijohn (1938). Manual of sedimentary petrography. New York, D. Appleton-Century Co., 549 pp.

Kurtz, E. B., and J. L. Liverman (1958). Some effects of temperature on pollen characters. Torrey Bot. Club Bull., v. 85, no. 2, p. 136–138.

————, J. L. Liverman, and H. Tucker (1960). Some problems concerning fossil and modern corn pollen. Torrey Bot. Club Bull., v. 87, no. 2, p. 85–94.

Kuyl, O. S., J. Muller, and H. T. Waterbolk (1955). The application of palynology to oil geology, with special reference to western Venezuela. Geol. Mijnbouw, new series, v. 17, no. 3, p. 49–70.

Leopold, E. B. (1956). Pollen size-frequence in New England species of the genus *Betula*. Grana Palynologica, v. 1, no. 2, p. 140–147.

Martin, A. R. H. (1959). South African palynological studies; I. Statistical and morphological variation in the pollen of the South African species of *Podocarpus*. Grana Palynologica, v. 2, no. 1, p. 40–68.

Martin, P. S., J. Schoenwetter, and B. C. Arms (1961). The last 10,000 years. Geochronology Laboratories, Univ. of Arizona, mimeographed book, 119 pp.

Pant, D. D., and G. K. Srivastava (1961). Structural studies on Lower Gondwana megaspores. Paleontographica, Abt. B, v. 109, p. 45–61.

Ting, W. S. (1961). On some pollen of Californian Umbelliferae. Pollen et Spores, v. 3, no. 2, p. 190–199.

Tokunaga, S. (1958). Palynological study on Japanese coal; I. Method of pollen analysis on Japanese coal. Geol. Survey Japan Rept. 177, 56 pp.

Whitten, E. H. T. (1961). Quantitative areal modal analysis of granitic complexes. Geol. Soc. America Bull., v. 72, no. 9, p. 1331–1360.

# Field Techniques

K. FAEGRI

*Botanisk Museum, University of Bergen, Norway*

J. IVERSEN

*Geological Survey of Denmark, Charlottenlund, Denmark*

The technique of pollen analysis has two different aspects—field work and laboratory work—and unless both are carried out with the greatest care, the results will be uncertain or have no value at all.

The aim of field work is to collect uncontaminated samples of the deposit, to define as exactly as possible the conditions under which the samples were taken, to determine the types of sediment, and to explain the stratigraphy.

The first problem is the choice of locality for taking samples—if there is any choice. If the locality itself forces upon the investigator a material that is less suitable for analysis, such as a deposit in which archaeological finds have been made, little can be done about that problem, but extreme caution is necessary in the interpretation of the results of analysis in such material.

Different problems in pollen analysis of Late Quaternary conditions demand deposits of different types. For paleophysiognomic work, spring bogs and marginal sediments of spring-fed lakes give the most perfect results, since they greatly depend upon climatic conditions, particularly precipitation; but they are practically worthless for pollen analysis, for the pollen is generally badly corroded and the flora is of a distinctly local, frequently aberrant character. The objection that the pollen flora is too local to give results of regional significance also applies to the deposits of very small basins, which are, together with marginal zones of larger ones, more suitable for macrofossil analysis.

The ideal deposits for ordinary pollen analysis are those in which the mother formation has not influenced the state of preservation of pollen grains or the composition of the pollen flora. They are, therefore, rather uninteresting from the paleophysiognomical angle. Older generations of paleobotanists preferred peat bogs, but these are not very suitable for pollen analysis, since the mother formation produces a great deal of pollen, at least of herbs and small shrubs. However, the central parts of extensive treeless bogs are rather free from local influence and may be used with advantage if the upland forest

Reprinted with modification, with permission of the authors and the publishers, Munksgaard, Copenhagen, from *Textbook of Pollen Analysis* (2nd ed., 1964) by K. Faegri and J. Iversen.

pollen is the sole object of investigation. The pollen produced by the mother formation is most easily recognized in lake deposits and can be more easily discounted there than the corresponding local pollen in other deposits. But the marginal vegetation may greatly influence the pollen from small lakes. But currents in large bodies of water may arise that destroy and redeposit sediments, thus resulting in difficulties of interpretation. Generally the state of preservation of pollen grains is better in lake deposits than in telmatic or terrestrial peats.

The following rules may be set up for the choice of a sampling site—if there is a choice.

1. Choose a lake deposit rather than a peat deposit.
2. Avoid lakes that are too small or too large (ideal magnitude, about 5000 m$^2$).
3. Choose lakes that are not surrounded by extensive bogs.
4. Choose a sample from a protected place, where there has been no wind or current action.
5. Avoid places where brooks enter a basin; otherwise, there will be the risk of contamination, oxidation, and currents.

Lakes that have filled in are, of course, especially favorable, because their sediments can be recovered from the surface, when it is firm enough to support investigator and equipment.

The principal object of field work, however, is to secure samples that are absolutely pure and free from contamination. To attain this goal, great care is necessary when samples are taken out of the deposit. Never touch a sample with your fingers; it must be handled with a pair of broad, smooth forceps (the ordinary, milled type is worse than anything), or a smooth spatula. Forceps are best for peats, whereas sediments are best treated with one or two spatulas. All instruments must, of course, be thoroughly cleaned between samplings. Each investigator soon develops his own procedure. We must, however, warn against the use of an ordinary piece of cloth, a towel, or a similar aid, which will very soon become so dirty as to present a serious contamination hazard.

It is much the safest and also the easiest to take samples directly from exposed profiles, working downward from the top of the deposit. When a suitable spot has been selected, the peat wall is cleaned with a knife, making horizontal cuts to avoid carrying material from one layer to another. A tape measure is then stretched vertically along the section and the sample tubes pressed into the wall, or small pieces can be taken out with forceps and spatula and transferred to tubes. For more exact work, a pillar ("monolith") of the deposit can be cut out and brought into the laboratory to be investigated in detail. In this case the problem is to keep the monolith suitably moist until it can be worked up (air-tight in plastic bag or foil).

Usually, however, one must work from the surface of the bog, in which case it is rarely profitable to dig to any depth. The surface samples, down to 15 or

20 cm, are usually taken out of a sod that is cut for the purpose; the others are then taken by some kind of peat sampler[1] (see fig. 1).

The general principles of these is that a closed chamber is pushed down

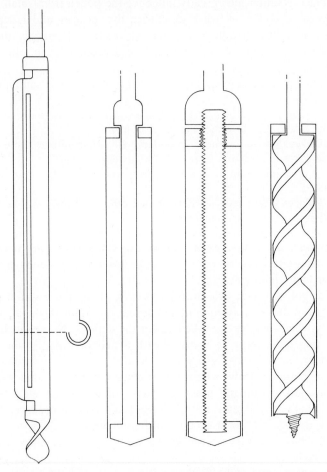

**Fig. 1.** *Types of peat samplers. Left to right: Hiller, Dach-nowsky, Reissinger, Douglas (Reissinger modifica-tion).*

through the deposit to the required depth, where it is opened. There are two main types of samplers—those that fill from the side and those that fill from the bottom. The Hiller type of sampler fills from the side. Filling is accomplished by turning the apparatus counterclockwise. A loose outer jacket with a projecting lip remains stationary while the inner chamber turns so that

---

[1] As all extra turning of the instrument tends to make a mess of any deposit, the instrument should be *pushed* down through the layers, not screwed; consequently we have preferred the neutral term "sampler" instead of the usual, but misleading, "borer" or "auger."

longitudinal slits of jacket and chamber coincide. By further counterclock-wise turning the jacket is rotated as well, the chamber fills with sediment, and is then closed by turning the sampler clockwise before pulling it up. After the sampler has been taken up, the chamber is opened and the samples taken out. It is difficult to preserve the undisturbed sequence if one tries to remove the sample in its entirety. It is better to take out smaller samples at regular intervals with forceps or spatula. Before opening the sampler, its surface must be cleaned with a knife (not a cloth). The parts of the sample that are in contact with the inner walls of the chamber must be considered contaminated and should be avoided. The exposed surface should be thoroughly cleaned. It is better to remove too much than too little!

A serious error may be caused if the sampler should gradually sink during the operation. The operator should take care (1) that the edge of the lip, especially the lower edge, is cutting sharp, not blunted, and (2) that the jacket is not too loose. After some use, especially in coarse sediments, the fit of the jacket may become so loose that contamination will result; such samplers should not be used.

Perhaps even more so than with other samplers the outer layers (and both ends) of a Hiller core should be regarded as contaminated and must be dis-carded. If these precautions are taken, and the chamber and jacket are thoroughly cleaned between each sampling, one should be able to avoid con-taminating the sample. We have found the Hiller sampler a very reliable in-strument, and Neustadt (1961) reports that he has used it through a 40 m deposit. For the fibrous undecomposed peat, especially, and for peat rich in woody remains, the Hiller sampler may be the only means of obtaining samples at all, though samples of such peats are never absolutely free from contamination. In sandy sediments results are not reliable, and in sticky or very loose muds it may be necessary to use an extra broad lip on the jacket to make it work (Faegri, 1944). At present the Hiller sampler is manufac-tured and sold by A/B Borros, Solna, Sweden.

The end-filling principle is used in the Dachnowsky sampler and in the recent modifications by Livingstone and others (see Rowley and Dahl, 1956). Its main parts are a piston and a jacket. When the instrument is pushed down, the piston blocks the lower opening of the jacket. When the right depth has been reached, the piston is pulled up into the upper part, and the jacket is pushed down an amount equal to its own length and thus filled. The piston is prevented from sliding down again either by a snap spring or by a bayonet fastening. In the original modification the piston is rigidly attached to the rod used to push the instrument down. A modified type has been proposed by Reissinger (1936, p. 17) in which the piston remains at a fixed level while the jacket is screwed farther down by turning the instrument counterclockwise. This corresponds to the Livingstone principle (see below), but is rather cumbersome.

In the Livingstone sampler the movement of the piston and that of the chamber itself are not linked, as in the Dachnowsky model. The piston (which can be made from rubber stoppers squeezed into a proper fit by means of screws and nuts) is attached to a loose cable that runs through the top of the sampler. While the sampler is pushed down to sampling level, it is closed by the piston. At the sampling level, the loose cable is pulled tight and anchored at the surface. When the sampler is pushed farther down the piston remains stationary, and a vacuum forms between piston and sediment that contributes to the filling of the sampler (the principle of the Kullenberg sampler).

In very hard sediments the piston may become dislocated before the sampler has reached the proper depth. To overcome this, a sampler has been designed [2] that combines the Dachnowsky and Livingstone principles—that is, the piston is divided into two parts, of which the upper, loosely fitting part is attached to the push rod, as in the Dachnowsky sampler. After the right depth has been reached, this part is pulled up, and during sampling the instrument functions as a Livingstone sampler. This may solve problems in some deposits, but if samples are taken continuously through the same hole the risk of premature dislocation of the piston is probably not very serious. One may alternatively employ a simpler instrument to make the hole and use the sampler only when the right depth has been reached.

In theory, one may use an end-filling sampling tube of the same length as the entire depth of sediments to be penetrated. However, the practical length is strictly governed by two considerations: (1) the danger of breakage, and (2) friction—external friction between sampler and sediment, and especially, friction between the core and the inner wall of the sampler. This latter friction will soon lead to serious compressions and distortions of the core.

For the problem of dealing with frozen deposits, Potzger (1955) has designed a sampler which is said to also give good results in firmly compacted sediments. It may prove difficult to clean.

All these samplers are pushed down by a rigid rod. The extensions of the rod should be locked in place in such a manner that they cannot unscrew themselves during operation. We find the extension rods of the Hiller sampler superior to any we have seen.

If samples are taken in open water, rods frequently bend too much, depending on the depth of water and the toughness of the sediment. This can be remedied by first lowering a casing tube, wide enough to accommodate the sampler. It is not necessary to drive the tube into the sediment, as the rod will stay straight anyhow.

Rods are heavy, however, and casing tubes even heavier, so that in deep basins this method becomes impracticable. Subaquatic sampling techniques have been developed to a high degree of perfection (Strøm, 1938, 1939; Jenkins and Mortimer, 1938; Jenkins, Mortimer, and Pennington, 1941; Kullenberg, 1947; Miller, 1953; Smith, 1959; Richards and Keller, 1961);

---

[2] Drawings have been loaned to us by Dr. H. E. Wright of the University of Minnesota.

unfortunately the most effective apparatus is too complicated and heavy to be transported to small lakes and operated from small boats or rafts.

It is unavoidable that distance to the sampling site and availability of transport will sometimes determine the choice of equipment. The only universal condition that should be laid down is that samples be reliable, both as to purity and as to stratigraphical position. To compromise on these points would be fatal. Much can be done to modify samplers so that they can be dismantled and transported in relatively light and easily packed units.

If the sampler cannot be pushed into the sediment by means of a rod, it must be weighted so that it will penetrate by itself. Three types of weights are in use: driving weights, pounding weights, and expendable weights. Driving weights are the simplest and most commonly used. They are permanently fixed to the sampler. Pounding weights have been described by Züllig (1956b) in his "Ramm-Kolben-Lot." In the Mackereth (1958) sampler the driving forces are a combination of vacuum and hydrostatic pressure.

A very ingenious "free corer" has been described by Moore (1961). The principle is that the weight driving the sampler into the sediment is sacrificed, and the sampler floats up again by means of an attached float. In this way there is, in principle, no limit to the water depth at which samples can be taken. Expendable weights can, of course, also be used with samplers that are pulled up by a cable.

None of these samplers penetrate beyond the surface layer of the sediment. The layers to be penetrated before sampling are, besides the water, very loose, flocculent deposits which are penetrated easily, without any appreciable external or internal friction. The sampler used in such sediments may therefore be an open-ended tube through the upper end of which the excess water passes. But when the sampler is to be pulled up again, the top end must be closed to create the vacuum that will keep the core from dropping out of the sampler. Züllig's "Schlammstecher" (1956a) fulfills this demand. If it is desirable to secure the loose, flocculent upper layers and the water-to-sediment transition, a flange may be mounted on the sampler to prevent its penetration beyond these layers.

If the aim is to penetrate to a greater depth of sediment than the length of the sampling tube, two complications arise: (1) the weights, whatever type, must be separated from the sampler by means of an extension rod (this results in a rather unwieldy instrument); (2) to reduce internal friction, the sampler must be closed until it reaches the sampling level. Incidentally, external friction is also reduced because the rod is thinner than the sampler. Accordingly some type of Livingstone sampler must be used, in this case operated by two cables, both of which must pass through the center of the weights. Very long samplers may be rather unstable, and may easily topple over. A stabilizer may therefore be useful.

In order to hit the same hole each time Reissinger (1936) uses a funnel connected to a piece of sheet iron that rests on the surface of the sediment.

When sampling through open water one may work from the ice, where practicable, or from a raft. A pontoon raft is generally preferable; especially when working in places that are inaccessible except on foot, light pontoons (inflated rubber!) are a must. The raft must be securely anchored, either by 3 or 4 grapnels or by strong wires attached to the shore (of small lakes). In shallow water the site may be marked by a stake driven into the bottom sediment, and the boat or raft may be moved up to the marker whenever another sample is to be collected.

Layers of sand offer serious difficulties in sampling. Though they are generally of little interest in pollen analysis—because pollen has either been destroyed or was never deposited—it may be necessary to penetrate the sand in order to reach polleniferous sediments at lower levels.

An ordinary $\frac{1}{2}$-inch pipe is used by I. J. Wilson for piercing sand and obtaining samples. It is closed at the bottom by a snugly fitting cork, and is lowered to the sand through a hole made by the ordinary peat sampler. The cork and sand are then forced into the pipe by pounding on the pipe with a sledge hammer (Wilson and Potzger, 1943, p. 388).

Only rarely do such primitive methods suffice. Geotechnicians have developed special methods for dealing with layers of sand, such as using casings to prevent the sand from caving in and blocking the hole.

Difficult deposits demand special measures, sometimes even measures in which the two primary demands—purity and stratigraphical exactitude—have not been fully complied with. For special purposes samples from these deposits may be of some value, but they are of little value in quantitative pollen analysis. Various, more or less obvious, devices may be resorted to in order to counteract contamination. Apart from exceptional circumstances, different deposits demand different equipment. The advantages and disadvantages of the side-filling type has been mentioned above. The end-filling type works best in homogeneous, fine-grained sediments, from which it gives a cleaner sediment core than the Hiller type. However, it should not be forgotten that the top of the core has traveled the whole length of the jacket. If material has adhered to the inside, contamination of the outer part of the core may be found. If there are strong differences in pollen contents, such contamination may be serious.

The following table summarizes the most expedient methods to be used under normal conditions for the situations shown. Thus a variety of samplers should be on hand, but extension rods and other accessories should be standardized and interchangeable.

Particularly when using the Hiller sampler one should always work two holes alternately, since the deposit is disturbed by the screw beneath the chamber as it turns back and forth. With end-filling samplers this is less important.

While it is impracticable to preserve the whole sediment from a Hiller sampler, end-filling samplers have the advantage that the whole core may be

| WORKING FROM | IN | EQUIPMENT |
|---|---|---|
| Open faces | All types of peat and sediment. | Spade, knife, and spatula/forceps. |
| Surface of deposit | Fibrous peat or coarse organic sediment. | Hiller sampler. |
| | Highly humified peat or medium- to fine-grained sediment. | End-filling samplers. |
| | Stiff clays and layers of sand. | Heavier core borers with casing, pipes. |
| Surface of lakes | Top deposit. | "Schlammstecher," core freezer. |
| | Ordinary deposit. | Livingstone sampler, free corer. Mackereth sampler (see Smith, 1959). |

pushed [3] out and preserved in its entirety, thus permitting the reconstruction of the whole sediment back in the laboratory. Overbeck (1958) pushes the sediment core out into a metal tube, the wall of which is longitudinally split and hinged. By opening this tube one may inspect the core for stratigraphical details, impurities, and so on. After inspection the tube is closed again, and the core pushed into a thin plastic tube that can be closed at both ends.

The danger inherent in all handling of samples is that they may be compressed and distorted. Various measures have been proposed: If the lower opening of the tube is equipped with a bit slightly narrower than the chamber itself, samples are easier to remove after this bit has been taken off (bayonet fastening!). Alternatively, a replaceable plastic tube may be mounted inside the (metal) sampler tube and held in place by rings at both ends. The plastic tube may then be taken out and samples kept in it until required. By careful vertical storage the stratigraphical sequence may be kept intact even in the loose, flocculent topmost layers—indeed, even a part of the water layer above the sediment may be preserved. The same may be done by using expendable chamber tubes. Clear plastic tubes have the advantage of giving visual inspection, but metal tubes are stronger. If it is possible to freeze the samples, either in the field or artificially, they can easily be stored without any danger of destroying even the most delicate stratigraphical details. Careful thawing of the surface layers permits the sample to be pushed out. The core freezer (Shapiro, 1958), which freezes the core in situ before it is retracted, is the ultimate refinement in this respect.

If possible, the core should be cut longitudinally—e.g., with a fine steel wire or nylon thread—and its stratification studied in the plane cut. Distortions can be checked upon more easily that way.

When the contents of the sampler are not to be brought to the laboratory

---

[3] In difficult cases, by pumping air into the upper part of the chamber.

in their entirety, small samples should be taken in the field from the sampler chamber at regular intervals. For general work the standard interval was 25 cm during the early days of pollen analysis; it is now 5 cm. This is not to say, however, that all 5-cm samples should be analyzed. Near transitions between different types of deposits, or in deposits which have accumulated very slowly, the sample distance must be reduced to 2.5 cm, or even 1 cm. As a general rule, more samples should be taken than may be needed for analysis, but in very rapidly growing deposits the distance between samples may generally exceed the usual standard.

If cores are preserved intact, samples for analysis may be taken out where needed, but sooner or later reference samples must be taken out at regular intervals, particularly with a view to the technical difficulties associated with the indefinite preservation of large cores.

Samples should be kept in glass tubes. Flat-bottom tubes are generally thin-walled and easily broken. Round-bottom tubes are stronger, but have the disadvantage that they will not stand on the table. Tubes with cork stoppers in both ends are well protected against breaking, but are more difficult to seal effectively. Samples should be kept moist until they are analyzed, as some humus colloids may be very difficult to disperse once they have dried out. Fragile pollen exines may also be more or less destroyed by volume changes and other effects of drying. A careful remoistening (5 percent cold KOH for a month or two) may counteract this. Samples should never be wrapped in cellophane or other material in which they dry up rapidly. To keep samples moist in the tubes, stoppers should be sealed with paraffin or other wax and/or some glycerol added to the samples to prevent desiccation. Large samples (entire chamber contents) may be kept in a seminatural state for some time when packed in airtight plastic tubes or foil. Precautions should be taken against mildew. Even when stored in evaporation-proof containers samples will frequently dehydrate irreversibly, changing in colloidal state and extruding water droplets. The mechanics of this process are unknown.

All samples should be clearly marked. Tube samples are most conveniently marked with consecutive numbers written with copying pencil or nonfading ball point pen on the cork stopper. In the notebook the corresponding depth is recorded together with notes on the nature of the deposit. Larger samples are more difficult to mark. The top must be clearly indicated. It should be kept in mind that slips of paper which have been in contact with wet peat or sediment for some time are usually so decayed that notes written on them are illegible. It is therefore most unwise to rely, even for a short time, on paper notes put into sample containers.

It is, of course, also possible to use small plastic cups with snap-on lids, provided they are sufficiently permanent and resistant to chemical action from the sample. Lids must be tight enough for the purpose, and there must be an easy method of permanently marking the cups. Some plastics demand special inks. Ordinary opaque paper should never be used for wrapping samples, not even temporarily, since its cleanness cannot be checked.

After samples for pollen analysis have been taken out of a core the rest of the contents of the sampler should be investigated macroscopically for determination of the type of deposit and should be examined for macrofossils. All plants cannot be identified from their pollen, and among indeterminable ones there may be important indicators, the macroscopic remains of which are more easily detected. Even if such an examination is in no way equivalent to a systematic macrofossil analysis, it may give results of some value, and findings should be noted down when made.

In very small bogs or lakes one single profile point may be sufficient, but it must be located as close as possible to the center of sedimentation (not always identical with the geometrical center). If the deposit studied is a uniform series of fine-grained sediments that have been deposited under uniform conditions, one section may also be sufficient in larger basins. Usually a profile across the basin should be investigated. A series of sections must be taken with the sampler to determine the nature of the deposits, the horizontal and vertical distances between points of investigation being determined with suitable instruments. Some simple leveling outfit is therefore necessary for work on land. The various sections are combined to give a profile of the deposit. Samples for analysis are taken from that part of the bog where the deposit is most complete and homogeneous; for the investigation of special problems additional samples may be taken from other points.

The more complex the sequence, the shorter the distance between sections (fig. 2). If the sequence is very intricate, and especially if archaeological objects or other traces of human activity are preserved in the deposit, open, near-vertical profiles are necessary. All important points should be marked— for example, by matches or more elaborate markers. Afterwards the whole profile should be leveled and the position of all markers either leveled directly or measured with tape measure from the leveled surface of the bog or a leveled reference line. This is necessary to secure sufficient detail to identify former bog surfaces and other features.

Even in apparently homogeneous sedimentary series, erosion may have caused great lacunae (see Lundquist, 1924), especially in the littoral parts. Samples should always be collected centrally, where the sequence is presumably most complete. Very sharp contacts between different types of deposit frequently indicate erosion. Other erosion contacts are indicated by thicker or thinner—sometimes exceedingly thin—layers of sand or silt.

One very difficult deposit is redeposited peat or sediment. Redeposition takes place where former peat bogs or littoral accumulations are eroded, either due to changes in water level or changes in the prevailing wind direction. Redeposited sediments contain a mixed pollen flora, partly deriving from contemporary, partly from an older vegetation. Typical redeposition sediments

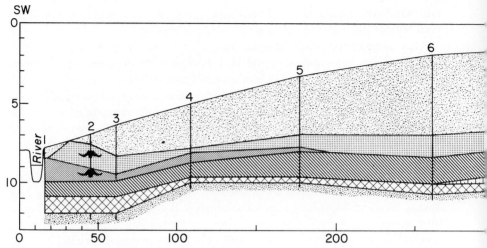

**Fig. 2.** *Peat-bog profile from Cloughmills, Co. Antrim, Ireland (from Jessen, 1949). The bog rests on clay and has started as an open lake (gytta bottom layer), which gradually filled in (Phragmites coming in from the right-hand shore) and was covered first by a birch forest with Phragmites, later by a drier birch forest without Phragmites. Subsequently, peat mosses occupied the area and built up a domed bog. The lower part was probably*

are often recognizable by an abnormally high content of coarse particles, the finer grains having been carried farther away. In the extremely oceanic blanket bogs small peat slides frequently lead to small-scale redeposition; however, since blanket peats are poor subjects for pollen analysis, this is of little importance. The deposits under floating quagmires are also among those in which redeposition may be suspected, as demonstrated by Troels-Smith (1955). Records of field work should contain—in addition to the numbering of samples, records of their depth, and profile data—a short description of the Recent vegetation of the bog and its immediate surroundings. A list of plants in flower when samples were taken is particularly necessary for control in case contamination is suspected. For studies of transgressions the altitude above sea level should be recorded. The accuracy of the macroscopic analysis of the deposit will vary with the aims of the investigation. Degree of humification, water content, fibrosity, contents of wood, and so on may be noted for each layer, especially if no samples are preserved.

In rainy weather field work is impossible, or nearly so. The notebook becomes wet, the pencil tears holes in the paper, rain drops into the sample and splashes the substance all over, and everything becomes hopelessly dirty in a short time. In such circumstances it is almost impossible to work with sufficient precision and to obtain pure samples. Only if some sort of shelter is handy can sampling be attempted, but even then it is very difficult to avoid contamination. If compelled to work under such conditions that absolute purity of samples cannot be guaranteed, one must resort to taking relatively

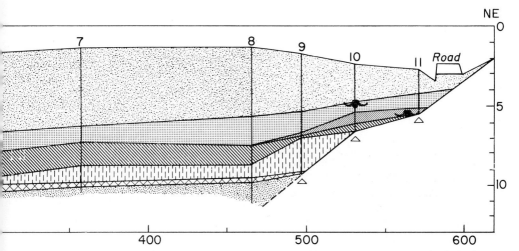

*formed under comparatively dry conditions (high degree of humification), the upper layers were formed under more humid conditions. The angular outlines used in this profile are customary in Denmark. Other investigators prefer to draw the boundary lines as curves between the individual points of observation (vertical lines). The former procedure is manifestly artificial; the latter may conceal undiscovered unconformities. (Scales in meters.)*

large samples, including the entire material of each sample for analysis. One can only hope that the contamination will be insignificant. But both sample and analysis must be considered very poor substitutes anyhow. No method can compensate for contamination of samples!

## REFERENCES

Faegri, K. (1944). Studies on the Pleistocene of Western Norway, III, Bømlo. Bergens Mus. Årb., 1943 Natv. rk. 8, p. 23.

Jenkins, B. M., and C. H. Mortimer (1938). Sampling lake deposits. Nature, v. 142, p. 834–835.

———, and W. Pennington (1941). The study of lake deposits. Nature, v. 147, p. 496.

Kullenberg, B. (1947). The piston core sampler. Svenska Hydrogr.-Biol. Kommissionen Skr., ser. 3, Hydrografi, v. 1, no. 2.

Lundquist, G. (1924). Utvecklingshistoriska insjöstudier. Sver. Geol. Unders., ser. C., p. 330.

Mackereth, F. J. H. (1958). A portable core sampler for lake deposits. Limnology and Oceanography, v. 3, p. 181–191.

Miller, M. M. (1953). A method for bottom sediment sampling in glacial lakes. J. Glaciology, v. 2, p. 287.

Moore, D. G. (1961). The free-corer; sediment sampling without wire and winch. J. Sed. Petrology, v. 31, p. 627–31.

Neustadt, M. J. (1961). Zur Geschichte der Seen im Holozän. Int. Ver. Limnol., Verh, v. 14, p. 279.

Overbeck, F. (1958). Ein Ergänzungsgerät zum Dachnowsky-Moorbohrer. Veröff. Geobot. Inst. Rübel Zürich, v. 34, p. 119.

Potzger, J. E. (1955). A borer for sampling in permafrost. Ecology, v. 36, p. 161.

Reissinger, A. (1936). Methode der Bohrungen in Seen zur Untersuchung von Sedimentschichten. Internat. Rev. Gesell. Hydrobiologie Hydrographie, v. 33, p. 1–24.

Richards, A. F., and G. H. Keller (1961). A plastic-barrel sediment corer. Deep-Sea Research, v. 8, p. 306–312.

Rowley, J. R., and A. O. Dahl (1956). Modifications in design and use of the Livingstone piston sampler. Ecology, v. 37, p. 849–851.

Shapiro, Joseph (1958). The core-freezer—a new sampler for lake sediments. Ecology, v. 39, p. 758.

Smith, A. J. (1959). Description of the Mackereth portable core sampler. J. Sed. Petrology, v. 29, p. 246–250.

Strøm, K. M. (1938). Recent bottom samplers securing undisturbed profiles of the upper sediment layer. Geol. Meere Binnengew., v. 2, p. 300.

―――― (1939). A handy sediment sampler. Norsk Geol. Tidsskr., v. 17, p. 50–52.

Troels-Smith, J. (1955). Karakterisering af løse Jordarter. Danm. Geol. Undersøg., rk. 4, v. 3, no. 10, 87 pp.

Wilson, I. J., and J. E. Potzger (1943). Pollen records from lakes in Anoka Country, Minnesota; A study on methods of sampling. Ecology, v. 24, p. 382.

Züllig, H. (1956a). Sedimente als Ausdrücke des Zustandes eines Gewässers. Schweizerisch Zeitschr. Hydrol, p. 18.

―――― (1956b). Das kombinierte Ramm-Kolben-Lot, ein leichtes Bohrgerät zur vereinfachten Gewinnung mehrerer meterlanger, ungeströrter Sedimentprofile. Ibid., v. 18, p. 208.

# Coring Devices for Lake Sediments

H. E. WRIGHT, E. J. CUSHING

*Department of Geology, University of Minnesota, Minneapolis*

D. A. LIVINGSTONE

*Department of Zoology, Duke University, Durham, North Carolina*

Many surficial lake and bog sediments contain sequences of Pleistocene and Holocene fossils that are useful for paleoecologic and paleoclimatic study

Contribution No. 9, Limnological Research Center, School of Earth Sciences, University of Minnesota.

as well as for stratigraphic purposes. Although pollen analysis has been the commonest objective of lake-sediment investigators, other paleontologic materials have been studied in a similar way—plant macrofossils (Vasari, 1962), Cladocera (Frey, 1961), midges (Stahl, 1959), molluscs (Sparks and West, 1959), and diatoms (Round, 1961). In addition, cores have been analyzed for hydrocarbons and other organic components (Swain and Prokopovitch, 1954; Vallentyne, 1955b) and for inorganic components as well (Hutchinson and Cowgill, 1963).

Where circumstances permit, commercial drill rigs of various kinds may be used to obtain samples of lake sediment. If the lake has dried up and it is possible to work directly on the exposed lake bed, a commercial well-drilling rig may be the best equipment to use (West, 1956; van der Hammen and Gonzalez, 1960). Such equipment is usually capable of boring to great depth even in hard sediments. Its principal disadvantages are high cost and the fact that core recovery is not always great enough for close stratigraphic work. Any method that employs drilling fluid or slurry carries the additional risk of contamination of samples (Traverse, et al., 1961).

This review will cover commercial drill rigs only incidentally. For a discussion of such equipment the reader may consult Hvorslev (1949). We are concerned chiefly with apparatus specifically designed for raising reasonably complete cores from lake and bog sediments for paleontologic investigation. Such apparatus is usually lighter and cheaper than standard engineering equipment. It is capable of higher core recovery and can be used from relatively light boats even on large and deep lakes, but it is less powerful than general-purpose well-drilling equipment and is less likely to penetrate deep deposits of very hard sediments.

Lake-sediment corers are conveniently considered in two size classes. The first consists of light, hand-operated samplers. These can be carried in a car or, less conveniently, on a man's back. The second consists of heavier, usually power-driven devices that must be carried by ship, truck, or trailer. Most of the devices, of either size category, utilize displacement boring (Hvorslev, 1949, p. 45) in obtaining successively deeper samples, but a few are augers or rotary drills or make use of wash boring to advance the hole.

Our treatment of drilling methods is not intended to be complete. Our own experience has been limited to augers of several types and to Naumann, Phleger, Davis, Hiller, Livingstone, Vallentyne, and Kullenberg samplers. We devote most of this review to devices and techniques that have performed well for us, with briefer accounts of the less satisfactory devices and of promising samplers that we have not used ourselves.

It should be emphasized that the key to successful coring is ingenuity in adapting the equipment to field conditions and in dealing with unexpected problems. It is essential to have a kit of the simpler wood- and metal-working tools and to be prepared to use them. A more extensive review of the problems of coring unconsolidated sediments is given by Hvorslev (1949), and certain theoretical and practical problems are discussed by Kjellman, et al. (1950) and Richards (1961).

## HAND-DRIVEN CORERS

### Free-fall Corers

For obtaining short cores of sediments from deep lakes and oceans the simplest instrument is probably the free-fall corer (Strøm, 1937). Those described by Lundquist (1925, p. 429–434), Naumann (1930, p. 20–26), Emery and Dietz (1941), Hvorslev and Stetson (1946), and Phleger (1951) are of this type. It consists of a weighted core tube that is allowed to fall freely through the water to penetrate as much sediment as possible in a single drive. The length of core recovered by such a sampler is limited and depends on the nature of the sediment, the diameter and wall-thickness of the core tube, and the height of the fall. Recovery can be improved by the addition of a check-valve or core retainer to help keep the core in the tube or by the addition of a piston that is held stationary while the tube descends into the sediment. The piston reduces the pressure over the top of the sediment core. The Kullenberg piston corer (1947) uses this principle, as do its many modifications (Silverman and Whaley, 1952; Heezen, 1952; Emery and Broussard, 1954; U. S. Hydrographic Office, 1955). The use of the Kullenberg corer on lakes is discussed in a later section.

With a free-fall sampler only a single drive is possible, for the original hole cannot be relocated for the purpose of obtaining deeper sediment. Furthermore, as the depth of penetration depends largely on dead weight, the device may be rather heavy, and a winch may be necessary to withdraw it from the bottom.

For operation from a sediment surface, or through water sufficiently shallow to permit relocation of the borehole, it is more profitable to lower a sampler by using a rigid assembly rather than a cable. For short cores in very shallow water a simple tube may suffice (Hanna, 1954). Extension rods can be used to push the sampler to successively greater depths, and a continuous series of core segments of the entire sediment can be recovered. Two general types of drive sampler will be discussed here: the side-intake sampler (Hiller sampler) and various types of piston corer.

### Hiller Sampler

The Hiller sampler has been manufactured commercially in Sweden (Beus and Mattson, Mora) since the beginning of this century and is used extensively in Scandinavian peat studies. According to information supplied by Magnus Fries, an open peat borer was used as early as 1773 in Sweden (Haglund, 1909), and the possible prototype for the Hiller sampler was described by Asbjørnsen in Norway in 1868 and was used by Blytt, the pioneer of bog stratigraphy. Even earlier types may have existed in Germany or England, where peat studies predate those in Scandinavia. The modern models are described by Lundquist (1925, p. 428), Erdtman (1943, p. 32), and Faegri and Iversen (1950, p. 51).

The sampling chamber, which is commonly 2.8 cm in diameter and 50 or 100 cm long, has a longitudinal slot that remains closed by a sliding cover during descent of the sampler through the sediment, provided a slight counter-clockwise torque is maintained on the rods. When the desired sampling level is reached, the sampler is rotated clockwise to open the chamber, and a longitudinal cutting flange that protrudes from the side of the chamber gathers sediment to fill the chamber as rotation is continued. The sampler is then rotated counterclockwise to close the cover, and the device is lifted to the surface, again with slight counterclockwise rotation. The chamber contents, once recovered, may be sampled on the spot; or if a liner was inserted the entire core can be removed intact from the chamber (Erdtman, 1935, p. 111–112; Livingstone, 1953, p. 11–12).

The extension rods used with the Hiller sampler must be of a design that transmits torque in either direction; threaded couplings are therefore un-suitable. The commercial model has a male-female joint held by a setscrew. When not in use the sampler and the rod couplings must be kept scrupulously clean and lightly oiled to prevent rusting, unless they are made of stainless steel.

The Hiller sampler is difficult to use in compacted sediment because the sediment must be displaced during penetration by the entire chamber and flange. Despite precautions in keeping the chamber closed during descent and ascent, water or loose sediment sometimes enters the chamber; such contami-nation is generally difficult to detect. The sample is always disturbed, and hence unsuitable for studies of sediment structure or bulk physical properties. The sampler will not operate properly in sandy sediments, for sand tends to jam the sliding cover. In spite of its disadvantages, the Hiller sampler is a valuable instrument for easily penetrated sediments because of its portability and its speed and simplicity of operation. It does not compress the sediments vertically and is the only device we have used successfully in certain types of fibrous or woody peats that tend to plug an open-ended coring tube.

### Davis Sampler

In a piston corer the sample enters the tube from the bottom rather than the side; consequently, the sample is less disturbed. The function of the piston is to keep the tube closed while the assembly is lowered to the desired sampling depth. Two basic designs are common, one with a retractable piston and one with a stationary piston.

The Davis sampler (Bastin and Davis, 1909) has a retractable piston. The commercial model (Eberbach Company, Ann Arbor, Michigan) is a tube 15 inches long with an inside diameter of $\frac{1}{2}$ inch. The piston is simply a loosely fitting interior rod that fills the tube during the initial drive of the device into the sediment. When the desired sampling level is reached, the rod is lifted until a spring catch near its lower end engages a collar at the upper end of the tube. This leaves the tube open. The sampler is then pushed farther into the sediment; a core about 10 inches long may be taken. The sampler is then withdrawn, the spring catch released, and the core extruded as the piston is forced back to its original position.

The Dachnowski sampler is similar in dimensions and manner of operation to the Davis sampler but instead of a catch the piston rod has two protruding longitudinal splines that slide through slots in the collar until, after the rod is given a half twist, their bottom ends come to rest on the collar (Faegri and Iversen, 1950, p. 52). The bearing surface during the operation that follows is therefore on the lower ends of the splines rather than on the less secure notch in a spring catch.

Both the Davis and the Dachnowski samplers can penetrate medium- or coarse-grained sands, but they may jam when one attempts to extrude the core. If a jam occurs, one must place the tube in a vise and hammer the piston through. The danger of jamming is reduced if the rod fits loosely through the collar of the tube. The piston end of the rod must fit tightly enough within the lower end of the tube, however, for the apparatus to remain closed while it is being lowered through water or loose sediment. If the fit is too tight or if the spring catch in the Davis sampler is too strong, then the piston cannot be easily retracted because the friction of the sediment may not be great enough to hold the tube. Cleaning of the sampler is simplified if the collar is attached to the tube by threads instead of pins.

Another difficulty with these samplers is that unwanted sediment may leak past the piston from above and partially fill the tube before the core is taken. If this happens the upper end of the core may consist entirely of stray material, which can only be recognized if it is less compact and lithologically different from the undisturbed remainder of the core. Sometimes the low pressure created within the tube by the retraction of the piston causes disturbed sediment to be drawn up into the tube from beneath it.

The Davis and Dachnowski samplers have the great advantage of light weight, simple operation, and simple maintenance. Because of the small diameter of the $\frac{1}{2}$-inch Davis model it can be pushed by hand through compacted or deep inorganic sediments that most other samplers will not penetrate. It is thus an essential item in a complete coring kit. In the commercial model of the Davis sampler the extension rods are too flexible for vigorous pushing in uncased holes through open water or soft sediments, but stronger rods can easily be substituted.

### Stationary-piston Corer

DESCRIPTION

Many of the disadvantages of the retractable-piston corers are overcome by the stationary-piston corer. In this design the piston is held at the lower end of the tube during the drive to the sampling depth, and it remains fixed at that depth while the core tube is driven past the piston farther down into the sediment to cut the core. The entry of excess sediment into the tube is thus prevented. A further advantage is that no hydrostatic pressure is created above the core, permitting the recovery of longer cores than is possible with the drive samplers just discussed. The stationary-piston sampler is the most successful and versatile hand-operated instrument that we have used. It can provide long cores of large diameter with little deformation of the sediment, although, as Kallstenius (1958) points out, it may fail to do so when the inside wall friction becomes very high.

Despite its importance in the development of lake-sediment sampling technique, the stationary-piston corer has a rather obscure history. Hvorslev (1949, p. 255) credits Olsson (1936) with the design of the first drive sampler with stationary piston, in use in Sweden since 1923 for soil coring. Reissinger (1936) describes a rather complete outfit employing a stationary-piston sampler for lake deposits and in addition refers to a sampler described by Perfiliev which made use of a piston and was suitable for deep water. Naumann (1930, p. 120) alludes to forthcoming papers by Perfiliev describing his sampler, in *Die Binnengewasser* and in Abderhalden's *Handbuch,* but neither seems to have appeared. We have not been able to check the reports of the Borodin Station, which are said to contain papers by Perfiliev (1927) on coring methods. Perfiliev was much concerned with problems of sampler design, and it seems quite possible that he may have been the originator of the stationary-piston principle, although we have been unable to locate a published description of his instrument.

Most students of lake sediments seem to have overlooked the papers of both Reissinger and Olsson. Reissinger's instrument was a rather complex one, making use of a screw to drive the sample tube into the sediment. Apparently no one who read his paper understood the principle on which his sampler was based well enough to recognize its basic simplicity and versatility. It was not until Kullenberg (1947) reintroduced the stationary piston with his deep-water corer that it was generally appreciated and incorporated into the standard working equipment of paleontologists. Kullenberg used his apparatus to obtain geological results of such general importance that it could not be overlooked. In the subsequent modification of piston samplers there has been much duplication of effort. For example, the idea of mounting such a sampler on rigid rod was advanced independently by Hvorslev (1949, p. 379), Livingstone (1953, 1955), and Reish and Green (1958).

Livingstone's (1953, 1955) sampler consisted of a tube about 4 feet long and 1.5 inches in diameter, attached by a head to extension rods. At the bottom of the tube a piston rimmed with leather washers was held in position by spring-loaded pins. A wire led from the piston through the head to the surface. As the tube was pushed down into the sediment the wire was held firmly, and the core entered the tube below the piston.

In sampling compacted sediments the piston was sometimes forced up from its lower position before the tube could be pushed all the way to the desired sampling level. Vallentyne (1955a) modified the apparatus by making the rod assembly pass through the head and extend down to the piston, which was thereby prevented from rising until the sampling level was reached. He also added a notched catch similar to that on the Davis corer near the lower end of the rod, which could be lifted to the top of the tube and secured there before the entire device was pushed deeper into the sediment to cut the core. Alternatively, splines can be placed near the lower end of the piston rod and the requisite slots cut in the head, according to the style of the Dachnowski sampler. We have had great success in using several samplers modified in this way.

If the leather-sealed piston is replaced with one made simply of two rubber stoppers on a threaded bolt (Rowley and Dahl, 1956; Ginsburg and Lloyd, 1956), the freedom of movement of the piston can be adjusted easily by tightening or loosening nuts that bear against the stoppers.

The Livingstone corer whose use is described below incorporates the Vallentyne and the Rowley and Dahl modifications as well as a few minor additional changes (Cushing and Wright, 1963). Its head is designed to accommodate core tubes of 1-inch diameter, but sleeves can be added to permit the use of larger tubes. Coring tubes 1 meter long are convenient and permit high recovery, but longer tubes can be used effectively if the sediment is soft and has a low coefficient of friction with the wall of the tube. Transparent plastic tubes allow observation of the core without extrusion, but the thick walls of such tubes make penetration into compacted sediments difficult. Thin-walled (0.035 inch) steel or aluminum tubes are best to use in compacted sediments.

Extension rods for this sampler must represent a compromise among weight, strength, and cost. Standard commercial water pipe and couplings are the cheapest—$\frac{1}{4}$-inch pipe is adequate for a light-weight rod where little bending is anticipated. Rods should be cut in 1- or 2-meter lengths. For heavier work standard $\frac{3}{4}$-inch black water pipe (outside diameter 1 inch) is inexpensive and rigid, although heavy. Threaded couplings can be handled easily with vise-grip pliers in any weather; recessed couplings are especially easy to use and provide extra support at the joints. In most sampling situations, however, Lichtwardt (1952) rods, made of high-strength aluminum alloy with special couplings covered by sleeves held in place by spring-loaded pins, are preferable. A similar type of coupling has been described by Taylor (1957). Lichtwardt rod has the advantages that it is extremely light, can be coupled and uncoupled at high speed, and can be used to apply torque in either direction. Water cannot be pumped through it for cleaning out the borehole, however, and the couplings may cause trouble in freezing weather. The relative expense of fabricating Lichtwardt rod is outweighed, we feel, by its portability and convenience in the field.

TAKING THE SAMPLE

High-energy sounding equipment (Hoskins, et al., 1961) is unnecessary on lake ships, but we have found it advantageous to make use of the best available echo sounder in choosing a coring station. Recording echo sounders are to be preferred, for they provide a permanent record of the depth and nature of the mud surface and of the depth to dense layers within the sediment. Even very cheap nonrecording echo sounders, such as the one sold in kit form by the Heath Company (Benton Harbor, Michigan), may provide useful information about the sediment.

The stationary-piston corer is operated easily from lake ice or from a peat-bog surface. On open water it may be manipulated, usually through a casing, from the stern of a rowboat or from a platform between two connected boats or pneumatic life-rafts. Where such craft are not obtainable an inexpensive raft may be made from three or four castoff (but airtight) truck-tire inner tubes which support a platform of two 3 by 6-foot plywood sheets held apart by two crosspieces secured by bolts and wing nuts. Such a raft is easily portable and can be assembled quickly. It provides working space for four persons, but it should not be used in waters frequented by dangerous animals (Richardson and Livingstone, 1962). Drilling craft are best anchored by long lines leading at shallow angles to at least three anchors (e.g., heavy stones, bags of sand), which may be set out before the coring station is occupied. If the water is shallow, poles or pipes placed next to the raft may be used to improve stability. Time spent in careful anchoring is saved later during coring operations, especially when winds are brisk. In water less than 3 meters deep a drilling platform may be constructed on four long pilings stabilized by two diagonal struts and four horizontal cross-members. Heavy rubber or plastic gloves on one or both hands provide good protection against cold water, clay, or frayed cables.

The assembled corer, with the piston at the lower end of the sampling tube, is lowered steadily to the desired sampling level by the string of rods. The piston wire is held to the rods during this operation so that it will play out at the same rate; if the sediment is loose, this precaution will assure that the sampling tube does not fall faster than the rods and engage the spring catch prematurely. If, on the other hand, the sediment is compacted, it may be necessary to apply strong downward pressure on the rod assembly to reach the required depth.

When the desired sampling depth is reached, the rod assembly is raised until the spring catch engages the head of the sampler. The desired length of drive is then marked on the rods (vise-grip pliers serve as a convenient marker), the piston wire is secured firmly to some stationary object close to the hole (vise-grip pliers may be used to secure it in a slot cut in the drilling platform), and the sampler is driven the desired sampling distance. The drive should be steady, without appreciable pause, to prevent the recurrence of inertial friction between the sediment and the core tube.

Measurements are checked and recorded before and after the pushing operation. Depths can be watched easily if a reference clip is moved on the piston wire below each drive. Care must be taken throughout the operation that there is no confusion about lengths of rod used and the depth of sampling.

The apparatus is then withdrawn from the hole. The piston wire should be held to the rods so that it rises at the same rate. As the assembly is withdrawn the extension rods are separated in groups of two to four so that they do not bend excessively. During the uncoupling operation one foot may be kept on the piston cable or a vise-grip pliers may be placed on the rod below the lowest exposed coupling so that the assembly does not slip down the hole accidentally.

In an ordinary sampling operation the weight of two or three persons may be applied to the rods to drive the sampler. After normal holding positions become ineffective, pushing is done best with the use of a pushing board, a 30-inch piece of 2 by 4 inch wood in which a slot reinforced with a metal plate has been cut. The slot is placed over one of the rod couplings or on vise-grip pliers locked at a convenient position, and the rods are forced down by the combined weight of several men. To withdraw the sampler, the pushing board may be used in reverse as a pulling board.

Hammering on the top of a piston sampler will increase the depth of penetration. It is convenient to connect a stem-jar to the top of the sampler, with an anvil at either end of the stem, so that the sampler can be hammered into the sediment and then hammered out again. The weight of the hammer should be about ten or fifteen pounds, if it is to be raised by hand. If power is available (Colinvaux, 1962, p. 133–142) the hammer can be made substantially heavier without harming the drill rod.

The disadvantage of hammering is that it results in deformation of the sediment (Hvorslev, 1949), and the core recovery is almost always lower than it would be with a single continuous drive. One should not hammer if the sampler can be forced into the sediment with a pushing-board, but when further penetration is impossible by ordinary means a hammer is useful. Hammering may cause certain sediments to become quick or fluid because of thixotropic effects; the core may then fall out as the tube is raised.

An alternative to hammering is the use of chain hoists to drive the sampler into the bottom (Cushing and Wright, 1963). Chain hoists that are light and compact enough to be classed as hand-operated equipment will permit a continuous drive of nearly 2 meters with up to 4000 pounds of force. The chain hoists are suspended from a simple yoke on the extension rods and hooked at the drilling-platform level. The reaction may be supplied by earth anchors in a bog, by a deadman under lake ice, or by the combined weight of an anchored raft and its crew. Steady cranking of the chain hoists will drive a piston corer into the most difficult sediment with little or no disturbance of the core. The same principle may be applied if a block and tackle is used instead of chain hoists to pull down the extension rods (Hvorslev, 1949, fig. 104).

In compacted sediments, especially clay, the force necessary to withdraw the filled sampler may exceed that necessary to drive it because of the low pressure beneath the core tube in the initial stage of withdrawal. The longer the sampler remains in the hole the harder it is to withdraw, owing to the buildup of friction on the outer wall of the tube. (In soft sediment, however, it is wise to leave the sampler in the hole a short time to allow the *internal* friction to increase and thus prevent the loss of the core during withdrawal of the sampler.) If manual force or hammering is insufficient for withdrawal, an automobile bumper jack may be used to advantage. Vise-grip pliers locked on the drive rod serve as an expedient lug for the application of the jack. A chain hoist makes the job even easier, if an overhead support can be rigged. Still another procedure is to bore a hole with an auger right beside the stuck corer to break the suction at the base. Then if the rod or cable is hammered, the tube may break loose from the clay. When operating on water the rod can be secured at one end of the boat and the crew moved to the opposite end to provide levering action. In apparently hopeless cases one may fill the boat with water, then secure the rod and bail out the boat—or even abandon the boat for the night to let the waves work the sampler loose.

FIELD TREATMENT OF THE CORE

Some workers prefer to extrude cores in the field to check the stratigraphy and completeness of recovery. Others detach the filled core tubes from the sampler and transport them untouched. The most satisfactory procedure is to extrude a pilot core in the field (to be saved or not) and then take a second core for retention in the tubes. In sealed tubes the moisture content, chemistry, and structure of the sediment will change very little until extrusion can be managed in the laboratory under controlled conditions. If the core is to be shipped in the tubes, the piston must be withdrawn from the top of the filled tube in the field and replaced by a cork or tape. If the sediment is loose one should have a small hole in the tube just below the piston to allow entrance of air as the piston is withdrawn; otherwise the loose sediment will be sucked up with the piston. Alternatively, one can insert a long-handled wrench into the top of the tube to release the pressure on the rubber piston and allow the air to enter. If one has a stock of extra pistons he need merely unscrew the wire from the piston and leave the piston in the filled tube.

Corking has the disadvantage that several centimeters of the core are distorted at each end of the tube when the corks are inserted. It is, however, a convenient way of dealing with the samples, particularly if they are to be shipped for a long distance by commercial carrier after they are collected. Care should be taken to decant any water that may be in the sample tube, particularly from the uppermost sample of sediment. The corks should fit tightly in the tube after they have been rolled and should be rammed home carefully so that all air is expressed from the sample. If this is done the cores may be shipped by sea or by rail over long distances without damage, and they will remain moist and chemically reduced so that microfossils in them are not damaged. Undoubtedly some water loss occurs, however, and the cores may not be suitable for careful measurements of shear strength after they have been stored for a long time in this way. If care is not taken to express all air from the tube at the time of corking, the corks may be driven out by expanding air when the tubes warm up, and the samples may be damaged by drying and oxidation.

If extrusion is to be managed in the field the sampler should first be washed on the outside to make the operation easier and cleaner. A plastic basin of water and a rag are suitable if open water is not convenient. If temperatures are far below the freezing level, a bucket of hot water should be at hand for continued application to the tube to prevent the core from freezing before it can be extruded.

To extrude the core the spring catch is released and the piston rod pushed into the tube until it comes against the top of the piston. An extrusion platform is prepared to receive the sample. This may be a clean ice surface, a flat board, a semicircular metal gutter, or a ribbed air mattress. Pieces of aluminum foil are cut for wrapping the samples. The sampler is laid horizontally and the piston rod is held stationary as the sampling tube is pushed steadily over the rod. In this way the sample emerges from the tube with least disturbance. If extrusion proves difficult, the main impediment may be the rubber stoppers. The necessary force may be materially reduced as the core tube is removed from the sampler head, the rubber piston pulled out, and a loose-fitting metal cylinder inserted as a substitute piston.

The length of the core is noted and the lithology and stratigraphy checked after the surface smear of disturbed sediment is removed transversely with a sharp knife. If the hole used for that particular core segment was new, there should be contamination at neither the top nor the bottom of the core. If the hole used was an old one that had been opened on the previous drive to the level directly above, then the top of the core may consist of material that fell into the hole between drives. If the least doubt exists about the purity of the whole core, the doubtful parts of the core should be discarded on the spot.

Recovery is sometimes incomplete—for example, a drive of one meter may yield a core only 50 cm long. Extent of recovery depends, among other factors, on the compaction and cohesion of the sediment and on the diameter and wall thickness of the core tube used. After a series of experiments with gravity corers, Emery and Dietz (1941) and Piggot (1941) concluded that only the first part of the core enters the tube without difficulty and represents a continuous sample of the sediment. As the core becomes longer the total sliding friction between the core and the inside walls of the tube becomes greater and the pressure at the mouth of the core tube increases; eventually the pressure exceeds the strength of the sediment, and sediment is forced aside instead of entering the core tube. The sample then becomes a composite of the remaining thickness of sediment penetrated, for some of the sediment enters the tube while some is squeezed aside. If the sediment is structureless, the deformation or the incompleteness may not be detected. Thus, for the example given above the top 30 cm of the recovered core may be complete, but the remaining 20 cm may contain decreasing amounts of material from 30 to 100 cm. The sediment in the borehole is disturbed to the depth of the total drive, of course, and the missing material cannot be recovered from the same hole. If continuous sampling is desired, it may be necessary to use adjacent holes alternately. Each drive should then start slightly above the level of the bottom of the preceding sample recovered from the alternate hole.

Recovery can be improved if a tube with a larger diameter is used, so long as the wall thickness does not increase proportionately. The pressure at the mouth of the core tube, which opposes the entry of sediment, decreases with an increase in the inside diameter of the tube but increases with an increase in the thickness of the tube wall; for greatest recovery the ratio of wall thickness to tube diameter should be kept as low as possible. Thus, the use of a liner within the core tube, although it has advantages, decreases sampler efficiency. We have found that a high-strength aluminum alloy tube with a wall thickness of 0.035 inch and a diameter of 1.5 inches is quite suitable for most ordinary coring operations. In normal sediment a recovery very close to 100 percent is obtainable for 1-meter samples taken in such tubes. The practice of making the diameter at the cutting edge smaller than the inside diameter of the core tube to provide a slight inside clearance is of questionable value for samplers with a tight-fitting stationary piston (Kjellman, et al., 1950, p. 13). Outside clearance, provided by a cutting shoe of greater diameter than the sample tube, does not appear to be necessary with rod-operated samplers if the core tube has a greater diameter than the extension rods.

With careful work in uniform sediment it is possible to obtain complete recovery with each sampling drive and nearly continuous sampling from a single borehole. Percent recovery cannot, however, always be predicted for a body of sediment of variable character. If time permits one should take test cores at various levels from a nearby borehole before the final core is taken so that optimum lengths of drive may be determined. Often the force necessary to drive the sampler increases appreciably when the core length begins to lag behind the distance penetrated. If such a situation develops, the drive should be stopped, the distance driven measured, the sampler withdrawn, and the core extruded and measured. If the core length is appreciably less than the length of drive, the length of drive for the next deeper coring operation is reduced accordingly. Peat, especially woody peat, is apt to give trouble because of its inhomogeneity and because of the formation of plugs in the tube, in which case the use of a Hiller peat borer is recommended.

If the cores are extruded in the field they may be cut to 30- to 50-cm segments for convenience in handling and transporting, although some prefer to wrap the entire length of the core uncut. Core segments may be wrapped tightly in aluminum foil and the joints completely sealed with masking tape to retard drying and oxidation. The top should be marked and the depth of penetration (or the number of the core segment) noted, as well as the code designation for the core. If storage for long periods is contemplated, it is advisable to wrap the core first in a thin plastic film (e.g., Saran Wrap) before wrapping in aluminum foil, for many sediments corrode aluminum. Packing the entire group of segments in a plastic bag further retards drying.

### SURFACE-SEDIMENT CORES

Collection of cores of the loose surface sediment from lakes presents a special problem which the stationary-piston sampler can handle adequately much in the manner described by Rowley and Dahl (1956). An accurate measurement of water depth is necessary. This may be difficult because the transition from water to organic sediment may be gradual. It is therefore best done with a perforated 10-inch metal disk suspended horizontally on the bottom of a line than with a simple sinker or rod. Alternatively, test cores may be taken to determine the top of the sediment. After the depth has been determined, the sampler is lowered at a spot free from the disturbance that may have been caused by the sounding. The piston should be at the bottom of the tube, but the spring catch should be engaged at the head. The piston sampler used for this purpose actually requires no head and no piston rod—a plastic tube with piston and wire may simply be firmly taped to the lower part of a string of rods. The tube should be allowed to fill with water from the top in order to equalize the pressure on the piston. The sampler can then be lowered to a depth a few centimeters above the effective top of the sediment, with the objective of sampling the lower part of the water itself. All movements of the sampler in the water must be made slowly so that the loose sediment will not be disturbed unduly. The piston wire is then secured in the usual manner, and the sampler is pushed into the sediment until the tube is full. It is wise to use a very long tube for this operation if the sediment is especially loose, or else the tube may not reach any sediment that is sufficiently compact to stay in the tube. If large plant roots or stems are present in the upper sediment, a plug often forms that prevents the entrance of further sediment into the tube, and under these conditions several trials may be necessary before a satisfactory core is obtained. A transparent plastic tube is preferable to a metal one for this operation because a successful core can be recognized at once.

The corer must be held vertically during and after withdrawal from the water. The core-filled tube is separated from the head of the corer and the wire unscrewed from the piston. The piston is left in the tube, and the core remains undisturbed. The base of the tube may be corked or taped. If the piston must be used for another operation, it may be withdrawn if the wall of the tube is punctured just below the piston to allow the entrance of air during the withdrawal. The puncture may then be sealed with tape. An even simpler technique is to saw off the plastic tube below the piston.

If the operation takes place in freezing weather the core-filled tube may be allowed to freeze in a vertical position before being transported. In warmer weather the cores may be frozen in an insulated receptacle containing dry ice and acetone, or they may be transported erect to a freezing room. Slow freezing may cause ice segregation in the core and drastically change the moisture content of the sediment. For extrusion, the tube is allowed to thaw slightly around the periphery, and the core is extruded as a solid cylinder. Enough of the surface should be thawed so that the peripheral smear from the inside of the tube may be scraped or washed off. The frozen core may then be cut into disks with a saw or a warm, sharp knife at requisite intervals and the disks placed in sample vials.

If freezing or vertical transportation of a short core is not practical, extrusion and sampling may be accomplished in the field if the tube is kept in a vertical position, the head removed, and a piston inserted at the bottom to permit extrusion out the top. Samples of soft sediment may be withdrawn from the top of the tube with a pipette or a spoon at appropriate intervals as the core is gradually extruded. Brown (1956) designed a special head for this purpose. Still another method is to allow the core to dry until it has enough cohesion to be extruded horizontally, in the normal manner; shrinkage is usually so drastic with this method, however, that depth measurements become inaccurate.

More elaborate surface-sediment corers have been designed for study of the microstructure or of the oxidized microzone at the top of the loose sediment. The Züllig (1953) or Jenkin (Mortimer, 1942) corers have valves which close the bottom of the tube to retain the loose core. Shapiro (1958) froze the sediment in place with the use of dry ice in a jacket around the tube.

### FOUR-INCH PISTON CORER

To provide larger samples for radiocarbon analyses and for separation of plant macrofossils and other organic materials, a special piston sampler 4 inches in diameter and 6 feet long has been used (Cushing and Wright, 1963). The device differs from the modified Livingstone sampler described above in that an internal rod rather than a wire is used to immobilize the piston. The drive rod is standard $\frac{3}{4}$-inch water pipe (1-inch outside diameter). It is screwed directly to the sampler head and encloses the piston rod, which is standard $\frac{1}{4}$-inch gas pipe with a $\frac{1}{2}$-inch outside diameter.

In operation, the apparatus is lowered with the piston held at the bottom of the tube by the piston rod. Water is allowed to enter through ports in the head to equalize the pressure. When the corer reaches the desired sampling level, the piston rod is secured to an overhead support, and the drive rod and core tube are forced as much as 1.5 meters into the sediment. The drive rod may be rotated a few times to be sure that the bottom of the core breaks from the sediment below. The entire apparatus is then pulled to the surface. Chain hoists may be necessary to drive in and pull out the sampler.

A 4-inch core is extruded and handled in much the same way as described for the smaller piston corers. If extrusion is difficult, a chain hoist may be attached to the sampler and used to draw the core tube against the piston and force out the core.

CASING

If sampling is to be carried out through open water or very loose sediment, casing is desirable to preserve the location of the borehole. Casing may also be necessary to prevent excessive bending and buckling of flexible drive rods under heavy driving pressure. A further purpose of casing is to keep the borehole vertical. If the drive rods are flexible or crooked they may be deflected out of the hole at depth, making penetration more difficult and introducing error in the depth measurements. For casing to depths of 15 meters the writers have used standard 2-inch water pipe in 5- and 10-foot lengths; although heavy, pipe is readily available and relatively inexpensive. Standard aluminum pipe, although more expensive, is lighter. Thin-walled aluminum tubing joined with heavy-duty aluminum pipe couplings is even lighter. This casing can be easily fitted in the laboratory. It has proved quite satisfactory in water as much as 30 meters deep. Standard couplings for electrical conduit can also be used to connect thin-walled tubing. Casing has not yet proved necessary for use with the 4-inch piston sampler, which is driven by relatively rigid rods. Ordinarily it is only necessary to use casing in the water and not in the borehole. When the hole must be cased, as in cohesionless sand, casing is driven and extracted in much the same way as the samplers. Casing is added in convenient lengths and driven deeper as the sampling progresses. The lower end of the casing must remain above the sampling depth. As the driving force necessary to take samples increases, the length of uncased borehole should be reduced to provide further support for the drive rods. A frustrating predicament often develops during withdrawal of the sampler when a coupling catches on the lower end of the casing; the situation can be obviated if the rod couplings and the end of the casing are beveled.

## Augers

Most pollen analysts unfamiliar with augers regard them as untrustworthy instruments because the sample they take is distorted and is open to contamination from overlying layers during removal to the surface. We do not wish to recommend the auger as an ideal instrument, but simply to point out some of the advantages that make it a valuable addition to the standard kit of sampling tools.

Augers are cheap and generally available. The single-fluted type used by ship's carpenters is preferred, as it distorts the sample less than the ordinary two-fluted carpenter's auger and provides a bigger sample. Sample size is important because one must always scrape off the smeared outer rind before taking a sample for microfossil analysis. Both types of auger are light, compact, and sturdy. They are capable of being driven by hand through very stiff sediments, and, being designed for the purpose, will penetrate even thick logs of sound wood, which no other ordinary sampler will do. This can be an advantage for work in bogs or fens. Unlike most samplers, they do not stick fast in tough sediments and defy removal, for they can always be screwed out along the path they made going in, and although this may mean losing the sample it is preferable to losing the instrument as well.

Sears (personal communication) and Hvorslev (1949, p. 60–61) recommend the Iwan posthole digger. Our experience with this instrument has been limited to permafrost drilling, for which it is essentially worthless. In our experience the most suitable auger for general purposes is a single-fluted one with Swedish rods and a long-handled lever jack for extrusion, described by West (1955, p. 4). We know of no other instrument which a single man can operate by hand in a drained cow pasture to penetrate a thick body of glacial till and sample an interglacial clay beneath it.

The auger does have disadvantages. Although it can be used, with appropriate care, to obtain uncontaminated samples from plastic clays and clay-gyttjas, it will not hold all other types of sediments as well. Sometimes the sample from a deep layer of soft sediment will not only be contaminated but will be removed completely as the auger is withdrawn through an overlying layer of stiffer material. The auger cannot be used with rods that are merely screwed together, and other kinds of rods are likely to be more expensive. It should be regarded as a useful adjunct, to be used for exploratory work or when special problems arise, rather than as a basic sampling instrument.

Related to augers is the hollow earth drill developed by Pchelkitsev (1951) for coring in permafrost. It consists of a cutting tube of hardened steel, with sharp cutting teeth ground into the lower end and a fitting for attachment to suitable extension rod at the upper end. The outer side of the cutting tube has spiral flutes to aid in forcing the sampler into the ground and to remove chips cut by the teeth. The sampler is rotated, with appropriate pressure on the rods, until it is filled with a plug of frozen sediment which is broken off and brought to the surface for sampling. Gerard (1954) has met the problem of sampling permafrost in a different way. He used an engine-driven force pump to jet a hole into the permafrost with water at the ambient summer air temperature and took a discontinuous core of short frozen plugs from the bottom of the hole as it was advanced. The plugs were taken by hammering a sample tube into the frozen sediment.

## HEAVY CORING DEVICES

### General

In the temperate zone, where investigation of lake and bog sediments began, most lakes are less than 15,000 years old and contain less than 20 meters of sediment. Most of this sediment is highly organic and rather soft, so that it can be penetrated easily by hand samplers. The only serious drilling problems are encountered in very large or deep lakes, such as the Laurentian Great Lakes, and the early workers were not ambitious enough to attempt these.

Oceanographers have led the way in the development of heavy coring devices. Their drilling problems have demanded powerful equipment, and the size of the vessels needed for simple travel on the ocean is great enough to make the use of heavy equipment feasible. Readers interested in the general problems and methods of meeting them at sea may consult the paper of Piggot (1941), Heezen (1952), Pratje (1952), Kullenberg (1947, 1955), Beckman, et al. (1960), Hersey (1960), Horton (1961), Moore (1961), Richards and Keller (1961), McLelland (1961), and Riedel, et al. (1961).

Most work on the development of heavy corers has been done on a rather empirical basis. A complete analysis of the dynamic properties of the piston cable has been made (Kullenberg, 1947, 1955), and a certain amount of careful engineering, usually not mentioned in the published descriptions, has obviously been applied to the construction and hydrodynamic properties of many samplers. There is, however, a scarcity of the quantitative data on sediment properties that must be available if corers are to fulfill their functions properly. Even Hvorslev's (1949) standard treatment of sampler technology is rather brief in its treatment of design problems, particularly those associated with single-shot, fixed-piston samplers like the Kullenberg device. In designing samplers for paleontologic work one must apply the theory developed for short-drive engineering samplers and mechanical data for terrestrial soils to problems where neither one is strictly applicable. The investigations of Richards (1961) into the mechanical properties of deep-sea sediments are very welcome, and there is a great need for similar information about lake sediments. In order to design efficient samplers for the collection of long cores with a high percentage of core recovery it is essential to be able to predict the relative importance of frictional, shearing, and plastic deformational forces on a long sample tube. At present they can hardly be estimated.

### Wilson Sampler

In many lakes there may be some difficulty in raising the basal few meters of sediment, which are likely to contain considerable quantities of clay, silt, sand, and gravel. It was in response to this problem that Wilson (1941) developed the first of the heavy-duty lake samplers. It is basically a simple tube without a piston but with a check valve to minimize loss of incohesive sediments. The tube and the rigid rod to which it is attached are made of standard iron pipe and are driven into the sediment with repeated blows of a sledge hammer. Because the sampler lacks a piston it will take only a short sample, usually less than 30 cm long, but its rugged construction permits it to be driven without harm into very resistant sediment. The outstanding feature of the sampler is the use of wash-boring to advance the hole, which is cased with standard pipe of sufficient size to accommodate the sampler. Lake water is driven by a manually operated force-pump down the hollow drill rod to clean out the cased hole. This feature makes the sampler particularly suitable for use in lakes where layers of cohesionless sand are likely to be encountered.

The original sampler described by Wilson was operated from a raft made of oil drums. The whole rig was of heavy construction. By giving some thought to ways of saving weight, particularly by using a pneumatic raft with a plywood deck and by substituting aluminum alloys for iron wherever possible, the apparatus could be made much lighter. A light gasoline engine could be used to drive the force pump and operate the running gear and would permit the use of a much larger sampler.

Few other paleontologists have followed Wilson's lead and exploited wash-boring, although it is sometimes used with power-driven equipment (Kjellman, et al., 1950; Cohenour, 1952; Zumberge, 1962). A light, hand-operated force pump could easily be included in the standard equipment that we describe in the first part of this paper, and its use might overcome much of the trouble with sandy sediments.

### Mackereth Sampler

Probably the most ingenious of the heavy-duty corers is that of Mackereth (1958), described also by Smith (1959). It is essentially a piston sampler forced into the sediment by pneumatic pressure. The reaction is furnished by a large sheet-metal drum anchored to the lake bottom hydrostatically, so that the apparatus can be operated from a light boat by its air hose, and there is no need for rigid drill rod or casing. Energy for anchoring the sheet-metal drum, for driving the sampler, and for bringing the equipment back to the surface of the water is provided by commercial cylinders of compressed air.

The Mackereth sampler takes a core about 6 meters long in a single, nicely machined tube. Sediment lying deeper than 6 meters can be sampled only by increasing the length of the core tube, which may become awkward to transport and handle. When many samples within this length limit are to be taken from the same lake or from a cluster of mutually accessible lakes, in water of moderate depth, the Mackereth sampler should receive very serious consideration. For such a purpose it is far superior to rod-operated samplers or to the Jenkin and Mortimer sampler (1938). It has the clear advantage over the Kullenberg sampler that it may be operated from a single rowboat.

### Colinvaux Sampler

Colinvaux (1962) has adapted a piston sampler of conventional design for power driving. His additions to the standard outfit consist of a 3.25 horse-power engine with a speed reducer and capstan head which is used to raise a 50-pound doughnut-shaped hammer riding on a heavy steel bar. The hammer is supported by a light steel tripod and is attached by its bar to standard $\frac{3}{4}$-inch aluminum alloy Lichtwardt drilling rod. The hammer stroke can be controlled by a turn of rope on the capstan head to drive the sampler into the sediment or to extract it. The apparatus has been used from the ice on Imuruk Lake, Alaska, to sample very resistant clay, silt, and fine sand that had defied the standard hand-driven samplers. The heavy hammer produced no noticeable deformation of the light aluminum drive rods, but the 1.5-inch solid steel bar on which the hammer rode up and down snapped after nine hours of hammering in extreme cold. Colinvaux advises the use of nonferrous metals under arctic conditions and also suggests that frozen couplings can be thawed conveniently, if dangerously, by dousing them with gasoline and then igniting it.

### Sampler with Metal Foils

The sliding fraction between the core and the inside walls of the core tube, which limits the core length obtainable with ordinary piston samplers, is eliminated in a remarkable sampler described by Kjellman, et al. (1950; see also Anonymous, 1960). The sampler is similar to other piston corers except that thin metal foils or ribbons are attached around the loose-fitting stationary piston. As the sampler descends into the sediment the foils, which are individually coiled in a storage space near the lower end of the sampler, are drawn into the core tube to form a liner between the core and tube walls. The core adheres to the foils, and the sliding friction is between the foils and the tube wall. The length of core obtainable is then limited only by the length and tensile strength of the metal foils.

Continuous undisturbed cores 20 meters long have been taken in a single drive with this sampler. Relatively heavy boring equipment is required for its operation, however, and since the core tube must extend to the surface, use of the sampler is confined to shallow water. Although the boring equipment and the careful machining required by its design make the sampler expensive, it is probably the most economical equipment to use in obtaining a large number of continuous samples from thick deposits. The sampler with metal foils is at present the only instrument available that can yield an uninterrupted and undisturbed core of a thick lacustrine deposit.

### Kullenberg Sampler

The raising of cores from very deep lakes presents some difficult problems. Although lakes with water depths of over 400 meters are not abundant

(Hutchinson, 1957, p. 168, lists only 19), they are of particular interest because they include the oldest lakes in the world, and many have a highly endemic fauna.

The Mohole project (Horton, 1961; McLelland, 1961; Riedel, et al., 1961) has demonstrated the feasibility of taking cores from very deep water with oil-drilling equipment, but it has also demonstrated the expense of that approach. In lakes that are connected with the sea, such as the Laurentian Great Lakes (Zumberge, 1962), this method is feasible; but in landlocked lakes one would be faced with the additional expense of constructing a drilling barge on the spot. Although it is reasonably certain that rod-operated samplers and casing could be used economically in deeper water than they have so far, we must consider other methods for lakes with depths near a thousand meters.

The best device that is currently available for dealing with deep lakes is the Kullenberg (1947, 1955) piston sampler. This was originally designed for use in the deep sea and has spawned a host of light, hand-operated offspring. The instrument is a simple tube with a piston attached to a long cable. It is lowered slowly until it is a few meters above the bottom. The cable is then arrested so that the piston is locked at that depth, and the sample falls freely around it under the force of gravity. The sample tube is weighted for greater penetration, and a trigger automatically releases the tube when it reaches the proper depth. The release removes the weight of the sample tube from the cable, and the winch operator brakes the winch when the strain on the wire relaxes.

At sea cores 20 meters long are sometimes taken with this instrument, although normally the length of core is somewhat less. The core recovery is usually very good, although, as Richards (1961) points out, it is often less than 100 percent. Although core disturbance is not great with stationary piston samplers, it may be sufficient to interfere with investigations of soil mechanics (Hvorslev, 1949, p. 320–321; Kallstenius, 1958). Most lake sediments are easier to penetrate than marine sediments, and there seems to be no reason why cores at least 20 meters long should not be raised from deep lakes with such a free-fall piston sampler.

We have had some experience with a Kullenberg sampler on the East African Great Lakes. The basic instrument was similar to Ewing's (Heezen, 1952) modification of the deep-sea sampler, but it was equipped with only about 250 kg of driving weights. The hoisting power was supplied by a 3.25 horsepower lawn mower engine through a reduction gear with an output speed of 600 rpm. The engine was coupled to a Beebe 2-ton winch that had 22:1 reduction gearing. The V-belt pulleys that coupled the engine and winch effected a further speed reduction. Faster hoisting speed would be desirable but would require a more powerful engine. The Beebe winch was stronger than necessary, but weaker winches do not have such low gearing nor such a good asbestos-shoed brake. The principal disadvantages of the winch are that it does not have a smooth-winding mechanism and that its drum capacity is limited to 150 meters of $\frac{3}{16}$-inch galvanized wire rope. For work in deeper water it is necessary to use auxiliary reels of wire, and this results in a lot of winding and unwinding that could be avoided with a bigger drum. When adding a new spool of wire rope to the sampler cable it is convenient to have an auxiliary 1-ton winch mounted on the derrick.

The apparatus was used on Lake Victoria in about fifty meters of water with thin-walled aluminum sample tubing such as is normally used with the hand-driven piston corer. Cores of up to eight meters were obtained in this way in soft organic gyttja, with only about fifty kilograms of driving weight. It was not possible to obtain longer cores because the light sample tube bent and broke. Black iron conduit used as sample tubing in 450 meters of water on Lake Tanganyika penetrated to a depth of 12 meters. In 20-meter lengths even the heavier tubing broke.

At sea the Kullenberg sampler is operated from larger vessels than are usually available for work on lakes. We were able to use it quite effectively by lowering the sampler through a hole in a plywood platform supported on two or more rubber dinghies or a steel catamaran. A wooden derrick with an appropriate block was used for hoisting the sampler. The sample tube was assembled vertically while suspended in the water through the hole in the raft.

In another modification of the Kullenberg sampler for use in deep Swiss lakes, Züllig (1956) added to the base of the sampler the lower part of a 50-cm-diameter steel barrel, with its bottom partially cut out, to rest on the sediment surface and provide support. The steel sample tube itself, with plastic liner, was then driven into the sediment by the use of an 8-kg weight, which was repeatedly raised and lowered about 30 cm by means of the single cable that reached to the water surface. The piston wire was held stationary at the top of the assembly that provided the guide rods for the ram-weight. After the 3-meter core was cut the entire apparatus was hoisted to the surface by a hand-operated winch mounted across two rowboats.

The factors limiting the length of core that can be taken by the Kullenberg sampler do not seem to have been investigated in detail. Presumably by simply increasing the diameter and the driving weight, the depth of penetration could be increased somewhat. Any great increase in driving weight, however, would lead to very serious problems at sea, for the cable strength would have to be increased correspondingly, and this would lead to a demand for stronger winches with much greater drum capacities. In lakes, where the depths of water are almost an order of magnitude less, these problems are not so serious, and although we have used a lighter sampler than the standard marine model in our experiments so far, it is quite possible that lake samplers can be made even heavier than marine samplers. In our experience, however, the factor limiting the depth of penetration was not the driving weight but the strength of the sample tubing, which often buckled and broke. At the beginning of a drive, when the tip of the sample tube first begins to encounter serious resistance from the sediment, there is a great length of unsupported tube between it and the weights at the upper end of the tube. Oceanographers have occasionally attempted to meet this problem by putting diamond stays on the sample tube, but these increase the resistance of the sample tube as it enters the sediment. Actually, only the part of the tube above the sediment needs lateral support, and it should be possible to provide it with a short length of casing suspended from the hoisting cable.

### Vibrodrills

Some workers have had considerable success in using vibrating corers for taking samples of marine and continental sediments (Barkan, 1957; Gumenskii and Komarov, 1961; Sanders, 1960). The vibration principle is particularly suitable for application to sandy material, but the design of an effective vibrating sampler to meet a particular drilling problem is not easily accomplished, and the unsuccessful attempts, although they are not recorded in the literature, appear to be at least as numerous as the successful ones. So far the method does not seem to have been applied to lake sediments, although it might be useful, particularly in small shallow lakes with silty or sandy sediments.

### Zumberge Method

Zumberge (1962) has succeeded in obtaining complete sections through the Pleistocene deposits of Lake Superior and also short cores from the underlying bedrock by the unorthodox application of fairly standard oil-well equipment. Lake Superior being accessible to ocean-going vessels, he engaged a converted Navy Patrol Craft fitted for deep drilling.

The vessel was anchored with a four-way mooring. Standard oil-well drill stem with an inside diameter of 2.06 inches was used without casing. The first 28 feet of sediment was taken by fitting the lower end of the drill string with a plastic liner and using it as a gravity sampler. The upper part of the sediment was composed largely of soft clay, and the recovery, after a trial period in which the technique was being mastered, was essentially 100 percent.

The bottom of the drill string was then fitted with a piston held by a shear pin. The device was lowered about 27 feet in the mud. An overshot was then sent down on a sand line to engage the piston, and the drill string was lowered around the piston by its own weight to cut the next 28 feet of core.

For greater depths a modified Reed inner core barrel 6 feet long and 1 inch in inside diameter was dropped down the drill string, and a punch core was taken by lowering the drill string another 6 feet. This procedure was repeated until bedrock was reached, when standard rotary drilling methods were employed. By this method it was possible to penetrate the bottom to 686 feet under 938 feet of water.

Although the overall recovery by this combination of methods was only 27 to 66 percent, the upper lacustrine parts of the section were recovered quite effectively, and most of the loss occurred in punch-coring through compact glacial till under the lake sediments.

This method could be applied to shallower lakes where only small craft are available, although the required derrick occasions dangerous loss of stability. It seems to be a promising method for raising complete cores from moderately deep lakes.

## SUMMARY

A wide variety of methods is now available for raising sediment cores from lakes of various depths. In shallow water, samplers may be driven into the sediment by rigid rods, and the choice of sampler usually depends on factors such as portability, cost, the nature of the sediment, and the sample requirements. The Hiller and Davis or Dachnowski samplers are well-suited to reconnaissance sampling. If larger or less-disturbed samples are needed, the sampler with stationary piston is perhaps the most useful type. With the addition of casing and lightweight equipment for pushing or hammering and extracting the sampler, it is possible to acquire nearly continuous undisturbed samples of a thick body of sediment in a single borehole with such a sampler. If still greater control is required, the sampler with metal foils can provide a single undisturbed core.

As water depth increases, drive rods become increasingly heavy and cumbersome, and other means of forcing the sampler into the lake bottom are more attractive. If the sediment is not too thick, or if the lower part of the deposit is not needed, a sampler operated by compressed air, like the Mackereth sampler, may be convenient. At still greater depths the Kullenberg sampler or other free-fall piston corers may afford the only practical means of obtaining samples. The raising of complete sections through thick lake deposits, with high recovery and low disturbance of the sample, from lakes of moderate to very great depth seems to be technically possible with present methods but only at very great cost.

## ACKNOWLEDGMENTS

We are indebted to many people who have helped us in the field while we were learning to core lake sediments, but particularly to Magnus Fries, John McAndrews, Kirk Bryan, Jr., Robert Kendall, and Jonathan Richardson. Paul Colinvaux, Richard West, and John Sanders have very kindly made available to us their opinions of samplers that we have not used ourselves. Dr. Sanders, Dr. West, Miss Myra Kerr and Mrs. Shirlee Cavaliere have given us bibliographic assistance. Samplers have been constructed and field experience gained with the aid of grants from The Hill Family Foundation, the Office of Naval Research, and the National Science Foundation.

## REFERENCES

Anonymous (1960). Demonstration of soil sampler and peat augers. Proc. 7th Internat. Bot. Cong., p. 881–882.

Barkan, D. D. (1957). Foundation engineering and drilling by the vibration method. Proc. 4th Internat. Conf. on Soil Mechanics and Foundation Engin., v. 2, p. 3–7.

Bastin, E. S., and C. A. Davis (1909). Peat deposits in Maine. U. S. Geol. Survey Bull. 376, 127 pp.

Beckman, W. C., C. L. Drake, and J. L. Worzel (1960). R. V. Vema deep-sea winch. Deep-Sea Research, v. 7, p. 48–52.

Brown, S. R. (1956). A piston sampler for surface sediments of lake deposits: Ecology, v. 37, p. 611–613.

Cohenour, R. E. (1952). Some techniques for sampling the bottom sediments of Great Salt Lake, Utah: M.S. Thesis, Univ. of Utah, 44 pp.

Colinvaux, P. A. (1962). The environment of the Bering Land Bridge: Ph.D. Thesis, Duke University, 147 pp.

Cushing, E. J., and H. E. Wright, Jr. (1963). Piston corers for lake sediments. Unpublished manuscript.

Emery, G. R., and D. E. Broussard (1954). A modified Kullenberg piston corer. J. Sed. Petrology, v. 24, p. 207–211.

Emery, K. O., and R. S. Dietz (1941). Gravity coring instrument and mechanics of sediment coring. Geol. Soc. America Bull., v. 52, p. 1685–1714.

Erdtman, Gunnar (1935). Pollen statistics—a botanical and geological research method, *in* R. P. Wodehouse (ed.), Pollen grains. New York, McGraw-Hill, p. 110–125.

———— (1943). An introduction to pollen analysis. New York, Ronald, 239 pp.

Faegri, Knut, and Johs. Iversen (1950). Textbook of modern pollen analysis. Copenhagen, Munksgaard, 168 pp.

Frey, D. G. (1961). Developmental history of Schleinsee. Verh. Internat. Verein. Limnol., v. 14, p. 271–278.

Gerard, Robert (1954). Pollen sampling in permafrost. Micropaleontologist, v. 8, no. 4, p. 38.

Ginsburg, R. N., and R. M. Lloyd (1956). A manual piston coring device for use in shallow water. J. Sed. Petrology, v. 26, p. 64–66.

Gumenskii, B. M., and N. S. Komarov (1961). Soil drilling by vibrations [transl. from Russian]. New York, Consultants Bureau, 80 pp.

Haglund, E. (1909). Om Torfborr. Svenska Mosskulturföreningens Tidsskr., 1909, p. 71–91.

Hanna, M. A. (1954). A simple coring tube for soft sediments. J. Sed. Petrology, v. 24, p. 263–269.

Heezen, B. C. (1952). Discussion of methods of exploring the ocean floor by R. S. Dietz, *in* J. D. Isaacs and C. O'D. Iselin (eds.), Symposium on oceanographic instrumentation. U. S. Office of Naval Research, p. 200–205; Natl. Acad. Sci.-Nat. Res. Council Pub. 309, 233 pp.

Hersey, J. B. (1960). Acoustically monitored bottom coring. Deep-Sea Research, v. 6, p. 170–172.

Horton, E. E. (1961). Preliminary drilling phase of Mohole project; I. Summary of drilling operations (La Jolla and Guadalupe sites). Am. Assoc. Petrol. Geologists Bull., v. 45, p. 1789–1792.

Hoskins, Hartley, and S. T. Knott (1961). Geophysical investigation of Cape Cod Bay, Massachusetts, using the continuous seismic profiler. J. Geology, v. 69, p. 330–340.

Hutchinson, G. E. (1957). A treatise on limnology, v. 1, New York, Wiley, 1015 pp.

——, and U. M. Cowgill (1963). Chemical examination of a core from Lake Zeribar, Iran. Science, v. 140, p. 67–69.

Hvorslev, M. J. (1949). Subsurface exploration and sampling of soils for civil engineering purposes. Am. Soc. Civil Eng., Comm. Sampling and Testing, Vicksburg, Mississippi, Waterways Expt. Sta., 521 pp.

——, and H. C. Stetson (1946). Free-fall coring tube; a new type of gravity bottom sampler. Geol. Soc. America Bull., v. 57, p. 935–950.

Jenkin, B. M., and C. H. Mortimer (1938). Sampling lake deposits. Nature, v. 142, p. 834–835.

Kallstenius, T. (1958). Mechanical disturbances in clay samples taken with piston samplers. Royal Swedish Geotechnical Inst. Proc., no. 16, 75 pp.

Kjellman, W., T. Kallstenius, and O. Wagner (1950). Soil sampler with metal foils; device for taking undisturbed samples of very great length. Royal Swedish Geotechnical Inst. Proc., no. 1, 75 pp.

Kullenberg, Börje (1947). The piston core sampler. Göteborg: Svenska Hydrografisk-Biologiska Komm. Skr., ser. 3, Hydrografi, v. 1, no. 1.

—— (1955). Deep-sea coring. Repts. Swedish Deep-Sea Expedition, v. 4, no. 2, p. 35–96.

Lichtwardt, R. W. (1952). A new light-weight shaft for peat samplers. Paleobotanist, v. 1, p. 317–318.

Livingstone, D. A. (1953). On the paleolimnology of arctic Alaska. Ph.D. Thesis, Yale University, 96 pp.

—— (1955). A lightweight piston sampler for lake deposits. Ecology, v. 36, p. 137–139.

Lundquist, G. (1925). Methoden zur Untersuchung der Entwicklungsgeschichte der Seen, *in* E. Abderhalden (ed.), Handbuch der biologischen Arbeitsmethoden, ser. 9, pt. 2, p. 427–462.

Mackereth, F. J. H. (1958). A portable core sampler for lake deposits. Limnology and Oceanography, v. 3, p. 181–191.

McLelland, J. I. (1961). Preliminary drilling phase of Mohole project; III. Summary of logging operations (La Jolla and Guadalupe sites). Am. Assoc. Petrol. Geologists Bull., v. 45, p. 1800.

Moore, D. G. (1961). The free-corer; sediment sampling without wire and winch. J. Sed. Petrology, v. 31, p. 627–630.

Mortimer, C. H. (1942). The exchange of dissolved substances between mud and waters in lakes; III and IV, summary and references. J. Ecology, v. 30, p. 147–201.

Naumann, E. (1930). Einführing in die Bodenkunde der Seen. Die Binnengewässer, v. 9, 126 pp.

Olsson, J. (1936). Method for taking earth samples with the most undisturbed natural consistency, *in* Second Congress on Large Dams, Washington, D.C., v. 4, p. 157–161.

Pchelkitsev, A. M. (1951). Novyi bur dlia vziatiia abraztsov merzlyk pochv i gruntov s nenarushchennoi strukturoi. Pochvovedenie Akad. Nauk USSR, v. 1, p. 57–58.

Perfiliev, B. (1927). Zur Methodik der Erforschung von Schlammablagerungen. Berichte der Biologischen Borodin-Süsswasser-Station 5.

Phleger, F. B. (1951). Ecology of Foraminifera, northwest Gulf of Mexico; I. Foraminifera distribution. Geol. Soc. America Mem. 46, p. 1–88.

Piggot, C. S. (1941). Factors involved in submarine core sampling. Geol. Soc. America Bull., v. 52, p. 1513–1524.

Pratje, Otto (1952). Die Erfahrungen bei der Gewinnung van rezenten, marinen Sedimenten in den letzten 25 Jahren. Geol. Gesell. Wien Mitt., v. 50, p. 118–197.

Reish, D. J., and K. E. Green (1958). Description of a portable piston corer for use in shallow water. J. Sed. Petrology, v. 28, p. 227–229.

Reissinger, A. (1936). Methode der Bohrungen in Seen zur Untersuchung von Sedimentschichten. Internat. Rev. Gesell. Hydrobiol. Hydrogr., v. 33, p. 1–24.

Richards, A. F. (1961). Investigations of deep-sea sediment cores; 1. Shear strength, bearing capacity, and consolidation. U. S. Navy Hydrographic Office Technical Report TR-63, 70 pp.

———, and G. H. Keller (1961). A plastic-barrel sediment corer. Deep-Sea Research, v. 8, p. 306–312.

Richardson, Jonathan, and D. A. Livingstone (1962). An attack by a Nile crocodile on a small boat. Copeia, p. 203–204.

Riedel, W. R., H. S. Ladd, and J. I. Tracey, Jr. (1961). Preliminary drilling phase of Mohole project; II. Summary of coring operations (Guadalupe site). Am. Assoc. Petrol. Geologists Bull., v. 45, p. 1792–1798.

Round, F. E. (1961). Diatoms from Esthwaite. New Phytologist, v. 60, p. 43–59.

Rowley, J. R., and A. O. Dahl (1956). Modifications in design and use of the Livingstone piston sampler. Ecology, v. 37, p. 849–851.

Sanders, J. E. (1960). Kudinov vibro-piston core sampler; Russian solution to underwater sand-coring problem. Internat. Geol. Rev., v. 2, p. 174–178.

Shapiro, Joseph (1958). The core-freezer—a new sampler for lake sediments. Ecology, v. 39, p. 758.

Silverman, Maxwell, and R. C. Whaley (1952). Adaptation of the piston coring device to shallow water sampling. J. Sed. Petrology, v. 22, p. 11–16.

Smith, A. J. (1959). Description of the Mackereth portable core sampler. J. Sed. Petrology, v. 29, p. 246–250.

Sparks, B. W., and R. G. West (1959). The paleoecology of the interglacial deposits at Histon Road, Cambridge. Eiszeitalter und Gegenwart, v. 10, p. 123–143.

Stahl, J. B. (1959). The developmental history of the chironomid and Chaoborus faunas of Myers Lake. Indiana Univ. Dept. Zoology, Invest. Indiana Lakes and Streams, v. 5, p. 47–102.

Strøm, K. M. (1937). A handy sediment sampler. Norsk Geol. Tidsskr., v. 17, p. 50–52.

Swain, F. M., and N. Prokopovich (1954). Stratigraphic distribution of lipoid substances in Cedar Creek Bog, Minnesota. Geol. Soc. America Bull., v. 65, p. 1183–1198.

Taylor, J. C. M. (1957). A light-weight auger with quickly detachable joints. J. Sed. Petrology, v. 27, p. 342–345.

Traverse, Alfred, K. H. Clisby, and F. Foreman (1961). Pollen in drilling-mud "thinners," a source of palynological contamination. Micropaleontology, v. 7, p. 375–377.

U. S. Hydrographic Office (1955). Instruction manual for oceanographic observations. Hydrographic Office Pub. 607, 210 pp.

Vallentyne, J. R. (1955a). A modification of the Livingstone piston sampler for lake deposits. Ecology, v. 36, p. 139–141.

——— (1955b). Sedimentary chlorophyll as a paleobotanical method. Canadian J. Botany, v. 33, p. 304–313.

van der Hammen, T., and E. Gonzalez (1960). Upper Pleistocene and Holocene climate and vegetation of the "Sabana de Bogota" (Colombia, South America). Leidse Geol. Mededeel., v. 25, p. 261–315.

Vasari, Yrjo (1962). A study of the vegetational history of the Kuusamo district (northeast Finland) during the Lake-Quaternary period. Ann. Bot. Soc. "Vanamo," v. 33, p. 1–140.

West, R. G. (1955). The Pleistocene vegetation and geology of East Anglia. Ph.D. Thesis, Cambridge Univ., 288 pp.

——— (1956). The Quaternary deposits at Hoxne, Suffolk. Roy. Soc. [London] Phil. Trans., ser. B, v. 239, p. 265–356.

Wilson, I. T. (1941). A new device for sampling lake sediments. J. Sed. Petrology, v. 11, p. 73–79.

Züllig, Hans (1953). Ein neues Lot zur Untersuchung der obersten Schlamm-schichten, zur Messung des Sedimentabsatzes und zur Erfassung bodennaher Wasserschichten. Schweiz. Zeitschr. Hydrologie, v. 16, p. 275–284.

——— (1956). Das kombinierte Ramm-Kolben-Lot, ein leichtes Bohrgerät zur vereinfachten Gewinnung mehrerer Meter langer, ungestörter Sedimentprofile. Schweiz. Zeitschr. Hydrologie, v. 18, p. 208–214.

Zumberge, J. H. (1962). A new shipboard coring technique. J. Geophys. Res., v. 67, p. 2529–2536.

# Sampling Lake Sediments by Use of the Livingstone Sampler

EDWARD S. DEEVEY, JR.

*Department of Biology, Yale University, New Haven, Connecticut*

The Livingstone sampler (Livingstone, 1955) is an adaptation of Kullenberg's deep-sea piston sampler (Kullenberg, 1947), designed for manual operation from a small raft in water shallow enough to permit the use of extension rods. It is not a peat borer, and cannot be used for bog sediments unless they are saturated with water. The maximum depth of water in which it has been operated successfully is 30 meters, but greater working depths are possible if the raft is exceptionally stable and strong. Cores have been taken through sediments as thick as 18 meters, including 1 meter or more of gravel or till, but in postglacial sediments the usual limitation is the first layer of impenetrable material (coarse sand, gravel, or rock), wherever it may lie. The core is taken in sections, ordinarily 1 meter long, although each section can be extruded in the field as taken, the customary practice is to carry enough sections of coring tube so that at least one complete boring can be made without reusing sections. Extrusion of samples is discussed in a later section; coring tubes which are made of hard aluminum (Dural; e.g., ALCOA 6061 T6) can be reused until they are accidentally dented or deformed.

The principle of operation is illustrated in fig. 1. The instrument consists basically of a removable *coring tube* (A), rigidly held to an *adapter* (B), through which a *cable* (C) passes to the *piston* (D). At the start of sampling the piston is fixed at the distal end of the coring tube (prevented from being prematurely pushed back by various devices, discussed below); the cable, which runs to the water surface, is slack. As sampling begins, the slack in the cable is taken up, holding the piston in position, and the instrument is pushed into the mud for a distance of 1 meter, or until the upper end of the piston-and-shackle assembly is met by the lower end of the adapter. Pushing is accomplished by the *extension rods* (E), also of hard aluminum, which are joined to each other and to the adapter by the mechanism devised by Lichtwardt (1952). The coring tube should be filled with water at the surface before the instrument is lowered; during sampling the water is smoothly

This account, circulated privately since 1959, has been slightly modified to incorporate more recent experience. Acknowledgment is made to Paul A. Colinvaux (see Colinvaux, 1964) for several valuable suggestions.

replaced by mud, which is driven into the coring tube by the excess hydrostatic pressure that is created when the pushing operation changes the relative positions of piston and tube—that is, the mud is *sucked* into the tube by a vacuum, which is proportional at all times to the height of the core being taken.

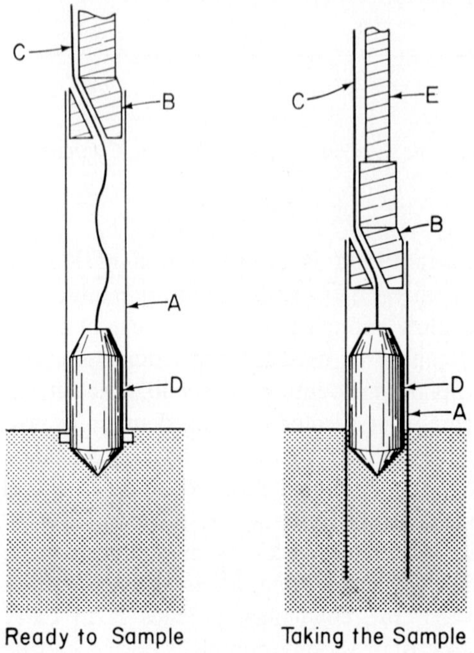

Ready to Sample          Taking the Sample

**Fig. 1**

*Principle of operation. A: coring tube. B: adapter. C: cable. D: piston. E: extension rod.*

## DETAILS OF PISTON

The piston, made of brass, is by far the most expensive part of the instrument, because of the machine work needed for the retractable pins incorporated in recent models. A detailed drawing is given in fig. 2. In this model, developed by Adrian A. Disco, Foreman of the Physics Shop, Gibbs Laboratory, Yale University, the pins are drawn medially as an internal shaft is pulled upward by the cable, the medial ends of the pins being provided with smaller pins set at right angles, which slide medially as they are forced downward, relative to the shaft, in grooves cut at a $35°$ angle to the axis of the piston. Thus, as long as the cable is slack, the pins prevent the mud from pushing the piston prematurely into the coring tube; as sampling begins, the projecting pins retract smoothly and automatically. The housing of this admirable device is filled with grease, and it should not be taken apart unless repairs are necessary.

Disco's model has superseded several earlier devices having the same function. Kullenberg's device—a spring-loaded pin—is practical only when, as in the 1500-kg deep-sea model, the coring tube is in fact a liner of a heavier outer tube or housing; the spring-pin then inserts into a groove in the housing tube. When Livingstone, in his first work in the arctic, was forced to discard the heavy brass housing and use the unprotected aluminum "liners" as coring tubes (as is now standard practice), he substituted a length of wire-solder for the spring pin. The wire-solder was inserted into the side of the piston to serve as a shear-pin. The disadvantage of this system is that shearing occurs only after considerable tension has been built up by the thrust into the mud against the taut cable. When the solder pin is suddenly sheared, the upper few centimeters of mud are violently sucked in, and distorted stratification can usually be seen in the upper 10 cm or so of each core. Vallentyne (1955) described a better device, consisting of a long shaft mounted above the piston,

which must be rotated 90° and locked into position before sampling. Still better, as suggested originally by Harald Krog, Danmarks Geologiske Undersøgelse, is a pair of retractable pins operated by a toggle arrangement, which retract when the cable is taut; this principle has been used in the large (2-inch) piston, but in the smaller ($1\frac{1}{2}$-inch) model there is too little space for insertion of two toggles, and Disco's device is the answer to that aspect of the problem.

One disadvantage of the retractable-pin devices is that the cable may be tightened inadvertently during rapid lowering, retracting the pins and allowing the piston to be pushed in prematurely. The first indication that this has happened, especially if the cable is being paid out by an inexperienced assistant, may be that the operator, attempting to sample below the chosen point, finds it impossible to push the instrument beyond the taut cable. It acts as though the sampling run were already finished, as in fact it is. Samples that are not

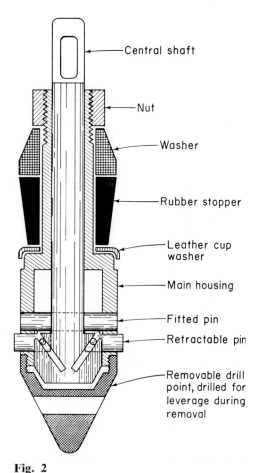

Central shaft

Nut

Washer

Rubber stopper

Leather cup washer

Main housing

Fitted pin

Retractable pin

Removable drill point, drilled for leverage during removal

**Fig. 2**

*Detail of piston. Not to scale.*

taken with a full 1-meter thrust beyond the chosen position must be discarded, unless there is another known reason (such as hard bottom) for the anomaly. Some protection against this heart-breaking experience can be obtained by taping the cable to the adapter or lowermost rod in a position known to be slack; Scotch electricians' tape, if used on a perfectly dry surface, may stick so well that considerable force will be needed to break it; but dry surfaces are not usual in sampling, and the optimal strength of seal can be quickly established with a little experience.

Leather cup-washers, used in earlier models to insure a tight fit between piston and coring tube, have been superseded by the rubber-stopper-under-compression described by Rowley and Dahl (1956). Since coring tubes are not invariably of the same inside diameter, and since piston and tubes may become worn with use, it is a great advantage to be able to adjust the piston's outer diameter to the dimensions of each coring tube as used. Such a rubber stopper is shown in Disco's piston (fig. 2). Incorporated in the older 2-inch model, the rubber unit has so improved its performance, at least in soft sediments, that the $1\frac{1}{2}$-inch model is now used only when a smaller core is particularly desired. Compressible rubber pistons 4 inches in diameter have been successfully used in mud-water-interface samplers, and the principle of a rubber stopper under adjustable compression is also used for the adapters of mud-water-interface samplers.

Colinvaux's piston, like that of Rowley and Dahl, consists almost entirely of rubber laboratory stoppers, without retractable pins, and is considerably cheaper to manufacture. Colinvaux's coring tubes are fitted at the distal end with a steel cutting bit of slightly smaller inside diameter than the coring tube; thus, the piston can be driven into the cutting bit before sampling, and retractable pins are considered unnecessary. However, release of this piston by a sudden jerk on the cable has the same disadvantage as release by shearing a solder pin.

## CARE OF SAMPLES

The coring tubes are affixed to the adapter by a tapered brass pin inserted through a hole in the side of each tube near its upper end. A light tap on this pin with the handle of a screw driver insures both firm seating and easy removal. (The pins are easily lost, and several spares should be carried into the field.) As long as the mud is safely inside, the position of the hole guarantees against confusion over which was the upper end. After extrusion other mnemonic devices must be used.

As the pin is removed and the coring tube with sample disengaged from the rod and adapter, the piston is still some 20 cm inside the tube, with water above it. This water should be poured out, and the piston then removed by pulling on the cable. (At this point the advantage of a good fit will be appreciated.) Very organic sediments may follow the piston upward as this is done, leaving space for a cork at the lower end. Ordinarily, however, the core must be driven far enough to be corked by gentle tapping of the upper end against the deck. When this is done, there is of course great danger that the core will break, or at least that the upper part will be poured out. Normally, therefore, after removal of the piston, the tube is gently inverted to pour out any water, and a cork is then driven down from the upper end against the top of the mud. This cork fits snugly inside the tube, but not so snugly that it prevents corking of the lower end, or causes difficulty later during extrusion. Correctly fitted corks, which cannot be lost inside, are then used to cork *both* ends. Although expensive, rubber stoppers are especially suitable, because Scotch electricians' tape makes a firm bond with dry rubber, and a stopper so sealed will withstand considerable internal pressure (resulting from warming of the cold sediment). It is necessary to dry the tubes thoroughly, however, if the tape is to stick tightly.

Extrusion is most conveniently done in the laboratory. A simple but effective piston can be made of one of the snugly-fitting corks, and two extension rods will deliver the thrust. The principle is to push the tube back against the piston, the core being caught in a suitable container as it is exposed; thus, at least 3 meters of working space are needed, backed at one end by a rigid structure, such as a wall, that serves to stabilize the 2-meter rod. In our practice semitubular aluminum sheets or troughs are used to catch the core; they are 110 cm long, and the distal end is clamped in position on the laboratory bench so that the distal end of the core, as it first appears after a few centimeters of initial thrust, is about 5 cm short of the end of the trough. (The marks of the C-clamp then serve as mnemonic devices until the upper and lower ends of the core can be adequately labeled.) A continuous thrust of almost exactly 100 cm, pushing the tube against the piston, drops the core smoothly into the trough.

Cores so extruded are normally too wet on the surface to be conveniently sampled by quantitative methods; a few hours' drying improves them greatly, but if moisture relations are critical the cores must be sampled at once, after slicing off the wet (and possibly contaminated) outer surface. For special purposes—e.g., study of plant pigments—the cores must be kept in a cold room. No material yet found is both completely waterproof and convenient for wrapping and rewrapping; Saran and DuPont Mylar have proved reasonably satisfactory, but polyethylene is much too permeable. If one could be sure that only the direst emergency would necessitate resampling, water-tight seals could be obtained by spraying the core with liquid latex, acrylate resin, or varnish. The "Albatross" cores were split lengthwise, and the "archival" half was treated in this way; the working half was wrapped in Briophan film. In our less careful practice we wrap the whole core in Mylar, knowing that it will dry almost completely within a year.

Note that for shipping long distances, the best container for a core is the aluminum sampling tube in which it was obtained and stoppered in the field. Extruded and wrapped cores can be partially protected inside cardboard mailing tubes, but their shipping is always more risky.

## FIELD OPERATION

The best raft or drilling platform is provided by two small boats, lashed side by side, with or without a special platform across them. Inflatable rubber boats are remarkably successful. Three anchors should be used, carried out and dropped from a boat so that their ropes form a Y; the ropes should be at least twice as long as the water is deep. The demand of extreme stability arises primarily from the need to use *casing* in water of any depth greater than 2 to 5 meters. The casing is needed to prevent bending of the rods and to insure that successive samples are taken in the same hole (if they are not, samples in mud deeper than 8 or 10 m will be impossible to take); casing must be absolutely vertical, for otherwise the casing binds the rods and may prevent sampling even at 1 or 2 meters in the mud. The casing is lowered just to the bottom for the first sample, or may be dispensed with for the first two or three samples. It is lowered farther into the mud as sampling progresses, but sampling must always be done beyond the casing if stratification is not to be disturbed. If the raft is perfectly stable, and if the casing is set vertically to begin with, sampling through casing can be trouble free. The chief problem that it presents, then, is the mental arithmetic needed to sample at predetermined depths (because the height of the casing above water must be subtracted from the absolute depth). Minor annoyance can be caused if the tapered pin which protrudes from the side of the adapter is caught on the lower end of the casing when the sampler is pulled up; jiggling will usually free it, but if the cable is allowed to become too slack during withdrawal, it may also be caught on the tapered pin or obstruct the casing itself. A serious kink in the stainless steel cable is an invitation to this trouble, and it may be necessary to shorten the cable in order to remove a kink.

For the first few meters the sampler will usually fall to the desired sampling position by its own weight, but the actual operation of sampling each meter normally requires direct thrust. It is important to be sure that enough rod is already attached to complete the sampling thrust; i.e., that at least 0.5 meter will remain above the water or above the top of the casing. Delivering the thrust is a skill that requires some practice, and inexperienced operators usually bend the rod instead. It is essential that the rod be vertical, and that the thrust be delivered by short jabs, making sure that the rod is drawn vertical between jabs, and using the shoulders and legs rather than the hands and wrists. The help of a second man at this point is normally undesirable, as two men are almost certain to bend the rods when the sediments are stiff and the water is deep. (Frey's model in which the Lichtwardt rods are 1 inch thick instead of $\frac{3}{4}$ inch, is less subject to bending and therefore easier to thrust than the Yale models.) If the operator finds it impossible to proceed, but is sure that more relatively soft sediment remains below, it may be that the instrument has left its original hole and is being driven at a slight angle into undisturbed sediments, which may be impenetrable *ab initio* below 6 or 8 meters. In this case a second, more careful lowering may be successful, or the casing may be lowered another meter or two to eliminate the angle. After the latter procedure it may be necessary to remove and discard some mud from the casing.

Driving by hammering is rarely necessary in organic sediments, but may be essential in stiff clay. The stainless steel T-handle, whose main use is in rotating the Hiller peat borer, may serve as a driving end if a sledge hammer is to be used. The ends of the aluminum rods should never be struck directly, even by wood, but the rod assembly is rigid and will withstand heavy blows. In sledge driving, one assistant should hold the rod assembly vertical between blows, while a second assistant protects the handle with a block of wood. Glancing blows cannot be entirely avoided, however, and for this reason Colinvaux's pile driver is preferable to a sledge hammer, especially as it can be inverted and used to drive the sampler up. It consists of a 10-pound cylindrical iron weight, provided with handles, lined with a bushing of hard plastic, which slides up and down an aluminum rod, striking against a steel collar that is rigidly fitted to the rod. The lower end of the rod has a Lichtwardt-type coupling. In our practice the sampler is never *jacked* into the sediment, as the aluminum rods are too soft to withstand the jack, but it may be jacked *out* by raising an automobile jack against the T-handle.

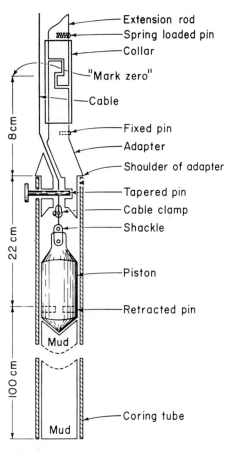

**Fig. 3**

*Detailed view of sampler when full, showing basis for reckoning depths. Not to scale.*

## MATERIALS

Full details of construction of Lichtwardt rods and Livingstone samplers appear not to have been published, though they are given in Livingstone's Ph.D. thesis (Yale University, 1953). The diagram in fig. 3 can be followed by any machinist, however, if he knows that the rods consist of $\frac{3}{4}$-inch Dural tubing, wall thickness 0.065 inch, end connections machined of $\frac{3}{4}$-inch Dural rod. The sliding sleeves are of $\frac{7}{8}$-inch Dural tubing, wall thickness 0.058 inch. Coring tubes are either $1\frac{1}{2}$ inch o.d., 0.035 inch wall, or 2 inch o.d., 0.065 inch wall. Alloy 6061 T6 is used throughout.

## RECKONING DEPTHS

A sample wrongly placed or wrongly recorded is worse than useless, and some routine mnemonic system is necessary to avoid confusion in the field. Coring tubes are 122 cm long; the extra 22 cm, beyond the 1-meter length of core, is needed to accommodate the piston assembly, and 122 cm is especially convenient as the tubing, in the U. S., is supplied in 12-foot lengths, which are cut into three 122-cm lengths with no waste. A one-meter core is assured if the distance from the retractable pins to the shoulder of the adapter is exactly 22 cm when the piston assembly is drawn up against the adapter (fig. 3). (Because the drill point of the piston projects below the coring tube, the uppermost 3 cm of each meter-sample will have been lost, or, if apparently present, will have been stratigraphically disturbed.)

The distance from the shoulder of the adapter to its upper end ("mark zero") is an additional 8 cm, so that the overall length of the sampler is 130 cm. Confusion is minimized if this length is added as a unit to the number of extension rods in use before sampling begins. For example, if the sampler is lowered until the end of the tenth meter of extension rod is at the water surface (recorded in the writer's notes as "mark 10"), *two* more lengths of rod should remain above the mark, and if the cable is then held and the sampler lowered to "mark 11," the sampled core runs from "10 plus to 11 plus," or 11.30 to 12.30 meters below the water surface. If casing is used, it is desirable to set its top at some even distance above the water, say 50 cm, recording this figure separately each time: "10 plus to 11 plus, minus casing 50 cm" would be later calculated as 10.80 to 11.80 below the water surface. The depth of water is determined separately, either by sounding line or by the sampler itself. In my experience, to attempt to sample even meters ("mark 9.70 plus to mark 10.70 plus = 11.00 to 12.00") is to invite confusion.

It follows from this that adjustment to the "mark plus" system should be made with the first sample; it should be started at an even mark, whether the additional 1.30 meters brings the sampler to the upper surface of the mud or not. A first sample that starts about 30 cm *above* the mud surface is especially desirable, since 70 cm of mud will not ordinarily fall out; overlying water and unconsolidated surface mud (which otherwise should be discarded) can be poured into a jar for later study (e.g., for comparison of the modern pollen assemblage with the surrounding vegetation), before the sample is stoppered. Samples of the mud-water interface are taken in this way by the transparent plastic samplers devised by Rowley and Dahl (1956) and Brown (1956). Such a sample, if taken in an aluminum tube, will of course suffer some loss at the top and also may be compressed during extrusion; accurate measurements on the uppermost sample are therefore best made in a transparent coring tube. (In my experience, compression during extrusion is negligible below 1 meter; cores are always 97 ± 1 cm long.)

## AVAILABILITY OF APPARATUS

Livingstone samplers, like the Yale model of the Hiller peat borer (also designed by Livingstone), are entirely custom made, and although they have been made on order for several scientific institutions outside Yale, the demand does not seem to justify their manufacture as a commercial venture. High labor costs in the U. S. make such apparatus expensive, especially as the Gibbs Laboratory shop must pay overtime wages for it, and it can undoubtedly be made more cheaply in some other countries. No part of the instrument is patented, nor does any appear patentable, and although the name as used at Yale appropriately honors Daniel A. Livingstone now of the Department of Zoology, Duke University, Durham, N. C., who drew the original plans and used the apparatus with great skill under exceptionally difficult field conditions, the piston principle is in the public domain and antedates both Livingstone and Kullenberg. Educational and scientific institutions wishing to purchase such apparatus should negotiate, not with the writer or the Department of Biology, but with Mr. Charles R. Wilson, Business Manager of the Department of Physics, Yale University, New Haven, Connecticut.

## REFERENCES

Brown, S. R. (1956). A piston sampler for surface sediments of lake deposits. Ecology, v. 37, p. 611–613.

Colinvaux, P. A. (1964). Sampling stiff sediments of an ice-covered lake. Limnology and Oceanography, v. 9, no. 1, p. 262–264.

Kullenberg, B. (1947). The piston core sampler. Svensk Hydrografisk-Biologiska Komm. Skr., ser. 3, Hydrografi, v. 1, no. 2.

Lichtwardt, R. W. (1952). A new light-weight shaft for peat samplers. Paleobotanist, v. 1, p. 317–318.

Livingstone, D. A. (1955). A lightweight piston sampler for lake deposits. Ecology, v. 36, p. 137–139.

Rowley, J. R., and A. O. Dahl (1956). Modifications in design and use of the Livingstone piston sampler. Ecology, v. 37, p. 849–851.

Vallentyne, J. R. (1955). A modification of the Livingstone piston sampler for lake deposits. Ecology, v. 36, p. 139–141.

# Extraction Techniques

JANE GRAY

*Paleoecology Laboratory, Museum of Natural History,*
*University of Oregon, Eugene*

The recovery of acid-insoluble microfossils (pollen, spores, hystrichospheres, and so on) from sediments and sedimentary rocks generally includes four steps: *cleaning, disaggregation and dispersal, chemical extraction,*[1] and *density separation.*

To clean means to remove from the outer surfaces of the rock any potential source of contamination by fresh pollen and spores or by fossil specimens of another age.

To disaggregate means to break the laboratory specimen into smaller aggregates, usually by physical means. Dispersal involves separating the aggregate particles to a state suitable for chemical and density separation: ideally, individual particles are put into a stable suspension, i.e., they remain dispersed and do not flocculate in liquid medium.

Disaggregation and dispersal usually continue in chemical extraction, as aggregates of mineral and organic matter are dissolved by various reagents. The chemical-extraction and density-separation methods, by destruction and removal of extraneous organic and mineral particles, also provide the means of concentrating the microfossils for study. Chemical treatment is generally tailored to the characteristics of the sediment or rock. Because the chemical removal of organic debris often constitutes the most difficult and critical stage in the extraction, it may be desirable to experiment with small samples to determine the most suitable technique. The chief difficulty may be to find a means of removing the organic debris without concurrently destroying some or all of the microfossils. If quantitive (statistical) analyses are to be meaningful, one should bear in mind that even minor deviations in treatment may cause considerable variations in microfossil assemblages.

A successful extraction fulfills certain objectives: the residue should be free from contaminants, i.e., microfossils that do not belong in the fossil assemblage; there should be a minimum of organic and inorganic detritus to conceal the microfossils and bias the results of the analysis; the maximum

---

[1] Most methods of chemical extraction disaggregate the matrix and disperse the particles as well as concentrate microfossils by dissolving matrix components. Because chemical extraction involves digestion or destruction of materials, the methods are here distinguished from those of disaggregation and dispersal, which are primarily physical in nature.

number of microfossils per volume of sediment should be recovered, together with the maximum diversity of types; the microfossils should be in a good state of preservation, i.e., they should not have been corroded or distorted during the extraction; the microfossils should be recovered in the same relative abundance with which they are preserved in the sediment, if statistical analysis is necessary, i.e., differential destruction of specimens should be at a minimum. The recovery of microfossils and the results of the statistical analysis should be reproducible by other palynologists.

There is no universal method of recovering plant microfossils from sediments and sedimentary rocks, which represent a variety of compositions and a variety of depositional environments. However, the technique for the removal of any specific mineral or organic compound is always essentially the same, no matter what the composition of the rock or sediment in which it occurs. Familiarity with standard methods, and with the principal problems in extraction, obviates the need for separate schedules for each different rock type, since only minor details differ. Minor variations are often primarily a matter of taste and depend on experience with specific sediments; many methods are restricted in their use. In this paper, a few variations are indicated, primarily to provide some idea of the latitudes possible when working with specific reagents. If each extraction is planned to take into account the lithology and compaction of the matrix and its age, the degree of weathering, and the probable pollen concentration (judged in part by the organic content of the sample), the extractionist can quickly learn which processing steps should be emphasized for certain types of matrices. Some ingenuity must, of course, be exercised in meeting the specific problems raised by each matrix. Frequent optical checks of wet residues with the microscope during processing will help to eliminate unnecessary steps and will provide a guide for directing the extraction.

Some of these factors also control the size of the sample to be extracted for each matrix type. A tenth of a gram may be adequate for some pollen-rich peats but 5 to 10 grams of matrix, or occasionally much more, may be necessary if matrix substances, organic and inorganic, so dilute the pollen as to make microfossils scarce in any given sample. Sample sizes are not always specified in extraction procedures and are best judged in terms of the specific matrix.

## CLEANING

Samples must be collected, transported to the laboratory, and processed under conditions which insure absolute cleanliness, to prevent contamination with fresh pollen or with microfossils from sediments of a different age. Analyses from samples which have not been handled to preclude contamination must always be considered suspect.

For unconsolidated sediments, or for a matrix that will break up in transport, cleanliness begins in the field, since these samples cannot be cleaned adequately after they are collected.

If the matrix is consolidated or semiconsolidated it may be cleaned in the laboratory; in collecting even these samples, however, it is well to remove the surface weathering face or any surface alteration before the samples are taken. The following methods can be used to clean samples in the laboratory:

1. Washing the sample thoroughly with water,[2] acetone, or alcohol.
2. Scraping or cutting off outside edges of the sample and throwing them away (the knife or other instrument used to cut or scrape the sample must be thoroughly cleaned between samples).
3. Brushing the sample thoroughly with a wire brush.
4. Burning combustible contaminants from the surface of the sample.
5. Blowing the sample with compressed air.
6. Treating the sample in an ultrasonic generator (p. 534).

## DISAGGREGATION AND DISPERSAL

Every matrix must be disaggregated, i.e., broken up or crushed by physical means, and dispersed or deflocculated by physical and/or chemical means, i.e., have its individual particles put into stable suspension, in the course of the extraction. In practice, with fine-grained sediments (those usually processed by palynologists) it is difficult to differentiate between processes of disaggregation and dispersion since they usually occur simultaneously, by a combination of physical and chemical means. Many unconsolidated materials need little treatment to achieve complete particle dispersal; hard, highly indurated, and cemented rocks may need severe and prolonged chemical treatment before good particle dispersal is achieved. In general, the more consolidated the matrix and the finer its grain size, the more difficult is the problem of attaining good disaggregation and dispersal.

Except for some unconsolidated sediments, for example, peats and clays, matrices are broken up with mortar and pestle before other treatment. Some highly fossiliferous peats, clays, silts, as well as soft shales and other uncemented sedimentary rocks, may occasionally be so effectively dispersed by dispersing agents and/or physical treatment, that chemical treatment to attack mineral and organic aggregates is unnecessary before density separation. Such procedure is seldom effective as a prime means of recovering pollen and spores, however, if organic detritus is extremely abundant.

Where acid-insoluble microfossils are the sole objects of study, consolidated and cemented matrices, after initial disaggregation with mortar and pestle, are usually placed directly in acid (p. 547) to effect further disaggrega-

---

[2] Throughout the discussion reference to water means distilled water or filtered tap water.

tion of mineral aggregates and particle dispersal. Because acid treatments are often time consuming and employ expensive chemical reagents that must be handled with care and because some microorganisms of palynological interest are destroyed by acids, palynologists may occasionally wish to disintegrate indurated samples by other methods that avoid the use of hydrochloric, hydrofluoric, and other acids.

Many methods of disaggregating and dispersing matrices without the use of chemicals have been developed by soil scientists, sedimentary petrologists (Krumbein and Pettijohn, 1938, p. 47–75), and by micropaleontologists (Camp and Hanna, 1937, p. 96–103). Although many of these could be used for, or adapted to palynological processing, their limited usefulness makes any detailed discussion beyond the scope of this paper. Some physical means of disaggregation, such as soaking or boiling in water to which dispersers (electrolytes) may be added to increase the effectiveness of the treatment, freezing-thawing methods, force of crystallization methods, and the use of various organic solvents, are discussed by Brown (1960). Most of these methods are as time consuming as acid treatment, and in general not particularly effective for most matrices. More effective methods use mechanical devices: crushing machines, pressure cookers, stirrers or agitators, shaking devices, miniature roller mills, and so on. Where salvaging the complete microflora and microfauna of samples is important, Felix (1963) has suggested, in place of acid treatment, the combined use of a miniature mechanical rotary washer (adapted from use in paleontology and petrography laboratories) and a microblender (using a 2.3 sp. gr. bromoform-toluene solution) for disaggregating and dispersing Tertiary shales. However, if such devices are to be effective for palynological work, the particle dispersal must be complete, the solution stable, and the sample relatively rich in microfossils as compared with other organic components.

### Mortar and Pestle

Except for peats, clays, and similar sediments, all samples are first broken up with mortar and pestle. Some unconsolidated or semiconsolidated sediments may be crushed with the fingers, but most matrices require more severe treatment. Using a mortar and pestle, the matrix should be broken to particles about 1 to 5 mm in size. Avoid powdering the sample to prevent damage to larger grains and spores. A crushing or gentle pounding (up-and-down) rather than a grinding (rotary) motion should be used, since grinding may break up the grains and tear off appendages. By screening, broken particles within the 1 to 5 mm range may be removed to prevent too fine a breakage while the remaining aggregates are being broken down.

After each sample is crushed, the mortar and pestle must be cleaned thoroughly with a brush and an abrasive cleaner (such as Ajax) and dried.

### Ultrasonic Generator

Dispersal by means of the ultrasonic generator may be inserted into the extraction process wherever necessary: this treatment is not limited to the beginning of the processing.

The ultrasonic generator is a multiple-purpose machine used in some pollen laboratories to disperse fine-grained sediments and sedimentary rocks by means of high-frequency vibrations.[3] The equipment consists of a generator and a transducer tank, the latter filled with water or a disperser into which material is immersed directly, or in a centrifuge tube, a beaker, or a flask which is immersed in the tank. Vibrations are transmitted through the fluid into the submerged container.

Ultrasonic generators are available in a wide range of sizes and frequencies.[4] Apparently machines with a capacity of 1 to 5 gallons and a frequency range of 30 to 50 kilocycles per second are the most advantageous for pollen work. Tschudy (personal communication, 1963) indicates that machines in the low-frequency ranges are unpleasantly noisy and need to be shielded during use, and that equipment using high frequencies, in addition to being expensive and needing a special cooling system, causes pollen breakage. He writes: "Some equipment in the frequency range of about 40 kilocycles does not produce much audible sound, and from the standpoint of palynology seems to work satisfactorily."

Ultrasonic equipment may be used for the following purposes:

1. To clean exposed surfaces of hard rock samples. Immerse rock directly in the liquid of the transducer tank.

2. To disaggregate and disperse some unconsolidated or semiconsolidated, fine-grained sediments and sedimentary rocks for example, silts, mudstones, and some soft shales. For this purpose, the matrix is usually broken up in a mortar, dried if damp, and then placed in a centrifuge tube with a hydrocarbon solvent (Varsol, Soltrol, etc.) and a small amount of a nonionic detergent, such as Lux or Joy, which acts as a disperser. The time of treatment (5 to 30 minutes) varies according to the compaction of the matrix and the resistance of the fossils.

3. To disperse precipitates or flocculates that commonly form during chemical processing of the samples. According to Tschudy, this step may follow each chemical treatment during the processing—e.g., after use of HF, of Schulze solution, and so on. A dispersing agent should be added to the residue (p. 536).

4. To break up any clumps of fine, insoluble, clinging particles, organic or inorganic, which may adhere to and obscure pollen grains and spores. The ultrasonic treatment breaks these clumps into their component parts, so that they are fine enough to wash away from the pollen by centrifugation (p. 571). Dispersal is facilitated by adding a dispersing agent.

---

[3] Gipson (1963) discusses the effectiveness of a probe-type ultrasonic instrument with various Paleozoic shales. This is the only account, in any way comprehensive, that I know to have been published on the use of ultrasonic equipment.

[4] A few sources are listed in this Handbook (p. 477).

Despite the seeming potential of the ultrasonic equipment for microfossil work, not all palynologists agree on its value, particularly for specific groups of microorganisms or specific matrices. Staplin, et al. (1960) remark, "Occasionally the method destroys the fossils, usually in somewhat metamorphosed samples." W. Evitt (personal correspondence, 1963) indicates that he has found evidence of breakage of hystrichospheres by the ultrasonic generator and has eliminated use of the equipment for study of these microorganisms. He further states that "almost all samples . . . can be treated satisfactorily without it. The problem of flocculation, which [the generator] was useful in combatting, can be managed with a combination of detergent washes and vigorous mixing with a Vortex Junior mixer, without the danger to specimens presented by the ultrasonic treatment." R. H. Tschudy writes (personal correspondence, 1963), "Experiments with modern pollen have demonstrated that ultrasonic cavitation can produce deleterious effects. The wings of pine pollen grains can be torn off during prolonged treatment. A 5-minute treatment of a mixture of pine, birch, and juniper pollen produced no recognizable changes. A 30-minute treatment resulted in some disattached pine wings, possibly a slight fraying of the juniper grains, birch pollen appeared to be unaffected. I have observed that a 5-minute treatment of Devonian spores produces a preparation in which larger than normal incidence of broken spores is observed. This may be the result of the more brittle nature of some fossilized material. I have found the ultrasonic equipment to be of greatest aid when used in disaggregating precipitates during sample processing."

**Organic Solvents**

Organic hydrocarbon solvents do not normally dissolve components of the matrix, but penetrate and fill pores of the rock or surround the individual mineral particles. In conjunction with water, they act as agents in disaggregation and dispersal by means which are yet poorly understood. According to L. R. Kittleman (personal communication), organic solvents usually are effective in disrupting rocks only if substantial amounts of bentonitic clays are present.

Gasoline and kerosene are effective with some clayey matrices; commercial hydrocarbon thinners and solvents,[5] such as Varsol, Soltrol, and Stoddard's Solvent may be equally useful. Dispersing and wetting agents may be added to aid in the penetration; other solvents, such as benzene and acetone, may also increase the effectiveness of the reaction with some matrices.

For disaggregating and dispersing noncemented sedimentary rocks such as claystones and siltstones, Staplin, et al. (1960) recommend Soltrol C and household detergent. If dispersal is complete it is sometimes possible to go from this treatment directly to heavy-liquid fractionation without chemical

---

[5] These are petroleum products that have distillation points between those of gasoline and kerosene. They are generally termed naphthas or petroleum solvents.

treatment. Essentially the same effect is achieved as with the use of the ultrasonic generator.

*Procedure*          1. Break sample into pea-size fragments and dry (if damp) at temperatures below 100°C.

2. Cover sample with a mixture of 75 percent Soltrol C and 25 percent liquid detergent Vel (or any nonionic detergent) or commercial detergent Polytergent J-400 (used only at concentrations of 5 to 10 percent since detergent will gel at concentrations of about 20 percent).[6] A 1 to 1 mixture of acetone and benzene may increase the effectiveness of the solution.

3. Allow mixture to stand overnight, stirring occasionally.

4. Pour off the solvent-detergent mixture and add boiling water to the sample, stirring vigorously. The matrix will break down into small particles.

5. Transfer the residue to centrifuge tubes and use a short-time controlled centrifugation (p. 571) until the supernatant liquid is clear. Dilute detergent may be added during the washing to promote dispersal of the finest particles.

Some shales may be disintegrated by kerosene, gasoline, Varsol, and other hydrocarbon solvents (see Brown, 1960). The shale is usually crushed and heated at temperatures from 90°C to 400°C until interstitial water is driven off; this may take only a few hours, or it may take several days. It is then immersed in the solution either while still hot or after cooling where it may be left for as much as 48 hours. After decanting the fluid, cold or boiling water is added to the residue and the sample disaggregates. Screening and the addition of dispersers may aid in the disaggregation at this stage. Brown reports varying degrees of success with this method and it is best used on a trial and error basis.

### Dispersing Agents

With fine-grained or colloidal materials, chemical dispersers (or electrolytes) are often necessary to get the particles into suspension in a liquid medium and to keep them from reaggregating or flocculating. Flocculation may be recognized by the rapid settling of clumps of particles, and under the microscope by adherence of particles to form clumps, chains, or strings; in the desired suspension each particle exists as an individual showing Brownian movement.

Good dispersion is extremely important because most of the fine-grained matrices in which pollen is found contain aggregates of very fine organic and inorganic particles that may coagulate with the microfossils, concealing them and making their study difficult or impossible. Dispersers are usually recom-

---

[6] These detergents are recommended since they are not flocculative with Soltrol C, as some are.

mended for use with the ultrasonic generator, although, as suggested by Evitt (personal correspondence), similar effects often can be achieved with the proper use of dispersing agents or in conjunction with less severe physical treatment than that provided by the rapid vibrations of the generator.

The theoretical basis for the use of dispersers, discussed in detail by Krumbein and Pettijohn (1938, p. 57–61), is summarized here. Particles in colloidal suspension often have either a positive or negative electrical charge. The charge exists because the atoms at the boundary of each particle have an unsatisfied valance and attract other ions in the solution. The ions arrange themselves around the solid particles imparting a charge to them. The oppositely charged ions in solution then swarm to the vicinity of the charged particle. In a stable suspension each particle maintains the same charge; when one particle approaches another with its swarm of charged ions, the two particles repel each other. If the charges are not great enough, if there is no charge, or if an electrolyte (HCl, for example) is added, colliding particles will adhere, forming aggregates that settle out of the suspension as a precipitate.

Dispersing chemicals, of which there are a large number, impart like charges to particles, build up stronger charges, or create a charged chemical coating. The critical effective charge of the particles varies with the concentration of the disperser. Thus, a suspension may be dispersed only with an exact quantity of disperser; it will flocculate if either too much or too little is used. The best dispersers for routine work are those that have a wide range of concentration that cause approximately the same degree of dispersion. Dispersers do not behave the same with all suspensions: some work with one matrix, but not with another; different concentrations may be necessary with different matrices. Some dispersers cannot be used satisfactorily when calcium or magnesium carbonates are present. It may be necessary to try several dispersers before the most satisfactory one for a specific matrix is found.

For clays, sodium carbonate ($Na_2CO_3$) is often used as disaggregant and disperser (Barghoorn, 1948; Dijkstra, 1949). The clay is boiled (time not specified) in 10 percent aqueous solution (Barghoorn, *ibid.*) or it is boiled for 15 minutes with a solution of 2 or 3 grams of $Na_2CO_3$ to 500 ml of $H_2O$ (Dijkstra, *ibid.*). Some clays may be dispersed with sodium pyrophosphate ($Na_4P_2O_7$), 1 to 5 percent aqueous solution, in 3 to 5 hours (Brown, 1960) or with a 5 to 10 percent aqueous solution of hydrogen peroxide ($H_2O_2$) in 10 to 20 minutes at room temperature (10 ml solution for 0.5 gram of clay) (Brown, 1960). Other dispersers used by sedimentary petrographers that might also prove useful with some clayey matrices include: sodium oxalate ($Na_2C_2O_4$), ammonium hydroxide ($NH_4OH$), sodium hexametaphosphate $[(NaPO_3)_6]$, lithium chloride (LiCl), and lithium hydroxide (LiOH) (see Krumbein and Pettijohn, 1938).

With peats, pollen and spores are often freed from entangling colloids by immersion in 5 to 10 percent aqueous solutions of sodium hydroxide

(NaOH), potassium hydroxide (KOH), or $NH_4OH$ for as much as 24 hours. Godwin (as quoted in Brown, 1960) heats peat in a centrifuge tube in a boiling-water bath with 10 percent NaOH or 10 percent KOH, from 10 minutes to 12 hours.[7] Ethyl alcohol (95 percent), either at room temperature or boiling, is also used to disperse peats (Geisler, 1935). Benninghoff (1947) uses 0.25 to 0.5 percent aqueous solution of trisodium phosphate ($Na_3PO_4 \cdot 12H_2O$) heated with peats for 2 hours in a 60°C oven. A wetting agent (Nacconol, for example) will hasten deflocculation by this method if the peat has been dried.

Some lignites (brown coals) may be dispersed by 5 to 10 percent KOH in 6 to 24 hours (Barghoorn, *ibid.*).

For some shales, NaOH, $(NaPO_3)_6$, $Na_4P_2O_7$ (Brown, 1960), $Na_2C_2O_4$, and $Na_2CO_3$ may prove useful dispersers (see Krumbein and Pettijohn, *ibid.*, p. 43–75).

Darvan[8] is mentioned in the pollen literature for dispersing finely divided insoluble material (Funkhouser and Evitt, 1959). The manufacturers recomment that Darvan be used at concentrations of 0.2 to 4 percent based on the weight of the dry material to be dispersed. Funkhouser and Evitt (1959) use 0.25 ml of saturated aqueous solution of Darvan No. 4 for 10 ml of suspended residue.

## CHEMICAL EXTRACTION

### General

Pollen-bearing rocks and sediments range from those that are accumulations of organized plant structures and/or amorphous organic residues with little or no mineral detritus (some peats, lignites, coals) to those composed largely of mineral constituents in the very fine silt ($3.9\mu$) to very fine sand ($125\mu$) grain size with minor amounts (1 to 2 percent) of organic debris (some shales, silts, water-laid volcanic ash). For purposes of extraction, however, differences are primarily quantitative rather than qualitative.

Chemical treatment for rocks or sediments with both mineral and organic fractions often consists of three steps: (1) demineralization, (2) solubilizing and/or chemical conversion to soluble products of residual organic matter, and (3) dispersion of maceration compounds evolved in the second step. For some peats and organic rocks, the chemical treatment must be directed toward removal of organic debris. A few rocks and sediments may need only demineralization and a density separation to yield microfossils. The specific

---

[7] A reflux condenser may be advisable for prolonged heating to keep the concentration of the alkaline solution constant.

[8] Four Darvans are available; No. 4, referred to in the pollen literature, is a monocalcium salt of polymerized aryl alkyl sulfonic acids. It belongs to the group of synthetic organic chemicals (surface-active agents) that includes most modern detergents and wetting agents. Darvan #4 is not recommended for use in the presence of soaps or of calcium salts (Technical Data Sheets of the R. T. Vanderbilt Co.).

procedure will depend on the mineralogical composition of the rock, on the relative proportion of organic and inorganic materials, and, occasionally, on the history of the rock or sediment since its deposition. Well-weathered outcrop samples of coal, for example, may need only treatment with alkaline solution or with an organic solvent to remove already oxidized humic complexes.

*Minerals* (*p. 547*). Minerals are routinely removed from the matrix by chemicals, following physical disaggregation and/or dispersal. Some are removed alternatively or in addition by density separation methods (p. 569). Most of the common minerals of sediments and sedimentary rocks are soluble in acids which generally do not attack the organic residue. Hydrofluoric, hydrochloric, and nitric acids, usually in aqueous solution, are most commonly used to remove mineral compounds.

*Organic Compounds* (*p. 552*). Plants contribute organic matter directly to the soil (which may be eroded and redeposited in lakes and streams) and to accumulating sediments in natural water bodies, as drift matter from the air, as finely divided material in water suspension, and in the form of leaves, twigs, cuticular material, cones, and even whole plants. Aside from the highly inert pollen and spore exines, this organic matter will include resins, waxes, proteins, carbohydrates (sugars, starches), derived carbohydrates (the polysaccharides: hemicelluloses, cellulose), and lignin. Because the chemical composition of the various structural elements in vascular plants has been essentially the same throughout geological time (i.e., waxes, polysaccharides, and lignin have always been present) this statement is true regardless of differences in the contributing vegetation (White, 1913).

Cellulose, hemicelluloses, and lignin especially command attention because of their abundance as contributed organic compounds and because they are the precursors, directly or through decomposition, of most of the finely divided organic debris or "unwanted organic matter" that must be removed from samples in extracting and concentrating microfossils.[9]

The purposes served by the chemical extractions of the palynologist can best be understood by some knowledge of the physical and chemical properties of these organic complexes and of the nature of the decomposition of plant material. In the following highly simplified discussion I have drawn freely on the following sources: Waksman (1936), Wise (1944), Wise and Jahn (1952), Brauns (1952), Stamm and Harris (1953), Pigman (1957), and Brauns and Brauns (1960).

*Abundance and Occurrence.* By weight, plants consist mostly of cellulose, hemicelluloses, and lignin. The carbohydrates constitute from 50 to 80 per-

[9] For purposes of this discussion marine-derived organic material is not considered; it seems likely, moreover, that much of the organic carbon in pollen-bearing marine rocks is ultimately derived from terrestrial sources.

cent (or on the average about 75 percent) of the dry matter of higher plants. In the same group of plants, the lignin content varies from about 15 to 30 percent (tables XI–XIX, p. 157–167, Brauns and Brauns).

Cellulose and lignin form the structural framework of plants; lignin also seems to protect cellulose from decay by presenting a physical barrier to microbial attack. The hemicelluloses comprise a variety of organic compounds; some serve in a skeletal capacity and are scarcely separable from cellulose, others serve as reserve food.

Cellulose is the major component of cell walls. Lignin lends mechanical strength in the secondary thickening of the walls, but is present chiefly in the cementing material between cells, constituting 70 to 75 percent of that substance.

The carbohydrates and lignin are usually partly or entirely combined in plants; opinion is divided, however, on whether there is a true chemical linkage or only a physical association between the two.

*Structure and Chemistry.* Cellulose is a high-molecular-weight carbohydrate, with the empirical formula $(C_6H_{10}O_5)n$; it is a long-chain polymer built upon a single pattern of repeating glucose anhydride units independent of source. Cellulose molecules form thread-like chains that are essentially parallel to one another and have interspersed amorphous regions, in which the threads are randomly interwoven, and crystalline regions, in which the threads are fitted together in ordered arrangement.

Hemicelluloses are complex polysaccharides without uniform chemical composition. They closely resemble cellulose in physical but not in chemical properties. However, the more insoluble hemicelluloses and "true cellulose" are scarcely distinguishable.

The chemistry and structure of lignin are yet obscure although lignin is generally thought to be an aromatic, long-chain, high-molecular-weight polymer with benzenoid-type rings. The repeating units, though not precisely known, are thought to be mainly, if not entirely, phenylpropane units; they vary from plant to plant, and are probably combined in different ways. Lignin has an irregular structure, without space lattice, and occurs in the plant in a "coherent ramified system" (Wise and Jahn, 1952, p. 414).

*Chemical Behavior.* Cellulose is insoluble in water, dilute alkali, most organic acids, and most common solvents (alcohols, chloroform, acetone, benzene, etc.) and is not susceptible to oxidation except under extreme conditions.

Cellulose is readily hydrolyzed by strong mineral acids to water soluble glucose. Acids depolymerize the cellulose chain by breaking glycosidic bonds of the amorphous regions. The primary cellulose molecule is broken into smaller and smaller component units and finally to the repeating unit itself. Among the acids which hydrolyze cellulose are 66 to 75 percent $H_2SO_4$; 42 to 45 percent HCl; 80 to 90 percent $H_3PO_4$; 70 to 75 percent HF, and various mixtures of these acids and other reagents.

Cellulose is readily esterified, and the ester derivatives are themselves soluble in some organic acids and solvents. Acetylation, esterification by acetic anhydride, is now the chief means used by palynologists to remove cellulose from matrices (p. 553): As usually conducted, acetylation produces a reaction faster and more complete than that of acid-hydrolysis (p. 553).

Most hemicelluloses enter solution readily in hot, dilute, mineral acids, forming simple sugars; they are also readily soluble in alkaline solutions.

Lignin is essentially unhydrolyzable by acids but extremely susceptible to oxidation, soluble in hot alkali (150 to 180°C, Waksman, 1936), and sparingly soluble in cold alkali. In the oxidation of lignin, carbon bonds are broken and the molecule is converted to the oxidized states of simpler compounds. The reaction is progressive once it is initiated, and attack continues on all of the remaining carbon-carbon bonds until lignin is degraded to gases and low molecular-weight water-soluble products, such as carbon dioxide, oxalic acid, acetic acid, and so on.

The oxidizable nature of lignin was recognized over 100 years ago by chemists attempting to isolate cellulose from wood. One of these chemists, Franz Schulze, used a mixture of potassium chlorate and nitric acid and then digested the residual fiber with dilute $NH_4OH$. Schulze was the first, according to Thiessen (1913), to apply this maceration reagent to the study of both lignite and hard coal. The mixture of potassium chlorate and nitric acid, known as Schulze solution, is still the principal oxidant used to extract acid-insoluble microfossils from sediments and rocks.

*Decomposition.* In aerobic conditions, the total decomposition of plant material means the accumulation of no organic residue. But at any stage in the decomposition, burial or submergence and a limited supply of oxygen can help to arrest biochemical decomposition. Even in anaerobic conditions, however, bacteria slowly degrade both the residual organic materials and their decomposition products.

Because of modifications by biochemical processes, the organic or humic fraction of sediments and sedimentary rocks rarely has the same composition as the original plant detritus nor are the proportions of constituent compounds the same as in the living plants. Many organic compounds in plants are water-soluble. Others are decomposed quickly by microorganisms on the ground surface or in well-aerated waters and are also readily solubilized. Still others are converted to gases through the metabolic activities of the aerobic microflora (fungi, bacteria) and to a lesser extent because of chemical processes of inanimate origin. Only the most stable constituents (lignin, waxes, resins) may survive the processes of decay and accumulate. Finally, the decomposition of plant debris and the synthetic activities of microorganisms give rise to organic complexes that have no exact counterpart among living plants.

Evidence indicates that lignin is the most stable of the three common plant constituents in aerobic conditions: in anaerobic conditions it is barely decomposed. For example, Waksman and Tenney (Waksman, 1936; Brauns, 1952) found lignin in soil either undecomposed, or insignificantly decomposed as compared with other plant constituents, over a period of 30 to 35 days. Hrubseky and Carpenter (Stamm and Harris, 1953, table 31, p. 83) compared decaying and sound Douglas fir wood and found a progressive increase in lignin from 26.7 percent in sound wood to 70.9 percent in fully decayed wood; cellulose and hemicelluloses showed a decrease from 73.5 to 28.1 percent. Jahn and Harlow (1942) found that 75 percent of the dry tissue of beech stakes from a prehistoric fishweir (the Boylston Street Fishweir) was lignin, which means that virtually none of it was lost, but 91 to 95 percent of the original pentosans and cellulose were destroyed. Gortner (1938) compared buried unfossilized Peorian and pre-Nebraskan spruce wood with modern spruce wood and found an increase in lignin and a decrease in cellulose and pentosans with increase in age of the wood. Similar results were reported by Mitchell and Ritter (1934) for buried, fossilized Miocene wood of pine, cedar, and redwood, all of which displayed a marked decrease in carbohydrates but little loss of lignin.

In natural deposits, both the composition of the organic detritus and its cellulose content are influenced in part by the composition of the original contributing plants (some, such as *Sphagnum,* contain no lignin), and in part by the immediate environment and prevailing climate, which affect the rapidity, nature, and extent of decomposition.

Among peats, for example, some, such as highmoor peats, contain large amounts of cellulose, fats, waxes and only minor amounts of lignin-humus complex; in lowmoor and forest peats, lignin or lignin-humus and proteins predominate; in sedimentary (estuarine, tidal-marsh, lake) peats, cellulose content is low, but ash and protein content is high. Under most conditions the carbohydrate content of both peats and lignites decreases with age. Although "coals" have been produced experimentally from cellulose or from a combination of cellulose and lignin, most natural coals are practically free from cellulose, and the belief is general that lignin is the parent material of coals.

Organic materials in soils, peat bogs, or water basins, under aerobic or anaerobic conditions, are in a dynamic state of decomposition and synthesis. The accumulation of organic constituents resistant to degradation, the formation of substances by chemical processes during the decomposition of less resistant constituents, and the synthesis of nitrogenous complexes by microorganisms, result in the formation and increase of amorphous, high-molecular weight, dark-brown or black organic complexes known as humus. Although humus possesses characteristic properties, it is extremely heterogeneous, and far from identical when isolated from soils, from bogs, or from lignites and coals. Waksman (1936) suggests that humus should be regarded as a "state of matter" rather than as a known chemical complex.

At least ten types of organic compounds, including a number of polymerized substances, have been isolated from humus, but two groups, with chemical counterparts in plant and animal constituents, are of major significance: (1) proteins, lignin, and lignin-like complexes, and (2) carbohydrates, fats, waxes, organic acids, alcohols, and other carbon compounds[10] (Waksman, *ibid.,* p. 186). Of these, lignin is present in "rather high concentrations in an unaltered form, in a modified form, or as condensation products with other complexes" (Waksman, *ibid.,* p. 141).

Until organic matter is preserved from further decomposition, or until it becomes no longer reactive, as in some "amorphous" peats, lignites, and coals, it is in a constant state of change. At any stage it may include (1) resistant structures, such as spores and cuticular tissues; (2) undecomposed plant residues; (3) organic debris in a state of modification or decay; and (4) complexes resulting from chemical processes, and from the activities of microorganisms, *i.e.,* humus. Organic residues differ because of variations in (1) the contributing plants (and animals); (2) the age of the deposit; (3) the state of decomposition; (4) the local microflora; and (5) the physical environment. For these reasons it is difficult to assign a definite composition to organic residues.

The heterogeneity of the organic fraction of sediments and sedimentary rocks accounts for the variety of methods of eradicating humic detritus used by palynologists. Complex organic detritus must be subjected to more than one kind of treatment if all of it is to be destroyed. Thus, much of the organic residue in some matrices is alkali-soluble (lignin-humus or "humic acids" of Faegri and Iversen, 1950; part (polysaccharides) can be made soluble by acetylation; still another part (lignin and "humic acids" of Erdtman, 1943) is susceptible to oxidation. Fully altered organic matter, as that in some coals and carbonaceous shales, is no longer reactive to alkali treatment or acetylation, and must be oxidized and the maceration compounds ("humic acids" of many authors) must be solubilized or dispersed by alkaline solutions. Of the three processes described below, oxidation is the most widely used, especially for sediments and rock samples of pre-Cenozoic age.

*Alkalies.* Aqueous alkaline solutions are used (1) to eliminate the large lignin-humus fraction of some sediments and sedimentary rocks, especially peats and some lignites, and (2) to solubilize humic maceration compounds of oxidized organic residues.

---

[10] According to Waksman (*ibid.*) this grouping more or less corresponds, but not quantitatively, to the older method of separating humus into "humic acids" chiefly characterized by their solubility in alkaline solutions and into "humins" and "crenic acids," or "fulvic acid." He advocates that the whole nomenclature of "humic acids" (humins, ulmins, crenic acid, fulvic acid, etc.) should be abandoned since these labels designate only substances of indefinite composition obtained by specific chemical procedures and not definite chemical compounds.

As a prime method for extracting microfossils, alkali treatment has limited application. It is most effective with some terrestrial peats, some lake and river-bottom sediments (sedimentary peats), and possibly with some lignites in which lignin-like substances are the major fraction of the organic residue. For most materials alkali treatment used in conjunction with acetylation provides the most effective means of recovering and concentrating microfossils. Alkaline solutions are decreasingly effective as organic residues are more thoroughly decomposed.

Alkali treatment as the usual follow-up to oxidation may be extremely hazardous, especially if samples are over-macerated. For some materials oxidation is sufficient without alkalies. Funkhouser and Evitt (1959) point out that if some samples react with alkali following oxidation, it indicates that the microfossils have been destroyed. For some well-weathered sedimentary rocks, on the other hand, alkali treatment may be sufficient to recover microfossils without oxidation.

*Acetylation.* Acetylation is the chief method used to solubilize the cellulose content of sediments and sedimentary rocks. Strong mineral acids originally used for cellulose degradation (Erdtman and Erdtman, 1933) are slow acting because the oxygen atoms they attack are deeply embedded in the cellulose molecule (L. H. Klemm, personal communication), and the reaction is often ineffective, stopping before completion.

Acetylation of cellulose does not produce water-soluble compounds; either glacial acetic acid or an organic solvent must be used to keep the cellulose ester in solution (see Faegri and Iversen, 1950, p. 63). The reaction is quite rapid, however, because it takes place at the OH groups along the periphery of the cellulose molecule (L. H. Klemm, personal communication).

Following Erdtman, palynologists have long called this process acetolysis. Acetylation and acetolysis are, however, distinct chemical processes. *Acetolysis* is the equivalent of two processes: hydrolysis followed by some acetylation. It brings about depolymerization, a process that primarily involves breakage of the carbon-oxygen bonds which join together the sugar units of the cellulose molecule. Acetylation may occur at the sites where these bonds are broken. The end products are water-soluble simple sugars or their partly acetylated derivatives. *Acetylation,* on the other hand, is an esterification reaction: larger acetyl ($CH_3CO$) groups are substituted for the hydrogen in the hydroxyl (OH) groups of the cellulose molecule, i.e., the process involves breakage of the hydrogen-oxygen bonds in the cellulose molecule. When acetylation goes to completion, cellulose is converted to cellulose triacetate (a derivative with the maximum number of acetyl groups per unit of the molecule). Cellulose triacetate is insoluble in water, but soluble in glacial acetic acid and some organic solvents. In general, the effect of increasing the time and the temperature of the acetylation reaction is to increase the probability that the reaction will be completed, i.e., that the cellulose molecule will be soluble. The shorter the acetylation, the greater the probability that the reaction is incomplete and that free OH groups (insoluble cellulose) are still present (L. H. Klemm, personal communication).

*Oxidation.* Oxidation is chiefly used to rid sediments and sedimentary rocks of unaltered lignin and of organic material in an advanced state of decomposition. Highly altered organic residue is often a highly condensed form of organic carbon of essentially benzenoid character. Condensation means that the original chemical compound is changed by an intermolecular reaction wherein two or more molecules come together to form a larger molecule with the concurrent elimination of one or more oxygen-containing smaller molecules (such as $H_2O$ and $CO_2$). Elimination of reactive groups takes place gradually with increasing maturity as may be indicated by a concurrent decreasing solubility in alkalies. For example, within the coal series, alkali-soluble substances are very abundant in peats and lignites; they are rare in bituminous coal; they are entirely absent from anthracite.

Strongly altered organic substances are rendered soluble in alkaline solutions and in some organic solvents by oxidation. The oxidation products have an acidic character, which is probably why they are usually referred to in pollen literature as "humic acids."

Palynologists use many of the oxidants of organic chemists and biochemists. Because many modified organic residues are colloidal complexes, and differ physically and biochemically from rock to rock, their reactions with different oxidants also vary: some matrices will respond well to one oxidant, but not to another. The reaction often varies with the maturity of the organic substance. The less reactive the material is to alkali, the stronger the oxidant necessary or the longer the time needed for the reaction to be completed, i.e., for carbonized materials to be broken down. Even within the same organic complex there may be ingredients that do not oxidize with the same ease or that are essentially unoxidizable (Thiessen, 1913).

Pollen and spores are also oxidizable and will be destroyed along with organic detritus if the reaction is not carefully monitored while it is in progress. In some cases, even reagents that may be used with relative confidence under some circumstances will destroy microspore specimens under other circumstances. All pollen and spores, moreover, do not have the same resistance to all oxidants, or for that matter, to some of the other chemical reagents used in their extraction. Kosanke (1962) reports, for example, that the genus *Crassispora* seems more resistant to fuming nitric acid than to Schulze solution. He notes also (*ibid.,* p. 13) that in some preparations small species in the 20 to $25\mu$ size range appear to be underrepresented when fuming nitric acid is used instead of Schulze solution. The state of preservation of the microfossils may determine whether they will be recovered with one oxidant but not with another.

Different oxidants used in chemical maceration may also affect microspore size. Specimens released from coal samples by Schulze solution and KOH were consistently larger (in mean diameter and limits) than the same species procured from coals processed only by fuming nitric acid (Butterworth and Williams, 1954). In two of nine species, the maximum mean diameter was as much as 11 to $14\mu$ larger when processed by Schulze solution than by $HNO_3$.

Oxidants used by palynologists include: nitric acid alone (p. 557), or with potassium chlorate (p. 558), or with bromine (p. 560); nitric acid with potassium dichromate[11] (Funkhouser and Evitt, 1959) or with chromium trioxide (p. 561); nitric acid with hydrochloric acid (p. 561); chlorine and sodium sulfite (p. 562); an aqueous solution of chlorine dioxide in 50 percent acetic or 50 percent monochloroacetic acid [12] (Erdtman and Erdtman, 1933; Bertsch, 1942; Sittler, 1955; Brown, 1960); sodium hypochlorite (p. 563); sodium chlorite (p. 563); sodium chlorate (p. 564); perchloric acid [13] (Leschik, 1956; Brown, 1960); perchloric and periodic acids (p. 564); hydrogen peroxide alone or with potassium hydroxide (p. 565); potassium permanganate alone[14] (Erdtman and Erdtman, 1933) or in sulfuric acid [15] (Staplin, et al., 1960); dichromic acid alone or with sulfuric acid [16,a,b] (Sittler, 1955; Brown, 1960); potassium dichromate and sulfuric acid [16,c] (Bertsch, 1942; Sittler, 1955); oxalic acid [17] (Bertsch, 1942; Sittler, 1955;

---

[11] $HNO_3$ (conc.) saturated with potassium dichromate ($K_2Cr_2O_7$).

[12] In the pollen literature a solution of $ClO_2$ in acetic or in monochloroacetic acid ($CH_2ClCOOH$) is referred to as Diaphanol. Diaphanol is not listed in the Merck Index or in trade name catalogues of chemical reagents, but according to C. Sittler (personal correspondence, 1963), Diaphanol is a commercial name for two reagents, of the composition indicated, manufactured in Germany for about 50 years. Diaphanol can be made in the laboratory, but the reaction is complicated and dangerous, since $ClO_2$ gas is unstable and explosive. According to Sittler (personal correspondence), Diaphanol is used primarily for young organic sediments rather than for indurated rocks. Erdtman and Erdtman say that $ClO_2$ in acetic acid acts "too slowly and not intensely enough" but Bertsch and Sittler claim that $ClO_2$ in $CH_2ClCOOH$ is more vigorous.

[13] Leschik (as cited in Brown, 1960) uses 30 to 40 percent $HClO_4$ and heats it with the organic residue for 1 to 2 hours in a water bath.

[14] $KMO_4$ is a powerful oxidant. Erdtman and Erdtman report some destruction of grains in peats from its use as well as from use of other alkaline oxidative agents such as sodium hypochlorite and sodium hypobromite. They regard acid oxidative agents as safer for pollen and spore extractions. According to Bone, et al. (1935), the susceptibility to $KMnO_4$ oxidation diminishes with the maturity of the material.

[15] $KMnO_4$ in $H_2SO_4$ is said to yield results comparable to Schulze solution, although an extra step is needed for decolorization.

[16] All of the following solutions are powerful oxidants, especially useful for the preparation of high rank coals. However, according to Sittler (personal correspondence, 1963), these reagents are dangerous, both for pollen and for man, and in his opinion they are less advantageous for extractions than Schulze solution.

   *a.* Concentrated (pure) dichromic acid ($H_2Cr_2O_7$) [$2CrO_3 + H_2O \longrightarrow H_2Cr_2O_7$]

   *b.* Concentrated $H_2Cr_2O_7$ + an excess of $H_2SO_4$ (conc.)

   *c.* A saturated solution of potassium dichromate ($K_2Cr_2O_7$) + an excess of $H_2SO_4$ (conc.) + $H_2O$ to keep the $H_2Cr_2O_7$ in solution.

   Although not specifically mentioned in any of these papers, chromium trioxide ($CrO_3$) + $H_2SO_4$ (conc.) is also a very strong oxidant that probably could be used with equal success.

[17] $(COOH)_2$ is a poisonous organic acid, used in 3 percent solution in direct sunlight as

Brown, 1960) and sodium perborate[18] (van Campo, 1950; Sittler, 1955; Brown, 1960).

Many of these reagents, for example, hydrogen peroxide and the halogen-oxygen compounds, are both oxidizing (delignifying or degrading) and de-colorizing agents (the destruction of coloring material by these reagents takes place under oxidizing conditions).

Other possible, but untested oxidizing agents suggested by Staplin, et al. (1960) include ceric sulfate [$Ce(SO_4)_2$], potassium bromate ($KBrO_3$), calcium hypobromite, and calcium hypochlorite [$Ca(ClO)_2$]. These and others may prove of value for some types of samples although, as already mentioned, alkaline oxidants appear destructive to pollen and spores.

## Inorganic Compounds

### CARBONATES

Anhydrous carbonates of the calcite group are the most common members of the carbonate suite in the sedimentary matrices likely to be examined by palynologists. Calcite ($CaCO_3$) and dolomite [$CaMg(CO_3)_2$] are the most common of these minerals.

Hydrochloric acid (HCl) is used in the routine removal of carbonates from sedimentary samples. Calcite dissolves in cold HCl; dolomite most readily in hot HCl. Carbonates must be completely removed from samples before residues are digested with HF, since calcium salts react with HF to form calcium fluoride ($CaF_2$), a fine precipitate that is difficult to eradicate from the sample (Walton, 1923; Sittler, 1955).

Before adding HCl, the matrix is broken into fragments, pea-size or smaller; if unconsolidated it may be boiled in water briefly to bring the particles into suspension. Hydrochloric acid, in an aqueous 10 percent solution, is added to the sample in a large beaker which is then set aside until the effervescence ceases. Fresh acid should be added from time to time and the concentration may be increased (up to 25 percent) to test whether the reaction is completed, since effervescence will cease when the acid is no longer potent, even if carbonates are still present. If effervescence is very vigorous, a few drops of acetone may be added to reduce the surface tension.

The reaction may be speeded up by increasing the concentration of the acid or by gently heating the solution; the latter step is necessary if dolomite is present. When the reaction ceases, decant the supernatant liquid, transfer the residue to centrifuge tubes, wash and centrifuge with water several times

---

an oxidant and bleach, primarily for young organic sediments. Samples may be pretreated with $KMnO_4$. $(COOH)_2$ is said to be less satisfactory than Schulze solution.

[18] $Na_2B_4O_8$ is an alkaline oxidant especially useful with peats and lignites, although said to be somewhat dangerous for fragile grains. A trace of $Na_2B_4O_8$ (1 gram or less) is used, usually in conjunction with 10 percent NaOH.

to complete the removal of all traces of calcium salts before proceeding with HF treatment.

A new method for solubilizing calcareous materials as well as for determining the calcite-dolomite ratio in carbonate rocks involves the use of EDTA, or ethylenediaminetetraacetic acid (Weissmann and Diehl, 1953; Glover, 1961; see also Bisque, 1961).[19] The EDTA concentration, the pH of the solution, the temperature, and the particle size of the carbonaceous rock, all affect the solution rate of calcareous material. For securing pollen preparations from calcareous rocks, Glover suggests the use of EDTA solution, pH 8.3 (the trisodium hydrogen salt, solubility 35 grams/100 ml), at temperatures just under boiling. Under these conditions, he says that the bicarbonate ion is present, rather than $CO_2$, which might cause some mechanical disruption of pollen grains.

Nitric acid ($HNO_3$) in an aqueous 10 percent solution will also remove carbonates (Faegri and Iversen, 1950). Arnold (1950) soaked coals in 10 percent $HNO_3$ for periods from several weeks to more than two years long for the purpose, he says, of removing "calcium held in combination with the humic substances." The process involved for such extended periods of time is, however, more likely one of oxidation, since the coal broke down "into a coarse black mud" in dilute KOH solution (p. 566).

Phosphoric or orthophosphoric acid ($H_3PO_4$)[20] is sometimes used to dissolve carbonates (Sarmiento, 1957; Staplin, et al., 1960). Sarmiento treated samples with cold $H_3PO_4$ until the reaction ceased; he then heated the mixture for 10 minutes (no temperature given). Staplin, et al. (1960) say that a 50 percent solution of $H_3PO_4$, mildly heated and/or agitated, is "more gentle but just as rapid as a hydrochloric acid solution." Moreover, according to them, $H_3PO_4$ will dissolve some Al, Ti, and Fe compounds that are insoluble in HCl. Two disadvantages of $H_3PO_4$ are the large volume of acid needed and the occurrence of newly formed phosphates, soluble, however, in $HNO_3$ or Schulze solution (p. 558).

Acetic acid ($CH_3COOH$) in 10 percent solution and formic acid (HCOOH) in 6 percent solution are also used to dissolve carbonate rocks. According to Brown (1960), HCOOH is gentler than 10 percent HCl in its action.

SULFATES

Anhydrite ($CaSO_4$) and gypsum ($CaSO_4 \cdot 2H_2O$) will probably be the most common sulfates in sedimentary samples examined by the palynologist.

---

[19] EDTA is an organic chelating agent: it reacts with the ions of Ca and Mg to form complex ions in which the Ca and Mg are very tightly bound (Weissmann and Diehl, 1953). According to Glover, commercially available forms of EDTA [known as Versene] include the free acid, the disodium dihydrogen salt, the trisodium hydrogen salt, and the tetrasodium salt. The solubility and the pH both increase in the order in which the forms are listed, the tetrasodium salt having a pH about 10.5.

[20] Pure $H_3PO_4$ is a deliquescent crystalline material; commercial $H_3PO_4$ is a liquid. Its high viscosity makes it somewhat difficult to handle.

Hot HCl or HNO₃ (in 10 percent aqueous solution) will dissolve both minerals. EDTA (the tetrasodium salt, p. 548) in 10 percent aqueous solution will also dissolve gypsum and anhydrite (Wagoner, et al., 1961). The reaction rate is greatly increased by use of the ultrasonic generator for two or three minutes during the solution period (W. L. Norem, personal communication, 1962).

Gypsum and anhydrite are also soluble in sodium thiosulfate, photographers "hypo" (Goldman, 1952, p. 70). Most effective is a solution of one part anhydrous "hypo" to four parts water, heated in a steam bath or gently boiled. According to Soefner (as quoted in Goldman), anhydrite and, presumably, gypsum are also soluble in ammonium sulfate ($NH_4SO_4$) solution. Nelson (cited by Brown, 1960) reports gypsum to be soluble in a hot supersaturated solution of sodium chloride (NaCl).

### SULFIDES

Pyrite ($FeS_2$) and marcasite ($FeS_2$) are common constituents of sedimentary rocks (Krumbein and Pettijohn, 1938). Pyrite is common in some coals, as is sulfur; marcasite is found occasionally. The blue and bluish-gray color of shales and mudstones sometimes associated with coal seams is usually due to finely disseminated iron sulfide (Raistrick and Marshall, 1948). Black marine muds deposited close to land frequently contain colloidal ferrous sulfide. These and other sulfide compounds are opaque; in pollen residues they may appear as well-crystallized angular particles or as globules or nodules that resemble small particles of carbon and clump with the microfossils.

Sulfide compounds are commonly soluble in cold, concentrated $HNO_3$ (from periods of 10 minutes to 24 hours) although it may be necessary to boil the specimen in $HNO_3$ if marcasite is present (in which case it will be decomposed with the separation of sulfur).[21] Pyrite is also commonly dissolved in boiling $HNO_3$ (Hurlbut, 1949).

Since $HNO_3$ is a very strong oxidant and will also attack organic matter, it may be preferable to remove metallic sulfides by heavy-liquid flotation.

### SILICATES

Since about 40 percent of the common minerals and nearly all of the igneous rock-forming minerals are silicates, it is not surprising that silicates, especially quartz, are extremely common in clastic rocks and sediments.

Hydrous hydrofluoric acid is the most effective reagent for removing silicates from sedimentary samples. If calcium carbonates are believed to be present in the matrix, the use of HCl or $HNO_3$ before the use of HF is advisable. Otherwise the introduction of the HF will cause precipitation of

---

[21] Xylene, and in decreasing order of effectiveness, amyl acetate, ethyl ether, petroleum ether, and alcohol, are sulfur solvents (Goldman, 1952). Carbon disulfide ($CS_2$) is also an effective sulfur solvent (L. H. Klemm, personal communication).

calcium fluoride (CaF$_2$), a flocculate which is troublesome to remove (p. 547). However, the introduction of some calcium via calcium-bearing silicates is often unavoidable. Thorough washing in water following HCl treatment will help to remove dissolved calcium salts.

In handling HF special care must be exercised. The vapor is irritating and poisonous, and the liquid will produce severe burns on the flesh that are not immediately detectable and that heal slowly and with difficulty.[22] Hydrofluoric acid must always be handled under a fume hood, and as an added precaution it is recommended that rubber gloves and apron be worn. It is also wise to wear a face shield.

The containers for hydrofluoric acid, including centrifuge tubes, should be made of a substance with which it will not react. The acid is extremely corrosive to glass, including Pyrex. Platinum or lead crucibles are recommended if the matrix is to be boiled with HF: nickel and copper crucibles may be used, but they will eventually be destroyed by the acid. Polyethylene centrifuge tubes and beakers are satisfactory although if the reaction when HF is first added to samples is strongly exothermic they may melt. Placing the beakers or centrifuge tubes in a cold water bath will dissipate some heat.

Anhydrous hydrofluoric acid dissolves in water in all proportions. The common commercial HF and that most often used by pollen workers is 48 percent to 52 percent acid. According to Norem (personal communication, 1962), 72 percent HF gives better results in breaking down siliceous matrices than the standard concentrations. Solutions up to 90 percent HF have been used by some palynologists (Klaus as cited in Brown, 1960). Others prefer a 1 to 1 solution of HF and 30 to 50 percent ethyl alcohol (Thiessen, 1913). According to Thiessen, the alcohol-HF solution penetrates more quickly and works more energetically than a water solution.

The time necessary to dissolve the silicates, from a few minutes to many hours, varies depending on their abundance and on the continuing potency of the acid solution. Some palynologists soak samples in HF for several weeks; Macko (1957) left samples in 40 percent HF for seven months, but it seems unlikely that such a prolonged treatment is really effective without the occasional addition of fresh acid. The usual treatment time for most matrices is 8 to 12 hours. Heating to gentle boiling will speed the reaction; Faegri and Iversen (1950) suggest boiling for 3 minutes. I have boiled samples for 10 to 20 minutes without damage to the microspores. Heat helps to volatilize silicon fluoride (SiF$_4$), which normally escapes as a gas in the reaction, and according to Staplin, et al. (1960), also helps to volatilize titanium as TiF$_4$.

---

[22] When a burn is suspected, immediately flood the area thoroughly with water and apply a paste of glycerin and magnesia oxide or glycerin and milk of magnesia. Information concerning safe handling of HF is provided in Chemical Safety Data Sheet SD-25 available from Manufacturing Chemists Assoc., Inc., 1625 Eye Street, N. W., Washington, D.C.

*Procedure*  1. Disaggregate sample with a small amount of $H_2O$ if it is not already in aqueous suspension. Add HF drop by drop, stirring after each addition and watching the reaction carefully. If the reaction is vigorous, generates much heat, and threatens to overflow the container, add no more acid for 5 to 10 minutes. Then continue to add acid slowly, or drop by drop, stirring after each addition, and watching the reaction carefully.

2. Set container aside, loosely covered and in fume hood, allowing it to stand overnight or longer. Stir occasionally. More HF may be added from time to time as the potency of that in the container decreases, or the spent acid may be completely decanted and fresh acid added. If desired, the residue may be boiled, or it may be boiled and then left to stand. Boiling should always be gentle, using the pilot light of a bunsen burner.

3. After the residue is fully settled, decant off as much of the supernatant HF as possible.[23] If the residue has been boiled, cooling before centrifugation will lessen laboratory fumes. Transfer residue to centrifuge tubes.

4. To keep the dissolved siliceous compounds in solution, rinse the residue with warm HCl (10 percent) before adding $H_2O$ (Faegri and Iversen, 1950; Sittler, 1955). In water environment, certain compounds and salts (colloidal silica, silicofluorides of aluminum, $CaF_2$, $MgF_2$, KF, NaF) may precipitate following the use of HF. Most of these are soluble, however, in hot, dilute (10 to 25 percent) HCl. It is usually most convenient to heat the centrifuge tube with HCl in a boiling water bath 1 to 3 minutes. It may be necessary to repeat the hot HCl treatment several times. Clisby and Sears (1955) suggest that certain dense gels that follow HF treatment of marls and ostracod microcoquinas can be precipitated in ammonium hydroxide ($NH_4OH$) and the precipitate dissolved in $HNO_3$.[24]

5. The organic residue should then be washed at least a half-dozen times with $H_2O$, centrifuging and decanting between each rinse, or the residue allowed to settle out of $H_2O$ in a large beaker several times, adding fresh $H_2O$ after each decanting.

---

[23] HF is very corrosive; if an acid-proof sink is not available, or if the acid is to be introduced into a sewerline, it is well to neutralize it with $Na_2CO_3$. It is also well to flush the drain system well with running water during and after the time when the acid is added.

[24] After completion of this paper, a technique developed by B. E. Balme (see Balme and Hassell, 1962, p. 4) for freeing organic residues of complex insoluble fluorides formed by the reaction of HF with minerals of the clay-mica suite, was called to my attention by Lucy M. Cranwell (personal correspondence, 1963). Balme and Hassell note that fine-grained marine matrices, especially those rich in chloritic minerals, yield a high proportion of insoluble reaction products with HF treatment; they claim to be able to eradicate these by the methods outlined by them. They do not, however, explain the nature of the chemical reactions involved.

## Organic Compounds

### BITUMINOUS SUBSTANCES

There are a variety of hydrocarbons, bituminous substances such as fats, waxes, wax-like materials, and resins, that occasionally are abundant in some sediments and rocks. Certain peats are rich in these "bitumens"; in some "pollen peats" they constitute approximately a third of the total organic matter (Waksman, 1936). Similar materials are often associated with lignites and bituminous coals, sometimes in large masses (Abraham, 1929). Bitumens may also form the cements of some sedimentary rocks (Krumbein and Pettijohn, 1938). Although waxes and resins are not especially common in plants, they are relatively resistant to decomposition under anaerobic conditions, and they will sometimes accumulate with other resistant organic compounds and increase in abundance with increasing age of the deposit (Waksman, 1936; Brauns, 1952).

Most bituminous substances are soluble in a variety of volatile organic solvents: acetone, alcohol, benzene, chloroform, ether, gasoline, kerosene, phenol, pyridine, Varsol, xylene, and so on. Pyridine ($C_5H_5N$) is sometimes used as a preoxidizing reagent for high rank coals. It acts both as a softener, to loosen the coal texture and swell the particles (Raistrick, 1934), and as a solvent. Two procedures are used: (1) boiling coal with $C_5H_5N$ for 16 hours (Kosanke, 1962); (2) soaking coal in $C_5H_5N$ for 24 hours (Raistrick, 1934). $C_5H_5N$ must be removed with dilute HCl, which converts it to a water-soluble compound. Rinse well with $H_2O$ following the use of HCl.

To help solubilize and soften some coals and thus reduce their oxidation time, Staplin, et al. (1960) and Wagoner, et al. (1961) recommend a solution of methanol-acetone-benzene in the proportions 15 to 15 to 70. A solution in the same proportions was used by Sittler (1955) to help solubilize asphalt and remove crude oil from residues before other treatment. Many of the other solvents mentioned are also satisfactory for this purpose. To extract organic remains from crude oil, Sittler (1955) diluted large quantities of oil with the benzene-methanol-acetone mixture before centrifugation. The centrifugate was washed with benzene, with a mixture of benzene-methanol-acetone, and with ethanol (95 percent) until the supernatant liquid was clear.

Although filtration of even very dilute solutions of oil through filter paper is too slow to be satisfactory, filters of other types may be used successfully to extract pollen and spores. Sanders (1937) used water-soluble substances (for example, $NH_4Cl$, NaCl) as filters to remove organic materials from waterless and slightly paraffin-base oils. Artamonova and Medvedeva (1962) propose the following filtration process as satisfactory for all types of oil. They use a Beuchner funnel with filter paper and a 12 to 15 mm layer of quartz sand (grain size $<0.25$ mm), mounted on a filtering (extraction) flask and connected to a water-jet pump (aspirator). The sand acts as the principal filter. Paraffin-base oils must be heated before filtration; others may be filtered cold or slightly warmed. After filtration the oil is removed from the filter by washing with heated kerosene and benzene; paraffin is removed by washing with hot water; the kerosene and benzene are removed with ethanol. The organic residue is recovered from the sand by flotation, and washed with acetone and alcohol and sieved to remove coarse impurities. Microspores are further concentrated by standard chemical treatment.

Waksman (1936) notes that the yield of ether- and alcohol-soluble complexes from some peats may be considerably increased if the peat is first extracted with solvents, then treated with hot, dilute (2 to 4 percent) HCl and then re-treated with solvents. The free fats and fatty acids go into solution with the first solvent extraction, but the HCl treatment liberates the combined fats and fatty acids, and these are dissolved by the second application of solvent. Waksman also points out that extracts of bituminous substances of peats and coals made under pressure yield oil, the amount of the yield increasing with the temperature.

### PROTEINACEOUS MATERIAL

Many of the proteins of decomposing plants are soluble in water. Others, however, that have been synthesized by the activity of microorganisms (Waksman, 1936, p. 278), may be abundant in organic residues of some samples, as already indicated. According to W. L. Norem (personal communication, 1962), "some samples containing proteinaceous debris can be cleaned up with a 10 to 30 minute treatment with N,N-dimethyl formamide." Norem cautions, however, that long treatment with this solvent is injurious to microfossils.

### CELLULOSE

**Acid-hydrolysis.** Erdtman and Erdtman (1933) rid samples of their polysaccharide fraction by hydrolysis with strong mineral acids. They used $H_2SO_4$ (1 cc or less of an 80 percent solution), in which the sample was allowed to stand for three hours or more.

Faegri and Iversen (1950, p. 62) note the possibility of removing cellulose with cold concentrated $H_2SO_4$, if plant material is left in it for 24 hours or longer. For hydrolysis to take place, however, $H_2O$ must be present; none will occur if concentrated (95 to 98 percent) $H_2SO_4$ is used (L. H. Klemm, personal communication).

For reasons discussed earlier (p. 544) acid-hydrolysis is generally slower and often less effective than acetylation, and has been generally abandoned by palynologists as a means of eradicating cellulose.

**Acetylation.** Acetylation is the prime method used by palynologists to solubilize cellulose (Erdtman, 1936, 1943; Faegri and Iversen, 1950). Oxidation is often combined with acetylation in the processing of peats and other sediments of low pollen content (Erdtman, 1936, 1943). Acetylation may be used independently, however, where oxidation is unnecessary or where alkali treatment preceding acetylation will remove most of the humus-lignin compounds that could be solubilized by oxidation (Faegri and Iversen, 1950, p. 62–63).

Recent evidence indicates that a combined treatment of oxidation and acetylation must be used cautiously, although the two treatments may be used independently with confidence. Hafsten (1959) extracted eight replicate samples by HF plus acetolysis and by oxidation plus HF plus acetolysis; he lost nearly 100 percent of the pine pollen grains in residues given the second treatment. However, a second set of eleven replicate samples treated with HF plus acetolysis and with HF plus oxidation showed no significant differences in amount of pine pollen, indicating that oxidation itself had little effect on the pollen content of the sample. If the two treatments are used in conjunction, Faegri and Iversen (1950) caution that the oxidation must always precede acetylation to avoid damage to grains.

*Needed reagents:* Acetic anhydride [$(CH_3CO)_2O$], sulfuric acid ($H_2SO_4$, concentrated), glacial acetic acid ($CH_3COOH$), or an organic solvent such as acetone.

The solution consists of nine parts of $(CH_3CO)_2O$ and one part concentrated $H_2SO_4$ as a catalyst. Make fresh mixture immediately prior to use by adding the $H_2SO_4$ to the $(CH_3CO)_2O$. The reaction is exothermic. Handle the solution with care. Add the solution to samples only after their dehydration with $CH_3COOH$. Following use, slowly decant the reagent into running $H_2O$. Do not permit $H_2O$ to enter the centrifuge tube during the processing as the solution is potentially explosive. If much cellulose is present in the original sample, the acetylated residue must be rinsed with glacial acetic acid, or with an organic solvent such as acetone, in order to keep cellulose acetate in solution (p. 544). The acetylation procedure is generally standard except for the time during which the organic residue is left in the reagent; this varies from 1 to 30 minutes. (For variations of acetylation with modern pollen see the article by Traverse in this Handbook, p. 598.)

*Procedure*    1. Wash pretreated organic residue thoroughly.

2. Add $CH_3COOH$ to residue in centrifuge tube. Thoroughly stir residue in acid, centrifuge, and decant. Repeat acid rinse if there is much residue to dehydrate.

3. Add the freshly mixed acetylation reagent (about 10 ml in a 15-ml centrifuge tube) while still hot to the residue, and stir to mix thoroughly.

a. As acetylation is practiced in the Pollen Laboratory, Danish Geological Survey, the centrifuge tube is placed in a gently boiling water bath for 60 seconds.[25]

---

[25] Of course, at high altitudes where water boils at lower temperatures, the acetylation time should be increased to obtain comparable results.

b. As acetylation is practiced by Erdtman (1960), the centrifuge tube is placed in a water bath at room temperature or at a maximum temperature between 70 and 80°C. When the bath begins to boil, heating is stopped, but the tube is left in the hot water for about 15 minutes.

c. Godwin (1956) acetylates material in a 100°C water bath for 5 to 30 minutes.[26]

4. Remove tube from water bath and centrifuge. Decant the acetylation mixture into running $H_2O$.

5. Wash residue with $CH_3COOH$ to prevent the precipitation of cellulose acetate now in solution following treatment; stir, centrifuge, and decant.

6. Wash 3 to 4 times with $H_2O$.

7. If the treatment was short and optical examination reveals the presence of much remaining organic detritus acetylation may be repeated.

LIGNIN, LIGNIN-HUMUS, AMORPHOUS
PHENOLIC DECOMPOSITION COMPOUNDS

**Alkalies.** Organic material in a dynamic state of decomposition becomes increasingly soluble in alkaline solutions and some organic solvents up to a point. The unaltered lignin molecule, which was only slightly soluble in hot alkali under pressure, becomes readily soluble in alkaline solution when it has been modified by decomposition.

The pollen and spores of some peats and similar sediments relatively free of minerals and unaltered organic debris may be effectively extracted by alkali treatment. Since the method provides for very little concentration of pollen, it is inadequate for sediments of low pollen content that do not fulfill the above requirements. Alkalies used are potassium hydroxide (KOH), sodium hydroxide (NaOH), and the somewhat weaker base, ammonium hydroxide ($NH_4OH$).

As described by Faegri and Iversen (1950), von Post briefly boiled a small amount of peat on a microscope slide with a few drops of dilute aqueous KOH. Generally, however, in order that the dispersed dark brown humic compounds may be washed free from the sample to facilitate its examination, it is preferable to heat the peat with alkaline solution in a porcelain evaporating dish or in a centrifuge tube in a boiling water bath for 5 to 10 minutes or so, followed by thorough $H_2O$ washes to remove the solubilized compounds. In either case, for the protection of the grains, the strength of the alkaline solution during the treatment should not rise above 10 percent (Faegri and Iversen, *ibid.*). If prolonged boiling is necessary, a

---

[26] Although there is general agreement that acetylation causes pollen grains to swell, the evidence regarding the effects of prolonged acetylation on the grains is conflicting. According to Faegri and Deuse (1960), the duration of acetylation has little effect on the size of the grains, but according to McIntyre (1963), prolonged heating causes excess swelling of the grains.

reflux condenser may be used to keep the concentration of the alkaline solution constant.

The alkali treatment may be repeated as long as the pollen and spores are
not attacked (determined by frequent optical checks), and until the residue
is free of alkali-soluble humic material. The removal of some coarse organic
detritus (wood, leaf fragments, etc.) may be facilitated by sieving the residue
through a fine metal or porcelain strainer with mesh size 0.15 to 0.2 mm
(i.e., large enough to allow large conifer grains and spores through). By
removing coarse detritus, the microfossils are concentrated, and residues that,
without sieving, appeared quite barren of pollen and spores may prove to
be excellent sources (see Faegri and Iversen, *ibid.,* fig. 6). If greater concentration of pollen is necessary, the sample may be acetylated following alkali treatment.

**Oxidation.** Sediments and sedimentary rocks in which undecomposed lignin
and/or altered humic complexes in the form of organic carbon are abundant,
must be oxidized to remove this material and extract the microfossils. Well-
weathered outcrop samples of such matrices will normally provide the only
exception to this generalization.

Because microfossils are susceptible to oxidation (p. 545), each sample
should be checked to determine that it contains material that cannot be removed in any other way. In addition, it is well to experiment with samples
requiring oxidation to determine the most effective oxidant and the optimal
time for its use. Although color change in the macerating reagent sometimes
provides a guide to the progress of oxidation, as a rule its advancement is
best controlled by trial and error, i.e., by examining washed samples of the
residue in dilute alkaline solution. If oxidation is carefully controlled by frequent optical checks of wet residues, the reaction can usually be stopped at
the point when extraneous organic material is removed but the microfossils
are not yet attacked.

Use the following simple test to determine the need for oxidation and to
monitor its progress during the course of the maceration.

Place a small untreated sample of the matrix on a microscope slide; if the
material is macerated first rinse the sample with $H_2O$. Add one or two drops
of a dilute (5 to 10 percent) alkaline solution (KOH, NaOH, or $NH_4OH$);
examine residue with the microscope. If the solid organic particles start to
disperse, possibly freeing some microspores and turning the fluid dark brown,
oxidation, whether natural or produced chemically, is complete. Oxidation
of such an untreated matrix may be bypassed in favor of alkali treatment (p.
566): macerated residue should be washed free of oxidant before alkaline
solution is added.

NITRIC ACID AND NITRIC ACID COMPOUNDS. Nitric acid reagents are usually
extremely vigorous in their action. The maceration must be controlled care-

fully to avoid degradation of microfossils. Nitric acid reagents are used effectively for coals, especially high-rank coals, carbonaceous shales, and similar rocks. All nitric acid maceration should be carried out in a fume hood.

*Nitric Acid.* Nitric acid is an efficient oxidant for organic compounds. Some pollen may be attacked (Thiergart, 1940). Dybová and Jachowicz (1957) note that spores may be completely dissolved when boiled in pure nitric acid, but they regard cold nitric acid as milder in reaction than Schulze solution, and say that even for high-rank coals, the maceration results with $HNO_3$ (and sometimes an admixture of $KClO_3$) are as good as those obtained with the use of $Br_2$ plus $HNO_3$.

The maceration time varies with the concentration of the acid and with the nature of the material. Pennsylvanian coal in 10 percent $HNO_3$ may require several weeks treatment; it may be left for extended periods (over two years) without harm to the spores (Arnold, 1950). Some matrices in concentrated $HNO_3$ may require a maximum of 1 to 2 hours treatment (Willrath, 1934). High-rank coals will require more extensive treatment than soft brown coal (lignites). Willrath (*ibid.*) notes that high carbon coals may require as much as 14 days (336 hours) maceration in concentrated $HNO_3$ before they decompose.

Lignites may be processed by the following schedule (Thiergart, 1940; see also Bertsch, 1942).

*Procedure* 1. Place 10 to 20 grams of sample, broken into fragments, into a liter flask.

2. Cover with a solution of 50 ml $H_2O$ and 50 ml of 50 to 60 percent $HNO_3$.

3. Leave 24 hours, or until the lignite is partly disintegrated or easily broken with a stirring rod. Frequent optical checks are recommended.

4. When the lignite is partly disintegrated, slow the reaction by filling the flask with $H_2O$. Humic matter will still be attacked, but the microfossils will not.

5. Twenty-four hours later decant the $HNO_3$ solution and add fresh $H_2O$.

6. If necessary, strain residue to remove large organic particles.

7. Wash residue thoroughly.

8. Complete the maceration with alkaline solution (p. 566).

Coals may be treated with fuming (pure) $HNO_3$ in the manner of Zetzsche and Kälin (Dybová and Jachowicz, 1957). Fuming $HNO_3$ is less stable than concentrated $HNO_3$ and therefore more hazardous. According to Butterworth and Williams (1954), when fuming nitric acid is used it is not necessary to disperse humic matter with alkaline solution following oxidation. Dyborá and Jachowicz use alkali treatment.

*Procedure*        1. Place 1 gram of crushed coal into a 1000-ml flask or beaker.

2. Every 15 minutes, over a 3-hour period, add fuming $HNO_3$ until 100 to 150 ml have been added. Stir residue after each addition, and *cool flask in a tub with running water to avoid the possibility of explosion or combustion.*

3. Maceration is completed in 3 to 48 hours depending on reactibility of matrix. Check optically at 1-hour intervals or oftener. Stir contents frequently.

4. When maceration is complete, fill flask with $H_2O$ and allow contents to settle. Decant and repeat until solution above settled material is neutral or weakly acid.

5. Add alkali (Dybová and Jachowicz use 5 ml of 30 percent aqueous $NH_4OH$, added drop by drop).

*Schulze Solution.* Schulze solution is the most popular oxidant used for the maceration of coals and other carbonaceous sedimentary rocks. In one or another of its many modified forms it may be used as an oxidant for almost any matrix. Although both $NHO_3$ and $KClO_3$ are powerful oxidants they do not act together as a double oxidant as some workers have suggested. Rather the chloric acid ($HClO_3$) evolved in the reaction is probably the active oxidizing and decolorizing agent and probably is more powerful than either $HNO_3$ or $KClO_3$ alone (L. H. Klemm, personal communication).

Descriptions of two procedures using Schulze solution follow. The first is the standard treatment suitable for high-rank coals including anthracite; the second is a less severe treatment suitable for the oxidation of organic detritus in any matrix.

*Needed reagents:* Potassium chlorate ($KClO_3$) or sodium chlorate ($NaClO_3$),[27] concentrated (70 percent) nitric acid ($HNO_3$) or fuming (pure) $HNO_3$ (sp. gr. 1.5).

1. Standard Schulze solution is usually prepared in one of two ways: *a.* One part saturated aqueous solution $KClO_3$ and two to three parts cold concentrated (or pure) $HNO_3$. *b.* One part $KClO_3$ or $NaClO_3$ crystals and one part dry sample and two to three parts concentrated (or pure) $HNO_3$.[28] The reaction will be speeded or made more effective for less readily oxidizable substances by increasing the proportion of $HNO_3$,[29] by gently warming the

[27] Either $KClO_3$ or $NaClO_3$ may be used, since only the anion ($ClO_3^-$) is important in the reaction. It should be noted, however, that $NaClO_3$ is far more soluble than $KClO_3$. Thus a saturated aqueous solution of $NaClO_3$ is a great deal stronger than a saturated solution of $KClO_3$, and a Schulze solution with $NaClO_3$ is both more powerful and more dangerous because of the greater possibility of exceeding the critical 30 percent concentration of $HClO_3$.

[28] This is the so-called dry method of Raistrick. Although the solution is the faster reacting of the two, extreme caution should be exercised in its use since chloric acid ($HClO_3$), formed during the reaction, is unstable and explodes spontaneously at concentrations above 30 percent.

[29] For example, for macerating coal, Raistrick (1934) used the following proportions: 3 parts coal + 3 parts $KClO_3$ crystals + 20 parts concentrated $HNO_3$.

reagent, or by exposing the macerating material to direct sunlight (Thiessen, 1913). Pretreatment of some coals with solvents may also help to speed oxidation by removal of "bitumens" (p. 552).

The time needed to macerate different rocks will depend on the maturity of the organic residue and the weathering state of the rock. No specific time can be recommended. The organic residue of some lignites, shales, and carbonates is broken down with Schulze solution in less than 5 minutes (Funkhouser and Evitt, 1959). Pennsylvanian high volatile bituminous coals may need treatment for from 6 to 206 hours depending on differences in the coal beds (Kosanke, 1950). Some coals, composed predominantly of un-oxidizable substances, may be untouched after several months in Schulze solution (Thiessen, 1913).

*Procedure*     1. Place sample, disaggregated, into flask or beaker. Add $KClO_3$ or $NaClO_3$ crystals or saturated aqueous solution of $KClO_3$ or $NaClO_3$ according to selected method.

2. Add concentrated or pure $HNO_3$. If dry method is used, add acid slowly: the reaction is extremely exothermic. Cool in running $H_2O$ or in a water bath if necessary. If the reaction appears extreme it may be slowed by adding $H_2O$.

3. Wth very reactive material, samples may be checked at short intervals (5 to 15 minutes) for the progress of oxidation. Otherwise, leave 24 hours or until test with alkaline solution (p. 556) indicates that oxidation is complete.

4. Add $H_2O$ to beaker and allowed residue to settle. Decant $H_2O$ and repeat step.

5. Pour residue into 50- or 100-ml centifuge tubes. Add $H_2O$, centrifuge and decant. Wash thoroughly.

II. Dilute Schulze solution may be used on coals of low rank, or on any organic residue for which it is necessary to solubilize phenolic detritus. The following schedule has been used successfully on a wide variety of sedimentary rocks to recover pollen and spores.

The use of increasing concentrations of $HNO_3$ with increasing age of the samples is based on the assumption that the older the material, the more mature, i.e., less reactive, is the organic residue. The following are suggested concentrations of $HNO_3$ for rocks of the ages indicated. The concentration is increased or decreased appropriately for specimens of other ages:

| | |
|---|---|
| Pliocene and Miocene samples | 35 percent $HNO_3$ |
| Eocene samples | 40 percent $HNO_3$ |
| Cretaceous samples | 45 percent $HNO_3$ |

*Procedure*     1. Transfer washed sample from centrifuge tube to beaker. The water that is used to transfer the sample is also used to dilute the

$HNO_3$ to the concentration desired. Therefore, it must be measured exactly.

For example:   35 percent 100 ml $H_2O$ to 100 ml $HNO_3$
                      40 percent  75 ml $H_2O$ to 100 ml $HNO_3$
                      45 percent  56 ml $H_2O$ to 100 ml $HNO_3$

Any amount of $H_2O$ and $HNO_3$, in the proper proportions, can be used depending on the size of the sample.

2. To the sample add approximately 1 gram $KClO_3$ or $NaClO_3$. Cover the beaker loosely and allow to stand overnight or for 18 to 24 hours.

3. Transfer residue to 50-ml centrifuge tubes, add $H_2O$, centrifuge, and decant. After centrifugation, wash until the supernatant fluid is clear. Follow with alkaline solution (p. 566).

*Nitric Acid–Bromine.* $HNO_3$–$Br_2$ was introduced for digestion of high grade coals by Zetzsche and Kälin (1932). The method is described in some detail by Dijkstra (1946) and by Bhardwaj (1957). See also the article in this Handbook by Dettman (p. 699). Both $Br_2$ and $HNO_3$ are strong oxidants; oxidation is begun by the $Br_2$ and completed by the acid.

*Needed reagents:* Concentrated or pure $HNO_3$ and bromine ($Br_2$).

Bromine is a reddish-brown liquid, with an unpleasant odor. The fumes are irritating to the eyes and throat. Painful sores are produced if $Br_2$ gets on the skin.[30] The preparator should wear rubber gloves and rubber apron, and a gas mask is recommended. The digestion must be carried out in a fume hood, and a cold-water or ice bath must be available.

*Procedure*       1. Place 5 to 20 grams of coal, in small pieces or crushed fragments (2 to 5 mm), in a beaker or a wide-mouthed bottle with a stopper.

2. Add $Br_2$ (Zetzsche and Kälin used 0.5 to 1 ml per gram of coal, less for soft coal; Bhardwaj, and Dijkstra 5 to 8 ml per 15 to 20 grams of coal). Shake vigorously. (Zetzsche and Kälin immediately place beaker in ice bath.) Leave sample in $Br_2$ from 4 hours to overnight or until most of the $Br_2$ is absorbed. Release excess pressure from time to time, or use external pressure to keep the flask stopper in place if the pressure is not released.[31]

3. Allow pressure to escape and the fumes and vapors to pass off. (Bhardwaj first placed the bottle in a sink which he filled with

---

[30] When working with $Br_2$ a 5 percent $NaHSO_3$ or $Na_2SO_3$ solution and glycerin should be available for use in case of burns. Information on safe handling of $Br_2$ is provided in Chemical Safety Data Sheet SD-49, available from Manufacturing Chemists Assoc., Inc., 1625 Eye St., N. W., Washington, D.C.

[31] Since there is risk of the flask being blown up, a far less dangerous procedure would be to use a $CaCl_2$ drying tube, a common and simple chemical apparatus that will allow constant escape of the gas HBr and will prevent moisture from entering the reagent bottle.

running $H_2O$ to a depth of 6 cm. Before opening the bottle, he added ice to the $H_2O$ if its temperature was higher than 5 to 10°C.) Add fuming or concentrated $HNO_3$ (Zetzsche and Kälin and Dijkstra used 100 ml; Bhardwaj used 2 to 4 ml at the beginning and then added 15 to 25 ml every 20 to 30 minutes until liter bottle was a third full). Place bottle in ice bath or in a box with crushed ice.

4. Allow bottle to stand until all humic material is dissolved. Depending on the nature of the matrix, this will take from 1 to 8 hours. Shake the bottle occasionally to insure uniform maceration. Leave bottle in running ice water, or packed in ice during this time.

5. Decant the acid carefully or fill bottle first with $H_2O$, adding small quantities at 10-minute intervals. (Dijkstra added ice inside the bottle and then after 5 minutes filled the bottle with cold $H_2O$.) Or neutralize the residue with ammonia and then add $H_2O$ to fill the bottle.

6. Filter the residue (100-mesh silk screen—Swiss miller's gauze —is recommended) and thoroughly wash the residue on filter paper with $H_2O$. The filtrate that passed the silk screen may be examined for microspores. The residue on filter paper will contain megaspores.

7. Both residues may be given alkali treatment (p. 566).

*Nitric Acid–Chromium Trioxide.*[32] $HNO_3$ plus $CrO_3$ is said to convert organic matter into soluble humic compounds much faster than Schulze solution, oxidizing even samples for which Schulze solution is ineffective. Yields of microfossils are also said to be better than with Schulze solution.

$HNO_3$ plus $CrO_3$ solution will adequately digest most coals in 5 to 10 minutes and may take a maximum of 30 minutes on a coal that might be digested only after several weeks with Schulze solution. With unweathered shales and carbonates the removal of organic detritus may take less than one minute. The excessive speed of the HNO plus $CrO_3$ reaction may make it difficult to control with some samples.

*Needed reagents:* Concentrated $HNO_3$ and chromium trioxide ($CrO_3$). The reagent consists of concentrated $HNO_3$ saturated with $CrO_3$ (Funkhouser and Evitt, 1959).

*Nitric Acid–Hydrochloric Acid (aqua regia).* Aqua regia is used occasionally by some palynologists (Funkhouser and Evitt, 1959) and routinely by others in macerating samples (Dr. Misaburo Shimakura).[33] Soft mudstones, soft sandstones, and sandy mudstones, in 20- to 50-gram samples, are pretreated

---

[32] Chromium anhydride and "chromic acid" are synonyms for chromium trioxide, a red toxic substance with acid properties.

[33] Dr. Kankichi Sohma, Tohoku University, Sendai, Japan, kindly translated five papers by Dr. Misaburo Shimakura, Nara Gakugei University, Nara, Japan, in which this method, or some variation of it, was used to prepare samples for pollen-spore studies.

with 10 percent NaOH; carbonaceous shales are pretreated with $HNO_3$. Following $H_2O$ rinse, the sample is allowed to settle and the finer grained material is transferred to a centrifuge tube to which a mixture of HCl plus $HNO_3$ (1 to 1 or 2 to 1) is added. The mixture is warmed for about a half minute, followed by centrifugation, decantation, and several $H_2O$ rinses. The residue may be further treated with alkalies, with HF, or by acetylation.

CHLORINE AND CHLORINE COMPOUNDS. The following oxidants (chlorine in aqueous solution, oxygen acids of chlorine, and salts of the oxygen acids) differ from most of those previously discussed in that under specific conditions the reaction may involve either degradation (oxidation or delignification) or bleaching (the destruction under oxidizing conditions of coloring matter present in the organic residue or in the microspores themselves).

In general, chlorine is the reactive molecule in these reagents, in acidic media acting as a chlorinating (bleaching) agent, and in alkaline media acting as a degrading (oxidizing) agent. Thus the relative degree of chlorination or degradation of any material is largely controlled by adjusting the hydrogen-ion concentration of the solution. The two phases of the reaction are related to the fact that the pH (acidity) of the solution determines the kind and amount of molecules and ions present (the composition of the solution) and the intensity of the oxidizing activity as measured by the oxidation potential. The amount of free chlorine present as well as the time of the exposure will help determine whether degradation or chlorination will predominate in any reaction. The chlorination or bleaching phase is fast, and its velocity and extent depend on the pH of the medium. Chlorination takes place in both acid and alkali media, but the reaction is much faster in acid solution. The degradation phase is much slower than the chlorination phase although its velocity is also faster in an acidic than in an alkaline medium. If the solution is very acid (pH 2 or less), chlorine acts only as a chlorinating agent and bleaching is very rapid. Because the degradation reaction is so much slower, a prolonged exposure to chlorine is necessary. After the fast chlorination phase, degradation then takes place in acidic conditions, reaching a peak when the medium is neutral. Under alkaline conditions, chlorination is generally suppressed in favor of degradation, although the oxidation potential also decreases between pH 5 and pH 11.0.

*Chlorine–Sodium Sulfite.* The deflocculation, delignification, and chlorination of peat may be accomplished by a series of brief chlorinations alternating with treatments with hot sodium sulfite (Barghoorn and Bailey, 1940). Cross and Bevan originally used this treatment to extract cellulose from wood (Haas and Hill, 1928). If the exposure to chlorine is brief, lignin and humic compounds are removed without degradation of cellulose; oxycelluloses are formed by overexposure of cellulose to chlorine (Haas and Hill, *ibid.*). The product formed by the chlorination of the lignin is solubilized in the sodium sulfite.

*Needed reagents:* Chlorine (Cl$_2$) in a saturated water solution and a 2 to 4 percent aqueous solution of sodium sulfite (Na$_2$SO$_3$).

*Procedure*

1. Wash sample thoroughly following other treatment.
2. Cover sample with saturated chlorine water for 2 to 5 minutes.
3. Centrifuge sample and decant chlorine solution.
4. Add 2 to 4 percent aqueous solution of hot Na$_2$SO$_3$. Shake residue vigorously in the centrifuge tube.
5. Allow Na$_2$SO$_3$ to act for a few minutes, centrifuge and decant liquid.
6. Repeat steps 2 through 5 as many times as necessary. According to Barghoorn and Bailey 3 to 10 times is normal.

*Sodium Hypochlorite.* Erdtman and Erdtman (1933) boiled peat with a solution of sodium hypochlorite (NaClO). They obtained a concentration of pollen, but report that there was some destruction of pollen grains.

Hoffmeister (1960) used Clorox (a 5.25 percent solution of NaClO) in place of Schulze solution on anthracite and bituminous coals, and on carbonaceous shales and similar rocks. He believes that the solution is superior to Schulze, in that it is cheap, fast, and gentle. According to Staplin, et al. (1960), Clorox is most effective with residues containing darkened or altered spores and pollen and with some coals.

*Needed reagents:* Clorox or an approximately 5 percent aqueous solution NaClO and concentrated HCl.

*Procedure*

1. Using a Pyrex beaker add Clorox full strength to cover the rock fragments; use Clorox about one-fourth to one-half strength for less severe reaction (Staplin, et al., 1960).
2. Add a few drops of concentrated HCl until chlorine is released. Oxidation time may vary from a few hours to a few days. Fresh solution may be added if necessary.
3. Check the residue occasionally with KOH as described on p. 566, to see if the oxidation is complete.
4. When oxidation is complete, wash residue with H$_2$O, and add alkaline solution to complete the maceration (p. 566).

*Sodium Chlorite.* The sodium salts of chlorous acid will solubilize lignin, other noncarbohydrates, and humic substances with a minimum of alteration to cellulose, unless exposure is prolonged. Sodium chlorite is an effective bleaching agent, and apparently has an oxidation potential between that of hypochlorites and hydrogen peroxide, even in fairly acid solutions. Chlorite solution may be used, according to Barghoorn (1948), on peats and "incompletely coalified brown coal" or on any "consolidated organic sediment," but has little effect on coals above the lignite rank.

*Needed reagents:* Sodium chlorite (NaClO$_2$) in 2 to 5 percent aqueous solution and dilute 10 percent HCl.

*Procedure*          1. Deflocculate sediment with KOH or Na$_2$CO$_3$. Although pretreatment with KOH is not necessary, it will accelerate the reaction.
2. Break apart material and acidify with dilute HCl.
3. Add an excess of 2 to 5 percent aqueous solution of NaClO$_2$. Chlorine gas and ClO$_2$ will be released. To speed the reaction, increase acid concentration and heat. Add fresh solution if necessary.
4. When residue is light brown, it is adequately oxidized, and the reaction can be stopped by washing the residue thoroughly with H$_2$O.

*Sodium Chlorate.* A rapid chlorination to clear darkened microfossils and delignify peaty and similar matrices may be accomplished in 30 to 60 seconds (some organic residue may take longer)[34] in a centrifuge tube by the sodium chlorate method introduced by Erdtman and Erdtman (1933) and described by Erdtman (1936, 1943) and Faegri and Iversen (1950). Like chlorite solution, chlorate solution has little effect on coals above the lignite rank.

*Needed reagents:* Glacial acetic acid (CH$_3$COOH), sodium chlorate (NaClO$_3$) in 30 percent aqueous solution (NaClO or NaClO$_2$ may be substituted), and concentrated HCl or 80 percent H$_2$SO$_4$.

The oxidizing solution can be made in the following ways, although other proportions are also cited in the literature: 8 ml CH$_3$COOH plus 4.5 ml NaClO$_3$ solution [(1) NaClO$_3$ to (2) H$_2$O] plus 1 ml 80 percent H$_2$SO$_4$ (Erdtman and Erdtman, 1933); 4 ml CH$_3$COOH plus 3 to 4 drops NaClO$_3$ solution plus 1 ml concentrated HCl (Erdtman, 1936); 4 ml CH$_3$COOH plus 5 to 6 drops NaClO$_3$ (30 percent aqueous solution) plus 1 ml concentrated HCl (Faegri and Iversen, 1950). The organic residue should be rinsed thoroughly with H$_2$O following the oxidation.

*Perchloric–Periodic Acids.* Wet oxidation by perchloric and periodic acids is reported to be much faster than by Schulze solution (Spielholtz, et al., 1962). The organic matter of coals and carbonaceous shales is said to be completely oxidized in 20 minutes, and the reaction can be stopped at any time by cooling the mixture or diluting it with water.

*Needed reagents:* Perchloric acid (HClO$_4$), periodic acid (para, H$_5$IO$_6$), and vanadium pentoxide (V$_2$O$_5$) or ammonium vanadate (NH$_4$VO$_3$) as catalyst. The oxidizing solution consists of 15 ml of 50 percent HClO$_4$,[35] 1.5 grams of para, H$_5$IO$_6$, and 1 or 2 milligrams of catalyst to 1 gram of crushed sample.

*Apparatus:* A 250-ml conical Pyrex flask with thermometer-well (Pyrex test tube) for 250°C thermometer and a water-cooled reflux condenser. (For details on reagents and apparatus see Spielholtz, et al., 1962).

---

[34] Originally, Erdtman and Erdtman (1933) left material in the NaClO$_3$ bleach for 12 hours at room temperature.

[35] Concentrations greater than 50 percent are to be avoided or some spores will be destroyed. 50 percent HClO$_4$ is obtained by diluting 10.0 ml vacuum distilled 70 percent acid with 5 ml H$_2$O.

*Procedure*     1. Place crushed coal in flask. Add oxidizing solution.

2. Insert condenser and thermometer. Heat mixture on a hot plate until a constant temperature is attained (10 to 20 minutes) and the acid is refluxing on the walls of the flask.

3. Cool mixture, dilute to 50 ml with $H_2O$, and neutralize solution with 10 percent NaOH until it turns dark brown.

4. Transfer to centrifuge tubes, centrifuge, and decant liquid. Wash residue thoroughly with $H_2O$.

HYDROGEN PEROXIDE. Commercial $H_2O_2$ is an aqueous solution, generally available in 3 to 50 percent concentrations; a stabilizer is usually added to decrease its rate of decomposition to $H_2O$ and $O_2$. Concentrations of 10 to 30 percent are most commonly used in palynology.

$H_2O_2$ is a bleach and a very strong oxidant that spontaneously oxidizes organic matter. It is sometimes used to prepare peats, lignites, and high-grade coals, although the method is somewhat dangerous for pollen and spores (Sittler, 1955). To prevent destruction of spores, A. H. V. Smith cautions specifically against vigorous boiling of samples in $H_2O_2$.

In discussing the $H_2O_2$ method, Sittler (1955) states that the maturity of the material ("le degré de fossilisation") determines the duration of the oxidation (5 to 45 minutes) and the concentration of the reagent (5 to 15 percent). He says that boiling certain residues for 10 minutes in a very dilute solution gives good results. The residue should be sieved, centrifuged, and washed with $H_2O$ before solubilizing the oxidized humic compounds.

Funkhouser and Evitt (1959) use 15 to 30 percent $H_2O_2$ alone or as a 1 to 1 solution with 5 percent KOH. Staplin, et al. (1960) mention use of a 1 to 1 solution of 10 percent $H_2O_2$ and 5 percent KOH as a bleach for material pretreated with Schulze solution; they caution that the reaction must be carefully watched in order to avoid overmaceration of the microfossils.

Kosanke (1962) reports that $H_2O_2$ preparation of coal samples in the 88 to 90 percent carbon range provided excellent results, comparable to, or better than, results from replicate samples processed by Schulze solution. The 90 percent carbon coal prepared with $H_2O_2$ had the best quality spores and the largest number of species. A. H. V. Smith (personal communication, 1963) prepared this coal sample by the following method:

1. Add about 50 ml of 100 volume $H_2O_2$[36] to 0.5 gram powdered coal (less than 0.4 mm) in a 100-ml beaker.

2. Boil very gently on a hot plate for several hours. *Do not boil vigorously, or the spores will be destroyed.*

3. Replenish the $H_2O_2$ from time to time to keep the volume of liquid constant.

[36] Smith writes that they do not often use the $H_2O_2$ method at the National Coal Board (Great Britain) and that they have not tried other strengths of $H_2O_2$. 100 volume $H_2O_2$ is approximately 30 percent $H_2O_2$. Volume notation refers to the number of volumes of free oxygen STP that can be obtained from a unit volume of aqueous solution $H_2O_2$.

The time of treatment varies with different coals—most take about 5 hours (high-carbon-content coals may take 10 hours according to Kosanke's report, 1962).

4. The color change of the $H_2O_2$ helps to indicate when the reaction is complete. The liquid first becomes black, then yellowish brown, and finally, colorless.

5. Test the residue from the pale brown stage onwards (p. 556). Stop the reaction when the spores are clean. The final solution is often cloudy but this can be corrected by adding a small quantity of concentrated hydrochloric acid (HCl). The HCl appears to dissolve some of the fine translucent debris.[37]

6. Alkaline solution is not required to solubilize the oxidation compounds.

**Oxidized Humic Compounds.** Oxidized humic compounds[38] are solubilized and dispersed by $H_2O$, by alkaline solutions, or by organic solvents such as alcohol and acetone. The usefulness of alkalies as compared with the organic solvents depends on the sample and on the degree of maceration.

Hydroxide solutions are the conventional postoxidation treatment, but they are often too vigorous and even when very dilute, may destroy microfossils especially in overmacerated residues. With some residues a weak alkali, such as $K_2CO_3$, may be preferable to a strong one. For example, in comparing the effects of a 30-minute treatment with 5 percent solutions of KOH, $NH_4OH$, and $K_2CO_3$ on an 84 percent carbon coal, slightly overmacerated, A. H. V. Smith found that $K_2CO_3$ and $NH_4OH$ caused less damage to spore exines than KOH (Kosanke, 1962). Staplin, et al. (1960) say that $K_2CO_3$ is gentler and less likely to corrode fossils than hydroxide solutions, in addition to the facts that the separation of fossils is more rapid and more complete and that the residues wash clean more rapidly. Tschudy (1958) found an 80 percent acetone-water solution preferable to a 2 to 10 percent NaOH solution for some coals. The alkaline solution destroyed the microfossils; the acetone mixture did not.

HYDROXIDES. Of the hydroxides commonly used to dissolve and disperse oxidized humic matter, KOH and NaOH are more potent than $NH_4OH$. All hydroxide solutions will be more penetrant but also more violent in their reactions, if they are made with alcohol rather than water, and if they are heated, rather than used cold (Thiessen, 1913). Thiessen used 70 to 85 percent alcohol on macerated coal before alkali treatment, not for its solvent power, but to withdraw from the coal the water, which "has the tendency to precipitate the substances already in solution." As the coal is studied, macerated fragments are placed in a watch glass with the alcohol and alkali is added to the desired strength.

Aqueous 5 to 10 percent hydroxide solutions are commonly used, although for some residues 1 to 2 percent solutions may be preferable to avoid corrosion of microfossils. A. H. V. Smith (Kosanke, 1962) actually found little

---

[37] Or perhaps it acts as an electrolyte and flocculates some of the fine debris.

[38] Carbon oxidation products may include colloidal "humic acid," carbonic anhydride, oxalic, benzene-carboxylic, acetic, succinic acids, etc. (Bone, et al., 1935).

difference between the effects of 5 percent and 10 percent KOH on spore exines, even after 16 hours of soaking.[39]

If oxidation has been carried far enough, alkaline solutions added to the washed residue will turn dark brown from the solubilizing and dispersal of humic material. The duration of the alkali treatment will vary with the residue: some samples may require short treatment (one to a few minutes); others may require treatment up to 12 hours or more. The completion of the reaction can best be determined by frequent optical checks of small samples of the residue to see if abundant pollen and spores are being freed cleanly from the matrix.

Following the treatment, the sample must be thoroughly washed to remove all traces of alkali and until the supernatant liquid is clear. As the solution is usually rather viscous following alkali treatment, it may be well to dilute the residue at the first centrifugation.

ALKALI CARBONATES. Staplin, et al. (1960) and Wagoner, et al. (1961) use a 5 percent aqueous solution of $K_2CO_3$ to disperse the oxidized humic material of some residues in place of stronger alkalies or organic solvents. $K_2CO_3$ may also be applied directly to well-weathered matrices that do not need oxidation. Other alkali carbonates, such as sodium carbonate ($Na_2CO_3$) and lithium carbonate ($Li_2CO_3$), though untested, should be equally effective.

According to Wagoner, et al. (*ibid.*), Schulze solution and $K_2CO_3$ react with excessive effervescence; the former reagent should therefore be washed from the residue before the carbonate solution is added. Wagoner, et al. (*ibid.*) allow the residue to stand with $K_2CO_3$ for 30 minutes, with a 5-minute treatment in the ultrasonic generator tank during this time to rid the fossils of clinging organic detritus.

ORGANIC SOLVENTS. Acetone and alcohol in the method of von Gümbel (Thiessen, 1913) are both less powerful dispersers of oxidized organic matter than alkaline solutions, but they may prove of some value with samples for which less action is preferable. Little material will be solubilized with either reagent, however, if oxidation is insufficient.

## NONCHEMICAL SEPARATION METHODS

### General

There are a number of relatively simple fractionation methods that may be used to free microfossil preparations of inorganic particles and of extraneous organic detritus. Similar methods have long been used by micropaleontologists (Hanna, 1927) and by sedimentary petrologists (Krumbein and Pettijohn, 1938).

---

[39] The exines were swollen but probably as a result of maceration damage rather than because of the strength of the KOH solution.

Some of these techniques are used to concentrate organic material before extensive chemical treatment, thereby reducing the size of the sample to be worked and eliminating some elaborate steps of the chemical treatment. Others are customarily used following chemical extraction to remove resistant mineral grains and residual organic detritus.

Nearly all of the separation methods described (Density-Separation Methods) depend upon differential settling velocities of mineral grains and organic particles, primarily determined by their densities (specific gravities). They are intended to float off the pollen, spores, and other microfossils, leaving heavier material, both mineral and organic, behind as a residue. Some also are effective for separating microfossils that are similar in density, but which differ in size and shape, and for eliminating finely divided organic detritus from fossiliferous residues. Density-separation methods are least successful if organic and inorganic particles intergrade in size and density, since there is then always a possibility of losing a certain fraction of the organic residue or of being unable to rid the organic residue of a certain fraction of the inorganic material.

The separation of pollen and spores from most of the unwanted inorganic components of the matrix is relatively easy, since the density of the microfossils is much less than that of most of the common minerals. Funkhouser and Evitt (1959) give the figures 1.3 to 1.7 as the density of organic particles, including microfossils, but according to Wenner (1947—as based on data from Pohl, 1937), the density of pollen and spores is "hardly more than 1.5, and often not half so much, in the case of our common tree pollens." On the other hand, essentially all of the common minerals encountered in pollen-bearing residues have densities of 2 to 3, for example, gypsum, 2.3; glauconite, 2.3; feldspar, 2.55 to 2.75; quartz, 2.6 to 2.66; calcite, 2.71 to 2.72; biotite, 2.7 to 3.1; dolomite, 2.8 to 2.9. Colloidal clay particles, as well as finely divided organic material that is similar in size and density to the smallest microfossils, may, however, be difficult to separate from pollen and spore preparations.

Most gravitational fractionation methods are relatively inexpensive and simple, requiring a minimum of equipment but often considerable patience. Two instruments, the Vibraflute (Tschudy, 1960) and the Vibroséparater (Dumait, 1962) have been designed to aid in fractionation of fine organic and inorganic debris in pollen-bearing residues. The latter combines vibration with heavy-liquid flotation in separating pollen from clastic sediments.

Heavy-liquid flotation is probably the most widely used of the fractionation methods. The separation of organic and inorganic debris made possible by heavy liquids is perhaps more gross than that possible through some of the alternative methods, but flotation has the advantage of being less time-consuming, and therefore, in the long run, probably the most satisfactory of the methods.

### Density-Separation Methods

SETTLING OR DECANTATION

Faegri and Iversen (1950) recommend removing coarse heavy-mineral particles from sediment samples by a simple "repeated decanting" of the residue in aqueous suspension. The success of the method depends on the differential settling rates of the heavy (inorganic) and light (organic) particles. The method also may be effective in eliminating both the coarse and the very finely divided fractions of organic detritus from some samples.

The sample is stirred well with water in a beaker, and a dispersing agent may be added to prevent flocculation. The time allowed for settling may be a few seconds to a few minutes, depending on the sample. The coarser, or heavier particles, both mineral and organic, will settle to the bottom of the container first, and the supernatant liquid with pollen and spores in suspension may then be poured into a second container. The settling and decanting process may be repeated any number of times, appropriately increasing both the time and the length of the column of water, as the remaining heavier or coarser particles approach the microfossils in size and density. The residue to be discarded must be centrifuged and examined microscopically each time the process is repeated to assure that microfossils are not discarded. When the microfossils settle to the bottom of the container, the process should be stopped.

As a further refinement, it seems probable that the settling technique could be made more effective for palynological purposes by determining the settling velocities of the microfossils. By basing the calculation on the settling time of the largest or heaviest pollen grains, spores or other microfossils in the sample, it should be possible to withdraw them and all smaller or lighter grains by pipette, while they are still in suspension, and to leave behind for disposal all larger or heavier particles, which will have settled.

The settling velocities of pollen grains can be determined by Stokes' Law (for derivation of Stokes' Law see Krumbein and Pettijohn, 1938, p. 95–96):

$$v = \frac{2(d_1 - d_2)gr^2}{9\eta}$$

$d_1$ = density of sphere (grain)
$d_2$ = density of fluid (usually water)
$v$ = velocity of sphere in cm/sec
$g$ = acceleration in cm/sec/sec (in Stokes' Law acceleration due to gravity—980 cm/sec/sec)
$r$ = radius of sphere (grain) in cm
$\eta$ = viscosity of the fluid (usually water) in poises

Before the suspended sample is stirred into water in a beaker, the time for the largest microfossils to settle through a certain distance is calculated from a known value of $v$ using the relation $t = (h/v)$ (where $t$ is the time in seconds, and $h$ is the height of the column of water in cm). When that time is reached, all larger and heavier particles will have settled out, and the suspended particles and supernatant fluid may be pipetted, without removing any of the matter on the bottom.

PANNING

The success of panning, as used in recovering pollen and spores, depends on differences in size, shape, and density of the mineral particles and the organic materials.

Faegri and Iversen (1950), who use a beaker for panning, suggest that the sample first be boiled with water to bring it into suspension. The beaker is then rotated by hand; the speed is best determined by the action of the individual sample. The heavy inorganic particles will collect in the middle of the beaker, at the bottom, and the liquid with the suspended organic fraction may be poured off. The process may be repeated varying the speed of the rotation and the time depending on the separation desired. As in the settling method, the heavier residue must be continually examined microscopically in order to determine the effectiveness of the treatment and the point at which it should be stopped.

Panning techniques used by sedimentary petrologists (Krumbein and Pettijohn, 1938) are similar to the method of panning gold. Most sedimentary petrologists use a shallow circular pan with flaring rim, and this gave Funkhouser and Evitt (1959) the idea of using a watch glass for the concentration of pollen and spores. They say that panning is more time-consuming than use of heavy liquids but that it is also more sensitive than flotation for samples rich in organic material, since it will cleanly separate particles of similar densities that differ in size and shape. Thus, they were able to divide samples into four separate residues: (1) pollen, spores, hystrichosphaerids, dinoflagellates; (2) coccoliths; (3) microforaminifera; (4) plant-tissue fragments, miscellaneous organic debris. Since the panning separation is affected by (1) diameter of watch glass, (2) volume of water suspension, (3) settling time before beginning of swirling motion, (4) speed of swirling movement, (5) amplitude of movement, and (6) position of pipette orifice, some experimentation is worthwhile with each sample when applying this technique. Some skill, moreover, is necessary for the method to be most effective: the results of the method, as practiced at the Paleoecology Laboratory, do not approach those claimed for it by Funkhouser and Evitt. Although we have been able to separate out fairly cleanly pollen grains of differing sizes, together with organic debris of the same general size range, we have had little success, with most samples, in separating all microspores from all plant fragments and organic debris. We find that controlled centrifugation and simple settling often are more successful in cleaning samples of organic detritus.

*Procedure*        1. Put 7 to 10 ml of well-mixed aqueous suspension of the residue in a smooth 3-inch watch glass. A dispersing agent should be
added to prevent flocculation and may be followed by treatment in
the ultrasonic generator (p. 534). Place watch glass on hard,
smooth, flat surface and allow particles to settle partly.

2. Rest heel of hand on surface and grasp watch glass between
thumb and fingers. Keep bottom of glass on surface, and keep rim
of glass level. Move glass smoothly in circles with amplitude of 2
to 4 mm. Avoid surface turbulence and side-to-side motion of liquid.
In general the heaviest particles will segregate in the center of the
glass, and the lightest and smallest particles will be kept in suspension.

3. Portions of the residue may be removed from the watch glass
with a pipette at the moment motion is stopped. These portions may
be placed in other glasses and the process repeated for further
separation.

## CONTROLLED CENTRIFUGATION

Centrifugation is a normal part of preparing samples for examination of
microfossils. The time necessary to centrifuge any sample will depend on
the viscosity of the suspending liquid, the size and density of the microfossils, the
size of the centrifuge tube, and the speed at which the centrifuge is run. The
effect of centrifugation is to increase the value of $g$ (acceleration) in the
equation for Stokes' Law (p. 569).

In normal centrifugation all material in liquid suspension is compacted at
the bottom of the centrifuge tube. In controlled centrifugation, a simple and
very effective means is provided for removing some organic and inorganic
debris from fossiliferous samples. The object is to vary the time or the rate
of rotation (rpm) and thus to control the nature of the material that is kept
in suspension in order that it may be decanted or pipetted from the sample.

The "short-time centrifugation" (which does not throw all particles to the
bottom of the tube) may be used for differential removal of finely divided
organic debris which remains in suspension longer than the microfossils, as
well as for removal of coarse, heavy debris which settles more quickly than
the microfossils. The method is generally ineffective when microfossils and
debris are approximately the same size and density. Funkhouser and Evitt
(1959) practice the short-time controlled centrifugation by centrifuging
polleniferous samples in water suspension at 1500 rpm for 45 seconds and
immediately decanting the supernatant liquid when the centrifuge stops. The
suggested rate is, of course, applicable only if the centrifuge used has arms of
the same radius as those of the machine used by Funkhouser and Evitt. This
is because the value of $g$ (acceleration) is governed by the number of rota-
tions per minute (the rpm) and by the radius of the centrifuge arms. Thus
comparisons of rates of rotation (rpm) are significant only if the radius of
the centrifuge arms is constant.

The material in suspension which is decanted should be saved, compacted by centrifugation, and examined for possible loss of large numbers of microspores, or for differential removal of microspores of small size. Controlled centrifugation may be repeated until the supernatant liquid is clear. By decreasing the time, but leaving the rpm constant, it is possible to remove finely divided detritus until too much pollen remains in the decanted liquid.

Brown (1960) practices controlled centrifugation by successively decreasing the rpm of the centrifuge. He suggests five centrifugations of one minute each at about 2000, 1750, 1500, 1250 and 1000 rpm. The supernatant liquid is removed each time, and the compacted residue at the bottom of the centrifuge tube is resuspended, until all finely divided organic material is removed. Of course, if no pollen is being lost at 1000 rpm, the preliminary centrifugations at higher speeds are unnecessary except as a safeguard.

To bring down only large heavy particles of organic or inorganic detritus one may decrease the duration of centrifugation very sharply, or run the centrifuge at very low rpm. Microfossils, having been kept in suspension, are then removed with the supernatant liquid.

The most effective speeds and times to achieve optimal results by controlled centrifugation with a particular centrifuge can be determined best by experimentation with different samples. It is not necessary to know the rpm in order for controlled centrifugation to be successful. It is only necessary to experiment with a few samples and record the position of the centrifuge control-dial setting found most effective.

### FLOTATION

The method of flotation involves the specific-gravity separation of the organic fraction of the sediment from the inorganic fraction by use of the so-called heavy liquids of high specific gravity. Heavy liquids are organic liquids, such as bromoform; solutions of inorganic salts, such as $ZnCl_2$; or molten inorganic salts, such as thallous mercurous nitrate. The method of flotation and most of the heavy liquids in use were introduced by mineralogists and petrographers and a wide literature exists on the subject (see Krumbein and Pettijohn, 1938; Sullivan, 1927, and references given by them).

To separate pollen and spores from the sedimentary matrix, flotation depends on the fact that the densities of the microfossils are less than those of many of the common minerals. The heavy liquids in use in palynology are those that are readily diluted to, or already have, specific gravities of approximately 1.5 to 2.5. Those most commonly used have a specific gravity of about 2.0. The specific gravity of any liquid may be determined with a pycnometer or a heavy-liquid hydrometer or by floating on the surface of the liquid a mineral of known specific gravity (a pure calcite fragment is commonly used for this purpose).

Heavy-liquid flotation may be used to concentrate the organic fraction of samples that have had little or no prior chemical treatment, but as used by most pollen workers, flotation usually follows full chemical treatment and is the final or one of the final steps in achieving a clean sample.

In essence, the flotation method consists of introducing the disaggregated and dispersed or the chemically macerated sample into an excess of the heavy liquid, shaking the mixture well, and allowing the organic particles, including pollen and spores, to float to the top of the liquid, while the heavy mineral particles settle to the bottom of the liquid. With pollen-spore work, the organic and inorganic particles involved are so fine that separation under gravity is slow, and often incomplete. Therefore, it is almost always necessary to use a centrifuge to separate light and heavy fractions in a reasonable length of time although some palynologists allow suitable samples to separate under normal effects of gravity (Staplin, et al., 1960). Thus flotation is usually carried out in a centrifuge tube, whose size depends on the amount of material involved in the separation.

If glass tubes are used in the centrifugation, low speeds are advisable, because even Pyrex tubes are likely to break from the pressure of the heavy liquid combined with high centrifugal force. If the centrifugation is a long one (30 to 45 minutes) and a very volatile diluent is used, it is best to stopper the tubes to prevent a change in the density of the flotation liquid. In centrifuging with heavy liquid, it is, of course, very important to make certain that the centrifuge is balanced.[40]

Many heavy liquids are available for mineralogical work, and some of these have been used or could be used in pollen-spore work. Most heavy liquids, however, have one or more undesirable characteristics. Almost all of them are toxic to some degree, either on contact or from inhalation of fumes. As normally used in pollen laboratories, however, several of the more common heavy liquids may be considered relatively safe. In general, a good heavy liquid will be (1) inexpensive, (2) noncorrosive, (3) chemically inert, (4) liquid at ordinary temperatures, (5) transparent or colorless, (6) easily diluted or miscible, and (7) readily available or easily made.

Some heavy liquids that have been used for pollen-spore work include carbon tetrachloride plus benzene, sp. gr. 1.25 to 1.27 (Bertsch, 1942); carbon tetrachloride, sp. gr. 1.58 (Sittler, 1955); sulfuric acid, sp. gr. 1.84 (Wenner, 1947; Faegri and Iversen, 1950); ethyl iodide, sp. gr. 1.94 (Wenner, 1947); an aqueous solution of stannic chloride (Urban, 1961; Davis, 1961);[41] an aqueous solution of potassium mercuric iodide and a variant

---

[40] With centrifugation, all the accessories and the tube loads should be balanced in pairs to reduce vibration and to put minimum strain on the bearings of the centrifuge. Balancing should be done by weighing the opposite specimen loads on a balance and equalizing their weights. Most accessories have been weighed in the factory and stamped with their weights; it is important to make certain that those on opposite sides have the same weight.

[41] In comparison with $ZnCl_2$ solution, stannic chloride is said to give better separation of microfossils, to be less reactive with fossils, to be much less viscous and much easier to remove from the light, organic fraction. Anhydrous stannic chloride ($SnCl_4$) is a

potassium cadmium iodide (p. 575); bromoform (tribromomethane, p. 575); acetylene tetrabromide (tetrabromoethane, p. 576); and aqueous solutions of zinc chloride and zinc bromide (p. 577).

Mineral-oil flotation, using Nujol and white, light U.S.P. paraffin oil, has been proposed by Ledingham and Chinn (1955) and by Kurtz and Turner (1957) for recovering spores and pollen from raw-soil samples. Kurtz and Turner report 90 percent recovery of specimens and a concentration of pollen per unit volume of residue as much as 100 times that of samples prepared by standard HF methods. However, success of the method depends on complete removal of all the oil. In evaluation of the paraffin-oil method, Brown (1960) reports that it is time-consuming and that the oil is difficult to filter and difficult to remove from the glassware. One of my colleagues, L. R. Kittleman, who has attempted paraffin-oil flotation, reports that it is extremely messy and time-consuming.

Descriptions of the use of five heavy liquids commonly mentioned in pollen literature follow: in general, the procedures outlined apply to the use of any heavy liquid.

**Potassium Mercuric Iodide Solution**[42] (Sonstadt's Solution, Thoulet's Solution, $HgI_2 \cdot 2KI$, sp. gr. 3.2). As described by Sonstadt (1874), his solution consists of a saturated solution of pure KI into which is stirred as much pure $HgI_2$ as will dissolve at room temperature. Alternate additions of KI and $HgI_2$ are then possible, but both iodides dissolve slowly. Since it is best not to apply heat to accelerate the process, considerable time is necessary to make a liquid of specific gravity 3 or higher. Lower specific gravities are attained through the addition of $H_2O$. The solution must be filtered before use; it may be reconcentrated, by evaporation with heat, without harm to it.

Goldschmidt (1881) gave the following proportions for a solution of $HgI_2 \cdot 2KI$ of specific gravity 3.196: 305 grams $HgI_2$ plus 246 grams KI plus 70 grams $H_2O$. The amount of $H_2O$ added is less important than the proportion of $HgI_2$ to KI, which optimally is 1 to 1.239. According to Sullivan (1927) a "small excess of KI is permissible, but an excess of $HgI_2$ causes a precipitation due to hydrolysis when water is added."

$HgI_2 \cdot 2KI$ solution may be used as a heavy liquid in the same manner as bromoform (p. 575). An excess of the liquid is added to the residue in a centrifuge tube, mixed thoroughly, and centrifuged until a clear separation is

liquid with specific gravity 2.23; crystalline forms of hydrous stannic chloride are also available.

[42] The use of $HgI_2 \cdot 2KI$ solution for flotation was first proposed by Sonstadt (1874), but its use by Thoulet in 1878 was publicized by Goldschmidt (1881) and the liquid has become widely known as "Thoulet's Solution." $HgI_2 \cdot 2KI$ is included here primarily because mention of the solution of this salt as Thoulet's solution is frequent in the pollen literature. The availability of several other equally suitable and safer heavy liquids suggests, however, that its use has been almost entirely superseded in palynology. The high maximum specific gravity, which makes $HgI_2 \cdot 2KI$ still of some value to the petrographer, is of no particular value to the palynologist.

obtained. The organic fraction, including pollen, floating at the top of the solution is decanted into another centrifuge tube, diluted with $H_2O$ to reduce the specific gravity of the float liquid, centrifuged down, and thoroughly washed with $H_2O$.

$HgI_2 \cdot 2KI$ has several disadvantages including the fact that it is very poisonous. It is viscous in solution, and it is expensive (Krumbein and Pettijohn, 1938; Brown, 1960), and Brown (*ibid.*) says that there is some evidence that the solution is corrosive to organic matter.

**Potassium Cadmium Iodide Solution** ($CdI_2 \cdot 2KI$, sp. gr. 2.5). This solution has been proposed as a substitute for $HgI_2 \cdot 2KI$.[43]

A solution with maximum specific gravity is made with the following proportions: 332 grams KI plus 366 grams $CdI_2$ plus enough $H_2O$ make a saturated solution. Lower specific gravities are attained by adding more $H_2O$. Before using this solution, the sample is macerated in the usual way and washed. A few drops of hydriodic acid (HI, approximately 9 percent) are added to acidify the residue, the centrifuge tube is filled with $H_2O$, the sample is centrifuged, and the $H_2O$ wash is repeated. The sample is then brought into suspension with the separating liquid and centrifuged (p. 577). The lighter, separated fraction of the suspension is poured into another centrifuge tube, $H_2O$ is added to dilute, and this portion is centrifuged. The liquid, including the diluted portion, may be collected, filtered, and evaporated for reuse. Before evaporation it should be neutralized with KOH.

According to Hallik (1957), a solution with specific gravity 2.0 gave the best pollen-spore preparations, even though a few pollen grains were lost in the residue. He suggests that the use of HF is best for a thorough investigation but believes that the $CdI_2 \cdot 2KI$ method gives good results for a rapid check. Brown (1960) obtained excellent results in pollen-spore separations using this liquid, which he says is noncorrosive to skin and plant tissue, and nonvolatile at ordinary temperatures. Cadmium compounds, like those of mercury, are, however, highly toxic.

**Bromoform** (Tribromomethane, $CHBr_3$, sp. gr. 2.87 at 20°C, chemically pure). Bromoform was first used by van der Kolk in 1895 for mineralogical purposes (Sullivan, 1927). It is an organic liquid which changes specific gravity with temperature (Sullivan, *ibid.*, fig. 5).

Bromoform is miscible in all proportions with carbon tetrachloride ($CCl_4$, sp. gr. 1.58), benzene (benzol, $C_6H_6$, sp. gr. 0.9), alcohol ($C_2H_2OH$, sp. gr. 0.8), and acetone ($CH_3COCH_3$, sp. gr. 0.8). These solvents vary in specific gravity, and the proportion in which they are used with bromoform will determine the specific gravity of the separating liquid.[44] When bromoform is

---

[43] The use of $CdI_2 \cdot 2KI$ solution as a flotation liquid was first proposed in a paper by Dorogenewskaja, Schenfinkel, and Gritschunk (1952) in Russian. Information given here is from a German abstract of the Russian paper prepared by Hallik (1957).

[44] Sullivan (*ibid.*, fig. 3, table 2) provides a curve and a table showing the specific

diluted with highly volatile reagents such as acetone or alcohol, only a fresh mixture should be used to assure that the heavy liquid has the specific gravity desired.

Bromoform has some objectionable features: (1) it is decomposed by strong light, (2) it deteriorates with heat, (3) it evaporates rapidly, (4) it is fairly expensive, and (5) it is toxic (Krumbein and Pettijohn, 1938).

Bromoform may be recovered for reuse,[45] if desired, by washing, by fractional distillation, by fractional crystallization, or by other methods (Krumbein and Pettijohn, 1938, and references given by them).

**Acetylene Tetrabromide** (Tetrabromoethane, $C_2H_2Br_4$, sp. gr. 2.96 at 20°C, chemically pure). Acetylene tetrabromide was first used by Muthmann in 1899 (Sullivan, 1927). It is an organic liquid that is similar to bromoform and that changes specific gravity with temperature (Sullivan, *ibid.*, fig. 5).

Acetylene tetrabromide is miscible in all proportions with carbon tetrachloride, benzene, or absolute alcohol (ethanol). Sullivan (*ibid.*, fig. 4, table 3) gives the specific gravity of mixtures of $C_2H_2Br_4$ and various proportions of $CCl_4$.

Acetylene tetrabromide can be recovered by fractional distillation, by evaporation, or by washing with $H_2O$, if alcohol is used as the diluent (see Krumbein and Pettijohn, 1938).

*Procedure for Fractionation with Bromoform or Acetylene Tetrabromide*

      The following is a general procedure for separating pollen and spores by means of heavy liquids and the centrifuge. Bromoform-acetone is used as an example although the method is equally applicable with acetylene tetrabromide-acetone and with mixtures of any other heavy liquid and its diluent.

      1. Pretreat sample (disaggregation and dispersal, HCl and HF and/or full chemical extraction).

      2. Wash sample thoroughly, centrifuging and decanting $H_2O$ several times.

      3. Rinse sample in acetone (or other diluting reagent) until all $H_2O$ is removed, centrifuging and decanting between each rinse.

      4. Mix bromoform and acetone (or other combination of heavy liquid and diluent) to specific gravity of approximately 2.0 to 2.3.[46]

---

gravity of mixtures of $CHBr_3$ and various proportions of $CCl_4$. Krumbein and Pettijohn (1938, fig. 148 and p. 324) provide a curve and a table for the specific gravity of mixtures of $CHBr_3$ and various proportions of acetone.

[45] Recovery from acetone and alcohol may be made simply by washing with $H_2O$; recovery from $CCl_4$, however, must be made by fractional distillation.

[46] A mixture of two parts of bromoform (or acetylene tetrabromide) to one part of acetone is usually satisfactory. A mixture of 75 percent bromoform and 25 percent acetone by volume will have a specific gravity of 2.3 at 20°C; 70 percent bromoform and 30 percent acetone by volume a specific gravity of 2.2; 65 percent bromoform and 35 percent acetone a specific gravity of 2.1. A bromoform-alcohol mixture of 43 percent alcohol and 57 percent bromoform by volume will have a specific gravity of 2.0. Because mixtures of alcohol or acetone and bromoform change in specific gravity very rapidly

The amount of flotation mixture necessary will depend on the size of the centrifuge tube being used (i.e., 15 or 50 ml) and on the amount of the sediment sample to be separated. Usually several volumes of heavy liquid to one volume of residual sediment is necessary to give a clean separation, for example, 5 to 10 ml of liquid to 1 gram of residue. If the flotation follows chemical treatment, the amount of the remaining residue is usually small and it is advisable to use 15-ml tubes for the separation.

Add the heavy-liquid mixture to the organic residue; stir and shake the suspension vigorously to disperse the sample in the liquid.

5. If flotation precedes chemical treatment, the organic fraction will probably float after a few minutes; centrifugation is usually necessary, however, especially if the flotation follows other treatment and the organic and inorganic particles of the residue are very finely divided. The centrifugation time must be adjusted according to the rpm (1500 rpm for 15 minutes is usually satisfactory for most samples, but less time can be used with greater speeds).[47] Allow the centrifuge to stop naturally: do not use a brake. The layers of heavy inorganic material at the bottom of the centrifuge tube and the upper layers of organic material must be well separated by clear liquid.

6. Decant the supernatant liquid with its floating organic fraction into a clean centrifuge tube that has been rinsed with acetone (or other diluting liquid).[48] The denser, predominantly inorganic, fraction may be discarded or it may be refloated if there is reason to believe that the separation was not as clean as possible.

7. Wash the organic residue thoroughly with acetone (or other diluting liquid), shake vigorously, centrifuge, and decant. The sample must be washed until all the bromoform has been removed.

8. If it is necessary to proceed with chemical treatment, the sample may be suspended in $H_2O$ before other treatment.

**Zinc Chloride (Zinc Bromide) Solution** ($ZnCl_2$, sp. gr. 1.96; $ZnBr_2$, sp. gr., see text). The use of solutions of $ZnCl_2$ or $ZnBr_2$ for flotation of the organic fractions of sediment samples apparently was proposed by Dorogenewskaja, Schenfinkel, and Gritschunk in 1952 (Brown, 1960). Both solutions appear to be in rather wide use by palynologists at the present time; both require the same steps in processing. However, according to Staplin, et al. (1960), $ZnBr_2$ has the following advantages over $ZnCl_2$: (1) its lower viscosity allows more rapid and more clear-cut fractionation of organic and inorganic materials and (2) the solution seems more stable.

---

owing to evaporation of the solvent, it is best to seal the centrifuge tubes during centrifugation.

[47] In some cases, it may be necessary to tailor both the specific gravity of the liquid and the duration of the centrifugation to the sample to achieve optimal results.

[48] A bottle should be kept available for collecting used bromoform if the liquid is to be reclaimed. It is desirable to filter the used bromoform as it is run into the bottle. The diluted bromoform recovered when the organic fraction is centrifuged may also be saved.

Funkhouser and Evitt (1959) use a saturated aqueous solution of $ZnCl_2$ of specific gravity 1.96. Staplin, et al. (1960) dissolve the $ZnBr_2$ crystals in 10 percent HCl until the saturation point is reached. Then they adjust the specific gravity of the solution to about 2.0 by adding $H_2O$. The maximum attainable specific gravity of the $ZnBr_2$ solution is not specified. Acidifying the solution prevents the precipitation of $Zn(OH)_2$ when the solution is added to the organic residue. It is also necessary to acidify the residue with 10 percent HCl before adding $ZnCl_2$ or $ZnBr_2$ solution and again after the flotation and before the first $H_2O$ rinse to prevent the precipitation of $Zn(OH)_2$. Because the reaction that takes place when $ZnCl_2$ and $ZnBr_2$ crystals dissolve is exothermic, Pyrex glassware should be used in preparing the solutions.

The $ZnCl_2$ and $ZnBr_2$ solutions have several advantages over many of the heavy liquids now in use. They are easy to handle and prepare, relatively nontoxic under ordinary laboratory conditions; they do not oxidize organic matter; and they are miscible in $H_2O$, which means that residues do not have to be evaporated with acetone or alcohol, for example, before the heavy liquids are introduced. In addition, $ZnCl_2$ is economical. The waste solutions can be filtered, then boiled under a fume hood to evaporate the $H_2O$; after adjusting to the desired specific gravity, they are again ready for use (Wagoner, et al., 1961).[49]

The following procedure is from Funkhouser and Evitt (1959) with some minor additions from schedules given by Staplin, et al. (1960) and Wagoner, et al. (1961). The procedure includes an innovation—the use of doubled plastic tubing—although the flotation can be carried out in an ordinary centrifuge tube in the conventional manner, previously detailed for use of bromoform. The use of plastic tubing appears to have several advantages: it minimizes the loss of fossils, it minimizes the amount of heavy liquid that is removed following the separation, and it minimizes the removal of heavy minerals that might still be in suspension below the floating organic fraction. It might be worth while to extend its use to flotations performed with other heavy liquids.

*Procedure*      1. Pretreat sample according to its characteristics. Wash.

2. In a test tube, acidify the organic residue by washing with HCl (10 percent). Centrifuge and decant. This will prevent precipitation of insoluble $Zn(OH)_2$ and other impurities when the $ZnCl_2$ solution is added to the residue.

---

[49] The solutions cannot be filtered through ordinary cellulose filter paper since the fibers of the paper will swell and the paper will eventually disintegrate. Wagoner (personal correspondence, 1964) states that Whatman borosilicate glass-fiber filter paper (grade GFA) can be used with a Büchner (porcelain) funnel and a vacuum filter apparatus for filtering zinc bromide solution. In the Paleoecology Laboratory we use a funnel with a fused, fritted, glass disk (4 to 5.5 microns pore size) of the type used for bacterial filtrations for filtering zinc chloride solution.

3. Transfer the $ZnCl_2$ sediment suspension from the test tube into a clear, flexible, thin-walled plastic tube that has been doubled in the middle and cut long enough to project about an inch above the centrifuge tube. The diameter of tubing used will vary with the size of centrifuge tube used; ⅜ inch is recommended for 50-ml tubes, ⅝ inch for 100-ml tubes, etc. Wash out any sediment remaining in the original tube with saturated $ZnCl_2$ solution from a squeeze bottle, and add this to the solution already in the plastic tube.

4. If necessary, add more of the saturated $ZnCl_2$ solution to the doubled plastic tube. Place thumbs over the open ends of the doubled tube, straighten it, and invert it several times until the contents are thoroughly mixed.

5. Redouble the tube in the middle, and after lubricating the outside with glycerin or vaseline, insert it into an ordinary centrifuge tube (either glass or plastic). Equalize the amount of $ZnCl_2$ solution in each side of the doubled tube, so that the level of the solution in each half is just above the rim of the centrifuge tube.

6. Centrifuge at about 1500 rpm from 5 to 30 minutes: the time required will be governed by the size and density of the mineral particles; the finer and lighter the particles the longer the time necessary. The same effect may be achieved by increasing the speed and correspondingly decreasing the time. Funkhouser and Evitt state that they centrifuge samples for about 15 minutes at 1500 rpm. Staplin, et al. (1960) use 700 rpm with 100-ml tubes, but give no time. During the centrifugation the mineral particles will fall to the bottom of the doubled plastic tube and the insoluble organic remains will float to the top, with a clear space between. Wagoner, et al. (1961) always let the organic residue stand in the separating solution 15 minutes or longer, both before and after centrifugation.

7. Occasionally, following centrifugation, there will be no separation—or incomplete separation—of the organic fraction from mineral particles. If everything has settled, the density of the float solution should be increased by adding more $ZnCl_2$ crystals to the solution already in the tube: if everything has floated, the density of the solution should be decreased by adding more $H_2O$ to the float solution. The solution should then be remixed as in step 4, and recentrifuged, as in step 6.

8. When a good separation has been achieved by centrifugation, the folded plastic tube is removed from the centrifuge tube and pinch clamps placed just below the organic material now floating at each end. This floating organic material is then poured into a single centrifuge tube and the ends of the tubing rinsed with $H_2O$ to recover all of the organic residue. The heavy residue is either discarded or saved for examination for other types of microfossils. The entire float process can be repeated if there is reason to suspect that the separation was inadequate.

9. Add a small amount of 10 percent HCl to the organic-rich solution in the centrifuge tube to prevent precipitation of $Zn(OH)_2$.

Fill the rest of the centrifuge tube with $H_2O$, making certain that the specific gravity is reduced, stir thoroughly, centrifuge for 2 or 3 minutes and carefully decant the supernatant fluid.

10. If 50-ml centrifuge tubes were used up to this point, it may be advisable to transfer the concentrated organic material to 15-ml centrifuge tubes, for the volume of material is so small that it may be lost if one continues to use the 50-ml tubes. To remove larger organic particles the residue may be strained through 50-mesh stainless-steel wire mesh (flamed to clean) when it is transferred to the 15-ml tubes.

11. Wash the organic residue several times with $H_2O$, centrifuging and decanting after each wash.

12. Follow up the flotation with additional chemical treatment (HF or HCl) if necessary.

## Other Separation Methods

Some other separation methods that are occasionally used are not dependent upon the density differential of organic and inorganic materials.

### SIEVING

Sieving is a simple technique that may be used on disaggregated samples at the beginning of processing, or at any time during processing, to remove large mineral and organic particles. If the volume of the sample is small, 3-inch diameter sieves are very convenient. In the Paleoecology laboratory, we have found 3-inch sieves of U. S. Standard or Tyler Standard tolerances 210 microns (65-mesh), 177 microns (80-mesh), and 149 microns (100-mesh) especially useful.

A concurrent sieving and deflocculation technique for extracting pollen and other small plant remains from peat was devised by Churchill (1957) who encases a peat sample in two stoppered concentric brass-gauze tubes (approximately $25 \times 27$ mm, 60-mesh; $35 \times 40$ mm, 100-mesh) while boiling it in KOH. This method provides simultaneous sieving and deflocculation, thus saving time, and it removes materials that might be broken down if sieving were postponed: a high concentration of pollen results.

Sieving techniques are used for recovery of megaspores as described by Dettman in this Handbook (p. 699). Eagar and Sarjeant (1963) have used a sieving technique to recover hystrichospheres from silty clay in place of the usual chemical extraction and concentration methods. The sample is dried, disaggregated in $H_2O$, and washed through a British Standard 200-mesh sieve (apertures 64 microns). The residue that does not pass the sieve is boiled with $Na_2CO_3$ (a disperser) and resieved: these steps are repeated until a clean organic residue remains. The hystrichospheres can then be picked out of the dried clay-free residue with the tip of a fine brush. The method has an inherent disadvantage in failing to retain the smallest members of the microfossil assemblage, which pass through the meshes of even the finest available sieve (37 microns).

### SILICATE-DEPRESSANT METHOD

Arms (1960) has devised a method of concentrating pollen from inorganic sediments in which the number of grains per unit volume of sediment is very low. This method helps reduce the volume of sediment that must be treated chemically to recover enough pollen for study, and helps overcome the formation of silica gel that often presents a problem with such sediment. The concentration usually obviates the extensive use of hydrofluoric acid.

*Needed reagents:* A 5 percent aqueous solution of Quebracho (American Cyanimide Company) as a silicate depressant;[50] a 5 percent aqueous solution of commercial pine oil as a flotation agent; a saturated aqueous solution of laboratory detergent as a flotation medium or frother.

The matrix, disaggregated but otherwise untreated, is frothed in a beaker with a solution of the three reagents by passing a stream of air or gas through the liquid. The Quebracho retards the flotation of the silicate grains, while the pollen grains and spores, coated with the pine oil, are floated off on bubbles of the detergent into a separate beaker. In principle this is a fractionation method, similar to the majority of the density-separation methods, but not depending on normal gravitational effects.

Dumait, et al. (1963) have proposed a similar technique in which a $1^0/_{00}$ (one part per thousand) solution of polyvinyl alcohol and water is used as the frother. The sample is powdered and placed with the flotation medium in the bottom of the long arm of a J-shaped glass tube, the short arm of which is bent over into a beaker. The introduction of $N_2$, through a fine-pored sinter filter in the bottom of the long arm, forms froth that carries the pollen into the beaker, leaving mineral particles behind.

A flotation method, which to date has been used only for processing foraminifera, could probably be adapted to palynological extractions (Journal of Paleontology, 1935). Sodium silicate solution is used as the silicate depressant, and thus one avoids any possibility of contamination through the use of Quebracho (Traverse, et al., 1961). The sodium silicate is added to the residue, then removed (after stirring), and a soap solution is added and frothed as with the Quebracho solution.

A somewhat similar frothing effect described by Brown (1960, p. 42) is produced by a mixture of hydrogen peroxide, hydrochloric acid, and marl. The marl effervesces readily with the two chemicals, and pollen and spores are carried out, with relatively little inorganic matter, on the foam.

---

[50] Quebracho is an extract of the wood of *Schinopsis lorentzii* (Griseb.) Engl., a South American tree. The pure extract has a small pollen and spore content (200 grains/gram) which is a possible source of contamination when the extract is used to prepare microfossil samples (Traverse, et al., 1961).

## SUMMARY

Outlined in the preceding pages is a sequence of steps that may be followed in extracting pollen, spores, and other acid-insoluble microfossils from sediments and sedimentary rocks. Some detailed schedules are provided as are procedures to be used in each step. It is emphasized that complete extractions are best programmed according to the individual characteristics of each rock or sediment and the desired results, rather than according to rote "cookbook" procedures. Thus, for example, the process of disaggregation and dispersal selected will depend on the induration of the sample and on whether one is interested only in acid-insoluble microfossils, or in the total microflora and microfauna. Similarly, whether a given sample needs both chemical extraction and density separation must be judged from the characteristics of the specific matrix and by optical examination during the extraction.

Nevertheless, procedures for destroying specific mineral and organic compounds are essentially standard, regardless of the composition of the sediment or rock in which they occur. However, in addition to the common methods and reagents there are others that may be used alternatively and which experiment may prove to be more satisfactory for certain matrices. In using oxidants, it is especially difficult to predict the nature of the reaction between matrix and reagent and the effect of the reagent on the microfossils. Thus, I have tried to mention many oxidizing agents: most of them should prove effective with at least one type of matrix.

In order to recover microfossils most effectively, the extractionist must have prior knowledge of all the available procedures; he must know in advance what he may expect to achieve by each step of the extraction, that is, he should know why he is using certain procedures and chemical reagents and what effect these may have on the fossiliferous residue; he should know the sequence of steps advisable in specific cases (for example, if both carbonate and silicate minerals are present in one sample, knowing that the removal of carbonates should precede the removal of silicates may save a great deal of time and effort) and finally, he should know the general mineralogical composition of his sample.

Armed with such information, experience with a wide variety of samples representing different matrix types will probably prove the best teacher.

## ACKNOWLEDGMENTS

Preparation of this manuscript has been supported in part by grants from the National Science Foundation for investigation of the pollen and spores of Tertiary sediments of the Pacific Northwest States.

I wish to thank my colleagues, Dr. L. R. Kittleman of the Paleoecology Laboratory, and Dr. L. H. Klemm of the Chemistry Department, The University of Oregon, for their help and suggestions concerning this manuscript. Dr. Pierre Grangeon, Ecole St. Julien, Brioude, Haute-Loire, France, Dr. K. Sohma, Tohoku University, Japan, and Dr. Joel McClure, The University of Oregon, provided help with several translations.

## REFERENCES

Abraham, H. (1929). Asphalts and allied substances (3rd ed.), New York, Van Nostrand, 891 pp.

Arms, B. C. (1960). A silica depressant method for concentrating fossil pollen and spores. Micropaleontology, v. 6, no. 3, p. 327–328.

Arnold, C. A. (1950). Megaspores from the Michigan coal basin. Univ. Mich. Mus. Paleontology Contr., v. 8, no. 5, p. 59–111.

Artamonova, S. V., and A. M. Medvedeva (1963). Methods of extracting spores and pollen from oils and the waters of oil deposits [transl. of a 1962 paper published in Russian in Paleontologicheskiy Zhurnal, no. 1, p. 157–158]. Internat. Geology Rev., v. 5, no. 11, p. 1510–1511.

Balme, B. E., and C. W. Hassell (1962). Upper Devonian spores from the Canning basin, Western Australia. Micropaleontology, v. 8, no. 1, p. 1–28.

Barghoorn, E. S. (1948). Sodium chlorite as an aid in paleobotanical and anatomical study of plant tissue. Science, v. 107, no. 2784, p. 480–481.

————, and I. W. Bailey (1940). A useful method for the study of pollen in peat. Ecology, v. 21, no. 4, p. 513–514.

Benninghoff, W. S. (1947). Use of trisodium phosphate with herbarium materials and microfossils in peat. Science, v. 106, no. 2753, p. 325–326.

Bertsch, K. (1942). Lehrbuch der Pollenanalyse. Stuttgart, Ferdinand Enke, 195 pp.

Bhardwaj, D. C. (1957). The palynological investigations of the Saar coals; I. Morphology of Sporae Dispersae. Palaeontographica, v. 101, ser. B, no. 5 & 6, p. 73–105.

Bisque, R. E. (1961). Analysis of carbonate rocks for calcium, magnesium, iron, and aluminum with EDTA. J. Sed. Petrology, v. 31, no. 1, p. 113–122.

Bone, W. A., L. G. B. Parsons, R. H. Sapiro, and C. M. Groocock (1935). Researches on the chemistry of coal; VIII. The development of benzenoid constitution in the lignin-peat-coal-series. Royal Soc. [London] Proc., ser. A, v. 148, p. 492–522.

Brauns, F. E. (1952). The chemistry of lignin. New York, Academic, 808 pp.

————, and D. A. Brauns (1960). The chemistry of lignin, Supplement Volume. New York, Academic, 804 pp.

Brown, C. A. (1960). Palynological techniques. Baton Rouge, C. A. Brown, 188 pp.

Butterworth, M. A., and R. W. Williams (1954). Descriptions of nine species of small spores from the British coal measures. Ann. Mag. Nat. History, v. 7, no. 82, p. 753–764.

Camp, C. L., and G. D. Hanna (1937). Methods in paleontology. Berkeley, Univ. California Press, 153 pp.

Campo, M. van (1950). Une méthode de préparation tres rapide des tourbes en vue de leur analyse pollinique. Soc. Bot. Française Bull., v. 97, nos. 7–9, p. 216–217.

Churchill, D. M. (1957). A method for concentrating pollen grains and small fossil remains from fibrous peats and moss polsters. Nature, v. 180, no. 4599, p. 1437.

Clisby, K., and P. B. Sears (1955). Palynology in southern North America; III. Microfossil profiles under Mexico City correlated with the sedimentary profiles. Geol. Soc. America Bull., v. 66, p. 511–520.

Davis, P. (1961). Use of stannic chloride for heavy-liquid flotation of palynological fossils. Oklahoma Geology Notes, v. 21, no. 10, p. 259–260.

Dijkstra, S. J. (1946). Eine monographische Bearbeitung der karbonischen Megasporen. Med. Geol. Stich., ser. C, v. 3, no. 1, p. 1–101.

———— (1949). Megaspores and some other fossils from the Aachenian (Senonian) in South Limburg, Netherlands. Med. Geol. Stich., new ser., no. 3, p. 19–32.

Dumait, P. (1962). Le Vibroséparateur. Pollen et Spores, v. 4, no. 2, p. 311–316.

————, L. Marceau, C. Devin, and M. van Campo (1963). Nouvelle méthode de concentration des pollens dans les sediments pauvres par microflottation. C. R. Acad. Sci. Paris, v. 256, p. 231–233.

Dybová, S., and A. Jachowicz (1957). Microspores of the Upper Silesian coal measures. Mikrospory, Instytut Geologiczny, Prace, v. 23, Warszawa, p. 319–326.

Eagar, S. H., and W. A. S. Sarjeant (1963). Fossil hystrichospheres concentrated by sieving techniques. Nature, v. 198, no. 4875, p. 81.

Erdtman, G. (1936). New methods in pollen analysis. Svensk Bot. Tidskr., v. 30, no. 2, p. 154–164.

———— (1943). An introduction to pollen analysis. Chronica Botanica, 239 pp.

———— (1960). The acetolysis method—A revised description. Svensk Bot. Tidskr., v. 54, no. 4, p. 561–564.

————, and H. Erdtman (1933). The improvement of pollen-analysis technique. Svensk Bot. Tidskr., v. 27, no. 3, p. 347–357.

Faegri, K., and J. Iversen (1950). Textbook of modern pollen analysis. Copenhagen, Ejnar Munksgaard, 168 pp.

Faegri, K., and P. Deuse (1960). Size variations in pollen grains with different treatments. Pollen et Spores, v. 2, no. 2, p. 293–298.

Felix, C. J. (1963). Mechanical sample disaggregation in palynology. Micropaleontology, v. 9, no. 3, p. 337–339.

Funkhouser, J. W., and W. R. Evitt (1959). Preparation techniques for acid-insoluble microfossils. Micropaleontology, v. 5, no. 3, p. 369–375.

Geisler, F. (1935). A new method for separation of fossil pollen from peat. Butler Univ. Bot. Studies, v. 3, no. 9, p. 141–145.

Gipson, Mack, Jr. (1963). Ultrasonic disaggregation of shale. J. Sed. Petrology, v. 33, no. 4, p. 955–958.

Glover, E. D. (1961). Method of solution of calcareous materials using the complexing agent, EDTA. J. Sed. Petrology, v. 31, no. 4, p. 622–626.

Godwin, H. (1956). The history of the British flora—A factual basis for phytogeography. London, Cambridge Univ. Press, 384 pp.

Goldman, M. I. (1952). Deformation, metamorphism, and mineralization in gypsum-anhydrite cap rock, Sulphur Salt Dome, Louisiana. Geol. Soc. America Mem. 50, 169 pp.

Goldschmidt, V. (1881). Ueber Verwendbarkeit einer Kaliumquecksilberjo-didlösung bei mineralogischen und petrographischen Untersuchungen. Neues Jahrb. Mineralogie, Geologie u. Paleontologie, v. 1, p. 179–238.

Gortner, W. A. (1938). Analyses of glacial and preglacial woods. J. Am. Chem. Soc., v. 60, no. 10, p. 2509–2511.

Haas, P., and T. G. Hill (1928). An introduction to the chemistry of plant products (4th ed.), v. 1, New York, Longmans, 530 pp.

Hafsten, U. (1959). Bleaching + HF + acetolysis a hazardous preparation process. Pollen et Spores, v. 1, no. 1, p. 77–79.

Hallik, R. (1957). Eine Flüssigkeit zur Trennung von organischen Material und Sand für die Pollenanalyse. Neues Jahrbuch Geologie u. Paläontologie, Monatsh., no. 4, p. 188–189.

Hanna, M. A. (1927). Separation of fossils and other light materials by means of heavy liquids. Econ. Geology, v. 22, p. 14–17.

Hoffmeister, W. S. (1960). Sodium hypochlorite, a new oxidizing agent for the preparation of microfossils. Oklahoma Geology Notes, v. 20, no. 2, p. 34–35.

Hurlbut, C. S., Jr. (1949). Dana's manual of mineralogy (15th ed.). New York, Wiley, 480 pp.

Jahn, E. C., and W. M. Harlow (1942). Chemistry of ancient beech stakes from the Fishweir (Chapter 7), *in* The Boylston Street Fishweir, Papers of the Robert S. Peabody Foundation for Archaeology, Andover, Mass., v. 2, p. 90–95.

Journal of Paleontology (1935). Recovery of foraminifera by means of flotation (Laboratory, N. V. De Bataafsche Petroleum Maatschappij; The Hague, Holland). J. Paleontology, v. 9, no. 8, p. 745–746.

Kosanke, R. M. (1950). Pennsylvanian spores of Illinois and their use in correlation. Illinois Geol. Survey Bull. 74, 128 pp.

——— (1962). Report to the Group on Coal Geology, Geol. Soc. Am., on the Fourth Meeting of the International Committee for Paleozoic Microflora, held in Liege, Belgium. (A mimeographed report, 18 pp.)

Krumbein, W. C., and F. J. Pettijohn (1938). Manual of sedimentary petrography. New York, Appleton-Century, 549 pp.

Kurtz, E. B., and R. M. Turner (1957). An oil-flotation method for the recovery of pollen from inorganic sediments. Micropaleontology, v. 3, no. 1, p. 67–68.

Ledingham, R. J., and S. H. F. Chinn (1955). A flotation method for obtaining spores of *Helminthosporium sativum* from soil. Canadian J. Bot., v. 33, no. 4, p. 298–303.

Leschik, Georg (1956). Sporen aus dem Salzton des Zechstein von Neuhof (bei Fulda). Palaeontographica, v. 100, ser. B, no. 4–6, p. 122–142.

Macko, S. (1957). Lower Miocene pollen flora from the valley of Klodnica near Gliwice (Upper Silesia). Prace Wroclawskiego Towarzystwa Naukowego, ser. B, no. 88, 314 pp.

McIntyre, D. J. (1963). Pollen morphology of New Zealand species of Myrtaceae. Royal Soc. [New Zealand] Trans., v. 2, no. 7, p. 83–107.

Mitchell, R. L., and G. J. Ritter (1934). Composition of three fossil woods mined from the Miocene Auriferous Gravels of California. J. Am. Chem. Soc., v. 56, no. 7, p. 1603–1605.

Pigman, W. (ed.) (1957). The carbohydrates: chemistry, biochemistry, physiology. New York, Academic, 902 pp.

Raistrick, A. (1934). The correlation of coal-seams by microspore-content; I. The seams of Northumberland. Inst. Mining Engineers Trans., v. 88, no. 3, p. 142–153.

——, and C. E. Marshall (1948). The nature and origin of coal and coal seams (2nd printing). London, The English Univ. Press. Ltd., 282 pp.

Sanders, J. M. (1937). The microscopical examination of crude petroleum. J. Inst. Petrol. Technology, v. 23, no. 167, p. 525–573.

Sarmiento, R. (1957). Microfossil zonation of Mancos group. Am. Assoc. Petrol. Geologists, Bull., v. 41, p. 1683–1693.

Sittler, C. (1955). Méthodes et techniques physico-chimiques de préparation des sédiments en vue de leur analyse pollinique. Rev. Inst. Française Petrol. Ann. Comb. Liquid., v. 10, no. 2, p. 103–114.

Sonstadt, E. (1874). Note on a new method of taking specific gravities, adapted for special cases. Chem. News, v. 29, p. 127–128.

Spielholtz, G., L. A. Thomas, and H. Diehl (1962). Isolation of spores by wet oxidation, Micropaleontology, v. 8, no. 1, p. 109–110.

Stamm, A. J., and E. E. Harris (1953). Chemical processing of wood. New York, Chem. Publishing Co., 595 pp.

Staplin, F. L., S. J. Pocock, J. Jańsonius, and E. M. Oliphant (1960). Palynological techniques for sediments. Micropaleontology, v. 6, no. 3, p. 329–331.

Sullivan, J. D. (1927). Heavy liquids for mineralogical analyses. Bur. Mines, Tech. Paper 381, p. 1–26.

Thiergart, F. (1940). Die Mikropaläontologie als pollenanalyse im Dienst der Braunkohlenforschung. Stuttgart, Ferdinand Enke, 82 pp.

Thiessen, R. (1913). Microscopic study of coal, *in* D. White and R. Thiessen eds.). The origin of coal. U. S. Bur. Mines Bull. 38, p. 187–304.

Traverse, A., K. H. Clisby, and F. Foreman (1961). Pollen in drilling-mud "thinners," a source of palynological contamination. Micropaleontology, v. 7, no. 3, p. 375–377.

Tschudy, R. H. (1958). A modification of the Schulze digestion method of possible value in studying oxidized coals. Grana Palynologica, new ser., v. 1, no. 3, p. 34–38.

—— (1960). Vibraflute. Micropaleontology, v. 6, no. 3, p. 325–326.

Urban, J. B. (1961). Concentration of palynological fossils by heavy liquid flotation, Oklahoma Geology Notes, v. 21, no. 7, p. 191–193.

Wagoner, D. L., T. L. Pruitt, and J. H. Thompson (1961). Palynological laboratory techniques and procedures. Richfield Oil Corp. (Mimeographed pamphlet, 14 pp.)

Waksman, S. A. (1936). Humus: origin, chemical composition, and importance in nature. Baltimore, Williams and Wilkins, 494 pp.

Walton, J. (1923). On a new method of investigating fossil plant impressions or incrustations. Ann. Bot., v. 37, no. 147, p. 379–391.

Wenner, C.-G. (1947). Pollen diagrams from Labrador. Geografiska Ann., v. 29, nos. 3 & 4, p. 137–373.

Weissmann, R. C., and H. Diehl (1953). A new method utilizing Versene for determination of the calcite-dolomite ratio in carbonate rocks. Iowa Acad. Sci. Proc., v. 60, p. 433–437.

Willrath, C. (1934). *in* R. Potonie II (ed.), Mikrobotanik des eocänen Humodils des Geisetals. Arb. Inst. Paläobot. Petr. Brennsteine, Preussischen Geologischen Landesanstalt, v. 4, p. 108–109.

Wise, L. E. (ed.) (1944). Wood chemistry. New York, Reinhold, 900 pp.

———, and E. C. Jahn (eds.) (1952). Wood chemistry (2nd ed.), v. 1, 2, New York, Reinhold, 1343 pp.

White, D. (1913). Regional Metamorphism of Coal, *in* D. White and R. Thiessen (eds.). The origin of coal. U. S. Bur. Mines B. 38, p. 91–130.

Zetzsche, R., and O. Kälin (1932). Eine Methode zur Isolierugn des Polymerbitumens (Sporenmembranen, Kutikulen usw. aus Kohlen). Halle, Braunkohle, p. 345–351.

# Mounting Media and Mounting Techniques

SVEND T. ANDERSEN

*Geological Survey of Denmark, Charlottenlund, Denmark*

Proper mounting techniques and mounting media are important for reliable results in pollen analysis. Because detailed pollen analysis requires complete quantitative records of fossil pollen and spore assemblages, the quantitative analysis should be as unbiased as possible, and the slides should permit ideal microscopic observation. It is also important, both for measurement and for identification of critical pollen grains, that the orientation of the grains can be changed during examination; in routine work, rotation of individual grains greatly facilitates the identification of damaged grains. As the identification of unfamiliar pollen grains must often be rechecked and "type specimens" preserved, the slides should be durable and the specimens should not change their appearance with time. Only in the most routine work is preservation of specimens unimportant. In any case, modern pollen used for comparison should be mounted in the same medium as the fossils in order to minimize variables in the comparison. Furthermore, as the mounting medium may affect the size of the pollen grains, the size of pollen from different sediments in relation to modern pollen should be known.

Careful mounting and the choice of a good mounting medium may help produce good results in pollen analyses and may reduce the amount of labor necessary to make them.

## MOUNTING PROCEDURE

After chemical treatment, the pollen-bearing residue is transferred from the final rinse water into the mounting medium. This procedure varies according to the solubility of the medium in water.

### WATER-SOLUBLE MEDIA

After centrifuging the residue with the final rinse water, decant the water and remove surplus water from the edge of the centrifuge tube by blotting with filter paper. If possible, the residue should be rinsed and centrifuged once with the mounting medium to remove remaining water. Afterwards, if the mounting medium is fluid, a small amount can be added to the residue in the tube.

### WATER-INSOLUBLE MEDIA

The residue is dehydrated following the final water rinse, and transferred into a suitable solvent before the mounting medium can be added. One method of dehydration is the following:

1. Rinse the residue with a few drops of water and 96 percent alcohol; centrifuge and decant.
2. Rinse a second time with 99 percent alcohol; centrifuge and decant.
3. Rinse with benzene[1] or some other highly volatile solvent; centrifuge and decant.

If the mounting medium is liquid, add the same solvent used in the third step in the dehydration procedure to the residue and transfer the mixture to a $\frac{1}{2}$ or 1 dram vial. Add mounting medium, and set the vial aside for evaporation of the solvent. If immediate use is necessary, some drops of the mixture are transferred to a small evaporating dish from which the solvent will evaporate quickly.

### FLUID MOUNTING MEDIA

Slides with *fluid mounting media* (for example glycerin, silicone oil) can be prepared without special precautions to keep the medium fluid during the process. The mounting medium is added to a porcelain evaporating dish, to which a few drops of the concentrated residue mounting-medium mixture has been transferred until optimal pollen-spore concentration is obtained (microscopic control). The residue is carefully stirred to disperse the pollen grains and to assure a proportional representation of all elements. A small nickel spatula that can be cleaned in a gas flame is useful for stirring and transferring the fluid. When a good pollen concentration is obtained, a small drop of the pollen-bearing medium is placed on a slide, and a cover slip is placed

---

[1] Only chemicals of a high purity grade should be used.

over it, allowing the droplet to spread under the cover slip. The droplet should be of a size that spreads slowly and uniformly in a thin film and does not ooze out from the edges of the cover slip. Because immersion lenses of high numerical aperture have a very short working distance, the cover slip, the layer of mounting medium, and the object slide, must be thin enough to permit immersion substage condensers and immersion objective lenses to focus on any level in the mounting-medium layer. All pollen grains should lie in a single thin layer, at a focal plane that can be seen with both low- and medium-power (high-dry) lenses, since small and large grains should have an equal opportunity to be detected during the analysis. As even a few mineral particles left in the organic residue may impede the processing of thin slides, such particles must be removed by the chemical treatment before the residue is mounted. It may be necessary to flatten large, organic, detrital particles by gently pressing the cover slip.

For ease and accuracy in making the analysis, pollen grains and any residual organic detritus should be well dispersed on the object slide so that small or inconspicuous pollen grains are not obscured; as few pollen grains as possible should appear at the same time in the field of vision at the magnification used for scanning and counting the slide.

SOLID MOUNTING MEDIA

This type of media must be kept fluid by heating (for example, glycerin jelly) or by presence of a solvent (for example, canada balsam). The former type of medium solidifies as the slides cool, the latter as the solvent evaporates. It may be difficult to prepare slides of correct concentration and thickness; and according to Jeffords and Jones (1959), it may be difficult to obtain complete dispersal, as some solid mounting media tend to promote clumping or flocculation of pollen and associated organic detritus.

## QUALITIES OF MOUNTING MEDIA

Before individual mounting media are mentioned, it will be useful to discuss the desirable characteristics of the various types.

VISCOSITY

Solid mounting media permit frequent handling of the slides without disturbing them or dislocating the pollen grains; this appears to be the main advantage of such media.

Fluid media, on the other hand, permit rotation of the individual grains. Well-sealed slides prepared with fluid mounting media (p. 595) are comparable in permanence to slides prepared with solid media. Pollen grains in sealed slides can be rotated if currents can be produced by tapping on the cover slip from above, but their movements are uncontrollable and many grains will remain immovable. In unsealed slides prepared with media of moderate viscosity, most pollen grains can be turned in any direction by gentle sideways pushing on the edge of the cover slip, but the film of mounting medium should be sufficiently thin so that the cover slip is held in place by adhesion and unwanted currents do not develop. Such unsealed slides must be handled with some care not to dislodge the grains. Anisol is a convenient immersion fluid for unsealed slides because of its volatility, which makes it unnecessary to clean the slide.

If the viscosity of the mounting medium is low, currents that will dislocate the pollen grains occur too easily. Highly viscous mounting media do not spread easily under the cover slip and thus are unsuitable for the preparation of thin slides.

VOLATILITY

Microscopic slides that are to be preserved must not dry out. Evaporation of volatile mounting media may be prevented by sealing, but it is safer to use a nonvolatile mounting medium. When water-miscible media are used, water should be removed from the residue before mounting, as otherwise the slides dry out too easily. Volatile media are, of course, not suitable for unsealed slides, especially when these are to be preserved for future examination.

INERTNESS

The mounting medium should be stable and the size of the pollen grains should not change with time. Acetolyzed pollen exines are somewhat swollen, unless water has been removed with a dehydrating agent (Anderson, 1960, fig. 5), and in some water-miscible media they tend to swell further, especially if exposed to pressure from the cover slip (Cushing, 1961).

REFRACTIVE INDEX

The index of refraction of most pollen exines is 1.55 to 1.60 (Christensen, 1954). To produce good contrast, both for visual observation and for photomicrography, the refractive index of the mounting medium should differ from that of the exines (Christensen, 1954; Berglund, et al., 1960; Andersen, 1960). Media with indices of 1.40 to 1.46 have proved favorable both for ordinary and for phase-contrast microscopy. Media with indices of 1.47 to 1.55 provide too little contrast, and the results, especially with phase contrast equipment, are disappointing. Mounting media with refractive indices higher than 1.60 are to be avoided, as they produce a confusing image (Christensen, 1954; Berglund, et al., 1960; Andersen, 1960).

Glycerin and glycerin jelly are the classic mounting media in pollen analysis probably because of ease in handling and a fairly favorable refractive index. However, the use of many other mounting media have been proposed in recent years (see especially Christensen, 1954; Brown, 1960; Andersen, 1960). The properties of the newer media are not always adequately described and some, obtained from commercial sources, are compounds of unknown composition and may be difficult to duplicate after a few years (see Brown, 1960, p. 133).

## LIQUID MOUNTING MEDIA

*Lactic acid* has a low refractive index (1.44) and low viscosity, but since it deteriorates with time, it is only suitable for temporary mounts (Barghoorn, 1947; Brown, 1960).

*Lactophenol* is mentioned by Brown (1960) as a "good temporary mounting medium." Its refractive index is not given. It is water-soluble, but as it is volatile, the slides must be sealed.

*Glycerin* is of a suitable viscosity. If completely water-free, its refractive index is 1.47, but as it is hygroscopic, glycerin always contains some water, which decreases the refractive index. Before mounting residues in glycerin their surplus water should be removed by centrifugation for about 10 minutes with glycerin, which has been heated slightly to reduce its viscosity. As glycerin is volatile, unsealed slides cannot be preserved. Even sealed slides are said to be difficult to preserve in hot climates (C. M. Gutjahr and E. M. Van Zinderen Bakker, personal communications). Acetolyzed modern pollen mounted in glycerin swells considerably if pressed by the cover slip (Cushing, 1961), and fossil pollen may also swell appreciably (Andersen, 1960, p. 9). If part of the medium escapes by evaporation, both fossil and modern pollen are extremely likely to swell owing to compression. Table I shows the average size of *Corylus avellana* pollen prepared by various treatments and mounted in glycerin (Andersen, 1960).

**Table I.** *Average Size of Postglacial and Modern* Corylus avellana *Pollen Mounted in Glycerin*

| DEPOSIT | TREATMENT | AVERAGE SIZE (100 GRAINS) |
|---------|-----------|---------------------------|
| Fossil | KOH, HF, acetolysis | $30.0 \pm 2.8\mu$ |
| Fossil | KHO, acetolysis | $34.9 \pm 1.9$ |
| Fossil | KOH, acetolysis | $33.5 \pm 3.2$ |
| Modern | KOH, acetolysis | $30.1 \pm 1.9$[1] |

[1] The modern pollen swelled quickly to a somewhat larger size (Andersen, 1960).

*Tricaproïn* and *tributyrin* (Andersen, 1960) are mounting media of low refractive index (1.44) and some stability, but their viscosity is too low. Residues are mounted from benzene.

*Aesculus-gum* (Christensen, 1954) and *Tanglefoot* medium (Andersen, 1960) are of suitable viscosity and stability, but their refractive index is too high (1.49). Residues are mounted from benzene.

*Silicone oil* is well suited for both fossil and modern pollen (Andersen, 1960). It is available in a wide range of viscosities that do not change with temperature; the refractive index is low (1.40); the oil is nonvolatile, water-repellent, and very stable. I prefer a viscosity of 2000 centistokes. I have used silicone oil for mounting fossil and modern pollen slides since 1958. The unsealed slides have remained essentially unchanged: *Corylus avellana* pollen contained in such slides showed little change in size over a period of four years (Table II).

**Table II.** *Average Size of Postglacial and Modern* Corylus avellana *Pollen Mounted in Silicone Oil*

| DEPOSIT | TREATMENT | AVERAGE SIZE (100 GRAINS) | |
|---------|-----------|:---:|:---:|
| | | 1958 | 1962 |
| Calcareous gyttja | KOH, HF, acetolysis | $22.7 \pm 1.3\mu$ | $22.6 \pm 1.3\mu$ |
| Calcareous gyttja | KOH, acetolysis | $23.5 \pm 1.3$ | $23.1 \pm 1.4$ |
| Non-calcareous gyttja | KOH, HF, acetolysis | $24.0 \pm 1.4$ | $23.7 \pm 1.5$ |
| Non-calcareous gyttja | KOH, acetolysis | $24.6 \pm 1.9$ | $23.4 \pm 1.4$ |
| Acid humus | KOH, HF, acetolysis | $24.9 \pm 1.6$ | $24.2 \pm 1.4$ |
| Acid humus | KOH, acetolysis | $25.9 \pm 1.6$ | $25.1 \pm 1.6$ |
| Modern | KOH, acetolysis | $26.6 \pm 1.3$ | $26.6 \pm 1.6$ |

Following the chemical treatment, the residue is rinsed with alcohol and benzene, as described on p. 588. During the last alcohol rinse, the residue may be stained with fuchsin. The slightly fluid residue-oil mixture may be preserved in a small vial for later use.[2] Residue samples are mounted as described on p. 588. In a properly made slide, the film of silicone oil should be so thin that the cover slip is held in place by adhesion and the slide may be turned on edge without dislodging the cover slip or the pollen grains. In such slides the pollen grains can easily be rotated in any direction by gentle pushing of the cover slip, and the slides can be preserved unsealed for future examination. There may, of course, be a chance of dislocating pollen grains earlier annotated by cross table coordinates, however, they can be reidentified without much trouble, provided the slides are thin, and the cover slips small (18 by 18 mm). If relocating annotated grains is found to be too difficult, the cover slip can, of course, be fixed with some sealing material (p. 595). Silicone oil is also convenient for routine examinations, as the slides are easy to make and can be used immediately.

---

[2] If too little silicone oil is added, the residue-oil mixture may become rubber-like after some years. If this should happen, the oil may be softened by adding benzene and letting it stand for a few days.

## SOLID MOUNTING MEDIA

Slides prepared with solid mounting media are usually durable, and may be handled quite roughly. However, they are little, if any, more durable than slides made with liquid media that have been effectively sealed.

Several solid mounting media have refractive indices above 1.50, which is too high for pollen and spore work. This is true of *canada balsam* with an index of 1.53 (Schopf, 1960), *hydroxyethyl cellulose* (Cellosize), with 1.50 to 1.51 (Jeffords and Jones, 1959), and *polyvinal alcohol,* with 1.54 (Funk-houser and Evitt, 1959).

*Poppy-seed oil* (*Oleum papaveri*) has a suitable refractive index, 1.46 to 1.47 (Christensen, 1954). The sample residue can be brought into the medium via alcohol and benzene. The oil is fluid, but hardens by slow polymerization.

*Glycerin jelly,* and several recipes for its preparation are mentioned in Brown (1960). Glycerin is the main component. The refractive index is about 1.43. Before mounting pollen in glycerin jelly, surplus water should be removed from the residue by centrifuging it with warm glycerin for 10 minutes. A little glycerin jelly is then added to the residue and melted by heating (e.g., in a water bath).

In glycerin-jelly slides the pollen grains swell appreciably if compressed by the cover slip (Cushing, 1961). Brown (1960) finds that it is difficult to prepare a jelly that will solidify in hot climates and that it is usually necessary to seal the slides. The following measurements of *Corylus avellana* pollen, mounted in glycerin jelly (Christensen, 1946) indicate average size in various sediments prepared according to various methods (standard derivations were not given by Christensen).

**Table III.** *Average Size of Postglacial and Modern* Corylus avellana *Pollen Mounted in Glycerin Jelly*

| DEPOSIT | TREATMENT | AVERAGE SIZE (100 GRAINS) |
|---|---|---|
| Calcareous gyttja | KOH, acetolysis | $33.0\mu$ |
| Non-calcareous gyttja | KOH, HF, acetolysis | 27.8 |
| Non-calcareous gyttja | KOH, acetolysis | 34.6, 35.0, 36.1 |
| Sphagnum peat | KOH, acetolysis | 34.9 |
| Modern | Acetolysis | 27.3–29.2 |
| Modern | KOH, acetolysis | 30.7, 32.2 |

*Clearcol* (Wilson, 1959) is a water-soluble medium with reference index of approximately 1.4. Residues are mounted on a cover slip, which is dried and fixed to the object slide with canada balsam or a similar compound (for details, see Wilson, 1959). Fungi mounted in Clearcol have been reported to be in excellent condition after 18 years.

*Gum arabic* is mentioned by Brown (1960) as a constituent of several water-miscible mounting media (refractive index 1.45: for example, Hoyer's, and Viscol, which is no longer available). Brown had difficulty preparing one which will not dry out.

Brown (1960) mentioned several other solid mounting media (euparal, diaphane, corn syrup, piccolyte, Permount, CMC-10) but does not give their refractive indices.

## STAINING

Staining of fossil pollen grains and spores is advocated for various reasons: (1) to increase contrast of morphological details, (2) to help differentiate pollen and spores from organic detritus and other microscopic objects, and (3) to make inconspicuous and thin-walled grains more visible.

Staining may be necessary to reveal sculptural details of badly swollen "pale" pollen grains. When the grains are normal, staining decreases the transparency of dense exines, and it is particularly unfavorable for phase-contrast microscopy, in which the use of contrast color filters is preferred. Light or short wavelength provides the best resolution, and greenish-blue filters produce excellent results with unstained pollen exines. Red filters may be necessary to increase light penetration of thick-walled grains and are useful in photography.

Selective staining of pollen grains and spores can be obtained in some residues, and may be useful for deposits low in pollen (see Faegri, 1936). Staining may also, in some cases, help in differentiating various pollen and spore types (Faegri, 1936; Brown, 1960).

Staining may be helpful in detecting small or thin-walled pollen grains, which are more easily overlooked than other grains during pollen analysis, especially if somewhat swollen.

The stains commonly used in pollen analysis are soluble in water or alcohol. Such stains may be added to the residue in the centrifuge tube from a dropping bottle, either during the final water rinse (if the mounting medium is water-soluble) or in the last alcohol rinse (if the residue is dehydrated before introducing it into the mounting medium). If soluble in the mounting medium and compatible with it (Brown, 1960)[3] the stain can be added to the medium or it may be added drop by drop to the mixture of residue and mounting medium. In any case, caution should be exercised in the use of stains as it is easy to overstain, which makes the pollen grains impenetrable to light. Since the color may intensify within a day or so, it is better to have a residue that appears slightly understained.

---

[3] Most mounting media are neutral. However, as noted by Brown (1960) a few, such as Hoyer's and Cellusolve, are acid and discolor basic dyes.

Faegri (1936; see Faegri and Iversen, 1963) advocates basic fuchsin for glycerin slides. For best results, the residue is heated with KOH after acetolysis and washed with water. The fuchsin, dissolved in alcohol, can be mixed into the glycerin before adding it to the residue, or the alcohol-fuchsin mixture can be added drop by drop to the residue-glycerin mixture in a porcelain evaporating dish until the optimal color intensity is obtained (microscopic control). In some cases only pollen grains and spores absorb the stain, the detritus remaining unstained.

For silicone-oil slides I use basic fuchsin, which is added to the last alcohol rinse (previous KOH-treatment is unnecessary). The benzene bleaches the stain somewhat, and a light-reddish stain is obtained. Due to the sharpness of contrast in this medium, staining is not essential and may be omitted.

Other stains mentioned by Brown (1960) are gentian violet, safranin, methyl green, and bismarck brown.

## SEALING

Sealing may be necessary to protect the cover slip from being dislodged when the slide is to be handled frequently and is essential for slides made with volatile mounting media. The sealing material may be applied on the edges of the cover slip, but if this is done, the outermost parts of the preparation cannot be examined. If the slides are prepared with fluid mounting media, the layer of medium must be thin enough so that it is not pressed outside the cover slip when the sealing material is applied. The sealing material used should not be dissolved by the liquids used for immersion lenses.

Nail polish is a simple and effective sealing material if properly applied, although it is to some degree attacked by anisol, if that is used as the immersion liquid. It is easily applied with the small brush which accompanies the bottle and hardens very quickly. Acetone can be used as a thinner and to clean the brushes. Cellulose paint may be used in the same manner as nail polish, and for larger applications it is cheaper.

Paraffin can be used as a sealing material if it is applied under the cover slip. According to Brown (1960), a small portion of residue is placed on a slide and surrounded by small bits of paraffin. A cover slip is placed on top and the slide is heated gently until the paraffin melts and expands around the droplet of material. Some experience is necessary to avoid air bubbles and it is difficult to produce thin slides. This sealing method is very effective and can be used for volatile media. However, it may be difficult to turn the pollen grains in a paraffin-sealed slide.

Several other sealing materials exist. Phenyl formaldehyde resin (Tufon #74) and vinyl acetate resin are mentioned by Barghoorn (1947). A disadvantage of Tufon is that it is attacked by anisol. Brown (1960) mentions gold size, asphaltum varnish, Duco cement, and Zut as other sealing materials.

Slides prepared with silicone oil need no sealing. If the cover slip must be fixed this can be done with nail polish or some other sealing material, or paraffin may be used as described above for reference slides of modern pollen.

## SPECIAL MOUNTING TECHNIQUES

Various methods have been developed for the processing of slides of fossil pollen and spores for purposes other than ordinary quantitative analysis.

Absolute pollen frequency can be indicated either gravimetrically or volumetrically. For a gravimetric indication a known weight of dried sample is treated chemically, and mounting medium is added until a known volume is reached (Dimbleby, 1961), or a known volume of mounting medium is added to the residue (Muller, 1959). Liquid mounting media are best suited for this technique. A drop of the mixture of residue and mounting medium measured with a standard pipette (Muller, 1959) or with a hypodermic syringe calibrated for drop size (Dimbleby, 1961) is covered with a standard-sized cover slip, and a specified area is scanned for pollen grains and spores. A representative part of the slide must be scanned in order to avoid the effect of possible sorting under the cover slip. More reliable results are obtained if an average is computed from several slides. If a volumetric indication is preferred, a known volume of fresh and undisturbed sediment must be used; the rest of the procedure is the same. As the pollen content of sediment varies widely, and as the digestive effect of the chemical treatment depends greatly on the nature of the sediment, the quantities of sediment and mounting medium used must be adjusted to obtain a reasonable concentration of pollen grains in the slides.

### MEASUREMENT OF LARGE POLLEN GRAINS

Large pollen grains easily become deformed by pressure from the cover slip. As such deformation may affect the dimensions measured, special thick slides should be made when large pollen grains are to be measured. Cushing (1961) used small bits of a cover slip or a few grains of fine sand to support the cover slip when making measurements of *Picea* and *Pinus* pollen grains. Fiberglass wool is also effective (Gray, personal communication). Such thick slides, of course, are unsuitable for the study of small pollen grains or for quantitative pollen analysis.

### DOUBLE COVER-GLASS SLIDES

Schopf (1960) developed a technique for making double cover-glass slides using a solid mounting medium (canada balsam). The cover-glass slide is fixed to an ordinary glass slide with adhesive tape. An advantage of the method is reported to be that individual pollen grains can be studied from either side. However, removing the tape and relocating the pollen grain to be studied after turning the slide seems to be a complicated operation. The air layer between the lower cover slip and the glass slide is optically disadvantageous.

## SINGLE-GRAIN SLIDES

This technique originally was designed by Faegri (1939) for preservation of outstanding pollen finds from Quaternary samples. It probably is not applied widely for this purpose today, as photomicrography is simpler and the original slides are ruined by the procedure. The technique seems to be widely used, however, for the isolation and preservation of pre-Quaternary type specimens. To make single-grain slides the cover slip is pushed aside, keeping the selected grain under microscopic observation until it is freed. Detritus is removed from the vicinity of the pollen grain with a fine dissecting needle and the pollen grain is caught on a small piece of glycerin jelly held on the tip of the needle, or sucked into a microcapillary tube, then transferred to another slide, and covered by a small cover slip. Klaus (1953) mounts the fossil grain between two cover slips held by a cardboard holder. Mädler (1956) even makes multiple-grain slides, arranging the single grains in rows. The glycerin jelly containing the pollen grains is dried almost completely before it is covered with fresh glycerin jelly and a cover slip. A micromanipulator using a thin microcapillary tube suitable for liquid mounting media is described by Andersen (1958) for capturing single pollen grains. Single-pollen-grain preparations may be sealed with paraffin.

## REFERENCES

Andersen, S. T. (1960). Silicone oil as a mounting medium for pollen grains. Danmarks Geol. Undersg., ser. 4, v. 4, no. 1, 24 pp.

Anderson, R. Y. (1958). A micromanipulator for single-mounting microfossils. Micropaleontology, v. 4, no. 2, p. 205–206.

Barghoorn, E. S. (1947). Use of phenol formaldehyde and vinyl resins in sealing liquid mounting media on microscope slides. Science, v. 106, no. 2752, p. 299–300.

Berglund, B., G. Erdtman, and J. Praglowski (1960). Några ord om betydelsen av inbäddningsmediets brydningsindex vid palynologiska undersökningar. Svensk Bot. Tidskr., v. 53, p. 462–468.

Brown, C. A. (1960). Palynological techniques. Baton Rouge, C. A. Brown, 188 pp.

Christensen, B. B. (1946). Measurement as a means of identifying fossil pollen. Danmarks Geol. Undersg., ser. 4, v. 3, no. 2, 22 pp.

——— (1954). New mounting media for pollen grains. Danmarks Geol. Undersg., ser. 2, v. 80, p. 7–11.

Cushing, E. J. (1961). Size increase in pollen grains mounted in thin slides. Pollen et Spores, v. 3, no. 2, p. 265–274.

Dimbleby, G. W. (1961). Soil pollen analysis. J. Soil Sci., v. 12, no. 1, p. 1–11.

Faegri, K. (1936). Einige Worte über die Färbung der für die Pollenanalyse hergestellten Präparate. Geol. Fören. Stockholm Förhandl., v. 58, p. 439–443.

——— (1939). Single-grain pollen preparations. Geol. Fören. Stockholm Förhandl., v. 61, no. 6, p. 513–514.

———, and J. Iversen (1963). Textbook of modern pollen analysis. 2nd ed. Copenhagen, Ejnar Munksgaard, 168 pp.

Funkhouser, J. W., and W. R. Evitt (1959). Preparation techniques for acid-insoluble microfossils. Micropaleontology, v. 5, no. 3, p. 369–375.

Jeffords, R. M., and D. H. Jones (1959). Preparation of slides for spores and other microfossils. J. Paleontology, v. 33, no. 2, p. 344–347.

Klaus, W. (1953). Zur Einzelpräparation fossiler Sporomorphen. Mikroscopie, v. 8, no. 1 & 2, p. 1–14.

Mädler, K. A. (1956). A technique for the preparation of multi-grain palynological slides. Micropaleontology, v. 2, no. 4, p. 399–401.

Muller, J. (1959). Palynology of Recent Orinoco delta and shelf sediments. Micropaleontology, v. 5, no. 1, p. 1–32.

Schopf, J. M. (1960). Double cover-glass slides for plant microfossils. Micropaleontology, v. 6, no. 2, p. 237–240.

Wilson, L. R. (1959). A water-miscible mountant for palynology. Oklahoma Geology notes, v. 19, no. 5, p. 110–111.

# Preparation of Modern Pollen and Spores for Palynological Reference Collections

ALFRED TRAVERSE

*Shell Development Company (A Division of Shell Oil Company), Exploration and Production Research Division, Houston, Texas*

Flowering plants first appear in the fossil record in the Lower Cretaceous. From that point on, through the Cenozoic, there is increasing utility, both for the paleoecologist and for the stratigraphically oriented palynologist, in comparing modern angiosperm pollen types with fossil angiosperm pollen. For fossil gymnosperm pollen and for fossil spores produced by ferns and other lower embryophytes, comparison with modern types can sometimes be rewarding even for late Paleozoic material. Such comparisons enable one to discover taxonomic and phylogenetic relationships and to interpret environments. They are also an aid in understanding pollen and spore morphology. A full knowledge of pollen and spores of recent plants can be helpful in interpreting features of fossil specimens, even when the identity of the specimens in question remains unknown. Thus, the comparative modern pollen

Shell Development Company Publication No. 316.

and spore collection is an essential working tool for most palynologists, and the time and care necessary to prepare, curate, and study the modern collection is well spent.

## COLLECTING POLLEN AND SPORES FOR POLLEN REFERENCE COLLECTIONS

### WHERE TO GET MATERIAL

A herbarium is the best source of pollen and spores for reference collections (Traverse, 1955). There are several reasons for this, of which the most important is identification. Herbarium specimens which have been collected and determined by competent taxonomic botanists ordinarily have a higher level of reliability of identification than material collected from a living plant by a palynologist. Furthermore, a herbarium specimen provides an anchor— a "voucher" it is usually called—the identity of which is amenable to investigation long after the polleniferous material has been removed. Secondary advantages of using material from an existing herbarium are the ease with which pollen from a large number of species from different parts of the world can be assembled, and the fact that if duplicate pollen slides are prepared for the herbarium, a contribution of potential taxonomic value is made to the herbarium.

A palynologist who collects his own material from living plants should make voucher herbarium specimens from each plant sampled, or from identical plants at the same location in the case of small herbs. It is wise for a palynologist to have the taxonomic identity of the vouchers checked. If his experience tallies with mine he will be humbled by how often he has been wrong in the field.

### HOW TO COLLECT MATERIAL FROM HERBARIUM SHEETS

It is, of course, necessary to get permission! If the herbarium curator has a modern attitude, and especially if you offer him duplicate slides, this is usually not a problem, though some curators have unfortunately had bad experiences with predatory palynologists and are very cautious about granting permission.

Inspect the sheets of a species in which you are interested. Avoid a sheet with so few flowers that it will be damaged by your work. All of the material from one pollen preparation should come from a single sheet. Use fine forceps, fine scissors, or razor blades to remove the flowers needed. If possible, collect flower buds on the point of opening. These will contain ripe pollen, but the pollen will not have shed. For amentiferous trees, such as *Betula* (birch), and for conifers, such as *Taxodium* (swamp cypress), take care to get portions of catkins or male cones containing abundant pollen, but which have not yet burst open and shed. For plants with separate male and female flowers, such as *Diospyros* or *Morus,* be sure to collect male flowers! It is important to use common sense in some other ways—don't take more material than you need. One or two heads from a plant such as *Ambrosia* (ragweed) will contain enough pollen to provide slides for every palynologist in North America. For plants with large flowers, such as *Liriodendron* (tulip tree) or *Opuntia* (prickly pear), it is only necessary to collect a few anthers. Collecting the whole flower in such instances is unnecessary and merely complicates later preparation techniques. When collecting from families whose flowering habits are unknown to you, refer to such plant taxonomy books as the Engler-Diels *Syllabus der Pflanzenfamilien* (Diels, 1936) so that you don't collect female flowers or small fruits.

In collecting from spore-bearing plants such as ferns, the same principles are followed, except that it is even more critical to take care that the spores have not already been shed. In many ferns the release of spores is very efficient, and if the sporangia have opened, little will be obtained on maceration but the annuli of the sporangia. Use a stereoscopic microscope, or at least a good hand lens, to examine the sori (groups of sporangia). In most ferns the sori are on the underside of the leaves, and the best way to collect them in the herbarium is to cut out a sector of a leaf with scissors or razor blade.

For complete records it is desirable to annotate the herbarium sheets to show that material has been removed for pollen preparation. Printed labels (fig. 1) are adequate for this purpose.

The buds, portions of catkins, and pieces of soriferous fern leaves, should be put into carefully labeled envelopes immediately on collection. A printed form envelope (fig. 1) is best for this purpose, since it assures that data will be obtained systematically on the name of the plant, the name of the collector and his field number, the location from which he collected the plants, and the herbarium where the sheet is deposited.

COLLECTION OF FRESH POLLENIFEROUS MATERIAL

As has already been emphasized, I advocate the collection of pollen-bearing plant material by the conventional methods of plant taxonomists—that is, preparation of pressed and dried plants, mounted on paper as herbarium specimens (for techniques, see Lawrence, 1951). Occasionally, however, one may wish to make pollen preparations from living plants without making voucher herbarium specimens. In these instances, collect flowers, male cones and so on, using the same precautions as mentioned for collecting from sheets in a herbarium. The polleniferous material is put into carefully labeled vials of glacial acetic acid. Alcohol or acetone are sometimes used but are too volatile for prolonged storage. Since it will be relatively troublesome to work on the material later, when it is wet with acetic acid, be sure to dissect off as much of the extraneous organs as possible—peduncles, involucres, sepals, and so forth. Subsequent treatment will destroy much of the substance of these organs, but the more removed during collection, the cleaner will be the final preparations.

**Fig. 1.** *Collecting a polleniferous flower bud from a herbarium sheet. Note the label applied just above the herbarium label, indicating that the sheet has been sampled for pollen. Note also the form envelope into which the bud will be placed.*

## MACERATION OF POLLENIFEROUS MATERIAL

The botanist who looked at pollen a century ago—usually for taxonomic purposes—made mounts of whole pollen by very simple techniques. Today some plant taxonomists, and nearly all pollen allergy specialists and investigators of pollen in honey, still do this. The grains are dissected out of anthers onto a microscope slide, sometimes treated with a little alcohol or ether to remove oil droplets, then mounted in glycerin, glycerin jelly, lacto-phenol, or lactic acid. Lactic acid has been a special favorite of plant tax-onomists. It "clears" the grains (makes them more nearly transparent), and also expands them. Unfortunately, the clearing action and expansion con-tinue indefinitely, the degree of disintegration being greater in some families of plants than in others—the exine of some groups is completely destroyed over a period of years (E. S. Barghoorn, personal communication).

The drawback shared by *all* techniques for mounting whole pollen is that, although the critical features of pollen morphology are those of the outermost shell (the exine), the presence of intine and cell contents in whole pollen obscures optical observation of the exine. Taxonomic botanists have long employed study of gross pollen morphology as an auxiliary tool in their in-vestigations of flowering plant relationships. For these studies they have tra-ditionally used temporary mounts of whole pollen, as described above. The technique is simple, rapid, and requires no fume hood or centrifuge. But since the important morphological features (sculpturing, pores, furrows, wall struc-ture) are features of the exine (see fig. 2), it is really desirable for nearly all purposes of comparative study of pollen to remove the protoplasmic contents of the grains, and the cellulosic inner layer of the shell (intine), as well as oil droplets and other substances that may adhere to the outside of the exine.

The exine is composed mostly of a C—H—O compound of amazing dura-bility, usually called sporopollenin. Fossil pollen consists only of this durable outer coat, which fortunately bears the distinctive features by which pollen is identified! Pollen destined to become fossil typically falls into water, expands fully, and soon loses its protoplasmic contents and nonsporopollenin shell constituents to the action of bacteria and hydrolysis. This paper will therefore be limited largely to the discussion of techniques that "fossilize"—destroy everything but the exine—modern pollen and spores. To recognize the optical advantages of macerating pollen, one need only compare pollen photos made from whole pollen (e.g., in Hyde and Adams, 1958) with photos of pollen prepared by techniques that "fossilize" (see, for example, Erdtman, et al., 1961).

One of the greatest contributions made by Erdtman to palynology was the introduction and popularization of the acetylation[1] technique for preparing modern pollen and spores. The method consists basically in briefly heating the pollen, or the floral material containing the pollen, in a mixture of acetic anhydride and sulfuric acid. Cellulosic floral tissues and all parts of the pollen except the exine are destroyed. Even the exine is somewhat modified, as reflected by chemical analysis, by the swelling of the grains and the produc-tion of burnt yellow to orange color in them. Moreover, Larson and Lewis's (1961) electron microscopic studies show that acetylation causes considera-ble change in the exine.

---

[1] Erdtman calls it *acetolysis,* and most palynologists have followed him, but the word used by chemists for anhydrous digestion of cellulose in acetic anhydride is *acetylation.*

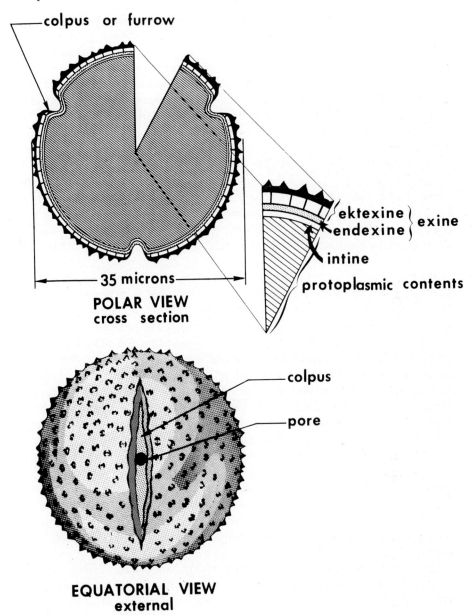

**Fig. 2.** *Polar and equatorial views of a hypothetical tricolporate pollen grain, showing the important anatomical and morphological features.*

Most palynologists who macerate modern pollen prepare it by some modification of the acetylation technique. As suggested above, however, acetylation is known to be quite rough on pollen. Hence there is some support for the gentler technique of alkali-maceration by boiling pollen briefly in 5 percent or 10 percent KOH. This treatment also removes intine and cell contents from pollen but affects the exine less than acetylation, provided that boiling is not prolonged. Continued boiling will destroy some exines. Pollen and spores have very little color after KOH treatment and should be stained with a red stain such as safranin or fuchsin. Red stains should be used, according to Faegri (personal communication), because optical systems are corrected for green light. If green light is used for microscopy (by employing a filter), optimum resolution is obtained with red-stained objects. Acetylated grains may also be stained, but can be studied and photographed (best with a green filter) quite satisfactorily without staining. Alkali-maceration is better than acetylation for some delicate pollen types, such as those of the family *Lauraceae*. But for palynologists who are interested in comparison of modern with fossil pollen, this refinement is hardly necessary; a pollen that does not survive acetylation very well, such as *Sassafras*, will not survive degradation in a sediment, let alone maceration of the sediment in the laboratory.

Whatever maceration technique is employed, the specimen in question is first assigned a laboratory number which is recorded in a permanent book. The number follows the specimen throughout its preparation, and much difficulty can be avoided if care is taken about this. (The number is written on the vial of the finished product, as well as scratched on the slides as they are prepared.) The specimen of floral material is next dissected on a fresh sheet of paper, removing with forceps and other tools as much as conveniently possible of the still remaining cellulosic and lignified accessory tissue. The remaining material containing the pollen is finely crushed; a mortar and pestle is used by some palynologists, followed by wet sieving in alcohol or acetone. I have used a set of stainless steel screens (see figs. 3 and 4). The floral material is crushed on the upper screen by rubbing with thumb and forefinger. The upper screen is removed, and a jet of acetone from a wash bottle is used to wash the material through the fine lower screen into a glass funnel, which stands in a centrifuge tube. More acetone is used to flush particles on the funnel into the centrifuge tube, in which the maceration is next carried out. The acetone serves to dissolve oil droplets and waxes that are present on some grains.

As already mentioned, acetylation turns pollen exines various hues of yellow and orange, depending mostly on the thickness of the exine. Some thick-walled types (e.g., *Malvaceae*) turn such a deep hue of orange-brown that they are nearly opaque. These grains must be bleached after acetylation in order to study them satisfactorily. Some form of chlorination is the usual method. Some palynologists regularly prepare slides that contain both bleached and unbleached grains. This may be an unnecessary refinement, however, because less than one percent of pollen types require bleaching, and it is a relatively easy matter to go back and bleach the few types that are too dark in the original preparations.

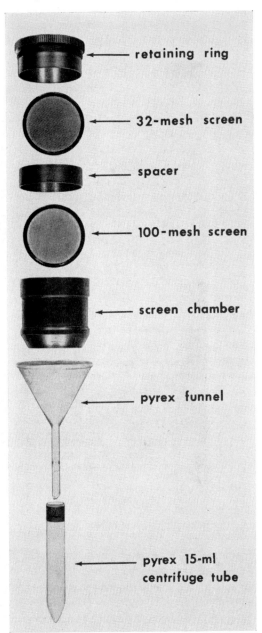

**Fig. 3**

*Exploded drawing of stainless steel screen set used to grind polleniferous material for preparation of modern pollen. Squares of screen placed directly over funnels can also be used, grinding the material through the coarse screen first, then washing (with acetone) the pulverized material through the fine screen into a second funnel and thus into a centrifuge tube.*

## MOUNTING MEDIA AND PERMANENCE OF PREPARATIONS

The majority of palynologists use glycerin jelly for mounting modern pollen on microscope slides. It has many advantages: (1) water solubility, permitting easy transfer from a final water wash of the maceration into mounting

**Fig. 4.** *Grinding polleniferous material through the screen unit shown in Figure 4, into a centrifuge tube.*

medium; (2) easy and low-temperature melting-gelation, making possible a variety of manipulations, such as Erdtman's slide technique (described later in this article) and the various single-grain techniques (see Schedule C-8); and (3) refractive index of 1.4258 (measured from commercially prepared glycerin jelly from W. H. Curtin Company), offering good contrast with the average refractive index of pollen exines, which is about 1.5 according to Ikuse (1953).

Glycerin jelly does have disadvantages. It is not as permanent as might be desired, and it will eventually dry out and crack. In my experience, all the more common mounting media, as well as several dozen of the newer plastics that seemed promising from their data sheets, have proved wanting in one respect or another. The most frequent objection to "substitutes" for glycerin jelly is the refractive index. Canada balsam, for example, has an index of 1.5, too close to that of pollen exines for best microscopic resolution.

Many of my preparations are now more than twelve years old. A selected group of these, for which measurements made in 1950 could be repeated in 1961, showed the following changes in condition (in percent):

| AMOUNT OF SWELLING | NUMBER OF SPECIES |
|:---:|:---:|
| 0 | 13 |
| 1–5 | 7 |
| 6–10 | 11 |
| 20 | 16 |
| >20 | 1 |

Of this selected group of 48 species, widely distributed among the seed plants and ferns, 73 percent showed some swelling. The more extreme cases of swelling are associated with some to considerable exine degradation. Cushing (1961) observed the same sort of swelling in pollen mounted in glycerin jelly and noted that it is correlated with the thickness of the layer of glycerin jelly between cover slip and slide. Cushing feels that the glycerin jelly causes the swelling, but I do not believe that this is so: Duplicate macerated pollen of the preparations for which the swelling data are listed above was stored in glycerin jelly in vials at the same time the slides were made in 1950. New slides made from the stored material of species which are badly degraded on the old slides show pollen in the quite fresh condition! (The value of saving duplicate material of modern pollen preparations is obvious: slides found in degraded condition can easily be replaced with new slides.) Contrary to Cushing, I believe that something happens to pollen in glycerin jelly on microscope slides that doesn't happen to pollen stored in glycerin jelly in vials. This observation proves that the observed degradation is not caused by the glycerin jelly but by compression, contact with glass, and/or by relatively greater exposure to the air.

Degradation of pollen on slides also occurs in other mounting media. In slides made with some of the new plastics, I found severe degradation in a matter of a day or two! Barghoorn (personal communication) has observed advanced degradation of exines in old canada balsam mounts. It is probable that thorough washing of the residues before mounting retards the reaction, or to put it the other way around, a poorly washed residue is likely to degrade more rapidly than a well-washed one.

NOTES ON SLIDE-MAKING TECHNIQUES

The older slide-making technique consisted in putting a drop of molten (about 50°C) glycerin jelly containing a representative portion of the pollen residue on a slide, covering it with a cover slip, and ringing it with some resin or varnish. Erdtman, Faegri, and others use a smaller amount of jelly, so that it doesn't reach the edge of the cover slip, and the slide is sealed by surrounding the jelly with paraffin wax. Cushing's (1961) evidence that the thinness of the glycerin jelly film may determine the degree of pollen degradation suggests that the wax technique might be beneficial in holding up the cover slip. Erdtman and others advocate hanging the freshly made slides upside-down to get the pollen to lie close to the cover slip for oil-immersion microscopy. It may be that Erdtman's wax-sealing technique produces such a thick film of glycerin jelly that this is helpful. I have had no difficulty in focusing an oil immersion objective on pollen in my old-style slides, which are made with thin cover slips (No. 0 and No. 1).

## PREPARATION SCHEDULES FOR MODERN POLLEN

### INTRODUCTORY NOTE

There are really only two techniques that are commonly used to prepare modern pollen: alkali maceration and acetylation (not counting whole mount techniques mentioned above). Of these acetylation is by far the most common. Other techniques have been described (see Brown, 1960), but they are of minor significance, and no practical purpose would be served by outlining them here. The same is true of the many variations on Erdtman's acetylation technique.

Erdtman's technique yields preparations of acetylated pollen or—if acetylated pollen is too dark—of a mixture of acetylated pollen and pollen chlorinated after acetylation. The purpose of the chlorination is to bleach pollen that has been turned too dark by acetylation. As previously pointed out, bleaching is not often really necessary.

### SCHEDULE A—ERDTMAN ACETYLATION TECHNIQUE (1960)

1. Grind pollen-bearing or spore-bearing material through fine bronze screen into a glass funnel standing in a centrifuge tube.
2. Wash down funnel into tube with acetylation mixture (1 volume conc. $H_2SO_4$, 9 volumes acetic anhydride). Add the acid to the anhydride slowly, with swirling to prevent buildup of hot spots. Make a fresh mixture each time.
3. Transfer the tube to a copper water bath, and heat from room temperature to boiling in a fume hood. Stir the tubes occasionally with glass rods. Stop heating when the water boils, and leave the tube in the bath for 15 minutes.
4. Centrifuge. Decant the acetylation mixture into a storage bottle for later safe disposal. Add a mixture of water and 95 percent alcohol (3:1) and shake very thoroughly. Pour suspension from the tube (A) through a fine brass screen into a funnel standing in another centrifuge tube (B).
5. Clean tube A and pour suspension from tube B through a screen into tube A,

as in step 4. Centrifuge, decant, and stand the tube upside-down on filter paper. If desired, make a test slide at this point to determine whether to bleach.

6. If bleaching is not required, add 50 percent glycerin to tube A, shake well, and allow to stand for at least 10 minutes. Centrifuge, decant, stand tube upside-down on filter paper, preferably in an oven at 50°C for 2 to 24 hours, to drain and dry.

7. If bleaching is required, fill tube A with water, shake and pour one-third to one-half of material into tube B. Centrifuge tube B, decant, transfer to fume hood. Add 2 ml glacial acetic acid, 2 to 3 drops sat. $NaClO_3$ solution, and last, 2 to 3 drops of concentrated HCl. Stir. Bleaching takes a minute or less. Centrifuge, decant, wash twice with water. Add water, shake, and recombine with unbleached material in tube A. Centrifuge, decant, add 50 percent glycerin, shake well, proceed as in step 6.

8. Get a bit of glycerin jelly about the size of a pinhead onto a clean platinum needle. Touch the jelly to the dry pollen residue in tube A. Put the bit of jelly with pollen on slide, melt by gentle heating, spread out evenly with needle, rewarm slide, cover. The polleniferous blob should be 2 to 3 mm in diameter. Melt a bit of paraffin wax on the slide near the cover slip so that the wax melts and runs under the cover slip. Lay the slide face down on a wooden frame until the wax hardens. Scrape off excess wax. Clean with xylol.

9. Store leftover dry pollen in glycerin or silicone oil.

Faegri's method is relatively complex, producing slides that contain pollen prepared in several ways. Such slides are favored by Faegri for critical study of pollen anatomy. Faegri's completed preparations contain pollen in the folowing conditions: (1) unmacerated, stained; (2) acetylated, alkali-treated, stained; (3) acetylated, chlorinated, alkali-treated, stained; and (4) *Corylus avellana* L. (hazelnut) pollen added to the original material so that each slide has *Corylus* pollen of known average size in conditions 1, 2, and 3.

Faegri's preparations are impressive. The staining is advantageous in some instances. Chlorination (bleaching) is seldom necessary, as already mentioned, yet is routine in Faegri's preparations. The addition of *Corylus* pollen is a good idea, if one wants an index that will show the effect of treatment on size of pollen for calculation of a size-correction factor. Faegri's elaborate preparation technique may seem unnecessarily demanding, but the extra steps have been reduced to such a routine in his laboratory that the total operation takes very little more time than straight acetylation takes me.

It will be noted that Faegri follows acetylation and chlorination with KOH boiling. The primary purpose of this is to remove the acidic reagents left over from acetylation, and hence prevent after-effects, which may cause deterioration of the pollen. The follow-up alkali treatment also serves to produce pollen comparable in size to that prepared by KOH boiling alone. (Some palynologists boil pollen in KOH *before* acetylation—for example, J. Iversen and his students, according to J. Gray, personal communication.) Schedule B is based on correspondence with K. Faegri and on notes made from personal observation in his laboratory.

SCHEDULE B—FAEGRI MODIFIED ACETYLATION METHOD

1. Grind anthers, or whole flowers if small, in a china mortar with a little chloroform, ether, or acetone, to dissolve wax and oils on grains.

2. Sieve through fine-meshed metal sieve under jet of 96 percent alcohol.

3. Add (to yield about 10 percent concentration) standard *Corylus avellana* L. pollen. Centrifuge the mixture, decant.

4. Divide residue into three portions (A, B, C). Set aside portion A, which should be much smaller than portions B and C because much of these portions is generally lost.

5. Acetylate portions B and C in a 9:1 mixture of acetic anhydride and concentrated $H_2SO_4$ mixture (see step 2, schedule A). Add the mixture to the samples in centrifuge tubes, and heat in water bath to 100°C. Centrifuge. Decant (see precautions in step 4, schedule A, and in step 3, schedule C).

6. Add glacial acetic acid. Separate portions B and C now if they were acetylated as one. Do not centrifuge.

7. Chlorinate portion B. (Add $\frac{1}{2}$ ml of a saturated solution of $NaClO_3$, 3 to 5 drops concentrated HCl.) Centrifuge portions B and C separately.

8. Keeping portions B and C separate, wash them with water, and then combine the two portions.

9. Bring the combined residue to a boil in 10 percent KOH. Centrifuge.

10. Wash the residue in water. Centrifuge. Add portion A and centrifuge. Repeat the washing. Add a suitable quantity of basic fuchsin solution to the wash water in the centrifuge tube, shake, centrifuge.

11. Transfer to a watch glass containing a little water. Add a small piece of glycerin jelly, and heat until the jelly is melted. Concentration of the jelly can be effected by evaporation.

12. Transfer a small piece of the jelly to a slide, and heat gently until the piece has rounded. Add some small pieces of high-melting-point paraffin wax, and heat until the paraffin has melted. The two liquids will appear to run together. Cover with a cover slip. The wax will separate from the jelly and form a neat protecting seal around the jelly. The piece of jelly should be small enough so that no jelly reaches the edge of the cover slip for the paraffin to form a complete seal.

SCHEDULE C—TRAVERSE ACETYLATION METHOD
WITH NOTES ON THE ALKALI METHOD AND
ON SINGLE-GRAIN SLIDES

1. Pulverize the pollen-bearing material by rubbing it with the fingers through a 32-mesh stainless steel screen disk into a funnel standing in a centrifuge tube. Wash this material with acetone through a 100-mesh screen into a second funnel and tube, or arrange the disks one above the other (see figs. 3 and 4), in which case the coarser screen can be removed after the original pulverizing and the acetone used to wash the pollen through the second, finer, screen and into the funnel. Wash down the funnel into the tube. (After use, the screens are cleaned with a toothbrush and, finally, by flaming.)

2. Centrifuge off the acetone and discard. Add enough acetylation mixture (see

step 2, schedule A) to the 15-ml centrifuge tube to nearly fill it. Put a stirring rod in the tube. Put the tube in an aluminum block at 100°C (see fig. 5). Leave the tube in the block for 7 to 10 minutes. Such blocks have many advantages over oil and water baths: they need never be refilled; are not messy; no water drops form on the inside of centrifuge tubes, spoiling the effectiveness of the acetylation mixture; aluminum is an excellent heat conductor.

3. Centrifuge, then decant the acetylation mixture into running water under a hood, or into a large container of water.

4. Wash the residue with glacial acetic acid. Centrifuge. Wash with water, stirring and shaking vigorously, and repeat this treatment until wash water is clear and no smell of acetic acid remains in it. Invert tubes on filter paper long enough to drain off excess drops of water.

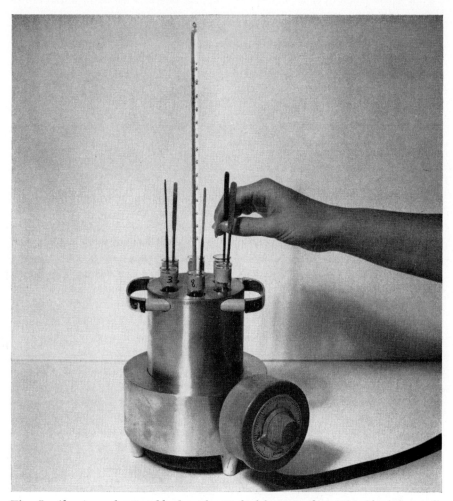

**Fig. 5.** *Aluminum heating block with attached heating plate. This block has wells that hold six 15-ml centrifuge tubes and a thermometer.*

5. Add molten (50°C) glycerin jelly to the residue. Make slides by placing a drop of this mixture on a slide and covering. The excess of glycerin jelly preparation can be stored in labeled vials. When the jelly on the slides has become firm, ring the cover slip with resin varnish that has been allowed to thicken in air before using, so that it will form a substantial coating around the cover slip. In some instances the jelly does not readily become firm on the slide. This can sometimes be corrected by heating the slides on a warming table for a few days to drive off excess water. Sometimes, however, the problem is that the gelatin has denatured. Such gelatin will never gel, in which case the only solution is to dissolve the original glycerin jelly residue in warm water, centrifuge, decant and add melted fresh jelly. Denaturation usually results from keeping jelly melted for long periods, remelting it too many times, or overheating it.

6. If examination of slides in step 5 shows that pollen is too dark, wash out the glycerin jelly from a portion of the residue with hot water, centrifuge, and bleach as follows: mix the residue with enough 5 percent solution of sodium chlorite ($NaClO_2$) to nearly fill a 15-ml centrifuge tube. Acidify with a few drops of 10 percent HCl. Bleach for 1 to 3 minutes, depending on how dark the pollen is. The amount of bleaching is dependent on time and pH. Since chlorine gas and $ClO_2$ are evolved, bleaching must be done under a hood. Centrifuge, wash until clear, centrifuging after each wash, and proceed as in step 5.

*Alkali-maceration method.* If examination of slides in step 5 shows that pollen was destroyed or degraded by acetylation:

1. Prepare material as in step 1, schedule C but take greater pains to remove extraneous matter, as alkali will not destroy as much of it as will acetylation.

2. After centrifuging off and discarding the acetone from the previous step, add enough 5 percent KOH nearly to fill a 15-ml centrifuge tube. Cook at 100°C for ten minutes in a water bath or aluminum heating block, as described in step 2. Centrifuge and decant.

3. Wash thoroughly with water until clear, shaking well and centrifuging with each water wash. (If it is desired to remove all the potassium, the first wash should be in dilute HCl. Considerable potassium combines chemically with the sporopollenin.) Add a drop of 0.5 percent aqueous solution of basic fuchsin stain or some other red stain to the final wash water. (The use of basic fuchsin ordinarily assumes that distilled water, *not acid,* was used for the washing.) Centrifuge, add molten glycerin jelly, and proceed as in step 5, schedule C.

*Single-grain preparations.* Slides containing only single pollen grains or spores can be made by means of techniques described by Faegri (1939), Faegri and Iversen (1950), Muller (as reported by Erdtman, 1952), and others. The most common method is first to isolate a desired pollen grain with needles, working at low microscopic power on a slide with no cover slip. The pollen residue on the slide is in a glycerin-alcohol mixture. (The alcohol reduces the viscosity of the glycerin to a workable level and must be replaced as it evaporates.) A small piece of glycerin jelly on the point of a needle is touched to the grain, which readily adheres, and the piece of jelly is transferred to a slide, which is warmed to melt the jelly, covered with a cover slip, and sealed with melted paraffin, which flows under the cover slip and surrounds the small bit of melted jelly containing the desired pollen grain.

## REFERENCES

Brown, C. A. (1960). Palynological techniques. Baton Rouge, C. A. Brown, 188 pp.

Cushing, E. J. (1961). Size increase in pollen grains mounted in thin slides. Pollen et Spores, v. 3, no. 2, p. 265–274.

Diels, L. (1936). A. Engler's Syllabus der Pflanzenfamilien. Berlin, Gebrüder Borntraeger, 419 pp.

Erdtman, G. (1952). Pollen morphology and plant taxonomy—angiosperms. Stockholm, Almquist and Wiksell, 539 pp.

————— (1960). The acetolysis method—a revised description. Svensk Bot. Tidskr., v. 54, no. 4, p. 561–564.

—————, B. Berglund, and J. Praglowski (1961). An introduction to a Scandinavian pollen flora. Grana Palynologica, v. 2, no. 3, p. 3–92.

Faegri, K. (1939). Single-grain pollen preparations, a practical suggestion. Geol. Fören. Förhandl., v. 61, no. 4, p. 513–514.

—————, and J. Iversen (1950). Textbook of modern pollen analysis. Copenhagen, Ejnar Munksgaard, 168 pp.

Hyde, H. A., and K. F. Adams (1958). An Atlas of airbourne pollen grains. London, Macmillan, 112 pp.

Ikuse, M. (1953). On the indices of refraction of pollen grains. J. Jap. Bot., v. 28, no. 6, p. 186–189.

Larson, D. A., and C. W. Lewis, Jr. (1961). Fine structure of *Parkinsonia aculeata* pollen; I. The pollen wall. Am. J. Botany, v. 48, no. 10, p. 934–943.

Lawrence, G. H. M. (1951). Taxonomy of vascular plants. New York, Macmillan, p. 234–262.

Traverse, A. (1955). Pollen analysis of the Brandon Lignite of Vermont. U. S. Bureau of Mines, R.I. 5151, 167 pp.

# Trapping Methods for Modern Pollen Rain Studies

DONALD M. LEWIS, EUGENE C. OGDEN

*New York State Museum and Science Service*

Much of the pollen found in the sediments of bogs and lakes was produced by anemophilous plants in the surrounding area. It was carried by air currents

Published by permission of the Assistant Commissioner, New York State Museum and Science Service.

and fell like rain onto the earth's surface. The composition of this pollen rain should reflect the composition of the vegetation that produced it. Assuming the fossil pollen assemblage to be indicative of the vegetation that produced it, a study of modern pollen rain in relation to present vegetation should aid in interpreting the environments responsible for the pollen recorded in pollen diagrams. However, determining the composition of modern pollen rains in relation to fossil pollen spectra has long posed a problem for analysts because methods which determine the composition of pollen in the air may not give a true indication of the pollen that becomes preserved in the sediments (Faegri and Iversen, 1950, p. 34).

In choosing a sampler which will accurately record the fall of pollen and other spores onto bog and lake surfaces, we must consider the factors that affect the pollen falling onto such surfaces (Gregory, 1961). These are essentially plane surfaces of minimal elevation in relation to adjacent topographic features, and as such are less influenced by the meteorological factors, wind speed and air turbulence; deposition is presumed to take place by gravity as well as by impaction. But differences in topography, surrounding forest density, and the nature of the surface upon which the pollen is deposited (open water, sphagnum mat, or low-growing shrub community) will influence local meteorological conditions and cause variation in the degree to which impaction is a factor in spore capture. Consideration of these factors makes it appear unlikely that any local study of modern pollen rain, regardless of how carefully executed, could have broad regional application.

Modern pollen-rain samplers should simulate, as nearly as possible, the manner in which pollen is trapped at the surface of bogs and lakes. Some of the methods employed to recover modern rains are the analyses of bryophytic polsters, surface soil and litter samples, and uppermost sediments of lakes. Artificial traps such as exposed petri plates and microscope slides, rain gauges, and pollen samplers for aerobiological studies are also used. All of these methods have shortcomings.

From modern pollen sampling we want to determine the kinds and amounts of pollen trapped on bog and lake surfaces to gain some insight into the relative production and dispersal of pollen of different species and their variation from year to year. This information may shed some light on questions of long-distance transport of pollens and their differential preservation, their differential loss in laboratory processing, their possible morphological modification, and so on. Most of the methods for sampling pollen rains mentioned above require centrifugation, filtration, or chemical treatment, and there is no guarantee that the original pollen deposit is not modified in the process. Even samples representing one or more recent growing seasons may have been modified by biotic, chemical, or mechanical means. The sample should allow for analysis without treatment as well as by the methods of processing usually employed in fossil pollen analyses, in order to give a comparison between the unmodified pollen rain and that affected by harsh chemical treatment. It should be borne in mind that modern pollen rains have not been extensively investigated [1] and that the following field and laboratory techniques are subject to improvement.

## BRYOPHYTIC POLSTERS

Analysis of polsters of mosses, liverworts, and lichens has been frequently employed to sample modern pollen rains (Carrol, 1943; Hansen, 1949; Potzger, et al., 1956; Benninghoff, 1960; Potter and Rowley, 1960). It has been found that the more compact growth forms are superior to the loose, many-branched forms as pollen traps (Carrol, 1943). The site for collections must be carefully selected, and should not be unduly influenced by the proximity of plants producing abundant pollen. Several samples should be taken according to some standard ecological technique. The polster collections should be representative of the pollen rain over the last few seasons. Problems of differential vertical migration of pollen and unusual deposition due to peculiar meteorological conditions must be considered. We are usually interested in obtaining proportional rather than quantitative pollen data, hence polster size need not be closely controlled, but the sample must be adequate for laboratory concentration of the pollen. To recover the pollen and other spores, the polsters are generally agitated in water or alcohol and the supernatant liquid decanted. The material in this liquid is then allowed to settle or is centrifuged, prepared by KOH or acetolysis methods, and mounted for microscopic examination.

## SOIL SURFACE

Samples may be taken from the surface of materials not generally incorporated in deposits analyzed for pollen. Chiefly these include forest litter and mineral soils (Dimbleby, 1957; Bent and Wright, 1963). Here again, control of the period of pollen accumulation is difficult, and soil microorganisms may degrade or destroy some of the pollen. The compactness of the soil or litter will probably also influence differential vertical migration of the spores. Litter samples usually are composed of coarse, lignified material. Extraneous matter may be removed by hand sorting or a procedure similar to that used with bryophytic polsters. Pollen is concentrated by the KOH-acetolysis method.

Soil samples may be taken with vials from the upper centimeter or so of a mineral soil surface. If the samples can be deflocculated easily a method of heavy liquid concentration of spores, such as the bromoform-acetone method, may be used. Otherwise, it may be necessary to employ hydrofluoric acid digestion. The concentrated organic fraction is prepared for analysis by one of the standard methods.

---

[1] For a review of early methods see Erdtman (1943) and Faegri and Iversen (1950).

## LAKE BOTTOM

Since many pollen analysts prefer to study cores taken from lake sediments rather than those taken from bogs, it is natural that they would attempt to correlate present vegetation with the pollen assemblages found in the upper-most sediments of the lakes being sampled. The simplest way of doing this is to correlate the pollen spectrum from the top layer of sediment in the core with the local vegetational analysis (Benninghoff, 1960). Samples may also be taken directly from the sediment surface with shell vials (Davis and Goodlett, 1960) or with equipment employed by limnologists, such as the Eckman dredge (Welch, 1948), especially designed to take a surface sample of sediments from relatively deep lakes. Samples are prepared routinely by the KOH or acetolysis methods. Samples that have been contaminated through stream action or erosion processes should be avoided; the presence of considerable mineral material is one of the clues. With lake sediment samples there is even less control of the period of accumulation than with polsters, and sedimentation rate may vary greatly from lake to lake. There may be no good way to determine whether a given sample of the "surface" may represent 5, 10, 20, or more years of accumulation; this will depend on sedimentation rate and whether there is free, restricted, or no vertical migration of pollen in this layer. Here too, we have to consider the possibility of differential flotation of pollens as reported by several workers and its possible effect on the pollen assemblage over different zones of the lake bottom (Hopkins, 1950; Faegri and Iversen, 1950, p. 96; Brown, 1960, p. 127). A straight-walled jar placed on the lake bottom may or may not yield a sample free from these problems.

## RAIN GAUGES AND SIMILAR DEVICES

These samplers cannot be considered true depositional devices. Anything constructed above the general ground surface will alter natural pollen sedimentation processes. There may be considerable differences in the collection efficiency of rain gauges, especially during windy periods (Ranson and Leopold, 1962). The accuracy of these traps in fair weather is suspect, but pollen "scrubbed" from the air in rain showers should provide good samples (McDonald, 1962). If these samplers are used during rainy periods they may give information on the importance of such conditions in differentially removing pollen from air. In these samples the pollen is concentrated by centrifuging and decanting the water contained in the trap. One must take into consideration the variation in pollen with regard to its ability to float for long periods and the effect of such variation on pollen recovery.

Stock watering tanks have been employed in the study of modern pollen rains, particularly in the southwestern United States (Hafsten, 1961; Martin and Gray, 1962). The effect of local air turbulence around these structures will influence pollen deposition as it does in rain gauges, but in spite of this drawback good correlation between the pollen recovered from these tanks and the composition of surrounding vegetation has been reported.

Sediment from the bottom of the tanks may be prepared for study in much the same manner as that from the uppermost part of the lake bottom. The worker has the advantage of greater knowledge of the age of deposits in these artificial traps.

## SUNKEN JARS

Straight-walled containers which collect spores in much the same manner as the standard rain gauge may also be used (Lewis, 1962). Several variations are employed in this type of sampling in attempts to minimize some of the defects. A battery jar may be buried to such a depth (preferably to within an inch of the top) that the exposed rim will not be a factor in creating local turbulence (fig. 1). A small amount of glycerin is added to cover the bottom

**Fig. 1.** *Two types of pollen rain samplers. A sunken jar, screened and surrounded by washed gravel, and adhesive film in a coded, metal frame.*

and prevent drying. The jar should be surrounded by a pollen-sterile area (washed gravel, polyethylene, or other material) to prevent contamination by splashing rain. It must be deep enough so that the accumulated water will not splash out. This trap is not an ideal one, as insects or wind-blown debris bearing considerable amounts of entomophilous pollen may become trapped along with pollen carried down in rain. Screening the jar may modify the entrance of raindrops, but will prevent a great deal of contamination.

Serious technical problems are encountered at the end of the sampling period. These may apply to any method of sampling pollen rain that employs water as a trapping medium. The jars are removed from the ground and the contents placed in storage receptacles if they are not to be processed immediately. The jars must be carefully washed, since pollen often adheres to the walls at the water line. Not all of the pollen will sink to the bottom of the storage receptacles, even after several months. The addition of 95 percent ethyl alcohol to bring the final concentration to 50 percent will aid in sinking most of the pollen and in preventing growth of microorganisms. In one test a sample was centrifuged and the supernatant liquid poured into a reserve receptacle and repeatedly recentrifuged. This resulted in a final concentration of 12 percent pine pollen in the centrifugate. The reserved supernatant liquid was then filtered on filter paper in which no contaminating grains were detected. The paper was digested by the acetolysis method and centrifuged. A large number of grains were recovered, consisting of over 80 percent pine pollen! A replicate sample filtered without previous centrifugation yielded 48 percent pine pollen.

The standard sediment-processing chemicals, as well as detergents and several other common reagents, have been used in efforts to sink fresh pollen in laboratory tests. The organic solvents, xylene and hexane, are among the most effective of these, but since they are not water miscible their use complicates an already complex processing sequence. It also has been found that pine pollen may be refloated and poured off with the supernatant liquid, apparently at any time during washing, so that preliminary treatment with these reagents probably aids little in pollen recovery.

Flotation of pollen after acetolysis does not seem to be a problem. Filtering the sample and digesting the filter paper by acetolysis may be the best method to avoid these serious laboratory errors in processing samples.

## ICE

Ice has been little investigated as a pollen trap (Heusser, 1954). Its applicability as a pollen-rain sampler is doubtful. Such a sample is necessarily restricted to glacier or other persistent ice and little is known about the receptivity of this material as a pollen trap. Spores are recovered by melting the ice, allowing the sediment to settle, and decanting excess water until the residue can be concentrated by centrifugation. This method may be subject to error due to differential flotation of pollen. In polar latitudes the amount of airborne pollen and other spores is very low (Barghoorn, 1960), and a considerable amount of ice has to be processed to recover enough pollen for statistically reliable analyses.

## PETRI PLATES

Petri plates containing a small amount of some trapping fluid such as mineral oil, glycerin, or glycerin-drenched filter paper have been used in studies of pollen rain (Potter and Rowley, 1961). If placed directly on the surface of the ground these should approximate true sedimentation of pollen. The shallow plates will not greatly influence local turbulence. Contamination of these traps by pollen-bearing insects might introduce serious errors, and since they are shallow they must be taken up during periods of rain to prevent a large part of the sample from splashing out. Processing is quite simple: the sample is washed from the plate and centrifuged, or else the filter paper is digested by acetolysis.

## MICROSCOPE SLIDES

Glass slides coated with a suitable medium such as silicone stopcock grease, rubber cement, or glycerin jelly may be placed directly on the surface of the ground (Federova, 1956) (but on boards or plastic to prevent local redeposition) in terrain selected to represent the natural area desired (bog or lake). In periods of fair weather such samples should accurately represent the pollen rain if it is reasonably uniform. It is unlikely that they will accurately record pollen washed from the air during periods of rain. These samples must be collected frequently to prevent a loss in retention of the sticky surface through drying (rubber cement and glycerin jelly) or incorporation of a large amount of debris. Any interfering debris should be removed before studying the slide. This method provides a direct sampling of the pollen rain without modification due to laboratory processing.

## ADHESIVE FILM

Transparent cellulose film with an adhesive surface, such as AEC fallout paper, may be substituted for microscope slides (Rosinski, 1957). This material is available commercially in sheets which may be exposed in suitable frames (fig. 1). The film may be exposed for periods of one week or greater without serious loss of the adhesive properties of the surface due to weathering or overloading of pollen and debris. The sample is prepared for microscopic examination by carefully removing coarse debris from selected areas of the film with forceps, applying a drop of melted, prestained glycerin jelly, and covering with a cover glass. After the mount has solidified, the film is cut around the cover glass with a razor blade and the sample is removed and affixed to a microscope slide with a suitable adhesive.

The remainder of the paper may be cut into small portions and placed into widemouthed jars and generously covered with hexane or heptane. The sticky film with its pollen may be dispersed in the solvent by placing the jars on an oscillating plate for an hour or more. The solvent is filtered or centrifuged to recover the pollen. The concentrated sample is then washed with acetone and treated by any of the standard methods of processing fossil pollen in order to provide a comparison with the unprocessed sample in the slide.

## DURHAM SAMPLER

Surveys of airborne pollen and other spores, usually made to determine the concentrations of aeroallergens in the atmosphere, may tell us something about pollen rain. The sampler usually used in such surveys and especially for reporting the daily pollen count of ragweed (*Ambrosia*) in North America is no more than a microscope slide held horizontally between two 9-inch disks (Durham, 1946). The upper surface of the glass slide is coated with a thin layer of petrolatum or silicone grease. Some of the spores in the air passing over the slide adhere to its surface.

Data obtained with this sampler have been used to estimate recent pollen rain in relation to existing vegetation (Potter and Rowley, 1960). These data do provide a rough indication but must be used with caution. Experiments have shown that pollen capture by the Durham sampler is determined by several factors in addition to the concentration of pollen in the air (Ogden and Raynor, 1960). The combined effects of wind speed and wind direction may introduce differences of over 500 percent for particles in the size range of pollen. It is doubtful whether proper correlations may be made to estimate the pollen deposited on the surface of the earth. Even if wind speed is measured and orientation of the slide with respect to wind direction is improved, the data are not satisfactory, since sampling efficiency depends on a number of variables which are not easily defined or measured.

## CYLINDER SAMPLERS

A family of instruments that appears to be more useful for determining pollen concentration per unit volume of air is based on the principle of particle impaction on the side of a vertical cylinder (Gregory, 1951; Harrington, et al., 1959; Raynor, et al., 1961). Such instruments have been tested for particles in the size range of pollen: their efficiency varies directly with wind speed, particle size, and particle density, and inversely with cylinder diameter. When wind speed and the efficiency of the sampler are known, the number of grains per unit volume is easily computed. The major defect of all such impaction devices is their varying efficiency with wind speed and the necessity of wind speed measurements, making their use for studies of modern pollen rain impractical.

## POWERED IMPACTION INSTRUMENTS

If the sampling surface is rotated at a linear speed as great as the maximum expected air speed, the instrument is essentially independent of wind speed and direction. One such machine is the rotorod sampler invented at the Stanford University Aerosol Laboratory (Perkins, 1957). Its sampling rods rotate at about 2500 rpm and have a linear speed of about 23 mph. It has an impaction efficiency of nearly 100 percent for particles $20\mu$ in diameter but its actual efficiency is somewhat lower. A slight modification of this instrument was developed at the University of Michigan: the rotobar sampler. Because the opaque bars, or rods, are difficult to read under a microscope, some prefer to attach transparent adhesive tape to them for taking samplers. The tape with the adhering pollen sample is removed and placed in a glass slide for microscopic examination.

A further modification of the rotorod sampler—being perfected at Brookhaven National Laboratory—is the rotoslide sampler, in which two standard glass microscope slides are substituted for the rods (fig. 2). The leading edge of each microscope slide is given a thin coating (5 to $15\mu$) of silicone grease. After the sample is taken the pair of slides is transferred to a special holder for microscopic examination. The two samples are prepared for study by painting (with a medicine dropper) two strips of warm glycerin jelly containing a suitable dye, such as basic fuchsin, on one face of a 22 by 50 mm cover glass. The cover glass is then inverted and placed on the slides so that the jelly is on the slide edges containing the samples. Routine scanning is usually done at $100\times$, but magnifications as high as $500\times$ are used.

This sampler overloads too quickly to be used for more than two or three hours at a time. In order to obtain samples over a longer period of time, a group of samplers may be operated sequentially, or a single unit may be used intermittently. Because this instrument is a highly efficient sampler even when not rotating, the slides must be covered if the sampler happens to be stopped with a collecting surface facing the wind. Intermittent use of the rotoslide may become popular for pollen surveys, yielding valuable qualitative and quantitative data on particles in the atmosphere, but such information may not reflect the kinds or amounts of these particles as they reach the surface of the sediments.

There are many other types of powered impaction samplers. Some indicate the variation in pollen concentration during the day. The Hirst Spore Trap (Hirst, 1952; Ritchie and Lichti-Federovich, 1963) draws air through an orifice oriented into the wind. The pollen is impacted on a microscope slide that moves across the orifice at 2 mm per hour by a clock mechanism. A continuous trace of the day's sample is deposited on an area 14 by 48 mm.

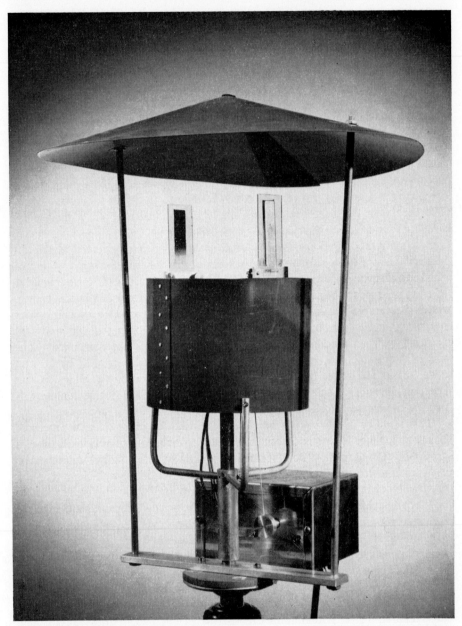

**Fig. 2.** *An intermittent rotoslide sampler. The sample accumulates on the leading edges of the rotating slides.*

## FILTER SAMPLERS

Several devices are available for sampling air which passes through a filter that retains the spores. These range from household vacuum cleaners to special high-volume samplers employing glass or fiber filters. The filter may be made transparent for direct analysis of the sample or it may be dissolved with a suitable chemical for processing by one of the methods used for sediment samples. Machines employing molecular-membrane filters have the advantage of retaining pollen and other spores on the filter surface, where they are easily seen under magnification.

With all such samplers, tests may indicate high efficiency in catching the spores that enter the machine, but we cannot assume that the sample gives an accurate indication of the spore concentration in the outside air. Unless the intake opening is continuously oriented into the wind and unless the speed of the air flowing through the sampler is equal at all times to the speed of the air approaching the intake, the system is subject to the serious errors of anisokinetic sampling. The number of grains per unit volume of air may be several times more or less than the actual number in the same volume of outside air. The ideal instrument for determining the actual content of free air is an isokinetic sampler which changes its flow rate rapidly and automatically to conform to changes in the wind speed while the sampling intake is oriented into the wind by a vane tail. This sampler is too complex for general use.

Identification techniques different from those for fossil pollen are often used in determinations of unmodified, direct visual samples. Some identification aids are restricted to fresh pollen:

1. The characteristic cell contents and staining properties of some grains (e.g., the starch granules of *Rumex*).
2. Information about the proximity of plants producing airborne pollen.
3. The time of flowering (e.g., seasonal variation in plants with betuloid pollen).

Among the factors making determination of fresh pollen difficult are:

1. The effect of cell contents obscuring typical morphological features.
2. The lack of control over the amount of pollen and debris found in a given sample.
3. The lack of adequate light at higher magnifications in many microscope systems when special collectors such as slide edges are used.

If fresh and fossil (or acetolyzed) pollen are to be compared in pollen rain studies it is desirable to have reference material representing both types.

Pollen surveys, as reported by aerobiologists, indicate great yearly differences in the quantity of pollen in the air and in the relative proportions of the species represented. Therefore it is necessary to collect pollen rain data for several years before they can properly be correlated with the existing vegetation.

## SUMMARY

Contemporary pollen rain sampling attempts to determine the kinds and amounts of pollen which are now being deposited on bog and lake surfaces. These data may shed light on such phenomena as differences in pollen production, dispersal, preservation, and laboratory recovery, and hence aid in the interpretation of fossil pollen diagrams.

Among the natural pollen traps which have been used are bryophytic polsters, upper surfaces of lake sediments, soil surfaces, and ice. Such samples are of doubtful value, however, owing to the lack of control over the period of pollen accumulation and to the lack of knowledge about the preservation (or movement) of the original deposit. Even laboratory processing may alter samples. Artificial devices constructed above ground level may have objectionable aerodynamic effects.

The devices ordinarily used by aerobiologists sample pollen primarily by impaction. Sedimentation, however, is a relatively important factor in the collection of pollen at bog and lake surfaces. Therefore, it is not yet known whether the results of aerobiological sampling can be correlated with pollen rains.

The "ideal" sampler should:

1. Collect airborne pollen in all kinds of weather with equal efficiency, as it is collected at the surface of bogs and lakes.
2. Provide direct visual samples and samples that may be treated in the manner of fossil pollen samples.
3. Require infrequent attention, but with rigid control of the sampling period.

Perhaps microscope slides or adhesive film placed directly on the surface of the ground best fulfill these criteria.

## REFERENCES

Barghoorn, E. S. (1960). Palynological studies of organic sediments and of coated slides. Scientific studies at Fletcher's Ice Island T-3, 1952–1955, v. 3, Geophys. Res. Paper 63, p. 86–91.

Benninghoff, W. S. (1960). Pollen spectra from bryophytic polsters, Inverness Mud Lake Bog, Cheboygan County, Michigan. Michigan Acad. Sci. Letters Paper 45, pls. 41–60.

Bent, A. M., and H. E. Wright (1963). Pollen analyses of surface materials and lake sediments from the Chuska Mountains, New Mexico. Geol. Soc. America Bull., v. 74, p. 491–500.

Brown, C. A. (1960). Palynological techniques. Baton Rouge, C. A. Brown, 188 pp.

Carrol, G. (1943). The use of bryophytic polsters and mats in the study of recent pollen deposition. Am. J. Botany, v. 30, p. 361–366.

Davis, M. B., and J. C. Goodlett (1960). Comparison of the present vegetation with pollen-spectra in surface samples from Brownington Pond, Vermont. Ecology, v. 41, p. 346–357.

Dimbleby, G. W. (1957). Pollen analysis of terrestrial soils. New Phytologist, v. 56, p. 12–28.

Durham, O. C. (1946). The volumetric incidence of atmospheric allergens, IV: A proposed standard method of gravity sampling, counting and volumetric interpolation of results. J. Allergy, v. 17, p. 78–86.

Erdtman, G. (1943). An introduction to pollen analysis. Chronica Botanica, 239 pp.

Faegri, K., and J. Iversen (1950). Textbook of modern pollen analysis. Copenhagen, Ejnar Munksgaard, 168 pp.

Federova, R. B. (1956). Dissemination of pollen of certain herbaceous plants in air [in Russian]. Izvestiva Akademii Nauk USSR 1, p. 104–108.

Gregory, P. H. (1951). Deposition of air-borne Lycopodium spores on cylinders. Ann. Appl. Biol., v. 38, p. 357–376.

——— (1961). The microbiology of the atmosphere. New York, Interscience, 251 pp.

Hafsten, U. (1961). Pleistocene development of vegetation and climate in the southern high plains as evidenced by pollen analyses, *in* Paleoecology of the Llano Estacado. Sante Fe, Mus. of New Mex. Press, 144 pp.

Hansen, H. P. (1949). Pollen content of moss polsters in relation to forest composition. Am. Midl. Naturalist, v. 42, p. 473–479.

Harrington, J. B., G. C. Gill, and B. R. Warr (1959). High-efficiency pollen samplers for use in clinical allergy. J. Allergy, v. 30, p. 357–375.

Heusser, C. (1954). Palynology of the Taku Glacier snow cover, Alaska and its significance in the determination of glacier regimen. Am. J. Sci., v. 252, p. 291–308.

Hirst, J. M. (1952). An automatic volumetric spore trap. Ann. Appl. Biol., v. 39, p. 257–265.

Hopkins, J. S. (1950). Differential flotation and deposition of coniferous and deciduous tree pollen. Ecology, v. 31, p. 633–641.

Lewis, D. M. (1962). Airborne pollen sampling and pollen rain: Intl. Conf. on Palynology, Tucson (abs.), Pollen et Spores, v. 4, p. 361.

Martin, P. S., and J. Gray (1962). Pollen analysis and the Cenozoic. Science, v. 137, p. 103–111.

McDonald, J. E. (1962). Collection and washout of airborne pollens and spores by raindrops. Science, v. 135, p. 435–437.

Ogden, E. C., and G. S. Raynor (1960). Field evaluation of ragweed pollen samplers. J. Allergy, v. 31, p. 307–316.

Perkins, W. A. (1957). The rotorod sampler. Second Semiannual Report, CML 186, Aerosol Laboratory, Stanford University.

Potter, L. D., and J. Rowley (1960). Pollen rain and vegetation, San Augustin Plains, New Mexico. Bot. Gaz., v. 122, p. 1–25.

Potzger, J. E., A. Courtemanche, B. M. Sylvio, and F. M. Hueber (1956). Pollen from moss polsters on the mat of Lac Shaw bog, Quebec, correlated with a forest survey. Butler Univ. Bot. Studies, v. 13, p. 24–35.

Ranson, J. F., and E. B. Leopold (1962). The standard rain gage as an efficient sampler of air-borne pollen and spores. Intl. Conf. on Palynology, Tucson (abs.), Pollen et Spores, v. 4, p. 373.

Raynor, G. S., M. E. Smith, I. A. Singer, and E. C. Ogden (1961). Pollen sampling and dispersion studies at Brookhaven National Laboratory. J. Air Pollution Control Assoc., v. 11, p. 557–561, 584.

Ritchie, J. C., and S. Lichti-Federovich (1963). Contemporary pollen spectra in central Canada; I. Atmospheric samples at Winnipeg, Manitoba. Pollen et Spores, v. 5, p. 95–114.

Rosinski, J. (1957). Some studies on the evaluation of gummed paper collectors used in determining radioactive fallout. Am. Geophys. Union Trans., v. 38, p. 857–863.

Welch, P. S. (1948). Limnological methods. Philadelphia, Blakiston, 381 pp.

# Photomicrography of Recent and Fossilized Pollen

K. E. SAMUELSSON

*Paleobotanical Department, Swedish Museum
of Natural History, Stockholm*

Improvements in the construction of microscope and camera equipment, the development of the electric exposure meter, increased knowledge about filters, and the new photographic emulsions coming out on the market have contributed hugely to improving opportunities for the microphotographer to reproduce the details of the pollen grain, which often lie on the limits of what a light microscope can resolve. The equipment commonly used consists of a stable microscope frame with monocular or binocular components and attachments for the camera, lenses, and phase contrast apparatus. In addition to the modern microscope, a fixed source of low-voltage lighting, a fixed

A modification of a paper that appeared in G. Erdtman, J. Praglowski, and S. Wilsson (1963), *An Introduction to a Scandinavian Flora* (v. 2) (English trans. by Ernest R. Manewal, Scandinavian Dept., Univ. of Washington; ed. by Jane Gray), Almquist and Wiksell, Stockholm, and in G. Erdtman (1963), "Introduction till Palynologin," *Natur och Kultur*.

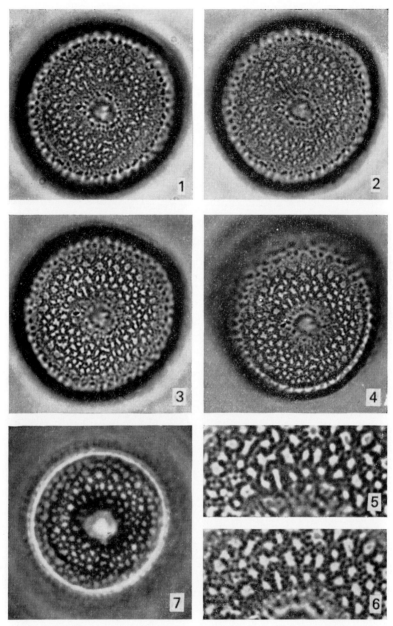

**Fig. 1.** *Detailed photography of pollen with lenses of different numerical aperture. Ilford chromatic film with yellow filter. Low-voltage lighting. (1–4 and 7) About 1500×. (5, 6) About 3000×. (1) Leitz Oel 100×, A 1.30. Periplan ocular 10×. (2) Leitz Pl Apo Oel 100×, A 1.32. Periplan ocular GF 10×. (3) Leitz Apo Oel 90×, A 1.40. Periplan ocular GF 10×. (4) Leitz Apo Oel 90×, A 1.40. Periplan ocular GF 10×. Result unknown: foreign light in the condenser. (5) Enlargement of 3. (6) Enlargement of 4. (7) Leitz phase contrast equipment P Apo Oel 90×, A 1.10. Periplan ocular GF 10×.*

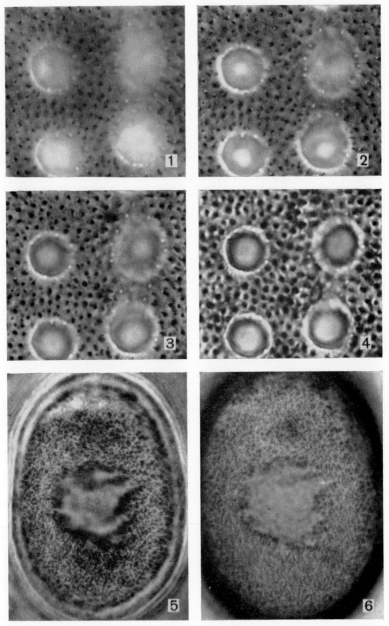

**Fig. 2.** *(1–4) Detailed photography of pollen wall with different diaphragm openings. Leitz lens PL Apo Oel 100×, A 1.32. Periplan ocular GF 10×. Chromatic film with yellow filter. Lowvoltage lighting. About 1500×. (1) Largest diaphragm opening. (2) Somewhat stopped down (6x). [x = diaphragm number on leitz condenser.] (3) Sharply stopped down (4x). (4) Extreme*

mirror, a frame with a bellows camera, and cut film holders for 9 by 12 cm film are needed. Other equipment includes a light meter, a set of filters, a micrometer, and nondrying immersion oil.

## LIGHTING

The usual source of light is a low-voltage lamp with a regulating transformer. At 6 volts the color temperature reaches 2800°K, at 5 amperes; 3000°K at 5.4 amperes; and 3200°K at 5.7 amperes. If the amperage is raised to the limit that the lamp will take, 6.1 amperes, the color temperature reaches 3400°K. When there is need for a very strong light, as when photographing very small details, a xenon light is used (Wild Xenon-Brenner XBO 162), which has a color temperature of 6300°K. The strength of the light used to take photographs should be high in order to ensure that the pollen grain be of a clear, light color, and to allow the small details to be brought sharply into focus.

## THE LAMP DIAPHRAGM AND THE DIAPHRAGM OPENING

The lamp diaphragm, which in earlier microscopes was on the light source, is now rightly placed on the microscope condenser; it is set so that it is the same as the objective aperture being used.

Choosing the correct diaphragm opening comes by experience. It must be done with the utmost care: by stopping down too much (small opening), the details can be blended and cause a misleading picture. Other difficulties are encountered when the diaphragm is incorrectly set—enlargement of details and, at extreme openings, loss of detail. For stained pollen, the film and filters, and not the diaphragm opening, should be depended upon to give the desired contrasts.

## OPTICS

An objective with good resolving power is needed when photographing pollen grain: the numerical aperture should be 1.30, 1.32, or 1.40. Objectives with A 1.40 have as a rule little working distance (about 0.08 mm). Suitable ob-

---

*stoppage (2x). (5, 6, and Fig. 3, 1) Detailed photography of pollen grain with very weak optical contrasts and weak colors. (5) Leitz phase contrast equipment with Pv Apo Oel 90×, A 1.10. Periplan ocular GF 10×. Ilford Special Rapid Panchromatic film. Low-voltage lighting. About 1500×. (6) Leitz lens Pl Apo Oel 100×, A. 1.32. Periplan ocular GF 10×. Ilford Thin-emulsion Half Tone film with blue-green filter. Xenon lighting (XBO 162). About 1500×.*

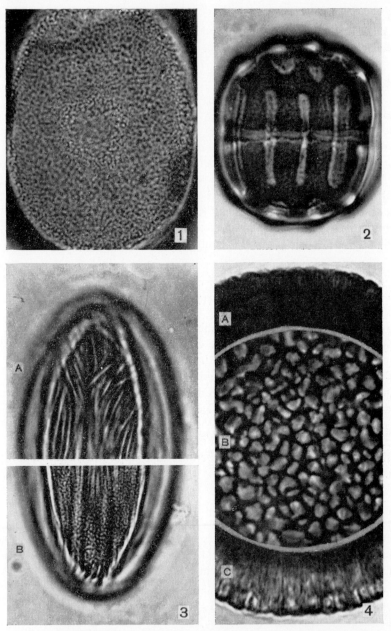

**Fig. 3.** *(1) (See legend to Fig. 2) Leitz lens Pl Apo Oel 100×, A 1.32. Periplan ocular GF 10×. Ilford chromatic film with yellow filter. Low voltage lighting. About 1500×. (1–4) Yellow pollen photographed in high (a) and low (b) focus. Leitz lens Pl Apo Oel 100×, A 1.32. Periplan ocular GF 10×. Low voltage lighting. About 1500×. (2) Ilford Chromatic film with yellow filter.*

jectives are now available with a maximum aperture of 1.32 and is provided with a large depth of focus (0.27 mm), so that even preparations under thick cover glass can be photographed. For simpler details, the resolving power of the objective can be increased by a factor of 2 if the light source is directed so that it enters the condenser at an angle. Phase contrast equipment is used primarily for fairly simple structures, but with more complicated subjects difficulties arise in separating the details photographically.

## FILM TYPES

Of the film types mentioned below, the orthochromatic and panchromatic are the ones most often used. Blue-sensitive and infrared-sensitive films are sometimes used for Recent as well as fossilized material.

*Non-color-sensitive film:* the speed ought to be slow, the contrast very high, and the grain very fine.
*Orthochromatic film:* normal speed, normal to high contrast, and fine grained.
*Panchromatic film:* normal speed, normal to high contrast, and fine grained.
*Infrared-sensitive film:* relatively high speed and contrast.

## FILTERS

When photographing pollen, filters are usually not used to bring out color tones but to heighten contrast. The color filters ordinarily used are blue or blue-green, yellow-green (for achromatic), light yellow, dark yellow, orange, red, and infrared.

To achieve the highest possible contrast with a filter, the filter color should be the same as the color of the details being photographed. If they are light yellow, with high focusing, a light-yellow filter must be used; the same filter is used at lower focusing, when the colors become reversed, the details dark, and the pollen grain light. This same rule applies even for the optical angle, with the exception of small outer details, where a blue or blue-green filter can be used to advantage.

For good results the choice of filter under all conditions should be made with regard to the type of film being used (table I).

---

*Yellow, orange, and red-brown pollen. Leitz lens Pl Apo Oel 100×, A 1.32. Periplan ocular GF 10×. Low-voltage lighting. About 1500×. (3) Ilford Special Rapid Panchromatic film with orange filter. Detailed photography of dark red pollen. Leitz lens Pl Apo Oel 100×, A 1.32. Periplan ocular GF 10×. Low voltage lighting. About 1500×. (4) a. Ilford Special Rapid Panchromatic film with red filter. b and c. Gevaert Scientia infrared film with red filter.*

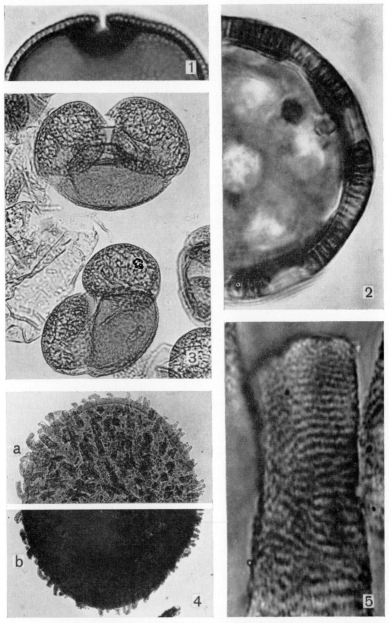

**Fig. 4.** (*1, 2*) *Optical section. Leitz lens Pl Apo Oel 100×, A 1.32.*
*Periplan ocular GF 10×. Low-voltage lighting. About 1500×.*
(*1*) *Ilford Chromatic film with blue-green filter.* (*2*) *Ilford*
*Chromatic film with yellow filter.* (*3*) *Schematic picture. Leitz*
*lens Apo 25×, A. 0.65. Periplan ocular GF 10×. Low-voltage*
*lighting. About 500×. Ilford Special Rapid Panchromatic film*

**Table I**

| FILTER | USED AS | FILM |
|---|---|---|
| Blue-green | Correction filter | Non-color sensitive |
| Blue-green<br>Yellow | Complement filter<br>Contrast filter | Orthochromatic |
| Yellow<br>Orange<br>Red | Contrast filter | Panchromatic |
| Red<br>Infrared | Contrast filter | Infrared sensitive |

## THE SUBJECT

In most cases the pollen grain exhibits color contrasts as well as optical contrasts; therefore, to get the best results the subject must be taken into account when choosing the film (table II).

**Table II**

| POLLEN | FILM | FILTER |
|---|---|---|
| Weak optical contrasts with very weak color | Non-color sensitive | Blue-green |
| Light optical contrasts with weak color | Orthochromatic | Blue-green |
| Light optical contrasts with yellow color | Orthochromatic | Light yellow<br>Medium yellow |
| Light optical contrasts with yellow, orange, and light-red colors | Panchromatic | Yellow<br>Orange<br>Red |
| Light optical contrasts with red and brown colors | Panchromatic<br>Infrared-sensitive | Red |
| Light optical contrasts with dark red and brown-black colors | Infrared-sensitive | Infrared |

*without filter. (4) Schematic picture of fossil specimen. Leitz lens 6/0.18. Periplan ocular 6×. Low-voltage lighting. About 80×. (4) a. Gevaert Scientia infrared film with infrared filter. b. Ilford Special Rapid Panchromatic film with red filter. (5) Detail of fossil specimen (from 4). Leitz lens Pl Apo Oel 100×, A 1.32. Periplan ocular GF 10×. Low-voltage lighting. About 1500×. Gevaert Scientia infrared film with infrared filter.*

## EXPOSURE TIME

A correctly chosen exposure time is just as important as the correct choice of filter and film. Underexposure or strong overexposure always means failure. If an electric exposure meter is used with good judgment, exposure problems can be completely avoided.

So that the exposure time can be determined for different bellows positions, a graduated scale must be made on the arm of the camera equipment. The camera bellows is collapsed and the arm is marked, beginning at the height of the film holder, every fourth centimeter and numbered from the bottom with 0, 1, 2, 3, 4, . . . , .

Next, a series of trial photographs is taken with the camera at zero position, the subjects being pollen grains enlarged until they cover slightly more than half the film surface. If the light value is 9 DIN (measured with Leitz Microsix) at the selected ocular position, and the exposure time—when using panchromatic film and an orange filter—is found to be five seconds in order to get a well-exposed negative, you have all the exposure-time information needed for the abovementioned types of film and filter. Table III gives the exposure times for other films and filters at light values ranging from 1 to 27 DIN.

If, for example, the camera bellows is extended to position 4, the exposure time is taken four steps to the right. If the light value is 6 DIN and the film and filter indicated in the following table are used, the time will be 2.5 seconds; at four steps to the right the correct exposure time at the selected camera extension is 6 seconds.

| FILM | FILTER | LIGHT VALUE (DIN) | | | | | | | | | | | | |
|------|--------|---|---|---|---|---|---|---|---|---|---|----|----|----|
| | | 0 | 1 | 2 | 3 | 4 | 5 | 6 | 7 | 8 | 9 | 10 | 11 | 12 |
| Panchromatic | Orange | | | 1 | 1.25 | 1.5 | 2 | 2.5 | 3 | 4 | 5 | 6 | 8 | 10 |

Only a change of ocular changes the exposure time. If a 10× ocular had been used to make the table, and if it were later replaced by a 6×, then the time would be six-tenths that shown in table III.

## DEVELOPER

In choosing a developer it is best to follow the film company's recommendations, which as a rule include data on development time and temperature.

## A SHORT SUMMARY FOR GOOD RESULTS

1. Use a relatively strong light source.
2. The opening of the lamp diaphragm should be the same as that of the objective aperture.

**Table III.** *Exposure Table (Exposure times must be adjusted if other brands of film are used)*

| FILM AND FILTER | LIGHT VALUE (DIN) | | | | | | | | | | | | | | | | | | | | | | | | | | |
|---|---|---|---|---|---|---|---|---|---|---|---|---|---|---|---|---|---|---|---|---|---|---|---|---|---|---|---|
| | 1 | 2 | 3 | 4 | 5 | 6 | 7 | 8 | 9 | 10 | 11 | 12 | 13 | 14 | 15 | 16 | 17 | 18 | 19 | 20 | 21 | 22 | 23 | 24 | 25 | 26 | 27 |
| **Ilford Thin Film** | | | | | | | | | | | | | | | | | | | | | | | | | | | |
| Half Tone | | | | | | | | | | | | | | | | | | | | | | | | | | | |
| Blue-green | | | | | | | 1 | 1.25 | 1.5 | 2 | 2.5 | 3 | 4 | 5 | 6 | 8 | 10 | 12 | 16 | 20 | 24 | 32 | 40 | | | | |
| **Ilford Chromatic** | | | | | | | | | | | | | | | | | | | | | | | | | | | |
| Blue | | | | | | | | | | | | 1 | 1.25 | 1.5 | 2 | 2.5 | 3 | 4 | 5 | 6 | 8 | 10 | 12 | 16 | 20 | 24 | 32 |
| Blue-green | | | | | | | | | | | 1 | 1.25 | 1.5 | 2 | 2.5 | 3 | 4 | 5 | 6 | 8 | 10 | 12 | 16 | 20 | 24 | 32 | 40 |
| Yellow | | | | | 1 | 1.25 | 1.5 | 2 | 2.5 | 3 | 4 | 5 | 6 | 8 | 10 | 12 | 16 | 20 | 24 | 32 | 40 | | | | | | |
| **Ilford Special Rapid** | | | | | | | | | | | | | | | | | | | | | | | | | | | |
| Panchromatic | | | | | | | | | | | | | | | | | | | | | | | | | | | |
| No filter | | | | 1 | 1.25 | 1.5 | 2 | 2.5 | 3 | 4 | 5 | 6 | 8 | 10 | 12 | 16 | 20 | 24 | 32 | 40 | | | | | | | |
| Yellow | | | 1 | 1.25 | 1.5 | 2 | 2.5 | 3 | 4 | 5 | 6 | 8 | 10 | 12 | 16 | 20 | 24 | 32 | 40 | | | | | | | | |
| Orange | | 1 | 1.25 | 1.5 | 2 | 2.5 | 3 | 4 | 5 | 6 | 8 | 10 | 12 | 16 | 20 | 24 | 32 | 40 | | | | | | | | | |
| Red | 1 | 1.25 | 1.5 | 2 | 2.5 | 3 | 4 | 5 | 6 | 8 | 10 | 12 | 16 | 20 | 24 | 32 | 40 | | | | | | | | | | |
| **Kodak Infrared** | | | | | | | | | | | | | | | | | | | | | | | | | | | |
| Extra-Rapid | | | | | | | | | | | | | | | | | | | | | | | | | | | |
| Red | | | | | | | | | | 1 | 1.25 | 1.5 | 2 | 2.5 | 3 | 4 | 5 | 6 | 8 | 10 | 12 | 16 | 20 | 24 | 32 | 40 | |
| Infrared | | | | | | | | | | | 1 | 1.25 | 1.5 | 2 | 2.5 | 3 | 4 | 5 | 6 | 8 | 10 | 12 | 16 | 20 | 24 | 32 | 40 |

3. Focus at the largest diaphram opening.
4. Use the diaphragm opening that gives best resolution.
5. Take into account the pollen grain color.
6. Use a suitable filter.
7. Use the appropriate film.
8. Determine the exposure time carefully.
9. Always develop at the same temperature.

# Statistical Methods for the Pollen Analyst: Multinomial and Negative Multinomial Techniques

JAMES E. MOSIMANN

*Geochronology Laboratories, University of Arizona*

The purpose of this paper is to place in the hands of the pollen analyst a collection of statistical tools, each of which is illustrated with a numerical example—a collection ready for use. If these tools are used, and the paper proves useful to research workers, then its major purpose will have been fulfilled.

This paper is written not for the casual reader, but for the pollen analyst who, being familiar with standard biostatistical techniques, is willing to study a particular statistical method to aid in the solution of a specific problem.

Many statistical applications in pollen analysis are not included in this paper. For example, the use of discriminant functions in distinguishing pollen types lies far afield of the coverage attempted here. So also do the important problems relating to absolute rather than to percent pollen falls (Davis and Deevey, 1963). The methods presented here deal largely with sampling. Other papers dealing with this general subject to which the reader may wish to refer are those of Deevey and Potzger (1951), Faegri and Ottestad (1949), Westenberg (1947a,b), Gray and Guennel (1961), and Mosimann (1962, 1963). All of these are concerned in some way with the binomial model as a basis for pollen studies.

At the heart of pollen analysis are the pollen counts themselves—the actual

Contribution No. 77. Program in Geochronology, University of Arizona. This study was supported by National Science Foundation Grant G 21944.
The author is now with the National Institutes of Health, Bethesda, Md.

raw data from which inferences concerning past vegetation and climates are to be made. Along with the need to point out the considerable effect that the sampling plan has on the variation and covariation of counts, there is the need to emphasize that one sampling plan may be more suited to the study of a given set of parameters that characterize a pollen population (i.e., pollen proportions) than some other plan. The choice of a sampling plan should not be arbitrary.

After a brief explanation of the models involved, there follows the section on methods, which constitutes the major part of this paper. About half of the methods presented are concerned with outside counts—counts outside the pollen sum. Most of these methods are, as far as I know, new, although they are analogous to well-known methods for counts inside the sum. A mathematical justification of these will appear elsewhere.

## WITHIN A SINGLE LEVEL: BERNOULLI TRIALS AND MULTIPLE BERNOULLI TRIALS

This section deals with models for variation of pollen counts within a single level of a profile, and highlights the manner in which this variation is affected by the sampling plan used in obtaining the counts. It is noted that, under the same assumptions, the distribution of counts inside the sum is multinomial, whereas that of counts outside the sum is negative multinomial.

### BERNOULLI TRIALS

An investigator looks at a pollen grain under the microscope and classifies it as AP or NAP (arboreal pollen or nonarboreal pollen). If one calls this action a *trial,* then the process of counting a number of grains can be thought of as a sequence of trials. If in a sequence of trials—each having only two possible outcomes (say AP or NAP)—the outcome of any trial is independent of the outcomes of any others, and if the probability, $P$, of AP occurring in any trial is constant, then the trials are said to be Bernoulli trials.

Suppose the assumptions of Bernoulli trials are met. This alone is not sufficient to determine the distribution of the investigator's counts. For such to be determined, consideration of the sampling plan becomes necessary. If it is decided to count until a fixed total number (say 200) of both AP and NAP grains are recorded, then the number $(X)$ of NAP grains counted follows a binomial distribution. If, instead, it is decided to count the number of NAP grains observed while counting to a fixed number (say 200) of AP grains then the number $(X)$ of NAP grains counted follows a negative binomial (or Pascal) distribution. That is, once the assumption of Bernoulli trials is made, the distribution of $X$ depends on the choice of the sampling plan. Thus, *the same basic assumptions which lead to the binomial distribution for a count within the pollen sum lead to the negative binomial distribution for a count outside the pollen sum.* This important point was recognized by Westenberg

(1947a, 1947b) but not made clear by Faegri and Ottestad (1949) in their discussion of his work. This effect of the sampling plan is equally important in the multivariate model next considered.

MULTIPLE BERNOULLI TRIALS

The only difference between multiple Bernoulli trials and ordinary ones is that there are three or more possible outcomes of each trial instead of only two. As before, the trials are independent, and each outcome has the same probability of occurrence in any trial.

Suppose the assumptions of multiple Bernoulli trials are met. If it is decided to count until a fixed number (say 200) of pine, grass, and composite grains is recorded, then the numbers counted of the three kinds of grains $(X_1, X_2, X_3)$ jointly follow the multinomial distribution. (Each $X$ by itself has a binomial distribution as before, since the remaining categories can always be considered as a single category, for example pine versus "not-pine.")

But if it is decided to count the number of grains each of grass and composites observed while counting to a fixed number (say 200) of pine grains, then the counts of grass and composites $(X_2, X_3)$ jointly follow a negative multinomial distribution. (Again $X_2$ or $X_3$ alone has a negative binomial distribution, for we can simply consider the counts of, for example, grass as if those of composites had not been made at all.) As before, once multiple Bernoulli trials are assumed, the joint distribution of all $X$ depends on the choice of a sampling plan.

Thus, *the same basic assumptions which lead to the multinomial distribution for counts within the pollen sum lead to the negative multinomial distribution for counts outside the sum,* and if one is interested in the counts of any single taxon (or the sum of any group of taxa), then *no matter how many types of grains are actually counted, the distribution of the single type alone is binomial or negative binomial,* depending on whether the counts are inside or outside the sum.

## BETWEEN-LEVEL VARIATION IN THE POLLEN PROFILE: CONSEQUENCES OF THE SAMPLING PLAN

When there are many levels in a profile, the true (population) proportions of the various types of pollen usually differ from level to level. Within any single level the sample counts can be used to estimate the true pollen proportions for that particular level. In what way can the counts from various levels be employed in studying level-to-level variation in the true proportions themselves, if within any single level Multiple Bernoulli (or simply Bernoulli) trials are assumed? A main point made is that counts inside the sum do reflect level-to-level variation in the true proportions, whereas counts outside the sum reflect level-to-level variation in ratios of true proportions. In general, these ratios do not seem to be particularly useful quantities.

## BETWEEN-LEVEL VARIANCE
## OF COUNTS INSIDE THE SUM

Suppose that at each of a number of levels counts are made of the following taxa: (1) pine, (2) grass, and (3) composites. Suppose also that Multiple Bernoulli trials are assumed within a single level.

First consider the case in which the sampling rule is to count to a fixed number of grains (say 200) at each level. The counts $X_1$, $X_2$, $X_3$ within any level will then follow a multinomial distribution. If one considers pine alone, then the distribution of pine counts will be binomial. But what of *between-level variation* in pine? This variation clearly depends on the past natural vegetation. Fortunately one can use the analysis of variance in separating between-level and within-level variation. This is possible since the needed replication of samples within a level is present, although somewhat hidden. A single sample of 200 grains per level can be just as easily regarded as two 100-grain samples, four 50-grain samples, or 200 1-grain samples. It is this property (*namely, that an n-trial binomial variable can be regarded as the sum of n independent 1-trial binomial variables*) *which enables one to partition the sum of squares as in the standard analysis of variance procedure.* Thus, one can separately estimate the within-level variance (or "binomial" variance) and the variance between levels (essentially the binomial variance plus the variance of the true pollen proportion). Using these two separate estimates one can then estimate the variance of the true proportions.

## BETWEEN-LEVEL VARIANCE
## OF COUNTS OUTSIDE THE SUM

Consider the case in which the sampling rule is to count the numbers of grass grains ($X_2$) and composite grains ($X_3$) observed while counting to a fixed number (say 150) of pine grains ("markers"). Counts of grass within a level would have a negative binomial distribution, but what of between-level variation in grass? Once more the needed replication of samples within a level is present, but hidden. The number of grains of grass noted while counting to 150 grains of pine can be thought of as 150 samples; the first, the number of grains of grass noted before encountering the first pine grain; the second, the number of grains of grass noted after the first pine grain and before the second; and so on. That is, *a negative binomial variable with n marker grains can be thought of as the sum of n independent negative binomial variables each with one marker grain.* Thus, one can again think of estimating within-level and between-level variances. Here, however, the between-level variance does not involve the variance of the true population proportion as it did for counts inside the sum. Rather it is equal to the within-level variance plus the level-to-level variance of the ratio (true-grass proportion/true-pine proportion). (The denominator of this ratio is always the proportion of marker grains.)

For counts outside the sum, the level-to-level variance is not that of a true proportion, but rather the variance of a ratio such as the one above. Although such a ratio might seem to be of little interest, ratios of this type have been used with interesting results by Maher (1961).

Suppose one counts the numbers of grass grains and composite grains observed while counting to a fixed number (say 150) of grains of pine, fir, and oak, such counts being made at each of several levels in the profile. If one assumes Multiple Bernoulli trials within any single level, then pine and fir counts from that level would follow a multinomial distribution with $n = 150$ trials. By reasoning similar to that used previously (but here extended to Multiple Bernoulli trials), one can regard a sample of 150 grains (trials) as 150 1-trial samples.

Correspondingly, grass and composite counts from a single level would follow a negative multinomial distribution with $n = 150$ marker grains. (Here the marker category is that of AP = pine + fir + oak.) By reasoning similar to that used before (but extended to Multiple Bernoulli trials), one can regard the single 150-marker sample as 150 1-marker samples.

Thus, as before, replicate samples within each level, needed to separately estimate within-level and between-level covariances, are present for counts both inside and outside the sum. For pine and oak, which are inside the sum, these separate estimates can be used to estimate the level-to-level covariance (and hence the correlation coefficient) of the *true proportions* of pine and oak. However, for grass and composite counts, which are outside the sum, use of the separate estimates of between-level and within-level covariances results in an estimate of the level-to-level covariance (and correlation coefficient) of two *ratios of proportions*—namely (true-grass proportion/true-marker proportion) and (true-composite proportion/true-marker proportion), the marker here being AP.

## BETWEEN-LEVEL VARIANCE AND COVARIANCE WITH LARGE POLLEN SUMS

Suppose the numbers of grass and composite grains observed while counting to a pollen sum of 150 AP grains (pine, fir, and oak) were recorded. What if the 150 were 1000 or 10,000 or any arbitrarily large number?

As before let $X$ denote an inside or outside count at some level, and consider that one has the same pollen sum ($n$) at each level. Then as the pollen sum ($n$) becomes larger and larger, the variance of the count ($\sigma_X^2$) divided by $n^2$ becomes equal to:

1. The variance of a proportion ($\sigma_P^2$) for an inside count.
2. The variance of a ratio ($\sigma_U^2$, where $U = P/P_k$ and $P_k$ is the proportion of marker grains) for an outside count.

Similarly, the covariance of two counts ($\sigma_{X_1 X_2}$) becomes equal to:

1. The covariance of the corresponding proportions ($\sigma_{P_1 P_2}$) for two inside counts.

2. The covariance of two ratios ($\sigma_{U_1 U_2}$, where $U_1 = P_1/P_k$ and $U_2 = P_2/P_k$) for two outside counts.

From the foregoing discussion of variance and covariance it is clear that *counts inside the sum are suited to the study of level-to-level variation in the true (population) proportions of pollen, whereas counts outside the sum are suited to the study of level-to-level variation in ratios of true proportions, the denominator always being the true proportion of marker grains.*

## METHODS

A method whose code number is preceded by an "A" is suitable for an inside-the-sum or fixed-*n* count. Such methods stem from the multinomial distribution. A method whose code number is preceded by a "B" is suitable for a count outside the sum. Such methods stem from the negative multinomial distribution. All numerical examples are in reduced type.

The examples, worked out in detail, are intended only for illustration, and use artificial data. In many sections the pollen analyst may find it easier to read the example first and then read the associated text.

All of the chi-square tests presented here can be validly applied when the pollen sum ($n$) is large. How large $n$ must be depends on the $p$ (for multinomial methods) and on the $u$ (for negative multinomial methods). The $np$ or $nu$ should not be too small, but it is not possible to give definite rules that would establish a lower limit. The following comments are in keeping with suggestions made by Cochran (1954). If the chi-square involves hypothetical values ($p^*$ or $u^*$), and if there are relatively few (say about one out of five) $np^*$ or $nu^*$ with values less than five, then some of these values can be as low as one. For chi-squares that do not involve hypothetical values, the same statement applies after substitution of an estimate, $n\hat{p}$, for $np^*$ (or $n\hat{u}$ for $nu^*$). When categories of rare taxa are included in the counts, they should be grouped until the above condition is roughly satisfied. Further study of negative multinomial chi-squares is needed.

**A.1** Point estimation of the true proportion, $p$, of a particular kind of pollen. One sample with $x$ NAP grains counted out of a total of $n$ grains. The point estimate of the true proportion of NAP pollen is

$$\hat{p} = x/n,$$

where the circumflex over the $p$ indicates that this is an estimate.

| | |
|---|---|
| *Example* | If out of 200 grains counted, 63 are NAP, then $\hat{p} = 63/200 = 0.315$; the point estimate of the true AP proportion $(1 - p)$ is $$1 - \hat{p} = 137/200 = 0.685.$$ |

**A.2** Point estimation of the true proportion, $p$, of a particular kind of pollen. Two or more ($N$) independent samples from the same level, with the number of NAP grains ($x$) recorded out of a given total number of grains ($n$) for each sample. The data can be arranged as follows.

|          | NUMBER OF NAP GRAINS | TOTAL NUMBER OF GRAINS |
|----------|:---:|:---:|
| Sample 1 | $x_1$ | $n_1$ |
| Sample 2 | $x_2$ | $n_2$ |
| ...      | ...   | ...   |
| Sample $N$ | $x_N$ | $n_N$ |
| Column totals | $x'$ | $n'$ |

The estimate of the NAP proportion is

$$\hat{p} = x'/n'.$$

*Example* | Three samples from the same level gave the following results.

|          | NUMBER OF NAP GRAINS | TOTAL NUMBER OF GRAINS |
|----------|:---:|:---:|
| Sample 1 | 102 | 200 |
| Sample 2 | 30  | 50  |
| Sample 3 | 47  | 100 |
| Column totals | 179 | 350 |

The point estimate of the NAP proportion $p$ is

$$\hat{p} = 179/350 = 0.511.$$

The point estimate of the AP proportion $1 - p$ is

$$1 - \hat{p} = 0.489.$$

*Remark:* The assumption that all the samples are from the same level can be tested by the method of (A.6).

**A.3** Confidence intervals (interval estimates) for $p$, the true proportion of a particular kind of pollen. One sample, or more than one ($N$) independent samples from the same level, with the number of NAP grains ($X$) recorded out of a total number of grains ($n$) for each sample.

Tables are given in Snedecor (1956, p. 4–5) for samples whose total count $n = 10, 15, 20, 30, 50, 100, 250$, or 1000. Graphs that can be used with any total count up to 1000 are given in Mainland (1952). Tables are also given by Mainland, Herrera, and Sutcliffe (1956).

If $n$ is fairly large, approximate 95 percent confidence intervals can be computed from

$$p_L = \frac{\hat{p} + [3.84/(2n)] \pm (1.96)\sqrt{[p(1-p)/n] + [3.84/(4n^2)]}}{1 + (3.84/n)},$$

where the larger value obtained is the upper limit, and the smaller value is the lower limit.

If a 99 percent confidence interval is desired, the formula

$$p_L = \frac{\hat{p} + [6.636/(2n)] \pm (2.576)\sqrt{[\hat{p}(1-\hat{p})/n] + [6.636/(4n^2)]}}{1 + (6.636/n)}$$

can be used when $n$ is fairly large.

In either of the above formulas the $\hat{p}$ can be for a single sample (as in A.1) or for several combined samples (as in A.2). If $\hat{p}$ is obtained from several combined samples, as in A.2, then $n$ in the above formulas should be replaced by $n'$, the sum of all $n$.

| | |
|---|---|
| *Example* | If there are 10 NAP in a total count of 50 grains, then $n = 50$, $x = 10$, and $\hat{p} = x/n = 0.2$. Substitution of these values into the formula for 95 percent limits gives $$p_L = \frac{0.2 + (3.84/100) \pm (1.96)\sqrt{(0.16/50) + (3.84/10000)}}{1 + (3.84/50)}$$ $$= \frac{0.2384 \pm 0.117}{1.0768},$$ resulting in the 95 percent limits $$0.11 < p < 0.33.$$ Snedecor (1956, p. 4) gives the limits 0.10 and 0.34, hence the approximation is quite accurate. The interval 0.11 to 0.33 contains the true NAP proportion, $p$, with a probability of 0.95. |
| *Example* | Using the data of A.2, $\hat{p} = 0.511$ and $n' = 350$. Substitution of these values into the formula for 99 percent limits gives $$p_L = \frac{0.511 + (6.636/700) \pm 2.576\sqrt{(0.2499/350) + (6.636/490,000)}}{1 + (6.636/350)}$$ $$= \frac{0.52048 \pm 0.0695}{1.01896},$$ resulting in the limits $$0.44 < p < 0.58.$$ In repeated sampling from this population 99 percent of the intervals computed as above will contain the true $p$. Hence one can say that the interval 0.44 to 0.58 contains the true NAP proportion with a probability of 0.99. |

*Remark:* The confidence limits used here are based on the asymptotic normality of the maximum likelihood estimate $\hat{p}$.

**A.4**   Simultaneous point estimation of the true proportions of any $k$ taxa counted in the sum. There are $x_1$ pine, $x_2$ oak, $x_3$ grass, $x_4$ sedge, $\cdots$, $x_k$ composite grains out of a total of $n$ grains. The simultaneous estimates are the same as those which would be obtained if each taxon were considered alone (as in A.1). That is,

$$\hat{p}_1 = x_1/n, \qquad \hat{p}_2 = x_2/n, \qquad \cdots, \qquad \hat{p}_k = x_k/n.$$

| | |
|---|---|
| *Example* | With 30 pine, 21 oak, 30 grass and 19 composite grains counted out of a total of 100 grains, simultaneous point estimates of the true $p$ are |

$$\hat{p}_1 = 0.30, \qquad \hat{p}_2 = 0.21, \qquad \hat{p}_3 = 0.30, \qquad \hat{p}_4 = 0.19.$$

**A.5**   Simultaneous point estimates of the true proportions of any $k$ taxa counted in the sum, where there are $N$ independent samples from the same level. Counts of pine $(x_1)$, oak $(x_2)$, $\cdots$, and composites $(x_k)$ were made for each of $N$ samples each totaling $n$ grains. The data can be arranged as follows.

| | NUMBER OF GRAINS | | | | |
|---|---|---|---|---|---|
| | PINE | OAK | $\cdots$ | COMPOSITES | TOTAL |
| Sample 1 | $x_{11}$ | $x_{21}$ | $\cdots$ | $x_{k1}$ | $n_1$ |
| Sample 2 | $x_{12}$ | $x_{22}$ | $\cdots$ | $x_{k2}$ | $n_2$ |
| $\cdots$ | $\cdots$ | $\cdots$ | $\cdots$ | $\cdots$ | $\cdots$ |
| Sample $N$ | $x_{1N}$ | $x_{2N}$ | $\cdots$ | $x_{kN}$ | $n_N$ |
| Column totals | $x_1'$ | $x_2'$ | $\cdots$ | $x_k'$ | $n'$ |

The simultaneous estimates of the true $p$ are the same as those obtained by considering any single taxon alone, as in A.2:

$$\hat{p}_1 = x_1'/n', \qquad \hat{p}_2 = x_2'/n', \qquad \cdots, \qquad \hat{p}_k = x_k'/n'.$$

| | |
|---|---|
| *Example* | The following three samples are from the same level: |

| | PINE | OAK | GRASS | TOTAL |
|---|---|---|---|---|
| Sample 1 | 6 | 3 | 1 | 10 |
| Sample 2 | 102 | 45 | 13 | 160 |
| Sample 3 | 26 | 14 | 5 | 45 |
| Column totals | 134 | 62 | 19 | 215 |

Simultaneous point estimates of the true proportions are:

$$\hat{p}_1 = 134/215 = 0.623, \quad \hat{p}_2 = 62/215 = 0.288, \quad \hat{p}_3 = 19/215 = 0.088.$$

*Remark:* The assumption that all samples are from the same level can be tested by the method of A.7.

**A.6** Test of the hypothesis that the true proportion, $p$, is the same for $N$ (two or more) samples. There are $N$ independent samples with counts of pine $(x)$ out of a given total number of grains $(n)$ for each sample. The data can be arranged as follows.

| | NUMBER OF PINE GRAINS | TOTAL NUMBER OF GRAINS |
|---|---|---|
| Sample 1 | $x_1$ | $n_1$ |
| Sample 2 | $x_2$ | $n_2$ |
| ... | ... | ... |
| Sample $N$ | $x_N$ | $n_N$ |
| Column totals | $x'$ | $n'$ |

Recall that $\hat{p} = x'/n'$. If each $n$ is large, the statistic

$$\chi^2 = \frac{(x_1 - n_1\hat{p})^2}{n_1\hat{p}(1-\hat{p})} + \frac{(x_2 - n_2\hat{p})^2}{n_2\hat{p}(1-\hat{p})} + \cdots + \frac{(x_N - n_N\hat{p})^2}{n_N\hat{p}(1-\hat{p})}$$

has approximately a chi-square distribution with $N - 1$ degrees of freedom under the hypothesis that the $N$ samples represent the same true proportion $(p_1 = p_2 = \cdots = p_N)$. If the value of the $\chi^2$ statistic is too large as compared with the tabulated critical value having $N - 1$ degrees of freedom (see Snedecor, 1956, p. 28), then the null hypothesis that the true pine proportion is the same for all samples is rejected.

The formula above can be used to compute $\chi^2$, and it is often illuminating to do so, for then the contribution of each sample to $\chi^2$ can be noted. However, the formula

$$\chi^2 = \frac{(\sum x^2/n) - [(x')^2/n']}{\hat{p}(1-\hat{p})}$$

is more suited to computation.
The term $\sum x^2/n$ is defined as

$$\sum x^2/n = \frac{x_1^2}{n_1} + \frac{x_2^2}{n_2} + \cdots + \frac{x_N^2}{n_N}.$$

When the total number of grains is the same for each sample $(n_1 = n_2 = \cdots n_N = n)$, the computations are easier, for then

$$\sum x^2/n = \frac{x_1^2}{n} + \frac{x_2^2}{n} + \cdots + \frac{x_N^2}{n}$$

$$= (1/n)(x_1^2 + x_2^2 + \cdots + x_N^2),$$

and it is not necessary to go through the tedious process of dividing each $x^2$ by a different $n$.

*Example*    Counts of pine pollen from five levels in a profile were:

|            | NUMBER OF PINE GRAINS | TOTAL NUMBER OF GRAINS |
|------------|:---------------------:|:----------------------:|
| Level 1    | 180                   | 200                    |
| Level 2    | 150                   | 160                    |
| Level 3    | 95                    | 110                    |
| Level 4    | 99                    | 115                    |
| Level 5    | 160                   | 175                    |
| Column totals | 684                | 760                    |

Do the five levels have the same proportions? (Does $p_1 = p_2 = p_3 = p_4 = p_5$?) The only term which is any trouble to compute is

$$\sum x^2/n = 180^2/200 + \cdots + 160^2/175 = 616.182.$$

Here $\hat{p} = 684/760$. Substitution of the appropriate numbers into the formula recommended for computation gives

$$\chi^2 = \frac{616.182 - [(684)^2/760]}{(684/760)[1 - (684/760)]} = 6.47.$$

This value is less than the critical value of $\chi^2$ with four degrees of freedom at the 0.05 level (9.49), and the proportions do not differ significantly.

*Remark:* The $\chi^2$ value here is exactly the one that would be obtained in computations from an $N$ by 2 contingency table; this test can also be viewed, however, as a comparison of a sample variance with an estimate of the binomial variance of a proportion. This test is a binomial homogeneity test.

**A.7**    Test of the hypothesis that $N$ samples have the same true proportions of $k$ taxa—a multinomial homogeneity test. Counts of pine $(x_1)$, oak $(x_2)$, $\cdots$, and composites $(x_k)$ were made for each of $N$ independent samples containing a total of $n$ grains for each sample. The data can be arranged as follows.

|              | NUMBER OF GRAINS |          |          |            |         |
|--------------|:----------:|:--------:|:--------:|:----------:|:-------:|
|              | PINE       | OAK      | $\cdots$ | COMPOSITES | TOTAL   |
| Sample 1     | $x_{11}$   | $x_{21}$ | $\cdots$ | $x_{k1}$   | $n_1$   |
| Sample 2     | $x_{12}$   | $x_{22}$ | $\cdots$ | $x_{k2}$   | $n_2$   |
| $\cdots$     | $\cdots$   | $\cdots$ | $\cdots$ | $\cdots$   | $\cdots$|
| Sample $N$   | $x_{1N}$   | $x_{2N}$ | $\cdots$ | $x_{kN}$   | $n_N$   |
| Column totals| $x_1'$     | $x_2'$   | $\cdots$ | $x_k'$     | $n'$    |

The question is whether the $N$ samples are homogeneous with respect to the true proportions of the taxa. Is the true pine proportion the same for each of the $N$ samples (does $p_{11} = p_{12} = \cdots = p_{1N}$) *and* the true oak proportion the same for the $N$ samples (does $p_{21} = p_{22} = \cdots = p_{2N}$) *and* ... *and* the true composite proportion the same for the $N$ samples (does $p_{k1} = p_{k2} = \cdots = p_{kN}$)?

Recall that $\hat{p}_1 = x'_1/n', \cdots, \hat{p}_k = x'_k/n'$. When $n$ is large for each sample, the statistic

$$\chi^2 = \frac{(x_{11} - n_1\hat{p}_1)^2}{n_1\hat{p}_1} + \frac{(x_{21} - n_1\hat{p}_2)^2}{n_1\hat{p}_2} + \cdots + \frac{(x_{k1} - n_1\hat{p}_k)^2}{n_1\hat{p}_k}$$

$$+ \frac{(x_{12} - n_2\hat{p}_1)^2}{n_2\hat{p}_1} + \frac{(x_{22} - n_2\hat{p}_2)^2}{n_2\hat{p}_2} + \cdots + \frac{(x_{k2} - n_2\hat{p}_k)^2}{n_2\hat{p}_k}$$

$$\cdots \qquad \cdots \qquad \cdots \qquad \cdots$$

$$+ \frac{(x_{1N} - n_N\hat{p}_1)^2}{n_N\hat{p}_1} + \frac{(x_{2N} - n_N\hat{p}_2)^2}{n_N\hat{p}_2} + \cdots + \frac{(x_{kN} - n_N\hat{p}_k)^2}{n_N\hat{p}_k}$$

is distributed approximately as chi-square with $(N - 1)(k - 1)$ degrees of freedom. One can compute with the above formula, and in doing so has the advantage of seeing which of the individual terms contribute most to the $\chi^2$ value, but computation is greatly facilitated by the formula

$$\chi^2 = \frac{\sum x_1^2/n}{\hat{p}_1} + \frac{\sum x_2^2/n}{\hat{p}_2} + \cdots + \frac{\sum x_k^2/n}{\hat{p}_k} - n',$$

which is mathematically identical to that above, and where

$$\sum x_1^2/n = (x_{11}^2/n_1) + (x_{12}^2/n_2) + \cdots + (x_{1N}^2/n_N).$$

Similarly,

$$\sum x_2^2/n = (x_{21}^2/n_1) + (x_{22}^2/n_2) + \cdots + (x_{2N}^2/n_N).$$

As in A.6, the calculations are simpler when all $n$ are equal ($n_1 = n_2 = \cdots = n_N = n$). For example, in such an event

$$\sum x_1^2/n = (1/n)(x_{11}^2 + x_{12}^2 + \cdots + x_{1N}^2),$$

hence the individual divisions are unnecessary.

| *Example* | Counts of pine, oak, grass, and composites were made to a predetermined total, $n$, at each of four levels. Results were: |

|  | | NUMBER OF GRAINS | | | |
|---|---|---|---|---|---|
|  | PINE | OAK | GRASS | COMPOSITES | TOTAL |
| Level 1 | 111 | 32 | 80 | 27 | 250 |
| Level 2 | 93 | 37 | 33 | 37 | 200 |
| Level 3 | 86 | 22 | 64 | 28 | 200 |
| Level 4 | 99 | 34 | 22 | 45 | 200 |
| Column totals | 389 | 125 | 199 | 137 | 850 |

The use of the formula for the computation of individual terms of the $\chi^2$ is illustrated. The estimates of the proportions of pine, oak, grass, and composites are:

$$\hat{p}_1 = 389/850 = 0.4576$$
$$\hat{p}_2 = 125/850 = 0.1471$$
$$\hat{p}_3 = 199/850 = 0.2341$$
$$\hat{p}_4 = 137/850 = 0.1612$$

Multiplying each of these by 250 gives

$$114.40, \quad 36.775, \quad 58.525, \quad 40.30,$$

and the terms of the $\chi^2$ from the first level are

$$\frac{(111 - 114.4)^2}{114.40} + \frac{(32 - 36.78)^2}{36.78} + \frac{(80 - 58.53)^2}{58.53} + \frac{(27 - 40.30)^2}{40.30}$$
$$= 0.10 + .62 + 7.88 + 4.39.$$

Multiplying each $\hat{p}$ by 200 gives

$$91.52, \quad 29.42, \quad 46.82, \quad 32.24,$$

and the terms of the $\chi^2$ from the second level are

$$\frac{(93 - 91.52)^2}{91.52} + \frac{(37 - 29.42)^2}{29.42} + \frac{(33 - 46.82)^2}{46.82} + \frac{(37 - 32.24)^2}{32.24}$$
$$= 0.02 + 1.95 + 4.08 + 0.70.$$

Similarly, the terms from the third level are

$$\frac{(86 - 91.52)^2}{91.52} + \frac{(22 - 29.42)^2}{29.42} + \frac{(64 - 46.82)^2}{46.82} + \frac{(28 - 32.24)^2}{32.24}$$
$$= 0.33 + 1.87 + 6.30 + 0.56,$$

and those for the fourth level are

$$\frac{(99 - 91.52)^2}{91.52} + \frac{(34 - 29.42)^2}{29.42} + \frac{(22 - 46.82)^2}{46.82} + \frac{(45 - 32.24)^2}{32.24}$$
$$= 0.61 + 0.71 + 13.16 + 5.05.$$

Summing the values for the four levels gives

$$\chi^2 = 12.99 + 6.75 + 9.06 + 19.53$$
$$= 48.33,$$

which, with nine degrees of freedom, is significant at the 0.005 level (see Snedecor, 1956, p. 28). The hypothesis that the four levels are homogeneous is rejected. It might be noted that the large terms of the $\chi^2$ come from the grass and composite counts. In fact if grass and composite counts are grouped as NAP, the data would be as follows.

|              | NUMBER OF GRAINS | | | |
|              | PINE | OAK | NAP | TOTAL |
|--------------|------|-----|-----|-------|
| Level 1      | 111  | 32  | 107 | 250   |
| Level 2      | 93   | 37  | 70  | 200   |
| Level 3      | 86   | 22  | 92  | 200   |
| Level 4      | 99   | 34  | 67  | 200   |
| Column totals | 389 | 125 | 336 | 850   |

The calculations for the first and second columns (pine and oak) are unchanged. For the NAP column (the sum of the grass and composite columns),

$$\hat{p}_3 = 0.3953.$$

Multiplying this value by 250 gives 98.83, and by 200 gives 79.06. The $\chi^2$ for all four levels is

$$\chi^2 = 0.10 + 0.62 + \frac{(107 - 98.83)^2}{98.83}$$

$$+ 0.02 + 1.95 + \frac{(70 - 79.06)^2}{79.06}$$

$$+ 0.33 + 1.87 + \frac{(92 - 79.06)^2}{79.06}$$

$$+ 0.61 + 0.71 + \frac{(67 - 79.06)^2}{79.06}$$

$$= 11.88,$$

which, with six degrees of freedom, is just slightly smaller than the critical value of 12.6 at the 0.05 level, and the result is not significant. It is revealing to compare this $\chi^2$ with the highly significant value obtained before composites and grasses were grouped as NAP. The data show that the grass proportion seems to increase only at the expense of the composite proportion, and that the heterogeneity of the levels seems to be less when the two are grouped as NAP.

**A.8** Test of the hypothesis that the true proportion, $p$, of a particular kind of pollen is a specified value $p^*$. One sample contains $x$ NAP grains counted out of a total of $n$ grains. Where $n$ is large, the statistic

$$\chi^2 = \frac{(x - np^*)^2}{np^*(1 - p^*)}$$

has approximately a chi-square distribution with one degree of freedom under the hypothesis that $p^*$ is the true $p$ ($p = p^*$). Thus the $\chi^2$ value computed with this formula can be compared with tabular values of chi-square and its significance evaluated. The formula

$$\chi^2 = \frac{(x^2/n) - 2p^*x + n(p^*)^2}{p^*(1 - p^*)}$$

(mathematically identical to that above) may on occasion be more convenient for computing purposes.

*Example* | Suppose that for theoretical reasons it is suspected that the NAP proportion for a given level is $1/3$. A sample is taken wherein 63 NAP grains are counted out of a total of 225 grains. Do the observations agree with the hypothesis?

Here $p^* = 1/3$; $x = 63$, $n = 225$, and $(x/n) = 0.280$. Thus,

$$\chi^2 = \frac{(3969/225) - (126/3) + (225/9)}{(2/9)}$$

$$= \frac{17.64 - 42 + 25}{(2/9)}$$

$$= 2.88.$$

Since this value is not significant at the 0.05 level with one degree of freedom, the hypothesis that $p = 1/3$ is not rejected.

**A.9**  Test of the hypothesis that the true proportion, $p$, of a particular kind of pollen is a specified value, $p^*$, when there are two or more $(N)$ independent samples purportedly from the same level, with the number of NAP grains $(x)$ recorded out of a total number of grains $(n)$ for each sample. The data can be arranged as follows.

|          | NUMBER OF NAP GRAINS | TOTAL NUMBER OF GRAINS |
|----------|:--------------------:|:----------------------:|
| Sample 1 | $x_1$                | $n_1$                  |
| Sample 2 | $x_2$                | $n_2$                  |
| ...      | ...                  | ...                    |
| Sample $N$ | $x_N$              | $n_N$                  |
| Column totals | $x'$            | $n'$                   |

When $n_1$ is large, then just as in A.8, the statistic

$$\chi^2 = \frac{(x_1 - n_1 p^*)^2}{n_1 p^*(1 - p^*)}$$

has approximately a chi-square distribution with one degree of freedom under the hypothesis that the first sample is from a population whose true $p$ is $p^*$. Similarly, when $n_2$ is large, then for the second sample,

$$\chi^2 = \frac{(x_2 - n_2 p^*)^2}{n_2 p^*(1 - p^*)},$$

which has approximately a chi-square distribution with one degree of freedom under the hypothesis that the second sample is from a population whose true $p$ is $p^*$. In fact, when each $n$ is large a $\chi^2$ statistic with one degree of freedom can be computed for each sample. But the sum of independent chi-square variables is itself a chi-square (for which the number of degrees of freedom is the sum of those of the individual chi-squares). Since our samples are independent, so are the individual $\chi^2$, and thus the statistic

$$\chi^2_N = \frac{(x_1 - n_1 p^*)^2}{n_1 p^*(1 - p^*)} + \frac{(x_2 - n_2 p^*)^2}{n_2 p^*(1 - p^*)} + \cdots + \frac{(x_N - n_N p^*)^2}{n_N p^*(1 - p^*)}$$

has approximately a chi-square distribution with $N$ degrees of freedom under the hypothesis that the $N$ samples are from a single population whose true NAP proportion is $p^*$. If the observed value of $\chi^2$ is too large compared with the tabular value (see Snedecor, 1956: p. 28), then the null hypothesis is rejected.

The null hypothesis might, however, be rejected here for more than one reason. First, not all samples may be from a single population. Second, even though all are from the same population, the hypothetical NAP proportion $(p^*)$ may not be the true NAP proportion.

In fact, the null hypothesis that all samples are from a population for which $p = p^*$ can be rephrased as follows:

1. All samples are from a population having the same NAP proportion $(p)$ regardless of the value of this $p$ (i.e., the samples are homogeneous).
2. The $p$ that is common to all samples is in fact $p^*$.

Correspondingly, the total $\chi_N^2$ already given can be regarded as the sum of two independent $\chi^2$:

1. A "heterogeneity" $\chi_{N-1}^2$ with $N-1$ degrees of freedom, whose value reflects whether the hypothesis of a common $p$ for all $N$ samples is feasible (i.e., whether the samples are homogeneous).
2. A "pooled" $\chi_1^2$ with one degree of freedom, whose value reflects whether $p^*$ is a likely candidate for the common $p$.

There are thus three $\chi^2$ statistics $(\chi_N^2, \chi_{N-1}^2, \chi_1^2)$, *none of which should be significant if the null hypothesis is to be accepted.* Further, where the null hypothesis is rejected, it is of interest to know whether this is due to a large "pooled" $\chi_1^2$, a large "heterogeneity" $\chi_{N-}^2$, or perhaps to both. If the heterogeneity is large and the pooled small, this indicates that the sampling is not from a single population. If the heterogeneity is small, but the pooled large, this indicates that although the sampling may be from a single population, the hypothetical $p^*$ is not the true $p$ of that population.

The formula for the total $\chi_N^2$ has already been given. Formulas for the heterogeneity and pooled $\chi^2$ are, respectively,

$$\chi_{N-1}^2 = \frac{(x_1 - n_1\hat{p})^2}{n_1 p^*(1 - p^*)} + \frac{(x_2 - n_2\hat{p})^2}{n_2 p^*(1 - p^*)} + \cdots + \frac{(x_N - n_N\hat{p})^2}{n_N p^*(1 - p^*)},$$

$$\chi_1^2 = \frac{(x' - n'p^*)^2}{n'p^*(1 - p^*)}.$$

The formula for the heterogeneity $\chi_{N-1}^2$ above is the same as that of the $\chi^2$ for testing homogeneity of samples in A.6, except that the denominators of the fractions therein contain an estimate, $\hat{p}$, rather than a hypothetical value $p^*$ as above. Thus, whereas the test of homogeneity in A.6 is made without regard to any specific hypothetical value of $p$, the test of homogeneity here is influenced somewhat by the choice of a hypothetical value $p^*$. If this value $p^*$ is reasonably close to the estimate $\hat{p} = x'/n'$, then the $\chi^2$ of A.6 and the heterogeneity $\chi^2_{N-1}$ here will give the same results.

The formulas already given for the total, heterogeneity, and pooled $\chi^2$ may be used in calculations from data. (In fact, using the formula already given for the total $\chi^2_N$, one obtains the $N$ separate values for the individual $\chi^2$ for each sample, and can observe which contribute most to the total $\chi^2_N$.) However, calculations are more conveniently made from the formulas below (each mathematically identical to its counterpart already presented). Formulas for the heterogeneity, pooled, and total $\chi^2$ are, respectively,

$$\chi^2_{N-1} = \frac{[\sum (x^2/n)] - [(x')^2/n']}{p^*(1 - p^*)},$$

$$\chi^2_1 = \frac{[(x')^2/n'] - 2p^*x' + (p^*)^2n'}{p^*(1 - p^*)},$$

$$\chi^2_N = \frac{[\sum (x^2/n)] - 2p^*x' + (p^*)^2n'}{p^*(1 - p^*)},$$

where the term $\sum (x^2/n)$ is equal to

$$(x_1^2/n_1) + (x_2^2/n_2) + \cdots + (x_N^2/n_N),$$

just as in A.6.

Since $\chi^2_N = \chi^2_1 + \chi^2_{N-1}$, the heterogeneity $\chi^2_{N-1}$ can be computed by subtracting $\chi^2_1$ from $\chi^2_N$.

*Example* | Three samples are taken from what is purportedly a single level. The numbers of pine grains counted out of a given total, and the pertinent calculations, are:

| | GRAINS COUNTED | | |
| | PINE | TOTAL | $x^2/n$ |
| --- | --- | --- | --- |
| Sample 1 | 55 | 230 | $3025/230 = 13.15217$ |
| Sample 2 | 38 | 140 | $1444/140 = 10.31428$ |
| Sample 3 | 44 | 215 | $1936/215 = \ \ 9.00465$ |
| | $x' = 137$ | $n' = 585$ | $\sum (x^2/n) = 32.47110$ |

Could these three samples be from a single level whose true proportion of pine is $1/2$ ($p^* = 1/2$)? Here

$$\chi^2_N = \frac{32.47110 - 137 + (585/4)}{(1/4)}$$

$$= 4(41.7211)$$

$$= 166.884.$$

Since $N = 3$, there are three degrees of freedom and $\chi^2_N$ is significant at the 0.005 level. To find the cause of this significance compute the pooled $\chi^2_1$:

$$\chi_1^2 = 4[137 - (585/2)]^2/585$$
$$= 4(24180.25/585)$$
$$= 165.3350,$$

which, with one degree of freedom, is significant at the 0.005 level. Subtracting $\chi_1^2$ from $\chi_N^2$ gives the heterogeneity $\chi_{N-1}^2$:

$$\chi_{N-1}^2 = 166.884 - 165.335$$
$$= 1.549.$$

Since $N - 1 = 2$, there are two degrees of freedom, and the value 1.549 is not significant at the 0.05 level. *Since the heterogeneity value is not significant, the three samples may well represent a single level; however, the highly significant pooled value indicates that the true pine proportion is not 1/2.*

Suppose that for the same three samples the hypothesis had been that $p^* = 1/4$. Then

$$\chi_N^2 = 2.84586, \qquad N = 3 \text{ degrees of freedom,}$$
$$\chi_1^2 = 0.78005,$$
$$\chi_{N-1}^2 = 2.06581, \qquad N - 1 = 2 \text{ degrees of freedom.}$$

None of these values is significant at the 0.05 level, and the hypothesis that $p = 1/4$ is not rejected.

A second series of three samples from what was purportedly a single level gave these results:

| | GRAINS COUNTED | | |
|---|---|---|---|
| | PINE | TOTAL | $x^2/n$ |
| Sample 1 | 130 | 250 | $16900/250 = 67.60000$ |
| Sample 2 | 61 | 200 | $3721/200 = 18.60500$ |
| Sample 3 | 101 | 145 | $10201/145 = 70.35172$ |
| | $x' = 292$ | $n' = 595$ | $\sum (x_i^2/n_i) = 156.55672$ |

Could these three samples be from a single level whose true proportion of pine is 1/2? Note that since the pine proportions for the three samples are 0.52, 0.31, and 0.70, heterogeneity may be suspected. The total chi-square statistic is

$$\chi_N^2 = \frac{156.55672 - 292 + 148.75}{(1/4)}$$

$$= 53.227,$$

which is significant at the 0.005 level with three degrees of freedom. The pooled is

$$\chi_1^2 = 4(292 - 297.5)^2/595 = 0.203,$$

which is not significant at the 0.05 level. The heterogeneity, however, is

$$\chi_{N-1}^2 = 53.227 - 0.203 = 53.024,$$

which, with $N - 1 = 2$ degrees of freedom, is significant at the 0.005 level. In this example although the overall pine proportions for three levels may be close to 1/2 (judging by the low pooled $\chi_1^2$), the levels are different (judging by the heterogeneity $\chi_{N-1}^2$), and thus the hypothesis that the samples are from a single level with $p = 1/2$ is rejected.

**A.10**  Test of the hypothesis that the true proportions of $k$ taxa are in fact specified values $(p , \cdots , p_k^*)$. One sample with $x_1$ pine $x_2$ oak, $x_3$ grass, $x_4$ sedge, $\cdots$, $x_k$ composite grains counted out of a total of $n$ grains. (The test of A.8 is a special case of this test where there are only two categories, $k = 2$.) When $n$ is large, the statistic

$$\chi^2 = \frac{(x_1 - np_1^*)^2}{np_1^*} + \frac{(x_2 - np_2^*)^2}{np_2^*} + \cdots + \frac{(x_k - np_k^*)^2}{np_k^*}$$

has approximately a chi-square distribution with $k - 1$ degrees of freedom under the hypothesis that the true $p$ are the $p^*$.

*Example*  A sample from a certain level has the following counts:

| pine | oak | grass | composites | total |
|------|-----|-------|------------|-------|
| 100  | 55  | 35    | 10         | 200   |

Since there are four categories, $k - 1 = 3$. Could the true proportions of pine, oak, grass, and composites be 0.40, 0.25, 0.25, and 0.10, respectively?

$$\chi^2 = \frac{(100 - 80)^2}{80} + \frac{(55 - 50)^2}{50} + \frac{(35 - 50)^2}{50} + \frac{(10 - 20)^2}{20}$$

$$= 5.0 + 0.5 + 4.5 + 5.0$$
$$= 15,$$

which, with three degrees of freedom, is significant at the 0.005 level (see the table in Snedecor, 1956, p. 28). If the null hypothesis were true, there would be only five out of a thousand occurrences of a value larger than 12.84 by chance. With a value of 15, the null hypothesis is rejected and the $p^*$ values 0.40, 0.25, 0.25, 0.10) are rejected as possible proportions for the level.

**A.11**  Test of the hypothesis that the true proportions of $k$ taxa $(p_1, \cdots, p_k)$ are given specified values $(p_1^*, \cdots, p_k^*)$ where there are $N$ independent samples purportedly from the same level. Counts of pine $(x_1)$, oak $(x_2)$, $\cdots$, composites $(x_k)$ were made for each of $N$ samples, each totaling $n$ grains. The data can be arranged as follows.

|  |  |  | NUMBER OF GRAINS |  |  |
|--|--|--|--|--|--|
|  | PINE | OAK | $\cdots$ | COMPOSITES | TOTAL |
| Sample 1 | $x_{11}$ | $x_{21}$ | $\cdots$ | $x_{k1}$ | $n_1$ |
| Sample 2 | $x_{12}$ | $x_{22}$ | $\cdots$ | $x_{k2}$ | $n_2$ |
| $\cdots$ | $\cdots$ | $\cdots$ | $\cdots$ | $\cdots$ | $\cdots$ |
| Sample $N$ | $x_{1N}$ | $x_{2N}$ | $\cdots$ | $x_{kN}$ | $n_N$ |
| Column totals | $x_1'$ | $x_2'$ | $\cdots$ | $x_k'$ | $n'$ |

Where $n_1$ is large, the statistic computed from the first sample,

$$_1\chi^2 = \frac{(x_{11} - n_1 p_1^*)^2}{n_1 p_1^*} + \frac{(x_{21} - n_1 p_2^*)^2}{n_1 p_2^*} + \cdots + \frac{(x_{k1} - n_1 p_k^*)^2}{n_1 p_k^*},$$

has approximately a chi-square distribution with $k - 1$ degrees of freedom under the hypothesis that the true $p$ are the $p^*$, just as in A.10. Similarly, where $n_2$ is large, the statistic computed from the second sample,

$$_2\chi^2 = \frac{(x_{12} - n_2 p_1^*)^2}{n_2 p_1^*} + \frac{(x_{22} - n_2 p_2^*)^2}{n_2 p_2^*} + \cdots + \frac{(x_{k2} - n_2 p_k^*)^2}{n_2 p_k^*},$$

has approximately a chi-square distribution with $k - 1$ degrees of freedom under the null hypothesis. Where each $n$ is large one can compute a similar $\chi^2$ statistic for each of the $N$ samples. The independence of these chi-squares follows from the independence of the samples, so that their sum is distributed approximately as chi-square with $N(k - 1)$ degrees of freedom under the hypothesis that the $N$ samples are all from a population for which $p_1 = p_1^*$ and $p_2 = p^*$ and $\cdots$ and $p_k = p_k^*$. This sum will be called the total $\chi^2$ and denoted by $\chi^2_{N(k-1)}$.

$$\chi^2_{N(k-1)} = {_1\chi^2} + {_2\chi^2} + \cdots + {_N\chi^2}.$$

As in A.9 the total $\chi^2$, (which in this case has $N(k - 1)$ degrees of freedom) can be regarded as the sum of two independent $\chi^2$: a pooled, with $k - 1$ degrees of freedom, and a heterogeneity, with $(N - 1)(k - 1)$ degrees of freedom. Thus,

$$\underset{\text{TOTAL}}{\chi^2_{N(k-1)}} = \underset{\text{POOLED}}{\chi^2_{(k-1)}} + \underset{\text{HETEROGENEITY}}{\chi^2_{(N-1)(k-1)}} \quad .$$

Just as in A.9, *none of these three $\chi^2$ should be significant if the null hypothesis is to be accepted.* Should the null hypothesis be rejected, the pooled and the heterogeneity $\chi^2$ can be interpreted just as before. The heterogeneity $\chi^2_{(N-1)(k-1)}$ reflects sample-to-sample variation in the proportions of the $k$ taxa—whether the $N$ samples are from a single population or not. The pooled $\chi^2_{k-1}$ reflects whether the $(p_1^*, \cdots, p_k^*)$ is a likely candidate for the true $(p_1, \cdots, p_k)$. *Interpretation of the heterogeneity and pooled $\chi^2$ is the same as in A.9,* the only difference being that conclusions are relevant to $k$ proportions rather than to a single proportion. Thus, the discussion of A.9 applies equally well to this section.

The total $\chi^2_{N(k-1)}$ can be computed by summing the individual $\chi^2$. The pooled $\chi^2_{(k-1)}$ can be computed from

$$\chi^2_{(k-1)} = \frac{(x_1' - n' p_1^*)^2}{n' p_1^*} + \cdots + \frac{(x_k' - n' p_k^*)^2}{n' p_k^*}.$$

The heterogeneity $\chi^2_{(N-1)(k-1)}$ is obtained by subtracting the pooled from the total:

$$\chi^2_{(N-1)(k-1)} = \chi^2_{N(k-1)} - \chi^2_{(k-1)}.$$

The heterogeneity $\chi^2_{(N-1)(k-1)}$ could be computed using the $\chi^2$ which was given for testing homogeneity in A.7 but replacing all $\hat{p}$ in the denominators (*not the numerators*) by the corresponding $p^*$. (This does not apply to the computing formula in A.7).

Whenever the $\hat{p}$ are sufficiently close in value to the $p^*$, the heterogeneity $\chi^2$ here and in A.7 will give the same results. The hypotheses tested by these two $\chi^2$ differ slightly. The heterogeneity $\chi^2$ of this section tests homogeneity under the hypothesis that the true $p$ are the $p^*$. The $\chi^2$ of A.7 tests homogeneity under the hypothesis that the $p$ for the $N$ samples are the same without regard to a specific set of $p^*$.

| | |
|---|---|
| *Example* | Four samples are taken from what is purportedly a single level. The numbers of pine, oak, grass, and composite grains counted up to a given total for each sample were: |

|          | NUMBER OF GRAINS | | | | |
|----------|-------|-----|-------|------------|-------|
|          | PINE  | OAK | GRASS | COMPOSITES | TOTAL |
| Sample 1 | 114   | 29  | 80    | 27         | 250   |
| Sample 2 | 93    | 37  | 33    | 37         | 200   |
| Sample 3 | 86    | 22  | 64    | 28         | 200   |
| Sample 4 | 99    | 34  | 22    | 45         | 200   |
| Column totals | 392 | 122 | 199 | 137      | 850   |

Could the true pine proportion be 0.45; that of oak, 0.15; that of grass, 0.25; and that of composites, 0.15? Here

$$p_1^* = 0.45, \qquad p_2^* = 0.15, \qquad p_3^* = 0.25, \qquad p_4^* = 0.15.$$

The pooled $\chi^2$, with $k - 1 = 3$ degrees of freedom, is

$$\frac{(392 - 382.5)^2}{382.5} + \frac{(122 - 127.5)^2}{127.5} + \frac{(199 - 212.5)^2}{212.5} + \frac{(137 - 127.5)^2}{127.5}$$

$$= 0.2359 + 0.2373 + 0.8576 + 0.7078$$
$$= 2.04.$$

With three degrees of freedom this value is not significant at the 0.05 level. Calculations for the total $\chi^2_{N(k-1)}$ involve first finding the individual $\chi^2$. These are:

$$_1\chi^2 = \frac{(114 - 112.5)^2}{112.5} + \frac{(29 - 37.5)^2}{37.5} + \frac{(80 - 62.5)^2}{62.5} + \frac{(27 - 37.5)^2}{37.5}$$

$$= 9.787;$$

$$_2\chi^2 = \frac{(93 - 90)^2}{90} + \frac{(37 - 30)^2}{30} + \frac{(33 - 50)^2}{50} + \frac{(37 - 30)^2}{30}$$

$$= 9.147;$$

$$_3\chi^2 = \frac{(86 - 90)^2}{90} + \frac{(22 - 30)^2}{30} + \frac{(64 - 50)^2}{50} + \frac{(28 - 30)^2}{30}$$

$$= 6.364;$$

$$_4X^2 = \frac{(99-90)^2}{90} + \frac{(34-30)^2}{30} + \frac{(22-50)^2}{50} + \frac{(45-30)^2}{30}$$

$$= 24.613.$$

Each of these individual $\chi^2$ has three degrees of freedom, and all but $_3\chi^2$ are significant at the 0.05 level ($_4\chi^2$ is significant at the 0.005 level). The total $\chi^2_{N(k-1)}$ is

$$9.787 + 9.147 + 6.364 + 24.613 = 49.911.$$

Here $N = 4$ and $k - 1 = 3$, so that this has twelve degrees of freedom. It is significant at the 0.005 level. The heterogeneity $\chi^2$ is obtained by subtracting the pooled from the total:

$$49.91 - 2.04 = 47.87,$$

which, with nine degrees of freedom, is significant at the 0.005 level.

Although the overall proportions of the four samples are not notably different from the hypothetical proportions (0.45, 0.15, 0.25, 0.15), as reflected by the low pooled $\chi^2$, the samples are quite heterogeneous, and the null hypothesis that the four samples are from a population with the specified proportions is rejected.

**B.1** Point estimation of the true proportion, $p$, of a particular kind of pollen. One sample, with $x$ NAP grains noted while counting to $n$ AP grains.

$$\hat{p} = x/(x + n).$$

The corresponding estimate for the proportion of AP pollen $(1 - p)$ is $1 - \hat{p}$.

*Example*    If while counting 20 AP grains, 4 NAP grains are observed, then the maximum likelihood estimate $\hat{p} = 4/24 = 0.167$. The corresponding estimate of the AP proportion $(1 - p)$ is $1 - \hat{p} = 20/24 = 0.833$.

*Remark:* The estimate for $p$ given here is the maximum likelihood estimate, and is biased. If an unbiased estimate is desired, then $\hat{p} = x/(x + n - 1)$ can be used.

**B.2** Point estimation of the true proportion, $p$, of a particular kind of pollen. Two or more ($N$) independent samples from the same level, with the number of NAP grains ($x$) recorded while counting to a given number ($n$) of AP grains for each sample. The data can be arranged as follows.

|  | NUMBER OF AP (MARKER) GRAINS | NUMBER OF NAP GRAINS |
|---|---|---|
| Sample 1 | $n_1$ | $x_1$ |
| Sample 2 | $n_2$ | $x_2$ |
| ... | ... | ... |
| Sample $N$ | $n_N$ | $x_N$ |
| Column totals | $n'$ | $x'$ |

The estimate of the NAP proportion, $p$, is

$$\hat{p} = x'/(x' + n').$$

The corresponding estimate of the proportion of AP pollen $(1 - p)$ is $1 - \hat{p}$.

*Example* | Four counts made from the same level give the following results.

| | NUMBER OF AP (MARKER) GRAINS | NUMBER OF NAP GRAINS |
|---|---|---|
| Sample 1 | 7 | 9 |
| Sample 2 | 100 | 95 |
| Sample 3 | 50 | 46 |
| Sample 4 | 200 | 189 |
| Column totals | 357 | 339 |

The estimate of the NAP proportion, $p$, is

$$\hat{p} = 339/696 = 0.487,$$

and the corresponding estimate of $1 - p$ is $1 - \hat{p} = 0.513$.

*Remark:* The estimate for $p$ given above is the maximum likelihood estimate, and is biased (although the bias is negligible for large samples). If an unbiased estimate is desired, then $\hat{p} = x'/(x' + n' - 1)$ can be used.

**B.3**  Point estimation of the ratio, $u$, of the true proportion, $p$, of a particular kind of pollen to the true proportion of marker pollen. One sample with $x$ NAP grains noted while counting to $n$ AP grains. In this example $u = p/(1 - p)$ is the NAP/AP ratio. The estimate of the NAP/AP ratio is

$$\hat{u} = x/n.$$

*Example* | With 147 NAP grains noted while counting to 100 AP grains, the estimate of the NAP/AP ratio is

$$\hat{u} = 1.47.$$

*Remark:* The estimate given is the maximum likelihood estimate, and is unbiased.

**B.4**  Point estimation of the ratio, $u$, of the true proportion, $p$, of a particular kind of pollen to the true proportion of marker pollen. Two or more ($N$) independent samples from the same level with the number of NAP grains ($x$) recorded while counting to a given number ($n$) of AP grains for each sample. [In this example $u = p/(1 - p)$ is the NAP/AP ratio.] The data can be arranged exactly as in B.2. The estimate of the NAP/AP ratio is

$$\hat{u} = x'/n'.$$

*Example* | If four independent samples give results exactly as in B.2, then
$$\hat{u} = 339/357 = 0.950.$$

*Remark:* The estimate given is the maximum likelihood estimate, and is unbiased.

**B.5** Confidence intervals (interval estimates) for $u$, the ratio of the true proportion of a particular kind of pollen to the true proportion of marker pollen. One or more independent samples $(N)$ from the same level, with the number of NAP grains $(x)$ recorded while counting to $n$ AP grains for each sample. [In this example $u = p/(1 - p)$ is the NAP/AP ratio.]

No tables are currently available, but with $n$ fairly large, approximate 95 percent confidence limits can be computed from

$$u_L = \frac{\hat{u} + [3.84/(2n)] \pm (1.96)\sqrt{[\hat{u}(1 + \hat{u})/n] + [3.84/(4n^2)]}}{1 - (3.84/n)},$$

where the larger value obtained is the upper 95 percent limit and the smaller value is the lower 95 percent limit. If one wishes 99 percent confidence limits, where $n$ is fairly large, approximate limits are given by

$$u_L = \frac{\hat{u} + [6.636/(2n)] \pm (2.576)\sqrt{[\hat{u}(1 + \hat{u})/n] + [6.636/(4n^2)]}}{1 - (6.636/n)}.$$

In either formula, if the limits are being estimated using a single sample, then $\hat{u} = x/n$ as in B.3. If the limits are being estimated using $N$ independent samples from the same level, then $\hat{u}$ is as in B.4 and $n$ in the above formulas should be replaced by the sum of the $n$; that is, $n'$.

*Example* | Using the example of B.3, we have
$$\hat{u} = 1.47 \quad \text{and} \quad n = 100,$$

so that approximate 95 percent confidence limits are obtained by solving

$$u_L = \frac{1.47 + (3.84/200) \pm (1.96)\sqrt{(3.6309/100) + (3.84/40,000)}}{1 - (3.84/100)}$$

$$= \frac{1.489 \pm 0.374}{0.9616},$$

giving

$$1.16 < u < 1.94.$$

Thus, this interval contains the true NAP/AP ratio with a probability of 0.95.

For an example using several independent samples, the example of B.4 is used. Here $\hat{u} = 0.950$ the sum of the $n$ is 357, so that approximate 99 percent confidence limits for $u$ are obtained by solving

$$u_L = \frac{0.950 + (6.636/714) \pm 2.576\sqrt{(1.8525/357) + (6.636/509{,}796)}}{1 - (6.636/357)}$$

$$= \frac{0.959 \pm 0.184}{0.9814},$$

giving

$$0.79 < u < 1.16.$$

Thus, this interval covers the true $u$ with a probability of 0.99. Note that in this example one individual $n$ is only 7; however, it is the total of the $n$ (357) that determines the accuracy of the approximation.

*Remark:* The confidence limits used here are based on the asymptotic normality of the maximum likelihood estimate $\hat{u}$.

**B.6**   Confidence intervals (interval estimates) for $p$, the true proportion of a particular kind of pollen. One or more independent samples ($N$) from the same level, with the number of NAP grains ($x$) recorded while counting to $n$ AP grains for each sample. Here $p$ is the true proportion of NAP pollen.

Tables are not available, but for fairly large values of $n$, approximate limits can be obtained by first finding limits for $u$ as in B.5 and then dividing each limit by one plus itself.

*Example*   In the first example of B.5 the following 95 percent confidence limits were found for $u$:

$$1.16 < u < 1.94.$$

Thus, the 95 percent confidence limits for $p$ are

$$[1.16/(1 + 1.16)] < p < [1.94/(1 + 1.94)],$$
$$0.54 < p < 0.66.$$

Therefore, this interval covers the true $p$ with a probability of 0.95.
Consider also the second example of B.5. There 99 percent confidence limits for $u$ were found to be

$$0.79 < u < 1.16.$$

Thus, the 99 percent confidence limits for the NAP proportion, $p$, are

$$(0.79/1.79) < p < (1.16/2.16),$$
$$0.44 < p < 0.54.$$

The probability that this interval covers the true $p$ is 0.99.

**B.7**   Simultaneous point estimates of the true proportions ($p_1, \cdots, p_k$) of any $k$ taxa, and simultaneous point estimates of the true ratios, $u$: $u_1 = p_1/p_k$, $u_2 = p_2/p_k$, $\cdots$ . There were $x_1$ grass grains, $x_2$ composite grains, $\cdots$, $x_{k-1}$ sedge grains counted while counting to $n$ grains of the $k$th category (AP).

Simultaneous point estimates of the true ratios $(u_1, \cdots, u_{k-1})$ are

$$\hat{u}_1 = x_1/n, \qquad \hat{u}_2 = x_2/n, \qquad \cdots, \qquad \hat{u}_{k-1} = x_{k-1}/n.$$

Let $t = x_1 + x_2 + \cdots + x_{k-1}$. Then simultaneous point estimates of the true proportions $(p_1, \cdots, p_k)$ are

$$p_1 = x_1/(t+n), \quad \cdots, \quad p_{k-1} = x_{k-1}/(t+n), \qquad p_k = n/(t+n).$$

| | |
|---|---|
| *Example* | 201 grass grains and 78 composite grains were counted while counting to 200 AP grains. Point estimates of $u_1$ and $u_2$ are $$\hat{u}_1 = 201/200 = 1.005,$$ $$\hat{u}_2 = \phantom{0}78/200 = 0.390.$$ Thus, the estimate of the grass/AP ratio is 1.0 and that of the composite/AP ratio, 0.39. Point estimates of the grass, composite, and AP proportions are, respectively, $$\hat{p}_1 = 201/479 = 0.42,$$ $$\hat{p}_2 = \phantom{0}78/479 = 0.16,$$ $$\hat{p}_3 = 200/479 = 0.42.$$ |

*Remark:* The estimates given above are maximum likelihood estimates. Those for the $u$ are unbiased. Those for the $p$ are biased, but the bias is negligible in samples where $n$ is at all large (see B.1).

**B.8** Simultaneous point estimates of the true proportions $(p_1, \cdots, p_k)$ of any $k$ taxa, and simultaneous point estimates of the true ratios, $u$: $u_1 = p_1/p_k$, $u_2 = p_2/p_k$, $\cdots$. For each of $N$ independent samples from the same level counts of grass $(x_1)$, composites $(x_2)$, $\cdots$, and sedges $(x_{k-1})$ were recorded while counting to $n$ AP (marker) grains. The data can be arranged as follows.

NUMBER OF GRAINS

| | MARKERS (AP) | GRASS | COMPOSITES | $\cdots$ | SEDGES | TOTAL EXCEPT MARKERS |
|---|---|---|---|---|---|---|
| Sample 1 | $n_1$ | $x_{11}$ | $x_{21}$ | $\cdots$ | $x_{k-1,1}$ | $t_1$ |
| Sample 2 | $n_2$ | $x_{12}$ | $x_{22}$ | $\cdots$ | $x_{k-1,2}$ | $t_2$ |
| $\cdots$ | $\cdots$ | $\cdots$ | $\cdots$ | $\cdots$ | $\cdots$ | $\cdots$ |
| Sample $N$ | $n_N$ | $x_{1N}$ | $x_{2N}$ | $\cdots$ | $x_{k-1,N}$ | $t_N$ |
| Column totals | $n'$ | $x_1'$ | $x_2'$ | $\cdots$ | $x_{k-1}'$ | $t'$ |

Simultaneous point estimates of the true ratios $(u_1, \cdots, u_{k-1})$ are

$$\hat{u}_1 = x_1'/n', \qquad \hat{u}_2 = x_2'/n', \qquad \cdots, \qquad \hat{u}_{k-1} = x_{k-1}'/n'.$$

Simultaneous estimates of the true proportions $(p_1, \cdots, p_k)$, where $p_k$ is the AP (marker) proportion, are

$$\hat{p}_1 = x_1'/(t'+n'), \qquad \cdots, \qquad \hat{p}_{k-1} = x_{k-1}'/(t'+n'), \qquad \hat{p}_k = n'/(t'+n').$$

*Example*

Three samples are collected from a single level. For each sample the numbers each of grass and composite grains are recorded while counting to a predetermined number of AP pollen grains (here $k = 3$). Results were:

| | NUMBER OF GRAINS | | | |
|---|---|---|---|---|
| | MARKERS (AP) | GRASS | COMPOSITES | TOTAL EXCEPT MARKERS |
| Sample 1 | 200 | 201 | 78 | 279 |
| Sample 2 | 300 | 270 | 132 | 402 |
| Sample 3 | 250 | 260 | 116 | 376 |
| Column totals | 750 | 731 | 326 | 1057 |

Point estimates of $u_1$ (the grass/AP ratio) and of $u_2$ (the composite/AP ratio) are

$$\hat{u}_1 = 731/750 = 0.97,$$
$$\hat{u}_2 = 326/750 = 0.43.$$

Point estimates of the grass, composite, and AP proportions in that order are

$$\hat{p}_1 = 731/1807 = 0.405,$$
$$\hat{p}_2 = 326/1807 = 0.180,$$
$$\hat{p}_3 = 750/1807 = 0.415.$$

*Remark:* The estimates used are the maximum likelihood estimates. Those for the $u$ are unbiased; those for the $p$ are biased, but the bias is negligible where $n'$ is at all large.

The assumption that all samples are from the same level can be tested by the method of B.10.

**B.9**   Test of the hypothesis that the true proportion, $p$, is the same for two or more ($N$) samples. For two or more ($N$) independent samples, counts of NAP grains ($x$) were made while counting to $n$ AP grains. Since to each value of the proportion, $p$, there corresponds only one value of the ratio $u = p/(1 - p)$, and vice versa, this is also a test of the hypothesis that the true ratio, $u$, is the same for $N$ samples. The data can be arranged as follows.

| | NUMBER OF AP (MARKER) GRAINS | NUMBER OF NAP GRAINS |
|---|---|---|
| Sample 1 | $n_1$ | $x_1$ |
| Sample 2 | $n_2$ | $x_2$ |
| ... | ... | ... |
| Sample $N$ | $n_N$ | $x_N$ |
| Column totals | $n'$ | $x'$ |

Recall that $\hat{u} = x'/n'$. With each $n$ large, the statistic

$$\chi^2 = \frac{(x_1 - n_1\hat{u})^2}{n_1\hat{u}(1 + \hat{u})} + \frac{(x_2 - n_2\hat{u})^2}{n_2\hat{u}(1 + \hat{u})} + \cdots + \frac{(x_N - n_N\hat{u})^2}{n_N\hat{u}(1 + \hat{u})}$$

has approximately a chi-square distribution under the hypothesis that the $N$ samples represent the same true proportion $(p_1 = p_2 = \cdots = p_N)$. If the value of the $\chi^2$ statistic is too large as compared with the tabulated critical value having $N - 1$ degrees of freedom (see Snedecor, 1956, p. 28), then the null hypothesis that the true NAP proportion is the same for all samples is rejected.

The formula above can be used in computation, and it is often illuminating to do so, for then the contribution of each sample to the $\chi^2$ can be noted. However, a formula more suited for computing purposes is

$$\chi^2 = \frac{(\sum x^2/n) - [(x')^2/n'],}{\hat{u}(1 + \hat{u})}$$

where the term $\sum x^2/n$ is defined as

$$\sum x^2/n = \frac{x_1^2}{n_1} + \frac{x_2^2}{n_2} + \cdots + \frac{x_N^2}{n_N}.$$

When the number of AP (marker) grains is the same for each of the $N$ samples, the calculation is easier, for then

$$\sum x^2/n = (1/n)(x_1^2 + x_2^2 + \cdots + x_N^2),$$

and the tedious process of dividing each $x^2$ by a different $n$ is avoided.

*Example* | Counts of NAP grains (made while counting to 200 AP grains at each of six levels) were:

| | NUMBER OF AP (MARKER) GRAINS | NUMBER OF NAP GRAINS |
|---|---|---|
| Level 1 | 200 | 40 |
| Level 2 | 200 | 300 |
| Level 3 | 200 | 65 |
| Level 4 | 200 | 180 |
| Level 5 | 200 | 250 |
| Level 6 | 200 | 95 |
| Column totals | 1200 | 930 |

The calculation of $\sum x^2/n$ is simplified by the fact that $n$ is the same for all levels:

$$\sum x^2/n = (1/200)[(40)^2 + (300)^2 + \cdots + (95)^2],$$
$$= 998.75.$$

To test the hypothesis that the true NAP proportion is the same for all six levels:

$$\chi^2 = \frac{(998.75 - 720.75)}{(930/1200)(2130/1200)}$$

$$= 202.1,$$

which, with five degrees of freedom, is significant at the 0.005 level (the critical value is 16.75 in Snedecor's table, p. 28), and the hypothesis that the six levels have the same NAP proportion is rejected.

As a second example consider the following counts of NAP grains made while counting to the stated number of AP grains:

|  | NUMBER OF AP (MARKER) GRAINS | NUMBER OF NAP GRAINS |
|---|---|---|
| Level 1 | 150 | 78 |
| Level 2 | 200 | 85 |
| Column totals | 350 | 163 |

$$\sum x^2/n = [(78)^2/150] + [(85)^2/200] = 76.69,$$

$$\chi^2 = \frac{76.69 - [(163)^2/350]}{(163/350)(513/350)}$$

$$= 1.14.$$

Since $N = 2$, then $N - 1 = 1$ degree of freedom. The value is not significant at the 0.05 level, and the hypothesis that the two levels represent the same true NAP proportion is not rejected.

**B.10**    Test of the hypothesis that $N$ samples have the same true proportions of $k$ taxa ($k - 1$ taxa counted while counting to $n$ grains of the $k$th taxon, the marker taxon)—a negative multinomial homogeneity test. For each of $N$ independent samples counts of grass ($x_1$), composites ($x_2$), $\cdots$, and sedges ($x_{k-1}$) were recorded while counting to $n$ AP (marker) grains. The data can be arranged as follows.

| | NUMBER OF GRAINS | | | | | |
|---|---|---|---|---|---|---|
| | MARKERS (AP) | GRASS | COMPOSITES | $\cdots$ | SEDGES | TOTAL EXCEPT MARKERS |
| Sample 1 | $n_1$ | $x_{11}$ | $x_{21}$ | $\cdots$ | $x_{k-1,1}$ | $t_1$ |
| Sample 2 | $n_2$ | $x_{12}$ | $x_{22}$ | $\cdots$ | $x_{k-1,2}$ | $t_2$ |
| $\cdots$ | $\cdots$ | $\cdots$ | $\cdots$ | $\cdots$ | $\cdots$ | $\cdots$ |
| Sample $N$ | $n_N$ | $x_{1N}$ | $x_{2N}$ | $\cdots$ | $x_{k-1,N}$ | $t_N$ |
| Column totals | $n'$ | $x_1'$ | $x_2'$ | $\cdots$ | $x_{k-1}'$ | $t'$ |

The question asked is are the $N$ samples homogeneous with respect to the true proportions of the taxa. Is the true grass proportion the same for the $N$ samples (does $p_{11} = p_{12} = \cdots = p_{1N}$) *and* the true composite proportion the same for the $N$ samples (does $p_{21} = p_{22} = \cdots = p_{2N}$) *and* . . . *and* the true AP proportion the same for the $N$ samples (does $p_{k1} = p_{k2} = \cdots = p_{kN}$)? If $p_1, \cdots, p_k$ are known, then so are $u_1, \cdots, u_{k-1}$ (where $u_1 = p_1/p_k$, $u_2 = p_2/p_k, \cdots$) and vice versa, the hypothesis of homogeneity of the $N$

samples with respect to the $p$ is the same as that of homogeneity with respect to the $u$.

Recall that $\hat{u}_1 = x_1'/n', \cdots, \hat{u}_{k-1} = x_{k-1}'/n'$. Let $\hat{t} = t'/n'$; then where the $n$ for each sample is large, the statistic

$$\chi^2 = \frac{(x_{11} - n_1\hat{u}_1)^2}{n_1\hat{u}_1} + \cdots + \frac{(x_{k-1,1} - n_1\hat{u}_{k-1})^2}{n_1\hat{u}_{k-1}} - \frac{(t_1 - n_1\hat{t})^2}{n_1(\hat{t} + 1)}$$

$$+ \frac{(x_{12} - n_2\hat{u}_1)^2}{n_2\hat{u}_1} + \cdots + \frac{(x_{k-1,2} - n_2\hat{u}_{k-1})^2}{n_2\hat{u}_{k-1}} - \frac{(t_2 - n_2\hat{t})^2}{n_2(\hat{t} + 1)}$$

$$\cdots \qquad \cdots \qquad \cdots \qquad \cdots$$

$$+ \frac{(x_{1N} - n_N\hat{u}_1)^2}{n_N\hat{u}_1} + \cdots + \frac{(x_{k-1,N} - n_N\hat{u}_{k-1})^2}{n_N\hat{u}_{k-1}} - \frac{(t_N - n_N\hat{t})^2}{n_N(\hat{t} + 1)}$$

has approximately a chi-square distribution with $(N - 1)(k - 1)$ degrees of freedom under the null hypothesis. Computation with the above formula offers the advantage of showing which of the individual terms contribute most to the $\chi^2$ value. The negative terms at the end of each row correct for the lack of independence of the grass, composite, . . . , and sedge counts within any sample.

The formula

$$\chi^2 = \frac{\sum x_1^2/n}{\hat{u}_1} + \frac{\sum x_2^2/n}{\hat{u}_2} + \cdots + \frac{\sum x_{k-1}^2/n}{\hat{u}_{k-1}} - \frac{(t' + \sum t^2/n)}{\hat{t} + 1},$$

which is mathematically identical to that above, facilitates computation. The terms therein are defined as follows:

$$\sum x_1^2/n = (x_{11}^2/n_1) + (x_{12}^2/n_2) + \cdots + (x_{1N}^2/n_N)$$

and

$$\sum x_2^2/n = (x_{21}^2/n_1) + (x_{22}^2/n_2) + \cdots + (x_{2N}^2/n_N)$$

and so on for the other sums up to $k - 1$. The term $\sum t^2/n$ is also defined in the same way:

$$\sum t^2/n = (t_1^2/n_1) + (t_2^2/n_2) + \cdots + (t_N^2/n_N).$$

When $n$ is the same for each of the $N$ samples, these sums are considerably easier to compute, for then

$$\sum x_1^2/n = (1/n)(x_{11}^2 + x_{12}^2 + \cdots + x_{1N}^2),$$

and division of the individual terms is no longer necessary. The same holds for the other sums.

In any event, if the $\chi^2$ value obtained is too high compared to the tabular value at the critical level, the hypothesis that the $N$ samples are homogeneous with respect to the true proportions is rejected.

*Example*  | The following counts of grass, composite, and sedge grains were obtained while counting to the specified number of AP pollen grains.

|         | AP  | GRASS | COMPOSITES | SEDGES | TOTAL EXCEPT AP |
|---------|-----|-------|------------|--------|-----------------|
| Level 1 | 100 | 96    | 72         | 40     | 208             |
| Level 2 | 130 | 100   | 88         | 55     | 243             |
| Level 3 | 150 | 97    | 94         | 70     | 261             |
| Level 4 | 90  | 56    | 60         | 41     | 157             |
| Column totals | 470 | 349 | 314      | 206    | 869             |

Here $N = 4$ and $k - 1 = 3$, so that the $\chi^2$ will have twelve degrees of freedom. The sums are

$$\sum x_1^2/n = [(96)^2/100] + \cdots + [(56)^2/90] = 266.65,$$
$$\sum x_2^2/n = [(72)^2/100] + \cdots + [(60)^2/90] = 210.32,$$
$$\sum x_3^2/n = [(40)^2/100] + \cdots + [(41)^2/90] = 90.61,$$
$$\sum t^2/n = [(208)^2/100] + \cdots + [(157)^2/90] = 1614.88.$$

Thus,

$$\chi^2 = \frac{266.65}{(349/470)} + \frac{210.32}{(314/470)} + \frac{90.61}{(206/470)} - \frac{(869 + 1614.88)}{[1 + (869/470)]}$$

$$= 8.7$$

which, with twelve degrees of freedom, is not significant at the 0.05 level (see Snedecor, 1956, p. 28), and the hypothesis of homogeneity of proportions for these four levels is not rejected.

**B.11**  Test of the hypothesis that the true proportion, $p$, of a particular kind of pollen is a specified value $p^*$ (and, equivalently, a test of the hypothesis that a true ratio, $u$, has a particular value, $u^*$). One sample with $x$ NAP grains counted while counting to $n$ AP grains.

If the hypothesis is given in terms of $p^*$, and the corresponding hypothesis in terms of $u^*$ is desired, then $u^*$ is found by the equation $u^* = p^*/(1 - p^*)$. If the hypothesis is given in terms of $u^*$, and the corresponding hypothesis in terms of $p^*$ is desired, then $p^*$ is found by the equation $p^* = u^*/(1 + u^*)$.

In any event, if the number of AP grains counted ($n$) is large, the statistic

$$\chi^2 = \frac{(x - nu^*)^2}{nu^*(1 + u^*)}$$

has approximately a chi-square distribution with one degree of freedom under the hypothesis that $u^*$ is the true $u$. Thus the $\chi^2$ value computed as above can be compared with tabular values of chi-square and its significance evaluated.

*Example*  | At a certain level 92 NAP grains were noted while counting to a predetermined number (150) of AP grains. Could the true NAP proportion for this level be $1/3$? Converting $p^* = 1/3$ to a value of $u^*$ gives

$$u^* = (1/3)/(2/3) = 1/2.$$

Thus, the hypothesis $p^* = 1/3$ is the same as the hypothesis $u^* = 1/2$. Could the true NAP/AP ratio $(u)$ be 0.5 where the sample ratio $(92/150)$ is 0.61?
One has

$$\chi^2 = \frac{[92 - (0.5)(150)]^2}{(150)(0.5)(1.5)} = \frac{(92 - 75)^2}{112.5}$$

$$= 2.57,$$

which has one degree of freedom and is not significant. (The 0.05 critical value is 3.84.) Hence the hypothesis is not rejected, and the true NAP/AP ratio might well be 0.5.

**B.12** Test of the hypothesis that the true proportion, $p$, of a particular kind of pollen is a specified value $p^*$ (and, equivalently, a test of the hypothesis that the true ratio $(u)$ has a particular value $u^*$). Two or more $(N)$ independent samples purportedly from the same level, with the number of NAP grains $(x)$ recorded while counting to a number $(n)$ of AP grains for each sample. The data can be arranged as follows.

|  | NUMBER OF AP (MARKER) GRAINS | NUMBER OF NAP GRAINS |
|---|---|---|
| Sample 1 | $n_1$ | $x_1$ |
| Sample 2 | $n_2$ | $x_2$ |
| ... | ... | ... |
| Sample $N$ | $n_N$ | $x_N$ |
| Column totals | $n'$ | $x'$ |

The null hypothesis in terms of $p^*$ can be converted to the null hypothesis in terms of $u^*$ and vice versa, exactly as in B.11.

If $n$ is large for each sample, then using the $\chi^2$ of B.11 $N$ times will give $N$ individual statistics, each distributed approximately as chi-square with one degree of freedom—one such for each sample.

|  | INDIVIDUAL $\chi^2$ FOR EACH SAMPLE | DEGREES OF FREEDOM |
|---|---|---|
| Sample 1 | $\dfrac{(x_1 - n_1 u^*)^2}{n_1 u^*(1 + u^*)}$ | 1 |
| Sample 2 | $\dfrac{(x_2 - n_2 u^*)^2}{n_2 u^*(1 + u^*)}$ | 1 |
| ... | ... | ... |
| Sample $N$ | $\dfrac{(x_N - n_N u^*)^2}{n_N u^*(1 + u^*)}$ | 1 |
| Column totals | $\chi_N^2$ | $N$ |

Since the samples are independent, so are the individual $\chi^2$, and their sum, $\chi_N^2$, has a chi-square distribution with $N$ degrees of freedom.

This total $\chi_N^2$ can be thought of as the sum of two independent $\chi^2$, a pooled $\chi_1^2$ with one degree of freedom and a heterogeneity $\chi_{N-1}^2$ with $N - 1$ degrees of freedom. Since

$$\chi_1^2 = \frac{(x' - n'u^*)^2}{n'u^*(1 + u^*)},$$

and since $\hat{u} = x'/n'$, then

$$\chi_{N-1}^2 = \frac{(x_1 - n_1\hat{u})^2}{n_1u^*(1 + u^*)} + \frac{(x_2 - n_2\hat{u})^2}{n_2u^*(1 + u^*)} + \cdots + \frac{(x_N - n_N\hat{u})^2}{n_Nu^*(1 + u^*)}.$$

*Although the formulas presented here differ from those of A.9, the interpretation of all $\chi^2$ is the same here as in A.9, and reference should be made to that section.*

Formulas mathematically identical to those already given, but more conveniently used in computation are

Heterogeneity:    $\chi_{N-1}^2 = \dfrac{[\sum (x^2/n)] - [(x')^2/n']}{u^*(1 + u^*)},$

Pooled:    $\chi_1^2 = \dfrac{[(x')^2/n'] - 2u^*x' + (u^*)^2n'}{u^*(1 + u^*)},$

Total:    $\chi_N^2 = \dfrac{[\sum (x^2/n)] - 2u^*x' + (u^*)^2n'}{u^*(1 + u^*)}.$

Since $\chi_N^2 = \chi_1^2 + \chi_{N-1}^2$, the heterogeneity value can be computed simply by subtracting the pooled from the total.

*Example* | Five samples are taken from what is purportedly a single level. For each level a number of NAP grains are observed while counting to a predetermined number of AP grains. Results are:

|  | NUMBER OF AP (MARKER) GRAINS | NUMBER OF NAP GRAINS |
|---|---|---|
| Sample 1 | 150 | 92 |
| Sample 2 | 200 | 81 |
| Sample 3 | 175 | 69 |
| Sample 4 | 200 | 120 |
| Sample 5 | 150 | 57 |
| Column totals | 875 | 419 |

Could these five samples be from a single level whose true NAP/AP ratio ($u$) is 0.5? First compute the $\chi^2$ with one degree of freedom for each sample. For example the calculation for the first sample is

$$\frac{[92 - 150(0.5)]^2}{(150)(0.5)(1.5)}.$$

For all five samples the individual $\chi^2$ are

| Sample 1 | $(92 - 75)^2/112.5 = 2.569,$ |
|---|---|
| Sample 2 | $(81 - 100)^2/150 = 2.407,$ |
| Sample 3 | $(69 - 87.5)^2/131.25 = 2.608,$ |
| Sample 4 | $(120 - 100)^2/150 = 2.667,$ |
| Sample 5 | $(57 - 75)^2/112.5 = 2.880.$ |

None of these values is significant at the 0.05 level (the critical value with one degree of freedom being 3.84). However, if the total $\chi_N^2$ is computed (by summing the five values), then

$$\chi_N^2 = 13.131,$$

which, with five degrees of freedom, is significant at the 0.025 level (the 0.025 value is 12.83). Thus, the information from all five samples together is sufficient to reject the hypothesis that the samples are from a single level with an NAP/AP ratio of 0.5.

To look further into the cause of rejection, compute the pooled $\chi_1^2$ where the five samples are treated as a single sample with 875 AP grains and 419 NAP grains:

$$\chi_1^2 = \frac{(419 - (0.5)875)^2}{(0.5)875(1.5)} = 342.25/656.25$$

$$= 0.522,$$

which has one degree of freedom and is not significant at the 0.05 level. The overall NAP/AP ratio for the five samples $(419/875 = 0.48)$ is quite close to 0.5, so that the non-significance of the pooled $\chi_1^2$ is readily understandable. The samples are not homogeneous, however, for the heterogeneity $\chi_{N-1}^2$ (computed by subtracting the pooled from the total) is

$$\chi_{N-1}^2 = 13.131 - 0.522$$
$$= 12.61,$$

which, with four degrees of freedom, is significant at the 0.025 level.

Thus, the hypothesis that the five samples are from a single level with an NAP/AP ratio of 0.5 is rejected because of the heterogeneity of the samples. This is reflected in the separate NAP/AP ratios for each sample—namely, 0.61, 0.41, 0.39, 0.60, and 0.38. Either the samples are not all from the same level or the samples were biased in different ways.

**B.13**    Test of the hypothesis that the true proportions of $k$ taxa are in fact specified values $(p_1^*, \cdots, p_k^*)$. One sample with $x_1$ grass, $x_2$ composite, . . . , $x_{k-1}$ sedge grains counted while counting to $n$ AP grains. Since from known values of $(p_1^*, \cdots, p_k^*)$ one can calculate the values of $(u^*, \cdots, u_{k-1}^*)$ and vice versa, the hypothesis can be equally well stated in terms of $u$.

Let $t^* = u_1^* + u_2^* + \cdots + u_{k-1}^*$, and $t = x_1 + x_2 + \cdots + x_{k-1}$. With $n$ large, the statistic

$$\chi^2 = \frac{(x_1 - nu_1^*)^2}{nu_1^*} + \cdots + \frac{(x_{k-1} - nu_{k-1}^*)^2}{nu_{k-1}^*} - \frac{(t - nt^*)^2}{n(t^* + 1)}$$

has approximately a chi-square distribution with $k - 1$ degrees of freedom under the hypothesis that the $u^*$ are the true $u$. Thus, the $\chi^2$ value computed above can be compared with the tabular value at an appropriate level and its significance evaluated.

If a hypothesis is given in terms of $p^*$, the equivalent $u^*$ can be found by means of the equations

$$u_1^* = p_1^*/p_k^*,$$

$$\cdots$$

$$u_{k-1}^* = p_{k-1}^*/p_k^*,$$

where $p_k^*$ is the proportion of marker grains (here AP) and is equal to one minus the sum of the other $p^*$; that is, $p_k^* = 1 - p_1^* - \cdots - p_{k-1}^*$. Correspondingly, $p^*$ can be found from known $u^*$ by means of the equations

$$p_1^* = u_1^*/(1 + u_1^* + \cdots + u_{k-1}^*),$$

$$\cdots$$

$$p_{k-1}^* = u_{k-1}^*/(1 + u_1^* + \cdots + u_{k-1}^*),$$

and

$$p_k^* = 1/(1 + u_1^* + \cdots + u_{k-1}^*).$$

*Example*

At a certain level 201 grass grains and 78 composite grains were counted while counting to a predetermined number (200) of AP pollen grains. From theoretical considerations, $u_1^* = 1$ (the grass/AP ratio $= 1$) and $u_2^* = 0.45$ (the composite/AP ratio $= 0.45$). Is the sample in agreement with these theoretical values?

$$\chi^2 = \frac{[201 - 200(1)]^2}{(200)(1)} + \frac{[78 - 200(0.45)]^2}{(200)(0.45)} - \frac{(279 - 290)^2}{(200)(2.45)}$$

$$= 1.358,$$

which, with two degrees of freedom, is not significant at the 0.05 level. There is no reason to reject the hypothesis. Incidentally, the hypothesis in terms of $p^*$ would be

$$p_1^* = 1/(1 + 1 + .45) = 0.41 \quad \text{(grass proportion)},$$
$$p_2^* = 0.45/2.45 \quad\quad\quad = 0.18 \quad \text{(composite proportion)},$$
$$p_3^* = 1/2.45 \quad\quad\quad\quad = 0.41 \quad \text{(AP proportion)}.$$

**B.14** Test of the hypothesis that the true proportions of $k$ taxa are in fact specified values $(p_1^*, \cdots, p_k^*)$. Two or more $(N)$ independent samples purportedly from the same level, with the counts of grass $(x_1)$, composite $(x_2)$, $\cdots$, sedge $(x_{k-1})$ grains noted while counting to $n$ AP grains for each sample. Since from known values of $(p_1^*, \cdots, p_k^*)$ one can calculate the values of $(u_1^*, \cdots, u_{k-1}^*)$ and vice versa, the hypothesis can be equally well stated in terms of $u$. The data can be arranged as follows.

NUMBER OF GRAINS

| | MARKERS | | | | | TOTAL EXCEPT |
| | (AP) | GRASS | COMPOSITES | $\cdots$ | SEDGES | MARKERS |
|---|---|---|---|---|---|---|
| Sample 1 | $n_1$ | $x_{11}$ | $x_{21}$ | $\cdots$ | $x_{k-1,1}$ | $t_1$ |
| Sample 2 | $n_2$ | $x_{12}$ | $x_{22}$ | $\cdots$ | $x_{k-1,2}$ | $t_2$ |
| $\cdots$ | $\cdots$ | $\cdots$ | $\cdots$ | $\cdots$ | $\cdots$ | $\cdots$ |
| Sample $N$ | $n_N$ | $x_{1N}$ | $x_{2N}$ | $\cdots$ | $x_{k-1,N}$ | $t_N$ |
| Column totals | $n'$ | $x_1'$ | $x_2'$ | $\cdots$ | $x_{k-1}'$ | $t'$ |

The null hypothesis expressed in terms of $p^*$ can be converted to the null hypothesis in terms of $u^*$ and vice versa, exactly as in B.13.

If $n$ is large for each sample, the $\chi^2$ of B.13 can be used $N$ times, once for each sample. Thus, there will be $N$ statistics, each distributed approximately as chi-square with $k-1$ degrees of freedom. Let $t^* = u_1^* + u_2^* + \cdots + u_{k-1}^*$. Then the individual $\chi^2$ for each sample are, in order,

$$_1\chi^2 = \frac{(x_{11} - n_1u_1^*)^2}{n_1u_1^*} + \cdots + \frac{(x_{k-1,1} - n_1u_{k-1}^*)^2}{n_1u_{k-1}^*} - \frac{(t_1 - n_1t^*)^2}{n_1(t^* + 1)},$$

$$_2\chi^2 = \frac{(x_{12} - n_2u_1^*)^2}{n_2u_1^*} + \cdots + \frac{(x_{k-1,2} - n_2u_{k-1}^*)^2}{n_2u_{k-1}^*} - \frac{(t_2 - n_2t^*)^2}{n_2(t^* + 1)},$$

$$\cdots$$

$$_N\chi^2 = \frac{(x_{1N} - n_Nu_1^*)^2}{n_Nu_1^*} + \cdots + \frac{(x_{k-1,N} - n_Nu_{k-1}^*)^2}{n_Nu_{k-1}^*} - \frac{(t_N - n_Nt^*)^2}{n_N(t^* + 1)}.$$

Each of the above has $(k-1)$ degrees of freedom. Since the samples are independent, so are these $\chi^2$; and their sum,

$$\chi^2_{N(k-1)} = {}_1\chi^2 + {}_2\chi^2 + \cdots + {}_N\chi^2,$$

has a chi-square distribution with $N(k-1)$ degrees of freedom.

This total $\chi^2_{N(k-1)}$ can now be thought of as the sum of two independent $\chi^2$, a pooled $\chi^2_{k-1}$ with $k-1$ degrees of freedom and a heterogeneity $\chi^2_{(N-1)(k-1)}$ with $(N-1)(k-1)$ degrees of freedom. *Although the formulas presented here differ from those of A.11, the interpretation of all $\chi^2$ is the same here as in A.11, and reference should be made to that section.* The formula for the pooled $\chi^2_{(k-1)}$ is

$$\chi^2_{k-1} = \frac{(x_1' - n'u_1^*)^2}{n'u_1^*} + \cdots + \frac{(x_{k-1}' - n'u_{k-1}^*)^2}{n'u_{k-1}^*} - \frac{(t' - n't^*)^2}{n'(t^* + 1)}.$$

The heterogeneity $\chi^2_{(N-1)(k-1)}$ is obtained by subtracting the pooled from the total

$$\chi^2_{(N-1)(k-1)} = \chi^2_{N(k-1)} - \chi^2_{k-1}.$$

The heterogeneity $\chi^2_{(N-1)(k-1)}$ here bears the same relationship to the $\chi^2$ of section B.10 as does the heterogeneity $\chi^2$ of A.11 to that of A.7.

*Example*

Three samples are collected from what is purportedly a single level. For each sample the numbers each of grass and composite grains are recorded while counting to a predetermined number of AP pollen grains. Results were:

NUMBER OF GRAINS

| | MARKERS (AP) | GRASS | COMPOSITES | TOTAL EXCEPT MARKERS |
|---|---|---|---|---|
| Sample 1 | 200 | 201 | 78 | 279 |
| Sample 2 | 300 | 270 | 132 | 402 |
| Sample 3 | 250 | 260 | 116 | 376 |
| Column totals | 750 | 731 | 326 | 1057 |

From theoretical considerations, $u_1^* = 1$ and $u_2^* = 0.45$. Is the set of three samples in agreement with this hypothesis? That is, could the grass/AP ratio be 1 and the composite/AP ratio be 0.45? In terms of proportions, the question would be: Could the grass proportion be 0.41; that of composites, 0.18; and that of AP, 0.41? (See the example of B.13.)

Computing the individual $\chi^2$ for each sample one has $u_1^* = 1$, $u_2^* = 0.45$, and $t^* = 1.45$. For the first sample the individual $\chi^2$ is

$$\frac{[201 - 200(1)]^2}{200} + \frac{[78 - 200(0.45)]^2}{90} - \frac{[279 - 200(1.45)]^2}{490} = 1.358.$$

For the second and third samples:

$$\frac{[270 - 300(1)]^2}{300} + \frac{[132 - 300(0.45)]^2}{135} - \frac{[402 - 300(1.45)]^2}{735} = 1.585,$$

and

$$\frac{[260 - 250(1)]^2}{250} + \frac{[116 - 250(0.45)]^2}{112.5} - \frac{[376 - 250(1.45)]^2}{612.5} = 0.211.$$

Each of the above three values has $k - 1 = 2$ degrees of freedom, and none is significant at the 0.05 level. The total $\chi^2_{N(k-1)}$ is the sum of the three values

$$1.358 + 1.585 + 0.211 = 3.154,$$

which has $N(k - 1) = 3 \times 2 = 6$ degrees of freedom. It is not significant at the 0.05 level. The pooled $\chi^2_{(k-1)}$ is

$$\frac{[731 - 750(1)]^2}{750} + \frac{[326 - 750(0.45)]^2}{337.5} - \frac{[1057 - 1087.5]^2}{1837.5} = 0.367,$$

which, with $k - 1 = 2$ degrees of freedom, is not significant at the 0.05 level. The heterogeneity $\chi^2_{(N-1)(k-1)}$ is

$$3.154 - 0.367 = 2.787.$$

With $(N - 1)(k - 1) = 2 \times 2 = 4$ degrees of freedom, this value is not significant at the 0.05 level.

Neither the pooled, nor the heterogeneity, nor the total $\chi^2$ is significant, hence there is no reason to reject the null hypothesis. The true $u$ may well be 1 and 0.45.

(Note that once all the calculations are finished, the last one or two decimal places in the $\chi^2$ above can be omitted if desired.)

## ACKNOWLEDGMENTS

I am grateful to Mr. Jacob E. Lieberman, Biometrics Branch, National Heart Institute for many pertinent suggestions. I would also like to thank Dr. Paul S. Martin, Mr. Peter J. Mehringer, Mr. David Peabody, and Mr. David Adams, all of the Geochronology Laboratories, University of Arizona, for many profitable hours of discussion. This study was supported by National Science Foundation Grant G21944.

## REFERENCES

Cochran, W. G. (1954). Some methods for strengthening the common $\chi^2$ test: Biometrics, v. 10, p. 417–451.

Davis, M. B., and E. S. Deevey, Jr. (1963). Estimation of absolute pollen rain from pollen frequencies in sediment of known accumulation rate. Ecol. Soc. America Bull., v. 44, no. 3, p. 81.

Deevey, E. S., Jr., and J. E. Potzger (1951). Peat samples for radiocarbon analysis. Am. J. Sci., v. 249, p. 473–511.

Faegri, K., and P. Ottestad (1949). Statistical problems in pollen analysis. Univ. Bergen, Arbok, Naturvitensk, rekka, 1948, no. 3, p. 1–29.

Gray, H. H., and G. K. Guennel (1961). Elementary statistics applied to palynologic identification of coal beds. Micropaleontology, v. 7, p. 101–106.

Maher, L. J., Jr. (1961). Pollen analysis and postglacial vegetation history in the Animas Valley region, southern San Juan Mountains, Colorado. Ph.D. thesis, University of Minnesota.

Mainland, Donald (1952). Introduction to elementary medical statistics (2nd ed., 1963). Philadelphia, W. B. Saunders, 327 pp.

———, L. Herrera, and M. Sutcliffe (1956). Statistical tables for use with binomial samples, contingency tests, confidence limits, and sample size estimates. Department of Medical Statistics, New York University College of Medicine.

Mosimann, J. E. (1962). On the compound multinomial distribution, the multivariate $\beta$-distribution, and correlations among proportions. Biometrika, v. 49, p. 65–82.

——— (1963). On the compound negative multinomial distribution and correlations among inversely sampled pollen counts. Biometrika, v. 50, p. 47–54.

Snedecor, G. W. (1956). Statistical methods. Iowa State College Press, Ames, *xiii* + 534 pp.

Westenberg, J. (1947a). Mathematics of pollen diagrams. K. Nederlandsche Akad. Wetensch., Proc., v. 50, p. 509–520.

——— (1947b). Mathematics of pollen diagrams. K. Nederlandsche Akad. Wetensch., Proc., v. 50, p. 640–648.

# A Method for Determination of Absolute Pollen Frequency

MARGARET B. DAVIS

*Department of Botany, University of Michigan, Ann Arbor*

It is often useful to determine the actual numbers of pollen grains in quantitative sediment samples. For this purpose, Erdtman (1943) has made pollen counts with a haemocytometer; Muller (1959) has used aliquot slides prepared from standard drops taken from glycerin-alcohol suspensions of pollen samples; and Benninghoff (1962) has used the ratio of the number of native pollen grains to that of exotic pollen grains added in known quantities to the samples prior to preparation.

The method described here is similar in principle to those of Erdtman and Muller but combines the advantages of both. The accuracy of the method is similar to that obtained with a haemocytometer, but the pollen counts are made under high magnification on ordinary microscope slides suitable for phase microscopy, photomicrography, and storage for future reference. The counts can therefore be used both for estimating absolute pollen frequencies and for calculating percentages.

Most workers are familiar with the principle of the method: the sample to be assayed is suspended in a measured quantity of liquid, and aliquots of the suspension are withdrawn for counting. The number of pollen grains in the original suspension is derived from the average number of grains found per aliquot. A significant error is introduced in any method of this kind in measuring the volume of small aliquots. This error can be reduced, however, by diluting the sample with a volatile liquid to a size where aliquots can be measured more accurately. After the aliquots have been measured, they are reduced in volume by evaporation to a practical size; the pollen grains contained in each aliquot are then counted.

## MATERIALS AND METHODS

### Materials

Silicone oil (viscosity 12,500 centistokes) is used as a mounting medium, and benzene as a solvent (Andersen, 1960; Whitehead, 1961). Silicone oil

The author is now with the Great Lakes Research Division, University of Michigan.

(viscosity 2000 centistokes) mixed with xylene, and Tanglefoot mounting medium No. 6 or No. 8 (Tanglefoot Co., Grand Rapids, Mich.) mixed with xylene have also been used successfully; presumably other combinations of volatile solvents and nonvolatile, viscous mounting media could be used, provided that hot solutions are not harmful to pollen. (Warm silicone oil and benzene do not appear to affect the gross morphology of pollen grains, but their effect on pollen size has not been investigated.)

Graduated 12- or 15-ml centrifuge tubes and 50-ml erlenmeyer flasks are used for sample dilution. Short-style glass pipettes, graduated to the tip with orifice size > 1 mm (cat. No. 12-318 spl, Bellco Glass Inc., Vineland, N. J.) and equipped with a rubber bulb or syringe attachment, are used for measuring aliquots. Glass tuberculin syringes are convenient for stirring solutions, as vigorous pumping will mix silicone oil and solvent without introducing moisture. A small magnetic stirring device (E. H. Sargent & Co., Chicago, Ill.) set at low speed is recommended for mixing pollen evenly in suspending fluid. Dichromate cleaning solution and Alconox detergent (Alconox Co., 853 Broadway, New York) are used for cleaning pipettes.

Modern pollen for use in testing the reliability of the method can be purchased from drug companies such as Greer Drug and Chemical Corporation, Lenoir, N. C.

Slides are prepared on a paraffin melting table or slide warming table at about 100°C. This must be done under a fume hood with ventilation sufficient to protect the investigator from benzene fumes.

### Method for Cleaning Glassware

After a thorough rinsing to remove silicone oil and benzene, glassware is soaked in dichromate cleaning solution and rinsed with water. This procedure is effective in removing all pollen grains.

Additional treatment is necessary, however, to prevent the glass surface from attracting pollen grains suspended in benzene. The attraction and adherence of pollen is not understood, but appears to be caused by attraction between electrical charges on the glass surface and ions carried by the grains from prior treatments. The effect is particularly noticeable in samples which were insufficiently dehydrated before suspension in benzene, but may also occur in samples that have been washed in acetone or soaked and washed repeatedly in 100 percent ethanol. Grains suspended in benzene will often adhere to the walls of a centrifuge tube where it has been touched by a metal stirring rod.

Pollen grains that have been washed in glacial acetic acid just before being washed with ethanol and then with benzene will not adhere to pipettes that were soaked in Alconox solution, rinsed with tap water and distilled water, and thoroughly dried. (Other detergents, such as Tween 20, Haemosol, and Dreft are less effective.) No procedure has been found that will prevent pollen in alkaline suspensions from adhering to glassware.

In the event that small amounts of pollen do stick to the walls of a centrifuge tube, adherence can sometimes be eliminated by diluting the sample further with benzene, adding a small amount of silicone oil, and pumping vigorously with a glass syringe. It has also been found that pollen grains sticking to a pipette, presumably because it was insufficiently clean and dry, can be rinsed out with absolute ethanol.

### Method of Preparing Aliquots

The procedure will be described using a specific example. The following method would be used to prepare aliquot slides each containing about 200 pollen grains from a sediment sample of known weight or volume that contains approximately 20,000 grains.

Pollen in the sediment sample is concentrated by the usual laboratory procedures. Care must be taken that the procedure used is effective in removing all large pieces of detritus from the sample, that pollen is neither lost from the sample nor destroyed during preparation, and that no clumping occurs. The pollen-bearing residue remaining upon completion of preparation procedures is washed successively with glacial acetic acid, ethanol, and benzene, and is then suspended in 2 or 3 ml of clean benzene. The suspension is transferred in its entirety, being carefully rinsed with benzene to avoid loss, into a graduated centrifuge tube or cylinder. The volume of the suspension is recorded, and the suspension is then transferred to a 50-ml erlenmeyer flask. The graduated vessel is rinsed carefully with measured quantities of benzene, which are then added to the flask, making the suspension up to a total volume of 10 ml. The flask is corked to prevent evaporation.

The desired aliquot size is one-hundredth of the total. Because about 0.01 ml of silicone oil is necessary per aliquot when 18-mm square cover glasses are used, 100 times this amount, or approximately 1 ml, of silicone oil is put into a graduated tube and dissolved in benzene. The solution is made up to a total volume of 10 ml, and is then added to and mixed thoroughly with the pollen suspension in the flask.

The erlenmeyer flask is then shaken vigorously for at least 5 seconds to suspend the pollen grains evenly in the fluid. This procedure is effective, but does produce air bubbles in the suspension, so that it becomes difficult to measure aliquots accurately. It is therefore preferable, if the equipment is available, to mix the sample thoroughly by shaking the flask and then to keep the pollen in suspension by means of a magnetic stirring device set at a speed that will produce turbulence rather than a strong vortex.

When the pollen is suspended evenly throughout the 20 ml of fluid, exactly one-hundredth of the total volume of the suspension, or 0.2 ml, is drawn up into a clean pipette. This must be done quickly, before the pollen falls out of suspension. The volume drawn up into the pipette must not exceed the desired aliquot size, because sedimentation will cause unequal distribution of pollen in the liquid contained within the pipette.

The outside of the pipette is wiped off, and the entire volume within the pipette is placed, drop by drop, on a glass microscope slide on a warming table. The benzene evaporates rapidly as the drops of suspension are placed on the warm glass. There will remain on the slide, therefore, only a small drop of silicone oil (one-hundredth of the total in the suspension; i.e., 0.01 ml) enclosing the pollen grains that were present in 0.2 ml, or one-hundredth, of the suspension. Then 0.2 ml of clean benzene is drawn up into the pipette as a rinse and added drop by drop to the preparation on the slide. When the benzene has evaporated completely, the drop of silicone oil and pollen is covered with an 18-mm square cover glass. Several replicate aliquot slides should be prepared in order to obtain an estimate of variance. It is very important that the suspension be shaken or stirred vigorously before each aliquot is subtracted.

Usually it is practical to make up several series of aliquot slides from a sample, one series containing small fractions of the sample for use in estimating the frequency of abundant pollen types, and others containing larger fractions of the sample for use in scanning for rare types. The following is the procedure that I use: The prepared sediment sample residue is diluted with benzene to a total volume of 10 ml, of which 5 ml is removed by pipette to a storage vial containing a quantity of silicone oil. The remaining half of the sample is diluted again and split unevenly. Each fraction is used to prepare a series of 3 or 4 aliquot slides, one series containing about 200 grains per slide, and the other several thousand.

After experience with a given sediment profile the investigator soon learns to estimate within a factor of 2 the fraction of the sample which must be used to obtain aliquots containing the desired number of grains. If a cursory inspection of the first aliquot slide prepared indicates that the slide contains too many grains, smaller aliquots can be taken from the suspension, provided supplementary mounting medium is placed on the glass slides before the aliquot of suspension is placed there. The investigator may also dilute the suspension further, taking into account in subsequent calculations the fraction that was removed for preparation of the first aliquot. If the slides contain too few grains, the investigator can use a larger aliquot and larger cover glasses, centrifuge the suspension and wash out the excess silicone oil, or prepare slides from another fraction of the original sample.

### Counting Methods

The entire area under the cover glass must be scanned under high magnification for accurate identification and tabulation of the pollen grains in the aliquot. For this purpose contiguous sweeps are made across the entire width of the preparation. The calibrations on the mechanical stage are used to advance the stage the width of the microscope field at the completion of each sweep. This is most easily done when the width of the field seen through the microscope is an integral fraction of a millimeter. In my microscope the field viewed at 200× (the magnification used for counting) was 0.665 mm in diameter when the oculars were a comfortable distance from one another. Therefore, I had diaphragms made to fit into the oculars, so that two parallel segments of the circular field are now blocked off from sight; the width of the remaining microscope field at 200× is 0.500 ± 0.003 mm (see fig. 1). (It should be mentioned that the change in magnification resulting from a change in the distance between the oculars of a binocular microscope is sufficient to introduce considerable error; for this reason ocular diaphragms must be custom-made for each investigator. They can be made quite inexpensively at a well-equipped machine shop.) Sweeps are made in a direction parallel to the straight sides of the field at 0.5-mm intervals across the slide. All pollen grains which lie within the field or which overlap the right-hand edge of the field (or upper edge if horizontal sweeps are made) are counted; grains which overlap the left-hand edge (or lower edge) of the field are not counted. In this way no grain will be counted more than once.

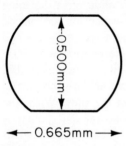

**Fig. 1**

*Size (in millimeters) and shape of field viewed in the author's compound microscope at 200× magnification.*

For rapid assay of modern pollen preparations, pollen counts can be made with a stereomicroscope at 75× magnification. If the pollen has been stained heavily it can be seen under incident light, provided graph paper is placed beneath the slide (which is placed with the cover glass side down) to reflect light and serve as a guide for sweeps across the preparation. Again, grains which overlap the right-hand, or upper, edge of the grid are counted, and those that overlap the left-hand, or lower, edge are not. Low-power counting is extremely rapid; for example, a slide containing more than 500 grains of a single type can be counted completely in 5 or 10 minutes.

I have experimented with methods that involve counting a fraction of the area of aliquot slides and estimating the count for the entire area. These methods have been generally unsatisfactory. Although with care the mounting medium can be made to spread out evenly under a cover glass, the pollen grains are rarely if ever evenly distributed. For this reason estimation of the pollen occurring over the entire area of the preparation from those observed in a fraction of that area is inaccurate: variance observed in aliquot counts estimated after scanning only five-eighths of the area of preparations was about twice as large as the variance in counts of the same aliquots made by scanning the entire preparation.

## RESULTS AND DISCUSSION

### Evidence of Reliability

ACCURACY OF MEASUREMENT OF ALIQUOT VOLUME

The investigator can test for accuracy by preparing several series of aliquots of unequal volume and comparing the pollen counts, which should be proportional to aliquot size. A suspension can also be subdivided and the accuracy of the subdivision tested by comparing aliquot series prepared from each fraction. Figure 2 shows pollen counts made in aliquots of varying size prepared from several fractions of a suspension of modern *Ambrosia* pollen. The ten points represent the mean number counted at $75\times$ magnification in three replicate slides, and the vertical bars show one standard deviation on either side of the mean. Five different symbols have been used to indicate which of the five subdivisions of the original suspension were used. The data show that the number of pollen grains counted is directly proportional to the size of the aliquot, and that the numbers of pollen grains in aliquots of the same size prepared from different fractions of the original sample are not significantly different.

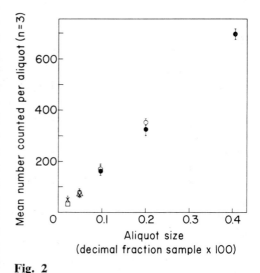

**Fig. 2**

*Comparison of numbers of grains counted per aliquot with aliquot size. For explanation see text.*

STATISTICAL EVIDENCE OF RELIABILITY

In order to test the hypothesis that a Poisson distribution could be used to describe the distribution of pollen grains among aliquots, several series of replicate slides were prepared from suspensions of modern *Tsuga* pollen and counted at $75\times$ magnification. The results, given in table I, show that the variance for each series is nearly equal to the mean number counted, as would be expected in Poisson distributions. In each series, the sum

$$\frac{\sum (X - \overline{X})^2}{\overline{X}},$$

was calculated, which for Poisson-distributed data is approximately $\chi^2$-distributed (Cochran, 1954). In no series was a significant departure from a Poisson fit established. It is therefore assumed in the following discussion that a Poisson distribution is to be expected.

**Table I.** *Variance Observed in Counts of Replicate Aliquot Slides Prepared from Suspensions of Modern* Tsuga *Pollen*

| NUMBER OF REPLICATES IN SERIES $n$ | MEAN NUMBER OF GRAINS COUNTED PER ALIQUOT $\overline{X}$ | RANGE | VARIANCE $s^2$ | $\dfrac{\Sigma(X - \overline{X})^2}{\overline{X}}$ |
|---|---|---|---|---|
| 10 | 27.2 | 19–32 | 13.96 | $\chi^2 = 4.6, p = 0.87$ (d.f. = 9) |
| 10 | 61.1 | 50–70 | 67.88 | $\chi^2 = 10.0, p = 0.35$ (d.f. = 9) |
| 10 | 74.1 | 58–96 | 100.5 | $\chi^2 = 12.2, p = 0.20$ (d.f. = 9) |
| 10 | 83.6 | 69–94 | 82.7 | $\chi^2 = 8.9, p = 0.45$ (d.f. = 9) |
| 10 | 239.9 | 215–262 | 148.3 | $\chi^2 = 5.6, p = 0.78$ (d.f. = 9) |
| 5 | 286.0 | 272–310 | 209.5 | $\chi^2 = 2.9, p = 0.57$ (d.f. = 4) |
| Total | | | | $\chi^2 = 44.2, p = 0.67$ (d.f. = 49) |

Investigators planning to use the method described here should repeat this experiment as a test for reliability. Pollen counts in sediment samples should be inspected routinely for excess variance; failure to achieve a Poisson distribution may be due to one or more of the sources of error discussed below.

### Confidence Interval for the Estimate of Absolute Pollen Frequency

The width of the confidence interval for the estimate of total number of pollen grains in the original sample can be calculated in two ways. Where it has been demonstrated that the grains are Poisson-distributed among aliquots, the width of the 95 percent confidence interval can be approximated by assuming that the variance is exactly equal to the number of grains in the sample counted and, therefore, that the standard deviation is equal to the square root of the number of grains counted. In this case it can be said with approximately 95 percent confidence that the true total number of grains in the original sample lies within the limits given by

$$T\left(\frac{D}{N}\right) \pm 2\sqrt{T}\left(\frac{D}{N}\right),$$

where $T$ is the total number of grains counted in all aliquots, $D$ is the dilution factor for a single aliquot, and $N$ is the number of aliquots. For example, if a total of 300 grains were counted in three aliquots, each of which represents one-thousandth of the original sample, the number in the original sample would be estimated to be

$$300\left(\frac{1000}{3}\right) \pm 2\sqrt{300}\left(\frac{1000}{3}\right) = 100,000 \pm 11,500.$$

Investigators will often wish to estimate in advance the number of grains that must be counted to achieve a given level of accuracy. Here it is useful to express the width of the confidence interval as a percentage of the total number in the original sample and to calculate the aliquot size necessary to achieve a confidence interval that equals, for example, ±20 percent of the estimated total number. This may be done easily by substituting different values of $T$ in the expression given above. Several series of aliquots can be prepared so that estimates of the numbers of abundant pollen types and of rare pollen types are based on counts of similar numbers of grains. The accuracy of estimates will increase with increasing num-

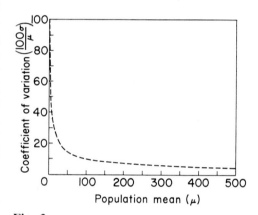

**Fig. 3**

*Theoretical relationship between coefficient of variation and mean number in the case of Poisson distribution.*

ber of grains counted because of the theoretical relationship in Poisson-distributed data shown in fig. 3. Figure 3 shows that the population standard deviation $\sigma$, when expressed as a percentage of the population mean $\mu$, decreases with increasing values of the mean $\mu$. This means that the width of the confidence interval, when expressed as a percentage of the total, will also decrease with increasing numbers counted, since we are assuming in calculating the confidence interval that $T$ is equal to $\mu$, and that $\sqrt{T}$ is equal to $\sigma$.

In all samples where it has not been demonstrated by rigorous testing that the pollen numbers per aliquot are Poisson-distributed, the confidence interval must be calculated using the mean number per aliquot ($\bar{X}$, or $T/N$) and the observed standard deviation ($s$). In this case the number of grains in the original sample is estimated with approximately 95 percent confidence to be within the limits given by

$$\frac{T}{N}(D) \pm \frac{t_a(s)}{\sqrt{N}}(D),$$

where $t_a$ is a value of Student's $t$ corresponding to $a = 0.95$ with $N - 1$ degrees of freedom. The value of $t_a$ will be large where $N$ is small. For example, if, as in the previous example, $T/N = 100$, $D = 1000$, $N = 3$, and $s = 10$, the number of grains in the total original sample is estimated by this method to lie within the limits

$$(100)(1000) \pm \frac{(4.303)(10)}{\sqrt{3}}(1000) = 100,000 \pm 24,900.$$

Comparison of the widths of the confidence intervals obtained by the two methods makes it obvious that a great advantage results from demonstration that the data are Poisson-distributed.

### Sources of Error

#### FAILURE TO MIX THE SAMPLE THOROUGHLY AND TO PLACE ALL POLLEN IN SUSPENSION

This source of error can result in a series of aliquots which give a consistently low estimate of the number of pollen grains in the total sample. Comparisons of aliquot series prepared from different fractions of the original sample (fig. 2) may be used to test for this effect. I usually find that, although the grains were placed in suspension, they were not randomly distributed in the suspending fluid at the time each aliquot was subtracted, resulting in unexpectedly high variance.

#### ADHERENCE OF POLLEN GRAINS TO THE INSIDE OF THE PIPETTE

This source of error can be extremely serious, particularly as loss of a large portion of each aliquot may not always be detectable as excess variance among replicate aliquots. The following experiment was done to measure the amount of pollen adhering to pipettes cleaned according to the procedure described under Methods.

From each of two suspensions, one containing a known number of modern *Ambrosia* pollen grains, the other a known number of *Tsuga* pollen grains, 0.2-ml aliquots were drawn up into clean pipettes and then expelled. The pipettes were then rinsed 5 times with 0.2 ml of clean benzene. Each rinse was evaporated onto a drop of silicone oil on a clean slide and the pollen contained in the rinse counted at $75\times$ magnification. After the last rinse the pipettes were inspected for remaining pollen under a stereomicroscope. The results shown in the following table indicate that in these cases less than 2 percent of the pollen grains in the aliquot were retained in the pipette; after the first rinse less than 0.6 percent of the sample remained in the pipette.

| | *Ambrosia* | | *Tsuga* | |
|---|---|---|---|---|
| | NUMBER | PERCENT OF NUMBER IN ALIQUOT | NUMBER | PERCENT OF NUMBER IN ALIQUOT |
| Aliquot | 31,000 (est.) | | 5000 (est.) | |
| 1st rinse | 415 | 1.34 | 3 | 0.06 |
| 2nd rinse | 57 | 0.18 | 4 | 0.08 |
| 3rd rinse | 66 | 0.21 | 1 | 0.02 |
| 4th rinse | 12 | 0.04 | 1 | 0.02 |
| 5th rinse | 12 | 0.04 | 2 | 0.04 |
| Remaining in pipette | 9 | 0.03 | 5 | 0.10 |
| Total lost from aliquot | 571 | 1.84 | 16 | 0.32 |

Because only a slight amount of moisture inside a pipette can cause some adherence of pollen, I have found it practical to inspect each pipette after use under the stereomicroscope; if an abnormally large number of grains remain within the pipette the aliquot slide that has been prepared must be discarded.

It may be mentioned that similar experiments have been done with glass tuberculin syringes. (The volume retained in the tip after discharge was measured and considered part of the aliquot volume.) Even repeated rinsing will not clear the syringe of pollen which settles at the base of the wide part of the barrel, just above the tip. For this reason syringes, despite their convenience, have not been recommended for aliquot preparation.

### SELECTIVE UPTAKE OF POLLEN GRAINS IN THE PIPETTE

Narrow bore pipettes are to be avoided, as they may lead to sorting of the grains and exclusion of some of the larger pollen types. No sorting has been observed with pipettes having a mouth bore greater than 1 mm. Furthermore, the percentages of fossil pollen counted on a series of aliquot slides are not significantly different at the 95 percent level of confidence, as indicated by a chi-square test (Faegri and Iversen, 1950), from those counted on a slide prepared in the traditional manner—using a spatula to place a drop of pollen sample suspended in viscous medium on a slide.

### COUNTING ERROR

The calibrations of most mechanical microscope stages are not sufficiently accurate to prevent occasional partial overlap of sweeps across the slide. The resulting counting error is small, however, because for each area of slide that is scanned twice there is an area of equal size that is not scanned at all.

Counting error will be expressed as variation in the results of repeated counts of the same slide. For example three counts of the same slide at 200× gave the results 356, 346, 346. The coefficient of variation is only 1.7 percent, indicating that the counting error is quite insignificant.

Counting error is often somewhat greater at 75× magnification, however, because grains that are torn or lightly stained may be overlooked, and because grains may be counted twice or not at all as the result of parallax effects in viewing the grid beneath the slide. The latter effect is greatly reduced by placing the slide so that the cover glass is down.

Counting error can also be assessed by counting the same slides under different microscopes. Table II shows comparisons of counts of the same slides made with the compound microscope at 200× magnification and with the stereomicroscope at 75× (cover glass up). The data show that the mean numbers counted per aliquot are closely similar.

Counting error resulting from pollen misidentification can be evaluated only by comparing analyses of different workers. However, inconsistencies in the criteria used by an individual worker for identification of a given pollen type may become apparent in the form of unexpectedly high (or low) inter-aliquot variance in counts of the pollen type in question.

**Table II.** *Comparison of Pollen Counts of the Same Slides Made with a Compound Microscope at 200× and a Stereomicroscope at 75× Magnification. Numbers Represent the Mean Number of Grains per Slide Counted in Each of Ten Series of Three Replicate Slides.*

| 200× | 75× |
|---|---|
| 34.0 | 32.3 |
| 70.3 | 72.6 |
| 78.3 | 81.0 |
| 168.3 | 168.3 |
| 349.3 | 346.7 |
| 351.3 | 344.3 |
| 442.3 | 443.0 |
| 579.0 | 578.3 |
| 697.7 | 701.0 |
| 772.0 | 780.7 |

When a cover glass is tapped to turn or move grains to facilitate their identification, care must be taken that the cover glass is moved over as short a distance as possible, and parallel to the direction in which sweeps are made across the slide. If the cover glass has been moved from its original position, sweeps must be extended beyond its edges in order to include in the count grains which have been left outside the area of the cover glass.

LOSS OF PORTION OF THE SAMPLE
DURING LABORATORY PREPARATION

No control for this source of error is provided here, and in this respect the method is inferior to that of Benninghoff (1962). Investigators can, however, check for loss or destruction of a pollen type during preparation by modifying Benninghoff's technique to perform percentage recovery experiments. After determining the numbers of grains in a suspension of modern pollen, the investigator should mix the suspension with a sediment sample in which that same pollen type occurs in known frequency (as determined from duplicate samples). By comparing the original number with the number of grains remaining in the sample after preparation, the investigator can assess the effect of standard preparation techniques.

## CONCLUSION

Investigators who have not previously used techniques similar to those described here will find it convenient to practice with suspicions of modern pollen before applying the method to fossil material. A large pollen type, such as *Tsuga,* is convenient to use because it can be counted easily at low magnification. Acetolysis is usually unnecessary; the pollen can simply be washed with glacial acetic acid and stained with fast green.

Once the technique has been mastered, preparation of at least two series of aliquot slides from a quantitative sediment sample can be accomplished in an hour. This is very little time compared with the number of hours that must be spent identifying and counting the pollen, but it is time well spent, as the counts from the quantitative slides can be used for estimating absolute pollen frequencies as well as for the more conventional calculation of pollen percentages.

## ACKNOWLEDGMENTS

I am very grateful to Richard D. Remington, Michael A. Schork, and Frederick E. Smith, all of the University of Michigan, for their helpful criticism and advice concerning the statistical aspects of this work. This project has been supported by the National Science Foundation.

## REFERENCES

Andersen, S. T. (1960). Silicone oil as a mounting medium for pollen grains. Danmarks Geol. Unders. IV R., v. 4, no. 1, 24 pp.

Benninghoff, W. S. (1962). Calculation of pollen and spores density in sediments by addition of exotic pollen in known quantities. Pollen et Spores, v. 4, no. 2, p. 332–3.

Cochran, W. G. (1954). Some methods for strengthening the common $\chi^2$ tests. Biometrics, v. 10, p. 417–451.

Erdtman, G. (1943). An introduction to pollen analysis. Chronica Botanica, 239 pp.

Faegri, K., and J. Iversen (1950). Textbook of modern pollen analysis. Copenhagen, Ejnar Munksgaard, 168 pp.

Muller, J. (1959). Palynology of recent Orinoco delta and shelf sediments. Micropaleontology, v. 5, p. 1–32.

Whitehead, D. R. (1961). A note on silicone oil as a mounting medium for fossil and modern pollen. Ecology, v. 42, p. 591.

# On the Cutting of Ultra-thin Sections

J. RADWAN PRAGLOWSKI

*Palynological Laboratory, Nybodagatan 5,*
*Stockholm-Solna, Sweden*

Before being embedded in methacrylate plastic, the pollen or spore material to be sectioned is washed in a centrifuge tube with distilled water (three times), then with 95 percent alcohol (twice), and finally with absolute alcohol (three times). The material should remain in absolute alcohol for 24 hours. The alcohol is then decanted and some methacrylate (methyl methacrylate one part, butyl methacrylate seven parts) is poured into the tube. (*Note:* Liquid methacrylate contains a stabilizer which impedes polymerization and must be washed away with 2 percent NaOH solution before the methacrylate is poured into the tube.) The methacrylate is renewed three times at 2-hour intervals and should be shaken often and thoroughly to prevent the pollen grains from settling. After the last refilling the fluid is shaken once again and transferred by means of a small pipette to gelatin capsules (No. 3 from Parke, Davis & Co.; see fig. 1). It is important to add a proper amount of pollen grains to the methacrylate. If too many grains are added the polymerization of the methacrylate may be rendered more difficult.

Reprinted with revision, with permission of the author and publisher, from G. Erdtman (1963), *Pollen and Spore Morphology/Plant Taxonomy* (v. 2), Uppsala, Almquist and Wiksell.

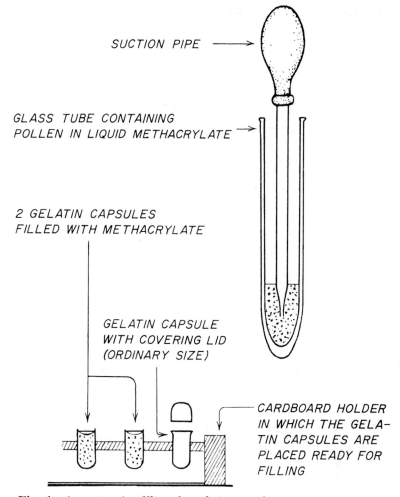

**Fig. 1.** *Apparatus for filling the gelatin capsules.*

## POLYMERIZATION IN UV LIGHT

The liquid methacrylate is polymerized—that is, solidified by exposure to UV radiation. This method is preferred to polymerization induced by heat with the aid of a catalyst, since the catalyst may oxidize the sporopollenine. The filled gelatin capsules are covered with lids and fastened in pairs to a length of tape. About ten capsules to every tape are fastened in this way and exposed to the light produced by a 120-watt UV lamp. The distance between the lamp and the tape should be about 15 cm. At the Palynological Laboratory, Bromma, the gelatin capsules are usually exposed to UV radiation for five nights, approximately 15 hours per night. During the first night, before the plastic hardens, the heat from the UV lamp should be controlled by a

Labels in figure:

SUCTION PIPE

GLASS TUBE CONTAINING POLLEN IN LIQUID METHACRYLATE

2 GELATIN CAPSULES FILLED WITH METHACRYLATE

GELATIN CAPSULE WITH COVERING LID (ORDINARY SIZE)

CARDBOARD HOLDER IN WHICH THE GELATIN CAPSULES ARE PLACED READY FOR FILLING

ventilator in order to prevent the formation of air bubbles in the sediment at the bottom of the capsules before the methacrylate solidifies (fig. 2). After about 80 hours of exposure to the UV lamp the plastic is usually hard enough to be cut.

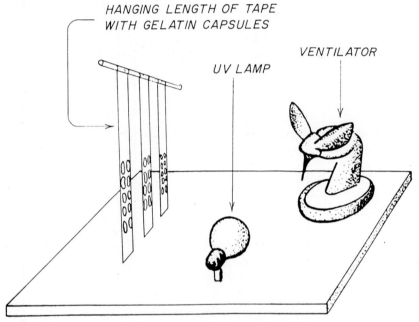

**HANGING LENGTH OF TAPE WITH GELATIN CAPSULES**

**VENTILATOR**

**UV LAMP**

**Fig. 2.** *Polymerization of the methacrylate with UV light.*

Cutting is rendered difficult if there are air bubbles in the methacrylate. The bubbles may be due to various causes: overheating during the initial stages of polymerization, the presence of impurities (different debris of plant tissue) in the pollen material to be embedded, an excess of pollen grains, or insufficient washings of the pollen material with methacrylate. A capsule with air bubbles can, nevertheless, be used for cutting if the pyramid (see below) is made either at the side of the bubble or just above it. Generally the embedded pollen grains form a thin sediment at the bottom of the gelatin capsule. This sediment may be difficult to cut because of the pollen concentration. To avoid this it is possible to re-embed the polymerized plastic unit in the following way (see fig. 3).

## CUTTING THE PYRAMID

After being soaked in water, the gelatin capsules can be easily removed from the plastic units which, when dry, are ready for cutting. A unit is fixed in a steel object-holder (made by LKB-Produkter, Stockholm 12) in such a way that three to four millimeters of the pollen-bearing part protrude from its

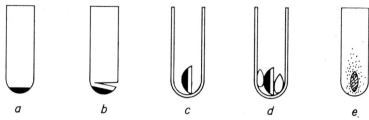

**Fig. 3.** (*a*) *Polymerized plastic unit with pollen sediment at the bottom.* (*b*) *The end of the plastic unit with the pollen sediment cut off horizontally.* (*c*) *The end with the pollen grains placed vertically in a new gelatin capsule.* (*d*) *To be kept in vertical position it must be supported by one or two wedges* (*cut from an old plastic unit*) *placed with the aid of forceps. Then the capsule is filled with new fluid methacrylate. Polymerize as before.* (*e*) *The ready plastic unit after polymerization and dissolution of gelatin capsule. Note vertical position of pollen sediment, where the pollen concentration is not so high, since the pollen grains have been to some extent spread out in the plastic unit. This makes cutting much easier.*

mouth (fig. 4). After trimming the top of the plastic unit with a razor blade (fig. 5), a thin four-sided projection—the pyramid—containing the pollen grains or spores for sectioning is carved from the apex.

When estimating the size of the pyramid, the following three factors should be taken into account:

1. The desired thickness of the sections. The thicker the sections the larger, and especially the higher, the pyramid must be.

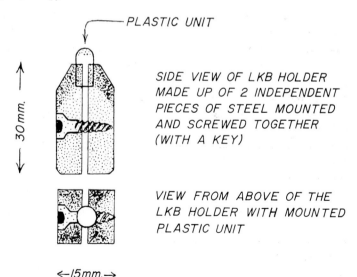

PLASTIC UNIT

30 mm.

SIDE VIEW OF LKB HOLDER
MADE UP OF 2 INDEPENDENT
PIECES OF STEEL MOUNTED
AND SCREWED TOGETHER
(WITH A KEY)

VIEW FROM ABOVE OF THE
LKB HOLDER WITH MOUNTED
PLASTIC UNIT

←15mm.→

**Fig. 4.** *LKB object holder with plastic unit mounted (1:1).*

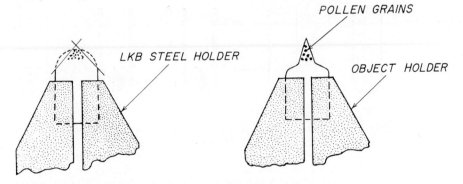

**Fig. 5.** (*Left*) *Preliminary cutting of the plastic unit.* (*Right*) *Plastic unit with ready-made pyramid.* (*The pyramid is enlarged about 5×; the rest of the figure, about 1.5×.*)

2. The size of the pollen grains. The size of the pyramid should be increased or decreased in proportion to the size of the pollen grains. If large pollen grains or spores (diameter about 80μ or more) are to be cut, sometimes as few as 1 to 3 pollen grains will be sufficient (see fig. 5).

3. The concentration of the pollen grains (see fig. 6). If the concentration is low, the dimensions of the pyramid must be made larger to increase the number of pollen grains to be sectioned.

The total height of the pyramid should not exceed half a millimeter if sections about 0.25 to 0.50μ in thickness are to be made. These recommendations have been followed when working with the modified Spencer microtome model 821 and are not always valid for ultrathin sectioning.

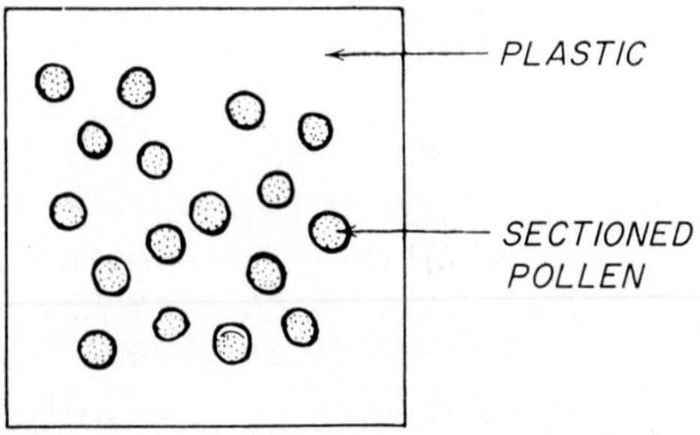

The best results are obtained by working with samples rich in pollen grains and absolutely clean. Organic debris renders cutting more difficult, shreds the sectioned pollen fragments, or covers them, and generally decreases the value of the sections. Inorganic material (e.g., silica or other mineral particles) will damage the microtome knife.

**Fig. 6**

*Section from the basal part of the pyramid. 100×.*

Figure 7 illustrates the order, directions, and so on, to be followed when molding the pyramid, but it goes without saying that many modifications can be made to suit the individual's techniques. Usually, the molding cannot be considered to be complete in eight cuts, and further fine trimming along the lines (illustrated in fig. 7) is

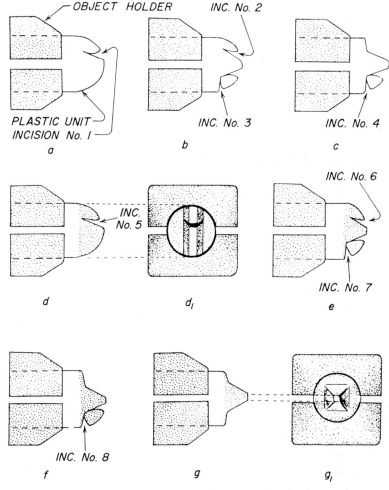

**Fig. 7.** *Molding the pyramid. Plastic unit 4:1, object-holder about 2:1. (a) Incision No. 1. (b) The object-holder is turned 180° and incisions Nos. 2 and 3 made. A part of the apex of the plastic unit will fall away with incision No. 3, after which the object-holder is again turned 180°. (c) Incision No. 4 cuts off the other part of the apex of the plastic unit. Two sides of the pyramid are now ready. The object-holder is then turned 90°. (d) Incision No. 5 (d₁) The object-holder with the plastic unit viewed from above after incision No. 5 (e) The object-holder is then turned 180° and incisions Nos. 6 and 7 made, after which it is again turned 180°. (f) Incision No. 8 cuts away the last part of the plastic unit, and the coarse cutting of the pyramid is now complete. (g) Side view. (g₁) Front view of the object-holder with ready-cut pyramid.*

always necessary. The height of a properly moulded pyramid is always greater than the base.

## GRINDING THE MICROTOME KNIFE

American Eversharp razor blades are used for cutting. After removing the fat with ether, the blade is mounted in a special holder (LKB-Produkter, Stockholm). Grinding is performed on a sheet of glass. A suitable amount of grinding powder (Type B 5125, Linde Air Products Co.) and teepol (one part teepol and four parts distilled water) should be available. The powder is thoroughly mixed with the teepol to a homogeneous, easy-flowing mixture. Ordinarily, grinding takes about 15 minutes. The pressure on the knife should be at a minimum during the last 5 to 8 minutes of grinding. After rinsing in running water and drying with a few drops of absolute alcohol, the knife is ready to use. It should be used immediately after grinding in order to avoid rust, contamination by dust, etc.

## SECTIONING

The knife is cleaned with acetone and mounted at an angle in a special trough (made by LKB-Produkter, Stockholm). Care must be taken to ensure that its edge is parallel with the end of the trough. The trough and the knife are then fixed in the microtome. The object-holder is tightly screwed into the moving part of the microtome. The screw controlling the thickness of the sections is adjusted in accordance with the desired thickness. A final adjustment of the pyramid in relation to the knife should be made. This process, as well as that of cutting, is followed through a binocular microscope ($20\times$).

With the motor off, the pyramid is brought by hand to the level of the knife. In order to prevent damage to the pyramid through the vertical movement of the microtome, the trough and the knife should be placed at a safe distance. The knife is then slowly brought forward to the apex of the pyramid.

Figure 8 outlines the moving part of the microtome, the knife-trough part (side view), and the vertical adjustment of the microtome lever with the mounted plastic unit. Figure 9 shows the knife-trough block and the microscope.

The final adjusting for sectioning is followed under the microscope. In the visual field will be seen the face of the knife, the liquid (20 percent alcohol in water) with which the trough has been filled, and the plastic unit with a part of its holder. One of the base lines of the pyramid must be parallel to the face of the knife, which should be brought as close as possible to the apex of the pyramid without coming into contact with it. The knife-trough block is then fixed, and the level of the liquid checked (the surface should be slightly convex).

The motor is then started. The initial movements of the microtome carry

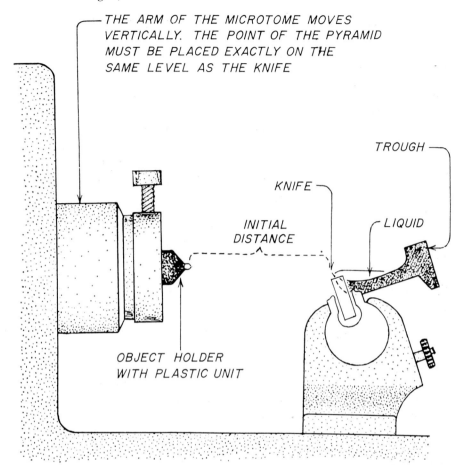

THE ARM OF THE MICROTOME MOVES
VERTICALLY. THE POINT OF THE PYRAMID
MUST BE PLACED EXACTLY ON THE
SAME LEVEL AS THE KNIFE

TROUGH

KNIFE

INITIAL
DISTANCE

LIQUID

OBJECT HOLDER
WITH PLASTIC UNIT

**Fig. 8.** *Adjusting the Spencer microtome model 821 for sectioning.*

the apex of the pyramid toward the knife. The object-holder advances at every second stroke. Normally the sections collect in the trough, forming wreaths, strips, or small flocks. If there is too much liquid they will disperse and water may adhere to the pyramid. Moreover, microscopic inspection of the sections will be rendered difficult or impossible because of light refraction, resulting from an exaggerated convexity of the liquid surface. Occasionally, the sections will roll up on the surface of the liquid, but they will regain their original shape if allowed to float in the trough for a few minutes before being picked up. The above methods of embedding, cutting, grinding, and sectioning have been recommended by, among others, F. S. Sjostrand, Karolinska Institutet, Stockholm. It is preferable to use pure distilled water (without adding alcohol) for cutting. If a water and alcohol mixture is used, the heavier sections sometimes sink to the bottom of the trough.

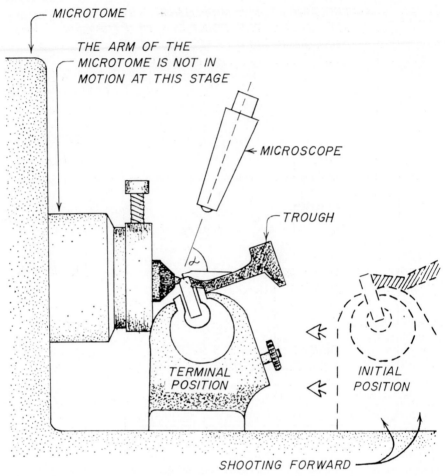

**Fig. 9.** *Adjusting the microtome for sectioning (continued).*

## PICKING UP THE SECTIONS

The sections in the trough are stretched with the aid of chloroform vapor, by passing a piece of blotting paper dipped in chloroform over the trough. The sections then immediately stretch out. They are picked up from the trough and transferred to a slide which has been thoroughly cleaned (albumin glycerin need not be used). A drop of alcohol (20 percent) is placed on the center of the slide. Previously, a soft, fine-pointed brush was used to pick up the sections and place them on the slide; today, however, the common practice is to use a thin copper or bronze wire with a small loop (about 4 mm²) at the end. It should have a "handle" about 5 cm long.

To fish out the sections the loop is lowered under the water surface and slowly moved toward the floating sections. When the loop is carefully lifted up there remains a water film carrying the sections. The loop is used to turn the sections upside down on a microscope slide on which a drop of water has been placed.

Further treatment depends on the number of sections transferred to the slide. If there are only a few it is better to allow the liquid on the slide to dry in the air. If there are many it is better to wash the slide with one or two drops of absolute alcohol. Although this procedure will probably wash away a number of the sections, it is nevertheless worth-while because the alcohol will separate the sections from each other and, at the same time, re-move any dust from the slide. When dry, the slide is rinsed once more with absolute alcohol. After the alcohol has evaporated, the plastic is dissolved in acetone.

## DISSOLVING THE PLASTIC; STAINING AND MOUNTING

The acetone usually dissolves the plastic in a few hours (generally, the slide is left overnight in the acetone). After inspection under the microscope at low magnification (about $60\times$) good section-bearing areas are marked with a diamond. The slide is then again carefully rinsed with absolute alcohol and with slowly running water. If the sections are not to be stained, the slide is ready for mounting.

Staining with fuchsin, safranine, or methylene blue is useful, and in fact often necessary, particularly if the thickness of the sections is only $0.5\mu$ or less. The stains are dissolved in a shallow dish filled with water (approxi-mately a knife's point to a dish). The material is stained in about 4 to 5 hours. Bismarck brown, malachite green, and other stains have been tried,

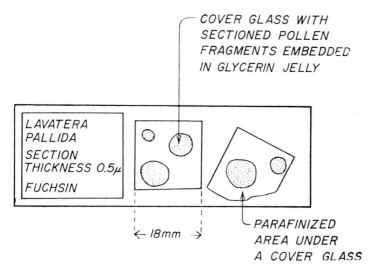

Fig. 10. *Microscope slide with sectioned pollen walls.*

but with less satisfactory results. Staining greatly facilitates the localization of the sections, as unstained sections thinner than $0.3\mu$ are often difficult to locate under an ordinary microscope.

After staining, the slide is rinsed with water and allowed to dry. Meanwhile, glycerine jelly cubes (about 1 mm³) are cut, and a number of cover slips carefully cleaned. The cubes are placed on those parts of the slide which have previously been marked with the diamond. The size of the cubes should vary in relation to the size of the section-bearing areas. A cover slip is then placed on top of each jelly cube, and the jelly slowly melted. Care should be taken to prevent the jelly from spreading to the edge of the cover slip.

The slide is then sealed by placing a small piece of paraffin (melting point about 70 centigrades) at the edge of the cover slip. It is then slowly heated in order to melt the paraffin, which is sucked in under the cover slip, forming a protecting zone around the section-bearing glycerin jelly (fig. 10). When the paraffin has cooled and hardened, the slide is cleaned with a knife and cotton wool soaked in benzol.

For further information see the brochure, "Sjostrand Ultra-Microtome. Instructions for Use," distributed by LKB-Produkter, Stockholm 12.

# A Method for Making Serial Sections
# of Pollen and Other Organic Microfossils

WILLIAM R. EVITT

*Stanford University, Stanford, California*

Thin sections of pollen and spores provide fundamental information on wall structure, yet sections have not been widely used in the study of fossil microspores and other microfossils of organic composition. Lack of suitable techniques is at least partly responsible for this. Identifying and orienting sections of grains prepared from fresh or herbarium material pose little problem for the preparator; the homogeneity of the sample from a plant of known identity assures that the sections studied represent the plant intended, and the abundance of randomly oriented specimens assures that some sections will show all possible orientations. With fossil material, however, a drop of the insoluble residue that is the starting point for section preparation usually contains a thorough mixture of grains representing many genera and species. The problem is how to select individual grains from such a fossil assemblage and cut them into sections with desired orientations.

In a recent paper Hughes, et al. (1962) suggested a method for sectioning fossil microspores and demonstrated in a convincing manner how sections can clarify critical uncertainties in the interpretation of fossil spore morphology. Each microtome block prepared by the technique developed by Mary Dettmann and described by Hughes, et al. (1962) provides a series of sections in known orientation through one individually selected and mounted spore (see also Dettmann's paper in this volume). Preparation of the microtome block requires a rather lengthy double-embedding sequence and careful control of specimen orientation, but there is no doubt about the position of the section and the identity of the grain.

The sectioning technique described below is an alternative to the Dettmann method. When multiple specimens of the fossil under study are available, it offers the advantages of relatively fast and simple preparation and the possibility of obtaining serial sections of many specimens from a single microtome block. However, orientation of individual grains is not controlled, and reliance is upon the random orientation of many grains to yield sections in all directions. The method is possibly applicable to smaller specimens than is the Dettmann technique, since grains are not individually manipulated into a precise position. Both sectioning procedures are applicable to many types of acid-insoluble microfossils with walls of organic composition.

### THE TECHNIQUE

1. A drop of insoluble microfossil-bearing residue in water suspension is placed on a microscope slide and a drop of glycerin added. The mixture is stirred and spread out; then the slide is placed on a warming table until the water has evaporated.

2. The slide is examined at about 100× under either a binocular dissecting microscope or a compound microscope. Specimens to be sectioned are withdrawn from the slide individually with the point of an eyelash that has been fixed (Duco cement is suitable) to the tip of a dissecting needle. To do this move the specimen through the glycerin to the edge of the smear, then pull it into a minute droplet of its own, free from the smear but still on the glass slide, then pick it up with a short quick movement, taking advantage of the surface tension which will hold the specimen to the eyelash. Specimens of each different kind to be sectioned are placed in a separate depression of a glass cavity slide that contains several drops of a solution of 50 percent water, 30 percent ethyl alcohol, and 20 percent *n*-butyl alcohol.

3. When all specimens of one type have been assembled in a cavity, the eyelash is used to pull them just above the surface of the liquid. The liquid is then withdrawn with a finely tipped eyedropper and the specimens are allowed to dry. *Note:* The low surface tension of the alcohol solution will permit uncompressed specimens with very thin and flexible walls to dry out without collapsing. If a noticeable amount of glycerin should remain on the specimens after evaporation of the solution, a second rinse in a few drops of the alcohol-water solution will remove it.

4. A few drops of 100 percent *n*-butyl alcohol are added to the cavity and the

specimens moved into it. After a few minutes the alcohol will have completely displaced the air in hollow specimens, which will then sink to the bottom of the cavity.

5. A few small chips of paraffin or Tissuemat are added to the cavity and allowed to dissolve. Then the slide is placed on a warming table (adjusted to a few degrees above the melting point of the wax) for an hour or so until the alcohol has evaporated.

6. A binocular dissecting microscope (about 100×) is arranged with the warming table as a stage. The fossil specimens are moved by means of the eyelash to the edge of the pool of melted wax. Then the specimens from a single cavity are gathered up on the fine tip of a dissecting needle by touching them one by one. When touched, each specimen will become fixed to the probe as the wax about it solidifies. Soon all specimens of a kind will be embedded in a tiny ball at the tip of the needle. The ball should be kept as small as possible so that the specimens are close together, with a minimum of wax between and around them. Thirty to 40 specimens can be collected in a ball 1 mm in diameter.

7. The ball with its enclosed specimens is dipped quickly into another container of the same melted embedding wax to which a little sudan black (or other fat-soluble stain) has been added. The thin, dark layer of wax thus added around the white ball will aid in locating the ball when it is mounted for sectioning.

8. A small block of wax is cut for mounting on the microtome, and a cavity into which the ball will fit is melted in one side of it with the warm, rounded end of a glass rod of suitably small diameter. While the wax is still melted, the tip of the rod is withdrawn and the dark ball inserted in its place. The needle is withdrawn, leaving the ball in the white block. Then the tip of a hot dissecting needle is carefully applied to seal the ball firmly in position.

9. The block is then trimmed square, close around the dark ball, with a razor blade, and mounted in the microtome. Sections are cut, expanded and arranged, and affixed to slides, following a standard technique (e.g., Weesner, 1960).

10. After the strips of sections are affixed to the slides and dried, the strips are outlined in India ink so that the lines of sections, which will be invisible to the unaided eye after the wax is removed, can be located easily in the completed slides.

11. The slides are then washed thoroughly in several rinses of xylene to remove all traces of wax and allowed to dry. Finally, the cover slips are affixed with a suitable mounting medium.

Grains sectioned according to this technique have been embedded in a paraffin-base wax (melting point 61°C). Both unstained grains (either naturally dark colored or made so by acetolysis) and grains stained before sectioning have been used. Aspects of the sectioning and staining methods described by Christensen (1950) and kindly called to my attention by Dr. Jane Gray also appear applicable to this technique, but have not yet been tried. The relatively hard carnauba-base wax used by Christensen should be particularly useful in reducing the distortion likely through compression of sections cut at less than $5\mu$.

**REFERENCES**

Christensen, B. B. (1950). Om mikrotomsnit af pollenexiner. Dansk Geol. Foren., Medd., v. 11, p. 441–448, pls. 7–9.

Hughes, N. F., M. E. Dettmann, and G. Playford (1962). Sections of some Carboniferous dispersed spores. Palaeontology, v. 5, p. 247–252, pls. 37–38.

Weesner, F. M. (1960). General zoological microtechniques. Baltimore, Williams & Wilkins Co., 230 pp.

# Techniques Used in the Study of Megaspores

MARY E. DETTMANN

*Department of Geology and Mineralogy, University of Queensland, St. Lucia, Queensland, Australia*

In botanical nomenclature, the term megaspore is used to denote the usually large spores which are borne by heterosporous plants and which germinate to form the multicellular female gametophyte. Megaspores are commonly much larger than the microspores produced by the same plant, but in several plants—for example, certain gymnosperms—the associated microspore is larger. Because palynologists have very little chance of determining whether a dispersed fossil spore is a true megaspore, they have set an arbitrary lower size limit of $200\mu$ for megaspores (Guennel, 1952).

Megaspores have been widely recognized as *sporae dispersae* in Devonian to Recent sediments; in particular, a great deal of attention has been given to those of Carboniferous age. Some have proven relationships with elements of the contemporaneous megaflora (see Chaloner, 1953) but the botanical affinities of the majority of described megaspore species remain largely obscure. Despite their large size and the fact that many probably derived from only the heterosporous plants, megaspores are often abundant in some continental sediments. For many years they have been utilized in stratigraphic geology, notably in the correlation of coal seams of Carboniferous age both in Europe and North America. Moreover, recent work testifies to their considerable stratigraphic importance in the intercontinental and world-wide correlation of other post-Silurian strata.

Megaspores may be recovered from sediments in conjunction with the extraction of microspores but in order to retrieve them in sufficient concentrations, several special recovery processes have been developed. Megaspores frequently possess a thick, opaque wall, and this has resulted in widespread use of incident light in their optical examination. However, the stratification of the megaspore wall and its structural and fine sculptural characteristics are seldom clearly visible in reflected light; thus, it is important to study these features in transmitted light.

## PREPARATION OF SAMPLES

### Coals

In the two procedures outlined below the coal is initially broken down into coarse fragments (approximately 5 to 10 mm in diameter). Five to 10 grams of coal is usually sufficient, but a greater or lesser amount may be processed, depending on the megaspore content of the sample.

#### Schulze Method (after Dijkstra, 1946)

1. The dry sample is placed in a large (50 to 100 cc) pyrex centrifuge tube or beaker, which is transferred to a fume hood and placed in a cold-water bath to counteract the exothermic reaction resulting from the next step.

2. Thirty to 50 cc of concentrated nitric acid and 3 to 5 grams of potassium (or sodium) chlorate crystals are added to the beaker and stirred cautiously with a glass rod. The time for adequate oxidation of individual samples varies from two hours to several days. In general, oxidation is sufficiently advanced when the top liquor is deep chocolate-brown and when the coal fragments have become partially disintegrated.

3. The acid solution is removed by centrifugation or decantation; the residue is then washed thoroughly in distilled water until the top liquor remains clear.

4. Subsequent alkali treatment varies considerably with the individual residue, and it is advisable to divide the residue into two or three parts before proceeding with this step. Indiscriminate use of alkali following oxidation may result in disorganization or total destruction of megaspore exines. In some cases, a 1 percent solution of ammonium hydroxide is sufficient to solubilize thoroughly excessive oxidation products; in others a 5 to 10 percent solution of potassium (or sodium) hydroxide is necessary. After addition of alkali the residue is stirred vigorously, immediately centrifuged, and then washed repeatedly with distilled water until the top liquor becomes clear. The residue is now ready to be sieved and subsequently searched for megaspores.

#### Zetzsche Method (after Dijkstra, 1946)

1. The coal sample is placed in a glass-stoppered liter flask (e.g., a kilner jar), which is transferred to the fume hood. Three to 4 cc of liquid bromine and 100 cc of fuming nitric acid are carefully added, then agitated, and allowed to stand for 3 to 4 hours. An alternative procedure is to place the coal in a centrifuge tube or a beaker to which 30 to 50 cc of fuming nitric acid is then added slowly and stirred carefully. The time for adequate maceration is shorter (1 to 4 hours) than

that recommended for the Schulze process. These alternative procedures should be carried out with extreme caution; rubber gloves and a face mask are recommended.

2. Following removal of acid by decantation or centrifuging, the residue is washed thoroughly in distilled water. It is then ready to be sieved.

## Clastic Sediments

### FRIABLE SEDIMENTS (CLAY, SILTS, ETC.)

Some noncemented sediments may be broken down readily by several hours' immersion in distilled water. Other sediments may have to be treated according to either of the following two methods. At least 10 grams of small lumps (about 1 or 2 cm in diameter) of sediment is used in each treatment.

*Sodium Carbonate Method (after Dijkstra, 1949)*. The dry sediment is immersed in boiling water containing 2 to 3 grams of anhydrous sodium carbonate. If the rock has not broken down after 15 minutes, the material is dried and the process repeated at least once.

*Ultrasonic Disintegration Method*. This method is often used in the recovery of microspores and is equally applicable in the extraction of megaspores.

### CONSOLIDATED SEDIMENTS

#### HYDROFLUORIC ACID METHOD

1. A polythene beaker or tube containing at least 10 g of sediment is transferred to a fume hood and approximately 50 cc of 50 to 60 percent hydrofluoric acid is added. Most sediments break down after a period of twelve hours to two days; frequent stirring and gentle heating hasten the process.

2. The hydrofluoric acid is removed, and the residue washed several times in distilled water.

3. Approximately 50 cc of 20 to 50 percent hydrochloric acid is added, and the mixture warmed, but not boiled, in a water bath for 5 minutes. The acid is then removed and the residue washed in distilled water.

## SIEVING, STORING, AND SORTING RESIDUES

After the coal or clastic sediment has been processed by one of the above methods, the residue is passed through one or more sieves. Copper or steel sieves are usually employed, although muslin or silk strainers may also be used. The mesh size of the sieve should not exceed the minimum diameter of the megaspores; a 100-mesh sieve (100 meshes to the inch, each mesh measuring about 150$\mu$ in diameter) retains the smallest megaspores. Some authors (Hughes, 1955; and others) recommend the use of three sieves (40-, 80-, and 100-mesh) to separate the residues into various size fractions. The fractions retained on the sieves may be *stored* before they are *sorted* for megaspores. Residues are commonly *stored* in sealed tubes containing either 50 percent glycerin plus a few drops of phenol solution or a mixture of glycerin and alcohol.

The sieved residues are transferred to petri dishes containing distilled water and then searched for megaspores by means of a binocular microscope at magnifications of 5× to 50×. Megaspores are extracted individually by means of a fine camel's-hair brush, flat needle, or pipette.

## MOUNTING AND OPTICAL EXAMINATION OF MEGASPORES

Arnold (1950), Chaloner (1953), Høeg, Bose, and Manum (1955), and other authors have emphasized the importance of examining megaspores in both reflected and transmitted light. Accordingly, both dry mounts, which are examined in reflected light, and translucent mounts, which are viewed in transmitted light, should be prepared for each megaspore species represented in the residues.

### Dry Mounts

Dry specimens are mounted in cardboard well slides, and, if desired, may be glued to the floor of the well with a water soluble gum (for example, gum tragacanth). Alternatively, the megaspores may be sealed under a cover slip in a glass cavity slide so that the spores can be examined from both sides. Any adherent mineral matter should first be removed by immersing the specimens in hydrofluoric acid for 1 to 2 hours.

### Translucent Mounts

Specimens examined in transmitted light are mounted in unstained glycerin jelly or, after dehydration in alcohol and xylene, in canada balsam, euparal, or polystyrene. Specimens with adherent mineral matter should be cleaned initially in hydrofluoric acid, and those which are insufficiently translucent may be cleared by either of the following procedures adopted by Dettmann (1961)

#### CLOVE OIL METHOD

The megaspores are allowed to stand briefly (approximately one minute) in each of 30 percent, 70 percent, and absolute alcohol, and xylene, and are then immersed in clove oil for 10 to 15 minutes. Cleared specimens to be mounted in canada balsam, euparal, or polystyrene are washed in xylene; those to be mounted in glycerin jelly are washed in xylene, absolute, 70 percent, and 30 percent alcohol, and distilled water.

#### NITRIC ACID METHOD

The megaspores are transferred to a small tube containing concentrated nitric acid or Schulze solution (15 cc concentrated nitric acid: 1 gram potassium chlorate). This and any subsequent treatment with alkali (very dilute ammonium hydroxide) should be observed continuously so that the reaction can be terminated before the megaspore wall dissolves or becomes disorganized. Care must be taken to wash the megaspores thoroughly after acid and alkali treatments. The megaspores are then mounted in glycerin jelly or, after dehydration, in canada balsam, euparal, or polystyrene.

In any systematic study, morphological descriptions, measurements, and photographs of both dry and translucent specimens should be given for each species. Pant and Srivastava (1961), Harris (1961), and Winslow (1959) have noted that there is a considerable size discrepancy between specimens mounted dry and those mounted in glycerin jelly and canada balsam. Furthermore, Pant and Srivastava (1961) commented that the morphological features of some spores may vary according to the chemical treatment to which they have been subjected.

External features are clearly seen in dry specimens viewed under a binocular microscope at magnifications of up to 100×. Fine sculptural and structural details are usually observed adequately in translucent specimens at magnifications of about 500×. In order to determine the wall stratification and structure of extremely thick-walled megaspores it may be necessary to study dissected and sectioned examples.

## Sectioning Technique

Microtoma sections of both megaspores and microspores may readily be cut at fine intervals (down to $1\mu$) following a modification of the embedding and sectioning techniques of Wigglesworth (1959). These procedures, in which the spores are double-embedded in agar (Japanese, fine powder) and ester wax (1960 formulation of British Drug Houses Ltd.) before being sectioned on a microtome (for example, a Cambridge rocking fine-section microtome), were adopted by Hughes, Dettmann, and Playford (1962).

1. Transfer selected spores to small porcelain or glass wells containing distilled water.

2. Place individual spores in embedding troughs (as shown in fig. 1,*a*) containing 5 percent agar solution at 55 to 60°C.

3. Orientate the spore under a binocular microscope so that the face to be cut lies parallel to the top or bottom surface of the agar (i.e., if polar sections are required, orient the spore so that its polar plane parallels the top or bottom surface of the agar). This procedure should be carried out with the trough standing on a hot plate.

4. Allow the agar to set at room temperature. Remove the agar block from the trough, and trim the block with a scalpel.

5. Transfer the trimmed agar block through the following solutions, allowing it to stand in each for 30 minutes: 30, 50, and 70 percent aqueous ethyl alcohol; 70 percent alcohol plus cellosolve (2:1); the same (1:2); pure cellosolve (three changes); cellosolve plus ester wax (1:1); pure ester wax (two changes).

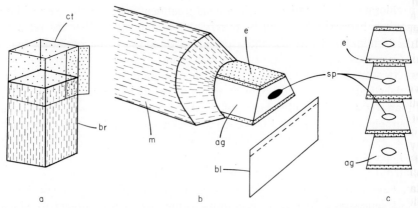

**Fig. 1.** (*a*) *Brass block (7 to 9 mm square in cross section) bound with cellulose tape to form embedding trough.* (*b*) *Mounted and trimmed agar block, showing position of spore.* (*c*) *Portion of ribbon containing spore sections. ct, cellulose tape; br, brass block; m, mount of microtome; e, ester wax; ag, agar; sp, spore; bl, blade.* [*From Hughes, Dettmann, and Playford, 1962.*]

6. Leave overnight in ester wax at 55 to 60°C.

7. Fill an embedding trough with molten ester wax.

8. Place the agar block containing the spore in the embedding trough so that the face to be cut rests near the bottom of the trough and parallel to it.

9. Allow the block to solidify rapidly by standing the trough in ice or a stream of running water. Do not allow the water to rise above the surface of the trough.

10. Trim and mount the agar-ester block as shown in fig. 1,*b*. An end-on view of the resultant mounted block shows narrow strips of ester wax constituting the two sides which parallel the cutting surface of the microtome blade. By following this procedure the sections subsequently obtained do not readily separate from one another and form a continuous ribbon as shown in fig. 1,*c*.

11. Cut the sections slowly (approximately 30 per minute) at required intervals using a sharpened microtome knife or a razor blade (e.g., the Pal or Personna type) mounted in a microtome holder.

12. Lay the ribbons on a sheet of paper, cut them into required lengths, and place the lengths on a slide smeared with adhesive albumen. By means of a fine pipette or dropper bottle apply two or three drops of 20 percent alcohol to one end of the slide, and allow the solution to flow below the ribbon, which, as a result, unfolds and flattens smoothly. The sections are then allowed to dry on the slide in an oven for 1 to 2 hours at 40 to 45°C.

13. Dewax the sections by placing the slide in xylene (5 minutes), and immerse the slide briefly (1 to 2 minutes) in 70 percent, 50 percent, and 30 percent alcohol. Finally, mount the sections in glycerin jelly under No. 0 cover slips.

### Photography

Translucent megaspores are photographed in transmitted light according to the procedures used in photographing microspores. Structural and sculptural details of thick-walled megaspores are usually depicted more clearly in photographs taken in infrared light.

Dijkstra and Piérart (1957) outline a method for photographing dry mounts in reflected light as follows:

1. Place the spore on a glass microscope slide which rests on white cardboard mounted on the microscope stage.

2. Illuminate the spore by means of a spot lamp (for example, an 8-volt Monla lamp). The spore is illuminated evenly either by means of light reflected from a small piece of white paper, which is mounted upright on the side of the spore opposite the light source, or by incident light directed onto the dark side of the spore from a second spot lamp.

3. Rotate the slide until the megaspore features are most clearly exhibited.

4. Insert a diaphragm (1.5-mm opening) into the objective lens (3–10:1) and photograph the spore at a magnification of 50× or 100× using a fine-grained film (Ilford Pan F) or plate (Ilford R.10).

Further techniques used in the photography of microfossils are detailed in Fournier (1956).

## REFERENCES

Arnold, C. A. (1950). Megaspores from the Michigan coal basin. Michigan Univ., Mus. Paleontology Contr., v. 8, no. 5, p. 59–111.

Chaloner, W. G. (1953). On the megaspores of four species of *Lepidostrobus*. Ann. Bot. [London], new series, v. 17, p. 263–93.

Dettmann, M. E. (1961). Lower Mesozoic megaspores from Tasmania and South Australia. Micropaleontology, v. 7, p. 71–86.

Dijkstra, S. J. (1946). Eine monographische Bearbeitung der karbonsichen Megasporen. Meded. Geol. Stichting, ser. C-III-I, no. 1, p. 1–101.

———— (1949). Megaspores and some other fossils from the Aschenian (Senonian) in South Limburg, Netherlands. Meded. Geol. Stichting, new series, no. 3, p. 19–32.

————, and P. Piérart (1957). Lower Carboniferous megaspores from the Moscow basin. Meded. Geol. Stichting, new series, no. 11, p. 5–19.

Fournier, G. (1956). New methods and techniques in the photography of microfossils. Micropaleontology, v. 2, p. 37–56.

Guennel, G. K. (1952). Fossil spores of the Alleghenian coals in Indiana. Rept. Progr. Indiana Geol. Survey, no. 4, 40 pp.

Harris, T. M. (1961). The Yorkshire Jurassic flora; 1. Thallophyta-Pteridophyta. British Museum of Natural History, London, 212 pp.

Høeg, O. A., M. N. Bose, and S. Manum (1955). On double walls in fossil megaspores. Nytt. Magasin für Botanik, v. 4, p. 101–107.

Hughes, N. F. (1955). Wealden plant microfossils. Geol. Mag., v. 92, p. 201–217.

————, M. E. Dettmann, and G. Playford (1962). Sections of some Carboniferous dispersed spores. Palaeontology, v. 5, p. 247–252.

Pant, D. D., and G. K. Srivastava (1961). Structural studies on Lower Gondwana megaspores; 1. Specimens from Talchir Coalfield, India. Palaeontographica, B, v. 109, p. 45–61.

Wigglesworth, V. B. (1959). A simple method for cutting sections in the 0.5 to 1$\mu$ range, and for sections of chitin. Quart. J. Micr. Sci., v. 100, p. 315–320.

Winslow, M. R. (1959). Upper Mississippian and Pennsylvanian megaspores and other plant microfossils from Illinois. Illinois Geol. Survey Bull., no. 86, 135 pp.

# Part IV

## BIBLIOGRAPHY ON PALEONTOLOGICAL TECHNIQUES

BERNHARD KUMMEL

# Bibliography on Paleon̄ Techniques

## BERNHARD KUMMEL

*Harvard University, Cambridge, M.*

I am extremely grateful to the great number of individuals who, over the years, have contributed references for this list. It is not possible to mention all of them by name, but I especially wish to acknowledge Dr. Siemon W. Muller of Stanford University and his paleontology-stratigraphy seminar who enthusiastically contributed many items plus suggestions on organization. Acknowledgment is made to the Milton Fund Small Grants Program of Harvard University for clerical assistance in the preparation of this section.

## CONTENTS

# A

## GENERAL

Camp, C. L. and G. D. Hanna (1937). Methods in paleontology. Univ. of California Press, Berkeley, 153 pp., 58 figs.

Goodwin, A. J. H. (1953), Method in prehistory. An introduction to the discipline of prehistoric archaeology with special reference to South African conditions. South African Archaeol. Soc., Handb. Ser. 1, 2nd ed., 184 pp., 15 figs. and front.

Grabau, A. W., and H. W. Shimer (1910). Hints for collecting and preparing fossil invertebrates, *in* North American Indev Fossils, v. 2, p. 803–819.

Heizer, R. F. (1949). A manual of archaeological field methods. National Press, Millbrae, Calif., vi + 72 pp., 12 figs.

Hennig, Edwin (1932). Wesen und Wege der Paläontologie. Eine Einführung in die Versteinerungslehre als Wissenschaft. Borntraeger, Berlin, 512 pp., 198 figs.

Mayr, Ernst, E. G. Linsley, and R. I. Usinger (1953). Methods and principles of systematic zoology. McGraw-Hill, New York, 328 pp.

# B

## COLLECTING

American Malacological Union (1961). How to collect shells. 2nd ed., Marinette, Wisc.

Baird, Donald (1951). See Sec. O, Vertebrate fossils.

Burns, N. J. (1941). List of materials used for collecting, cleaning and preserving specimens. Field Manual for Mus., U. S. Dept. Interior, Natl. Park Service, p. 221–239

Condra, G. E., and M. K. Elias (1944). Study and revision of Archimedes (Hall); technique in collecting and preparation. Geol. Soc. Am., Spec. Paper no. 53, p. 11–13.

Demanet, A. F. (1935). The systematic collecting of fossils. What is the best way of forming a palaeontological collection? Mus. J., London, v. 35, no. 8, p. 288–294.

Flint, J. M. (1886). See Sec. M(2), Micropaleontology—Foraminifera.

Grabau, A. W., and H. W. Shimer (1910). Hints for collecting and preparing fossil invertebrates. North American Index Fossils, v. 2, p. 803–819.

Gunnell, F. H., and P. S. Morey (1932). See Sec. M(7), Micropaleontology—Conodonts.

Hibbard, C. W. (1948). Technique of collecting microvertebrate fossils. Geol. Soc. Am., B. 59, 1330 pp.

———— (1949). Techniques of collecting microvertebrate fossils. Michigan Univ., Mus. Paleontology, cont. v. 8, no. 2, p. 7–19.

Höglund, Hans (1947). See Sec. M(2), Micropaleontology—Foraminifera. [p. 6–7 on collection.]

Holden, F. H. (1914), (1916). See Sec. O, Vertebrate Fossils—General. [Packing.]

Hudson, G. H. (1916). Some notes on fossil collecting, and on the Edrioasteroidea. Ottawa Nat., v. 30, p. 21–25, 40–46.

Janensch, W. (1914). Bericht über den Verlauf der Tendaguru-Expedition. Arch. Biont., v. 3, H. 1, p. 28–38. [Collecting and packing.]

Kindle, E. M. (1916). Fossil collecting. Ottawa Nat., v. 29, p. 117–124.

Klebs, R. (1910). Über Bernsteineinschlüsse im Allgemeinen. Phys.-oek. Ges., Schr., Pr., v. 51, p. 216–233. [Collecting and packing.]

Langston, Wann, Jr. (1948). Vertebrate paleontological field technique and its application to archeological collecting. Texas Archeol. Paleont. Soc., B., v. 19, p. 88–99.

Lee, J. J., Stanley Pierce, Marilyn Tentchoff, and J. J. A. McLaughlin (1961). Growth and physiology of foraminifera in the laboratory, Part 1, Collection and maintenance. Micropaleontology, v. 7, no. 4, p. 461–466.

Malan, B. D. (1944). Excavation method in South African prehistoric caves. African Mus. Assoc., B., Dec., p. 1–8. [Reprint.]

Mann, Albert (1922). See Sec. M(4), Micropaleontology—Diatoms.

Matthew, W. D. (1926). Early days of fossil hunting in the high plains. Nat. Hist., v. 26, p. 449–454.

McKenna, M. C. (1962). Collecting small fossils by washing and screening. Curator, v. 5, no. 3, p. 221–235.

Meléndez, Bermudo (1953). Los métodos de trabajo en paleontología: Arbor, v. 26, no. 93–94, 34–49, 7 figs.

Morris, P. A. (1947). A field guide to the shells of our Atlantic Coast. Houghton Mifflin, Boston, 190 pp.

Olsen, S. J. (1961). Scuba as an aid to archeologists and paleontologists. Curator (Am. Mus. Nat. Hist.), v. 4, no. 4, p. 371–378, 3 figs.

Patterson, Bryan (1940) Collecting fossil vertebrates. Chicago Nat., v. 3, no. 1, p. 3–10, 4 figs.

———— (1947). Use of aerial photographs in fossil hunting. Chicago Nat. Hist. Mus., B., v. 18, no. 5, p. 7.

Phleger, F. B., and F. L. Parker (1951). Ecology of foraminifera, Northwest Gulf of Mexico. Geol. Soc. Am., Mem. no. 46, 64 pp.

————, and W. R. Walton (1950). Ecology of marsh and bay foraminifera, Barnstable, Mass. Am. J. Sci., v. 248, p. 275–276.

Prokhorov, M. G. (1929). Instructions for excavating, preparing and mounting fossil vertebrates: Acad. Sci. U.S.S.R., Geol. Mus. Leningrad, p. 1–75, 7 pls., 6 figs. [In Russian.]

Reimann, I. G. (1952). A new material for the paleontologist. J. Paleontology, v. 26, p. 529. [Use of plastic impregnated fabric.]

Salomon-Calvi, Wilhelm (1933). Aufsammlungen und Ausgrabungen von Fossilien. Badische Geol. Abh. Jahrg. 5, H. 2, 4 pp. [Reprint.]

Schenck, H. G., and R. T. White (1942). Collecting microfossils. Am. Midl. Nat., v. 28, p. 424–450.

Schuchert, Charles (1895). Direction for collecting and preparing fossils. U. S. Natl. Mus., B. 39, pt. K, p. 5–31.

Simpson, G. G. (1937). How fossils are collected. Am. Mus. Nat. Hist., v. 39, no. 5, p. 329–333.

Stürmer, Wilhelm (1951). Zur Technik der Auffindung von Graptolithen-Kieselschiefern in den Main-Geröllen. Senckenbergiana, v. 32, no. 1–4, p. 157–159.

Tassin, W. (1895). Directions for collecting minerals. U. S. Natl. Mus., B. 39, pt. H, p. 3–6.

Unwin, Max (1951). A new method for the impregnation of wet objects in the field. Mus. J. London, v. 50, no. 10, p. 237.

Ward's Natural Science Establishment (1950). First steps in field collecting of fossils. Ward's Nat. Sci. Bull., v. 23, no. 5, p. 75–76.

Weidenreich, Franz (1941). The site and the technique of the excavations of fossil man in Choukoutien, China. N. Y. Acad. Sci., Tr., ser. 2, v. 4, no. 1, p. 23–31. [Lecture.]

Wood, J. M., and K. L. Segroves (1963). Method for collecting coal and shale samples. Micropaleontology, v. 9, no. 3, p. 340.

# C

## LABELING AND STORAGE

Bartenstein, Helmut (1953). Die DMW–Zelle, eine neuartige Zelle zur Aufbewahrung von Mikrofossilien. Erdöl Kohle, Jahrg. 6, no. 6, p. 329, 1 fig.

Dahmer, G. (1933). Cellophan als Zettelschutz in Gesteinsammlungen. Natur. Mus., v. 63, p. 29.

Frizzell, D. L. (1949). Flat filing cabinets for cardboard microslides. Micropaleontologist, v. 3, no. 2, p. 30.

Gage, S. H. (1936). See Sec. I, Microscopy. [Chapter 11 on labeling and storage.]

Howell, B. F. (1928). Marking of type specimens. Geol. Soc. Am., B., v. 39, no. 1, p. 287–288.

———— (1929). Third report of special committee on marking of type specimens. Geol. Soc. Am., B., v. 40, no. 1, p. 215–220, 1 pl.

Marsh, O. C. (1898). The value of type specimens and importance of their preservation. 4th. Int. Cong. Zool., Pr., p. 158–162.

North, F. J. (1949). Notes for students; Labels, their function, preparation, and use. Mus. J. London, VI–VIII, v. 49, no. 2, p. 26–30; no. 3, p. 55–62; no. 4, p. 80–86.

Richards, H. G. (1954). An analysis of the methods of storing invertebrate fossils. J. Paleontology, v. 28, no. 4, p. 486.

Sahni, B. (1945). Permanent labels for museum specimens in damp tropical climates. J. Mus. Assoc. India, Prince of Wales Mus., v. 1, no. 2, p. 107–108.

Schenck, E. T., and J. H. McMasters (1948). Types and storage of type material, *in* Procedure in taxonomy. Stanford Univ. Press (2nd ed. revised by A. M. Keen and S. W. Muller), p. 6–12.

Shaub, B. M. (1936). See Sec. G, Sectioning.

Spencer, L. J. (1931). Paper for museum labels. Mus. J. London, v. 31, p. 391–395.

Steineke, F. S. (1927). Filing and indexing a micropaleontologic collection. Micropaleontology, B., v. 1, no. 4, art. 15, p. 2–4.

Stephenson, L. W. (1933). The preservation of type specimens. J. Paleontology, v. 7, p. 442–443.

Stohler, R. (1952). Techniques for the internal labeling of bio-plastics. Ward's Nat. Sci. Bull., v. 25, no. 5, p. 74–75.

Walker, P. H. (1933). Gold and silver paints for use in marking type specimens. Paleont. Soc. Serv. Comm. Inf. B, no. 10, p. 4.

Warthin, A. S., Jr. (1939). "Spotting" specimens for catalogue numbers. Science, n.s., v. 89, p. 324.

Wentworth, C. K. (1934). Rational tray sizes for geologic specimens. Science, v. 80, no. 2065, p. 98–99.

Wilson, J. H. (1949). Labels which last. Mus. J., London, v. 49, no. 5, p. 114–116.

# D

## PRESERVATION

Bachmayer, Friedrich (1954). Ursache und Bekanpfung des Zerfalles von schwefelkiesdurch–setzten fossilen Knochen. Paläont. Zs., v. 28, no. 1–2, p. 77–80, illus.

Bannister, F. A. (1933). The preservation of pyrites and marcasite. Mus. J., London, v. 33, p. 72–75.

Bather, F. A. (1908). The preparation and preservation of fossils. Mus. J., London, v. 8, p. 76–90.

Boettcher, F. L. J. (1912). Preservation of osseous and horny tissues. U. S. Natl., Mus. Pr., v. 41, p. 697–705.

Borger, Harvey (1939). Recovery and preservation of marcasitized and pryritized microfossils. Ill. State Acad. Sci., Tr., v. 32, no. 2, p. 166.

Brink, A. S. (1957). On the uses of glyptal in palaeontology. Palaeont. Africana, v. 4 (1956), p. 124–130.

Burns, N. J. (1941). See Sec. B, Collecting.

Cameron, E. N. (1934). Notes on the synthetic resin hyrax. Am. Miner., v. 19, p. 375–383.

Case, E. C. (1925). The use of Bakelite in the preservation of fossil material. Science, v. 61, p. 543–544.

Cushman, J. A. (1940). See Sec. M(2), Micropaleontology—Foraminifera. [p. 25–26 on preservation.]

Davidson, C. F. (1932). The Arctic clay of Errol, Perthshire. Perthshire Soc. Nat. Sci., Pr. Tr., v. 9, pt. 2, 1930/31, p. 55–68. [p. 67, Note on vinyl acetate.]

Frentzen, K. (1932). Über Durol, ein neues Konservierungsmittel für fossile und subfossile Knochen und andere mürbe oder leicht zerfallende Fossilien. Zentralb. Miner., Geol., Paleont., Abt. B, p. 65–66.

Geemann, H. B. (1940). Die Konservierung angetriebener meerischer Holzund Torffunde mit I. G. Wachs. Senckenbergiana, v. 22, p. 402.

Gunn, W. A. (1924). Celluloid as a preservative. Mus. J., London, v. 24, p. 154.

Harden, C. E. (1963). How to preserve animal and other specimens in clear plastic. Naturegraph, Healdsburg, Calif., 64 pp., 23 figs.

Mann, L. McL. (1933). Preservation of fossil bones. Nature, v. 131, p. 366.

Marie, Pierre (1921). Sur la conservation des pyriteux dans les collections. Mus. Natl., d'Hist. Nat., B. ser. 2, v. 13, p. 606–608.

Nature (1933). Preservation of fossil bones. Nature, v. 131, p. 127.

Nicols, H. W., and P. C. Orr (1932). Bakelite impregnation of fossil bones. Mus. J., London, v. 32, no. 2, p. 47–53.

Oehmichen, Et. (1944). Traitement d'antioxydation des fossiles pyriteux. Soc. Géol. France, C. R., p. 65–67.

Radley, E. G. (1929). The preservation of pyritised and other fossils. Naturalist, no. 867, p. 143–146; no. 868, p. 167–173; no. 869, p. 196–202.

Raistrick, A., and C. E. Marshall (1939) (reprinted 1948). The nature and origin of coal and coal seams. Engl. Univ. Press Ltd., London, p. 269–270. [Treatment of fragile specimens.]

Rathgen, Friedrich (1915). Die Konservierung von Altertumsfunden . . . 1. Teil. Stein und steinartige stoffe. Handb. k. Mus. Berlin, 153 pp., 91 figs.

Reimann, I. G. (1952). A new material for the paleontologists. J. Paleontology, v. 26, no. 3, p. 529. [Plastic preservative.]

Sternberg, L. (1956). The use of "Gelva" in the vertebrate laboratory. Soc. Vert. Paleont. News B., no. 48, p. 33.

Swinton, W. E. (1933). Bakelite and the preservation of fossils. Mus. J., London, v. 33, p. 76–80.

Timon-David, Jean (1943). Un procédé d'examen et de conservation des insectes fossiles. Marseille, Fac. Sci., C. R., ser. 1, v. 1, f. 8, p. 123–124.

Todd, William (1941). A vacuum process for the preservation of bone and similar materials. Tech. Studies, v. 9, no. 3, and Mus. News, 1944, v. 21, no. 13, p. 7–8.

Wagstaffe, Reginald, and J. H. Fidler (1955). The Preservation of Natural History Specimens, v. 1. Invertebrates. Witherby, London, 205 pp., 139 figs.

White, T. C. (1891). A new method of infiltrating osseous and dental tissues. Toy. Micros. Soc. J., pt. 1, p. 307–308.

# E

## MECHANICAL METHODS OF PREPARATION

Bernard, H. M. (1894). On the application of the sand-blast for the development of trilobites. Geol. Mag., v. 1, p. 553–557, 2 figs.

Biggs, D. L. (1957). Cavitation as a means of cleaning silt grains. Iowa Acad. Sci., Proc., v. 64, p. 382–384.

Brough, James (1931). On the fossil fishes from the Karroo System, and some general considerations on the bony fishes of the Triassic period. Pr. Zool. Soc. London, p. 235–296, 4 pls., 19 figs. [With a note by D. M. S. Watson on the use of the wire brush in cleaning specimens.]

Buckman, S. S. (1911). A method of removing the test from fossils. Am. J. Sci., ser. 4, v. 32, p. 163. [Mechanical.]

Cummings, R. H. (1956). Gyratory sieving and straining applied to geological research. Colliery Guardian, v. 192, no. 4951, p. 94–95, illus.

——— (1956). Gyratory sieving speeds research. World Oil, v. 143, no. 5, p. 137–139, illus.

Kesling, R. V. (1954). An instrument for cleaning small fossils. Michigan Univ. Mus. Paleont. Contr., v. 11, no. 10, p. 193–199, illus.

Morse, W. C. (1916). A power chisel for paleontologic laboratories. Science, n.s., v. 44, p. 142–143.

Osborn, H. F. (1904). On the use of the sandblast in cleaning fossils. Science, n.s., v. 19, p. 256. [Abstract.]

Riggs, E. S. (1903). The use of pneumatic tools in the preparation of fossils. Science, n.s., v. 17, p. 747–749.

Spreng, A. C. (1962). Airbrasive cleaning tool. J. Paleontology, v. 36, no. 6, p. 1391–1392.

Stevens, C. H., D. H. Jones, and R. G. Todd (1960). Ultrasonic vibrations as a cleaning agent for fossils. J. Paleontology, v. 34, p. 727–730, 2 pls.

Stucker, G. F. (1961). Salvaging fossils by jet. Curator, v. IV, no. 4, p. 332–340.

Tschudy, R. H. (1960). "Vibraflute." Micropaleontology, v. 6, no. 3, p. 325–326.

Wetzel, W. (1950). Ultraschall-Aufbereitung von Gesteinsproben. Erdöl u. Kohle, v. 3, p. 212–214, 3 figs.

# F

## CHEMICAL, THERMAL, AND WASHING METHODS OF PREPARATION

Beckmann, Heinz (1952). Zur Anwendung von Essigsäure in der Mikropaläontologie. Paläont. Zs., v. 26, no. 1–2, p. 138–139.

——— (1952). The use of acetic acid in micropaleontology. Micropaleontologist, v. 6, no. 3, p. 39. [Conodonts.]

Bell, W. C. (1946). Etching "corneous" brachipods. Geol. Soc. Am., B., v. 57, no. 12, pt. 2, p. 1177. [Abstract.]

—————— (1948). Acetic acid etching technique applied to Cambrian brachipods. J. Paleontology, v. 22, p. 101–102.

Bolli, H. M. (1950). Disintegration of indurated siliceous rocks. Micropaleontologist, v. 4, no. 3, p. 20–21. [Sodium hydroxide techniques.]

—————— (1952). Note on the disintegration of indurated rocks. Micropaleontologist, v. 6, no. 1, p. 46–48, illus.

Böse, Emil, and Victor von Vigier (1907). Ueber die Anwendung von Aetzkale beim Praparieren von Versteinerungen. Zentralbl. Miner., Geol., Paleont., p. 305–313.

—————— (1907). Sobre la aplicación de la potasa caustica a la preparacion de fósiles. Inst. Geol. Mexico, Parergones, v. 2, p. 49–59.

Bourdon, M. (1956). Études micropaléontologiques; utilisation de l'acide acétique dans la desagrégation des roches dures. Inst. Franç. Pétrole, Rev., v. 12, no. 1, p. 14–15.

Buckman, S. S. (1911–1912). A method of removing tests from fossils. Am. J. Sci., ser. 4, v. 32, p. 163; v. 33, p. 593–594.

Bulman, O. M. B. (1931). Note on *Palaeospondylus gunni* Traquair. Ann. Mag. Nat. Hist. (10), v. 8, p. 179–190. [Carbonized specimen transferred to slide and etched with HCl and HF.]

—————— (1944). Caradoc (Balclatchie) graptolites from limestones in Laggan Burn, Ayrshire. Palaeontogr. Soc., London, v. 98, pt. 1, p. 1–42.

Chamney, T. P. (1957). A micropaleontological disintegration method. Alberta Soc. Petrol. Geol., J., v. 5, no. 9, p. 215–221, illus.

Crowley, A. J. (1952). Method of extracting foraminifera from refractory shale. Am. Assoc. Petrol. Geol., B., v. 36, no. 11, p. 2185.

Drevermann, Fritz (1928). Beobachtungen bei der Präparation von Solnhofener Versteinerungen. Paläont. Zs., v. 10, p. 289–292, 2 figs.

Driver, H. L. (1928). An aid in disintegrating samples for micro-organic study. J. Paleontology, v. 1, no. 4, p. 253–254. [Pressure cooking.]

Dunn, P. H. (1933). Microfaunal technique in the study of older Paleozoics. Illinois State Acad. Sci., Tr., v. 25, no. 4, p. 140–141.

Elliot, G. F. (1949). The brachial development of *Kraussina* (Brachiopoda). Ann. Mag. Nat. Hist., s. 12, v. 2, no. 19, p. 538–546. [Methods of study of dried and preserved recent brachs.]

Evitt, W. R. (1951). Paleontologic techniques. J. Paleontology, v. 25, no. 5, p. 693–695. [Acid cleaning solution.]

Ewing, J. F. (1950). A new technique for removing bones from limestone breccia. Antig., v. 24, p. 102–105.

Funkhouser, J. W., and W. R. Evitt (1959). Preparation techniques for acid-insoluble microfossils. Micropaleontology, v. 5, no. 3, p. 369–375.

Hanna, G. D. (1925). The extraction of fossils from refractory rocks. J. Geology, v. 33, no. 5, p. 545–547.

—————— (1926). Disintegrating shales by mechanical attrition. Micropaleontology, B., v. 1, no. 3, p. 1–2.

——————, and C. C. Church (1928). Freezing and thawing to disintegrate shales. J. Paleontology, v. 2, p. 131.

Hoffmeister, W. S. (1959). Sodium hypochlorite, a new oxidizing agent for the preparation of microfossils. Oklahoma Geol. Notes, v. 20, no. 2, p. 34–35.

Holm, G. (1890) Gotlands Graptoliter. Bih. K. Svenska Vet.-Akad., v. 16, pt. iv., no. 7, p. 1–34, 2 pls. [Balsam embedment on glass plus HCl etching.]

Kirchner, Z. M. (1958). A new method of hard-rock maceration. Micropaleontology, v. 4, no. 3, p. 327–328, illus.

Knights, A. J. (1951). Micropaleontological technique. Geol. Mag., v. 88, no. 2, p. 150. [Shale disentegration by heat.]

Kühne, Walter G. (1961). Präparation von flachen Wirbeltierfossilien auf künstlicher Matrix. Pälaont. Zs., Bd. 35, no. 3–4, p. 251–252.

Layne, N. M., Jr. (1950). A procedure for shale disintegration. Micropaleontologist, v. 4, no. 1, p. 21. [Gasoline technique.]

Lejeune, Maria (1936). Sur un moyen d'isoler les microfossiles inclus dans les silex. Acad. Sci. Paris, C. R., v. 203, no. 7, p. 435–437.

MacVicar, D. G., Jr. (1951). Heat treatment frees Pre-Cambrian fossils. Sci. News-Letter, v. 59, no. 17, p. 261.

———— (1951). Extraction of fossils by heat. Micropaleontologist, v. 5, no. 3, p. 15.

———— (1952). Thermal disintegration of sedimentary rock. Am. J. Sci., v. 250, no. 4, p. 271–274, illus.

Moore, R. C. (1948). Assembly-line paleontological laboratory at the University of Kansas. Compass of Sigma Gamma Epsilon, v. 25, no. 2, p. 5–11.

Moysey, L. (1908). On a method of splitting ironstone nodules by means of an artificial freezing mixture. Geol. Mag., v. 5, p. 220–222.

Ostrom, M. E. (1961). Separation of clay minerals from carbonate rocks by using acid. J. Sed. Petrol., v. 31, no. 1, p. 123–129.

Owen, E. F. (1955). The use of sugar solution in the differentiation of the internal structures of Upper Chalk brachiopods. Proc. Geol. Assoc., v. 66, p. 369–370.

Pierce, W. D. (1955). Use of propylene glycol in paleontology. So. Calif. Acad. Sci. Bull., v. 54, pt. 2, p. 104. [Use in softening insect-bearing interglacial peat and in making insect-bearing onyx marble translucent.]

Puri, H. S. (1948). Chemical treatment of rocks for removing microfossils. Micropaleontologist, v. 2, no. 3, p. 18.

Rasetti, Franco (1941). Action de l'acide oxalique sur les calcaires fossilifères. Assoc. Can.-Franç. Av. Sci., Ann., v. 7, p. 91. [Abstract.]

Redmond, C. D. (1953). Further notes on the disintegration of shale samples. Micropaleontologist, v. 7, no. 2, p. 47–48.

Reid, R. E. H. (1958). A use for acetic acid in the study of fossil sponges. Geol. Mag. v. 95, no. 1, p. 82–83.

Rixon, A. E. (1949). The use of acetic and formic acids in the preparation of fossil vertebrates. Mus. J., London, v. 49, p. 116–117.

Rowe, A. W. (1896). The preparation and mounting of chalk fossils. Nat. Sci., v. 9, p. 303–311.

St. Clair, D. W. (1935). The use of acetic acid to obtain insoluble residues. J. Sed. Petrol., v. 5, no. 3, p. 146–149.

Sohn, I. G. (1956). The transformation of opaque calcium carbonate to translucent calcium fluoride in fossil Ostracoda. J. Paleontology, v. 30, no. 1, p. 113–114, 1 pl.

Stürmer, Wilhelm (1951). Zur Technik der Auffindung von Graptolithen-Kieselschiefern in den Main-Geröllen. Senckenbergiana, v. 32, no. 1–4, p. 157–159.

―――― (1952). Zur Technik an Graptolithen und Radiolarien in Main-Kiesel-schiefern. 2. Senckenbergiana, v. 32, p. 351–355, 4 pls.

Thursch, Horst (1958). Ein neues Verfahren zur Präparation von Kalkproben mit Essigsäure. N. Jb. Geol., Palaeont., Mh., H. 6, p. 283–284.

Tolmachoff, I. P. (1932). Crystallization of certain salts used for the disintegration of shales. Science, n.s., v. 76, no. 1963, p. 147–148.

Toombs, H. A. (1948). The use of acetic acid in the development of vertebrate fossils. Mus. J. London, v. 48, no. 3, p. 54–55, 1 pl.

―――――, and A. E. Rixon (1950). [Letter re: ". . . development of fossils from rocks of all geological ages by chemical methods, . . ."]. Antig., v. 24, p. 141.

―――― (1959). The use of acids in the preparation of vertebrate fossils. Curator, v. II, no. 4, p. 304–312.

Udluft, Hans, and Hans Matern (1926). Ein Beitrag zur Präparation von verkiesten Fossilien. Senckenbergiana, v. 8, p. 17–22, 3 figs.

Upshaw, C. F., R. G. Todd, and B. D. Allen (1957). Fluoridization of microfossils. J. Paleontology, v. 31, no. 4, p. 793–795.

Wetzel, Otto (1948). Micro-organisms in chert. Micropaleontologist, v. 2, no. 2, p. 32.

―――― (1957). Fossil "microforaminifera" in various sediments and their reaction to acid treatment. Micropaleontology, v. 3, no. 1, p. 61–64.

Williams, Ernest (1953). Acetic acid preparation in England. Soc. Vert. Paleont., News B., no. 38, p. 22–25.

Wulff, R. (1916). Ein Beitrag zur Präparation fossiler Korallen. Zentralbl. Miner., Geol., Paleont., p. 445–446.


# G

## SECTIONING—THIN, SERIAL, AND POLISHED

Arnold, Z. M. (1958). A precision sectioning instrument for microfossils. Micropaleontology, v. 4, no. 1, p. 103.

Bassler, R. S. (1922). The Bryozoa, or moss animals. Smithson. Inst., Ann. Rept. for 1920, p. 348–349. [On thin-section technique.]

Baumann, H. N., Jr. (1957). Preparation of petrographic sections with bonded diamond wheels. Am. Mineralogist, v. 42, no. 5–6, p. 416–421, illus.

Beck, C. B. (1955). A technique for obtaining polished surfaces of sections of pyritized plant fossils. Torrey Bot. Club, B., v. 82, no. 4, p. 286–291, illus.

Beckmann, H. (1951). Hilfsmittel zum Schleifen von Mikrofossilien. Paläont. Zs., v. 24, no. 1–2, p. 91–94.

Berry, Willard (1931). Sectioning orbitoid foraminifera. Science, v. 73, no. 1894, p. 426–427.

Birket-Smith, Jørgen (1950). Serial sections of small fossils, a new method. Danm. Geol. Unders., v. 3, no. 7, 32 pp.

Boddy, R. G. H. B. (1934). The preparation of thin sections of coal using Bakelite as an embedding medium. Fuel Sci. Pract., v. 13, p. 269–271, 3 figs.

Bulman, O. M. B. (1925). Notes on the structure of an early *Dictyonema*. Geol. Mag., v. 62, p. 50–67, 12 figs. [Serial sectioning.]

Caldwell, F. E. S. (1935). A simple method of taking serial sections. Geol. Mag., v. 72, p. 521–523, 1 fig.

Carpenter, W. B. (1856). Monograph of the genus *Orbitolites*. Roy. Soc. London, Philos. Tr., v. 146, p. 187–236, 9 pls.

Carroll, D. L. (1929). Scientific apparatus and laboratory methods: New methods in the study of fossil shark teeth. Science, n.s., v. 70, p. 331–332.

Christensen, B. B. (1949). Om mikrotomsnit af pollenexiner-Microtome sectioning of pollenexines. Dansk Geol. Foren., Meddel., v. 11, H. 4, p. 441–444, illus. [In Danish, with English summary.]

Cochran, Manning, and A. G. King (1957). Two new types of holders used in grinding thin sections. Am. Mineralogist, v. 42, no. 5–6, p. 422–425, illus.

Corrington, J. D. (1941). See Sec. L, Microscopy. [Chapters 12–14 on sectioning.]

Creaser, C. W., and W. J. Clench (1923). The use of sodium silicate as a mounting medium. Am. Micros. Soc. Tr., v. 42, no. 1, p. 69–71.

Croft, W. N. (1950). A parallel grinding instrument for the investigation of fossils by serial sections. J. Paleontology, v. 24, no. 6, p. 693–698, 5 figs.

——— (1953). A simplified parallel grinding instrument. Ann. Mag. Nat. Hist., ser. 12, v. 6, no. 72, p. 915–918, illus.

Cummings, R. H. (1950). Oriented thin-sectioning of microfossils. Cushman Lab. Foram. Res., Contr., v. 1, pt. 3–4, p. 66–67.

——— (1952). Developments in micropaleontological technique. J. Paleontology, v. 26, no. 1, p. 123. [Serial sectioning and peel projection for drawings.]

Douglass, R. C. (1960). The foraminiferal genus *Orbitolina* in North America. U. S. Geol. Survey Prof. Paper 333, p. 1–52. [Sectioning, p. 25–26.]

Dunbar, C. O. (1954). A new technique for making sections of invertebrate fossils. J. Paleontology, v. 28, no. 1, p. 112.

Dunbar, C. O., and G. E. Condra (1927). See Sec. M(2), Micropaleontology—Foraminifera.

Dunbar, C. O., and L. G. Henbest (1942). See Sec. M(2), Micropaleontology—Foriminifera.

Dunn, J. A. (1937). Polished and thin section technique in the laboratory of the Geological Survey of India. Geol. Survey India, Rec., v. 72, pt. 2, p. 207–226, 2 pls., 3 figs.

Emiliani, Cesare (1951). Notes on thin sectioning of smaller foraminifera. J. Paleontology, v. 25, no. 4, p. 531–532.

Exley, C. S. (1956). A method of impregnating friable rocks for the cutting of thin sections. Miner. Mag., v. 31, no. 235, p. 347–349, illus.

Farris, E. J. (1932). Aloxite as an abrasive for grinding bone sections for histological purposes. Science, n.s., v. 75, no. 1945, p. 389–390.

Fowler, J. W., and J. Shirley (1947). A method of making thin sections from friable materials and its use in the examination of shales from the coal measures. Geol. Mag., v. 84, p. 354–359.

Fritz-Gaertner, R. (1878). The preparation of rocks and fossils for microscopial examination. Am. Naturalist, v. 12, p. 219–225.

Fuller, H. C. (1933). Mounting polished surfaces in bakelite. Econ. Geol., v. 28, p. 393–395.

Gabelman, J. W. (1947). Method of preparing thin sections. Compass of Sigma Gamma Epsilon, v. 24, no. 3, p. 174–180.

Gage, S. H. (1936). See Sec. L, Microscopy. [Chapter 12 on sectioning.]

Gille, F. (1952). Herstellung von Dünnschliffen und AnDünnschliffen, insbesondere von wasserempfindlichen Proben. N. Jahrb. Miner., Mh., H. 10, p. 277–287.

Glaessner, M. F. (1947). See Sec. M(1), Micropaleontology—General.

Goodman, A. J. (1956). Shortcuts in slide making. Alberta Soc. Petrol. Geol., J., v. 4, no. 1, p. 13–15, 23.

Gordon, W. T. (1926). The preparation of thin rock-sections. British Assoc. Adv. Sci., Rept., p. 348–349.

Granger, W. C. (1948). See Sec. M(2), Micropaleontology—Foraminifera.

Grayson, H. J. (1910). Modern improvements in rock section cutting apparatus. Roy. Soc. Victoria, Pr., n.s., v. 23, pt. 1, p. 65–81, 4 pls. [Reprinted in part in Roy. Micros. Soc., 1911, p. 703–709, 4 pls.

Hagn, Herbert (1953). A new method of preparing oriented thin sections of foraminifera and other small paleontologic specimens. Micropaleontologist, v. 7, no. 1, p. 34–43.

———— (1953). Ein neues Verfahren zur Anfertigung orientierter Dünnschliffe kleiner paläontologischer Objekte. Paläont. Zs., v. 24, no. 1–2, p. 26–31.

————, and K. W. Barthel (1956). Neuere Erfahrungen mit Polestar bei präparativen Arbeiten. Paläont. Zs., v. 30, no. 3–4, p. 207–212, illus.

Hallimond, A. F. (1954). Polishing mineral specimens. Miner. Mag., v. 91, no. 4, p. 208–210, illus.

———— (1956). Preparation of polished specimens. Miner. Mag., v. 95, no. 5, p. 271–276, illus.

———— (1961). Aluminum laps for polished sections. Miner. Mag., v. 32, no. 252, p. 738–739.

Hanna, M. A. (1927). A simple thin-section lap. J. Paleontology, v. 1, p. 219.

Heeger, W. (1913). Ueber die mikrochemische Untersuchung fein verteilter Carbonate im Gesteinsschliff. Zentralbl. Miner. Geol., Paleont., no. 2, p. 44–51.

Hendry, R. D., A. J. Rowell, and J. W. Stanley (1963). A rapid parallel grinding machine for serial sectioning of fossils. Palaeontology, v. 6, pt. 1, p. 145–147, 1 pl.

Hodson, Floyd, and Helen Hodson (1926). See Sec. M(2), Micropaleontology—Foraminifera.

Honda, Sakuro (1956). A method of thin section making for powder specimens. Japanese Assoc. Mineralogists, J., v. 40, no. 3, p. 130–131.

Honjo, Susumu (1960). A study of some primitive *Neoschwagerina* by a new serial section technique. J. Faculty Sci., Hokkaido Univ., ser. IV, Geol. and Miner., v. 10, no. 3, p. 457–470.

Huene, Rudolph von (1949). Notes on Lakeside no. 70 transparent cement. Am. Mineralogist, v. 34, p. 125–127.

Ikeda, S. (1961). How to make thin sections of rocks by hand. Nat. Sci. and Mus. (Tokyo, Natl. Sci. Mus.), v. 28, no. 9–10, p. 14–23. [In Japanese.]

Ireland, H. A. (1950). Curved surface section for microscopic study of calcareous rocks. Am. Assoc. Petrol. Geol., B., v. 34, no. 3, p. 1737–1739.

Jefferies, R. P. S., J. B. Adams, and R. C. Miller (1962). Automatic serial sectioning machine for fossils. Nature, v. 193, no. 4821, p. 1166–1167.

Keyes, I. W. (1962). A new instrument for the serial grinding of invertebrate fossils. New Zealand J. Geol. Geophys., v. 5, p. 46–54.

Keyes, M. G. (1925). Making thin sections of rocks. Am. J. Sci., 5th ser., v. 10, p. 538–550.

King, A. G. (1957). Technique for thinned polished sections. Am. Mineralogist, v. 42, no. 9–10, p. 689–694, illus.

Koslowski, Roman (1932). Sur un procédé simple et précis d'effectuer les coupes sérielles des fossiles. Paläont. Zs., v. 13, p. 316–318.

Kremp, Gerhard, and Walter Johst (1952). Einige Mikrofossilien des Oberkarbons und Verfahren zur Gewinnung von Schliffen solcher oft sehr harten Objekte. Germany, Geol. Landesanst., Geol. Jb., v. 66, p. 151–161.

———— (1952). Preparation of oriented sections of microfossils. Micropaleontologist, v. 7, no. 1, p. 29–33.

Krieger, P., and P. H. Bird (1932). Mounting polished surfaces in bakelite. Econ. Geol., v. 27, p. 675–678, 1 fig.

Kruk, P. (1951). Sporzadzanie phytek cienkich z utworów spykich. Préparation des plaques minces des roches non cohérantes et meubles. Polsk. Tow. Geol, Rocznik (Soc. Géol. Pologne, Ann.), v. 20 (1950), no. 1–2, p. 193–196, illus. [In Polish, with Russian and French summaries.]

Lang, A. J., Jr., and H. W. Smedes (1951). Preparation of large size thin sections. Am. J. Sci., v. 249, no. 9, p. 676–682, 1 pl., 3 figs.

Laude, P. P., R. G. Janes, and J. D. Boyd (1949). A simplified machine for making ground sections of teeth or bone. Anat. Rec., v. 104, no. 1, p. 11–15.

Leclercq, S. (1928). La méthode J. Walton pour la préparation des lames minces. Soc. Geol. Belg., Ann., v. 52, B. 10, p. 24–27.

Lees, Alan (1958). Etching techniques for use on thin sections of limestones. J. Sed. Petrol., v. 28, no. 2, p. 200–202, illus.

Levinson, S. A. (1950). A technique for sectioning microfossils. Science, v. 111, no. 2873, p. 60.

———— (1951). See Sec. M(6), Micropaleontology—Ostracods.

Lockwood, W. N. (1950). Impregnating sandstone specimens with thermosetting plastics for studies of oil-bearing formations. Am. Assoc. Petrol. Geol., B., v. 34, no. 10, p. 2061–2067, 4 figs.

Loeblich, A. R., Jr. (1940). A fine abrasive for use in thin-sectioning. J. Paleontology, v. 14, no. 4, p. 378.

Löffler, Karl (1952). Phtalopal G, ein neues synthetisches Einbettunsmittel. Geol., Berlin, Jahrg. 1, no. 5, p. 384–389.

Lorant, Michael (1950). Expansion method for micro-sectioning. Microscope, v. 8, no. 4, p. 94–97.

Mangin, J. P. (1953). See Sec. P(3), Photomicrography.

Mathews, R. D. (1945). A technique for simultaneous sectioning of foraminifera. J. Paleontology, v. 19, no. 6, p. 657–658.

McGugan, Alan (1959). Comments on "A simplified method of grinding foraminifera." Micropaleontology, v. 5, no. 1, p. 76.

McNair, A. H. (1938). The preparation of oriented thin sections and a method of cleaning small fossils. J. Paleontology, v. 12, p. 397–398.

Merrill, G. P. (1895). Directions for collecting rocks and for the preparation of thin sections. U. S. Natl. Mus., B. 39, pt. 1, p. 3–15, 17 figs. [p. 8–15 relevant.]

Meyer, Charles (1946). Notes on the cutting and polishing of thin sections. Econ. Geol., v. 41, p. 166–172.

Morkhoven, C. P. C. M. van (1958). A simplified method of grinding foraminifera. Micropaleontology, v. 4, no. 2, p. 209–210.

Muir-Wood, H. M. (1953). Techniques employed in grinding and illustrating serial transverse sections of fossil brachiopods. Ann. Mag. Nat. Hist., ser. 12, v. 6, no. 72, p. 919–922, illus.

Murata, K. J. (1935). A neglected method for making thin sections of fossils. J. Paleontology, v. 9, p. 359–361.

Murray-Hughes, R. (1935). Making thin sections, simplified method. Econ. Geol., v. 30, p. 192–193.

Nagappa, Y. (1954). See Sec. P(3), Photomicrography.

Ohtsuka, T. (1953). Study on preparing thin section of soft rocks in permeated synthetic resins under low pressure. J. Geol. Surv. Jap., B., v. 4, no. 7, p. 37–42.

Olsen, F. R., and F. C. Whitmore, Jr. (1944). Machine for serial sectioning of fossils. J. Paleontology, v. 18, no. 2, p. 210–215.

Penseler, W. H. A. (1932). The preparation of translucent sections of Waikato coal. New Zealand J. Sci., v. 13, p. 189–197.

Pessagno, E. A., Jr. (1960). Thin-sectioning and photographing smaller foraminifera. Micropaleontology, v. 6, no. 4, p. 419–423, 2 pls.

Reed, F. S., and J. L. Mergner (1953). Preparation of rock thin sections. Am. Mineralogist, v. 38, no. 11–12, p. 1184–1203, illus.

Ross., C. S. (1924). A method of preparing thin section of friable rock. Am. J. Sci., 5th ser., v. 7, p. 483–485.

——— (1926). Methods of preparation of sedimentary materials for study. Econ. Geol., v. 21, p. 454–468, 1 fig.

Sartory, P. K. (1949). An interesting slide repair. Quekett Micros. Club, J., ser. 4, v. 3, p. 58–59.

Sayles, R. W. (1921). Microscopic sections of till and stratified clay. Geol. Soc. America Bull., v. 32, p. 59–62, 3 figs.

Schaffer, R. J., and P. Hirst (1930). The preparation of thin sections of friable and weathered material by impregnation with synthetic resin. Geol. Assoc., v. 41, p. 32–43.

Schlossmacher, K. (1919). Ein Verfahren zur Herrichtung von schiefrigen und lockeren Gesteinen zum Dünnschleifen. Zentrbl. Miner., Geol., Paleont., p. 190–192, 1 fig.

Seilacher, A. (1962). Die Sphinctozoa, eine Gruppe fossiler Kalkschwämme. Abh. Mathem.-Naturwiss. Klasse der Akad. d. Wiss. u. d. Lit. (Mainz), Jahrg. 1961, nr. 10, p. 723–790 9 pls., 8 figs. [Sectioning.]

Shaub, B. M. (1936). A simple method of making, mounting, and filing polished sections. Econ. Geol., v. 31, no. 2, p. 212–218, 2 figs.

Simpson, G. G. (1933). A simplified serial sectioning technique for the study of fossils. Am. Mus., Nov., no. 364.

Sognnaes, R. F. (1947). Preparation of thin "serial" ground sections of whole teeth and jaws and other highly calcified and brittle structures. Anat. Rec., v. 99, no. 2, p. 133–144.

Sollas, W. J. (1903). A method for the investigation of fossils by serial sections. Roy. Soc. London, Philos. Tr., ser. B, v. 196, p. 259–265, 2 figs.

Thiessen, R., G. C. Sprunk, and H. J. O'Donnell (1938). Preparation of thin sections of coal. U. S. Bur. Mines Inform., Circ., no. 7021, p. 1–8.

Tolman, Frank (1929). A note on some refinements in the technique of making thin sections of Foraminifera. Micropaleontology, B., v. 1, no. 10, art. 39, p. 1–2.

Tourtelot, H. A. (1961). Thin sections of clay and shale. J. Sed. Petrology, v. 31, no. 1, p. 131–132.

Von Staff, H. (1910). Zur Herstellung der Dünnschliffe. Zoologica, v. 22, H. 58, p. 7–9.

Weatherhead, A. W. (1940). A new method for the preparation of thin sections of clays. Miner. Mag., v. 25, no. 169, p. 529–533, 1 fig.

Wentworth, C. K., and F. T. Suzuki (1936). Multiple grinding of thin-section chips. Am. J. Sci., ser. 5, v. 31, p. 93–96, 1 fig.

Weymouth, A. A. (1928). Simple methods for making thin sections. Econ. Geol., v. 23, p. 323–330.

Willden, C. R., and D. C. Arnold (1955) Spot grinding, a technique for finishing rock thin sections. Am. Mineralogist, v. 40, no. 3–4, p. 357–359.

Wood, Alan (1948). Sectioning small foraminifera. J. Paleontology, v. 22, no. 4, p. 530.

Wulff, R. (1916). Ein Beitrag zur Präparation fossiler Korallen. Zentralbl. Miner., Geol., Paleont., Jahrg. 1916, no. 18, p. 445–446.

Zdansky, Otto (1938). An improved apparatus for the serial sectioning of fossils. Science, n.s., v. 88, no. 2286, p. 385–386, 1 fig.

Zeidler, W. (1952). Die Verwendung von Zahnzement und Amalgamen als Einbettungsmittel für die Herstellung mikroskopischer Präparate. Germany, Geol. Landesanst., Geol. Jahrb., v. 66, p. 162–163.

Zirkl, E. J. (1953). Notiz über eine praktische Beschriftungsmethode für Dunnschliffe. Tschermaks Miner. Petrog. Mitt., F. 3, v. 3, H. 3, p. 282.

# H

## PEEL TECHNIQUES

Abbott, M. L. (1950). A paleobotanical transfer method. J. Paleontology, v. 24, no. 5, p. 619–621.

Abbott, R. E., and M. L. Abbott (1952). A simple paleobotanical transfer technique. Ohio J. Sci., v. 52, no. 5, p. 258–260.

Andrews, H. N., Jr. (1947). The peel or collodion film method; ancient plants. Comstock, Ithaca, N. Y., p. 114–115.

Appel, J. E. (1933). A film method for studying textures. Econ. Geol., v. 28, no. 4, p. 383–388.

Barnes, B., and H. Duerden (1930). On the preparation of celluloid transfers from rocks containing fossil plants. New Phytologist, v. 29, p. 74–76.

Bissell, H. J. (1957). See Sec. I, Staining.

Buehler, E. J. (1948). The use of peels in carbonate petrology. J. Sed. Petrol., v. 18, no. 2, p. 71–73.

Butler, A. J. (1935). Use of cellulose films in paleontology. Nature, v. 135, no. 3413, p. 510; Mus. J., London, v. 33, p. 235–236; v. 35, p. 111–112.

Darrah, W. C. (1936). The peel method in paleobotany. Harvard Univ., Bot. Mus. Leaflets, v. 4, no. 4, p. 69–83.

Dollar, A. T. J. (1942). Laminar moulds in cellulose acetate for the study of rock and mineral structures. Geol. Mag., v. 79, no. 4, p. 253–255.

——— (1943). Recording low relief in metallic surfaces by cellulose acetate moulds. Nature, v. 152, no. 3852, p. 248.

——— (1948). Recording crevices in plane surfaces by pigment fillings held in cellulose acetate moulds. Nature, v. 161, no. 4088, p. 358.

Duerden, H. (1931). On the preparation of cellulose films of fossil plants. Ann. Bot., v. 45, p. 376–378.

Dwivedi, J. N. (1959). Possibility of taking peel sections of silicified plant parts. Sci. Culture, v. 24, no. 10, p. 481–482.

Easton, W. H. (1942). See Sec. P(2), Illustrations—Photography.

Edmund, Gordon (1956). See Sec. P(2), Illustrations—Photography.

Fenton, M. A. (1935). Nitrocellulose sections of fossils and rocks. Am. Midl. Nat., v. 16, p. 410–412.

Graham, Roy (1933). Preparation of palaeobotanical sections by the peel method. Stain Tech., v. 8, p. 65–68.

Heezen, B. C., and G. L. Johnson III (1962). A peel technique for unconsolidated sediments. J. Sed., Petrol., v. 32, no. 3, p. 609–613.

Joy, K. W., A. J. Willis, and W. S. Lacey (1956). A rapid cellulose peel technique in palaeobotany. Ann. Bot., v. 20, no. 80, p. 635–637.

Kesling, R. V. (1957). See Sec. M(6), Micropaleontology—Ostracods.

Koenig, J. W. (1954). Application of cellulose peel technique to fenestrate sections. J. Paleontology, v. 28, no. 1, p. 76–78, illus.

Koopmans, R. G. (1929). Celluloidpreparat anstatt Dünnschliff. Geol. Bur. Nederl. Minjngeb., Jv., 1928, p. 131–132.

Lane, D. W. (1962). Improved acetate peel technique. J. Sed. Petrol., v. 32, no. 4, p. 870.

Lang, W. H. (1926). A cellulose-film transfer method in the study of fossil plants. Ann. Bot., v. 40, p. 710–711.

McCrone, A. W. (1963). Quick preparation of peel-prints for sedimentary petrography. J. Sed. Petrol., v. 33, no. 1, p. 228–230.

Mercier, Jean (1928). Application des empreintes à la celluloidine pour l'étude des Echinodermes fossiles. Soc. Linn. Normandie, B., ser. 8, v. 1, p. 129–132.

Miller, T. H., and R. M. Jeffords (1962). Some properties of acetate films used in peels. J. Paleontology, v. 36, no. 6, p. 1382–1383.

Miloradovich, B. V. (1940). A study of the microstructure of paleontological objects by the celluloid imprints method. Akad. Nauk S.S.S.R., B., sér. Géol., no. 4, p. 171–175, 1 pl. [In Russian, with English summary.]

Nathorst, A. G. (1907). Kollodiumaftrudk sasom hjälpmedel vid undersökning of fossila växter. Geol. Fören. Stockh. Förh., v. 29, p. 221–227.

——— (1908). Über die Anwendung von Kollodiumabdrucken bei der Untersuchung fossiler Pflanzen. Ark. Bot., v. 7, no. 4, p. 1–7.

Nicolesco, Constant (1918). Application des empreintes au collodion à la reproduction des cloisons des Ammonoides. Soc. Geol. Fr., B., ser. 4, 18, p. 217–221.

Noé, A. C. (1930). Celluloid films from coal balls. Bot. Gaz., v. 89, p. 318–319.

Sampson, D. N. (1949). See Sec. P(2), Illustrations—Photography.

Sternberg, R. M., and H. F. Belding (1942). Dry-peel technique. J. Paleontology, v. 16, no. 1, p. 135–136.

Taylor, T. N. (1962). The coal ball peel technique. Fast J., April-May, p. 5–6.

Toombs, H. A., and A. E. Rixon (1950). The use of plastics in the "transfer method" of preparing fossils. Mus. J., London, v. 50, no. 5, p. 105–107, 1 pl.

Troedsson, G. T. (1938). Voigt's Lackfilmmetod. Geol. Fören. Stockh. Förh., v. 60, H. 4, p. 646–648.

Voiht, Ehrhard (1933). Die Übertragung fossiler Wirbeltierleichen auf Zellulose-Filme, eine neue Bergungsmethode für Wirbeltiere aus der Braunkohle. Paläont. Zs., v. 15, p. 72–78, 3 figs.

———— (1936). Die Lackfilmmethode, ihre Bedeutung und Anwendung in der Paläontlogie, Sedimentpetrographie und Bodenkunde. Deutsche Geol. Ges., Zs., v. 88, H. 4, p. 272–292, 3 pls.

Walton, John (1923). See Sec. N, Paleobotany.

———— (1927). Recent developments in palaeobotanical technique. Cong. Av. Études Strat. Carbon., C. R., p. 749–754.

———— (1928). A method of preparing sections of fossil plants contained in coal balls or in other types of petrifaction. Nature, v. 122, no. 3076, p. 571.

———— (1928). Recent developments in palaeobotanical techniques. Cong. Av. Études Strat. Geol. Carbon. C. R. Geol. Mijnb. Gen. Ned. Liege, p. 749–754.

———— (1930). Improvements in the peel method of preparing sections of fossil plants. Nature, v. 125, no. 3150, p. 413–414.

———— (1952). Notes on the preparation and permanence of peel sections. Cong. Av. C. R., 3rd, v. 2, p. 651–653, illus.

———— (1953). Level table for use in preparation of peel sections. Int. Cong. Bot., Pr., 7th, Stockholm, p. 584–585.

————, and R. Koopmans (1928). Preparation of cellulose films and their use in making serial sections of coal ball plants. Rept. British Assn. at Glasgow, p. 615 and 688.

# I

## STAINING

Artusy, R. L., and J. C. Artusy (1956). The use of food coloring as a new technique for staining microfossils. J. Paleontology, v. 30, no. 4, p. 969.

Beckmann, Von Heinz (1959). Verunreiningung von Mikroproben beim Schlämmen. Paläont. Zs., v. 33, no. 1–2, p. 124.

Bissell, H. J. (1957). Combined preferential staining and cellulose peel technique. J. Sed. Petrol., v. 27, no. 4, p. 417–420.

Conn, H. J. (1929). Biological stains; a handbook on the nature and uses of the dyes employed in the biological laboratory. Geneva, N. Y., The Commission (on standardization of biological stains), 224 pp.

Deflandre, Georges (1935). Présence de microdiaclases dans les éclats de silex; leur importance dans les colorations artificielles des microfossiles et en particulier des forminiféres. Acad. Sci. Paris, C. R., v. 200, no. 11, p. 953–955.

Fairbanks, E. E. (1925). A modification of Lemberg's staining method. Am. Mineralogist, v. 10, p. 126–227.

Ferns, J. F. (1950). Standardized stains. Quekett Micros. Club, J. ser. 4, v. 3, p. 179–185.

Friedman, G. M. (1959). Identification of carbonate minerals by staining methods. J. Sed. Petrol., v. 29, no. 1, p. 87–97.

Gage, S. H. (1936). See Sec. L, Microscopy. [Chapter XII on staining.]

Hamblin, W. K. (1962). Staining and etching techniques for studying obscure structures in clastic rocks. J. Sed. Petrol., v. 32, no. 3, p. 530–533.

Henbest, L. G. (1930–31). The use of selective stains in paleontology. J. Paleontology, v. 5, p. 355–364; Abstract in Pan.-Am. Geol., v. 53, 1930, p. 156, and in Geol. Soc. Am., B., v. 41, 1930, p. 201.

Horn af Rantzien, Henning (1953). Staining and plastic embedding of small mineralized plant fossils. Nature v. 171, no. 4351, p. 516–517, illus.

Kosanke, R. M. (1945). Staining plant remains in calcareous coal balls. J. Paleontology, v. 19, no. 658.

Kraft, P. (1926). Eine neue Methode zür Entfarbung des rezenten und fossilen Chitins. Naturwissenschaften, 17 Jahrg., p. 85–86.

Levinson, S. A. (1951). The Triebel technique for staining ostracodes. Micropaleontologist, v. 5, no. 2, p. 27.

Mitchell, J. (1956). A note on a method of staining to distinguish between calcite and dolomite. Colonial Geol. Min. Res., v. 6, no. 2, p. 182.

Pantin, H. M. (1960). Dye-staining techniques for examination of sedimentary microstructures in cores. J. Sed. Petrol., v. 30, no. 2, p. 314–316.

Rodgers, John (1940). Distinction between calcite and dolomite on polished surfaces. Am. J. Sci., v. 238, no. 11, p. 788–798.

Vavrinova, Milada (1951). Investigation of the colouring methods and their use in distinguishing closely related species of Foraminifera. Ústřed. Ústav. Geol., Věstn., v. 26, p. 334–340.

Warne, S. St. J. (1962). A quick field or laboratory staining scheme for the differentiation of the major carbonate minerals. J. Sed. Petrol., v. 32, no. 1, p. 29–38.

Wolf, K. H., and S. St. J. Warne (1960). Remarks on the application of Friedman's staining methods. J. Sed. Petrol., v. 30, no. 3, p. 496–497.

# J

## X-RAY, INFRARED, AND ULTRAVIOLET LIGHT TECHNIQUES

Barber, E. J. (1932). Note on radiography of prehistoric bones. British J. Radiology, v. 5, p. 591.

Barbour, E. P. (1950). A study of the structure of fresh and fossil human bone by means of the electron microscope. Am. J. Phys. Anthrop., n.s., v. 8, no. 3, p. 315–328, 1 pl.

Barnard, J. E., and F. V. Welch (1936). See Sec. L, Microscopy.

Bataller, J. R. (1933). Los rayos X y las investigaciones paleontológicas. Ibérica, Añ. 20, v. 40, no. 1004, p. 366–368, 5 figs.

Bertnistle, A. P. (1932). Prehistoric bones. British J. Radiology, v. 5, p. 589–591.

Boni, Alfredo (1939). Radiografie di fossili particolarmente di brachiopodi. Soc. Geol. Italiana, Bull., v. 57, f. 3, p. 265–286, 1 pl.

—— (1940) Fluorescenze di fossili eccitate con luce visible. Riv. Italiana Paleont., v. 46, f. 3–4, p. 61–71, 1 Taf.

Branco, W. (1906). Die Anwendung der Röntgenstrahlen in der palaeontologie. K. Preuss. Akad. Wiss. phys.-mat. Kl., Abh., p. 1–55, 4 pls.

Brumberg, E. M. (1946) See Sec. L, Microscopy.

Clark, Walter (1946). See Sec. P(2), Illustrations—Photography.

Combee, B., J. Houtman, and A. Recourt (1955). A sealed-off X-ray tube for contact-microradiography. British J., Radiology, v. 28, no. 334, p. 537.

Dake, H. C., and Jack DeMent (1941). Fluorescent light and its applications. Chemical Publishing, New York, xi + 256 pp.

Debeauvais, M., et al. (1954). Über die Lokalisierung von Wismut in Gesteinen mit Kernemulsionsplatten. Tschermaks Miner. Petrog. Mitt., F. 3, v. 5, H. 1–2, p. 129–136, illus.

Drevermann, Fritz (1927). Versteinerungen in ultraviolettem Licht. Senckenberg. Naturf. Ges., Natur. u. Museum, v. 57, p. 193–201, 6 figs.

Duval, A. G. (1949). Application des rayons X à l'étude des structures internes des Echinides actuels et fossiles et en particulier à quelques espèces du genre *Scutella* Lamarck 1816. Mus. natl. d'Hist. Nat., Bull., ser. 2, v. 21, p. 399–407.

Engström, Arne (1956). Stereoscopic techniques in X-ray microscopy, *in* Physical techniques in biological research (ed. by Gerald Oster and A. W. Pollister), Academic Press, New York, v. 3, p. 503–508, 6 figs., 1 table.

Field, R. M. (1915). The use of the Roentgen ray in paleontology; skiagraphy of fossils. Am. J. Sci., ser. 4, v. 39, p. 543–550.

Fischer, E. (1914). Zur Anwendung der Röntgenstrahlen in der Paläontologie. Naturf. Ges. Mitt., v. 4, p. 1–8.

Fonton, M. E. de, Rodger Michaud, and Guy Périnet (1951). Étude par diffraction des rayons X de la fossilisation d'ossements préhistoriques. Acad. Sci. Paris, C. R., v. 233, p. 706–707.

Fournier, Fernand (1954). Les microtechniques utilisant les rayons x. Soc. Franç. Minér., Bull., v. 77, no. 4–6, p. 741–747, illus.

Goby, P. (1913). New application of the X-rays; microradiography. Roy. Micros. Soc., J., pt. 4, p. 373–375.

Haas, Fritz (1934). Neue Landschnecken des Senckenberg-Museums. Senckenbergiana, v. 16, no. 2–3, p. 94–98, 16 figs. [Ultraviolet light.]

Hamblin, W. K. (1962). X-ray radiography in the study of structures in homogeneous sediments. J. Sed. Petrol., v. 32, no. 2, p. 201–210.

Hanzawa, S. (1935). Study of fossils in ultraviolet ray. Geol. Soc. Japan J., v. 42, no. 506, p. 733–735, 1 fig. [In Japanese.]

Harris, J. E., and E. Latham (1951). See Sec. P(2), Illustrations—Photography.

728                          *Bibliography on Paleontological Techniques*

Hartman-Weinberg, A., and S. A. Reinberg (1925). Die fossilhaltigen Gesteins-formationen in Röntgenbilde. Akad nauk S.S.S.R., Bull., p. 279–292, 2 pls.

Hedley, R. H. (1957). Microradiography applied to the study of foraminifera. Micropaleontology, v. 3, no. 1, p. 19–28.

Hooper, Kenneth (1959). X-ray absorption techniques applied to statistical studies of foraminifera polulations. J. Paleontology, v. 33, no. 4, p. 631–640.

Johnson, B. K. (1931). See Sec. L, Microscopy.

Kalabis, Vladimír (1935). Roentgenovy x paprsky v paleontologii. Příroda, roč. 28, č. 9, p. 274–278, 3 figs. [In Czech, with German summary.]

Klinger, F. E. (1934). Erfahrungen bei Mikroaufnahmen von Kohlendünnschliffen mit ultraroten Strahlen. Montanistische Rundschau; Berlin, Vienna, Jahrg. 26, no. 14, 4 pp. 9 figs.

Lambert, J. M. (1906). Étude sur les échinides da la molasse de Vence. Soc. lettr., sci. arts Alpes maritimes, Ann., v. 20, p. 57–61.

Lambrecht, Kalman (1928). Die Verwendung der Fluorographie in der paläon-tologishen Forshung. Zool-bot. Ges. Wien, Verhandl., v. 78, p. 62–70, 3 figs.

———— (1928). Fluorographische Beobachtungen an den "elastischen Fasern" des Pterosaurier-Patagiums. Arch. Mus. Teyler, ser. 3, v. 6, p. 40–50, 2 pls.

———— (1928). Die Verwendung der Flurographie in der paläontologischen Forschung. Zool.-bot. Ges., Verh., v. 78, p. 62–70, 3 figs.

Lehmann, W. M. (1937). Neue Entdeckungen in alter Museumschatzen. Rönt-gendurchleuchtung von Versteinerungen des Hunsruckschiefers. Die Umschau (Frankfort), Jahrg. 25, p. 1–5 (of reprint), 8 figs.

———— (1934). Röntgenuntersuchung von *Asteropyge* sp. Broili aus dem rhein-schen Unterdevon. N. Jahrb. Miner., Geol., Paleont., v. 72, Abt. B., p. 1–14, 1 pl., 2 figs.

———— (1938). Die Anwendung der Röntgenstrahlen in der Paläontologie. Oberrhein. Geol. Ver., Jber. Mitt., N. F., v. 27, p. 16–24, 6 pls.

———— (1939). Neue Beobachtungen an Versteinerungen aus dem Hunsrück-schiefer. K. Preuss. Akad. Wiss., mat.-naturw. Kl., Abh., no. 13, p. 1–17, 7 pls.

———— (1951). Neue Beobachtungen an Lunaspis. N. Jahrb. Geol. Paleont., Abh., v. 94, p. 93–100, 2 pls. 3 figs. [X-rays.]

Lemoine, M. (1896). De l'application des rayons Röntgen à l'étude des ossements fossiles des environs de Reims. Soc. Biol. C. R., ser. 10, v. 3, no. 48, p. 878–881.

Maier, Dorothea, and Walter Wetzel (1958). Fluoreszenzmikroskopie geologischer und paläontologischer Objekte. Zeiss-Mitt. Fortschr. technisch. Optik, v. 1, p. 127–131, 6 figs. [In color.]

Maresh, Charles (1953). See Sec. P(3), Illustrations—Photomicrography.

Michaud, R., and G. Périnet (1950). Étude de la fossilisation des ossements préhistoriques par la diffraction des rayons X. Minist. Educ. nation., Centre Rech. Sci. Industr. Marit. Marseille, Note, no. 233, 13 pp., 2 pls.

Miethe, A., and A. Born (1928). Die Fluorographie von Fossilien. Paläont., Zs., v. 9, H. 4, p. 343–356, 6 pls.

Miranda, Raúl de (1945). Os raios x e a estrutura dos fósseis. Coimbra Univ., mus. miner. e geol., Publ; Mem. Not., no. 16, p. 43–46, 1 photo.

Moss, A. A. (1954). The application of X-rays, gamma rays, ultra-violet and infra-red rays to the study of antiquities. London Mus. Assoc., Handbook for Museum Curators, part B, sec. 7, 16 pp., 8 pls., 1 fig.

Mutschke, F. (1953). Infrarot-Aufnakmen von Fossilien. Naturwiss. Rundschau, fg. 6, no. 2, p. 74–75, 4 figs.

Niggli, Ernst, C. J. Overweel, and I. M. van der Vlerk (1953). An X-ray crystallographical application of the fluorine-dating method of fossil bones. K. Akad. Wetens., Pr., ser. B., v. 56, no. 5, p. 538–542.

Putnam, Brenda (1947). Animal X-rays; A skeleton key to comparative anatomy. Putnam, New York, 96 pp.

Radley, J. A., and J. Grant (1933). Fluorescence analysis in ultraviolet light. Van Nostrand, New York, 219 pp. [p. 156–157, note on study and photography of fossils by ultraviolet fluorescence.]

Roger, Jean (1947). Sur l'application des rayons aux études paléontologiques. Mus. natl. d'Hist. nat., Bull., v. 19, no. 1, 2, p. 118–120, 224–229.

——— (1947). Paléontologie et rayons X. Acad. Sci. Paris, C. R., v. 225, no. 17, p. 757–759.

——— (1947). Résultats fournis par l'application des rayons X à la paléontologie. Soc. Géol. Fr., Bull., ser. 5, v. 17, p. 483–491, 4 pls.

Schmidt, R. A. M. (1946). Application of X-rays to paleontology. Geol. Soc. America, B, v. 57, no. 12, pt. 2, p. 1228. [Abstract.]

——— (1948). Radiographic methods in paleontology; a progress report. Am. J. Sci., v. 246, p. 615–627.

——— (1952). Microradiography of microfossils with X-ray diffraction equipment. Science, v. 115, p. 94–95.

Swartz, J. H. (1928). Some X-ray studies of fossils. Elisha Mitchell Sci. Soc., J., v. 44, p. 22. [Abstract.]

Trillat, J. J., and J. Roger (1947). L'utilisation des rayons X en paléontologie. Rev. Sci., an. 85, f. 6, no. 3270, p. 335–342, illus.

Wagner, E. (1928). Zur Fluorographie von Fossilien. Ein neues und einwandfreies Glasfilter. Paläont. Zs., v. 10, p. 298.

Walker, J. J., and L. Slater (1935). See Sec. P(2), Illustrations—Photography.

Walton, John (1935). See Sec. P(2), Illustrations—Photography.

Young, R. S. (1954). Preliminary X-ray investigation of solid hydrocarbons. Am. Assoc. Petrol. Geol., Bull., v. 38, no. 9, p. 2017–2020, illus.

Zangerl, Rainer (1948). The use of X-rays in the study of fossils. Non-destructive testing. J. Geology, p. 29–31.

# K

## CASTING AND MOLDING

Afford, A. E. (1928). A method for making small rubber articles for laboratory use. Science, v. 107, no. 2786, p. 552.

Baird, Donald (1951). Latex molds in paleontology. Compass of Sigma Gamma Epsilon, v. 28, no. 4, p. 339–345.

——— (1955). Latex micro-molding and latex-plaster molding mixture. Science, v. 122, no. 3161, p. 202.

Bather, F. A. (1926). Plaster casts *in* A cargo of notions. Mus. J. London, v. 25, p. 278–280.

Battetta, J. (1947). Constitution de collections paléontologiques, préhistoriques, ethnographiques par un procédé simplifié de moulage. Soc. Linn. Lyon, Bull. mens., v. 16, p. 147–150.

Bell, J. F. (1939). Notes on the uses of methyl methacrylate "Lucite" in a geological laboratory. Econ. Geol., v. 34, p. 804–811.

Boardman, E. T. (1950). Technique of life casting of small vertebrates. Mus. News, v. 28, no. 11, p. 7–8.

Bowsher, A. L., and W. J. Greer, Jr. (1948). Mounting fossil specimens in plastic. Compass of Sigma Gamma Epsilon, v. 25, no. 2, p. 68–70.

Clarke, C. D. (1938, 1940). Molding and casting. Lucas, Baltimore, 308 pp.

Conkin, J. E. (1956). Plastic spray in laboratory and field. J. Sed. Petrol., v. 26, no. 1, p. 68.

Cooper, G. A. (1933). A method for the preparation of fossils. Science, n.s., v. 77, no. 394. [Paraffin mounting.]

Feiss, J. W. (1926). Casting invertebrate fossils in sealing wax and type metal. Geol. Soc. America, Bull., v. 37, no. 1, p. 235. [Abstract.]

Fischer, Alfred (1939). Rubber casts and molds of fossils. J. Paleontology, v. 13, no. 6, p. 621.

Fuehrer, O. F. (1938). Liquid rubber, a new casting medium. Mus. News, v. 15, no. 16, p. 7.

———— (1939). Liquid rubber as an enlarging medium. Mus. News, v. 16, no. 14, p. 8.

Garner, M. R. (1953). The preparation of latex casts of soil cavities for the study of tunneling activities of animals. Science, v. 118, no. 3066, p. 380–381.

Gill, E. D., K. E. Caster, and P. C. R. Boswell (1956). Simple apparatus for vacuum injection of moulding latex. Austral. J. Sci., v. 18, no. 6, p. 198–199.

Hagerman, Tor, and Lennart Nyström (1952). Impregnering av porösa material med plast för mikroundersökningar. Geol. Fören. Stockh. Förh., v. 74, p. 212–217, 3 figs.

Hasluck, P. N. (1908). Clay modelling and plaster casting. Cassell, London, 106 pp.

Jensen, J. A. (1961). A new casting medium for use in flexible and rigid molds. Curator, v. 4, no. 1, p. 76–90, 12 figs.

Keyes, I. W. (1959). Paleontological casting and moulding techniques. New Zealand J. Geol. and Geophysics, v. 2, no. 1, p. 56–65, 10 figs.

Lawson, P. F. (1952). Plastics in the museum. Art Galleries Mus. Assoc. Australia and New Zealand, News Bull., Jan., no. 6, p. 9–13.

Leclercq, Suzanne, and M. Discry (1950). De l'utilisation du Plastique en paléontologie végétale. Soc. Géol. Belg., Ann., v. 72, B, no. 3–7, p. 151–155.

Moore, B. P., and B. J. Southgate (1953). Embedding specimens in methyl methacrylate; a new cold-casting technique. Mus. J., London, v. 53, p. 219–222.

Muñoz Amor, Joaquín (1952). Un nuevo méthodo de reproducciones plásticas con fines paleontológicos. Inst. Geol. Min., España Not. Com., no. 27, p. 159–167.

Newark Museum Association (1931). Making a durable modeling material. The Mus. (Newark Mus. Assoc.), p. 182–183.

Peyer, Bernhard (1949). Galvanoplastische Nachbildungen von Fossilien. Schweiz. Naturf. Ges., Verh., v. 129, p. 142.

Purves, P. E., and R. S. J. Martin (1950). Some developments in the use of plastics in museum technology. Mus. J., London, v. 49, p. 293.

Quinn, J. H. (1940). Rubber molds and plaster casts in the paleontological laboratory. Field Mus. Nat. Hist., Tech. Ser., no. 6, 21 pp., 7 figs.

—— (1940). Use of latex in paleontology. Mus. News, v. 18, no. 9.

—— (1940). Latex in paleontology, *in* The rubber age, v. 47, no. 4, Palmerton, New York.

—— (1952). Concerning rubber molds and plaster casts. Soc. Vert. Paleont., News Bull., no. 36, p. 28.

—— (1957). Mud matrix for rubber molds. Soc. Vert. Paleont. News Bull., no. 49, p. 31.

Rasetti, Franco (1944). Moulage en métal de petits fossiles. Assoc. Can.-Franc. Av. Sci., Ann., v. 10, p. 81.

—— (1947). Notes on techniques in invertebrate paleontology. J. Paleontology, v. 21, p. 397–399. [Metal casting.]

Rau, Reinhold (1955). Abformen von Naturkörpern mit Latex-Gummi. Nat. Volk, v. 85, H. 10, p. 321–326.

St. Joseph, J. K. S. (1938). The Pentameracea of the Oslo region. Norsk Geol. Tidsskrift, v. 17, H. 4, p. 225–336. [Beeswax models.]

Schlossmacher, K. (1919). Ein Verfahren zur Herrichtung von schiefrigen und lockeren Gesteinen zum Dünnschleifen. Zentralb. Miner., Geol., Paleont., p. 190–192, 1 fig.

Sella, Emil (1951). Plastics and other media in museum exhibits. Mus. News, v. 29, no. 3, p. 4–6.

Shrock, R. R. (1940). "Lucite" as an aid in studying hard parts of living and fossil animals. J. Paleontology, v. 14, no. 1, p. 86–88.

Slocum, A. W. (1907). New processes of taking impressions of natural molds of fossils. Science, n.s., v., 25, no. 641, p. 591–592.

Ståhl, Eric (1951). A new casting-method for paleontological purposes, *in* V. Jaanusson, Brachiopoda from the Tertiary Nahuel Huapi formation of the Patagonian Cordillera. Uppsala Univ., Miner.-Geol. Inst., B, v. 34, no. 7.

—— (1956). A casting-method for palaeontological purposes. Uppsala Univ., Miner.-Geol. Inst., Bull. v. 36, pt. 4, p. 285–295, illus.

Steedman, H. F. (1953). A new modelling medium. Mus. J., London, v. 53, p. 199–200.

Tugby, D. J., and P. C. R. Boswell (1953). A new method for making internal cranial casts. Austral. J. Sci., v. 15, no. 5, p. 154–158.

Unwin, Max (1950). New plastic for the taking of impressions. Mus. J., London, v. 50, no. 7, p. 155.

—— (1951). A new moulding jelly. Mus. J., London, v. 50, no. 11, p. 267.

—— (1951). The uses of plastics and other new materials in archaeology. Archaeol. Newsletter, v. 3, no. 11, p. 175–178.

Verniory, René (1957). Utilisation des mouillants cationiques en micropaléontologie. Arch. Sci., v. 10, f. 1, p. 116–125.

Vernon, R. O. (1957). New technique for casting fossils and forming molds. J. Paleontology, v. 31, no. 2, p. 461–463.

White, Charles (1891). A new method of infiltrating osseous and dental tissues. Roy. Micros. Soc., J., p. 307–308.

Whittard, W. F., and J. E. Sisson (1940). Phenolformaldehyde resin as a casting material. Geol. Mag., v. 77, no. 6, p. 478–481.

Ward's Natural Science Establishment (1950). How to embed in Bioplastic. Ward's Bull., 20 pp.


# L

## MICROSCOPY

Adams, J. W. (1954). A simple microspectroscope. Am. Miner., v. 39, no. 3–4, p. 393–394, illus.

Anderson, F. W. (1956). L'application des techniques microscopiques à l'étude d'échantillons de sondages. Rev. Ind. Minér., num. spéc. 1R, p. 415–424, illus.

Barnard, J. E., and F. V. Welch (1936). Fluorescence microscopy with high powers. Roy. Micros. Soc., J., ser. 3, v. 56, p. 361–364, 1 pl., 1 fig.

——— (1936). Microscopy with ultra-violet light. A simplification of method. Roy. Micros. Soc., J., ser. 3, v. 56, p. 365–371, 2 pls., 4 figs.

——— (1937). The principles of fluorescence microscopy. Roy. Micros. Soc., J., ser. 3, v. 57, p. 256–259.

Belling, John (1930). The use of the microscope; a handbook for routine and research work. McGraw-Hill, New York, xi + 315 pp., 28 figs.

Brumberg, E. M. (1946). A microscope for visual colour microscopy in the ultra-violet rays. Akad. Nauk S.S.S.R., C. R., v. 52, p. 499–502.

Burkhardt, P., and J. G. Helmcke (1954). Der Elmigraph 1, Ein Photogrammetrisches Auswertgerät mit Selbstkartierung fur Electronenmikroskopische Stereoaufnahmen. Int. Conf. Elect. Mic., Pr., London, p. 651.

Chamot, E. M. and C. W. Mason (1938). Handbook of chemical microscopy. Wiley, New York, 2nd ed., v. 1, 478 pp., 165 figs.

Corrington, J. D. (1941). Working with the microscope. Whittlesey House, London, and McGraw-Hill, New York, 418 pp., 121 figs.

Cowan, R. S. (1947). A mirror device for studying lower surfaces of small objects using a dissecting microscope. Science, v. 105, p. 555–556.

Cullison, J. S. (1934). A suitable tray for comparative examination of minute opaque objects under the binocular microscope. J. Paleontology, v. 8, no. 2, p. 247.

Deflandre, Georges, and C. Fert (1953). Application du microscope electronique à l'étude des coccolithophoridés; technique et résultats liminaires. Soc. Hist. nat. Toulouse, Bull., v. 88, f. 3–4, p. 301–312.

Dixon, H. H. (1953). Use of reflected light in the examination of fossils. Nature, v. 135, no. 3423, p. 958, 1 fig.

Duijn, C. van, Jr. (1948). A simple opaque illuminator. Microscope, v. 7, no. 3, p. 75–76, 1 photo, 1 fig.

Dupuis, Roger (1952). Un nouveau projecteur à l'usages multiples. Cahiers géol., no. 15, p. 121–122, illus.

———— (1951). Un nouvel instrument d'optique cristalline. Cahiers géol., no. 4, p. 37–40, illus.

———— (1953). Microprojecteur à trois objectifs. Cahiers géol., no. 19, p. 161–162, illus.

Frederickson, A. F. (1954). A method of effectively increasing the resolving power of a microscope to reveal unsuspected detail in thin sections. Am. Mineralogist, v. 38, 1953, no. 9–10, p. 815–526, illus.; discussion by B. F. Strengham and E. W. Roedder with title, Occurrence of "Channels" in thin sections, v. 39, 1954, no. 3–4, p. 384–386; reply by author, p. 386–390, illus.

Freund, Hugo, ed. (1952). Handbuch der Mikroskopie in der Technik; Band II, Mikroskopie der Bodenschätze, Teil 1, Mikroskopie der Steinkohle, des Kokses und der Braunkohle: Umschau Verlag, Frankfurt, 759 pp., illus.

Fritz-Gaertner, R. (1878). The preparation of rocks and fossils for microscopical examination. Am. Naturalist, v. 12, p. 219–225.

Gage, S. H. (1917). The microscope; an introduction to microscopic methods and to histology (12th ed.). Comstock, Ithaca, N.Y., 472 pp. (later editions up to 17th ed.).

———— (1936). The microscope (16th ed.). Comstock, Ithaca, N.Y., 617 pp.

Goldman, M. I. (1925). Testing and adjusting the binocular microscope and suggestions on the use of microscopes in general. Am. Assoc. Petrol. Geol., Bull., v. 9, p. 175–180.

Gysin, Marcel (1952). Sur un petit perfectionnement apporté au microscope polarisant à lumière réfléchie. Arch. Sci., v. 5, f. 3, p. 179–180, illus.

Hanna, G. D. (1931). The adjustment of low power binocular microscopes. Micropaleont. Bull., v. 3, no. 1, p. 1–3, 2 figs.

———— (1937). An illuminator for opaque objects. Roy. Micros. Soc., J., ser. 3, v. 57, p. 11–14.

Harding, J. P., and C. C. H. Washtell (1950). The Labgear-Harding micro-dissector. Quekett Micros. Club, J., ser. 4, v. 3, p. 89–92.

Hartridge, H. (1950). The visual perception of the colours of microscopic objects. Quekett Micros. Club, J., ser. 4, v. 3, p. 163–170.

Hegre, E. S., and R. F. Blount (1945). A chin-operated focus adjustment for the dissecting microscope. Science, v. 101, no. 2614, p. 126–127.

Hewitt, P. C. (1954). An inexpensive microscope illuminator. Am. Mineralogist, v. 39, no. 7–8, p. 664–667, illus.

Holmes, A. (1921). Petrographic methods and calculations. Murby, London, 515 pp. 4 pls., 83 figs.

Johnson, B. K. (1931). Notes on ultra-violet microscopy. Roy. Micros. Soc., J., v. 51, p. 268–271, 4 pls.

Kooman, A. (1951). Über die Messung mikroskopischer Objekte, speziell zur Verwendung bei Kerninhaltsbestimmungen. Zs. Wiss. Mikros., v. 60, H. 1–2, p. 16–25.

Kufferath, A. (1937). Die Mikroskopiertechnik der Gegenwart im Dienste der geologischen Forschung. Zs. prakt. Geol., Jg. 45, H. 4, p. 60–64, 4 figs.

Lamar, J. E. (1929). A simple accessory stage for the microscope. J. Paleontology, v. 3, p. 185–188.

Leclercq, Suzanne (1933). Application de la lumière infrarouge à l'étude micro-scopique des végétaux fossiles. Soc. Géol. Belg., Ann., v. 56, p. 351–356.

Locquim, Marcel (1942). Extension aux coupes optiques des méthodes de recon-struction graphique en technique microscopique: Soc. Linn. Lyon, Bull., Mens., 11th an., no. 9, p. 143–144.

Maniéro, Jordano (1951). O microscópio electrônico como novo recurso da geologica. Acad. Brasil. Sci., An., v. 23, no. 1, p. 135–138, illus.

McLean, J. D., Jr. (1951). Comparison microscope—a tool with unique possi-bility. Am. Assoc. Petrol. Geol., Bull., v. 35(1), p. 96–101.

Metzner, P. (1930). Einfache Einrichtungen zur Fluoreszenzmikroskopie und Fluoreszenzmikrophotographie. Biol. Generalis, v. 6, p. 415–432, 4 pls., 5 figs.

Mickey, G. H. (1950). Foot focusing device for binocular dissecting microscope. Stain Tech., v. 25, p. 217–218.

Nygaard, Gunnar (1949). A simple micromanipulator. Science, v. 110, no. 2850, p. 165–166.

Pierce, R. L. (1959). Converting coordinates for microscope-stage scales. Micro-paleontology, v. 5, no. 3, p. 377–378.

Porter, J. J. (1962). Electron microscopy of sand surface texture. J. Sed. Petrol., v. 32, no. 1, p. 124–135.

Rosenblum, Sam (1954). Rotating stage for projecting rock thin sections in polarized light. Geol. Soc. Am., Bull., v. 65, no. 7, p. 713–714, illus.

Rosenfeld, M. A. (1954). A modification of the Chayes point counter stage. Am. Mineralogist, v. 39, no. 9–10, p. 834–836, illus.

Schenck, E. T. (1932). See Sec. M(1), Micropaleontology—General.

Schneiderhohn, H., Paul Randohr, et al. (1934). Lehrbuch der Erzmikroskopie. Borntraeger, Berlin, v. 1, H. 1, xi + 312 pp., 2 pls., 145 figs.

Scott, T. L. (1944). New lamps for old. Microscope, v. 5, no. 7, p. 166–171, 3 photos, 2 figs. [Lamps for direct lighting with microscope.]

——— (1948). Plastic light conductors. Microscope, v. 7, no. 4, p. 87–91, 2 figs.

Stach, Erich (1949). Lehrbuch der Kohlenmikroskopie. Volume 1: Kettwig. Glückauf, Essen, 285 pp., 50 figs.

Thompson, I. M. (1926). A simple improvised dissecting microscope. Anat. Rec., v. 34, p. 37–40, 1 fig.

Tolansky, S. (1952). A high-resolution surface-profile microscope. Nature, v. 169, no. 4298, p. 445–446.

Traverse, Alfred (1960). Still more on conversion of microscope coordinates. Micropaleontolgy, v. 6, no. 4, p. 424.

Voigt, Ehrhard (1950). Mikroskopische Untersuchungen an fossilen tierischen Weichteilen und ihre Bedeutung für Systematik und Paläobiologie. Deutsch. Geol. Ges., Zs., v. 101, p. 99–104.

Wesley, A. (1954). A short synopsis of some microscopical methods in palaeo-botany. Leeds Phil. Lit. Soc., Pr., Sci. Sec., v. 6, pt. 3, p. 168–179, illus.

Wise, F. C. (1949). The development of the binocular microscope. Quekett Micros. Club, J., ser. 4, v. 2, no. 6, p. 305–321.

Wishart, G., and T. H. Stovell (1948). A portable light for a dissecting micro-scope. Science, v. 108, no. 2793, p. 46.

Wright, H. G. S. (1948). A home-made binocular body. Microscope, v. 7, no. 4, p. 94–96, 2 figs.

Young, M. R. (1961). Principles and techniques of fluorescence microscopy. Quart. J. Micros. Sci., v. 102, p. 419–449, 4 pls., 3 figs.

# M (1)

## MICROPALEONTOLOGY—GENERAL

Anderson, Lee, and Ervin Hoffman (1963). Concentration of microfaunal samples by the use of a Syntron. Micropaleontology, v. 9, no. 1, p. 105–106.

Anderson, R. Y. (1958). A micromanipulator for single-mounting fossils. Micropaleontology, v. 4, no. 2, p. 205–206.

Arnold, Z. M. (1955). The construction and use of a simple die for plastic micropaleontological slides. Micropaleontology, v. 1, no. 4, p. 365–367.

——— (1958). See Sec. G, Sectioning.

Artusy, R. L., and J. C. Artusy (1956). See Sec. I, Staining.

Baker, W. H. V. (1951). A simple technique for extracting microfossils. Micropaleontologist, v. 5, no. 4, p. 39–40.

Barghoorn, E. S. (1947). Use of phenol formaldehyde and vinyl resins in sealing liquid mounting media on microscope slides. Science, v. 106, no. 2752, p. 299–300.

Bartenstein, Helmut (1953). See Sec. C, Storage.

Beckmann, Heinz (1950). Eine einfache Schlämm-Einrichtung für Gesteine mit hohen Rückständen. Senckenbergiana, v. 31, p. 355–356, 1 fig.

——— (1951). See Sec. G, Sectioning.

——— (1952). See Sec. F, Preparation.

Berry, Willard (1931). See Sec. G, Sectioning.

Bolli, Hans (1950). See Sec. F, Preparation.

——— (1952). See Sec. F, Preparation.

Boltovskoy, Esteban (1953). Über Zersetzungserscheinungen bei mikro-paläontologischem Sammlungsmaterial. Paläont. Zs., v. 27, no. 3–4, p. 237–240.

Bourdon, M. (1956). See Sec. F, Preparation.

Brooks, H. K. (1954). A method for removing platy fragments of fossils and minerals from microfossil concentrates. Micropaleontologist, v. 8, no. 4, p. 39–40.

Brotzen, F. (1950). Methods and techniques in routine work; separating and washing; fractionation. Micropaleontologist, v. 4, no. 2, p. 18–20.

Campbell, C. B. (1951). The Campbell micro-fossil washer. Iowa Acad. Sci. Pr., v. 58, p. 275–277.

Carter, J. F. (1955). A technique in the study of microfossils. Compass, v. 33, no. 1, p. 18–20.

Chamney, T. P. (1957). See Sec. F, Preparation.

Cohee, G. V. (1937). Inexpensive equipment for reclaiming heavy liquids. J. Sed. Petrol., v. 7, no. 1, p. 34–35, 1 fig.

Colenutt, G. W. (1941). A method for obtaining clean residues from fossiliferous clays and marl. Geologists' Assoc. Pr., v. 52, p. 194–197.

Craig, G. Y., and J. Hogg (1962). A rapid sorting device for microfossils. Micropaleontology, v. 8, no. 1, p. 107–108.

Crowley, A. J. (1952). See Sec. F, Preparation.

Cummings, R. H. (1950). See Sec. G, Sectioning.

———— (1952). Development in micropaleontological techniques. J. Paleont., v. 26, p. 123.

———— (1956). See Sec. P(3), Illustrations—Photomicrography.

Cuvillier, Jean (1945). La micropaléontologie; ses méthodes, ses buts, ses résultats. Assoc. Franc. av. sci., C. R., Paris, v. 64, no. 3, p. 30–31.

Dahl, Eilif (1951). On the composition of "Viscol" and the employment of gum arabic for mounting media. Stain Tech., v. 26, no. 2, p. 97–101.

Deflandre, Georges (1935). Technique micropaléontologique appliquée à l'étude des silex: Soc. franç. Micros., Bull., v. 4, p. 104–111.

———— (1935). See Sec. I, Staining.

————, and M. O. Deflandre-Rigaud (1943). Constitution et différentiation d'un fichier micropaléontologique général. Soc. Géol. Fr. C. R. somm., p. 186–188.

Driver, H. L. (1928). See Sec. F, Preparation.

———— (1931). Sample washer. Micropaleont. Bull., v. 2, no. 4, p. 76–79, 1 pl.

Dunn, P. H. (1933). See Sec. F, Preparation.

Eckert, R., W. W. Hay, G. Lorenz, and P. Vogt (1961). The magnetic separator as a tool in micropaleontology. J. Paleontology, v. 35, no. 4, p. 876.

Edwards, A. R. (1963). A preparation technique for calcareous nannoplankton. Micropaleontology, v. 9, no. 1, p. 103–104.

Ellis, B. F. (1948). The universal stage and the sorting stage. Micropaleontologist, v. 2, no. 4, p. 22.

———— (1949). A new mounting device. Micropaleontologist, v. 3, no. 1, p. 23.

Ellison, S. P., Jr. (1954). Television microscopy for micropaleontology. Cushman Lab. Foram. Res. Contr., v. 5, pt. 3, p. 106.

Fisher, J. C. (1962). Laboratory reagents as a possible source of microfossil contamination. Micropaleontology, v. 8, no. 4, p. 508.

Franke, Adolf (1922). Die Präparation von Foraminiferen und anderen mikroskopischen Tierresten, *in* Konrad Keilhack, Lehrbuch der praktischen Geologie, Stuttgart, v. 2, p. 509–533.

———— (1927). Neuere Erfahrungen über die Präparation und Aufbewahrung von Mikrofossilien. Paläont. Zs., v. 9, p. 109–111.

———— (1929). Mikrofossilien, ihre Gewinnung und Aufbewahrung: Naturwissenschaftliche monatschrift des Deutschen Lehrervereins fur Naturkunde E. V. aus der Heimat. Jahrg. 42, H. 11, p. 357–365, 4 figs.

———— (1935). Ein einfacher Auslesetisch für Mikrofossilien. Senckenbergiana, v. 17, no. 1–2, p. 87–89, 1 fig.

———— (1935). Sammeln, Präparieren und Aufbewahren von Mikrofossilien. Senckenbergiana, v. 17, no. 3–4, p. 124–137, 6 figs.

———— (1939). A simple apparatus for sorting microfossils. J. Paleontology, v. 13, p. 225–227.

Frey, D. G. (1955). A differential flotation technique for recovering microfossils from inorganic sediments. New Phytologist, London, v. 54, no. 2, p. 257–258.

Frizzell, D. L. (1949). See Sec. C, Storage.

Funkhouser, J. W., and W. R. Evitt (1959). See Sec. F, Preparation.

Galliher, E. W. (1929). Mounting medium. Micropaleont. Bull., v. 1, no. 12, art. 49, p. 2.

Glaessner, M. F. (1947). Principles of micropaleontology. Wiley, New York, 296 pp., illus.

Goodchild, C. G. (1951). See Sec. Q, Measurement.

Gullentops, F. (1954). A new slide for microfossils. Micropaleontologist, v. 8, no. 4, p. 41.

Hagn, Herbert (1952). A new plexiglass slide for microfossils. Micropaleontologist, v. 6, no. 3, p. 39–40.

———— (1953). See Sec. G, Sectioning.

Hanna, G. D. (1925). See Sec. F, Preparation.

————, and C. C. Church (1928). See Sec. F, Preparation.

———— (1927). Synthetic resin as a mounting medium. Science, n.s., v. 65, no. 1693, p. 575–576.

Hanna, M. A. (1927). Separation of fossils and other light materials by means of heavy liquids. Econ. Geol., v. 22, no. 1, p. 14–17.

Hay, W. W. (1961). Note on the preparation of samples for Discoasterids. J. Paleontology, v. 35, no. 4, p. 873.

Hecht, Franz (1933). Arbeitsweisen der Mikropaläontologie. Senckenbergiana, v. 15, p. 346–362.

———— (1934). Eine neue Verteilungszelle zum Aufbewahren von Mikrofossilien, vornehmlich Foraminiferen. Senckenbergiana, v. 16, p. 152-155.

———— (1934). See Sec. P(3), Photomicrography.

Hedley, R. H. (1957). See Sec. J, X-Ray.

Hiltermann, Heinrich (1948). Notes on proper sampling of material. Micropaleontologist, v. 2, no. 2, p. 11–13. [Untitled; part of "news" correspondence of the issue.]

———— (1956). Mikropaläontologische Arbeitsmethoden in den Vereinigten Staaten von Amerika–Bericht über eine Studienreise nach Californien. Erdöl Kohle, Jahrg. 9, no. 11, p. 750–753, illus.

Hoffmeister, W. S. (1959). See Sec. F, Preparation.

Hofker, J. (1930). The study of plankton by means of Canada balsam preparations. Stazione Zool. di Napoli Publ., v. 10, f. 2, p. 279–283.

Howe, H. V. (1941). Use of soap in the preparation of samples for micropaleontologic study. J. Paleontology, v. 15, no. 6, p. 691; abstract in Oil Gas J., v. 39, no. 47, p. 65.

Hucke, K. (1933). Über die Gewinnung von Mikrofossilien aus Geschieben. Zs. Geschiebeforschung, v. 9, H. 1, p. 42–48, 3 figs.

Hussey, K. M., and C. B. Campbell (1951). A new method of sample preparation. J. Paleontology, v. 25, p. 224–226.

Järnefors, Björn (1953). A method of mounting mineral grains for statistical microscopic study. Uppsala Univ., Geol. Inst. Bull., v. 34, p. 115–122, illus.

Jeffords, R. M., and D. H. Jones (1959). See Sec. M(5), Micropaleontology—Pollen.

Jekhowsky, B. de (1959). Une technique standard de préparation des roches pour l'étude des microfossiles organiques. Inst. Franç. Pétrole., Rev., v. 14, no. 3, p. 315–320.

Kennard, M. C., and A. J. Smith (1961). A simple microsample splitter. J. Paleontology, v. 35, no. 2, p. 396–397.

Kirby, Harold (1950). Materials and methods in the study of protozoa. Univ. of California Press, Berkeley, 73 pp.

Kirchner, Z. M. (1958). See Sec. F, Preparation.

Knights, A. J. (1951). See Sec. F, Preparation.

Knox, A. S. (1942). The use of bromoform in the separation of noncalcareous microfossils. Science, n.s., v. 95, no. 2464, p. 307–308.

Kornicker, L. S. (1953). See Sec. P(3), Illustrations—Photomicrography.

—————— (1954). Elimination of static charge from celluloid-covered micropaleontologic slides. Micropaleontologist, v. 8, no. 1, p. 36.

—————— (1957). Spirally designed picking tray. Micropaleontology, v. 3, no. 2, p. 189.

Kremp, Gerhard (1953). See Sec. G, Sectioning.

——————, and Walter Johst (1952). See Sec. G, Sectioning.

Kugler, H. G. (1957). See Sec. Illustrations—Photomicrography.

Layne, N. M., Jr. (1950). See Sec. F, Preparation.

Lehmann, E. P. (1956). See Sec. P(3), Illustrations—Photomicrography.

Lejeune, M. (1936). See Sec. F, Preparation.

Le Roy, L. W. (1949). Subsurface laboratory methods. Micropaleontological analysis. Colorado School of Mines Quart., v. 44, p. 58–86, 3 pls.

Levinson, S. A. (1950). See Sec. G, Sectioning.

MacVicar, D. G., Jr. (1951). See Sec. F, Preparation.

—————— (1952). See Sec. F, Preparation.

Malyskek, V. T. (1940). Method of separation of microfauna from the sediments by centrifugal method on heavy liquids. Azerbeidzhan. Petrol. Industr., no. 9, p. 4–6, 5 figs.

Marlière, R. (1948). Frontières et disciplines de la micropaléontologie. Soc. Géol. Belg. Ann., v. 71, p. 285–298, 1 fig.

McNair, A. H. (1938). See Sec. G, Sectioning.

Micropaleontologist (1948). Sorting stages for microfossils. Micropaleontologist, v. 2, no. 4, p. 22–23.

Napoli, Enrico di (1955). See Sec. P(6), Illustrations—Drawings.

Nelson, D. O. (1950). Method of eliminating gypsum from samples. Micropaleontologist, v. 4, no. 3, p. 21.

Nichols, W. H., and S. K. Roy (1932). Preparation of microfossils. Mus. J., London, v. 32, p. 261–262, 1 fig.

Olinomikado, T. (1949). Assemblage slide used in the laboratory of Imperial Oil Co., Tokyo, Japan. Micropaleontologist, v. 3, no. 2, p. 32, 1 fig.

Oyen, F. H. van (1953). Methods applied in the examination of the microfauna of the South Limburg Carboniferous. Micropaleontologist, v. 7, no. 4, p. 31. [Hydrogen peroxide technique.]

Plummer, H. J. (1929). See Sec. P(3), Illustrations—Photomicrography.

Pokorny, Vladimir (1958). Grundzüge der Zoologischen Mikropaläontologie. Deutsch. Verlag Wiss., Berlin. v. I, 582 pp., 549 figs.; v. II, 453 pp.

Puri, H. S. (1948). See Sec. F, Preparation.

Redmond, C. D. (1953). See Sec. F, Preparation.

Ross, C. S. (1926). Methods of preparation of sedimentary materials for study. Econ. Geol., v. 21, p. 454–468, 1 fig.

Sander, N. J. (1955). See Sec. P(3), Illustrations—Photomicrography.

Schenck, E. T. (1932). A universal stage for microfossils. Micropaleont. B., v. 3, no. 3, p. 75–76, 1 fig.

Schenck, H. G., and R. T. White (1942). See Sec. B, Collecting.

Schenck, H. G., and B. C. Adams (1943). Operations of commercial micropaleontologic laboratories. J. Paleontology, v. 17, p. 554–583, 97 pls., 13 figs.

Schmidt, R. A. M. (1948). Magnetic separation of microfossils. J. Paleontology, v. 22, p. 530–531.

——— (1952). See Sec. J, X-Rays.

Smith, M. L. (1954). A method of selecting sample sizes. J. Paleontology, v. 28, no. 1, p. 116–117, illus.

Stainforth, R. M. (1949). Work in comfort. Micropaleontologist, v. 3, no. 2, p. 29–30. [Work bench design for micropaleontologists.]

Steineke, F. S. (1927). See Sec. C, Storage.

Sud, C. P. *in* B. Sahni (1947). The age of the saline series in the salt range, second symposium. Natl. Acad. Sci. India, Pr., v. 16, pts. 2–4, p. xxxix. [Rubber tube as container for macerating siliceous rocks containing organic remains.]

Tolmachoff, I. P. (1931). A method of cleaning microscopical fossils. Science, n.s., v. 73, no. 1879, p. 15–16.

——— (1932). See Sec. F, Preparation.

Triebel, Erich (1938). Über das Auslesen von Mikrofossilien. Senckenbergiana, v. 20, p. 292–296.

——— (1947). Methodische und Technische Fragen der Mikropaläontologie. W. Kramer, Frankfurt, 47 pp.

Turner, J. P. (1931). A simple apparatus for washing Protozoa. Science, n.s., v. 74, no. 1908, p. 99–100, 1 fig.

Turnovsky, K. (1948). Arbeitsmethoden der angewandten Mikropaläontologie. Mikroskopie, v. 3, p. 181–188, 2 figs.

Upshaw, C. F., R. G. Todd, and B. D. Allen (1957). See Sec. F, Preparation.

Verniory, René (1956). Extraction des microfossiles; une nouvelle méthode rapide. Arch. Sci., v. 9, f. 4, p. 487–492.

——— (1957). See Sec. K, Casting and molding.

Wetzel, Otto (1948). See Sec. F, Preparation.

——— (1957). See Sec. F, Preparation.

Wicher, C. A. (1936). Die Aufbereitungsmethoden in der Mikropaläontologie. Zs. prakt. Geol. Jahrg. 44, H. 11, p. 174–176.

Witwicka, E., W. Bielecka, O. Styk, and J. Sztejn (1958). The methods of working out microfossils. Polan. Inst. Geol., B., 156 pp., 1 pl., 69 figs.

Wood, Alan (1945). See Sec. P(6), Illustrations—Drawings.

# M  (2)

## MICROPALEONTOLOGY—FORAMINIFERA

Aitken, W. E. (1927). Notes on sorting and mounting foraminifera. Micropaleont. Bull., v. 1, no. 4, art. 17, p. 6.

Altpeter, O. (1913). Beiträge zur Anatomie und Physiologie von *Alveolina*. N. Jahrb., Stuttgart, Beil., v. 36, p. 86–90.

Bakx, L. A. J. (1936). Making prints of foraminifera: J. Paleontology, v. 10, no. 2, p. 145–146.

Bé, A. W. H. (1959). A method for rapid sorting of Foraminifera from marine plankton samples. J. Paleontology, v. 33, no. 5, p. 846–848.

Berry, Willard (1931). See Sec. G, Sectioning. [Orbitoid Foraminifera.]

Birch, D. C. (1932). Technique in the handling and picking of Foraminifera. Micropaleont. Bull., v. 3, no. 2, p. 26–27.

Blow, W. H. (1955). Dissection of highly perforate calcareous foraminifera. Micropaleontology, v. 1, no. 2, p. 190.

Brönnimann, Paul (1951). A model of the internal structure of *Discocyclina* s.s. J. Paleontology, v. 25, p. 208–211.

Brotzen, F. (1950). Methods and techniques in routine work. Micropaleontologist, v. 4, no. 2, p. 18–20.

Carpenter, W. B. (1856). See Sec. G, Sectioning.

———— (1862). Introduction to the study of the Foraminifera. Roy. Soc. London Publ., 319 + 22 pp., 22 pls.

Carson, C. M. (1933). A method of concentrating Foraminifera. J. Paleontology, v. 7, p. 439. [Bromoform.]

———— (1953). Heavy liquid concentration of Foraminifera. J. Paleontology, v. 27, no. 6, p. 880–881.

Chapman, Frederick (1902). The Foraminifera. Longmans, Green, London [Chapter 19 on the collection, examination, and mounting of Foraminifera; p. 291–326.]

Corrington, J. D. (1941). See Sec. L, Microscopy. [Chapter 10 on Foraminifera, etc.]

Crowley, A. J. (1952). Method of extracting foraminifera from refractory shale. Am. Assoc. Petrol. Geol. Bull., v. 36, no. 11, p. 2185.

Cushman, J. A. (1924). The use of foraminifera in geologic correlation. Am. Assoc. Petrol. Geol. Bull., v. 8, p. 485–491.

———— (1925). And introduction to the morphology and classification of the Foraminifera. Smithson. Misc. Coll., v. 77, no. 4, p. 1–77.

———— (1926). Sec. P(3), Illustrations—Photomicrography.

———— (1928–1940). Foraminifera, their classification and economic use. Cushman Lab. Foram. Res. Contr., no. 1; 1st ed, 401 pp., 59 pls.; 2nd ed., 1934, 426 pp., 71 pls; 3rd ed., 535 pp., Harvard Univ. Press.

Debes, E. (1911). Zur Technik der Foraminiferen-Präparation. Naturf. Ges., Leipzig Sitzungsber., Jahrg. 1910, v. 37, p. 3–34.

Donnay, J. D. H., and E. W. Galliher (1929). Method of studying the internal structure of Foraminifera. Micropaleontol. Bull., v. 1, no. 10, p. 3–4.

Douglass, R. C. (1960). See Sec. G, Sectioning.

Driver, H. L. (1926). The wet method of Foraminiferal examination. Micropaleont. Bull., v. 1, p. 2–4.

Dunbar, C. O., and G. E. Condra (1927). The Fusulinidae of the Pennsylvanian system in Nebraska; method of study. Nebraska Geol. Survey Bull., 2, 2nd ser., p. 49–52, 2 tables, 15 pls., 12 figs.

———, and L. G. Henbest (1942). Pennsylvanian Fusulinidae of Illinois. Illinois State Geol. Survey, Bull. 67, 218 pp., 23 ps. [p. 65–74 relevant.]

Dunn, P. H. (1942). Silurian Foraminifera of the Mississippi Basin. J. Paleontology, v. 16, no. 3, p. 317–342. [Arenaceous foraminifera.]

Earland, Arthur (1899). Collection and preparation of Foraminifera. Sci. Gossip, v. 6, no. 61, p. 8–9; no. 62, p. 53–54; no. 63, p. 74, 5 fig.

Eisenack, Alfred (1931). Neue Mikrofossilien des Baltischen Silurs. Paläont. Zs., v. 13, p. 74–118, 5 pls. [Arenaceous forms, techniques used.]

Elcock, C. (1882). How to prepare Foraminifera. Postal Micros. Soc. J., Bath, v. 1, p. 25–29, 139–145, 1 fig.

Ellis, B. F. (1933). A sorting stage for Foraminifera. Science, n.s., v. 78, no. 2029, p. 461–462.

——— (1949). Models of foraminifera. Micropaleontologist, v. 3, no. 4, p. 22.

——— (1950). The models of foraminifera. Micropaleontologist, v. 4, no. 4, p. 11.

——— (1951). A model of Triticites. Micropaleontologist, v. 5, no. 3, p. 14.

Emiliani, Cesare (1951). See Sec. G, Sectioning.

Flint, J. M. (1886). On the collection and method for studying Foraminifera. Am. Monthly Micros. J., v. 7, p. 105–108.

Fournier, George (1950). See Sec. P(3), Illustrations—Photomicrography.

——— (1954). See Sec. P(3), Illustrations—Photomicrography.

——— (1956). See Sec. P(3), Illustrations—Photomicrography.

Granger, W. C. (1948). Preparation of Fusulinidae thin sections. Compass of Sigma Gamma Epsilon, v. 25, no. 2, p. 77–79.

Grimsdale, T. F., and F. P. C. M. van Morkhoven (1955). The ratio between pelagic and benthonic foraminifera as a means of estimating depth of deposition of sedimentary rocks. World Petroleum Congress, Pr. 4th, sec. 1, p. 473–491, illus. [Gulf of Mexico.]

Hagn, Herbert (1953). See Sec. G, Sectioning.

Hecht, Franz (1934). Sec. P(3), Illustrations—Photomicrography.

——— (1935). See Sec. P(3), Illustrations—Photomicrography.

Hedley, R. H. (1957). See Sec. J, X-Ray.

Hodson, Floyd, and Helen Hodson (1926). Shortcuts in picking out and sectioning formanifera. Am. Assoc. Petrol. Geol. Bull., v. 10, p. 1173–1174.

Hofker, Jan (1950). See Sec. P(3), Illustrations—Photomicrography.

Höglund, Hans (1947). Foraminifera in the Gullmar Fjord and the Skagerak. Zoologiska bidrag från Uppsala, v. 26, p. 1–329, 32 pls., 312 fig., 2 maps, 7 tab. [Preparations and collecting, p. 6–9.]

Honjo, Susumu (1960). See Sec. G, Sectioning.

Hooper, Kenneth (1959). See Sec. J, X-Ray.

Hulme, S. G. (1961). A mechanized method of breaking down and washing foraminiferal rock samples. Micropaleontology, v. 7, no. 1, p. 107–113.

Journal of Paleontology (1935). Recovery of Foraminifera by means of flotation. J. Paleontology, v. 9, p. 745–746. [Laboratory, N. V. De Bataafsche Petroleum Maatschappij, The Hague, Holland.]

Kornicker, L. S. (1954). Plastic models of Foraminifera. Cushman Lab. Foram. Res. Contr., v. 5, pt. 3, p. 107.

Lee, J. J., et al. (1961). See Sec. B, Collecting.

Lemardeley, F., and P. Frémy (1946). Préparations microscopiques du test de foraminifères. Soc. Linn. de Normandie, Caen, Bull., ser. 9, v. 4, p. 15–19.

Mathews, R. D. (1945). See Sec. G., Sectioning.

McGugan, Alan (1959). See Sec. G., Sectioning.

Morikawa, R. (1953). A method of observation for fusilinids by "Sump-figures." Geol. Soc. Japan, J., v. 59, no. 689, p. 59–63, illus. [In Japanese, with English summary.]

Morkhoven, F. P. C. M. van (1958). See Sec. G, Sectioning.

Noth, Rudolf (1947). Tetrachlorkohlenstoff als Aufhellungsmittel für Foreaminiferenuntersuchungen. Austria Geol. Bundesanst., Verh., Wien 1945, H. 1–3, p. 83–85, 1 pl.

Pessagno, E. A., Jr. (1960). See Sec. G, Sectioning.

Phleger, F. B., and F. L. Parker (1951). See Sec. B, Collecting.

Plummer, H. J. (1951). Foram surgery. Micropaleontologist, v. 5, no. 1, p. 26–28, 6 figs.

Reed, R. D. (1928). The preservation of Foraminifera. Micropaleont. Bull., v. 1, no. 7, art. 29, p. 1–3.

Sander, N. J. (1955). See Sec. P(3), Illustrations—Photomicrography.

Scheffen, W. (1934). Ein Universaltisch zum Auslesen von Foraminiferen in transparente Zellen. Senckenbergiana, v. 16, no. 4–6, p. 303–308, 6 figs.

——— (1937). Die besonderen Vorteile der Transparent-Zelle bei der Untersuchung von Klein-und Gross-Foraminiferen. Senckenbergiana, v. 19, no. 3–4, p. 193–200.

Schenck, H. G., and R. T. White (1942). See Sec. B, Collecting.

Secrist, M. H. (1934). Technique for the recovery of Paleozoic arenaceous Foraminifera. J. Paleontology, v. 8, no. 2, p. 245–246.

Simon, L. J. (1949). Foraminiferal picking tray. Micropaleontologist, v. 3, no. 3, p. 21–22, 1 fig.

Špalek, Vladimír (1937). Preparátové schránky na foraminifery. Priroda, Brno (Brünn), roč. 30, leden 1937, cislo 1, p. 16–18, 1 fig.

Stelzner, A. W. (1890). Über die Isolierung von Foraminifern aus dem Badener Tegel mit Hilfe von Jodidlösung. Ann. K. K. Naturh. Hofmuseums, Wien, v. 5, p. 15–19.

Thomas, E. T. (1925). An aid to the study of foraminifera. Am. Assoc. Petrol. Geol. Bull., v. 9, p. 667–669.

Tolman, Frank (1929). See Sec. G, Sectioning.

Troelsen, J. C. (1954). Foram Surgery. Micropaleontologist, v. 8, no. 4, p. 40–41.

——— (1954). Glass needles used in dissection of foraminifera. Micropaleontologist, v. 8, no. 1, p. 37.

Vavrinova, Melada (1951). See Sec. I, Staining.

Veen, F. R. van (1957). Microforaminifera. Micropaleont. (Am. Mus. Nat. Hist.), v. 3, no. 1, p. 74.

Vorce, C. M. (1880). Cleaning Foraminifera. Am. Month. Micros. J., v. 1, p. 24.

Walton, W. R. (1952). Techniques for recognition of living foraminifera. Cushman Lab. Foram. Res. Contr., v. 3, pt. 2, p. 56–60.

White, M. P. (1950). A fusulinid slide rule. J. Paleontology, v. 24, p. 123–129.

e recent Foraminifera of Great Britain. Roy.
29, 107 pp., 8 figs., 7 pls.
ister (1952). Small Foraminifera. Micropale-
lus.
ctioning.

## OLOGY—RADIOLARIA

c. L, Microscopy. [Chapter 10, Foraminifera,

ur (1951). Paleocene Radiolaria from South-
nes Metall. Bull., Tech. Ser. no. 77, p. 1–41.

aren zur Freilegung von Radiolarien aus Kiesel-
schieiern. ................ 6, p. 239–244.

# M (4)

## MICROPALEONTOLOGY—DIATOMS

Bailey, J. W. (1856). New Method of disintegrating masses of fossil Diatomaceae. Am. J. Sci., ser. 2, v. 21, p. 356–357.

Caballero, E. (1927). The technique of mounting diatom and other type slides. Roy. Micros. Soc. J., ser. 3, v. 47, p. 9–28.

Elyashev, A. A. (1957). O prostom sposobe prigotovleniya vysokoprelomlya-yushchei sredy dlya diatomovogo analiza. Wauch.-Issled. Inst. Geol. Arktiki, Sbornik Statei Paleont. i Biostratig. vyp. 4, p. 74–75 (processed).

Hanna, G. D. (1930). Hyrax, a new mounting medium for diatoms. Roy. Micros. Soc. J., ser. 3, v. 50, pt. 4, p. 424–426.

———, and W. M. Grant (1939). Preliminary note on a technique for mounting diatoms in realgar and other substances. Roy. Micros. Soc. J., v. 59, p. 174–176.

——— (1940). Apparatus for mounting diatoms in realgar and other substances. Roy. Micros. Soc. J., ser. 3, v. 60, p. 152–160, 1 pl., 4 figs.

Lohman, K. E. (1941). Geology and biology of north Atlantic deep-sea cores between Newfoundland and Ireland. Part 3, Diatomaceae. U.S. Geol. Survey Prof. Paper 196-B, p. 55–86, 6 pls.

Mann, Albert (1922). Suggestions for collecting and preparing diatoms. U.S. Natl. Mus. Pr., v. 60, no. 2410, p. 1–8.

Okuno, Haruo (1956). Electron-microscopic fine structure of fossil diatoms. Palaeont. Soc. Japan, Tr. Pr. n.s. no. 13, 14, p. 125–130, 143–147, 1954; no. 19, p. 53–58, 1955; no. 21, p. 133–138, illus. [In English, with Japanese summary.]

Swatman, C. C. (1949). Cleaning diatoms for microscopic use. Microscope, v. 7, no. 5, p. 132–136.

Van Heurck, H. F. (1896). A treatise on the Diatomaceae. Wesley, London, 558 pp., 35 pls., 291 figs.

Wise, F. C. (1950). Mounting diatoms. Quekett Micros. Club, J., ser. 41, v. 3, p. 127.

# M  (5)

## MICROPALEONTOLOGY—POLLEN AND SPORES

Afzelius, B. M. (1957). On new methods in physical cell research and their application in studies of pollen grains and spores, *in* Pollen and spore morphology/ Plant taxonomy, An introduction to palynology II, Almqvist & Wiksell, Stockholm, p. 125–134.

Andersen, S. Th. (1960). Silicone oil as a mounting medium for pollen grains. Danm. Geol. Undersøg., ser. 4, v. 4, no. 1, p. 5–24.

Anderson, S. J. (1959). See Sec. P(2), Photography.

Arms, B. C. (1960). A silica depressant method for concentrating fossil pollen and spores. Micropaleontology, v. 6, no. 3, p. 327–328.

Assarsson, G., and E. Granlund (1924). En method för pollenanalys av minerogena jordater. Geol. Fören. Stockh. Förh., v. 46, p. 76–82.

Avetissian, N. M. (1950). Méthode simplifée d'acetolyse dans la préparation des pollen. J. Bot. U.R.S.S., v. 35, no. 4, p. 385–386.

Barghoorn, E. S., and I. W. Bailey (1940). A useful method for the study of pollen in peat. Ecology, v. 21, no. 4, p. 513–514.

Bertsch, Karl (1942). Lehrbuch der Pollenanalyse (Handbücher der praktischen Vorgeschichtsforschung Band 3), Enke, Stuttgart, 195 pp., illus. [A textbook of the fundamentals of pollen analysis.]

Cain, S. A. (1939). Pollen analysis as a paleoecological research method. Bot. Rev., v. 5, no. 12, p. 232–236.

———— (1944). Size-frequency characteristics of *Abies Fraseri* pollen as influenced by different methods of preparation. Am. Midl. Nat., v. 31, no. 1, p. 232–236.

Campo, M. Van (1950). Une méthode de préparation très rapide des tourbes en vue de leur analyse pollinique. Soc. Bot. Fr., B., v. 97, no. 7–9, p. 216–217.

Christensen, B. B. (1949). See Sec. G, Sectioning.

———— (1954). New mounting media for pollen grains. Danm. Geol. Undersøg. ser. 2, no. 80, p. 7–11.

Cushing, Edward J. (1961). Size increase in pollen grains mounted in thin slides. Pollen et Spores, v. 3, no. 2, p. 265–274. [In English, with French summary.]

Deevey, E. S., Jr., and J. E. Potzger (1951). Peat samples for radiocarbon analysis; problems in pollen statistics. Am. J. Sci., v. 249, no. 7, p. 473–511.

Doroganievka, E. A., I. E. Chenfinke, and V. P. Gritchouk (1952). Nouveau liquide dense pour l'analyse sporopollinique, Iza. Akad. Nauk S.S.S.R., Sed. Geog., no. 4, p. 73–74.

Erdtman, Gunar (1934). Über die Verwendung von Essigsäureanhydrid bei Pollenuntersuchungen. Sv. Bot. Tidskr., v. 28, ser. 2, p. 354–358.

―――― (1935). Pollen statistics, a botanical and geological research method, *in* R. P. Wodehouse, Pollen grains, McGraw-Hill, New York, p. 110–125.

―――― (1936). New methods in pollen analysis. Svensk Botanisk Tidskr., v. 30, ser. 2, p. 154–164.

―――― (1943). An introduction to pollen analysis. Chronica Botanica Co., Waltham, Mass., xv+ 239 pp. (2nd. ed., with minor changes, 1954.)

――――, and H. Erdtman (1933). The improvement of pollen analysis technique. Sv. Bot. Tidskr. v. 27, ser. 3, p. 347–357.

Faegri, Knut (1939). Single-grain pollen preparations. Geol. Fören. Stockh. Förh., v. 61, pt. 4, no. 419, p. 513–514.

―――― (1951). An unrecognized source of error in pollen analysis. Geol. Fören. Stockh. Förh. v. 73, pt. 1, no. 464, p. 51–56.

――――, and Johs. Iversen (1950). Textbook of modern pollen analysis. Munksgaard, Copenhagen, p. 1–168.

Felix, C. J. (1963). Mechanical sample disaggregation in palynology. Micropaleontology, v. 9, no. 3, p. 337–339.

Fernández-Morán, H., and A. O. Dahl (1952). Electron microscopy of ultrathin frozen sections of pollen grains. Science, vo. 116, no. 3018, p. 465–467.

Geisler, F. (1935). A new method of separation of fossil pollen from peat. Butler Univ. Studies, v. 3, p. 141–145.

Gerard, R. (1954). Pollen sampling in permafrost. Micropaleontologist, v. 8, no. 4, p. 38.

Godwin, H. (1934). Pollen analysis. An outline of the problem and potentialities of the method: New Phytologist, Pt. 1, Technique and interpretations, v. 33, no. 4, p. 278–305; Pt. 11, General applications, v. 33, no. 5, p. 325–358.

Gross, Karl (1948). Die Präparation von Sporen aus devonischen Tonschiefern und anderen Gesteinen. Neues Jb. Geol. U. Paläont., Abt., B, Jahrg. 1945–1948, no. 1–4, p. 49–53.

Guennel, G. K. (1956). Systematic methods for Paleozoic plant microfossils. Micropaleontology, v. 2, no. 4, p. 393–395.

Jeffords, R. M., and D. H. Jones (1959). Preparation of slides for spores and other microfossils. J. Paleontology, v. 33, n. 2, p. 344–347.

Kirchheimer, F. (1933). Über die Herstellung von Präparaten zur Kontrastreichen Wiedergabe fossilen Pollens. Paleont. Zs., v. 15, p. 78–79, 1 pl.

Klaus, Wilheim (1953). Zur Einzelpräparation fossiler Sporomorphen. Mikroscopie, v. 8, no. 1–2, p. 1–14.

Kurtz, E. B., and R. M. Turner (1957). An oil flotation method for the recovery of pollen from inorganic sediments. Micropaleontology, v. 3, no. 1, p. 67–68.

Kuyl, O. S. (1961). The pollen preparation of calcareous sediments. Netherlands, Geol. Stichting Med., n.s., no. 13, p. 27–28.

Ledingham, R. J., and S. H. F. Chinn (1955). A flotation method for obtaining spores of *Helminthosporium sativum* from soil. Canadian J. Bot., v. 33, no. 4, p. 298–303.

Mädler, K. A. (1956). A technique for the preparation of multigrain palynological slides. Micropaleontology, v. 2, no. 4, p. 399–401.

——— (1958). Zur Einzelkornpräparation fossiler Sporomorphen. Paläont. Zs. v. 32, no. 1–2, p. 14. [Abstract.]

Norem, W. L. (1953). Separation of spores and pollen from siliceous rocks. J. Paleontology, v. 27, no. 6, p. 881–883.

——— (1956). An improved method for separating fossil spores and pollen from siliceous rocks. J. Paleontology, v. 30, no. 5, p. 1258–1260.

Petzger, J. E. (1942). Influence of location of borings in bogs on completeness of pollen profiles; pollen records from sediments of four lakes in Anoka County, Minnesota. A study on method of sampling. Am. Phil. Soc. Yearb., 1941, p. 164–165.

Praglowski, J. R. (1957). On the cutting of ultra-thin sections, *in* Pollen and spore morphology/Plant Taxonomy. An introduction to palynology II, Almqvist & Wiksell, Stockholm, p. 135–147.

Puri, H. S. (1948). Methods and techniques. Micropaleontologist, v. 2, no. 3, p. 18. [With spores.]

Schopf, J. M. (1960). Double cover-glass slides for plant microfossils. Micropaleontology, v. 6, no. 2, p. 237–240.

Sears, P. B., and L. R. Wilson (1954). Plant microfossils. Methods and techniques. Micropaleontologist, v. 8, no. 2, p. 31–35.

Sittler, C. (1955). Méthodes et techniques physicochimiques de préparation des sédiments en vue de leur analyse pollinique. Inst. Franc. Pétrole., Rev. Ann. Comb. liquid., v. 10, no. 2, p. 103–114.

Spielholtz, Gerald, L. A. Thomas, and Harvey Diehl (1962). Isolation of spores by wet oxidation. Micropaleontology, v. 8, no. 1, p. 109–110.

Staplin, F. L., S. J. Pocock, J. Jansonius, and E. M. Oliphant (1960). Palynological techniques for sediments. Micropaleontology, v. 6, no. 3, p. 329–331.

Thompson, Paul W. (1953). Aufbereitung von Sporomorphen in Braun- und Steinkohlen. Int. Bot. Cong., 7th Stockholm, Pr., p. 887. [Abstract, with discussion.]

Traverse, Alfred (1958). Locating plant microfossils on mixed slides. Micropaleontology, v. 4, no. 2, p. 207–208.

Venkatachary, S., *in* B. Sahni (1947). The age of the Saline series in the salt range, second symposium. Natl. Acad. Sci. India, Pr., v. 16, pts. 2–4, p. xxxvi–xxxviii. [Spore preparation by macerating mixture of $HNO_3$ and chlorate of potash, and desilicification by HF. Gives technique for single-spore mounts.]

Von Post, L, (1933). On improvements of the pollen-analysis technique. Geol. Fören. Stockh. Förh., v. 55, no. 3, p. 523–527.

Wenner, Carl-Gösta (1944). Om separeringsmethodik för pollenanalys av sandiga jordarter. Geol. Fören. Stockh. Förh., v. 66, pt. 3, no. 438, p. 695–698.

Wolfram, Alfred (1954). Versuche zur Trennung der Sporomorphen von organischen und anorganischen Beimengungen unter Berüchsichtigung der Wirkung des Ultraschalls auf Kohlenmazerati. Geol. Berling. Jahrg. 3, pt. 5, p. 655–658, illus.

Zetzsche, Fritz, and Oskar Kälin (1932). Eine Methode zur Isolierung des Polymerbitumens (Sporenmembranen, Kutikuine, usw.) aus Kohlen. 7. Mettulung zu. Untersuchungen über die Membran der Sporen und Pollen., Braunkohle, v. 20, p. 345–351, 363–366.

# M (6)

## MICROPALEONTOLOGY—OSTRACODS

Alexander, C. I. (1933). Preparation and study of fossil Ostracoda. Micropaleont. Bull. v. 4, no. 1, p. 1–11, 1 fig.

Friebel, Erich (1958). Ostracoden, *in* Hugo Freund (ed.), Handbuch der Mikroskopie und der Technik, v. 2, pt. 3, p. 193–236, 8 pls.

Kesling, R. V. (1951). The morphology of ostracod molt stages. Illinois Univ. Biol. Monog., v. 21, no. 1–3, 324 pp.

——— (1953). A slide rule for the determination of instars in ostracod species. Michigan Univ. Mus. Paleont. Contr., v. 11, no. 5, p. 97–109, illus.

——— (1957). A chart useful for study of ostracod carapaces. Michigan Univ. Mus. Paleont. Contr., v. 14, no. 2, p. 17–20, illus.

——— (1957). A peel technique for ostracod carapaces, and structures revealed therewith in *Hibbardia lacrimosa* (Swartz and Oriel). Michigan Univ. Mus. Paleont., Contr., v. 14, no. 4, p. 27–40, illus.

Kornicker, L. S. (1957). Concentration of ostracods by alcohol flotation. J. Paleontology, v. 31, no. 5, p. 1030.

Levinson, S. A. (1951). Sec. I, Staining.

——— (1951. A technique for anesthetizing freshwater ostracodes. Am. Midl. Nat., v. 46, no. 1, p. 254–255.

——— (1951). Thin sections of Paleozoic Ostracoda and their bearing on taxonomy and morphology. J. Paleontology, v. 25, no. 5, p. 533–560.

——— (1956). The identification of ostracod genera and species in thin sections. J. Paleontology, v. 30, no. 4, p. 1010. [Abstract.]

Martin, G. P. R. (1957). A new method of recovering remains of the chitinous integument of fossil Ostracoda. Micropaleontology, v. 3, no. 3, p. 291–292.

Schubert, Edmund (1943). Erste Ergebnisse einer neuen Untersuchungsmethode von Ostracodenschalen. Akad. Wiss. Wien, mat.-nat. Kl., Anz. Jahrg. 80, p. 22–23.

Sohn, J. G. (1960). Cleaning ostracod valves with ultrasonic vibrations. Geol. Soc. Am., Bull., v. 71, p. 1982.

——— (1961). Techniques for preparation and study of fossil ostracods, *in* R. C. Moore (ed.), Treatise on invertebrate paleontology, Part Q, Arthopoda 3, Geol. Soc. America and Univ. Kansas Press, p. 64–70.

——— (in press). Lower Tertiary ostracods from Western Pakistan with a section on the preparation and study of Ostracoda. Pakistan Geol. Surv., Mem. Paleontologia Pakistanica, v. 3, pt. 2.

——— (1956). See Sec. F, Preparation.

Sylvester-Bradley, P. C. (1941). The shell structure of the Ostracoda and its application to their paleontological investigation. Ann. Mag. Nat. Hist., ser. 11, v. 8, p. 1–33, 18 figs.

Ulrich, E. O., and R. S. Bassler (1923). Paleozoic Ostracoda; their morphology, classification and occurrence. Md. Geol. Survey Silurian v., p. 271–391, 26 figs.

# M (7)

## MICROPALEONTOLOGY—CONODONTS

Branson, E. B., M. G. Mehl, and E. R. Branson (1933). Conodont studies. Univ. Mo. Studies, v. 8, p. 1–349, 28 pls. (Issued in 4 nos.)

Collinson, Charles (1963). Collection and preparation of Conodonts through mass productin techniques. Illinis State Geol. Survey, circ. 343, p. 1–16.

Dow, V. E. (1960). Magnetic separation of Conodonts. J. Paleontology, v. 34, no. 4, p. 738–743.

Eller, E. R. (1941). Removal of scolecodonts from the matrix. Pennsylvania Acad. Sci. Pr., v. 15, p. 119–120.

Ellison, Samuel (1944). The composition of conodonts. J. Paleontology, v. 18, p. 133–140.

Gunnell, F. H. (1931). Conodonts from the Fort Scott limestone of Missouri. J. Paleontology, v. 5, p. 244–252, 1 pl.

———, and P. S. Morey (1932). The preparation of conodonts for study. Micropaleont. Bull., v. 3, no. 3, p. 77–78.

Schmidt, Hermann (1934). Conodonten-Funde in ursprünglichem Zusammenhang. Paleont. Zs., v. 16, p. 76–85, 1 pl., 8 figs.

Tasch, Paul, and B. L. Shaffer (1961). Study of scolecodonts by transmitted light. Micropaleontology, v. 7, no. 3, p. 369–371, 1 pl.

Ulrich, E. O., and R. S. Bassler (1926). A classification of the toothlike fossils, conodonts, with descriptions of American Dëvonian and Mississippian species. U.S. Natl. Mus. Pr., v. 68, no. 2613, p. 1–63, 11 pls.

# N

## PALEOBOTANY

Abbott, M. L. (1950). See Sec. H, Peels.

Abbott, R. E., and M. L. Abbott (1952). See Sec. H, Peels.

Andrews, H. N., Jr. (1946). Preservation of plants as fossils. Earth Sci. Digest, v. 1, no. 5, p. 3–7.

——— (1947). See Sec. H, Peels.

Barghoorn, E. S. (1948). Sodium chlorite as an aid in paleobotanical and anatomical study of plant tissues. Science, v. 107, p. 480–481.

Barnes, B., and H. Duerdon (1930). See Sec. H, Peels.

Beck, C. B. (1955). See Sec. G, Sectioning.

Benninghoff, W. S. (1947). Use of trisodium phosphate with herbarium material and microfossils in peat. Science, v. 106, no. 2753, p. 325.

Boddy, R. G. H. B. (1934). See Sec. G, Sectioning.

Chamberlain, C. J. (1932). Methods in plant histology (5th ed.), Chicago Univ. Press, xiv + 416 pp.

Danzé, Jacques (1953). Une nouvelle méthode de transfert des limbes fossiles carbonifères; II, Considérations sur la fossilisation. Soc. Geol. Nord., Ann., v. 73, p. 142–153.

———— (1954). Les différentes méthodes de transfert des limbes fossiles carbonifères. Int. Cong. Bot., Pr. 8th Rapp., p. 168–173.

Darrah, W. C. (1939). Principles of paleobotany. Chronica Botanica, Leiden, Holland, 239 pp.

———— (1941). Studies of American coal balls. Am. J. Sci., v. 239, no. 1, p. 33–53.

———— (1952). The materials and methods of paleobotany. Paleobotanist, v. 1, p. 146–153, illus.

Duerden, H. (1931). See Sec. H, Peels.

Dwivedi, J. N. (1959). See Sec. H, Peels.

Elias, M. K. (1953). Tertiary grasses and other prairie vegetation from high plains of North America. Am. J. Sci., ser. 5, v. 29, p. 24–33, 1 pl.

Fischer, Paul-Henri, and Jean Saddy (1948). Examen des nacres actuelles et fossiles en lumière de Wood. Acad. Sci. Paris C. R., v. 227, no. 3, p. 218–219.

Foster, A. S. (1953). Techniques for the study of venation patterns in the leaves of angiosperms. Internat. Cong. Bot, Pr. 7th, 1950, p. 586–587.

Graham, Roy (1933). See Sec. H, Peels.

Hafsten, Ulf (1959). Bleaching plus HF plus acetolysis, a hazardous preparation process. Pollen et Spores, v. 1, no. 1, p. 77–79.

Harris, T. M. (1926). Note on a new method for the investigation of fossil plants. New Phytologist, v. 25, p. 58–60.

Horn af Rantzien, Henning (1953). See Sec. I, Staining.

Huntington, Ellsworth (1925). Tree-growth and climatic interpretations. Carnegie Inst. Washington, Publ. 352, p. 157–204.

Jähnichen, von Hellmut (1959). Die Kutikulananalyse fossiler Blätter im Rahmen der mikropaläobotanischen Komplexmethode. Geologie, v. 8, no. 7, p. 758–768, 5 pls.

Joy, K. W., A. J. Willis, and W. S. Lacey (1956). See Sec. H, Peels.

Kisser, J. G. (1931). The preparation of anthracograms from thin sections of fossil plants. J. Ind. Bot. Soc., v. 10, no. 1, p. 60–62.

Kosanke, R. M. (1945). See Sec. I, Staining.

Kräusel, Richard (1953). Neue Präparationsmethoden. Int. Cong. Bot., Pr. 7th, p. 585–586.

Lacey, W. S. (1953). Methods in palaeobotany. North Western Naturalist, v. XVIV, p. 234–249.

Lang, W. H. (1926). See Sec. H, Peels.

Maslov, V. P. (1947). Materials for the investigation of fossil algae of the USSR. Fossil Chara—their importance, anatomy and the methods of their study. Bull. Soc. Nat. Moscow, v. 52 (ser. geol. 22, no. 3) p. 73–90.

Nathorst, A. G. (1908). See Sec H, Peels.

Noé, A. C. (1930). See Sec. H, Peels.

Penseler, W. H. A. (1932). See Sec. G, Sectioning.

Raistrick, Arthur, and C. E. Marshall (1939; reprinted 1948). The nature and origin of coal and coal seams. English Universities Press, London, p. 266–270.

Reymanowna, M. (1960). Brytyjskie metody badan paleonbotanicznych. Prezegl. Geol. Polska, v. 8, no. 1, p. 48–51.

Sahabi, Yadollah (1936). Quelques méthodes d'étude des empreintes carbonisées de végétaux fossiles. Soc. Geol. Nord, Ann. v. 61, p. 147–153, 2 pls.

Sommer, F. W. (1950). Métodos de pesquisa paleobotânica; a maceração, base the análise cuticular. Acad. Brasil. Sci., An. v. 22, no. 4, p. 421–439, illus.

Stach, Erich (1949). See Sec. L, Microscopy.

Taylor, T. N. (1962). See Sec. H., Peels.

Thiessen, Reinhardt (1931). Recently developed methods of research in the constitution of coal and their applications to Illinois coal. Illinois Geol. Survey, Bull. 60, p. 117–147.

———, G. C. Sprunk, and H. J. O'Donnell (1938). See Sec. G. Sectioning.

Thomas, H. H. (1912). On some methods in Paleobotany. New Phytologist, v. 11, p. 109–114.

Tschudy, H. (1958). A modification of the Schulze digestion method of possible value in studying coals. Grana Palynologica, n.s., v. 1., no. 3, p. 34–38.

Vallentyne, J. R. W. (1955). Sedimentary chlorophyll determination as a paleo-botanical method. Canadian J. Botany, v. 33, no. 4, p. 304–313, illus.

Walton, John (1923). On a new method of investigating fossil plant impressions or incrustations. Ann. Botany, v. 37, p. 379–391.

——— (1927). See Sec. H, Peels.

——— (1930). See Sec. H, Peels.

——— (1935). See Sec. P(2), Illustrations—Photography.

——— (1940). An introduction to the study of fossil plants. Black, London, 188 pp.

——— (1952). See Sec. H, Peels.

——— (1953). See Sec. H, Peels.

Wesley, A. (1954). See Sec. L, Microscopy.

Weston, W. H., Jr. (1935). See Sec. P(1), Illustrations—General.

Wienert, Herbert (1960). See Sec. P(2), Illustrations—Photography.

# O

## VERTEBRATE PALEONTOLOGY

Alimen, H. (1952). Aspects modernes des méthodes préhistoriques. La Nature, Sept., no. 3209, p. 257–262.

Baird, Donald (1951). Field expedients in vertebrate collecting. Compass of Sigma Gamma Epsilon, v. 28, no. 2, p. 112–114.

Barber, E. J. (1932). See Sec. J, X-Ray.

Barbour, E. P. (1950). See Sec. J, X-Ray.

Basa, M. N. (1943). Museum method and the process of cleaning and preserva-tion. Calcutta Univ., Asutosh Mus., ser. no. 2, April 1943. [Fossils, p. 24–25.]

Bassini, Transesco (1900). Di un Congegno Per Facilitare L'Isolamento Dei Fossili. Estratto Dagli Atti der R. Instituto d'Incoraggiamento di Napoli, ser. 5, v. 2, no. 4.

Bertnistle, A. P. (1932). See Sec. J, X-Ray.

Carroll, D. L. (1929). See Sec. G, Sectioning.

Cooke, S. F. (1951). Chemical analysis of fossil bone. Michigan Univ., Mus. Anthropol. Paper, no. 8, p. 73–84.

———, and R. F. Heizer (1953). The present status of chemical methods for dating prehistoric bone. Am. Antiq., v. 18, no. 4, p. 354–358.

Efremov, I. A., and F. M. Kuzmin (1932). Die Präparierung der in harten Gesteinen eingeschlossenen Reste der Ältesten Tetrapoda. Trav. Inst. Paléozool. Acad. Sci. U.S.S.R., p. 207–15, illus. [In Russian, with German summary; describes methods in Sushkin's lab.]

Evans, F. Gaynor, C. C. Coolbaugh, and Milton Lebow (1951). An apparatus for determining bone density by means of radioactive strontium. Science, v. 114, no. 2955, p. 182–185.

Ewing, J. F. (1950). See Sec. F, Preparation.

Farris, E. J. (1932). See Sec. G, Sectioning.

Furon, Raymond (1945). Formulaire technique du prehistorien. Lechevalier, Paris, 118 pp., 45 figs.

Goodwin, A. J. H. (1953). Method in prehistory. An introduction to the discipline of prehistoric archaeology with special reference to South African conditions (2nd ed.). African Archaeol. Soc., Handb. Ser. no. 1, 184 pp.

Griffeth, J. (1954). A technique for the removal of skeletal remains from bone-bed. Geol. Assoc., Pr., v. 65, pt. 2, p. 123–124.

Gromova, V. J. (1950). Un nouveau manuel, de determination des Mammifrères sur pièces osseuses. Vest. Acad. Nauk, S.S.S.R., 5, p. 117–118. [In Russian.]

Heizer, R. F. (1949). A manual of archaeological field methods. National Press Millbrae, Calif., 72 pp. (Prepared for use by California Archaeol. Survey of Univ. of California.)

Hermann, Adam (1908). Modern methods of excavating, preparing, and mounting, and mounting fossil skeletons. Am. Naturalist, v. 43, Jan., p. 43–47.

——— (1909). Modern laboratory methods in vertebrate paleontology. Am. Mus. Nat. Hist. Bull., v. 26, p. 283–331.

Hibbard, C. W. (1948). See Sec. B, Collecting.

——— (1949). See Sec. B, Collecting.

Holden, F. H. (1914), (1916). A method of cleaning skulls and disarticulated skeletons. Condor, v. 16, p. 239–241; v. 18, p. 231.

Hopkins, M. L. (1957). A practical box for bone cleaning. Soc. Vert. Paleont., News Bull., no. 51, p. 16–18.

Laming, A. (ed.). (1952). La découverte du passé. Progrès récents et techniques nouvelles en préhistoire et en archéologie. Picard, Paris, 363 pp.

Langston, Wann, Jr. (1948). See Sec. B, Collecting.

Laude, P. P., R. G. Janes, and J. D. Boyd (1949). See Sec. G, Sectioning.

Lepper, H. A., Jr., and G. E. Lewis (1941). Materials for preparation of vertebrate fossils. An analysis of their effectiveness. Am. J. Sci., v. 239, p. 17–24.

Mann, L. McL. (1933). See Sec. D, Preservation.

Mathew, W. D. (1926). See Sec. B, Collecting.

McKenna, M. C. (1962). See Sec. B, Collecting.

Michaud, R., and G. Périnet (1950). See Sec. J, X-Rays.

Moodie, R. L. (1915). Some methods of studying fossil Amphibia embedded in coal. Kansas Univ. Sci. Bull., v. 9, p. 185–193, 1 pl., 3 figs.

Moody, R. O. (1903). On the use of clay modeling in the study of Osteology. Johns Hopkins Hospital, Bull., v. 14, no. 144–145, p. 1–10, 2 pls.

Nicols, H. W., and P. C. Orr (1932). See Sec. D, Preservation.

Niggli, Ernst, et al. (1953). See Sec. J, X-Rays.

Nocera, J. A. (1955). On the removal of gypsum from vertebrate bones. Soc. Vert. Paleont., News Bull., no. 44, p. 19.

Oakley, K. P. (1950). An account of the "fluorine text" for determining the relative antiquity of fossil bones. Geol. Soc. London, Abs., no. 1454–1466, p. 29–31.

Ørvig, Tor (1951). Histologic studies of placoderms and fossil elasmobranchs. 1: The endoskeleton, with remarks on the hard tissues of lower vertebrates in general. Ark. Zool., ser. 2, v. 2, no. 2, p. 321–454, 8 pls.

Osborn, H. F. (1901). Des méthodes précises mises actuellement en oeuvre dans l'étude des vertébrés fossiles des États-Unis d'Amérique. Congrès Géol. internati., extrait, C. R. Paris, p. 353–356.

Patterson, Bryan (1940). See Sec. B, Collecting.

——— (1947). See Sec. B, Collecting.

Prokhorov, M. G. (1929). See Sec. B, Collecting.

Reith, Adolf (1939). Geschichte und Methoden der Fossil-Bergung. Kosmos, Feb., p. 58–64.

Riggs, E. S. (1952). The discovery of the use of plaster of Paris in bandaging fossils. Soc. Vert. Paleont., News Bull., no. 34, p. 24–25.

Rixon, A. E. (1949). See Sec. F, Preparation.

Schultz, C. B., and H. P. Reider (1943). Modern methods in the preparation of fossil skeletons. Compass, My., p. 268–278, 13 pls.

Snow, C. E. (1951). The Kentucky skull rig. Am. J. Phys. Anthrop., n.s., v. 9, no. 4, p. 475–478.

Sognnaes, R. F. (1947). See Sec. G, Sectioning.

Stensiö, E. A. (1927). The Downtonian and Devonian vertebrates of Spitsbergen. Pt. I, Family Cephalospidae. Skrifter om Svalbard og Nordishavet, no. 12, A, 391 pp., 112 pls.

Sternberg, L. (1956). See Sec. D, Preservation.

Swinton, W. E. (1948). Making bones live. Illus. London News, v. 123, no. 3208, p. 438–439.

Todd, William (1941). See Sec. D, Preservation.

Toombs, H. A. (1948). See Sec. F, Preparation.

———, and A. E. Rixon (1959). See Sec. F, Preparation.

Vésignié, Louis (1949). Sur un procédé de dégagement des os dans les brêches. B. Mém. Soc. Anthrop., v. 10, p. 128.

Weidenreich, Franz (1941). See Sec. B, Collecting.

# P  (1)

## ILLUSTRATIONS—GENERAL

Clarke, C. D. (1939). Illustration; its technique and application to the sciences. Lucas, Baltimore, 386 pp.

German, J. C. (1943). Scientific illustration. Mus. News, Nov., v. 21, no. 10, p. 7.

Hanna, G. D. (1931). Illustrating fossils. J. Paleontology, v. 5, no. 1, p. 49–68, 1 pl., 2 figs.

Reeside, J. B., Jr. (1930). The preparation of paleontologic illustrations. J. Paleontology, v. 4, no. 3, p. 299–308, 1 pl.

Ridgway, J. L. (1920). The preparation of illustrations for reports of the U. S. Geol. Survey with brief descriptions of processes of reproduction. Dept. of Interior, U. S. Geol. Survey, 101 pp., 9 pls., 11 figs.

———— (1938). Scientific illustration. Stanford Univ. Press, 173 pp., 23 pls., 23 figs.

Weston, W. H., Jr. (1935). The use of celluloid in botanical illustrations. Am. J. Bot. v. 22, p. 384–391, 3 figs.

# P (2)

## ILLUSTRATIONS—PHOTOGRAPHY

Anderson, S. J. (1958). Phase-contrast photography of pollen. Veröff. Geobot. Inst. Rübel Zürich, no. 34, p. 20.

Beach, F. K. (1946). Photography of megafossils. Am. Assoc. Petrol. Geol. Bull., v. 30, p. 620–624.

Burling, L. C. (1911). Photographing fossils by reflected light. Am. J. Sci., 4th ser., v. 31, p. 99–100.

Clark, Walter (1946). Photography by infrared, its principles and applications (2nd ed.), Wiley, New York, xviii + 472 pp., 93 figs.

Clarke, C. D. (1934). See Sec. P(6) Illustrations—Drawings.

Eastman Kodak Co. (1961). Infrared and ultraviolet photography (7th ed.). Kodak Advanced Data Book No. M-3, 48 pp., Rochester, N. Y.

Easton, W. H. (1942). An improved technique for photographing peel sections of corals. J. Paleontology, v. 16, no. 2, p. 261–263.

Eaton, J. E. (1945). Photography of megafossils. Am. Assoc. Petrol. Geol. Bull., v. 29, p. 1494–1511.

Edinger, Tilly (1925). Photographie verschwundener Weichteile. Paläont. Zs., v. 7, p. 141–144.

Edmund, Gordon (1956). Photographic prints from peel sections. Soc. Vert. Paleont. News Bull., no. 48, p. 40.

Eggert, John (1935). Die Photographie im Dienste der paläontologischen Wissenschaft. Die Naturwiss., Berlin. Jahrg. 23, p. 168. [Abstract.]

———— (1936). La photographie au service de la paleontologie. International Congress of Photography, 9 Paris, 1935, Procès-ver-baux, rapports et mémoires, p. 737–741, 6 figs.

Evitt, W. R., II (1949). Stereophotography as a tool of the paleontologist. J. Paleontology, v. 23, p. 566–570, 1 pl.

Foldyna, Jan (1959). Použití stereoskopichých snímku v paleontologii (Emploi de photographies stéréoscopiques en paléontolgu). Čas. Mineral. geol., Českosl. v. 4, no. 2, p. 198–200.

Gott, P. F. (1945). Procedure of simplified stereophotography of fossils: J. Paleontology, v. 19, no. 4, p. 390–395, 1 pl.

Groom, H. B., Jr. (1953). Photographing minerals with the Leica. Leica Photog., v. 6, no. 3–4, p. 8, 44–45, illus.

Gutschick, R. C. (1960). Photography of Paleozoic arenaceous Foraminifera. J. Paleontology, v. 34, no. 4, p. 756–758.

Harris, J. E., and E. Latham (1951) Infra-red photography of fossils. Medical and Biol. Illus., v. 1, no. 3, p. 130.

Haverstick, E. J. (1931). Photographic method for securing copies of diagrams, etc., without use of a camera. Rev. Sci. Instrum., v. 2, p. 287–289.

Hay, Alfred (1930). Photographisches Praktikum für Mediziner und Natur-wissenschaftler. Springer, Vienna, 531 pp., 3 pls., 299 figs.

Hubendick, Bengt (1950). A photographical method of studying morphological variation. Arkiv. Zool., v. 42A, no. 5, p. 1–3, 1 pl.

Jeffords, R. M., and T. H. Miller (1960) See Sec. P(4), Illustrations—Coating of fossils.

Karth, E. G. (1936). Biological illustrations and the photo-engraver. Biol. Photo. Assoc., J., v. 4, p. 151–161.

Lawrence, A. S. C. (1941). The scientific photographer. Macmillan, New York, 180 pp.

Luckiesh, M. (1916). See Sec. P(6), Drawings.

McNair, A. H. (1941). A method of photographing impressions of fossils. J. Paleontology, v. 15, p. 91.

Mehl, M. G. (1921). Some suggestions for photographing fossils. Science, n.s., v. 54, p. 358.

Miethe, A. (1927). Über die Photographie von Fossilien bei ihrem eigenen Fluoreszenzlicht. Photogr. Korrespondenz, v. 63, p. 69–70.

————— (1927). Fossilien-Photographie; Koralle. Magazine f. alle Freunde von Natur. u. Technik, Jahrg. 3, p. 145–147, 6 figs.

Moyd, Louis (1949). A simple method for making stereoscopic photographs and micrographs. Min. Eng., v. 1, p. 383–384, Am. Inst. Min. Met. Eng. Tr. 184.

Pence, R. J. (1953). A simple stage for single-lens three-dimensional photo-macrography. Turtox News, v. 31, no. 9, p. 173–176.

Radley, J. A., and J. Grant (1933). See Sec. J, X-Rays.

Ramanadham, R., and K. N. Rao (1960). A simple inexpensive automatic camera for photographing at required intervals. J. Sci. Indust. Res., v. 20D, no. 4, p. 135–136.

Rasetti, Franco (1946). Optimum conditions for the photography of fossils. J. Paleontology, v. 20, p. 514–516.

Redini, Roberto (1938). Stereoscopia applicata allo studio dei fossili. Riv. Italiana Paleont., v. 44, p. 51–60.

Resser, C. E. (1933). Notes on photographing for the illustration of fossils. Paleont. Soc. Service Comm. Infrm. Bull., no. 10, p. 4–6.

Richter, R. (1951). Mikrokopie (Mikrofilm) bewirkt für die Paläontologie keine Veröffentlichung. Paläont. Zs., v. 24, p. 101–103.

Rotarides, M. von (1943). Über das Photographieren von Schnecken- und Muschelschalen. Ann. Hist. natur. Mus. natl. hungarici. Zool., Budapest, v. 36, p. 208–220.

Sampson, D. N. (1949). Photographic prints from cellulose-acetate transparencies. Geol. Mag., v. 86, no. 6, p. 386–387.

Sass, D. B. (1962). Improved techniques for the photographing of fossils. J. Paleontology, v. 36, no. 1, p. 171–172.

Seegert, Bruno (1928). Fluoreszenz-photographie von Fossilien. Die Umschau, Jahrg. 32, p. 134–136, 6 figs.

Seemann, Hans (1954). Beschreibung einer neuen Schwenk-Kamera. Chemie Erde, v. 17, H. 1, p. 29–37, illus.

Solle, Gerhard (1952). Neue Ergebnisse paläontologischer Arbeitstechnik. Paleont. Zs., v. 26, no. 3–4, p. 255–264, 1 pl. [Photography of small fossils.]

Spelvin, G. P. (1954). My subjects are old fossils. Leica Photog., v. 7, no. 3, p. 10–12, illus.

Toba, G. (1931). Methods of photographing shell specimens. Venus Kyote, v. 2, p. 198–199.

Van Ingen, Gilbert (1901). A method of facilitating photography of fossils. Science, n.s., v. 13, p. 710–711. [Abstract.]

Walker, J. J., and L. Slater (1935). Infra-red photography of coal. Nature, v. 135, p. 623.

Walton, John (1935). An application of infra-red photography to palaeobotanical research. Nature, v. 135, p. 265.

Wienert, Herbert (1960). Techniques in the photography of fossilized plants. Michigan Univ. Mus. Paleont., Contr., v. 15, no. 6, p. 125–132.

———— (1960). A simple device for single-lens sterophotography of paleontological specimens. Michigan Univ. Mus. Paleont. Contr. v. 15, no. 5, p. 121–124.

Williams, H. S. (1901). The photography of fossils. Science, n.s., v. 13, p. 790.

# P  (3)

## ILLUSTRATIONS—PHOTOMICROGRAPHY

Allen, R. M. (1941). Photomicrography. Van Nostrand, New York, 365 pp., 2nd ed. 1958, 441 pp.

Aprile, Guiseppi (1955). Microfotografie con riferimento fotografato sul negativo. Servizio Geol. d'Italia, B., v. 77, 1° f., p. 121–122.

Bachofen-Echt, A. (1926). Mikrophotographien von Bernsteininsekten. Paläont. Zs., v. 7, p. 162–163.

———— (1927). Farben-Photographien von in Bernstein und Kopal eingeschlossenen Insekten. Paläont. Zs., v. 9, p. 283–284.

Barnard, J. E. (1911). Practical photomicrography. Arnold, London, 322 pp., 10 pls., 79 figs.

————, and F. V. Welch (1925). Practical photomicrography (2nd ed.). Arnold, London, 316 pp., 16 pls. 86 figs.

———— (1936). Practical photomicrography (3rd ed.). Longmans, Green, 352 pp.

Batters, R. J. (1949). Adjustment and illumination when photographing with the aid of a microscope. Lincolnshire Nat.-Union, Tr., v. 12, p. 83–90.

Brünner, G. (1949). Kombinierte Beleuchtung in der Mikroskopie und Mikrophotographie. Mikrokosmos, v. 38, p. 207–209.

Burke, Frederick (1942). A simple plate camera for photomicrography. The Microscope, v. 5, no. 4, p. 78–81, 2 figs.

Butterfield, J. V. (1942). Faults in photomicrography. Biol. Photo. Assoc., J., v. 10, p. 175–183.

Chilton, L. V. (1945). Microfilm and other means of documentary reproductions. Nature, v. 156, p. 24–26.

Corin, F. (1931). Une méthode simple permettant d'obtenir de bonnes microphotographies. Soc. Sci. Bruxelles Ann., v. 51, p. 205–207, 1 fig.

Cummings, R. H. (1956). Preparation of microfossils for photography. Micropaleontology, v. 2, no. 4, p. 402.

Cushman, J. A. (1926). Photographing Foraminifera. Cushman Lab. Foram. Res. Contr., v. 2, pt. 1, p. 1–3.

Denne, M. T. (1923). An improved apparatus for the production of photomicrographs. Roy. Micros. Soc., J., p. 157–162.

Duijn, C. van, Jr. (1949). A photomicrographic stand for use with twin-lens reflex cameras. Microscope, v. 7, p. 217–218, 1 fig.

Earle, W. R. (1938). A simple photoelectric exposure meter for use in photomicrography. Biol. Photo. Assoc., J., v. 7, p. 54–58.

Fournier, George (1950). Photographing small foraminifera. Micropaleontologist, v. 4, no. 1, p. 19–21.

——— (1954). Use of the pinhole diagram in photomicrography. Micropaleontologist, v. 8, no. 3, p. 58–62, tfs. 1–5.

——— (1954). Photographing smaller foraminifers. Micropaleontologist, v. 4, no. 1, p. 19.

——— (1956) New methods and techniques in the photography of microfossils. Micropaleontology, v. 2, no. 1, p. 37–56.

——— (1957). Construction of pinhole diaphragms for use in photomicrography. Micropaleontology, v. 3, p. 85–87.

Gage, S. H. (1936). See Sec. L, Microscopy. [Chapter X on photographing with microscope.]

Gravelle, P. O. (1938). Surface illumination in low and medium power photomicrography. Biol. Photo. Assoc., J., v. 7, p. 27–32, 64–68.

Grove, B. H. (1932). A simple photomicrographic apparatus for obtaining depth of focus. Science, n.s., v. 75, p. 53.

Hanna, G. D. (1927). The photography of small objects. Am. Micros. Soc. Tr., v. 46, p. 15–25.

Headland, C. I. (1924). A simple and rapid photomicrograph for embryological sections. Anat. Rec., v. 27, p. 145–150.

Hecht, Franz (1934). Einfache Geräte zum Fotografieren von Mikrofossilien, ins-Besondere Foraminiferen. Senckenbergiana, Frankfurt, v. 16, p. 65–77.

——— (1935). Foraminiferen unterm Foto-objektiv. Senckenberg. Naturf. Ges. Abh., Berlin, v. 65, p. 295–303, 8 figs.

Hefley, H. M., and A. I. Smith (1942). A method for determining exposures for photomicrographs. Biol. Photo. Assoc., J., v. 10, p. 164–171.

Henbest, L. G. (1934). Exposure determination in photomicrography. Biol. Photo. Assoc., J., v. 3, no. 1, p. 2–23, 1 fig.

Hind, H. L., and W. B. Randles (1913). Handbook of photo-micrography. Dutton, New York; 2nd ed., 1927.

Hofker, Jan (1950). Photographing small foraminifera. Micropaleontologist, v. 4, no. 2, p. 21.

Hughes, R. J., Jr. (1954). Photomicrostereographs as an aid in interpreting textures and structures. J. Sed. Petrol., v. 24, no. 1, p. 20–26, illus.

Koch, W. (1941). Increasing the depth of focus in photomicrography by incident light. Roy. Micros. Soc., J., ser. 3, v. 61, p. 86–87.

Kornicker, L. S. (1953). A method of mounting microfossils for photographing. Micropaleontolgist, v. 7, no. 4, p. 32.

Kraft, Paul (1932). Neue optische Wege in der Mikrophotographie und Mikroskopie in Dienste del Geologie und Paläontologie. Zs. Deutsch, geol. Jes., v. 84, p. 651–652.

Kugler, H. G. (1957). Preparation of microfossils for photography. Micropaleontology, v. 3, no. 2, p. 190.

Lehmann, E. P. (1956). A technique of stereophotomicrography for illustrations in micropaleontology. J. Paleont., v. 30, no. 3, p. 757–759.

Linssen, E. F. (1949). The problem of simultaneous stereo-photomicrography. Microscope, v. 7, no. 5, p. 127–131, 2 figs.

Locquin, M. (1945). Microstéréosynthèses et reconstructions photographiques au grossissement élévés. Bull. mens. Soc. Linnéenne Lyon, 14, p. 18–23.

Loveland, R. P. (1943). Simplified photomicrography with a hand camera. Science, n.s., v. 97, p. 24–26.

Mangin, J. P. (1953). Photography of thin sections. Micropaleontologist, v. 7, no. 3, p. 67; discussion by Y. Nagappa, 1954, v. 8, no. 1, p. 38.

Maresh, Charles (1953). Infrared photomicrography with the electron image converter tube. J. Biol. Photogr. Assoc., v. 21 (3), p. 14–23, 20 figs.

McLean, J. D., Jr. (1957). Photomicrography of opaque specimens. McLean Paleont. Lab. Rept., no. 3, p. 5–11, illus.

McWhorter, F. P. (1927). A simple and inexpensive method of making photomicrographs. The Camera, v. 35, p. 381–384.

——— (1939). Application of fine-grain processing and condenser illumination enlarging to photomicrography. Stain Tech., v. 14, p. 87–96.

Mettler, F. A. (1938). Negative enlargement in photomicrography. Biol. Photo. Assoc., J., v. 7, p. 21–26.

Metzner, P. (1930). Einfache Einrichtungen zur Fluoreszenzmikroskopie und Fluoriszenz-mikrophotographie. Biol. Generalis, Wien-Leipzig, v. 6, p. 415–432, 4 pls., 5 figs.

Michel, K. (1940). Grundzüge der Mikrophotographie. Zeiss-Nachr., Sonderheft 4, Jena.

Nagappa, Y. (1954). Photography of thin sections. Micropaleontologist, v. 8, no. 1, p. 38.

Nicholas, J. W. (1947). The recording of exposure data in photo-micrography. Microscope, v. 6, no. 10, p. 263–265.

Pence, R. J. (1947). A simple device to increase background contrast in photomicrography. Science, v. 105, p. 503–504.

——— (1948). A simple attachment to increase depth of focus of microscope objectives for photomicrography. Science, v. 107, p. 631–632.

Pessagno, E. A., Jr. (1960). See Sec. G, Sectioning.

Petrunkevitch, Alexander (1920). Standardized microphotography. Anat. Rec., v. 19, p. 289–307.

—— (1921). The object factor. Am. Nat., v. 55, p. 178–180.

Piéchaud, M. (1952). Intérêt de la photomicrographie sur film inversible. Bull. Micros. Appliqué, ser. 2, v. 2, no. 7–8, p. 106–109.

Plummer, H. J. (1929). Photographic slide mount for micro-fossils. J. Paleontology, v. 3, no. 2, p. 189–195.

Pocock, S. A. (1959). See Sec. Q, Measurement.

Raeburn, L. T. (1944). Side-focusing eyepiece for small micro-cameras. Roy. Micros. Soc., J., ser. 3, v. 64, p. 147–148.

Rau, P. J. (1949). The use of microphotographic objective to improve image definition in photomicrography of semimicro objects. Turtox News, v. 27, no. 10, p. 239–242.

Sander, N. J. (1955). An apparatus for photographing foraminifera and other small objects. Micropaleontology, v. 1, no. 3, p. 251–256.

Shillaber, C. P. (1944). Photomicrography in theory and practice. Wiley, New York, 773 pp.

Soares, J. M. P., and E. C. Dos Santos (1952). The Sebattier effect in photomicrography. Microscope, v. 9, no. 1, p. 5–12, 2 pls. [Bas-relief in photomicrography.]

Stevens, R. B., and J. H. Taylor (1948). Photomicrography at your convenience. Science, v. 108, p. 420–421.

Strömberg, Arne (1952). A method for rapid photographing of microscopical objects. Geol. Fören. Stockh. Förh., v. 74, p. 386–389.

Thiery, G. (1949). L'emploi d'artifices photographiques en technique microphotographique; le "bas-relief," la "solarisation." Hist. Appl. Bull., v. 26, no. 1, p. 22–25.

Triebel, Erich (1947). See Sec. M(1), Micropaleontology—General. [Photomicrography, p. 29–45.]

Walmsley, W. H. (1902). The A.B.C. of photo-micrography. Tennant and Ward, New York, 155 pp.

Whittington, H. B. (1956). Photographing small fossils. J. Paleontology, v. 30, no. 3, p. 756–757.

# P (4)

## ILLUSTRATIONS—COATING OF FOSSILS

Cooper, C. L. (1935). Ammonium chloride sublimate apparatus. J. Paleontology, v. 9, p. 357–359.

Jeffords, R. M., and T. H. Miller (1960). Air brush for whitening fossils, and notes on photography. J. Paleontology, v. 34, no. 2, p. 275–276, 1 pl.

Poulsen, Charles (1957). Improved method for whitening fossils for study. J. Paleontology, v. 31, no. 5, p. 1029.

Rasetti, Franco (1947). Notes on techniques in invertebrate paleontology. J. Paleontology, v. 21, p. 397–398.

Teichert, Curt (1948). A simple apparatus for coating fossils with ammonium chloride. J. Paleontology, v. 22, p. 102–104.

Ulrich, E. O., and R. S. Bassler (1923). Paleozoic Ostracoda; their morphology, classification and occurrence. Maryland Geol. Survey [Reports on the systematic geology and paleontology of Maryland], Silurian, p. 281–283.

# P (5)

## ILLUSTRATIONS—FIELD PHOTOGRAPHY

Blackwelder, Eliot (1926). Photography for the field geologist. Wash. Acad. Sci. J., v. 16, p. 93–97.

———— (1931). Hints for better geological photographs. Science, v. 73, p. 241.

Graton, L. C. (1927). Underground photography without flash-light. Econ. Geol., v. 22, p. 388–399.

Thwaites, F. T. (1936). Field photography for geologist. Am. Assoc. Petrol. Geol. Bull., v. 20, no. 2, p. 186–214, 827–828.

Wentworth, C. K. (1925). Photographic practice for field geologists. Iowa Univ., Studies Nat. Hist., v. 11, no. 89, p. 17–40, 5 pls.

Wood, F. D. (1945). Color photography applied to stratigraphy. Connecticut Acad. Arts Sci. Tr., v. 36, p. 879–882.

# P (6)

## ILLUSTRATIONS—DRAWINGS

Bassé, Éliane (1930). Procédé simple permettant de reproduire les cloisons d'Ammonites et de Nautiles. Soc. géol. Fr., Bull., v. 30, p. 269–271.

Bather, F. A. (1917). Drawing in scientific work. Conf. Educat. Assoc. (Rept.), p. 1–44.

Begg, A. S. (1915). A simple form of drawing apparatus. Anat. Rec., v. 9, p. 715–717.

Böse, Emil (1907). Ein verbesserter Apparat zur photographischen Reproduktion von Ammonitensuturen und Ambulakren von Seeigeln. Zentralbl. Miner., Jahrg. 1907, p. 422–429.

Brown, Barnum (1935). Art studies in the field. Nat. Hist., v. 35, no. 1, p. 84. [Note.]

———— (1941). The methods of Walt Disney productions. N. Y. Acad. Sci., Tr., ser. 2, v. 3, no. 4, p. 100–105. [Abstract.]

Chapin, C. van A. (1946). An artist looks at the zoo. Animal Kingdom, v. 49, no. 4, p. 149–151.

Clarke, C. D. (1934). Combining drawing and photography for composite illustration. Biol. Photo. Assoc., J., v. 3, no. 2, p. 37–49.

———— (1938). The airbrush and its use. Biol. Photo. Assoc., J., v. 6, p. 101–124.

Colbert, E. H., and Chester Tarka (1960). Illustration of fossil vertebrates. Medical and Biol. Illus., v. 10, p. 237–246, 9 figs.

Cummings, R. H. (1952). See Sec. G, Sectioning.

Elias, M. K. (1933). Cephalopods of the Pierre formation of Wallace County, Kansas. Kansas Univ., Sci. Bull., v. 21, p. 290–293.

———— (1938). Studies of Late Paleozoic ammonoids. I. Methods of drawing sutures; bibliography. J. Paleontology, v. 12, p. 87–89.

Foldyna, Jan (1957). Use of stereoplotter STD-2 in paleontology for the morphological evaluation of fossil shells. Photogram. Engin., v. 23, no. 5, p. 935–937, illus.

Furnish, W. M., and A. G. Unklesbay (1940). Diagrammatic representation of ammonoid sutures. J. Paleontology, v. 14, no. 6, p. 598–602.

Gage, S. H. (1936). See Sec. L, Microscopy. [Chapter IX on drawing with microscope.]

Gilles, E. (1942). Un appareil destiné à la reproduction de dessins ou d'objets a diverses échelles. Soc. Linn. Lyon, Bull. mens., 11th Année, no. 8, p. 121–124.

Hudson, G. H. (1913). The use of the stereogram in paleobiology. N. Y. State Mus. Bull. 164, p. 103–130, 13 pls.

Hultgren, Ken (1950). The art of animal drawing. Construction, action, analysis, caricature. McGraw-Hill, New York, Toronto, London, 134 pp.

Hutchings, Geoffrey E. (1960). Landscape drawing. Methuen, London, 134 pp.

Innes, A. D. (1927). A description of a simple laboratory apparatus for obtaining accurate tracings of objects. Anat. Rec., v. 36, p. 195–198.

Knight, C. R. (1947). Animal anatomy and psychology for the artist and layman. Whittlesey House, McGraw-Hill, New York, London, 149 pp.

Kuhl, W. (1949). Das wissenschaftliche Zeichnen in der Biologie and Medizin. Kramer, Frankfurt, 108 pp., 103 figs. (Herausgegeben von Senckenberg. naturf. Gesells.)

Lapage, Geoffrey (1949). Draughtmanship in zoological work. Endeavour, v. 8, no. 30, p. 70–79.

Luckiesh, M. (1916). Light and shade and their applications. Van Nostrand, New York, 265 pp., 135 illus., 10 tables. [Chapter XII, p. 190–215, light and shade in photography.]

Lupher, A. W., R. L. Lupher, and E. L. Packard (1930) An apparatus for the reproduction of suture-lines of ammonites. J. Paleontology, v. 4, no. 1, p. 22–23.

Napoli, Enrico di (1955). A new type of microfaunal diagram. Micropaleontology, v. 1, no. 2, p. 133–139.

Nature (1930). The Leakey-Harper drawing machine. Nature, v. 126, p. 220–222, 3 figs.

Naylor, Ernest (1931). Pen and ink drawings from photographs. Science, n.s., v. 73, no. 1879, p. 15.

Nicholson, J. L. (1933). Dupont cement as a fixative for pencil drawings. Micropaleont. Bull., v. 4, no. 2, p. 47.

Nicolesco, Constant (1918). Application des empreintes au collodion à la reproduction des cloisons des Ammonoides. Soc. géol. Fr., Bull., Sér. 4., v. 18, p. 217.

Souèges, René (1934). Coffret-support pour dessin à la chambre claire de Malassez: Soc. Franç. Micros., Bull., v. 3, p. 119–122, 3 figs. [Drawing from microscope.]

Staniland, L. N. (1953). The principles of line illustration with emphasis on the requirements of biological and other scientific workers. Harvard Univ. Press, 212 pp.

Stanley, J. (1930). A method of copying biological reconstructions with any desired factor of magnification. Anat. Rec., v. 48, p. 13–18, 3 figs.

Swinnerton, H. H., and A. E. Trueman (1957). The morphology and development of the ammonite septum. Geol. Soc. London, Quart. J., v. 73, p. 26–58.

Weidenreich, Franz (1926). Ein verbesserter Günther-Metzscher Zeichenapparat der Firma G. Leitz in Wetzlar für Osteologisch-Anthropologische Zwecke. Zs. Morphologie, Anthropologie, v. 26, H. 1, p. 181–184.

Williams, S. R. (1917). Scientific drawing in biology. Ohio J. Sci., v. 17, no. 6, p. 205–212.

Wilwerding, W. J. (1946). Animal drawing and painting. Watson-Guptill, New York, 147 pp., illus.

Wood, Alan (1945). A rapid method of making accurate drawings of small and microscopic objects. Geol. Assoc. Pr., v. 56, p. 18–19.

# P (7)

## ILLUSTRATIONS—CHARTS AND GRAPHS

Arkin, Herbert, and R. R. Colton (1936). Graphs, how to make and use them. Harpers, New York and London, 224 pp.; revised ed., 1940, 236 pp.

Hovanitz, William (1948). A graphic method of illustrating ecological and geographical distributions. Ecology, v. 29, no. 1, p. 121.

Karsten, K. G. (1923). Charts and graphs. Prentice-Hall, New York, 724 pp.

Swinnerton, H. H. (1921). The use of graphs in palaeontology. Geol. Mag., v. 58, p. 357–364, 397–408.

Tasch, Paul (1955). The triangular graph in population analysis—uses and limitations. J. Paleontology, v. 29, no. 1, p. 171–177, illus.

Walford, L. A. (1946). A new graphic method of describing the growth of animals. Biol. Bull., v. 90, p. 141–147.

# P (8)

## ILLUSTRATIONS—CAMERA LUCIDA

Cutright, P. R. (1930). Black paper for camera lucida drawings. Science, n.s., v. 72, no. 1864, p. 299.

Harding, J. T. (1941). Simple modification of the camera lucida for making larger drawings. Nature, v. 148, p. 754–755, 2 figs.

Hobson, G. D. (1942). Construction of perspective drawings from contoured maps by means of a camera lucida. Geol. Mag., v. 79, p. 147–152.

Richards, G. L. (1931). Camera lucida drawings. Micropaleont. Bull., v. 2, p. 107.

Stensiö, E. A. (1927). Description of the Spitsbergen forms; material and methods. Skrifter om Svalbard og Nordishavet, Oslo, no. 12, pt. 1, p. 18–19. [Camera lucida.]

# P (9)

## ILLUSTRATIONS—LANTERN SLIDES

Copeland, D. E. (1948). Automatic masking of lantern slides. Science, v. 107, p. 401.

Fuller, H. J. (1948). AAAS meetings and lantern slides. Science, v. 107, p. 140–141.

Moore, C. A. (1942). Preparation of lantern-slide copy. Am. Assoc. Petrol. Geol. Bull., v. 26, p. 1656–1671.

Neuberger, Hans (1948). A method for making lantern slides. Science, v. 107, p. 23.

Sommer, W. (1946). Lantern slides of diagrams, formulae, etc. Nature, v. 158, p. 591.

Van Pelt, J. R. (1950). Lantern slides and such. Quart. J. Speech, v. 36, p. 44–50.

# Q

## MEASUREMENTS

Ashton, E. H., and W. J. Pardoe (1950). A craniostat and projector for the measurement of mammalian skulls. Man, Aug., no. 163, p. 1–3.

Breathnach, A. S. (1950). The measurement of palatal height and length by means of the travelling microscope. Man, London, Apr., v. 50, art. 47, p. 37–40, 1 pl.

Diver, D. (1931). A method of determining the number of the whorls of a shell and its application to *Cepoea hortensis* Müll. and *C. nemoralis* L. Malacol. Soc. London, Pr., v. 19, pt. 5, p. 234–239.

Dunbar, C. O., and L. G. Henbest (1942). Pennsylvanian Fusulinidae of Illinois. Illinois State Geol. Survey Bull., no. 67, 218 pp. [p. 57–64 on measurement.]

Fujita, Tunetaro (1949). On the standard of the measurement of teeth. Anthrop. Soc. Nippon, J., v. 61, no. 690, p. 27–32. [In Japanese.]

Goodchild, C. G. (1951). Measurement of small microscopic objects by microprojection. Am. Micros. Soc., Tr., v. 70, no. 4, p. 348–350.

Hamilton, J. D., and M. L. Barr (1948). An elliptometer. A simple method of measuring the areas of structures in microscopic sections. Stain Tech., v. 23, p. 123–127.

Hanna, G. D. (1931). Illustrating Fossils. J. Paleontology, v. 5, no. 1, p. 49–68, 1 pl., 2 figs. [p. 65–68 on measurement.]

Kalinko, M. K. (1955). O novykh geologicheskikh izmeritelnykh priborakh. Geol.

Sbornik (Vsesoyuz. Neft. Nauch.-Issled. Geol.-Razv. Inst.), v. 3, pt. 6, p. 293–313, illus. [New types of geologic measuring instruments.]

Kornicker, L. S. (1960). Methods of measuring the internal volume of shells. J. Paleontology, v. 34, no. 3, p. 595–596.

Lamberton, Charles (1947). Un nouvel appareil pour les mesures craniométriques. Acad., Malgache, B. (for the years 1944–1945), n.s., v. 26, p. 143–144.

Mangili, G. (1947). Di un nuevo metodo grafico craniometrico. Riv. Antropol., v. 35 (1944–1947), p. 443–449, 1 fig.

Pocock, S. A. (1959). Scales for making direct measurements from photomicrographs. Micropaleontology, v. 5, no. 3, p. 349–350.

Richards, C. M. (1948). Formulae for museum measurements. Museum News, v. 25, no. 19, p. 7–8.

Simmons, Gene (1959). The photo-extinction method for the measurement of silt-sized particles. J. Sed. Petrol., v. 29, no. 2, p. 233–245.

Sloan, R. E. (1951). A new instrument for measuring fossils. J. Paleontology, v. 25, no. 4, p. 525–526, 1 fig.

Steggerda, Morris (1949). Anthropometric instruments. Am. J. Phys. Anthropology, n.s., v. 7, no. 3, p. 473–474.

Stewart, T. D. (1942). Variation in the technique of measuring skulls. Anthrop. Briefs, no. 2, Aug., p. 1–6.

White, M. P. (1950). See Sec. M(2), Micropaleontology—Foramanifera.

# R

## RESTORATION AND RECONSTRUCTION

Abel, Othenio (1925). Geschichte und Methode der Rekonstruktion Vorzeitlicher Wirbeltiere. Gustav Fisher, Jena, 327 pp.

Avinoff, Andrey (1941). Rept. Dept. Geol., Ann. Rept., Field Mus. Nat. Hist., v. 12, no. 2, publ. 497, p. 227–235, 1 pl. [Skeleton and restoration of *Leptomeryx*.]

Beck, H. T. (1942). Reconstruction of prehistoric animals. Los Angeles Mus. Quart., v. 2, no. 2, p. 17–19, 1 fig.

Boonstra, L. D. (1952). Reconstructing life-sized models of prehistoric reptiles. 200,000,000 years ago in the South African Karroo. Samab., v. 5, no. 7, p. 179–183.

Engel-Baiersdorf, E. C. von (1949). The method of reconstructing human and animal remains in sculpture and in paintings. Mus. Art Notes, ser. 2, v. 1, no. 1, p. 5–11.

German, J. C. (1943). From rock to canvas. Nat. Hist., v. 51, no. 4, p. 166–175. [Restoration.]

Hill, F. C. (1886). On the mounting of fossils. Am. Naturalist Extra, Apr. 1896.

Hoagland, Clayton (1943). They gave life to bones. Sci. Monthly, Feb., v. 56, p. 114–133.

Jagt, E. R. van der (1931). Reconstruction work by the use of cellophane. Science, n.s., v. 74, p. 601.

Johnston, C. S. (1941). How to make a mastodon. Students of paleontology reconstruct a model of *Amebelodon* from fossils (at West Texas College, Dept. of Paleontology). Sci. Am., v. 165, 6, p. 333–334.

Keller, Gerhard (1939). Das Steinkohlen wald-Diorama in Ruhrland-Museum in Essen. Museumskunde, v. 2, H. 3–4, p. 144–150, 1 pl.

Kleinschmidt, Adolf (1951). Über eine Rokonstruktion des Schädels von *Archaeornis siemensi* Dames 1884 im Naturhist. Museum, Braunschweig. Pr. 10th. Internatl. Ornithol. Cong. in 1950, 1951, p. 631–635.

Koch, G. V. (1913). Über Versuche mit Zellon bei zoologischen und paläontologischen Präparationen sowie einige Worte über Gipsabgüsse. Museumskunde, Berlin, v. 9, p. 216–219.

König, Friedrich (1911). Fossil reconstruktionen: Bemerkengen zu einer Reihe plastischer Habitusbilder fossiler Wirbeltiere. Dultz, München.

Lake, Philip (1943). Restoration of the original forms of distorted specimens. Geol. Mag., v. 80, p. 139–147, 1 pl.

Orr, P. C. (1940). An adjustable frame for mounting fossil skeletons. Mus. J., v. 39, no. 10, p. 420–421, 2 pls.

Pusey, H. K. (1939). Methods of reconstruction from microscopic sections. Roy. Micros. Soc. J., ser. 3, v. 59, p. 232–244.

Ruedemann, Rudolf, and Winifred Goldring (1931). Some museum methods developed in the New York State Museum. N.Y. State Mus. Bull., 288, p. 71–83, 8 figs.

Stewart, T. D. (1952). Wishful thinking in the reconstruction of skulls. Am. J. Phys. Anthropology, n.s., v. 10, no. 4, p. 520–521.

Strasser, H. (1887). Ueber die Methoden der plastischen Reconstruction. Zs. f. Wiss. Mikros. und. Mikros. Technik, v. 4, H. 2–3, p. 168–208, 330–339, 6 figs.

# Part V

## COMPILATION OF BIBLIOGRAPHIES OF USE TO PALEONTOLOGISTS AND STRATIGRAPHERS

BERNHARD KUMMEL

# Compilation of Bibliographies of use to Paleontologists and Stratigraphers

BERNHARD KUMMEL

*Harvard University, Cambridge, Massachusetts*

The growth of paleontology and stratigraphic geology over the past 150 years has resulted in an accumulation of literature that has reached staggering proportions. Knowledge of the many and diverse bibliographic sources is essential. General discussions on the source and kind of geological literature available are very ably discussed by Pearl [1] and Mason.[2]

The following list is the outgrowth of my attempts over many years to teach students about library resources. The list is in no sense complete; some selectivity had to be exercised, hence some items have been excluded.

The individual references are grouped by subject or by country; cross references are included to facilitate efficient use of this list. The abbreviations used in journal citations are those used by the U. S. Geological Survey and the Geological Society of America. The numbers given in the Contents refer to the first item under each category. Acknowledgment is made to the Milton Fund Small Grants Program of Harvard University for clerical assistance in the preparation of this section.

---

[1] R. M. Pearl (1951). *Guide to Geologic Literature.* New York, McGraw-Hill, 239 pp.
[2] Brian Mason (1953). *The Literature of Geology.* 155 pp.

## CONTENTS

# Contents

## STANDARD CURRENT BIBLIOGRAPHIES

1. United States Geological Survey (1732 to date) Bibliographies covering Central and North America from Panama northward, the West Indies, Greenland, and the Hawaiian Islands. The older bibliographies of this series are not listed here because they are summarized in Darton (1896) and Nickles (1923–1924).

   Darton, N. H. (1896) Catalogue and index on contributions to North American Geology, 1732–1891. U.S. Geol. Surv. Bull. 127, 1045 pp.

   Nickles, J. M. (1923–1924) Geologic literature on North America, 1785–1918. *Ibid.,* Bull. 746, Pt. I, Bibliography, 1167 pp., 1923; Pt. II, Index, 658 pp., 1924.

   ———— (1931) Bibliography of North American Geology, 1919–1928. *Ibid.,* Bull. 823, 1005 pp.

   Thom, E. M. (1944) *Ibid.,* 1929–1939, Bull. 937, 1546 pp. (1942) 1940 and 1941, Bull. 938, 479 pp. (1945) 1942 and 1943, Bull. 949, 460 pp. (1947) 1944 and 1945, Bull. 952, 496 pp.

   ————, M. Hooker, and R. R. Dunaven (1949) *Ibid.,* 1946 and 1947, Bull. 958, 658 pp. (1950) 1948, Bull. 968, 309 pp. (1951) 1949, Bull. 977, 273 pp.

   Hooker, Marjorie (1952) *Ibid.,* 1950, Bull. 985, 394 pp.

   King, R. R., V. M. Jussen, J. S. Pomeroy, and V. L. Skitsky (1955) *Ibid.,* 1951, Bull. 1025, 378 pp. (1956) 1952–1953, Bull. 1035, 714 pp. (1957) 1940–1949, Bull. 1049, Pt. 1, Bibliography, p. 1–1034, Pt. 2, Index, p. 1035–2205. (1957) 1954, Bull. 1054, 484 pp. (1958) 1955, Bull. 1065, 511 pp. (1959) 1956, Bull. 1075, 554 pp. (1960) 1957, Bull. 1095, 531 pp. (1961) 1959, Bull. 1145, 605 pp.

2. Geological Society of America (1934 to date) Bibliography and index of geology exclusive of North America. v. 1, 1933; v. 2, 1934; v. 3, 1935; v. 4, 1936; v. 5, 1937; v. 6, 1938; v. 7, 1939; v. 8, 1940; v. 9, 1941–1942; v. 10, 1943–1944; v. 11, 1945–1946; v. 12, 1947; v. 13, 1948; v. 14, 1949; v. 15, 1950; v. 16, 1951; v. 17, 1952; v. 18, 1953; v. 19, 1954; v. 20, 1955; v. 21, 1956; v. 22, 1957; v. 23, 1958; v. 24, 1959; v. 25, 1960; v. 26, 1961.

3. Neues Jahrbuch (1807 to date) [This has been an extremely important source of original geological articles, abstracts, and bibliographies for more than 150 years. It has undergone many title changes and modifications in the course of its publication. The Zentralblatt listed at the end of this series is the current abstract and review journal.]

   1807–1824: Taschenbuch für die gesammte Mineralogie [After 1819 had the subtitle Mineralogisches Taschenbuch]

   1825–1829: Zeitschrift für Mineralogie, Taschenbuch.

   1830–1832: Jahrbüch für Mineralogie, Geognosie, Geologie und Petrefaktenkunde

   1833–1862: Neues Jahrbuch für Mineralogie, Geognosie, Geologie und Petrefaktenkunde.

1863–1925: Neues Jahrbuch für Mineralogie, Geologie und Paläontologie. Jahrgäńge [Annual volumes, original contributions and review abstracts; after 1923, reviews and abstracts only] Beilagebände (Vol. 1: 1881) [Original contributions only]

1900–1924: Centralblatt für Mineralogie, Geologie, und Paläontologie [Brief original contributions and communications]

1925–1942: Neues Jahrbuch für Mineralogie, Geologie und Paläontologie (Abt. B: Geologie–Paläontologie). 1925–1927: Referate, Abt. B [Reviews and abstracts] 1928–1942: Referate, Teil II and III [Reviews and abstracts] 1925–1942: Beilagebände, Abt. B [Vols. 52–87, original contributions only]

1925–1942: Zentralblatt für Mineralogie, Geologie, und Paläontologie, Abt. B [Brief original contributions and communications]

1943–1949: Neues Jahrbuch für Mineralogie, Geologie und Paläontologie (Abt. B) Abhandlungen, Abt. B [Vols. 88–91, original contributions only; previously Beilagebände, Abt. B] Monatshefte, Abt. B [Brief original contributions and communications; previously Zentralblatt, etc., Abt. B]

1943–1949: Zentralblatt für Mineralogie, Geologie und Paläontologie, Teil II and III [Reviews and abstracts; previously N. Jahrb. etc., Referate, Teil II and III; not published 1943–1947]

1950–present: Neues Jahrbuch für Geologie und Paläontologie. Abhandlungen [Beginning with Vol. 92, original contributions only] Monatshefte [Brief original communications]

1950–present: Zentralblatt für Geologie und Palaeontologie [Reviews and abstracts] Teil I, General and applied geology including geology of deposits, regional geology. Teil II, Historical geology and paleontology.

The following indices for these journals have been published: for 1830–1839, 1840–1849, 1850–1859, 1860–1869, 1870–1879, 1880–1884, 1885–1889, 1890–1894, 1895–1899, 1900–1904, 1905–1909, 1910–1924 (I and II), 1925–1929 (I and II), 1930–1935 (I and II), 1936–1940 (I and II), 1946–1949 (I and II).


## SPECIAL AND OLDER
## NORTH AMERICAN BIBLIOGRAPHIES

4. United States Geological Survey. Publications of the Geological Survey. [A complete list and index of the survey publications exclusive of topographic maps. This booklet is revised and reissued from time to time. The catalogue is supplemented by a bimonthly list of publications, issued in pamphlet form, free on application.]

5. Albertson, G. H. (1931) Geologic index of the publications of the United States Geological Survey. Denver, Geological Publishing Co., 420 pp. (1932) Suppl., 15 pp.

6. Howell, J. V., and A. I. Levorsen (1946, 1957) Directory of geological material in North America. Am. Assoc. Petrol. Geol. Bull., v. 30, no. 8,

pt. 2, p. 1321–1432. (1957) Second ed., revised and enlarged, Natl. Res. Council Pub. 556, Am. Geol. Inst., 208 pp.

7. Heath, D. W. (1947) Comprehensive index of publications of the American Association of Petroleum Geologists 1917–1945. Amer. Assoc. Petrol. Geol., 603 pp.

8. Turner, D. S. (1954) Bibliography of geology theses: Colleges and universities of the United States. Micro-RESEARCH-Card Petroleum Geology Library. Denver, The Petroleum Research Company, 483 pp.

9. Chronic, John, and Halka Chronic (1958) Bibliography of theses written for advanced degrees in geology and related sciences at universities and colleges in the United States and Canada through 1957. Boulder, Colo., Pruett Press, Inc.

10. Little, H. P. (1922) List of manuscript bibliographies in geology and geography. Natl. Res. Council, Reprint and Circular Series, no. 27, 17 pp.

11. Mathews, E. B. (1923) Catalogue of published bibliographies in geology, 1896–1920. Natl. Res. Council, Pub. no. 36, 228 pp.

12. Long, H. K. (1958) Manual of reference sources in geology. Washington Univ. Libr. Reference Manual, no. 5, 21 pp.

13. Smithsonian Institution Editorial Division (1947) A list and index of the publications of the United States National Museum (1875–1946). U. S. Natl. Mus. Bull. 193, 306 pp.

14. Bradley, W. H. (1938) A brief annotated bibliography on cyclic variations in climate as indicated by pre-Pleistocene non-glacial varves. Am. Meteorol. Soc. Bull., v. 19, no. 5, p. 162–163.

15. Girard, Charles (1852) Bibliographia Americana historico-naturalis: A.D. 1851. Smithson. Publ. no. 48, p. 1–60.

16. Hasse, A. R. (1899) Reports of explorations printed in the documents of the United States Government (A contribution toward a bibliography). Washington, D.C., Government Printing Office, 90 pp.

17. Academy of Natural Sciences of Philadelphia (1913) An index to the scientific contents of the Journal and Proceedings of The Academy of Natural Sciences of Philadelphia 1817–1910. Philadelphia, Acad. Nat. Sci., 1433 pp. [This index is particularly important for Tertiary stratigraphy and paleontology, because many of the early publications of the Academy dealt with geology of the Gulf and Atlantic Coastal Plains.]

18. Schmeckebier, L. F. (1904) Catalogue and index of the publications of the Hayden, King, Powell, and Wheeler Surveys, etc. U. S. Geol. Surv. Bull. 222, 208 pp.

19. Haskell, D. C. (1942) The United States exploring expedition 1838–1842, and its publications 1844–1874. A bibliography. New York, The New York Publ. Library, 188 pp.

20. Meisel, Max (1924–1929) A bibliography of American natural history: the pioneer century, 1769–1865. The role played by the scientific societies, scientific journals, natural history museums and botanic gardens, state geological and natural history surveys, federal exploring expeditions in the rise and progress of American botany, geology, mineralogy, paleontology and zoology. Brooklyn, Premier Pub. Co., 3 v. (1) Annotated bibliography of history, biography and bibliography of the period 1769–1865,

with a classified subject and geographic index. (2) Institutions founded between 1769 and 1844. History and detailed account of the publications, including publication dates. (3) Institutions founded between 1845 and 1865. Bibliography of books. Chronological Tables. Index of Authors and Institutions. Addenda to Volume 1.

## SPECIAL AND OLDER FOREIGN BIBLIOGRAPHIES

21. Société Géologique de France (1923–1960) Bibliographie des sciences géologiques. Paris, The Société. Pt. 1, v. 1–7 (1923–1929); citations only, in the form of the tables of contents, number by number, of current issues of the serials it covers, including government survey publications; pt. 2, v. 1 (1931); changed so titles are listed by subject.

22. Bibliographie Scientifique Francaise (1902 to date) Paris, Bureau Française du Catalogue International de la Littérature Scientifique. [Issued in two parts: pt. 1, Sciences mathématiques et physiques; pt. 2, Sciences naturelles et biologique.]

23. Bureau de Recherches Géologiques et Minères, Service d'Information Géologique. Bibliographical card index. [World-wide coverage, cards obtained monthly by subscription (74, rue de la Federations, Paris).]

24. Société Géologique de Belgique (1920 to date) Revue de géologie et des sciences connexes. Liége, Vaillant-Carmanne.

25. Woodward, B. B. (1903–1940) Catalogue of books, manuscripts, maps and drawings in the British Museum (Natural History). London, British Mus., vols. 1–8.

26. International catalogue of scientific literature (1903–1920) (G) Mineralogy, including petrology and crystallography; (H) Geology; (K) Paleontology. Published for the Internat. Council by the Royal Soc., 14 v.

27. Geological Society of London (1894–1934) Geological literature added to the Geological Society's library during the year ended December 31, etc. Geol. Soc. London, 1894–1934. [World wide in scope, nearly complete, good cross index. Discontinued in 1934.]

28. Comptoir Géologique de Paris (1885–1893) Annuaire géologique universel et guide du geologue. v. 1–10. [World-wide in coverage.]

29. The Geological Record (1874–1884) London [13 volumes only. Covers world literature for 1874–1884.]

30. Royal Society of London (1867–1925) Catalogue of scientific papers, 1800–1900. V. 1–6 for 1800–1863; v. 7–8 for 1864–1873; v. 9–11 for 1874–1883; v. 12 for 1800–1883, Suppl.; v. 13–19 for 1884–1900.

31. Mourlon, M. F. (1899–1901) Bibliographia geologica, series A, v. 1–7 (lists publications printed before 1896); series B, v. 1–4 (after 1896). Brussels, Academie Royale de Belgique.

32. Margerie, E. de (1896) Catalogue des bibliographies géologiques [1726–1896] rédigé avec le concours des nombres de la Commission Bibliographique du Congrès. Pt. 1, General; pt. 2, Regional. Paris, Gauthier-Villars et fils, 733 pp.

33. Dewalque, G. (1884) Catalogue des ouvrages de géologie, de minéralogie et de paléontologie. Liége, Societié Géologique de Belgique, Vaillant-Carmanne, 394 pp.
34. Cotta, Bernhard (1877) Beiträge zur Geschichte der Geologie. Erste Abtheilung, Geologisches Repertorium [1546–1876] Leipzig, 400 pp.
35. Giebel, C. G. (1851) Bericht über die Leistungen im Gebiete der Paläontologie mit besonderer Berücksichtigung der Geognosie während der Jahre 1848 und 1849. Berlin, 282 pp.
36. Agassiz, Louis (1848–1854) Bibliographia zoologiae et geologiae. A general catalogue of all books, tracts, and memoirs on zoology and geology. London, Ray Society, 4 volumes, 506 pp., 492 pp., 657 pp., 604 pp.
37. Englemann, Wilhelm (1846) Bibliotheca Historico-Naturalis. Verzeichniss der Bücher über Naturgeschichte welche in Deutschland, Scandinavien, Holland, England, Frankreich, Italien und Spanien in den Jahren 1700–1846 Erschienen sind. Leipzig. 786 pp.
38. Keferstein, Christian (1840) Geschichte und Litteratur der Geognosie. Halle, 281 pp.
39. Boehmers, D. G. R. (1786–1789) Handbuch der Naturgeschichte Oeconomie und anderer damit verwandten Wissenschaften und Künste. Pt. 1, Allgemeine Schriftsteller, v. 1, 778 pp., 1785; v. 2, 772 pp., 1786. Pt. 2. Thierreich, v. 1, 604 pp., v. 2, 536 pp., 1786. Pt. 3, Gewaechsreich, v. 1, 808 pp., 1787, v. 2, 642 pp., 1787. Pt. 4, Mineralreich, v. 1, 510 pp., 1788, v. 2, 412 pp., 1789. Pt. 5, Wasserreich, nehst Allgemeinen Register, 704 pp., 1789.

## CATALOGUES OF SCIENTIFIC PERIODICALS

40. Scudder, S. H. (1879) Catalogue of scientific serials of all countries including the transactions of learned societies in the natural, physical and mathematical Sciences, 1633–1876. Cambridge, 358 pp.
41. Bolton, H. C. (1885) A catalogue of scientific and technical periodicals, 1665–1882, together with chronological tables and a library check list. Smithson. Misc. Coll. 514, 718 pp.
42. Smith W. A., ed. (1925, 1927) A world list of scientific periodicals published in the years 1900–1921. New York, Oxford Univ. Press, v. 1, 499 pp. (1925); v. 2, 344 pp. (1927).
43. Brown, Peter, and G. B. Stratton, ed. (1963) World list of scientific periodicals published in the years 1900–1960. Washington, D.C., Butterworths, v. I, A–E, 531 pp. [Additional volumes to be published.]
44. Gregory, Winifred (1932) List of the serial publications of foreign governments, 1815–1931. New York, H. W. Wilson Co., 720 pp.
45. ——— (1938) International congresses and conferences, 1840–1937. A union list of their publications available in libraries of the United States and Canada. New York, H. W. Wilson Co., 229 pp.
46. ——— (1961) Union list of serial in libraries of the United States and Canada. New York, 3rd ed,

**47.** Biological Abstracts (1955) Biological sciences serial publications: World list, 1950–1954. Philadelphia, Biological Abstracts, 269 pp.
**48.** Lomský, Josef (1959) Soupis periodik geologických věd; periodica geologica, palaeontologica et mineralogica, Prague, Českoslov. Akad. Věd, 501 pp. [An alphabetic compilation of periodical titles in which papers on geology, paleontology, and mineralogy are published; includes subject indexes.]
**49.** Buttress, Frederick A. (1960) World List of Abbreviations of Scientific Technoloical and Commercial Organizations. 2d ed. London, Leonard Hill, 300 pp.

## REGIONAL BIBLIOGRAPHIES

### United States

#### *Alabama*

**50.** Harper, R. M. (1935) Bibliography of Alabama geology. *In* Alabama Geol. Surv. Bull. 42, p. 59–108.
**51.** Jones, W. B. (1937) Complete list of publications of the Geological Survey of Alabama to January 1, 1937. Alabama Geol. Surv., Univ. Ala., 16 pp.
**52.** Harper, R. M. (1940) Supplementary bibliography of Alabama geology. *In* Alabama Geol. Surv. Bull. 44, p. 47–55.
**53.** Hildreth, Ellen, and P. M. Foster (1942) Know Alabama! The geology and mineral resources of Alabama: A bibliography for schools. Alabama Geol. Surv. Bull. 51, 56 pp., 9 figs. incl. index map.
**54.** See 525 (Cenozoic Stratigraphy)

#### *Alaska*

**55.** Fuller, G. H. (1943) Aleutian Islands: A list of references. Washington, D.C., Lib. of Cong., Div. of Bib., 41 pp.
**56.** Dutro, J. T., Jr. (1956) Annotated bibliography of Alaskan Paleozoic paleontology. *In* U. S. Geol. Surv. Bull. 1021-H, p. 253–287.

#### *Arizona*

**57.** Lutrell, Estelle (1915) Bibliography of Arizona mining, metallurgy and geology. Univ. Arizona, Bull. 23, Arizona Bur. Mines, 49 pp.
**58.** Jenkins, O. P. and E. D. Wilson (1920) List of United States Geological Survey publications relating to Arizona. Univ. Arizona Bull. 104 (Geol. ser. no. 1), 40 pp.
**59.** Wilson, E. D. (1939) Bibliography of the geology and mineral resources of Arizona. Arizona Bur. Mines Bull. 146, Geol. ser. 13 (Univ. Bull., vol. 10, no. 2), 164 pp., 1 fig. index map.
**60.** Anthony, J. W., E. D. Wilson, and R. T. Moore (1953) Bibliography of the geology and mineral resources of Arizona, 1939–1952. Ariz. Bur. Mines Bull. no. 161, Geol. Ser., no. 20, 62 pp.

### Arkansas

**61.** Branner, J. C. (1894) Bibliography of the geology of Arkansas. *In* Arkansas Geol. Surv. Ann. Rept. 1891, v. 2, p. 319–340.

**62.** ———, and A. H. Purdue (1909) Bibliography of the geology of Arkansas. *In* Arkansas Geol. Surv., Slates of Arkansas, p. 97–164.

**63.** See 525 (Cenozoic Stratigraphy)

### California

**64.** Vodges, A. W. (1896) A bibliography relating to the geology, paleontology and mineral resources of California: Calif. State Mining Bureau, Bull. 10, 121 pp. (1904) *ibid.*, Bull. 30, 290 pp.

**65.** Shedd, Solon (1931–1940) Bibliography of the geology and mineral resources of California to the end of 1929. Calif. Dept. Nat. Res. Div. Mines Bull. 104 (preliminary ed.), 205 pp., 1931; to December 31, 1930, Bull. 104, 376 pp., 1932; for the years 1931 to 1936, inclusive (supplementing the master bibliography, Bull. 104), Bull. 115, 125 pp., 1938; for the year 1937 (supplementing Bull. 104 and 115 of the Division of Mines), Calif. J. Mines and Geol., v. 35, no. 3, 1939, p. 275–307.

**66.** Jenkins, O. P. (1943) Glossary of the geologic units of California: Compilation based largely on the work of M. Grace Wilmarth and Alice S. Allen, abstracted and revised by Olaf Pitt Jenkins. *In* Calif. Dept. Nat. Res., Div. Mines Bull. 118, pt. 4, p. 667–687.

**67.** Chapin, E. L., Jr. (1953) A selected bibliography of southern California maps. Berkeley and Los Angeles, Univ. Calif. Press, 124 pp.

**68.** Jennings, C. W., and R. G. Strand (1963) Index to graduate theses on California geology to December 31, 1961. Calif. Div. Mines Geol., Spec. Rept. 74, 39 pp.

### Colorado

**69.** Jones, O. M. (1914) Bibliography of Colorado geology and mining, with subject index, from the earliest explorations to 1912. Colorado Geol. Surv. Bull. 7, 493 pp.

**70.** Johnson, J. H. (1923) Bibliography of the geology of the Denver Basin of Colorado. Colorado School of Mines, Circular of Information, 7 pp.

**71.** ——— (1924) Bibliography of the geology of northwestern Colorado. Colorado School of Mines, Circular of Information, 7 pp.

**72.** ——— (1924) Bibliography of the geology of southwestern Colorado. Colorado School of Mines, Circular of Information, 7 pp.

**73.** ——— (1925) Bibliography of the geology of northeastern Colorado. Colorado School of Mines, Circular of Information, 12 pp.

**74.** ——— (1925) Bibliography of the geology of southeastern Colorado. Colorado School of Mines, Circular of Information, 11 pp.

**75.** ——— (1925) Bibliography of Colorado maps published by the State and Federal governments. Colorado School of Mines, Quart., v. 20, no. 4, 40 pp.

**76.** ——— (1926) Bibliography of geophysical principles, apparatus, and methods applied to prospecting. Colorado School of Mines Mag., v. 15, no. 10, p. 11–16, 21.

77. —— (1926) Bibliography of the geology and related subjects of northwestern Colorado (revised to June 1, 1926). Colorado School of Mines, Quart., v. 21, no. 3, 52 pp.

78. —— (1927) Bibliography of the geology of north-central Colorado. Colorado School of Mines, Quar., vol. 22, no. 4, 38 pp.

79. —— (1928) Bibliography of the geology of south-central Colorado. Colorado School of Mines, Quar., vol. 23, no. 4, 30 pp.

## Connecticut

80. Gregory, H. E. (1907) Bibliography of the geology of Connecticut. State Geol. and Nat. Hist. Surv. Conn. Bull. 8, 123 pp.

## Florida

81. Sellards, E. H. (1908) Bibliography of Florida geology. *In* Florida Geol. Surv. Ann. Rept. 1, p. 73–108.

82. *California Company* (1953) Bibliography of geology: Florida. New Orleans, La., The California Co., 29 pp.

83. Ray, C. E. (1957) A list, bibliography, and index of the fossil vertebrates of Florida. Fla. Geol. Surv. Spec. Pub., no. 3, 175 pp.

84. Sherman, H. B. (1952) A list and bibliography of the mammals of Florida, living and extinct. Fla. Acad. Sci. Quar. J., v. 15, no. 2, p. 86–126.

85. See 525 (Cenozoic Stratigraphy)

## Georgia

86. Cave, H. S. (1922) Historical sketch of the Geological Survey of Georgia: Bibliography and other data. Georgia Geol. Surv., Bull. 39, 154 pp., 7 pls., 2 figs. incl. map.

87. See 525 (Cenozoic Stratigraphy)

## Idaho

88. Ross, C. P. (1959) Annotated bibliography of papers related to the geology of Idaho, 1941–1957. Idaho Bur. Mines and Geol. Pamph. no. 119, 219 pp

## Indiana

89. Marsters, V. F., and E. M. Kindle (1894) Geological literature of Indiana (stratigraphy and economic). *In* Pr. Indiana Acad. Sci., p. 156–191.

90. Woodard, G. S. (1954) List of geologic publications and maps of Indiana. Bloomington, Ind. Geol. Surv., 66 pp.

## Iowa

91. Keyes, C. R. (1913) Annotated bibliography of Iowa geology and mining. Iowa Geol. Surv., v. 22, 908 pp.

92. Kay, G. F. (1944?) The bibliography of the Pleistocene geology of Iowa: Pt. 3 of The Pleistocene geology of Iowa. Iowa Geol. Surv. Spec. Rept. [Des Moines, Iowa?], 55 pp.

### Kansas

**93.** ver Wiebe, W. A., and B. N. Cooper (1938) Bibliography of Kansas Geology, 1823–1938. Municipal Univ. Wichita, Univ. Studies Bull. 5, 70 pp.

### Kentucky

**94.** Jillson, W. R. (1923) Geological research in Kentucky: A summary account of the several geological surveys of Kentucky, including a complete list of their publications and a general bibliography of 806 titles pertaining to Kentucky geology. Kentucky Geol. Surv., ser. 6, v. 15, 228 pp., 10 pls. (maps and portraits).

**95.** ——— (1950) A bibliography of early books, pamphlets, articles and maps pertaining to the geology, paleontology, and seismology of Kentucky 1744–1854 (with annotations). Frankfort, Ky., Roberts Printing Co., 53 pp.

**96.** ——— (1951) A bibliography of Cumberland County, Kentucky: An annotated list of titles of books, pamphlets, articles, and maps pertaining to geology, paleontology, petroleum, mineralogy, and history. Frankfort, Ky., Roberts Printing Co., 46 pp.

**97.** ——— (1953) A bibliography of Mammoth Cave (1798–1949). Frankfort, Ky., Roberts Printing Co., 81 pp.

**98.** ——— (1954) A bibliography of Casey County, Kentucky. Frankfort, Ky., Roberts Printing Co., 19 pp.

**99.** ——— (1956) A bibliography of Floyd County, Kentucky: Citations of printed and manuscript sources touching upon its history, geology, cartography, coal, salt, oil and gas, with annotations (1750–1956). Frankfort, Ky., Perry Pub. Co., 29 pp.

**100.** ——— (1957) A bibliography of Estill County, Kentucky (1784–1956). Lawrenceburg, Ky., Anderson Press, 34 pp.

**101.** ——— (1957) A bibliography of county geological reports in Kentucky during the past century, 1856–1956. Frankfort, Ky., Roberts Printing Co., 18 pp.

**102.** ——— (1957) A bibliography of Barren County Kentucky. Frankfort, Ky., Roberts Printing Co., 36 pp., illus.

**103.** ——— (1958) A bibliography of Knox County, Kentucky: Citations of printed and manuscript sources touching upon its history, geology, cartography, coal, salt, oil and gas, with annotations (1750–1956). Frankfort, Ky., Perry Pub. Co., 34 pp.

**104.** ——— (1958) A bibliography of Elliott County, Kentucky: Citations of the printed sources touching upon its history, geology, cartography, coal, dikes, ores, oil and gas, with annotations (1861–1957). Frankfort, Ky., Perry Pub. Co., 21 pp.

**105.** ——— (1959) A bibliography of Wayne County, Kentucky: Citations of printed and manuscript sources touching upon its history, geology, cartography, coal, salt, oil and gas, with annotations (1744–1958). Frankfort, Ky., Perry Pub. Co., 34 pp.

### Louisiana

**106.** Dunbar, C. P. (1933) A list of some of the available publications dealing with the geology and mineral resources of Louisiana and related areas. *In*

Louisiana Dept. Conserv. Bull. 22 (General Bull. Handbook, Minerals Division), p. 235–269.
**107.** See 525 (Cenozoic Stratigraphy)

### Maine

**108.** Babb, C. C. (1913) Bibliography of Maine geology. *In* Maine, State Water Storage Comm. Ann. Rept. 3, v. 10, p. 185–242.
**109.** Maine Geological Survey (1958) Bibliography on Maine geology, 1836–1957. Dept. Econ. Devel., 143 pp. (1959) First suppl., 10 pp.

### Maryland

**110.** Mathews, E. B. (1897) Bibliography and cartography of Maryland, including publications relating to the physiography, geology, and mineral resources. *In* Maryland Geol. Surv. v. 1, p. 229–401.

### Massachusetts

**111.** Johansson, W. I. (1952) A bibliography of the paleontology of Massachusetts, 1821–1949. Mass. Univ., Dept. Geol. and Miner., Spec. Dept. Pub. no. 3, 28 pp.
**112.** Cassidy, Martin (1962) A partial bibliography of the geology of Massachusetts through 1958. Cambridge, Harvard Univ., Dept. Geol. Sci., 90 pp.

### Michigan

**113.** Martin, H. M., and M. T. Straight (1956) An index of the geology of Michigan, 1823–1955. Mich. Geol. Surv., pub. 50, 461 pp.

### Minnesota

**114.** Gregory, Winifred (1915) Bibliography of Minnesota mining and geology. Minnesota Univ., School of Mines Exp. Station, Bull. 4, 157 pp. (1920) Suppl., Bull. 8, 43 pp.
**115.** Melone, T. G., and L. W. Weis (1951) Bibliography of Minnesota Geology. Minnesota Geol. Surv. Bull., v. 34, 124 pp.

### Mississippi

**116.** See 525 (Cenozoic Stratigraphy)

### Missouri

**117.** Sampson, F. A. (1890) A bibliography of the geology of Missouri. Missouri Geol. Surv. Bull. 2, 158 pp.
**118.** Keyes, C. R. (1896) Bibliography of Missouri geology. *In* Missouri Geol. Surv. Bull. 10, p. 219–523.
**119.** Greger, D. K. (1945) Bibliography of the geology of Missouri. Missouri Geol. Surv. and Water Res., v. 31, 2d ser., 294 pp.
**120.** Clark, E. L., N. L. Scofield, and J. W. Koenig (1956) Bibliography of the geology of Missouri, 1945–1955. Missouri Geol. Surv. and Water Res., v. 38, 2d ser., 146 pp.
Koenig, J. W. (1957) Bibliography of the geology of Missouri, 1956. Missouri Geol. Surv. and Water Res., 48 pp. (1958) 1957, 35 pp. (1959) 1958, 36

pp. (1960) 1959, 44 pp. (1961) 1955–1960, *ibid.,* Info. Circ. no. 16, 104 pp. (1962) 1961, 53 pp. (1963) 1962, 33 pp.
Vineyard, J. D. (1964) *Ibid., 1963, ibid.,* 56 pp.

### Montana

**121.** Montana Bureau of Mines and Geology (1942) Bibliography of the geology and mineral resources of Montana. Montana Bur. Mines and Geo. Mem. 21, 356 pp., 3 pls., correl. charts, index map.
**122.** Peck, L. B. (1952) Preliminary list of graduate theses on Montana geology. Butte, Mont. School of Mines, 15 pp.
**123.** Pye, W. D. (1954) Contributions to the geology of the Bighorn–Beartooth region by the Yellowstone–Bighorn Research Association. *In* Billings Geol. Soc. Guidebook, 5th Ann. Field Conf., p. 137–139.
**124.** Petroleum Research Corporation (1957) Selected geologic bibliography of Crazy Mountain basin and south central Montana. *In* Billings Geol. Soc. Guidebook, 8th Ann. Field Conf. p. 99–105.

### Nebraska

**125.** Barbour, E. H. (1910) List of publications of the Nebraska Geological Survey. *In* Nebraska Geol. Surv., Bull. 4, p. 7–16.
**126.** ——— and C. A. Fisher (1902) The geological bibliography of Nebraska. *In* Nebraska State Board Agr., Ann. Rept. 1901, p. 248–266.

### Nevada

**127.** Gianella, V. P. (1945) Bibliography of geologic literature of Nevada, by Vincet P. Gianella, and Bibliography of geologic maps of Nevada areas, by Robert W. Prince. Nevada Univ. Bull., v. 39, no. 6, Geology and Mining ser. no. 43, 205 pp. 1 pl., road map.

### New Jersey

**128.** Black, G. F. (1916) List of works relating to the geology, mineralogy, and paleontology of New Jersey. New York Pub. Library, 36 pp.
**129.** Grametbaur, A. B. (1946) Bibliography and index of the geology of New Jersey. New Jersey Dept. Conserv., Geol. Ser. Bull. 59, 42 pp.

### New Mexico

**130.** Wootton, T. P. (1930) Geologic literature of New Mexico. New Mexico Bur. Mines and Mineral Resources Bull. 5, 127 pp.
Bates, R. L., and M. R. Burks (1945) Geologic literature of New Mexico through 1944. *Ibid.,* Bull. 22, 147 pp.
Burks, M. R., and J. H. Schilling (1955) *Ibid.,* 1950. Bull. 43, 198 pp.
Schilling, C. F., and J. H. Schilling (1956) *Ibid.,* 1951–1955. Bull. 52, 136 pp.

### New York

**131.** Ellis, Mary (1903) Index to publications of the New York State Natural History Survey and New York State Museum, 1837–1902; also including

other New York publications on related subjects. New York State Mus.,
Bull. 66, 653 pp.

## North Carolina

132. Laney, F. B., and K. H. Wood (1909) Bibliography of North Carolina
geology, mineralogy, and geography, with a list of maps. North Carolina
Geol. Surv. Bull. 18, 428 pp.
133. Holland, Alma (1934) Publications in the field of science from the University of North Carolina (1759–1934). Elisha Mitchell Sci. Soc. J., v. 50,
nos. 1–2, p. 303–415

## North Dakota

134. Budge, C. E. (1946, 1948, 1952) Bibliography of the geology and natural
resources of North Dakota, 1814–1944. North Dakota Research Foundation Bull. 1, 214 pp. (1948) First Suppl., *ibid.*, Bull. 4, 90 pp. (1952)
Second Suppl., *ibid.*, Bull. 6, 61 pp.

## Ohio

135. Derby, A. G. (1906) A subject index of the publications of the Geological
Survey of Ohio, from its inception to and including Bulletin number eight,
series four. *In* Ohio Geol. Surv. Bull. 6, p. 15–233.
    Prosser, M. W. (1906) A bibliography of the publications relating to the
geology of Ohio other than those of the State Geological Survey. *In* Ohio
Geol. Surv. Bull. 6, p. 235–332.
136. Watkins, D. G. (1953) Bibliography of Ohio geology, 1819–1950. Ohio
Geol. Surv. Bull. 52, 103 pp., illus. incl. geol. map.
    Smyth, Pauline (1963) Bibliography of Ohio Geology, 1951–1960. Ohio
Geol. Surv., Info. Circ. no. 32, 63 pp.

## Oklahoma

137. Trout, L. E., and G. H. Myers (1915) Bibliography of Oklahoma geology,
with subject index. Oklahoma Geol. Surv. Bull. 25, 105 pp.
138. Finnerty, Lucy (1954) Bibliographic index to University of Oklahoma theses
[geology and geological engineering]. Tulsa Geol. Soc. Digest, v. 22, p.
180–203.
139. Taaffe, F. D. (1956) Published papers on Oklahoma geology in the year
1955. Okla. Geol. Notes, v. 16, nos. 5–6, p. 43–55.
    Curtis, N. M., Jr. (1957) *Ibid.* 1956, v. 17, no. 4, p. 34–38. (1958) 1957,
v. 18, no. 3, p. 34–57. (1959) 1958, v. 19, no. 3, p. 51–71.

## Oregon

140. Henderson, C. W., and J. B. Winstanley (1912) Bibliography of the geology,
paleontology, mineralogy, petrology, and mineral resources of Oregon,
with subject index by Graham J. Michael. Oregon Univ. Bull. n.s. 10, no.
4, 49 pp.
141. Jillson, W. R. (1923) A bibliography of the geology and paleontology of the
John Day Region, Oregon. Frankfort, Ky., Roberts Printing Co., 7 pp.

142. Dixon, D. E. (1926) Bibliography of the geology of Oregon. Oregon Univ. Pub., Geol. ser., v. 1, no. 1, 125 pp.
143. Treasher, R. C., and E. T. Hodge (1936) Bibliography of the geology and mineral resources of Oregon, with digests and index to July 1, 1936. Port-Ore., Oregon State Plann. Bd., 224 pp.
144. Hodge, E. T. (1936) Bibliography of Oregon geology. Geol. Soc. Oregon Country Newsletter, v. 2, no. 6, p. 1–21.
145. Appleton, J. B. (1939) The Pacific Northwest, a selected bibliography covering completed research in the natural resources and socio-economic fields, an annotated list of in-progress and contemplated research, together with critical comments thereon, 1930–39. Portland, Ore,. Northwest Regional Council, 456 pp.
146. Allen, J. E. (1947) Bibliography of the geology and mineral resources of Oregon (Supplement), July 1, 1936 to December 31, 1945: Compiled by John Eliot Allen, geologist, with contributions by Elinor Kinsley, Hazel Quasdorf, and Raymond Clarence Treasher. Ore. Dept. Geol. and Min. Indust. Bull. 33, 108 pp.
147. Schlicker, H. G. (1959) Bibliography of theses on Oregon geology. Ore. Dept. Miner. Indust. Misc. Paper, no. 7, 14 pp.

### Rhode Island

148. Quinn, A. W., and D. H. Swann (1944) Bibliography of the geology of Rhode Island. R. I. Indust. Commission, Min. Res. Comm., 23 pp., 1 pl., 2 figs, index maps.
——— (1950) Bibliography of the geology of Rhode Island. 2d ed., 26 pp., index maps. Providence, R.I., R.I. Port and Indust. Dev. Comm. [This second edition adds the references for 1944–1949 inclusive and a few prior ones not given in the first edition.]

### South Carolina

149. Petty, J. J. (1950) Bibliography of the geology of the state of South Carolina. Univ. S.C. Pub. Phys. Sci., ser. 2, Bull. 1, 86 pp. (1957) Ibid. 9 pp.

### Tennessee

150. Cockrill, E. (1911) Bibliography of Tennessee geology, soils, drainage, forestry, etc., with a subject index. Geol. Surv. Tenn. Bull. I, pt. B, p. 1–117.
151. Wilson, C. W., Jr. (1953) Annotated bibliography of the geology of Tennessee through December 1950. Tenn. Dept. Conserv., Div. Geol. Bull. 59, 308 pp., index map.
152. See 525 (Cenozoic Stratigraphy)

### Texas

153. Simonds, F. W. (1900) A record of the geology of Texas for the decade ending December 31, 1896. *In* Trans. Texas Acad. Sci., v. 3, p. 19–285.
154. Sellards, E. H. (1932) Bibliography and subject index of Texas Geology. *In* Univ. Texas Bull. 3232, v. 4, p. 819–996.
155. Ellison, S. P., Jr. (1954) Bibliography of the geology of Erath County, Texas, and vicinity. *In* Abilene Geol. Soc. Guidebook, p. 51–52.

**156.** Girard, R. M. (1959) Bibliography and index of Texas geology, 1933–1950. Texas Univ. Pub., no. 5910, 238 pp.

**157.** See 525 (Cenozoic Stratigraphy)

*Utah*

**158.** Stringham, B. F. (1944) Bibliography of the geology and mineral resources of Utah to December 31, 1942. Utah Univ. Bull., v. 34, no. 15, Geol. Ser., v. 1, no. 1, 99 pp.

**159.** Buss, W. R. (1950) Bibliography of Utah geology to December 31, 1950. Utah Geol. Mineral Surv. Bull. 40, 219 pp.

**160.** Wengerd. S. A., and M. E. King (1952) Geological bibliography of the Four Corners Region. *In* Four Corners Geol. Soc., [1st] Geological symposium of the Four Corners Region, p. 133–145.

*Virginia*

**161.** Watson, T. L. (1897) A bibliography of the geological, mineralogical, and paleontological literature of the State of Virginia. Bull. Am. Paleont. no. 7, 109 pp.

**162.** Roberts, J. K. (1942) Annotated geological bibliography of Virginia. Charlottesville, Va., Alderman Library, 726 pp.

**163.** Bevan, A. C. (1942) Publications on the geology and mineral resources of Virginia. Va. Geol. Surv. Circ. 2, 57 pp., illus.

**164.** Huddle, J. W., Eloise Jacobsen, and A. D. Williamson (1956) Oil and gas wells drilled in southwestern Virginia before 1950. *In* U.S. Geol. Surv. Bull. 1027-L, p. 501–573.

*Washington*

**165.** Arnold, Ralph (1902) Bibliography of literature referring to the geology of Washington. *In* Wash. Geol. Surv. Bull. 1, p. 321–338.

**166.** O'Donnell, Gretchen (1913) Bibliography of Washington geology and geography. Wash. Geol. Surv., Bull. 12, 63 pp.

**167.** Bennett, W. A. G. (1939) Bibliography and index of geology and mineral resources of Washington, 1814–1936. Wash. Dept. Conserv. and Devel., Div. Geol., Bull. 35, 140 pp.

**168.** University of Washington, Department of Oceanography (1953) Puget Sound and approaches: a literature survey. Seattle. v. 1, Hydrology, p. 85–130; v. 2, Geology, p. 2–47; Volcanology, p. 49–51; Seismology, p. 53–61; Geomagnetism, p. 63–67, illus.

**169.** See 145

*West Virginia*

**170.** Lucke, J. B. (1937) Bibliography and index of West Virginia geology and natural resources to July 1, 1937. West Va. Geol. Surv. Bull. 4, 84 pp.

*Wyoming*

**171.** Bovee, G. G. (1918) Bibliography and index of Wyoming geology, 1823–1916. *In* Wyom. Geol. Office, Bull. 17, p. 317–446.

## North America (exclusive of the United States)

### Canada

172. Dowling, D. B. (1900) Geological Survey of Canada: General index to the reports of progress, 1863 to 1884. Geol. Surv. Canada, 475 pp.
173. Nicholas, F. J. (1908) Geological Survey of Canada: General index to reports 1885–1906. Geol. Surv. Canada Pub. no. 1000, 1014 pp.
174. —————— (1921) General index of the reports of the Ontario Bureau of Mines, v. 1–25, 1891–1916. Ontario Dept. Mines, 871 pp., 2 maps.
175. —————— (1923) Index to separate reports, 1906–1910 and summary reports 1905–1916. Geol. Surv. Canada, 305 pp.
176. —————— (1925) Index to paleontology: Geological Publications 1847–1916. Geol. Surv. Canada Pub. no. 2034, 383 pp.
177. —————— (1930) Index to paleontology: Geological publications of the Geological Survey of Canada, 1917–1926. *In* Geol. Surv. Canada Misc. Ser. 2, p. 385–482.
178. —————— (1932) Index to Memoirs, 1910–1926; Bulletins, 1913–1926; Summary Reports 1917–1926; Sessional Papers (Administrative), 1921–1926. Geol. Surv. Canada Misc. Ser. no. 3, 666 pp.
179. Cockfield, W. E., E. Hall, and J. F. Wright (1962) Index to Reports of Geological Survey of Canada from 1927–50. Geol. Surv. Canada, 723 pp.
180. Ferrier, W. F. (1920) Annotated catalogue of and guide to the publications of the Geological Survey of Canada, 1845–1917. Geol. Surv. Canada Pub. 1823, 544 pp.
181. Reinecke, Leopold (1912) Bibliography of Canadian geology for the years 1908–1911, inclusive. Proc. Trans. Roy. Soc. Canada, ser. 3, v. 6, sec. 4, p. 139–226.
    Malcolm, Wyatt, (1915) *ibid.*, 1912–1913, v. 8, sec. 4, p. 287–350. (1916) 1914, v. 9, sec. 4, p. 279–305. (1917) 1915, v. 10, sec. 4, p. 131–168.
182. Dresser, J. A., and T. C. Denis (1941) Geology of Quebec, v. 1: Bibliography and index. Quebec Bur. Mines, 180 pp.
183. Quebec Bureau of Mines (1949) Annotated list of publications of the Department of Mines of the Province of Quebec, 1883–1944. Quebec (province) Bur. Mines, Quebec, 45 pp.
184. Moran, P. J. (1945) Catalogue of published maps of the Geological Survey of Canada, 1917–1945 inclusive. Ottawa, Ontario, Dept. Mines Res. Canada, 77 pp.
185. Kupsch, W. O. (1952) Annotated bibliography of Saskatchewan geology, 1823–1951 incl. Saskatchewan Geol. Surv. Report, no. 9, 106 pp., illus. incl. geol. map, 1952; (1954) 1952 and 1953, supp. to no. 9, 31 pp.; (1959) Revised edition, 198 pp.
186. Alberta Society of Petroleum Geologists (1954) Lexicon of geologic names in Alberta and adjacent parts of British Columbia and Northwest Territories. Calgary, The Society, Geologic Names and Correlations Committee, 172 pp.
187. McCrossan, R. G., and others (1958) Annotated bibliography of geology of the sedimentary basin of Alberta and adjacent parts of British Columbia

and Northwest Territories, 1945–1955. Calgary, Alberta Soc. Petrol. Geol. J., 499 pp.

**188.** Mills, B. A. (1959) Bibliography of geology, paleontology, industrial minerals, and fuels in the post-Cambrian regions of Manitoba, 1950–1957. Manitoba Dept. Mines Nat. Res., Mines Br. Pub. 57-4, 32 pp.

**189.** Alberta Society of Petroleum Geologists (1960) Lexicon of geologic names in the western Canada sedimentary basin and arctic archipelago, The Society, 380 pp.

**190.** Whiteaves, J. F. (1901) Catalogue of the marine invertebrata of eastern Canada. Geol. Surv. Canada, Pub. 722, 271 pp.

**191.** Bolton, T. E. (1960) Catalogue of type invertebrate fossils of the Geological Survey of Canada. Geol. Surv. Canada, v. 1, 215 pp.

**192.** See 522, v. VII (Stratigraphic Lexicon)

### Newfoundland

**193.** Betts, R. M. W. (1936) Bibliography of the geology of Newfoundland. Newfoundland Dept. Nat. Res., Geol. Sec., Bull. 5, 35 pp.

**194.** Baird, D. M., C. R. Gillespie, and J. H. McKillop (1954) Bibliography of the geology of Newfoundland, 1936–1954; Bibliography of the geology of Labrador, 1814–1954. Newfoundland Dept. Mines Res. Bull. 36, 47 pp.

### Greenland

**195.** John Crerar Library (1940) Union Catalogue of literature on Greenland. The Library, Ref. List. No. 45, 45 pp.

**196.** Vortual, Hroar (1935) Bibliographie des ouvrages norvegiens relatifs au Greenland (y compris les ouvrages islandais anterieurs à l'an 1814). Skrifter om Svalbard og Isharet, v. 54, 119 pp.

**197.** Koch, Lauge (1954) Literature from the Danish East Greenland expeditions published in the Meddeleser om Grønland. Meddel. om grønland, v. 143, no. 3, 20 pp.

**198.** See 283, 315, 522, v. I, fasc. 1a (Stratigraphic Lexicon)

### Mexico

**199.** Aguilar y Santillán, R. (1898) Bibliografía geológica y minera de la República mexicana. México Inst. geol., Bol. 10, 158 pp.

**200.** ——— (1902) Bibliography of Mexican geology and mining. Am. Inst. Min. Eng., Trans., v. 32, p. 605–680.

**201.** ——— (1908) Bibliografía geológica y minera de la República mexicana completada hasta el año de 1904. México Inst. Geol., Bol. 17, 330 pp.

**202.** ——— (1918) Bibliografía geológica y minera de la República mexicana. Mexico Dept. Minas, Bol. min., v. 5, nos. 3–6; v. 6, nos. 1–3, 55 pp.

**203.** ——— (1936) Bibliografía geológica y minera de la República mexicana correspondiente a los años de 1919 a 1930. México, Talleres Gráficos de la Nación.

**204.** Thayer, W. N. (1914) A bigliography of Mexican geology, geography, and mining, 1902–1912. Mining Science, v. 70, Aug. p. 52–56, Sept. p. 53–56, Oct. p. 53–58.

205. Maldonado-Koerdell, Manuel (1954) Nomenclatura, bibliografía y correlación de las formaciones arqueozóicas y paleozóicas de México. Assoc. Mex. Geól. Petrol. Bol., v. 6, nos. 3–4, p. 113–137, illus.
206. —— (1958) Nomenclatura, bibliografía y correlación de los formaciones continentales (y alyunes marinas) del Mesozoico de México. Assoc. Mex. Géol. Petrol. Bol., v. 10, nos. 5–6, p. 287–308.
207. Richards, A. F. (1959) Bibliography, cartography, discovery, and exploration of the Isles Revillagigedo [Mexico]. Calif. Acad. Sci. Proc., v. 29, no. 9, p. 315–360.
208. See 522, v. V, fasc. 1 (Stratigraphic Lexicon)

### Caribbean Region

209. Rutten, L. M. R. (1938) Bibliography of West Indian geology. Geog. Geol. Mededeel, Physiog, geol. Reeks 16, 103 pp.
210. Bermudez, P. J. (1938) Bibliografía geológica cubana. Publicaciones de la Revista "Universidad de la Habana," 86 pp.
211. Reid, C. F., N. Habit, F. D. Clark, and C. Simonini (1941) Bibliography of the Virgin Islands of the United States. New York, H. W. Wilson Co., 225 pp.
212. Brown, A. D. (1943) British possessions in the Caribbean area: A selected list of references. Washington, D.C., Div. Bib., Lib. Cong., 192 pp.
213. —— (1943) Puerto Rico: A selected list of recent literature. Washington, D.C., Div. Bib., Lib. Cong., 44 pp.
214. See 263; 522, v. V, fasc. 2b,c (Stratigraphic Lexicon); 596 (Foraminifera)

### Central America

215. Maldonado-Koerdell, Manuel (1958) Geological and paleontological bibliography of Central America. Pan. Am. Inst. Geog. Hist. Pub. 204, 288 pp.
216. See 522, v, V, fasc. 2a (Stratigraphic Lexicon)

### South America

*General*

217. Fuller, G. H. (1942) Latin America: A list of recent bibliographies. Washington, D.C., Lib. Cong., Div. Bib., 16 pp.
218. Singewald, J. T., Jr. (1943) Bibliography of economic geology of South America. Geol. Soc. Am. Special Paper 50, 159 pp.
219. Morgan, K. L. (1944) Journals dealing with the natural, physical and mathematical sciences published in Latin America: A tentative directory. Washington, D.C., Division of Intellectual Cooperation Pan American Union, 62 pp.
220. Pan American Union (1962) Guide to Latin American Scientific and Technical Periodicals: An annotated list. Washington, D.C., Pan American Union; Mexico City, Centro de Documentación Científica y Técnica de México, 187 pp.
221. See 531 (Geologic Maps)

## Argentina

222. Sparn, Enrique (1920) Bibliografía de la geología, mineralogía, y paleontología de la República Argentina, 1900–1914. Acad. Nac. Cienc. Córdoba, Misc. no. 2, p. 1–58. (1921) Pt. 2, hasta 1899, Misc. no. 3, p. 1–93. (1922) Pt. 3, 1915–1921, Misc, no. 5, p. 1–50. (1925) Pt. 4, 1922–1924, Misc. no. 11, p. 1–37. (1928) Pt. 5, 1925–1927, Misc. no. 17, p. 1–44. (1935) Pt. 6, 1928–1931, Acad. Nac. Cienc. Córdoba, Bol., v. 32, p. 337–379. (1936) Pt. 7, 1932–1935, v. 33, p. 221–280. (1939) (incluso de la Antártica Americana) pt. 8, 1936–1938, v. 34, p. 227–336. (1942) pt. 9, 1939–1941, v. 35, p. 309–417. (1946) Pt. 10, 1942–1945, v. 38, p. 3–132. (1950) Pt. 11, 1946–1959: *ibid.,* v. 39, p. 77–210.

—— (1937) Bibliografía geológica y minera de las provincias de Salta y Jujuy, con especial atención al petroleo, hierro y carbón del norte argentina. Acad. Nac. Cienc., Córdoba, Boll., v. 34, p. 32–95.

223. —— (1950) Bibliografía de los yacimientos de minerales y rocas de aplicación de la provincia de Córboda, Argentina. Córdoba, Univ., Rev. año 37, no. 3–4, 41 pp.

—— (1953) Bibliografía de la mineralogía, geología y paleontología de la provincia de Córdoba, Argentina. Córdoba, Univ. Nac., 76 pp.

224. Castellanos, Alfredo, Pierina Pasotti, and Cortés Plá (1940) Crónica bibliográfica, mineralogía y minería, geología, petrografía, geografía, paleontología, A–1939. Rosario, Univ. Nac. Litoral., Inst. Fis. Geol. Pub., v. I, 50 pp.
Castellanos, Alfredo, and Pierina Pasotti (1941) *Ibid.,* B–1940, v. II, 66 pp. (1942) C–1941, v. III, 70 pp. (1943) D–1942, v. IV, 163 pp. (1944) E–1943, v. V, 90 pp.

——, and Pedro Epstein (1945) *Ibid.,* F–1944, v. VI, 48 pp. (1946) G–1945, v. VI, 58 pp. (1947) H–1946, v. VII, 47 pp. (1948) I–1947, v. VII, 157 pp.
Pasotti, Pierina (1959) *Ibid.,* J–1958, v. IX, 52 pp. Parts A–E, republished as one volume, 1944; parts E–J, republished as one volume, 1959.

225. See 522, v, V, fasc. 8 (Stratigraphic Lexicon)

## Bolivia

226. Oppenheim, Victor (1943) Bibliografía geológica de Bolivia: Soc. Geog. La Paz, Bull. año 43, no. 65, 19 pp. [Reprint.]

227. Muñoz Reyes, Jorge (1945) Contribución a la bibliografía minera y geología de Bolivia. Minería Boliviana, año 2, no. 15, p. 19–21; no. 16, p. 19–22; no. 17, p. 20–23; no. 18, p. 22–26.

228. See 52, v. V, fasc. 6a (Stratigraphic Lexicon)

## Brazil

229. Branner, J. C. (1903) A bibliography of the geology, mineralogy, and paleontology of Brazil. Mus. Nac. Rio de Janeiro, v. 12, 115 pp.

230. —— (1909) Bibliography of the geology, mineralogy, and paleontology of Brazil. Geol. Soc. Am., Bull. 20, 132 pp.

231. Diniz Gonsalves, Alpheu (1928) Bibliographía da geología, mineralogía e paleontología do Brasil. Brazil. Ministerio da Agricultural. . . . Servico Geol. Miner. Brazil, v, 27, 205 pp.

232. Campos, J. M. (1940) Notas bibliográficas sôbre os terrenos onduânicos do Brasil. Brasil, Departamento Nacional Producão Mineral, Div. de Geol. e Miner., Bol. no. 108, 39 pp.

233. Iglesias, Dolores (1943) Bibliografía e indice da geología do Brasil, 1641–1940. Brasil, Departamento Nacional Producao Mineral, Div. de Geol. Miner., Bull. 111, 323 pp.

———, and Maria de Lourdes Meneghezzi (1944) *Ibid.*, 1941–1942. Bol. 117, 35 pp.

——— (1949) *Ibid.*, 1943–1944. Bol. 131, 45 pp.

234. Mendes, J. C. (1944) Bibliografía geológica, mineralógica, petrográfica e paleontológica do estado de São Paulo. São Paulo, Inst. Geog. Geol., 57 pp.

235. Murta, Domicio de Figueiredo (1946) Literatura geológica do estado de Minas Gerais. Belo Horizonte, Imprensa Oficial, 2 v. 182, 253 pp.

236. Mezzalira, Sergio (1947) Resumo histórico das pesquisas paleontológicas no Brasil no período 1939–1946. São Paulo, Inst. Geog. Geol., Rev. v. 5, no. 2, p. 213–220.

237. ———, and Armando Wohlers (1952) Bibliografía da geología, mineralogía, petrografía e paleontología do estado de São Paulo. São Paulo, Inst. Geog. Geol., Bol. no. 33, 62 pp.

238. International Geologie Congress (1951) Bibliographie du système Gondwana an Brésil. *In* Int. Geol. Cong., 19th, Algeria, Symposium . . . Gondwana, p. 325–338.

239. See 522, v. V, fasc. 10a (Stratigraphic Lexicon)

### Chile

240. Brueggen, J. (1919) Bibliografía minera y geológica de Chile. Bol. Soc. Nac. Minería, Santiago, ser. 2, v. 31, p. 441–513, 539–607.

——— (1926) Bibliografía minera y geológica de Chile. Bol. Soc. Nac. Minería, Santiago, ser. 2, v. 38, p. 870–889, 989–1007.

241. Porter, C. E. (1933) Notas bibliográficas: Los estudios sobre ciencias naturales relativas a paises extranjeros publicados en Chile. Anales de la Univ. de Chile, Fasc. I, p. 1–79.

242. Cristi, J. Muñoz, and J. Karzulovic Kokot (1955) Bibliografía geológica de Chile, 1927–1953. Univ. of Chile, Anales Facul. Ciencias Físicas Math., v. 12; Inst. Geol. Pub. no. 5; 121 pp.

243. See 522, v. V, fasc. 7 (Stratigraphic Lexicon)

### Columbia

244. Wokittel, R. (1934) Bibliografía sobre la minería y geología del Choco. Minería (Medellín, Colombia, Asociación Colombiana de Mineros) año 3, no. 28, p. 1890–1893.

245. Royo y Gómez, José (1945) Bibliografía geológica, geográfica y minera de Colombia. Colombia, Serv. Geol. Nac., Compilación Estud. Geol. Ofic. Colombia v. 6, 127 pp.

——— (1950) Adiciones y correcciones v. 8, p. 313–344.

246. Ramirez, J. E. (1951) Bibliografía de la biblioteca del Instituto Geofísico de los Andes Colombianos sobre geología y geofísica de Colombia. Inst. Geofís. Andes Colombianos, s. C (Geol.), Bull. no. 2, 267 pp.

247. Venegas Leyva, Alicia (1960) Bibliografía de los informes del Instituto Geológico Nacional. Colombia, Serv. Geol. Nac., Compilación Estud. Geol. Ofic. Colombia v. 9, 587 pp.
248. See 263; 522, v. V, fasc. 4 (Stratigraphic Lexicon)

### Ecuador

249. See 522, v. V, fasc. 5a (Stratigraphic Lexicon)

### Paraguay

250. See 522, v. V, fasc. 9b (Stratigraphic Lexicon)

### Peru

251. Broggi, J. A. (1934) Bibliografía geológica, botánica y zoológica del Perú: Síntesis crítica de las publicaciones aparecidas especialmente en el último lustro 1929–1933. Soc. Geol. Peru, Bol., v. 6, f. 2, p. 23–123.
252. Castro Bastos, Leonidas (1954) Datos bibliográficos sobre minería y geología del carbón en el Péru. *In* Peru, Inst. Nac. Inves. Fom. Min., Ser. Mem. no. 2, p. 25–37.
253. ―――― (1960) Bibliografía geológica del Perú. Lima [privately published], 317 pp.
254. See 522, v. V, fasc. 5b (Stratigraphic Lexicon)

### Surinam (Dutch Guiana)

255. Steenhuis, J. F. (1934) De geologische literatuur over van belang voor Nederlands Guyana (Suriname) en de Nederlandse Westindische Eilanden. 'S-Gravenhage, Mouton and Co., 89 pp. (1951) Suppl. 2–6, for 1934–1950, 108 pp.
256. See 522, v. V, fasc. 10b (Stratigraphic Lexicon)

### Uruguay

257. Marstrander, Rolf (1917) Bibliografía de la geología, mineralogía y paleontología de la República Oriental del Uruguay. *In* Pan-Am. Sci. Cong., Proc. 1915–16, Washington, D.C., v. 8, p. 659–674.
258. Lambert, Roger (1939) Bibliographie géologique de la République Orientale de l'Uruguay. Uruguay, Inst. Geol., Bol. 26, 81 pp.
259. See 522, v. V, fasc. 9a (Stratigraphic Lexicon)

### Venezuela

260. Hedberg, H. D. (1938) Lista de los nombres de las formaciones geológicas de Venezuela: List of formation names. Bol. Geol. Min., Caracas, Venezuela, v. 2, no. 2–3–4, p. 270–280; Engl. trans. p. 243–251.
261. ―――――, and F. Hedberg (1945) Bibliografía e índice de la geología de Venezuela. Rev. Fomento, Venezuela, año 7, nos. 58–59, p. 43–123, 1 pl. (map).
262. Venezuela. Ministerio de Minas e Hidrocarburos (1956) Léxico estratigrafico de Venezuela. Geología Pub. Especial no. 1, 728 pp.
263. Douglass, I., and others (1958) Bibliografía de artículos concerniente a Venezuela, Colombia y Trinidad publicados en los boletines de la AAPG.

Asoc. Venezolana Geol., Min. Petróleo, Bull. Inf. v. 1, no. 3, p. 101–107.
**264.** See 522, v. V, fasc. 3 (Stratigraphic Lexicon)

### Falkland Islands

**265.** Sparn, Enrique (1954) Bibliografía de la geología y del clima de las islas Malvinas (Falkand Islands). Cordoba, Univ., 29 pp.
**266.** See 522, v. V, fasc. 9c (Stratigraphic Lexicon)

## Europe

### Albania

**267.** Magnani, Mario (1939) Bibliografía geologica e geografico-física della regione Albanese. Italy, R. Uff. Geol., Bol. v. 64, suppl., 66 pp. (1941) Second ed., 106 pp.
**268.** See 274; 522, v. I, fasc. 12b,c (Stratigraphic Lexicon)

### Austri,

**269.** Srbik, R. R. (1935) Geologische Bibliographie der Ostalpen von Graubünden bis Kärnten. Deutscher u. Österreichischer Alpenverein. München, R. Oldenbourg, 2 v., 1411 pp.
———— (1937) Geologische Bibliographie der Ostalpen von Graubünden bis Kärnten: 1, Forsetzung. Innsbruck, J. Winkler and Co., 388 pp.
**270.** Exner, Christof, and J. Windbrechtinger (1951) Geologische Literatur in Österreich 1945–1950. Austria, Geol. Bundesanst., Verh. Sonderb. B, 44 pp.
**271.** See 522, v. I, fasc. 8 (Stratigraphic Lexicon)

### Balkan Countries

**272.** Anonymous (1889) Bibliographie géologique de la Péninsule Balkanique. Ann. Géol. Pénin. Balkan. v. 1, p. 133–160. (1890) *ibid.,* v. 2, p. 195–209. (1891) *ibid.,* v. 3, p. 271–313. (1893) *ibid.,* v. 4, p. 182–207. (1893) *ibid.,* v. 5, p. 326–353 (fasc. 1). (1900) *ibid.,* v. 5, p. 100–146 (fasc. 2). Petkovic, V. K. (1911) 1904–1909. *Ibid.,* v. 6, p. I–LIX.
————, and J. S. Tomic (1925) 1910–1918. *Ibid.,* v. 8, p. 154–190. Stratimirovic, V. (1926) 1919–1925. *Ibid.,* v. 8, p. 171–219. Milojević, S. P. (1928) 1926. *Ibid.,* v. 9, p. 142–158; Suppl. for 1910–1925, p. 159–187. (1930) 1927. *Ibid.,* v. 10, p. 170–184 (fasc. 1). (1931) 1928. *Ibid.,* v. 1, p. 149–165 (fasc. 2). (1932) 1929. *Ibid.,* v. 11, p. 111–128 (fasc. 1). (1933) 1930. *Ibid.,* v. 11, p. 285–305 (fasc. 2). (1934) 1931–1932. *Ibid.,* v. 12, p. 257–301. (1937) 1933. *Ibid.,* v. 14, p. 224–241. (1937) 1934. *Ibid.,* v. 14, p. 242–258. (1938, 1939) 1935–1937. Ibid., 15, p. 447–461; v. 16, p. 144–184. (1949) 1938. *Ibid.,* v. 17, p. 176–193. (1950) 1939. *Ibid.,* v. 18, p. 253–270. (1951) 1940–1948. *Ibid.,* v. 19, p. 256–289.
**273.** Toula, Franz (1903) Übersicht über die geologische Literatur der Balkanhalbinsel mit Moreas des Archipels mit Kreta und Cypern, der Halbinsel Anatolien, Syriens und Palästinas. *In* Int. Geol. Cong. IX Vienne, C. R., p. 185–330

—— (1906) Zusammenstellung der neuesten geologischen Literatur über die Balkanhalbinsel mit Morea, die griechischen Inseln, Ägypten und Vorderasien. Naturwiss. In Orientverens, Jahresber. 1905, p. 36–75.

**274.** Conover, H. F. (1943) The Balkans: A selected list of references, I, General, 73 pp.; II, Albania, 24 pp.; III, Bulgaria, 34 pp.; IV, Rumania, 70 pp.; V, Yugoslavia, 63 pp. Lib. Cong., Div. Bib., Washington, D.C.

## Belgium

**275.** Dargent, J. L. (1953) Bibliographie des thèses et mémoires geographiques belges, 1904–1953. Brussels, Comm. Belge Bib., Bibliog. Belgica 3, 35 pp.

**276.** Dumont, M. E., and L. de Smet (1960) Bibliographie géographique de la Belgique. Brussels, Comm. Belge Bib., Bibliog. Belgica 48, 210 pp.

**277.** See 522, v. I, fasc. 4 (Stratigraphic Lexicon)

## Bulgaria

**278.** Bončev, Ekim, ed. (1959) Abstracts of Bulgarian scientific literature; geology and geography, v. 1 (1957–1958), Sofia, Bulgar. Acad. Sci., Dept. Sci. Tech. Inf. Doc., 52 pp.

—— and others (1960) *Ibid.*, v. 2, 1959, 95 pp.

Spasov, K. H., and others (1961) *Ibid.*, v. 3, 1960, 72 pp.

**279.** See 274; 522, v. I, fasc. 13b (Stratigraphic Lexicon)

## Czechoslovakia

**280.** Procházka, V. J. (1897) Repertorium literatury geologické a mineralogicke 'Královstrí Českého Markrabstri Moravského a Vvodství Slezského od roku 1528 oz de 1896. Prague, 299 pp.

**281.** Schwarz, Rudolf, and Milada Vavřínová (1948) Mineralogickogeologica bibliographie CSR za rok 1945 a 1946. Prague Státní Geol. Ústav Československe Rep., 43 pp.

Vavřínová, Milada (1948) *Ibid.*, 1947, 35 pp. (1949) 1948, 45 pp.

Bartusek, Václav (1951) *Ibid.*, 1949, 61 pp. (1951) 1950, 124 pp. (1952) 1951, 24 pp. (1953) 1952, 115 pp. (1954) 1953, 137 pp. (1955) 1954, 153 pp.

Tvrznik, Břetíslav, and Jan Havle (1956) *Ibid.*, 1955, 107 pp. (1957) 1956, 173 pp. (1958) 1957, 180 pp.

**282.** See 522, v. I, fasc. 6b (Stratigraphic Lexicon)

## Denmark

**283.** Litteraturfortegnelse omfattende Skrifter af geologisk eller lignende Natur og som ved Emne, Forfatter eller Udgivelsessted er knyttede til Danmark og grønland samt Island. Dansk Geol. Foren., Meddel. (1926) 1921–1924, v. 7, Heft. 1, p. I. (1926) 1925, v. 7, Heft. 1, p. II–VI. (1927) 1926, v. 7, Heft. 2, p. VII–X. (1928) 1927, v. 7, Heft. 3, p. XI–XV. (1929) 1928, v. 7, Heft. 4, p. XVII–XX. (1930) 1929, v. 7, Heft. 5, p. XXI–XXIV. (1931) 1930, v. 8, Heft. 1, p. I–IV. (1932) 1931, v. 8, Heft. 2, p. V–VIII. (1933) 1932, v. 8, Heft. 3, p. IX–XII. (1934) 1933, v. 8, Heft. 4, p. XIII–XVI. (1935) 1934, v. 8, Heft. 5, p. XVII–XIX. (1936) 1935, v. 9, Heft. 1, p.

II–V. (1937) 1936, v. 9, Heft. 2, p. VI–IX. (1938 1937, v. 9, Heft. 3, p. X–XIII. (1939) 1938, v. 9, Heft. 4, p. XIV–XVII, 1940, (1939), v. 9, Heft, 5, p. XIX–XXI. (1941) 1940, v. 10, Heft. 1, p. I–IV. (1942) 1941, v. 10, Heft. 2, p. V–VI. (1943) 1942, v. 10, Heft. 3, p. VIII–X. (1944) 1943, v. 10, Heft. 4, p. XI–XIV. (1945) 1944, v. 10, Heft. 5, p. XVI–XVIII. (1946) 1945, v. 11, Heft. 1, p. II–IV. (1947) 1946, v. 11, Heft. 2, p. VI–VIII. (1948) 1947, v. 11, Heft. 3, p. IX–XI. (1949) 1948, v. 11, Heft. 4, p. XIII–XIV. (1950) 1949, v. 11, Heft. 5, p. XVII–XIX. (1951) 1950, v. 11, Heft. 1, p. I–III. (1952) 1951, v. 12, Heft. 2, p. VII–VIII. (1953) 1952, v. 12, Heft. 2, p. VIII–X. (1954) 1953, v. 12, Heft. 4, p. XII–XIII. (1955) 1954, v. 12, Heft. 6, p. XVII–XX. (1956) 1955, v. 13, Heft. 2, p. III–VI. (1957) 1956, v. 13, Heft. 4, p. X–XIII. (1958) 1957, v. 13, Heft. 6, p. XVII–XVIII. (1959) 1958, v. 14, Heft. 2, p. V–VII. (1960) 1959, v. 14, Heft. 3, p. XI–XIII. (1961) 1960, v. 14, Heft. 4, p. XVII–XXII. (1962) 1961, v. 15, Heft. 1, p. III–VIII. (1963) 1962, v. 15, Heft. 2, p. X–XII.

**284.** See 522, v. I, fasc. 2d (Stratigraphic Lexicon)

### Finland

**285.** Laitakari, Aarne (1934) Geologische bibliographie finnlands, 1555–1933. Comm. Géol. Finlande, Bull. 108, 224 pp.

**286.** Okko, Marjatta, and M. Hannikainen. (1960) Guide to the publications of the Geological Survey of Finland, 1879–1960. Helsinki, Geol. Tutkimuslaitos, 106 pp., map.

**287.** See 522, v. I. fasc. 2a,b (Stratigraphic Lexicon)

### France

**288.** Kilian, W., and O. Nicaud (1922) Répertoire de la bibliographie géologique du sud est de la France (Alpes francaises et Provence), comprenant les publications relatives à la géologie, la paléontologie, la minéralogie, la pétrographie et les sciences connexes. Grenoble Univ., Sec. Sci. Med., Ann., v. 12, p. 1–322. (1923) *Ibid.,* v. 13, p. 1–102.

Gignoux, M., L. Moret, and F. Blanchet (1931) *Ibid.,* Troisième liste suppl. (1922–1930), *Ibid.,* v. 15, p. 155–183.

———, and ——— (1939) *Ibid.,* Quatrième list suplémentaire (1931–1940). *Ibid.,* v. 16, p. 111–139. (1940) *Ibid.,* v. 22, p. 173–201. (1951) Cinquième list supplémentaire (1940–1950): *Ibid.,* v. 28, p. 113–135.

**289.** See 522, v. I, fasc. 4 (Stratigraphic Lexicon)

### Germany

**290.** Rüger, Ludwig (1948) FIAT review of German science 1939–46; geology and palaeontology. Office of Military Govt. for Germany, Field Information Agencies Technical. Wiesbaden, Dieterich'sche Verlagbuchhandlung, 247 pp., 1 fig.

**291.** Gallwitz, Hans (1951) Die geologische Literatur des Harzes seit 1913. Halle. Jb. Mittedeut. Erdgeschichte Bd. 1, Lf. 3, p. 159–173, illus.

**292.** Schwarzbach, Martin (1952) Geologische Forschung in Schlesien: eine Bibliographie der Jahre 1914–1945, gleichzeitig ein Rückblick auf die

Arbeit deutscher Geologen (Osteuropa und der deutsche Osten R. 2). Cologne Univ., 63 pp., illus. incl. map.

**293.** Pietzsch, Kurt (1953) Die geologische Literatur über Sachsen 1921–1950. Berlin, Geologie, Beihefte, nos. 5–6, 320 pp.

**294.** See 522, v. I, fasc. 5 (Stratigraphic Lexicon)

### Great Britain

**295.** Royal Society of London (1950) A list of periodicals and bulletins containing abstracts published in Great Britain. Cambridge Univ. Press, 79 pp.

**296.** Ward, W. S. (1953) Index and Finding List of Serials Published in the British Isles, 1789–1832. Lexington, Univ. Kentucky Press, 185 pp.

**297.** Bassett, D. A. (1961) Bibliography and index of geology and allied sciences for Wales and the Welsh borders 1897–1958. Cardiff, Amgueddfa Genedlaethol Cymru—Natl. Mus. Wales, 376 pp.

**298.** See 522, v. I, fasc. 3 (Stratigraphic Lexicon)

### Greece

**299.** Haralambous, Diomedes (1961) Geological and physicogeographical bibliography of Greece. Athens, Greece, Inst. Geol. Subsurface Res., 236 pp., map.

**300.** See 273; 522, v. I, fasc. 12b,c (Stratigraphic Lexicon)

### Hungary

**301.** Anonymous (1900) Bibliographia geologica hungarica 1899 (early title, Repertorium der auf Ungarn bezüglichen Geologischen Literatur): Földtani Közlöny, v. 30, p. 40–43. (1901) 1900, v. 31, 43–46. (1902) 1901, v. 32, p. 57–62. (1903) 1902, v. 33, p. 65–73. (1904) 1903, v. 34, p. 65–73. (1905) 1904, v. 35, p. 88–97. (1908) 1907, v. 38, 58–66. (1909) 1908, v. 39, p. 33–46. (1910) 1909, v. 40, p. 39–56. (1911) 1910, v. 41, p. 115–130. (1912) 1911, v. 42, p. 157–176.

Timko, E. (1913) 1912, *ibid.*, v. 43 p. 230–248. (1914) 1913, v. 44, p. 435–454. (1917) 1914–1915, v. 47, p. 93–111.

Anonymous (1926) 1925, *ibid.*, v. 55, p. 395–400. (1927) 1926, v. 56, p. 261–267. (1929) 1927–1928, v. 58, p. 245–256. (1930) 1929, v. 59, p. 134–139. (1934) 1930–1933, v. 64, p. 63–64; 175–176; 268–272; 366–372. (1935) 1934, v. 65, p. 78–80, 152; 276–280. (1936) 1935, v. 66, p. 233–240. (1937) 1935–1936, v. 67, p. 96–98; 230–240. (1940) 1938, v. 70, p. 43–53. (1948) 1940–1947, v. 77, p. 87–108.

**302.** See 522, v. I, fasc. 9 (Stratigraphic Lexicon)

### Ireland

**303.** See 522, v. I, fasc. 3b (Stratigraphic Lexicon)

### Italy

**304.** Portis, A., and M. Baretti (1881). Bibliographie géologique et paleontologique de l'Italie, par les soins du comité d'organisation du 2me Congrès Géologique International à Bologne. Bologne, 630 pp.

**305.** Italy. Reale Ufficio Geologico (1900–1939) Bibliografia geologica italiana per l'anno 1898. R. Uff. Geol., p. 1–105. (1901) 1899, *ibid.*, p. 1–154; 1900, *ibid.*, p. 1–181. (1902) 1901, p. 1–152. (1903) 1902, p. 1–141. 1904) 1903, p. 1–137. (1905) 1904, p. 1–120. (1906) 1905, p. 1–110. (1907) 1906, p. 1–152. (1908) 1907, p. 1–134. (1909) 1908, p. 1–147. (1911) 1909, p. 1–126. (1912) 1910, p. 1–144. (1913) 1911, p. 1–156. (1915) 1912, Bol, v. 44, p. 1–154. (1916) 1913, v. 45, p. 1–106. (1917) 1914, v. 46, p. 1–122. (1923) 1915–1920, v. 48, p. 1–38. (1928) 1921– 1926, v. 53, p. 1–74; 1927, v. 53, p. 1–13. (1929) 1928, v. 54, p. 1–17. (1931) 1929, v. 56, p. 1–18. (1932) 1930, v. 57, p. 1–21. (1933) 1931, v. 58, p. 1–22. (1934) 1932, v. 59, p. 1–21.

**306.** Italy. Reale Ufficio Geologico (1934–1939) Bibliografia geologica italiana per gli anni 1915–1933, N. 1, Lettera A, 72 pp., Suppl. v. 59 Bol. R. Ufficio Geol. Italia, 1934. N. 2, Lettera B, p. 73–188, Suppl. v. 60, *ibid.*, 1935. N. 3, Lettera C, p. 189–268, Suppl. v. 63, *ibid.*, 1938. N. 4, Lettera D, p. 269–400, Suppl., v. 64, *ibid.*, 1939.

**307.** Società Geografica Italiana (1953) Bibliografia geografica della regione italiana, f. 21–24, 1945–1948. Rome, 193 pp.

**308.** Bibliographia Geologica d'Italia (1956–1959) v. 1, 1956, Lazio, i–xii + 173 pp.; v. 2, 1957, Lombardia, i–vii + 300 pp.; v. 3, 1958, Campania, 533 pp.; v. 4, 1959, Calabria, i–viii + 121 pp.; v. 5, 1959, Puglia, i–xxvi + 252 pp.

**309.** See 328 (Sicily); 522, v. I, fasc. 11 (Stratigraphic Lexicon)

### Luxemburg

**310.** Lucius, Michel (1940–1941) Beiträge zur Geologie von Luxemburg, Bd. 2. Luxembourg, Serv. Carte Geol., Pub. (Luxemburg, Geol. Landes- aufnahmedienst, Veröff.) 381 pp., 4 figs., 9 pls. (incl. g. map. 1:100,000), 1940. [Contains Bibliography of geology of Luxemburg.]

**311.** See 522, v. I, fasc. 4 (Stratigraphic Lexicon)

### Netherlands

**312.** Jonker, H. G. (1907) Lijst van geschriften, welke handelen over of van belang zijn voor de geologie van Nederland (1734–1906). Verh. akad. wetensch., v. 13, Meded. geol. Nederland, v. 36, 154 pp.

Steenhuis, J. F. (1922) Geologie van Nederland, 1907–1920: Verbolg van het onder, Gelÿknomigen titel uitgageven geschrift von Wijlen Pro. Dr. H. G. Jonker (1734–1906). Netherlands R. Geol. Dienst. Med. ser. A, no. 1, 134 pp.

———— (1934) Lijst van geschriften, welke handelen over of van belang zijn voor de geologie van Nederland, 1552–1920: Supplement op de onder Gelijknamigen titel uitgegeven lijsten van wijlen Prof. Dr. H. G. Jonker, 1734–1906, en van den schrijver, 1907–1920. *Ibid.*, no. 4, 109 pp. (1939) 1921–1925, no. 6, 65 pp. (1940) 1926–1930, no. 7, 65 pp. (1941) 1931–1935, no. 8, 66 pp. (1947) 1936–1944, Netherlands, Geol. Stichting, Med. n.s., no. 2, 99 pp.

———— (1952) *ibid.*, 1945–1948. Netherlands, Geol. Stichting, Med. n. 3, no. 6, 51 pp.

**313.** Steenhuis, J. F. (1930) Lijst der Proefschriften ter verkrijging van den Doctoralen Graad over onderwerpen van geologischen of Mijnbouw-kundigen aard, of met de geologie of den Mijnbouw van Het Rijkinen Buiten Europa verband Houdende, Geschreven Door Nederlanders aan Binnen of Buitenlandsche Inrichtingen voor Hooger Onderwijs, 1781–1929. Jaarbock 1930 von het Geolog. Mijn. Gen. voor Ned. en Kol., 36 pp.

**314.** See 522, v. I, fasc. 4 (Stratigraphic Lexicon); 593 (Foraminifera)

### Norway

**315.** Rosendahl, Halvor (1934) Littérature géologique concernant la Norvège avec Svalbarde et la territoire des recherches de la mer glaciale et la mer norvégienne et groenlandienne. Norsk Geol. Tidssk. v. 13, H. 1–4, p. 129–301. [Geologic literature on Norway, Svalbard, Greenland, and the Arctic Ocean, 1916–1932.]

**316.** Dons, J. A. (1956) Kart-katalog: Norges berggrunn. Catalogue of maps: Bed-rock geology of Norway. Norges Geol. Unders. no. 193, 146 pp., maps.

**317.** See 522, v. I, fasc. 2a, b (Stratigraphic Lexicon)

### Poland

**318.** Danysz-Fleszarowa, R. (1921?–1947) Bibljografja geologiczna Polski. Bibli-ographie Géologique de Pologne. no. 1, 1914–1920: Serv. Géol. Pologne, p. 1–24, (n.d.) No. 2, 1921–1923, p. 1–24. (n.d.) No. 3, 1924, p. 1–11. (n.d.) No. 4, 1925, p. 1–11. (n.d.) No. 5, 1926, p. 1–12. (n.d.) No. 6, 1927, p. 1–15. (1930) No. 7, 1928, p. 1–20. (1931) No. 8, 1929, p. 1–16. (1932) No. 10, 1931, p. 1–16. (1933) No. 11, 1932, p. 1–16. (1934) No. 12, 1933, p. 1–19. (n.d.) No. 13, 1914–1933, p. 1–24. (1936) No. 14, 1934, p. 1–30. (1937) No. 15, 1935, p. 1–28. (1938) No. 16, 1936, p. 1–59. (1938) No. 17, 1937, p. 1–51. (1947) No. 18, 1938–1939, p. 1–25.

Rühle, Edward (1947) *Ibid.*, No. 19, 1940–1944, p. 1–10.

Wardeska, C. (1949) *Ibid.*, No. 20, 1945–1947, p. 1–24. (1950) No. 21, 1948, p. 1–23. (1951) No. 22, 1949, p. 1–27. (1952) No. 23, 1950, p. 1–23. (1953) No. 24, 1951, p. 1–16. (1955) No. 25, 1952, p. 1–32. (1956) No. 26, 1953, p. 1–24.

Bukowski, C. Z., and M. W. Bukowska (1957) *Ibid.*, No. 27, 1954: p. 1–118. (1957) No. 28, 1955, p. 1–163. (1959) No. 29, 1956, p. 1–235. (1960) No. 30, 1957, p. 1–265. (1962) No. 31, 1958, p. 1–253.

**319.** Stach, Jan (1947) Wykaz prac z dzialu nauk matematyczno-przyrodnicych wykomanych w Polse w okresie okupacji niemieckiej w latach 1939–1945. List of the works achieved in the field of mathematics and sciences in Poland during the German occupation, 1939–1945. Kraków, Polska Akad. Umiejetnósci, 289 pp. [Classified list in English; sections on geography (p. 165–179), geology (p. 180–219), and mineralogy (p. 237–239) are included.]

**320.** Fleszarowa, Regina (1957–1958) Retrospektywna bibliografia geologiczna Polski; oraz prac Polaków, z zakresu nauk o ziemi. Retrospective geo-

logical bibliography of Poland, containing also works of Polish authors dealing with sciences of earth, Part 1, 1900–1950. Warsaw, Poland, Inst. Geol., Muz. Ziemi, v. 1, (A-L), 478 pp., 1957; v. 2 (L-Z), 624 pp., 1958.
**321.** See 522, v. I, fasc. 6a; (Stratigraphic Lexicon); 608 (Micropaleontology)

*Portugal*

**322.** Choffat, Paul (1895–1898) Bibliographie géologique du Portugal et de ses colonies (1893–1897) Portugal. Serv. Geol., Comm., v. 3, p. 104–108, 294–299. (1900–1901) 1894–1897, v. 4, p. 228–236. (1904) 1898–1902, v. 5, p. 254–277. (1904–1907) 1902–1904, v. 6, p. 197–210, 213, 365–376. (1907–1909) 1906–1907, v. 7, p. 187–221. (1910–1911) 1908–1909, v. 8, p. 181–216. (1912–1913) 1910–1912: v. 9, pp. 248–288.
———, and E. Fleury (1914) *Ibid.,* 1913, v. 10, p. 234–263. (1915–1916) 1914, v. 11, p. 145–198.
**323.** Acciainoli, Luís de Menezes Corrêa (1957–1958) Geologia de Portugal: ensaio bibliográfico. Lisbon, Dir.-Geral Minas-Serv. Geol., 2 vols., 674 pp.
**324.** See 522, v. I, fasc. 10 (Stratigraphic Lexicon)

*Rumania*

**325.** Roman, D., and A. Codarcea (1926) Bibliografía geologiča a României. Publ. Inst. geol. României, 155 pp. (1929) Supplement, 103 pp.
Kräutner, Theodor (1939) Bibliografía geologiča a României: al II supliment, 80 pp., Inst. Geol. României, Bucuvesti.
——— (1943) Bibliographie des travaux scientifiques parus en 1941; géologie: Acad. Roumaine, Sec. Sci., B, v. 24, p. 727–734. (1943) *Ibid.,* 1942, v. 25, p. 694–698.
Atanasia, I. (1946) 1943: *ibid.,* v. 26, p. 782–786. (1947) 1944: *ibid.,* v. 27, p. 786–790.
**326.** See 274; 522, v. I, fasc. 13a (Stratigraphic Lexicon)

*Sardinia*

**327.** Taricco, M., and T. Sotgia (1923) Bibliografia geologica, paleontologica, mineralogica e mineraria della Sardegna: Soc. geol. Ital. Bull., v. 41, p. 373–437.
**328.** Hellman, F. S. (1942) Sicily and Sardinia: A bibliographical list. Washington, D.C., Lib. Cong., Div. Bib., 38 pp.

*Spain*

**329.** Primitivo Hernandez, Sampelayo (1942) Explicacion del nuevo mapa geológico de España, tomo 2, El Sistema Siluriano, fasc. 2 (Especies, bibliografía, cuadro), p. 593–848, Mem. Inst. Geol. Min. España.
**330.** Battaler Calatayud, José R. (1945) Bibliografía del Cretácico de España. Madrid, Inst. Investig. Geol. "Lucas Mallada," Estud. Geol., no. 1, p. 7–108, 1 pl.
**331.** Meseguer Pardo, José (1947) Catálogo de las publicaciones del Instituto Geológico y Minero de España. Madrid, Tip. Lit. Coullaut, 366 pp.

332. San Miguel de la Cámara, Maximino (1952) Bibliografía vulcanológica española. Bol. Volcan. s. 2, v. 12, p. 203–214.

333. Spain. Instituto Geológico y Minero (1955) Catálogo de las publicaciones del Instituto Geológico y Minero de España. Madrid, 326 pp.

334. See 522, v. I, fasc. 10 (Stratigraphic Lexicon)

### Soviet Union

335. Berg, Ernst V. (1862) Repertorium der Literatur uber die Mineralogie, Geologie, Palaeontologie, Berg und Hüttenkunde Russlands. St. Petersburg, 227 pp.

336. Nikitin, S. (1887) Bibliotheque géologique de la Russie 1886. Bull. Comité Geol., Suppl. v. 6, p. 1–184. (1888) 1887, Suppl. v. 7, p. 1–178. (1889) 1888, Suppl. v. 8, p. 1–201. (1890) 1889, Suppl. v. 9, p. 1–187. (1891) 1890, Suppl. v. 10, p. 1–225. (1892) 1891, Suppl. v. 11, p. 1–234. (1893) 1892, Suppl. v. 12, p. 1–245. (1894) 1893, Suppl. v. 13, 1–200. (1895) 1894, Suppl. v. 14, p. 1–202. (1896) 1895, Suppl. v. 15, p. 1–223. (1897) 1896, Suppl. v. 16, p. 1–244. (1901) 1897, Edition du Comité Geol., p. 1–280.

337. Anonymous (1935) A bibliography of Novaya Zemlya. Leningrad, Admin. of the Northern Sea Route, 240 pp.

338. Samorodova, Anna (1936) Bibliography of paleontology and stratigraphy 1934–1935. Problems Paleont. (Moscow, Univ., Lab. Pub.) v. 1, p. 275–322. (1937) 1935–1936, v. 2–3, p. 713–807. (1938) 1936–1937, v. 4, p. 407–537. (1938) 1937–1938, v. 5, p. 397–453.

339. Snezhinskaya, M. V. (1938) The USSR nonperiodical literature on geological sciences for 1937. Acad. Sci. USSR, B, Sér. Géol. no. 5–6, p. 837–854 (Russ.).

340. Anonymous (1940) Literature. Molotov, Univ. (M. Gorky), Sci. Mem. v. 3, no. 3, pp. i–xx. [A bibliography of the geology of the Perm region and the Urals, Russia.]

341. Edelshtein, Ya. S. (1941) Chronologic list of the geological papers and monographs published by the Russian Academy of Sciences. Bibliothek Geologicheskaia literature USSR, Akad. Nauk USSR. v. 1, 1728 to 1928, 471 pp.; v. 2, 1929 to 1937, 656 pp.

342. Brookhaven National Laboratory (1948 to date) Guide to Russian scientific periodical literature. Vol. 1, 1948 to present. Upton, N. Y.

343. Dorosh, J. T. (1950) Guide to Soviet bibliographies: A selected list of references. Washington, D.C., Lib. Cong., General Ref. Bib. Div., 158 pp.

344. Anonymous (1953) Bibliografiya sovetskoi literatury po paleontologii i biostratigrafii paleozoya SSSR za 1940–1951 gg. (materialy vystavki vo vremya soveshchaniya). Mater. Paleont. Soveshchaniya Paleozoyu, Akad. Nauk SSSR, Paleont. Inst.–Inst. Geol. Nauk, p. 194–257.

345. Pauliuc, Simon, and A. Holan (1958) Revista de referata geologie-geografie din literature sovietica de specialitate, no. 6, [Bucharest] Acad. Republicii Populare Romîne, Inst. Studii Romîno-Soviet., 221 pp. [An annotated bibliography of geologic and geographic papers published in the Soviet Union in 1958, classified by subject, with abstracts in Romanian and author and subject indexes.]

**346.** Smits, Rudolf (1958) Serial publications of the Soviet Union, 1939–1957. Washington, D.C., Lib. Cong., Cyrillic Bibliographic Project, Processing Dept., 459 pp.

**347.** National Science Foundation (1961) List of Russian scientific journals available in English. Washington, D.C., The Foundation, 39 pp.

**348.** Union Library Catalogue of the Philadelphia Metropolitan Area (1961) Union list of English translations of Russian journals. Philadelphia, 9 pp.

**349.** Vsesoyuznaya Geologicheskaya Biblioteka (Vsegei) (1934 to date) Geologicheskaya Literatura U.S.S.R. [Annual volumes, but coverage not complete, for 1934–1955; from 1956 published as quarterly.]

**350.** Referativnyi Zhurnal Geologiya (1954 to date) Inst. Acad. Sci., U.S.S.R. [Abstract journal, issued monthly.]

**351.** See 522, v. II; (Stratigraphic Lexicon); 537, 539 (Marine Geology)

### Sweden

**352.** Ahlander, F. E. (1901) Förteckning öfuer svensk geologisk, paleontologisk, petrografisk och mineralogisk litteratur för åren 1899–1900. Geol. Foren. Stockholm, v. 23, p. 185–198. (1904) 1901–1903, v. 25, p. 432–448 (1903). (1907) 1904–1906, v. 29, p. 49–67. (1919) 1907–1917, v. 41, p. 539–606. (1920) 1918 och 1919: *ibid.,* v. 42, p. 453–464. (1921) 1920, v. 43, p. 663–668. (1922) 1921, v. 44, p. 777–782. (1923) 1922, v. 45, p. 598–605. (1924) 1923, v. 46, p. 696–703. (1925) 1924, v. 47, p. 512–520. (1926) 1925, v. 48, p. 584–592. (1927) 1926, v. 49, p. 588–596.

Sandegren, R. (1928) *Ibid.,* 1927, v. 50, p. 788–798. (1929) 1928, v. 51, p. 580–588.

———, and N. Magnusson (1930) *Ibid.,* 1929, v. 52, p. 689–754.

——— (1932) Revue annuelle de la littérature géologique suédoise 1930. *Ibid.,* v. 53, p. 471–520. (1934) 1931–1933, v. 56, p. 531–595. (1935) 1934, v. 57, p. 637–661. (1936) 1935, v. 58, p. 567–595. (1937) 1936, v. 59, p. 469–502. (1938) 1937, v. 60, p. 555–589. (1939) 1938, v. 61, p. 463–489. (1940) 1939, v. 62, p. 309–331. (1941) 1940, v. 63, p. 341–371. (1942) 1941, v. 64, p. 369–398. (1943) 1942, v. 65, p. 337–370. (1944) 1943, v. 66, p. 777–806. (1945) 1944, v. 67, p. 469–497. (1946) 1945, v. 68, p. 531–554. (1947) 1946, v. 69, p. 433–459. (1948) 1947, v. 70, p. 551–574. (1949) 1948, v. 71, p. 545–576. (1950) 1949, v. 72, p. 405–436. (1951) 1950, v. 73, p. 571–602. (1952) 1951, v. 74, p. 395–426. (1953) 1952, v. 75, p. 411–464. (1954) 1953, v. 76, p. 613–660. (1955) 1954, v. 77, p. 449–477. (1956) 1955, v. 78, p. 579–674.

Larsson, Walter (1960) *Ibid.,* 1956–1957, v. 82, p. 433–604.

**353.** Sandegren, Ragnar (1959) Register över Sveriges Geologiska Undersöknings publikationer 1858–1958. Sveriges Geol. Unders., Årsb. 53, no. 1, s. C, no. 563, 330 pp.

**354.** See 522, v. I, fasc. 2c (Stratigraphic Lexicon)

### Switzerland

**355.** Rollier, Louis (1907, 1908) Bibliographie géologique de la Suisse pour les années 1770 à 1900. Mater. Carte Geol. de la Suisse, v. 29, p. 1, A

(Géologie générale et géognosie de la Suisse) jusqu'a K-11 (Stratigraphie des terrains molassiques, pp. 1–540 (1907); pt. 2, L-1 (Hydrodynamique et glacialisme) jusqu'à V (Reliefs géologiques), p. 541–1025 (1908).

Gogarten, E. and W. Hauswirth (1913) *Ibid.*, 1900 à 1910, v. 70 (n.s. no. 40), p. 1–412.

Jeannet, Alphonse (1927) *Ibid.*, 1910 à 1920, v. 86, pt. 1, Catalogue par noms d'auteurs, p. 1–462; pt. 2, Catalogue par matières, p. 463–855. (1936) 1921 à 1930, v. 103, 496 pp.

**356.** Schweizerische Naturforschende Gesellschaft (1934) Bibliographie der Schweizerischen Naturforschenden Gesellschaft, 1817–1930. Bern, Buchler and Co., 340 pp. (1941) 1931–1940, Bern, Buchler and Co., 89 pp.

**357.** Schweizerische Naturforschende Gesellschaft (1946) Katalog der Publikationen der Geologischen Kommission und der Geotechnischen Kommission. Bern, Kümmerly and Frey, 36 pp., 3 pls.

**358.** See 522, v. I, fasc. 7 (Stratigraphic Lexicon)

## Yugoslavia

**359.** See 272; 274; 522, v. I, fasc. 12a (Stratigraphic Lexicon)

## Middle East

### General

**360.** Keller, Alexandre (1933) Bibliographie géologique et géographique de la Syrie, du Liban et des régions limitrophes. Rev. Géog. Phys. Géol. Dyn., v. 6, f. 4, p. 453–512.

**361.** Dost, H. (1953) Bibliography on land and water utilization in the Middle East. Wageningen, Univ., 115 pp.

**362.** Field, Henry (1958) Bibliography of southwestern Asia. Univ. of Miami Press, 275 pp.

**363.** Avnimelech, M. (1961) Bibliography of Levant geology (incl. Sinai, Israel, Jordan, Lebanon, Syria, and Cyprus). Provisional edition, not for publication. Jerusalem, Hebr. Univ. Geol. Dept., 112 pp.

**364.** See 273; 522, v. III, fasc. 10c (Stratigraphic Lexicon)

### Arabia

**365.** Macro, Eric (1958) Bibliography of the Arabian peninsula: Univ. of Miami Press, 80 pp.

**366.** See 522, v. III, fasc. 10b (Stratigraphic Lexicon)

### Cyprus

**367.** See 522, v. III, fasc. 9d (Stratigraphic Lexicon)

### Iran

**368.** See 522, v. III, fasc. 9b (Stratigraphic Lexicon)

## Iraq

**369.** See 522, v. III, fasc. 10a (Stratigraphic Lexicon)
**370.** Allouse, B. E. (1954) A bibliography on the vertebrate fauna of Iraq and neighbouring countries: I, Mammals. p. 1–34, Iraq Natural History Museum, Ar-Rabitta Press, Baghdad. [II, Birds; III, Reptiles and Amphibians and IV, Fishes: to appear later.]

## Turkey

**371.** Fuller, G. H. (1944) Turkey: A selected list of references. Washington, D.C., Lib. Cong., General Ref. Bib. Div., 114 pp.
**372.** Lahn, E. (1948) Türkiye jeolojik bibliyografyasi. Bibliographie géologique de la Turquie. Turk. Jeol. Kurumu, Bull., v. 1, no. 2, p. 96–135.
**373.** Jones, L. (1953) Bibliography on geology and mineral resources of Turkey. U. S. Bureau Mines, 43 pp.
**374.** See 522, v. III, fasc. 9c (Stratigraphic Lexicon)

# Asia

## General

**375.** Garde, P. K. (1956) Directory of reference works published in Asia. Paris, Nijmegen, UNESCO Bibliographical Handbooks, No. 5, 139 pp.

## Afghanistan

**376.** See 522, v. III, fasc. 9a (Stratigraphic Lexicon)

## Ceylon

**377.** Wadia, D. N. (1944) Bibliography of Ceylon geology. *In* Ceylon, Dept. Miner. Records, Prof. Paper no. 1, p. 33–38.
**378.** See 522, v. III, fasc. 8 (Stratigraphic Lexicon)

## China

**379.** Wang, Chung Yu (1912) Bibliography of the mineral wealth and geology of China. London, 63 pp.
———— (1917) Bibliography of the mineral wealth and geology of China from 1912 to 1917. Shanghai Commercial Press, 21 pp. (1918) Suppl., 15 pp. (1925) 1918–1924. Jr. Assoc. Chinese Amer. Engineers, v. 6, no. 5, 17 pp.
**380.** Anonymous (1934) Bibliographic review of modern literature on northern Manchuria: I, Geology. Club. Nat. Sci. Geog. YMCA, Ann. (Ezhegodnik), v. 1, p. 246–250, (1933).
**381.** Young, T. I. (1935) Bibliography of Chinese geology up to 1934. Peiping, Nat. Acad., 241 pp.
**382.** Chi, Y. S. (1936) Science bibliography of China: V, Section of geology [1934–1935] Nanking, Nat. Res. Council (Academia Sinica), 57 pp.
———— (1942) Bibliography of Chinese geology for the years 1936–1940. Pehpei, Nat. Geol. Surv. China, 147 pp.

**383.** Tseng, T. C. (1946) Bibliography of geology and allied sciences of Tibet and regions to the west of the Chinshachiang. Nanking, Nat. Geol. Surv. China, 114 pp.

**384.** Li, Hsiao-Fung (1947) Bibliography of geology and geography of Sinkiang. Nanking, Nat. Geol. Surv. China, 213 pp.

**385.** See 522, v. III, fasc. 1 (Stratigraphic Lexicon)

### India

**386.** Oldham, R. D. (1888) A bibliography of Indian geology: Being a list of books and papers relating to the geology of British India and adjoining countries published previous to the end of A.D. 1887. Calcutta, Government Printing, India, 145 pp.

**387.** La Touche, T. H. D. (1917–1926) A bibliography of Indian geology and physical geography, with an annotated index of minerals of economic value. Calcutta, India Geological Survey. Pt. 1A, A bibliography of Indian geology and physical geography (1917); pt. 1B, An annotated index of minerals of economic value (1918); pt. 2, Index of localities (1921); pt. 3, Index of subjects (1923); pt. 4, Paleontological Index (1926).

**388.** Radhakrishna, B. P. (1957) Bibliography of Mysore Geology. Mysore Geol. Assoc. Bull. no. 44, 16 pp.

**389.** See 449 (Goa); 522, v. III, fasc. 8 (Stratigraphic Lexicon)

### Korea

**390.** See 522, v. III, fasc. 2a (Stratigraphic Lexicon)

### Manchuria

**391.** Manchukuo Geological Institute (1940) List of literatures on the geology of Manchuria. Manchukuo Geol. Inst., Bull. no. 98 (appendix), 6 pp. (Jap.).

**392.** See 522, v. III, fasc. 2b (Stratigraphic Lexicon)

### Pakistan

**393.** See 386, 387; 522, v. III, fasc. 8 (Stratigraphic Lexicon)

### Southeast Asia

**394.** Mason, J. B., and H. C. Parish, (1918) Thailand bibliography. Univ. Florida Libraries, Bibliographic Series No. 4, 247 pp.

**395.** Hellmen, F. S. (1943) British Malaya and British North Borneo: A bibliographical list. Washington, D.C., Lib. Cong., Div. Bib., 103 pp.

**396.** Hobbs, C., G. H. Fuller, H. D. Jones, J. T. Dorosh, and I. M. Socko (1950) Indochina: A bibliography of the land and people. Washington, D.C., Lib. Cong., Ref. Dept., 367 pp.

**397.** Hobbs, C. (1952) Southeast Asia: An annotated bibliography of selected reference sources. Washington, D.C., Lib. Cong., Orientalia Div., 163 pp.

**398.** See 522, v. III, fasc. 6 (Stratigraphic Lexicon)

## Pacific and Southwest Pacific Regions

### *Australia*

399. Etheridge, R. (1872) A catalogue of Australian fossils, stratigraphically and zoologically arranged. Cambridge Univ. Press, Cambridge, England, 240 pp.

400. —— and R. L. Jack (1881) Catalogue of works, papers, reports, and maps on the geology, paleontology, mineralogy, mining and metallurgy, etc. of the Australian Continent and Tasmania. London, 196 pp.

401. —— (1902) A monograph of the Cretaceous Invertebrate fauna of New South Wales: Appendix I, Catalogue of the Cretaceous fossils of Australia, by R. Etheridge and W. S. Dun, Appendix II, Bibliography of Australian Cretaceous Geology and Palaeontology, by W. S. Dun; N. S. Wales Geol. Surv., Mem. Pal. 11, 120 pp.

402. Keble, R. A., and W. N. Benson (1939) Graptolites of Australia: Bibliography and history of research. Melbourne, National Museum Memoir, no. 11, p. 11–99.

403. Singleton, F. A. (1941) The Tertiary geology of Australia. Roy. Soc. Victoria, Proc., v. 53, pt. 1, p. 1–125, 15 figs., 6 pls. maps [Bibliography of 705 titles.]

404. Fuller, G. H. (1942) A selected list of references on Australia. Washington, D.C., Lib. Cong., Div. Bib., 101 pp

405. Clark, H. L. (1946) The echinoderm fauna of Australia; its composition and its origin. Carnegie Inst. Washington, Publ. no. 566, 567 pp.

406. Dall, W., and W. Stephenson (1953) A bibliography of the marine invertebrates of Queensland. Univ. Queensland Papers, Dept. Zoology, v. 1, p. 21–49.

407. Crespin, Irene (1955) A bibliography of Australian foraminifera. Micropaleontology, v. 1, no. 2, p. 172–188.

408. Teesdale-Smith, E. N. (1959) Bibliography of South Australian geology. S. Aust. Dept. Mines, Geol. Surv., 240 pp.

409. See 522, v. VI, fasc. 5 (Stratigraphic Lexicon)

### *Indonesia*

410. Verbeek, R. D. M. (1924) Geologisch Mijnbouwkundige Bibliographie von Nederlandsch-Indië. Geol. Mijnb. Gen. Nederland en Kol., Deel III, p. 1–20. (1925) p. 21–43.

411. Wing-Easton, N. (1926) *Ibid.,* p. 45–70. (1926) p. 45–70. (1927) p. 71–94. (1928) p. 95–115. (1929) p. 117–134. (1930) p. 135–152. (1931) p. 153–174. (1932) p. 175–194. (1933) Algemen Register voor Deel III, 1923–1932, p. 195–208.

—— (1935) Opgave van geschriften over geologie en mijnbouw van Nederlandsch Oost-Indië. *Ibid.,* Deel IV, pt. 1, 2, p. 1–18. (1937) pt. 3, 4, p. 19–36.

Steenhuis, J. F. (1951) Opgave van geschriften over geologie en mijnbouw van Indonesië, drieentwintigste vervolg; Geologisch-mijnbouwkundige bibliografie van Indonesië. *Ibid.,* Deel IV, pt. 5–10, p. 37–118.

412. Klompé, Th. F. F. (1954) Publications on the geology and geophysics of Indonesia and adjacent areas, 1952–1953. Madjalah Ilmu Alam Indonesia (Indones. J. Nat. Sci.) v. 110, no. 4–6, p. 216–246.

—— (1955) Publications on the geology and geophysics of Indonesia and adjacent areas, 1954. Madjalah Ilmu Alam Indonesia (Indones. J. Nat. Sci.) v. 111, no. 4–6, p. 214–243; Addenda. . . . 1952–1953, p. 244–250.

413. See 449 (Portuguese Timor); 522, v. III, fasc. 7 (Stratigraphic Lexicon); 594 (Foraminifera)

### Japan

414. Japan. Imperial Geological Survey (1932) List of publications of the Imperial Geological Survey of Japan, 1880–1932. Tokyo, Imp. Geol. Surv., 62 pp.

415. Hatai, K. M. (1937) Classified list of papers and reports bearing on paleontology published in Japan during 1900–1936 (with several earlier works). Pt. 1. Invertebrata, Mammalia and Stratigraphic paleontology. pt. 2, Botany and paleobotany. Sendai, Saito Ho-On Kai Mus. Res. Bull. 13, p. 189–277.

—— (1940) List of papers and reports bearing on palaeontology and geology published by Japanese workers during 1937, with supplement. Sendai, Saito Ho-On Kai Mus., Res. Bull. 19, p. 211–229.

—— (1940) Genera, subgenera, and higher systematic rankings published by palaeontologists of Japan. Sendai, Saito Ho-On Kai Mus., Res. Bull. 19, p. 171–210.

416. Hanzawa, Shoshiro, and Kotora Hatai (1951) Alphabetic list of papers and reports published in Japan on stratigraphy, paleontology and marine ecology for the period 1947–1951. Tokyo, U. S. Geol. Surv., Military Geol. Branch, 130 pp.

417. Endo, Riuji (1951) Bibliography of Japanese paleontology and related sciences 1941–1950. Paleont. Soc. Japan, Sp. Paper 1, 71 pp.

418. Fujimoto, Haruyoshi (1956) Bibliography of the geology of Japan, 1873–1955: rev. ed. Tokyo, Chijin Shokan, 711 pp.

419. Takoi, Fujuji (1962) Bibliography of Japanese paleontology and related sciences, 1951–1960. Palaeont. Soc. Japan, Sp. Paper 9, 338 pp.

420. Bonn, G. S. (1960) Japanese journals in science and technology, an annotated checklist. New York, The New York Public Library, 119 pp.

421. See 522, v. III, fasc. 3a,b (Stratigraphic Lexicon); 538 (Marine Geology); 595, 605 (Foraminifera).

### New Zealand

422. Allan, R. S., and B. W. Collins (1951–1952) Bibliography of New Zealand geology since 1908. New Zealand Geol. Surv., Geol. Rept. no. 28 and Suppl., 235 pp.

423. Jenkins, A. P., and D. L. Jenkins (1954) Subject index to a bibliography of New Zealand geology since 1908. Otago, Univ. Christchurch, 121 pp.

**424.** Adkin, G. (1954) Bibliographic index of New Zealand stratigraphic names to 31 December 1950. New Zealand Geol. Surv., Mem. 9, 121 pp.
**425.** See 522, v. VI, fasc. 4 (Stratigraphic Lexicon); 542 (Oceanography).

### Pacific Region

**426.** Reid, C. F., N. Habit, V. Jay, and C. Simonini (1939) Bibliography of the Island of Guam. New York, H. W. Wilson Co., 102 pp.
**427.** Conover, H. F. (1943) Islands of the Pacific: A selected list of references. Washington, D.C., Lib. Cong., Div. Bib., 181 pp. (1945) Supplement, 68 pp.
**428.** Leivin, Evans (1944) The Pacific region: A bibliography of the Pacific and East Indian islands exclusive of Japan. Royal Empire Soc. Bibl. no. 11, 76 pp.
**429.** U. S. Army Forces, Far East, Office of the Engineer, Intelligence Division, Geological Surveys Branch (1954) Catalogue of translations of Japanese geological literature of the Pacific Islands. [Tokyo], 34 pp.
**430.** —— (1954) Catalogue of translations of Japanese geological literature of Far Eastern areas. [Tokyo], 17 pp.
**431.** Foster, H. L. (1956) Annotated bibliography of geologic and soils literature of western north Pacific islands: [Tokyo] U. S. Army, Chief Eng., Intelligence Div., Headquarters U. S. Army Forces Far East, 879 pp., maps.
**432.** See 522, v. VI, fasc. 1, 2, 3 (Stratigraphic Lexicon).

### Philippine Islands

**433.** Teves, Juan S. (1953) Bibliography of Philippine geology, mining, and mineral resources. Philippines Bur. Mines, Bib. Ser. no. 1, 155 pp.
**434.** Daleon, B. A. (1957) Bibliography of Philippine paleontology and stratigraphy, 1861–1957. Phil. Geol., v. 12, no. 1, p. 16–32.
**435.** See 522, v. III, fasc. 5 (Stratigraphic Lexicon)

### Taiwan

**436.** Yen, T. P., C. S. Ho, and P. Y. Chen (1947) Bibliography of geology of Taiwan. Taipeh, Taiwan Geol. Surv., 58 pp.
**437.** See 522, v. III, fasc. 4 (Stratigraphic Lexicon)

### Tasmania

**438.** Twelvetrees, W. H. (1915) Catalogue of publications issued by the government of Tasmania, relating to the mines, minerals, and geology of the state to 31 December, 1914. Tasmania Geol. Surv., Bull. 22, 28 pp.
**439.** See 522, v. V, fasc. 5d (Stratigraphic Lexicon)

## Africa

### General

**440.** Stefanini, G., and C. de Stefani (1925) Bibliographie des travaux des géologues italiens sur l'Afrique. *In* C. R. Congr. Géol. Intern., Belg. 1922, v. 8, p. 1073–1086.

**441.** Conover, H. F. (1942) The British Empire in Africa: Selected references. I. General, 37 pp.; II. British West Africa, 32 pp.; III. British Eastern and Central Africa, 45 pp.; IV. The Union of South Africa, 77 pp. Washington, D.C., Lib. Cong., Div. Bib.

**442.** Conover, H. F. (1942) French Colonies in Africa: A list of references. Washington, D.C., Lib. Cong., Div. Bib., 89 pp.

**443.** Hopwood, A. T., and J. P. Hollyfield (1954) An annotated bibliography of the fossil mammals of Africa (1742–1950). British Mus. (Nat. Hist.), Fossil Mammals of Africa, no. 8, 194 pp.

**444.** Kufferath, Hubert (1956) Liste bibliographique de travaux concernant les algues fossiles et protistes fossiles d'Afrique (première liste). Soc. Belge Géol., Bull., v. 65, f. 2, p. 359–366.

### Algeria

**445.** Blondel, Fernand (1937) Bibliographie géologique et minière de la France d'outre-mer: tome 1, édition provisoire. Paris, Bur. d'Études Géol. et Min. Coloniales, 563 pp.

———— (1941) Bibliographie géologique et minière de la France d'outre-mer. Paris, Bur. Études Géol. et Min. Coloniales, Pub. no. 11, v. 1 and 2, 1037 pp. (1952) 2nd ed. v. 1, 567 pp.

**446.** Hilly, Jean, and Maurice LeLubre (1954) Bibliographie geologique de l'Algérie: no. 1, Liste des publications récentes; arrêtée au 28 février 1954. Algeria, Serv. Carte Géol. Bull., n.s. no. 1, pt. 2, p. 211–250. (1955). . . . . no. 2, *ibid.*, no. 5, p. 581–604.

LeLubre, Maurice (1956) *Ibid.*, no. 3, *ibid.*, no. 8, p. 363–391. (1957) no. 4, *ibid.*, no. 13, p. 219–252.

———— (1958) Bibliographie géologique annuelle de l'Algérie. Algérie du Nord et Sahara algérien: no. 5. *Ibid.*, no. 20, p. 95–111.

LeGallic, M. L., and G. Busson (1959) *Ibid.* no. 6. *Ibid.*, no. 25, p. 305–330.

**447.** See 522, v. IV, fasc. 1b (Stratigraphic Lexicon)

### Angola

**448.** Mouta, F. (1938) Bibliografía geológica de Angola (Africa Ocidental Portuguesa) em Dezembro de 1934: Portugal, Serviços Geol., Commun. v. 20, p. 39–52.

**449.** Goncalves, Francisco, and Jaime Caseiro (1959) Bibliografía geológica do ultramar portugues. Junta Investig. Ultramar, 273 pp.

**450.** See 522, v. IV, fasc. 7b (Stratigraphic Lexicon)

### Cameroun

**451.** Denaeyer, M. E. (1933) Bibliographie géologique de l'Afrique Equatoriale Française, du Cameroun et des régions limitrophes. Acad. Sci. Coloniales, Ann. v. 6, p. 355–431.

**452.** Denaeyer, A., and F. Blondel (1944) Bibliographie géologique du Cameroun. Soc. Études Camerounaises, Bull., 1944, no. 6, p. 41–60.

## Central Africa

453. Cornet, J. (1913–1914) Bibliographie géologique du Bassin du Congo. Soc. Géol. Nord., Ann. 41, pp. 1–81.
——— (1916) Bibliographie géologique du Bassin du Congo. Ann. Soc. géol. Belgique, Liége, 81 pp.
454. Association Services Géologiques Africains (1937) Bibliographie geologique de l'Afrique Centrale (Edition provisoire). Liége, Assoc. Serv. Géol. Africains, Publiée avec le concours de la Sociéte Géol. de Belgique., 298 pp.
Jamotte, A. (1948) Compléments à la bibliographie géologique de l'Afrique centrale publiée en 1937: Congo Belge, décade 1935–1944 et addenda à l'édition de 1937. Paris, Assoc. Serv. Géol. Africains, Bur. Études Géol. Min. Coloniales, 38 pp.
——— (1951) Compléments à la bibliographie géologique de l'Afrique Centrale publiée en 1937: Congo belge, periode 1945–1949; addenda et errata aux editions de 1937 et 1948. Paris, Assoc. Serv. Géol. Africains, Bur. Études Geol. Min. Coloniales; Brussels, Min. Colonies Belgique, Comm. Géol., 29 pp.
455. Heyse, Theodore (1946) Bibliographie du Congo belge et du Ruanda-Urundi, 1939–1945. Cahiers Belges et Congolais no. 4. Brussels, G. van Campenhout, 42 pp.
456. Cahen, Lucien (1952–1961) Bibliographie geologique du Congo Belge et du Ruanda-Urundi. Brussels, K. Mus. Belg. Congo (Mus. Roy. Congo Belge). (1955) v. 1, 1818–1924, 173 pp. (1953) v. 2, 1925–1934, 188 pp. (1952) v. 3, 1935–1944, 131 pp. (1955) v. 4, 1945–1954, 232 pp. (1957) v. 5, 1955–1956, 90 pp. (1959) v. 6, 1957–1958, 109 pp. (1961) v. 7, 1959–1960, 183 pp. Name of issuing agency changed to K. Mus. Midden-Afrika (Mus. Roy. L'Afrique Centrale), Teruren, Belgique.
457. See 449; 522, v. IV, fasc. 6, 7a (Stratigraphic Lexicon)

## Egypt

458. Sherborn, C. D. (1910) Bibliography of scientific and technical literature relating to Egypt. Cairo, National Printing Dept., 155 pp.
459. Egypt. Survey Department (1915) Bibliography of scientific and technical literature relating to Egypt, 1800–1900. Preliminary edition. Cairo, 155 pp.
460. Keldani, E. H. (1941) A bibliography of geology and related sciences concerning Egypt up to the end of 1939. Cairo, Dept. Surv. Mines, 428 pp.
461. Conover, H. F. (1952) Egypt and the Anglo-Egyptian Sudan: A selected guide to background reading. Seattle, Univ. of Washington Press, 26 pp.
462. Said, Rushdi, and E. M. El Shazly (1957) Review of Egyptian Geology, v. 1. Cairo, Egyptian Rev. Sci., Sci. Council, 91 pp.
463. Said, Rushdi (1960) Bibliography on Sinai. *In* Sinai Volume. Cairo, Science Council, p. 383–416.
464. See 522, v. IV, fasc. 4b (Stratigraphic Lexicon)

## Ethiopia

**465.** See 522, v. IV, fasc. 5a (Stratigraphic Lexicon)

## Ghana

**466.** James, W. T. (1937) A bibliography of Gold Coast geology, mining, and archaeology to March, 1937. Gold Coast Geol. Surv., Bull. 9, 55 pp.

## Guinea

**467.** Furon, Raymond (1943) Géologie de la Guinée française. Paris, Bur. Études Géol. Min. Col., Pub. no. 19, 47 pp., 12 figs. (incl. g. map 1:400,000). [An extensive bibliography is included.]

## Kenya

**468.** See 522, v. IV, fasc. 8a (Stratigraphic Lexicon)

## Libya

**469.** Desio, Ardito (1950) Bibliografia geologica italiana dell'Africa sino al 1948 incluso. Rome, Ufficio Studi Ministero dell'Africa Italiana, 83 pp.
**470.** Desio, Ardito (1953) Bibliografia geologica della Libia dal 1941 al 1952. Mus. Libico Storia Nat., Ann. v. 4, p. 195–200.
**471.** See 522, v. IV, fasc. 4a (Stratigraphic Lexicon)

## Morocco

**472.** Gaudefroy, C., and F. Permingeat (1956) Bibliographie régionale: Maroc. Soc. Franc Minér., Bull., v. 79, nos. 1–3, p. 184–191.
**473.** See 445; 522, v. IV, fasc. 1a (Stratigraphic Lexicon)

## Mozambique

**474.** See 449; 522, v. IV, fasc. 10a (Stratigraphic Lexicon)

## Northern Rhodesia

**475.** Snowball, G. J. (1960) A bibliography of Northern Rhodesia geology. Northern Rhodesia, Geol. Surv., Rec., 1959, p. 35–76.
**476.** See 522, v. IV, fasc. 9a–c (Stratigraphic Lexicon)

## Nyasaland

**477.** See 522, v. IV, fasc. 9a–c (Stratigraphic Lexicon)

## Portuguese Guinea

**478.** See 449

## Somaliland

**479.** Italy, Reale Ufficio Geologico (1936) Bibliografia geologica italiana per gli anni 1915–1933; Africa orientale italiana. Italy, R. Uff. Geol., Bol., v. 61, suppl. 2, 116 pp.
**480.** See 469; 522, v. IV, fasc. 5 (Stratigraphic Lexicon)

### South Africa

481. Saunders, H. P. (1897) Bibliography of South African geology, being a list of books, papers and reports on the subject. Parts 1 and 2. Capetown, Geol. Comm., South African Museum, 56 pp.
482. Anderson, W. (1901, 1904, 1907) Bibliography of Natal and Zululand geology. *In* First Report of the Geological Survey of Natal and Zululand, 1901, p. 29–36; 2nd Report, 1904, p. 29–35; 3rd Report, 1907, p. 37–44: Natal, Surveyor General's Department.
438. Wilman, M. (1905) Catalogue of printed books, papers and maps relating to the geology and mineralogy of South Africa. S. Afr. Phil. Soc. Trans. 15, pt. 5, p. 283–467.
484. Hall, A. L. (1922) A bibliography of South African geology to the end of 1920: Authors index. Union of South Africa Geological Survey Mem. 18, 376 pp. (1927) 1921–1925, Authors Index, Mem. 25, 117 pp. (1931) 1926–1930, Mem. 27, 160 pp. (1937) 1931–1935, Mem. 30, 168 pp.

———— (1939) A subject index to the literature of South African geology and mineral resources for the years 1921 to 1935 (inclusive). *Ibid.,* Mem. 37, 288 pp.
485. Vermeulen, P. H. (1959) Bibliography and subject index of South African geology, 1957. Pretoria, South Africa, Geol. Surv., 60 pp.
486. Haughton, S. H., and A. S. Brink (1954) A bibliographical list of Reptilia from the Karroo beds of Africa. Palaeont. Africana, v. 2, 187 pp.
487. Haughton, S. H. (1956?) Geological bibliography of Africa south of the Sahara—Bibliographie géologique de l'Afrique au sud du Sahara: Bibliography of the Karroo system—Bibliographie du système Karroo, no. 1. London, Comm. Tech. Co-operation Africa South of Sahara, 111 pp.
488. See 522, v. IV, fasc. 10b (Stratigraphic Lexicon)

### Sudan

489. Andrew, Gerald (1945) Sources of information on the geology of the Anglo-Egyptian Sudan. Anglo-Egyptian Sudan, Geol. Surv., Bull. no. 3, 36 pp.
490. See 461; 522, v. IV, fasc. 4b (Stratigraphic Lexicon)

### Tanganyika

491. Reck, Hans (1936) Literaturübersicht über die bergwirtschaftliche und geologische Arbeit in Ostafrika während der Jahre 1935 und 1936. Tropenpflanzer, Berlin, Jg. 39, no. 12, p. 530–537.
492. Hennig, Edwin (1937) Die geologische Erschliessung Deutsch-Ostafrikas in der Nachkriegszeit. Deut. Geol. Ges., Zs., v. 89, no. 8–9, p. 509–526. [Extensive bibliography.]
493. Spence, J. (1954) Bibliography of the Tanganyika Karroo. *In* Int. Geol. Cong., 19th, Algeria, C. R. f. 21 (Assoc. Serv. Géol. Africains, pt. 2), p. 103–109.
494. See 522, v. IV, fasc. 8c (Stratigraphic Lexicon)

## Togoland

**495.** Kachinsky, V. (1933) Bibliographie géologique et minières du Togo. La chronique des mines coloniales (Bur. d'Études Géol. Min. Coloniales), an. 2, no. 21, p. 517–526.

## Tunisia

**496.** Castany, Gilbert (1954) Bibliographie géologique de la Tunisié, no. 1. Tunisia, Serv. Mines, Tunis, 15 pp. (1955) no. 2, Tunisia Serv. Geol., Tunis, 22 pp.
**497.** See 445; 522, v. IV, fasc. 1c (Stratigraphic Lexicon)

## Uganda

**498.** Uganda. Geological Survey (1934) Bibliography of Uganda geological literature. *In* Ann. Rep. and Bull. Geol. Surv. Uganda, 1933, p. 82–88.
———— (1939) Bibliography of Uganda geological literature. *In* Uganda Geol. Surv. Bull. 3, p. 183–196.
**499.** See 522, v. IV, fasc. 8b (Stratigraphic Lexicon)

## Western Africa

**500.** Masvier, L. (1952) Bibliographie et carte géologique de l'Afrique occidentale française. Dakar, Dir. Fédérale Mines Géol., 29 pp., maps.
**501.** See 522, v. IV, fasc. 2 (Stratigraphic Lexicon)

## Madagascar

**502.** Madagascar Service des Mines (19—?) Bibliographie géologique de Madagascar. Madag. Serv. Mines, Annales Géologique. [Annual bibliographies published in this journal.]
**503.** See 522, v. IV, fasc. 11 (Stratigraphic Lexicon)

## Polar Regions

### General

**504.** Chavanne, J. (1878) Die Literatur über die Polar-Regionen der Erde. Vienna, K. K. Geog. Gesell., 335 p.
**505.** Hulth, J. M. (1910) Swedish Arctic and Antarctic explorations 1758–1910: Bibliography. K. Svenska Vet. Arsbok, 1910, Bilaga 2, 189 pp.
**506.** Denuce, J. (1913) Bibliographie Antartique. *In* Proc.-verb. Comm. Polaire Intern. 1913, Rome, p. 25–293.
**507.** Dutilly, Artheme (1945) Bibliography of bibliographies on the Arctic. Arctic Inst. Pub. 1B. Washington, D.C., Catholic Univ. America, 47 pp.
**508.** United States Navy Department (1951) Antarctic bibliography. Navaer 10-35-591. Washington, D.C., 147 pp.
**509.** Arctic Institute of North America (1953–1961) Arctic bibliography, Marie Tremaine, editor. U.S. Dept. Defense. (1953) v. 1, p. 1–1498; v. 2, p. 1499–2967; v. 3, p. 2968–4478. (1954) v. 4, 1591 pp. (1955) v. 5, 1268 pp. (1956) v. 6, 1208 pp. (1957) v. 7, 1071 pp. (1959) v. 8, 1281 pp. (1960) v. 9, 1599 pp. (1961) v. 10, 1467 pp.

**510.** United States. Works Progress Administration (1939?) Selected list of bibliographies on the Polar regions, Part 1. New York, U. S., W.P.A., 41 pp.

**511.** Adkin, G. L., and others (1955?–1957?) Preliminary bibliography of the Ross Dependency [1955?] 7 pp; suppl. 1 [1957?] 3 pp. Geol. Soc. New Zealand, Antarctic Res. Subcomm.

**512.** See 315; 522, v. VI, fasc. 6 (Stratigraphic Lexicon)

### Faeroes

**513.** Rasmussen, Joannes (1946–1947) Oversigt over den geologiske litteratur vedrørende Faerøerne (med bemaerkninger om forfatterne og deres citerede arbejder). Dansk Geol. Foren., Meddel. v. 11, p. 66–96, 1946; Copenhagen, Univ. Mus. Miner. Geol., Misc. no. 13, 1947. [Bibliography of geology of the Faeroes, 1673–1945: brief biographic data are included for the authors cited in the list.]

**514.** See 522, v. I, fasc. 1b–d (Stratigraphic Lexicon)

### Iceland

**515.** See 522, v. I, fasc. 1b–d (Stratigraphic Lexicon)

### Svalbard (Spitsbergen)

**516.** Orvin, A. K. (1947) Bibliography of literature about the geology, physical geography, useful minerals, and mining of Svalbard. Norges Svalbard-og Ishavs-Unders., Skr. no. 89, 121 pp.

**517.** See 522, v. I, fasc. 1b–d (Stratigraphic Lexicon)

## STRATIGRAPHY

**518.** Weeks, F. B. (1902) North American geologic formation names; bibliography, synonymy and distribution. U.S. Geol. Surv. Bull. 191, 448 pp.

**519.** Willis, Bailey (1912) Index to the stratigraphy of North America. U.S. Geol. Surv. Prof. Paper 71, 894 pp.

**520.** Wilmarth, M. G. (1938) Lexicon of geologic names of the United States: U.S. Geol. Surv. Bull. 896, 2396 pp. [Contains names, definitions, approximate distribution, and geologic age of named mappable units, such as formations, members, etc., with selected literature references and quotations.]

**521.** Wilson, Druid, W. J. Sando, and R. W. Kopf (1957) Geologic names of North America introduced in 1936–1955. U.S. Geol. Surv. Bull. 1056A, p. 1–405.

Wilson, Druid, G. C. Keroher, and B. E. Hanson (1959) Index to the geologic names of North America. U.S. Geol. Surv. Bull. 1056B, p. 406–622.

**522.** Centre National de la Recherche Scientific (1956 to date) Lexicon stratigraphic international. Paris.

VOLUME I: EUROPE

Fascicule 1: *a*, Greenland, 116 pp., 1956; *b,c,d*, Iceland, Svalbard, Faeröe Islands, 101 pp., 1956. Fascicule 2: *a,b*, Norway and Finland, 101 pp., 1956; *c*. Sweden, 498 pp., 1958; *d*, Denmark, 44 pp., 1957. Fascicule 3:

*a,* England, Wales, Scotland—I, General introduction and index, in press; II, Precambrian, 87 pp., 1960; III, Cambrian, 95 pp. 1959; IV, Ordovician, 296 pp., 1960; V, Silurian, 273 pp., 1961; VI, Devonian, 131 pp., 1959; VII, Lower Carboniferous, in press; VIII, Upper Carboniferous, 365 pp., 1960; IX, New Red Sandstone, in press; X, Jurassic, in press; XI, Cretaceous, in press; XII, Paleogene, 82 pp., 1958; XIII, Neogene and Pleistocene, in press. *b,* Ireland, 98 pp, 1956. Fascicule 4: *a,* France, Belgium, Netherlands, Luxembourg—I, Precambrian and Lower Paleozoic, 432 pp., 1957; II, Upper Paleozoic, 224 pp., 1957; III, Triassic, 54 pp., 1956; IV, Lias, 107 pp., 1956; V, Jurassic, 169 pp., 1956; VI, Cretaceous, 403 pp., 1957; VII, Tertiary, 217 pp., 1957; VIII, Bibliography, 316 pp., 1957. *b,* Quaternary, 231 pp., 1957. Fascicule 5, Germany: *a,* Precambrian, Cambrian-Silurian, in press; *b,* Devonian, 388 pp., 1963; *c,* Carboniferous, Permian, 307 pp., 1963; *d,* Triassic (Germanic), in press; *e,* Triassic (Alpine), in press; *f,* Jurassic, in press; *g,* Cretaceous, in press; *h,* Tertiary, in press; *i,* Quaternary, in press; *j,* Bibliography, in press. Fascicule 6: *a,* Poland, 75 pp., 1956; *b,* Czechoslovakia, 369 pp., 1957. Fascicule 7, Switzerland, 314 pp., 1961. Fascicule 8, Austria, 646 pp., 1962. Fascicule 9, Hungary, 174 pp., 1956. Fascicule 10: *a,b,* Spain and Portugal, 145 pp., 1958. Fascicule 11, Italy, 186 pp., 1956. Fascicule 12: *a,* Yugoslavia, 54 pp., 1956; *b,c,* Greece and Albania, in press. Fascicule 13: *a,* Rumania, 119 pp., 1956; *b,* Bulgaria, 36 pp., 1957. Fascicule 14, Table générales, in press.

VOLUME II: SOVIET UNION

Fascicule 1, A-J, 564 pp., 1958. Fascicule 2, K-R, p. 565–1212, 1958. Fascicule 3, S-Z, p. 1213–1738, 1958. Fascicule 4, Bibliography and index, 477 pp., 1959.

VOLUME III: ASIA

Fascicule 1, China, in press. Fascicule 2: *a,* Korea, 83 pp., 1956; *b,* Manchuria, 68 pp., 1956. Fascicule 3: *a, b,* Japan and Ryu Kyu, 183 pp., 1956. Fascicule 4, Taiwan, 143 pp., 1957. Fascicule 5, Philippines, 167 pp., 1957. Fascicule 6: *a.* Indochina, 140 pp., 1956; *b, c, d,* Malaya, Thailand, Burma, 115 pp., 1956. Fascicule 7, Indonesia, British Borneo, Malaya, 315 pp., 1956. Fascicule 8, India, Pakistan, Nepal, Bhutan, Burma, Ceylon, 404 pp., 1957. Fascicule 9: *a,* Afganistan, 171 pp., 1961; *b,* Iran, in press; *c,* Turkey, 96 pp., 1960; *d,* Cyprus, 47 pp., 1960. Fascicule 10, Arabian Peninsula: *a,* Iraq, 333 pp., 1959; *b,* Arabia, in press; *c,* Eastern Mediterranean region, in press—I. Syria, Jordan; II. Israel; III. Sinai. Fascicule 11, Tables générales, in press.

VOLUME IV: AFRICA

Fascicule 1: *a,* Morocco, 208 pp., 1956; *b,c,* Algeria, Tunisia, 204 pp., 1962. Fascicule 2, French West Africa, Sahara, 80 pp., 1956. Fascicule 3, English East Africa, 68 pp., 1956. Fascicule 4: *a,* Libya, in press; *b,* Egypt and Sudan, in press. Fascicule 5: *a, b,* Ethiopia and Somaliland, 80 pp., 1956. Fascicule 6, French Equatorial Africa, 60 pp., 1956. Fascicule 7: *a,* Congo, Ruanda-Urundi, 124 pp., 1956; *b,* Angola, 56 pp., 1956. Fascicule 8: *a, b.* Kenya and Uganda, 124 pp., 1956; *c,* Tanganyika, 170 pp., 1957. Fascicule 9: *a, b, c,* Nyasaland, Rhodesia, 80 pp., 1956. Fascicule 10: *a,* Mozambique, in press; *b,* Union of South Africa and Southwest Africa, in press. Fascicule 11, Madagascar, 96 pp., 1956. Fascicule 12, Table générales, in press.

VOLUME V: LATIN AMERICA

Fascicule 1, Mexico, in press. Fascicule 2: *a,* Central America, 367 pp., 1960; *b,* Antilles, 495 pp., 1956; *c,* Cuba, 140 pp., 1959. Fascicule 3, Venezuela, 740 pp., 1956. Fascicule 4, Colombia, in press. Fascicule 5: *a,* Ecuador, 191 pp., 1956; *b,* Peru, 132 pp., 1956. Fascicule 6, Bolivia, in press. Fascicule 7, Chile, 444 pp., 1957. Fascicule 8, Argentina, in press. Fascicule 9: *a,* Uruguay, in press; *b, c,* Paraguay and Falkland Islands, 59 pp., 1958. Fascicule 10: *a,* Brasil, in press; b, Guianas, 77 pp., 1962. Fascicule 11, Tables générales, in press.

VOLUME VI: OCEANIA

Fascicule 1, Bibliographia, in press. Fascicule 2, Oceania proper, 286 pp., 1956. Fascicule 3, Marginal Oceania, in press. Fascicule 4, New Zealand, 527 pp., 1957. Fascicule 5, Australia: *a,* Queensland, 182 pp., 1858; *b,* New South Wales, 210 pp., 1959; *c,* Victoria, in press; *d,* Tasmania, 176 pp., 1959; *e,* South Australia, 103 pp., 1958; *f,* West Australia, 238 pp., 1963; *g,* Northern Territory, 137 pp., 1962; *h,* Bibliography, in press. Fascicule 6, Antarctica, in press.

VOLUME VII: NORTH AMERICA

In preparation.

**523.** Agout, Marthe (1949) Bibliographie des livres, thèse et conférences relatifs à l'industrie du petrole. Paris, Gauthier-Villars, 322 pp.

**524.** Pugh, W. E. (1950) Bibliography of organic reefs, bioherms, and biostromes. Tulsa, Okla., Seismograph Service Corporation, 139 pp.

**525.** Murray, G. E. (1950) Bibliography of Gulf-Coast Cenozoic formations, including Texas, Louisiana, Mississippi, Alabama, Georgia, Florida, Arkansas, and Tennessee, through June 1949. Austin, Univ. Texas Geol. Soc., 94 pp.

**526.** Pugh, W. E., and B. G. Preston (1951) Bibliography of stratigraphic traps. Tulsa, Okla., Seismograph Service Corporation, 195 pp.

**527.** Nazdik, G. C., and K. M. Tagg (1957) Annotated bibliography of high-calcium limestone deposits in the United States including Alaska, to April 1956. *In* U.S. Geol. Surv. Bull., 1019I, p. 675–713.

## MAPS

**528.** Marcou, J., and J. B. Marcou (1884) Mapoteca geologica Americana: A catalogue of geological maps of America (North and South) 1752–1881. U.S. Geol. Surv. Bull. 7, 184 pp.

**529.** Thiele, Walter, and A. F. Kuhlman (1938) Official map publications: A historical sketch, and a bibliographical handbook of current maps and mapping services in the United States, Canada, Latin America, France, Great Britain, Germany, and certain other countries. Chicago, American Library Assoc., 356 pp.

**530.** Ireland, H. A. (1943) History of the Development of geologic maps. Geol. Soc. Am. Bull., v. 54, p. 1227–1280.

**531.** Sullivan, H. B. (1922) A catalogue of geological maps of South America. Amer. Georg. Soc. Res. Series, no. 9, 191 pp.

**532.** Cobb, G. C. (1943) Bibliography on the interpretation of aerial photographs and recent bibliographies on aerial photography and related subjects. Geol. Soc. Am. Bull., v. 54, p. 1195–1210.

**533.** Jillson, W. R. (1950) The geological map of the United States, a narrative outline and annotated bibliography (1752–1946). Frankfort, Ky., Roberts Printing Co., 23 pp.


## MARINE GEOLOGY

**534.** Centro Nazionale di Studi Talassografici (1929 to date) Bibliographia Oceanographica, v. 1 (1929) to present. Venezia.

**535.** Senckenbergische Naturforschende Gesellschaft (1934) Senckenberg am Meer: Schriftenreihe der Forschungsanstalt für Meeres-geologie und Meerespaläontologie "Senckenberg" in Wilhelmshaven. Senckenbergiana v. 16, no. 1, p. 34–37.

**536.** Groschopf, Paul, and C. Johannsen (1937) Neuerscheinungen. Geol. Meere Binnengew. v. 1, H. 1, p. 132–155, H. 2, p. 381–399. (1938) v. 2, H. 1, p. 159–171.

Groschopf, Paul, Kurt Lamcke, and C. Johannsen (1938) Limnogeologische Literatur (seit 1930) *Ibid.*, v. 2, H. 2, p. 334–349.

Wasmund, Erich (1939) *Ibid.*, v. 3, H. 1, p. 107–113.

Groschopf, Paul (1942) *Ibid.*, v. 6, H. 1, p. 104–114.

**537.** Klenova, M. V. (1938) Spisok rabot sektora geologii morya Vsesoyunznogo Nauchno-Issledovatelskogo Instituta Rybnogo Khozyaistva i Okeanografii (VNIRO), b. Gos. Okeanograficheskogo Instituta (GOIN), ranee Morskogo Nauchnogo Instituta (MNI). Moskov. Gos. Univ., Uchenye Zapiski, v. 19 (Geol.), p. 289–293. [Chronologic list of papers published from 1924 to 1938 by the marine geological sections of several Russian oceanographic institutions.]

**538.** Yoshimura, Shinkichi (1938) Classified list of papers and reports bearing on oceanic geology published in Japan during 1927–1937. Geol. Meere Binnengew. Bd. 2, p. 451–476.

**539.** Smirnov, V. I. (1938) Materialy po bigliografii poberezhya Belogo myra. Moskov. Gos. Univ., Uchenye Zapiski, v. 19 (Geol.) p. 294–305. [Bibliography of geologic, geographic, gemorphologic, hydrologic, and other papers on the coasts of the White Sea, USSR.]

**540.** Geyer, R. A. (1948) Annotated bibliography of marine geophysical and geological surveys. Geol. Soc. Am. Bull., v. 59, p. 671–696.

**541.** ——— (1950) A bibliography on the Gulf of Mexico. Texas J. Sci., v. 2, p. 44–93.

**542.** New Zealand. Department of Scientific and Industrial Research (1955) Bibliography of New Zealand Oceanography, 1949–1953. Geophysical Mem. 4, 19 pp.

543. Woods Hole Oceanographic Institution (1962) A partial bibliography of the Indian Ocean. Woods Hole, Mass., The Institution, 395 pp.

544. Food and Agricultural Organization (1962) World List of Periodicals for Aquatic Sciences and Fisheries. Fisheries Technical Paper no. 19, v. 1.

## GEOLOGIC TIME MEASUREMENT

545. Marble, J. P., and R. C. Wells (1935) Bibliography of recent articles relating to the measurement of geologic time. Nat. Research Council Ann. Report, Div. Geol. Geog., App. K, Exhibits A–X, p. 22–36.

Marble, J. P. (1936) Bibliography on geologic time, April, 1935 to April, 1936. *Ibid.,* app. K, Exhibits 1–13, p. 9–34. (1937) April, 1936 to March, 1937, *Ibid.,* App. A, p. 7–31.

——— (1938) Annotated bibliography on geologic time, March, 1937 to April, 1938. *Ibid.,* App. J, Exhibits 1–12, p. 7–52.

——— (1939) Annotated bibliography of articles related to the measurement of geologic time. *Ibid.,* App. A, Exhibits 1–11, p. 10–63.

———(1940) Annotated bibliography of selected articles dealing with the measurement of geologic time. *Ibid.,* App. G, Exhibits 1–14, p. 4–54.

——— (1941) Annotated bibliography of articles dealing with geologic time, 1940–41. *Ibid.,* App. E, Exhibits 1–12, p. 7–48.

——— (1942) Annotated bibliography of articles relating to geologic time [1941–42]. *Ibid.,* App. F, Exhibits 1–8, p. 4–37. (1943) [1942–1943], *ibid.,* App. F, Exhibits A–E, p. 3–21. (1947) 1943, 1944, 1945, 1946, App. F, Exhibits A–E, p. 10–56. (1948) 1946–1947, App. F, Exhibits A–E, p. 6–38. (1949) 1947–1948, App. 4, p. 29–76. (1949) 1948–1949, App. 4, p. 83–138. (1950) 1949–1950, App. C, p. 52–112. (1952) 1950–1951, Pub. 212, p. 29–97. (1953) 1951–1952, Pub. 245, p. 25–115. (1954) 1952–1953, Pub. 319, p. 22–130.

## PALEONTOLOGY

### General, Special Groups, and Ages of Fossils

546. McGuire, Ignatius (1930) General bibliographies for paleontology. Geol. Soc. Am. Bull., v. 41, p. 188–195.

547. Royal Society of London (1864 to date) The zoological record . . . being records of zoological literature. London, v. 1, 1864 to date.

548. Biological abstracts (1926 to date) A comprehensive abstracting and indexing journal of the world's literature in theoretical and applied biology. V. 1, December, 1926, to date. Philadelphia, University of Pennsylvania.

549. ——— (1962 to date) B.A.S.I.C. (Biological Abstracts Information Dissemination System). A computer-prepared title permutation subject index to Biological Abstracts. [Issued bimonthly.]

550. Giebel, C. G. (1852) Deutschlands Petrefacten: Ein systematisches Verzeichniss aller in Deutschland und den angrenzenden Ländern vorkommenden Petrefacten nebst Angabe der Synonymen und Fundorte. Leipzig, 706 pp.

551. White, C. A., and H. A. Nicholson (1878) Bibliography of North American

invertebrate paleontology. U.S. Geol. Surv. Terr., Misc. Publ. 10, 132 pp. (1879) Supplement, Bull. U.S. Geol. Surv. Terr., v. 5, p. 143–152.

552. Marcou, J. B. (1885) A list of the Mesozoic and Cenozoic types in the collections of the U.S. National Museum. U.S. Nat. Mus., Proc. 8, p. 290–344.

553. ———— (1885) Bibliography of publications relating to the collection of fossil invertebrates in the United States National Museum, including complete lists of the writings of F. B. Meek, C. A. White, and C. D. Walcott. U.S. Nat. Mus., Bull. 30, 333 pp.

554. Miller, S. A. (1889) North American geology and paleontology for the use of amateurs, students, and scientists. Cincinnati, 664 pp. (1892) First appendix, p. 665–718. (1897) Second appendix, p. 719–793. [Index to American fossils described before 1897.]

555. Boyle, C. B. (1893) A catalogue and bibliography of North American Mesozoic invertebrata. U.S. Geol. Surv. Bull. 102, 315 pp.

556. Keyes, C. R. (1894) A bibliography of North American paleontology, 1888–1892. U.S. Geol. Surv. Bull. 121, 251 pp.

557. Weller, Stuart (1898) A bibliographic index of North American Carboniferous invertebrates. U.S. Geol. Surv. Bull. 153, 653 pp.

558. Grabau, A. W., and H. W. Shimer (1909–1910) North American index fossils. New York, A. G. Seiler and Co., v. 1, 853 pp.; v. 2, 909 pp.

559. Bassler, R. S. (1915) Bibliographic index of American Ordovician and Silurian fossils, v. 1 and 2. U.S. Nat. Mus. Bull. 92, 1521 pp.

560. Whitney, M. A. (1928) Bibliography and index of North American Mesozoic Invertebrata. Bull. Am. Paleont., v. 12, no. 48, 448 pp.

561. Sherborn, C. D. (1940) Where is the collection? An account of the various natural history collections which have come under the notice of the compiler, Dr. Charles Davies Sherborn, between 1880 and 1939. Cambridge Univ. Press, 150 pp.

562. Shimer, H. W., and R. Shrock (1944) Index fossils of North America. New York, Wiley, 837 pp.

563. Paul, Henry (1944) Schrifttum des Unterkarbons. Germany, Reichsamt Bodenf., Abh. no. 198, 515 pp. [A chronologic list, from 1780 through 1937, of writings on the lower Carboniferous, with an appendix including titles of papers published from 1938 to 1940, and with geographic, paleontologic, and author indexes.]

564. Branson, C. C. (1948) Bibliographic index of Permian invertebrates. Geol. Soc. Am. Mem. 26, 1049 pp.

565. Clapp, W. F., and R. Kenk (1956) Marine borers: A preliminary bibliography. Washington, D.C., Lib. Cong. Tech. Inform. Div., 346 pp.

566. Brotzen, Fritz (1959) On Tylocidaris species (Echinoidea) and the stratigraphy of the Danian of Sweden, with a bibliography of the Danian and the Paleocene. Sveriges Geol. Unders., Arsb. 54 (1960), no. 2, s. C, no. 571, 81 pp., illus. incl. maps.

567. Fossilium Catalogus (1913–1963) Berlin, W. Junk.

SERIES I: ANIMALIA

Pt. 1: Frech, F., Ammoneae devonicae, 42 pp., 1913. Pts. 2 and 15: Teppner, W., Lamellibranchiata tertiaria 'Anisomyaria' I, II, 296 pp., 1914 and 1922. Pt. 3: Schuchert, Ch., Stelleroidea palaeozoica, 53 pp., 1914. Pt. 4: Huene, F. de, Saurischia et Ornithischia triadica, 21 pp., 1914. Pt. 5: Felix J., Anthozoa palaeocretacea, 84 pp., 1914. Pt. 6: Felix, J., Anthozoa cenomanica, p. 85–144, 1914. Pt. 7: Felix, J., Anthozoa neocretacea, p. 145–273, 1914. Pt. 8: Diener, C., Cephalopoda triadica, 369 pp., 1915. (See also part 56.) Pt. 9: Hennig, F., Stegosauria, 16 pp., 1915. Pt. 10: Diener, C., Brachiopoda triadica, 109 pp., 1920. Pt. 11: Bülow-Trummer, E., Cephalopoda dibranchiata, 313 pp., 1920. Pt. 12: Lambrecht, K., Aves, 104 pp., 1921. Pt. 13: Diener, C., Cnidaria triadica, 46 pp., 1921. Pt. 14: Diener, C., Ammonoidea permiana, 36 pp., 1921. Pt. 16: Handlirsch, A., Insecta palaeozoica, 230 pp., 1922. Pts. 17, 18, 20–23, 32, 38, 40, 43, and 46: Wenz, W., Gastropoda extramarina tertiaria, 3,387 pp., 1923–1930. Pt. 19: Diener, C., Lamellibranchiata triadica, p. 1–259, 1923. (See also part 51.) Pt. 24: Posthumus, O., Otolithi Piscium, 42 pp., 1924. Pt. 25: Diener, C., Eurypterida, 29 pp., 1924. Pt. 26: Kieslinger, A., Medusae fossiles, 20 pp., 1924. Pts. 27 and 50: Nopcsa, F. von, Osteologia Reptilium fossilium et recentium, 391 pp., 1926. Supplement (pt. 50), 62 pp., 1931. Pt. 28: Felix, J., Anthozoa eocaenica et oligocaenica, p. 1–296, 1925.(See also pts. 35 and 44.) Pt. 29: Diener, C., Ammonoidea neocretacea, 244 pp., 1925. Pt. 30: Deecke, W., Trigoniidae mesozoicae, 306 pp., 1925. Pt. 31: Dietrich, W. O., Gastropoda mesozoica, Fam. Nerineidae, 164 pp., 1925. Pt. 33: Deecke, W., Pisces triadici, 201 pp., 1926. Pt. 34: Diener, C., Glossophora triadica, p. 1–244, 1926. (See also pt. 81.) Pt. 35: Felix, J., Anthozoa miocaenica, p. 297–488, 1927. (See also pts. 28 and 44.) Pt. 36: Kühn, O., Hydrozoa, 114 pp., 1928. Pt. 37: Richter, R. et E., Trilobitae neodevonici, 160 pp. 1928. Pt. 39: Deecke, W., Echinoidea jurassica, 540 pp., 1929. Pt. 41: Glaessner, M. F., Crustacea decapoda, 464 pp., 1929. Pt. 42: Schuchert, Ch., and C. M. Le Vene, Brachiopoda, 140 pp., 1929. Pt. 44: Felix, J., Anthozoa pliocaenica et plistocaenica, p. 489–668, 1929. (See also pts. 28 and 35.) Pt. 45: Plieninger, F., Pterosauria, 84 pp., 1930. Pt. 47: Simpson, G. G., Post-Mesozoic Marsupialia, 87 pp., 1930. Pt. 48: Straelen, V. van, Crustacea Eumalacostraca, 98 pp., 1931. Pt. 49: Liebus, A., Bibliographia foraminiferum recentium et fossilium II (1911–1930), 36 pp., 1931. (See also pts. 59–60.) Pt. 51: Kutassy, A., Lamellibranchiata triadica II, p. 260–477, 1931. (See also pt. 19.) Pt. 52: Hummel, K., Trionychia fossilia, 106 pp., 1932. Pts. 53 and 65: Haber, G., Gastropoda, Amphineura et Scaphoda jurassica, 400 pp., 1932–1934. Pt. 54: Kühn, O., Rudistae, 200 pp., 1932. Pt. 55: Schilder, F. A., Cypraeacea, 276 pp., 1932. Pt. 56: Kutassy, S., Cephalopoda triadica, p. 370–382, 1933. (See also pt. 8.) Pt. 57: Gross, W., Antiarchi, 40 pp., 1932. Pt. 58: Hühn, O., Theodontia, 32 pp., 1933. Pts. 59–60: Liebus, A., and H. Thalmann, Bibliographia foraminiferum recentium et fossilium; I (to 1910), 179 pp., 1933; III (1911–1930, Supplementum), 28 pp., 1933. (See also pt. 49.) Pt. 61: Kuhn, O., Labyrinthodontia, 114 pp., 1933. Pt. 62: Kuhn, O., Placodontia, 15 pp., 1933. Pt. 63: Kuhn, O., Ichthyosauria, 75 pp., 1934. Pt. 64: Stralen, V. van, and G. Schitz, Crustacea Phyllocarida (Archaeostraca), 246 pp., 1934. Pt. 66: Biese, Walter, Crinoidea triadica, 255 pp., 1934.

Pt. 67: Bassler, R. S., Bryozoa, generum et genotyporum, 229 pp., 1934. Pt. 68: Kutassy, A., Pachyodonta mesozoica (Rudistis exclusis), 202 pp., 1934. Pt. 69: Kuhn, O., Sauropterigia, 127 pp., 1934. Pts. 70, 73, and 76: Biese, Walter, Crinoidea jurassica, 739 pp., 1935–1937. Pt. 71: Kuhn, O., Rhynchocephalia (Eosuchia), 39 pp., 1935. Pt. 72: Lambrecht, K. and W. and A. Quenstedt, Palaeontologi; Catalogus biobibliographicus, 495 pp., 1938. Pt. 74: Quenstedt, W. and A., Hominidae fossiles, 456 pp., 1936. Pt. 75: Kuhn, O., Crocodilia, 144 pp., 1936. Pt. 77: Biese, W., and Hertha Sieverts-Doreck, Crinoidea cretacea, 254 pp., 1937. Pt. 78: Kuhn, O., Ornithischia (Stegosauriis exclusis), 81 pp., 1936. Pt. 79: Kuhn, O., Cotylosauria et Theromorpha, 209 pp., 1937. Pt. 80: Biese, W., and Hertha Sieverts-Doreck, Crinoidea caenozoica, 151 pp., 1939. Pt. 81: Kutassy, A., Glossophora triadica II, p. 243–477, 1940. (See also pt. 34.) Pts. 82, 89, 92: Wolf, B., Fauna fossilis cavernarum, I–III, 320 pp., 1938–1941. Pt. 83: Bassler, R. S., Pelmatozoa Palaeozoica: 194 pp., 1938. Pt. 85: Kuhn, O., Protorosauria, 8 pp.; Mesosauria, 6 pp.; 1939. Pt. 86: Kuhn, O., Squamata, 89 pp.; Lacertilia et Ophidia, 33 pp.; 1939. Pt. 87: Kuhn, O., Saurischia, 124 pp., 1939. Pt. 88: Sieverts-Doreck, Hertha, and Biese, W., Supplementum ad Crinoidea triadica, jurassica, cretacea, et caenozoica, 81 pp., 1939. Pt. 90: Zeuner, F. E., Saltatoria Ensifera fossilia, 108 pp., 1940. Pt. 91: Paul, H., Lamellibranchiata infracarbonica, 348 pp., 1941. Pt. 93: Huene, Fr. von., Mammalia triadica, 13 pp., 1940. Pt. 94: Kuhn, O., Testudinata triadica: 12 pp., 1941. Pt. 95: Moll, F., Teredinidae: 89 pp., 1941. Pt. 96: Zeiss, A., Hecticoceratinae (Ammonoidea jurassica), 143 pp., 1959. Pt. 97: Kuhn, O., Amphibia (Supplementum), 161 pp., 12 pls., 1960. Pt. 98: Kuhn, O., Reptilia, Supplementum I (Millerosauria, Placodontia, Eunotosauria, Bolosauria, Weigeltisauria, Thalattosauria, Pleurosauria, Araeoscelidia, Choristodera), 47 pp., 5 pls. and frontispiece, 1961. Pt. 99: Kuhn, O., Reptilia, Supplementum I (2) (Protorosauria (Prolacertilia), Eosuchia, Proganosauria (Mesosauria), Trilophosauria, Amphisbaenia, Captorhinomorpha, Diadectomorpha, Pareiasauria, Procolophonia, Pterosauria, Rhynchocephalia, Thecodontia, Icthyosauria, Pelycosauria), 163 pp., 15 pls., 1961. Pt. 100: Quenstedt, W., Solenomyidae fossiles, 46 pp., 1962. Pt. 101: Kuhn, O., Ichnia Tetrapodorum, 176 pp., 12 pls., 1963. Pt. 102: Quenstedt, W., Clavis bibliographica, 115 pp., 1963. Pt. 103: Kuhn, O., Serpentes (Supplementum I): 45 pp., 1963.

SERIES II: PLANTAE

Pts. 1, 15, 16, 18, 21, 22. Jongmans, W., Lycodiales, 1331 pp., 1913–1937. Pts. 2–5, 7, 9, 11. Jongmans, W., Equisetales, 831 pp., 1914–1924. Pt. 6: Nagel, K., Juglandaceae, 87 pp., 1915. Pt. 8: Nagel, K., Betulaceae, 177 pp., 1916. Pt. 10: Nagalhard, K. (formerly Nagel), Ulmaceae, 84 pp., 1922. Pt. 12: Posthumus, O., Inversicatenales (Botryopterideae et Zygopterideae), 56 pp., 1926. Pt. 13: Dixon, H. N., Muscineae, 116 pp., 1927. Pt. 14: Edwards, W. N., and Wonnacott, F. M., Sapindaceae, 84 pp., 1928. Pt. 17: Edwards, W. N., Dicotyledones (Ligna), 96 pp., 1931. Pt. 19: Groves, J., harophyta, 74 pp., 1933. Pt. 20: Edwards, W. N., Anacardiaceae, 73 pp., 1935. Pt. 23: Kirchheimer, F., Umbelliflorae; Cornaceae, 188 pp., 1938. Pt. 24: Kirchheimer, F., Rhamnales I; Vitaceae, 153 pp., 1939. Pts. 27, 28, 30–32: Jongmans, W. J., Filicales, Pteridospermae, Cycadales, p. 1–366, 1954–1957. (See also pts. 33–55.) Pt. 29: Wonnacott, F. M., Celastraceae, 149 pp., 1955. Pts. 33–35: Jongmans, W. J. and Dijkstra, S. J., Filicales, Pteridospermae, Cycadales, p. 367–2,658, 1958–1963. (See also pts. 27, 28, 30–32.)

**568.** See 56 (Paleozoic Paleontology, Alaska); 111 (Paleontology, Massachusetts); 176, 177, 190, 191 (Paleontology, Canada); 338, 344 (Paleontology, Soviet Union); 399 (Paleontology, Australia); 401 (Cretaceous Fossils, Australia); 406 (Marine Invertebrates, Australia); 415–417, 419 (Paleontology, Japan); 434 (Paleontology, Phillippine Islands); 444 (Protista, Africa)

## Nomenclatural Indexes

**569.** Fischer de Waldheim, G. (1834) Bibliographia palaeonthologica animalium systematica. Mosque, Typis Universitatis Caesareae, 414 pp.

**570.** Agassiz, Louis (1842–1847) Nomenclator zoologicus. Soloduri, 26 parts. [Each part has separate paging and its own bibliography.]
———— Nomenclatoris zoologici index universalis. Soloduri, 1846, 393 pp. [Forms part 2 of the Nomenclator. Another edition with different format, is dated Soloduri, 1848, and has 1135 pp.]

**571.** Herrmannsen, A. N. (1846–1852) Indicis generum Malacozoorum primordia: v. 1, 2 and suppl. Cassellis (v. 1, 637 pp. [1846–1847]; v. 2, 717 pp. [1847–1849]; Suppl., 140 pp. [1852]).

**572.** Bronn, H. G. (1848–1849) Index Palaeontologicus oder übersicht der bis jetzt bekannten Fossilen Organismen, unter mitwirkung der H. H. Prof. H. R. Göppert und Herm. v. Meyer: pt. I, Nomenclator palaeontologicus, A.–M, p. 1–775, 1848; pt. 2, N–Z, p. 776–1384; pt. 3, Enumerator palaeontologicus, p. 1–1106, 1849.

**573.** Marschall, A. (1873) Nomenclator zoologicus: Continens nomina systematica generum animalium tam viventium quam fossilium, secundum ordinem alphabeticum disposita. Vindobonae, C. R. Societatis Zoologico-Botanicae, 482 pp. [Covers generic names for 1842–1868.]

**574.** Scudder, Samuel Hubbard (1882) Nomenclator zoologicus: An alphabetical list of all generic names that have been employed by naturalists for recent and fossil animals from the earliest times to the close of the year 1879. U.S. Nat. Mus. Bull. 19, pt. 1, Supplemental list, 376 pp.; pt. 2, Universal Index, 340 pp.

**575.** Sherborn, C. D. (1899) Index to the "Systema naturae" of Linnaeus. Manchester Museum, Owens College, Museum Handbook 25, 108 pp.

**576.** Hulth, J. M. (1907) Bibliographia Linnaeana: Matériaux pour servir a une bibliographie Linnéenne. Uppsala, 170 pp.

**577.** British Museum (1907) A catalogue of the works of Linnaeus (and publications more immediately relating thereto) preserved in the libraries of the British Museum (Bloomsbury and The British Museum (Natural History) South Kensington. London, 27 pp.

**578.** Waterhouse, C. O. (1902, 1912) Index zoologicus, an alphabetical list of names of genera and subgenera, proposed for use in zoology as recorded in the "Zoological record" 1880–1910. Together with names not included in the "Nomenclator zoologicus" of S. H. Scudder. London, Zoological Society, 2 v.

**579.** Sherborn, C. D. (1902, 1922–1933) Index animalium: Sive, index nominum quae ab. A. D. (1758) generibus et speciebus animalium imposita sunt, societatibus eruditorum adiuvantibus, a Carlo Davis Sherborn confectus. Cambridge Univ. Press. Part 1 covers 1758 to 1800, complete in one volume, with a literature list (1902). Part 2 covers 1801 to 1850, in 9 volumes (1922–1933).

**580.** Schulze, F. E., W. Kükenthal, K. Heider, and T. Kuhlgatz (1926–1940). Nomenclator animalium generum et subgenerum (1758–1922). Im auftrage der Presussischen Akademie der Wissenschaften zu Berlin, herausg. von F. E. Schulze. W. Kükenthal, fortgesetzt von K. Heider. Schriftleiter Th. Kuhlgatz. Berlin, v. 1, A–B; v. 2, C–E; v. 3, F–M; v. 4, N–P; v. 5, Q–Z.

**581.** Poche, Franz (1939) Supplement zu C. D. Sherborn's Index animalium. In Festschrift zum 60 Geburstage von Professor Dr. Embrick Strand, Riga, v. 5, p. 477–615.

**582.** Neave, S. A. (1939–1950) Nomenclator zoologicus: A continuation of Sherborn's Index animalium, covering the years 1758–1945. London, Zoological Society, 5 v.

### Bacteria

**583.** Mcoy, E., and L. S. McClung (1939) The anaerobic bacteria and their activities in nature and disease: A subject bibliography. V. 1, Author index, 295 pp.; v. 2, Subject index, 602 pp., Berkeley and Los Angeles, Univ. Calif. Press.

**584.** Zobell, C. E. (1957) Bacteria: An annotated bibliography. *In* Ladd, H. S., ed., Paleoecology, Geol. Soc. Am. Mem. 67, p. 693–697.

### Foraminifera

**585.** Woodward, Anthony (1886) The bibliography of the Foraminifera, recent and fossil, including Eozoon and Receptaculites. *In* Minn. Geol. Surv., Ann. Rept. 14, p. 167–311.

**586.** Sherborn, C. D. (1888) A Bibliography of the Foraminifera, 1565–1888. London, Dulau, 152 pp.

**587.** Sherborn, C. D. (1893, 1896) An index to the genera and species of the Foraminifera. Smithsonian Misc. Coll. v. 37, pt. 1, publ. 856 (1893), p. 1–240; pt. 2, publ. 1031 (1896), p. 241–485.

**588.** Beutler, K. (1910) Palaeontologisch–stratighaphische und zoologischsystematische literatur über marine Formaniferan fossil und rezent bis Endo 1910. Muenchen, 144 pp.

**589.** Cushman, J. A. (1932) Bibliography of American Foraminifera. Cushman Lab. Foram. Res. Special Publ. no. 3, 40 pp.

**590.** Thalmann, H. E. (1933) Bibliography and index to new genera, species, and varieties of Foraminifera for the year 1931. J. Paleont., v. 7, p. 341–355. (1934) Suppl., v. 8, p. 238–244; 1932, v. 8, p. 356–387. (1935) 1933, v. 9, 715–743. (1936) 1934, v. 10, p. 294–322. (1938) 1935, v. 12, p. 177–208. (1939) 1936, v. 13, p. 425–465. (1941) 1937 and 1938: v. 15, p. 629–690. (1942) 1939, v. 16, p. 489–520. (1943) 1940, v. 17, p. 388–408. (1944) 1941, v. 18, p. 387–404. (1945) 1942, v. 19, p. 396–410. (1945) 1943, v. 19, p. 648–656. (1946) 1944, v. 20, p. 172–183; 1945, with supplements for the period 1936–1944, v. 20, p. 591–619. (1947) Supplements for 1940–1945, v. 21, p. 278–281; 1945, with supplements for 1939–1944 and addenda, 1942–1945, v. 21, p. 355–395. (1948) 1946, v. 22, p. 193–221. (1949) 1947, v. 23, p. 395–418; 1948, v. 23, p. 641–668; Supplements and corrections for the period 1931 to 1947, v. 23, p. 498–506. (1950) 1949, v. 24, p. 699–745. (1952) 1950, v. 26, p. 223–268; 1951, v. 26, p. 953–992. (1953) 1952, v. 27, p. 847–876. (1954) 1953, v. 28, p. 840–873. (1956) 1954, v. 30, p. 352–388. (1958) 1955, v. 32, p. 737–762. (1959) 1956, v. 33, p. 1069–1114.

**591.** Todd, M. R. (1950) Recent literature on the Foraminifera. Cushman Found. Foram. Res. Centr., v. 1, pts. 1, 2, p. 38–40; pts. 3, 4, p. 91–92. (1951) v. 2, pt. 1, p. 30–32; pt. 3, p. 111–113; pt. 4, p. 147–148. (1952) v. 3, pt. 1, p. 32–34; pt. 2, p. 103–104. (1953) v. 4, pt. 1, p. 37–40; pt. 2, p. 84–86; pt. 3, p. 106–108; pt. 4, p. 156–157. (1954) v. 5, pt. 1, 42–43; pt. 2, p. 88–89; pt. 3, p. 45–46; pt. 4, p. 192–193. (1955) v. 6, pt. 1, p. 54–55; pt. 2, p. 83–84; pt. 4, p. 150–151. (1956) v. 7, pt. 1, p. 31–33; pt. 2, p. 67–68; pt. 3, p. 102–104; pt. 4, p. 152–153. (1957) v. 8, pt. 1, p. 41–44; pt. 2, p. 90–92; pt. 3, p. 122–125; pt. 4, p. 149–152. (1958) v. 9, pt. 1, p. 22–24; pt. 2, p. 49–52; pt. 3, p. 78–81; pt. 4, p. 112–116. (1959) v. 10, pt. 1, p. 21–24; pt. 2, p. 65–69; pt. 3, p. 106–110, pt. 4, p. 137–140. (1960) v. 11, pt. 1, p. 42–45; pt. 2, p. 69–72; pt. 3, p. 104–107; pt. 4, p. 134–138. (1961) v. 12, pt. 1, p. 27–32; pt. 2, p. 71–76, pt. 3, p. 115–119; pt. 4, p. 49–152. (1962) v. 13, pt. 1, p. 24–30; pt. 2, p. 64–67; pt. 3, p. 111–117; pt. 4, p. 153–159. (1963) v. 14, pt. 1, p. 32–56, pt. 2, p. 71–75.

**592.** Silvestri, Alfredo (1933) Bibliografia delle fusulinidi. Pontifica Accad. Sci. Nuovi Lincei Mem. s. 2, v. 17, p. 523–554.

**593.** Dam, A. ten (1946) Publications on Foraminifera issued during the years 1940–1945 in the Netherlands. J. Paleont., v. 20, p. 184–185.

**594.** Neve, G. A. de (1950–1951) Bibliography of micropalaeontological publications concerning Indonesia and covering the period 1940–1950. De Ingenieur in Indonesie, jg. 2, no. 5, IV, p. 27–28, 1950; jg. 3, no. 1, IV, p. 6–11, 1951; Supplement, p. 11–12, 1951.

**595.** Oinomikaro, Tsuneteru (1951) Bibliography of Japanese papers on Cenozoic and Recent Foraminifera published prior to 1950. Tokyo, Hosokawa Printing Co.

**596.** Bronnimann, Paul (1952) Micropaleontologic literature 1941–1951 on Trinidad, Tobago, and Barbados, B.W.I. Micropaleontologist, v. 6, no. 1, p. 23–42.

**597.** Toomey, D. F. (1954) A bibliography of the family Fusulinidae. J. Paleont.,

v. 28, no. 4, p. 465–484. (1956) Addendum, v. 30, no. 6, p. 1360–1366.

**598.** Dunbar, C. O. (1957) Fusuline Foraminifera: An annotated bibliography. *In* Ladd, H. S., ed., Paleoecology, Geol. Soc. Am. Mem. 67, p. 753–754.

**599.** Hilterman, Heinrich (1956) Annotated bibliography of micropaleontology in Germany for 1955. Micropaleontology, v. 2, no. 4, p. 385–392. (1957) 1956; v. 3, no. 4, p. 399–406. (1958) 1957; v. 4, no. 4, p. 431–438. (1959) 1958; v. 5, no. 4, p. 487–496. (1960) 1959; v. 6, no. 4, p. 425–432.

**600.** De Flandre, Georges (1957) Annotated bibliography of micropaleontology in France, 1952–1956 (exclusive of Foraminifera and Ostracoda). Micropaleontology, v. 3, no. 3, p. 263–267.

**601.** Cooper, C. L. (1957) Paleozoic Foraminifera (exclusive of Fusulinidae): An annotated bibliography. *In* Ladd, H. S., ed., Paleoecology, Geol. Soc. Am. Mem. 67, p. 747–752.

**602.** Fox, S. K., Jr. (1957) Foraminifera of the Mesozoic: An annotated bibliography. *In* Ladd, H. S., ed., Paleocology, Geol. Soc. Am. Mem. 67, p. 755–756.

**603.** Cole, W. S. (1957) Foraminifera of the Cenozoic: An annotated bibliography. *In* Ladd, H. S., ed., Paleoecology, Geol. Soc. Am. Mem. 67, p. 757–762.

**604.** Toomey, D. F. (1959) Annotated bibliography of Late Paleozoic nonfusulinid Foraminifera. Cushman Found. Foram. Res. Centr., v. 10, pt. 3, p. 71–105.

**605.** Takayanagi, Yokichi (1960) Annotated bibliography of the Cretaceous Foraminifera from Japan. Tohoku Univ., Sci. Rept., s. 2, Spec. v. no. 4, p. 309–315.

**606.** Hiltermann, Heinrich (1961) Fortschritte der Mikropaläontologie in Deutschland mit einer Bibliographie für das Jahr 1960. Paläont. Zs. Bd. 35, no. 3–4, p. 209–230.

**607.** ———— (1961) Bibliographie stratigraphisch wichtiger mikropaläontologischer Publikationem von etwa 1830 bis 1958 mit Kurzreferaten. Stuttgart, E. Schweizerbart, 403 p.

**608.** Pożaryska, Krystyna (1961) Annotated bibliography of micropaleontology in Poland. Micropaleontology, v. 7, no. 1, p. 115–118.

**609.** See 407 (Foraminifera, Australia)

### Radiolaria

**610.** Campbell, A. S., and E. A. Holm (1957) Radiolaria: An annotated bibliography. *In* Ladd, H. S., ed., Paleoecology, Geol. Soc. Am. Mem. 67, p. 737–743.

### Silicoflagellata

**611.** Hanna, G. D. (1957) Silicoflagellata: An annotated bibliography. *In* Ladd, H. S., ed., Paleoecology, Geol. Soc. Am. Mem. 67, p. 745.

## Porifera

**612.** Vosmaer, G. C. J. (1928) Bibliography of sponges, 1551–1913. Edited by G. P. Bidder and C. S. Vosmaer-Röell. Cambridge Univ. Press, 234 pp.

**613.** Okulitch, V. J., and S. J. Nelson (1957) Sponges of the Paleozoic: An annotated bibliography: *In* Ladd, H. S., ed., Paleoecology, Geol. Soc. Am. Mem. 67, p. 763–769.

**614.** DeLaubenfels, M. W. (1957) Sponges of the post-Paleozoic: An annotated bibliography. *In* Ladd, H. S., ed., Paleoecology, Geol. Soc. Am., Mem. 67, p. 771–772.

## Coelenterata

**615.** Lang, W. D., S. Smith, and H. D. Thomas (1940) Index of Palaeozoic coral genera. London, British Museum Nat. History, 231 pp.

**616.** Bassler, R. S. (1950) Faunal lists and descriptions of Paleozoic corals. Geol. Soc. Am., Mem. 44, 315 pp.

**617.** Perkins, B. F. (1951) An annotated bibliography of North American upper Cretaceous corals, 1785–1950. Fondren Sci. Series, no. 3. Dallas, Texas, Southern Methodist Univ. Press, 45 pp.

**618.** Wells, J. W. (1957) Corals: An annotated bibliography. *In* Ladd, H. S., ed., Paleoecology, Geol. Soc. Am. Mem. 67, p. 773–782.

**619.** See 567, Pts. 5 (Anthozoa palaeocretacea); 6 (Anthozoa cenomanica); 7 (Anthozoa neocretacea); 13 (Cnidaria triadica); 26 (Medusae fossiles); 28 (Anthozoa eocaenica et oligocaenica); 35 (Anthozoa miocaenica); 36 (Hydrozoa); 44 (Anthozoa plioaenica et plistocaenica)

## Conularida

**620.** Sinclair, G. W., and E. S. Richardson, Jr. (1954) A bibliography of the Conularida. Bull. Am. Paleont., v. 34, no. 145, 143 pp.

## Bryozoa

**621.** Nickles, J. M., and R. S. Bassler (1900) A synopsis of American fossil Bryozoa including bibliography and synonymy. U.S. Geol. Surv. Bull. 173, 663 pp.

**622.** Neviani, A. (1901, 1903) Materiali per una bibliografia italiana degli studi sui Briozoi viventi e fossili dal 1800 al 1900. Bol. nat. Sienna, v. 21, pp. 4–8, 29–33, 47–50, 66–67, 102–105, 129–133; v. 23, pp. 11–15, 31–34, 46–50, 59–62, 75–76, 90–91, 101–102, 109–113.

——— (1905) Bibliografia degli studi sui Briozoi viventi e fossili dal 1800 al 1900: Bol. nat. Sienna, v. 25, pp. xxi–xxxii.

**623.** Canu, Ferdinand (1915) Bibliographie primitive relative aux Bryozoaires. Soc. géol. France, Bull. 4th ser., v. 15, p. 287–292.

**624.** ——— (1915) Bibliographie paléontologique relative aux Bryozoaires du Bassin de Paris. Soc. Géol. France, Bull. 4th ser., v. 15, p. 293–304.

**625.** Duncan, Helen (1957) Bryozoans: An annotated bibliography. *In* Ladd, H. S., ed., Paleoecology, Geol. Soc. Am. Mem. 67, p. 783–799.
**626.** See 567, Pt. 67 (Bryozoa)

## Brachiopoda

**627.** Davidson, T. (1851–1886) British fossil brachiopoda: Bibliography. *In* Paleont. Soc. Mon. v. 6, p. 1–163.
**628.** Dall, W. H. (1877) Index to the names which have been applied to the subdivisions of the class Brachiopoda. U.S. Nat. Mus., Bull. 8, 88 pp.
**629.** Schuchert, Charles (1897) A synopsis of American fossil brachiopoda including bibliography and synonymy. U.S. Geol. Surv., Bull. 87, 464 pp.
**630.** Bryant, D. L. (1955) Index, type species, and bibliography of productid genera. J. Paleont., v. 29, no. 2, p. 283–94.
**631.** Cooper, G. A. (1957) Brachiopods: An annotated bibliography. *In* Ladd, H. S. ed., Paleoecology, Geol. Soc. Am. Mem. 67, p. 801–804.
**632.** See 567, Pts. 10 (Brachiopoda triadica), 42 (Brachiopoda)

## Mollusca

**633.** Binney, W. G. (1863–1864) Bibliography of North American conchology previous to the year 1860. Smithsonian Misc. Collections, v. 5, pt. I, American authors (1863); pt. II, Foreign authors (1864).
**634.** Carpenter, P. P. (1872) List of papers on American Mollusca published in European works by P. P. Carpenter. *In* Smithsonian Misc. Collections 252, v. 10, p. ix–xii.
**635.** Dall, W. H. (1885) List of marine Mollusca comprising the Quaternary fossils and Recent forms from American localities between Cape Hatteras and Cape Roque including the Bermudas. U.S. Geol. Surv., Bull. 24, 336 pp.
**636.** Dall, W. H. (1909) Material toward a bibliography of publications on the post-Eocene marine mollusks of the northwest coast of America, 1865–1908. *In* U.S. Geol. Surv., Prof. Paper 59, p. 192–216.
**637.** Parona, C. F. (1916) Saggio bibliografico sulle rudiste con indici dei nomi de autore, di genere e di specie. Italy. Com. Geol., Bull. 6, 78 pp.
**638.** Johnson, C. W. (1934) List of marine Mollusca of the Atlantic Coast from Labrador to Texas. Proc. Boston Soc. Nat. Hist., v. 40, no. 1, p. 1–203.
**639.** Schenck, H. G. (1934) Literature on the shell structure of pelecypods. Mus. roy. d'hist. nat. Belgique, Bull. 10, no. 34, 20 pp.
**640.** Henderson, J. (1935) Fossil non-marine Mollusca of North America. Geol. Soc. Am., Special Paper 3, 313 pp.
**641.** Keen, A. M. (1937) An abridged check list and bibliography of West North American marine Mollusca. Stanford Univ. Press, 84 pp.
**642.** Kindle, E. M., and A. K. Miller (1939) Bibliographic index of North American Devonian Cephalopoda. Geol. Soc. Am., Special Paper 23, 179 pp.
**643.** Knight, J. B. (1941) Paleozoic gastropod genotypes. Geol. Soc. Am., Special Paper 32, 510 pp.

**644.** Keen, A. M., and H. Bentson (1944) Check list of California Tertiary marine Mollusca. Geol. Soc. Am., Special Paper 56, 280 pp.

**645.** Branson, C. C. (1957) Pelecypoda of the Paleozoic: An annotated bibliography. *In* Ladd, H. S., ed., Paleoecology, Geol. Soc. Am. Mem. 67, p. 817–818.

**646.** Bowsher, A. L. (1957) Gastropods of the Paleozoic: An annotated bibliography. *In* Ladd, H. S., ed., Paleoecology, Geol. Soc. Am. Mem. 67, p. 821–825.

**647.** Yochelson, E. L. (1957) Scaphopods and Chitons of the Paleozoic: an annotated bibliography. *In* Ladd, H. S., ed., Paleoecology, Geol. Soc. Am. Mem. 67, p. 819–820.

**648.** Flower, R. H. (1957) Nautiloids of the Paleozoic: An annotated bibliography. *In* Ladd, H. S., ed., Paleoecology, Geol. Soc. Am. Mem. 67, p. 829–852.

**649.** Miller, A. K. (1957) Ammonoids of the Paleozoic: An annotated bibliography. *In* Ladd, H. S., ed., Paleoecology, Geol. Soc. Am. Mem. 67, p. 853–859.

**650.** Kummel, Bernhard (1957) Mollusks of the Triassic: An annotated bibliography. *In* Ladd, H. S., ed., Paleoecology, Geol. Soc. Am. Mem. 67, p. 861–866.

**651.** Imlay, R. W. (1957) Mollusks of the Jurassic: An annotated bibliography. *In* Ladd, H. S., ed., Paleoecology, Geol. Soc. Am. Mem. 67, p. 867–870.

**652.** Bergquist, H. R., and W. A. Cobban (1957) Mollusks of the Cretaceous: An annotated bibliography. *In* Ladd, H. S., ed., Paleoecology, Geol. Soc. Am. Mem. 67, p. 871–884.

**653.** Woodring, W. P. (1957) Cenozoic mollusks of California: An annotated bibliography. *In* Ladd, H. S., ed., Paleoecology, Geol. Soc. Am. Mem. 67, p. 891–892.

**654.** Gardner, Julia, and H. S. Ladd (1957) Cenozoic mollusks of the Atlantic and east Gulf coastal plains: An annotated bibliography. *In* Ladd, H. S., ed., Paleoecology, Geol. Soc. Am. Mem. 67, p. 885–886.

**655.** Stenzel, H. B. (1957) Cenozoic mollusks of the west Gulf [Coast]: An annotated bibliography. *In* Ladd, H. S., ed., Paleoecology, Geol. Soc. Am. Mem. 67, p. 887–889.

**656.** ———— (1957) Cenozoic nautiloids: An annotated bibliography. *In* Ladd, H. S., ed., Paleoecology, Geol. Soc. Am. Mem. 67, p. 893-894.

**657.** Pfitzenmeyer, H. T., and C. N. Shuster, Jr. (1960) A partial bibliography of the soft shell clam, *Mya arenaria* L. Md. Dept. Res. Ed., Chesapeake Biol. Lab., Contr. 123 and Univ. Del. Marine Lab., Info. Ser., Publ. 4, 29 pp.

**658.** Clarke, A. H., Jr. (1962) Annotated list and bibliography of the abyssal marine molluscs of the world. Natl. Mus. Canada, Bull. no. 181, Biol. ser. no. 67, 114 pp.

**659.** See 567, Pts. 1 (Ammoneae devonicae); 2, 14 (Lamellibranchiata tertiaria); 8, 56 (Cephalopoda triadica); 11 (Cephalopoda dibranchiata); 14 (Ammonoidea permiana); 17, 18, 20–23, 32, 38, 40, 43, 46 (Gastropoda extramarina tertiaria); 19, 51 (Lamellibranchiata triadica); 29 (Ammonoidea neocretacea); 30 (Trigoniidae mesozoica); 31 (Gastropoda mesozoica); 34, 81 (Glossophora triadica); 53, 65 (Gastropoda, Amphineura et Scaphopoda jurassica); 54 (Rudistae); 55 (Cypraeacea); 68 (Pachydonta mesozoica); 91 (Lamellibranchiata infracarbonica); 94 (Testudinata triadica); 95 (Teredinidae); 96 (Hecticoceratinae)

## Arthropoda

660. Vogdes, A. W. (1890) A bibliography of Paleozoic crustacea from 1698 to 1889, including a list of North American species and a systematic arrangement of genera. U.S. Geol. Surv., Bull. 63, 177 pp.

661. ———— (1893–1925) A classed and annotated bibliography of the Paleozoic crustacea, 1698–1891, to which is added a catalogue of North American species (with supplements): San Francisco, Calif. Acad. Sciences, Occasional Papers, v. 4, p. 1–412, 1893; Calif. Acad. Sci., Proc., v. 5, 2nd ser. 1895, p. 53–76; Trans. San Diego Soc. Nat. Hist., v. 3, no. 1, p. 1–141, 1917 (for years 1895-1917); *ibid.*, v. 4, p. 1–115, 1925.

662. Bassler, R. S., and B. Kellett (1934) Bibliographic index of Paleozoic Ostracoda. Geol. Soc. Am., Special Paper 1, 500 pp., 24 figs.

663. Agnew, A. F. (1942) Bibliographic index of new genera and families of Paleozoic Ostracoda since 1934. J. Paleont., v. 16, no. 6, p. 756–763; reprinted as Illinois Geol. Survey Circ. 86. (1944) Addenda and errata to bibliography of Paleozoic ostracods. J. Paleont., v. 18, p. 218–219.

664. Téllez-Girón, G. (1951) Additions to the bibliography of Paleozoic ostracods. Micropaleontologist, v. 5, no. 3, p. 18.

665. Petrunkevitch, Alexander (1953) Paleozoic and Mesozoic Arachnida of Europe. Geol. Soc. Am., Mem. 53, 128 pp.

666. Levinson, S. A. (1953) Bibliography and index to new genera of Ostracoda, 1950–1952. Micropaleontologist, v. 7, no. 3, p. 51–64. (1955) 1953, Micropaleontology, v. 1, no. 3, p. 273–286. (1956) 1954, v. 2, no. 1, p. 79–90; 1955, v. 2, no. 4, p. 375–384. (1957) 1956, v. 3, no. 4, p. 367–392. (1959) 1957, v. 5, no. 2, p. 241–260. (1962) 1958–1959, v. 8, no. 1, p. 75–105.

667. Kornicker, L. S. (1957) Bibliography of ostracod theses. Micropaleontology, v. 3, no. 3, p. 287–290.

668. Brooks, H. K. (1957) Chelicerata, Trilobitomorphia, Crustacea (exclusive of Ostracoda) and Myriapoda: An annotated bibliography. *In* Ladd, H. S., ed., Paleoecology, Geol. Soc. Am. Mem. 67, p. 895–929.

669. Agnew, A. F. (1957) Ostracodes of the Paleozoic: An annotated bibliography. *In* Ladd, H. S., ed., Paleoecology, Geol. Soc. Am. Mem. 67, p. 931–935.

670. Sohn, I. G. (1957) Ostracods of the post-Paleozoic: An annotated bibliography. *In* Ladd, H. S., ed., Paleoecology, Geol. Soc. Am. Mem. 67, p. 937–941.

671. Pierce, W. D. (1957) Insects: An annotated bibliography. In Ladd, H. S., ed., Paleoecology, Geol. Soc. Am. 67, p. 943–951.

672. Coryell, H. N. (1964) A bibliography of the Mesozoic Ostracoda and their classification. Univ. of Dayton Press, 1175 pp.

**673.** See 567, Pts. 16 (Insecta palaeozoica); 25 (Eurypterida); 37 (Trilobitae neodevonici); 41 (Crustacea decapoda); 48 (Crustacea Eumalacostraca); 64 (Crustacea Phyllocarida)

## Vermes

**674.** Howell, B. F. (1957) Vermes: An annotated bibliography. *In* Ladd, H. S., ed., Paleoecology, Geol. Soc. Am. Mem. 67, p. 805–816.

## Echinodermata

**675.** Klem, M. J. (1904) A revision of the Paleozoic Paleëchinoidea, with a synopsis of all known species. St. Louis Acad. Sci., Trans., v. 14, p. 1–97.
**676.** Kew, W. S. W. (1920) Bibliography of Pacific Coast Cretaceous and Cenozoic Echinoidea. Univ. Calif. Publ. Bull. Dept. Geol. Sci., v. 12, no. 2, p. 49–51.
**677.** Greger, D. K. (1934) Bibliographic index of North American species of the Eublastoidea. St. Louis Acad. Sci., Trans., v. 28, no. 3, p. 119–181.
**678.** Bassler, R. S., and M. W. Moodey (1943) Bibliographic and faunal index of Paleozoic pelmatozoan echinoderms. Geol. Soc. Am., Special Paper 45, 734 pp.
**679.** Sinclair, G. W. (1957) Cystoids: An annotated bibliography. *In* Ladd, H. S., ed., Paleoecology, Geol. Soc. Am. Mem. 67, p. 953–954.
**680.** Cline, L. M., and Harold Beaver (1957). Blastoids: an annotated bibliography. *In* Ladd, H. S., ed., Paleoecology, Geol. Soc. Am. Mem. 67, p. 955–960.
**681.** Laudon, L. R. (1957) Crinoids: An annotated bibliography. *In* Ladd, H. S., ed., Paleoecology, Geol. Soc. Am. Mem. 67, p. 961–971.
**682.** Berry, C. T. (1957) Asterozoa of the post-Paleozoic: An annotated bibliography. *In* Ladd, H. S., ed., Paleoecology, Geol. Soc. Am., Mem. 67, p. 975–978.
**683.** Cooke, C. W. (1957) Echinoids of the post-Paleozoic: An annotated bibliography. *In* Ladd, H. S., ed., Paleoecology, Geol. Soc. Am. Mem. 67, p. 981–982.
**684.** Frizzell, D. L., and Harriet Exline (1957) Holothurians: An annotated bibliography. *In* Ladd, H. S., ed., Paleoecology, Geol. Soc. Am. Mem. 67, p. 983–986.
**685.** Cooper, G. A. (1957) Echinoids of the Paleozoic: An annotated bibliography. *In* Ladd, H. S., ed., Paleoecology, Geol. Soc. Am. Mem. 67, p. 979–980.
**686.** Cooper, G. A. (1957) Asterozoa of the Paleozoic: An annotated bibliography. *In* Ladd, H. S., ed., Paleoecology, Geol. Soc. Am. Mem. 67, p. 973–974.
**687.** See 405 (Echinoderms, Australia); 567, Pts. 3 (Stelleroidea palaeozoica); 39 (Echinoidea jurassica); 66, 88 (Crinoidea triadica); 70, 73, 76, 88 (Crinoidea jurassica); 77, 88 (Crinoidea cretacea); 80, 88 (Crinoidea caenozoica); 83 (Pelmatozoa Palaeozoica)

## Graptolites

**688.** Bulman, O. M. B. (1957) Graptolites: An annotated bibliography. *In* Ladd, H. S., ed., Paleoecology, Geol. Soc. Am. Mem. 67, p. 987–991.
**689.** See 402 (Graptolites, Australia)

## Stromatoporoidea

**690.** Galloway, J. J., and J. St. Jean, Jr. (1956) A bibliography of the order Stromatoporoidea. J. Paleont., v. 30, no. 1, p. 170–85.
**691.** Flügel, Érik (1956) Zur Bibliographie der Stromatoporen. Naturw. Ver. Steiermark, Mitt. Bd. 86, p. 26–31.

## Conodonts

**692.** Holmes, G. B. (1928) A bibliography of the conodonts with descriptions of early Mississippian species. U.S. Nat. Mus., Proc., v. 72, art. 5, 38 pp., 11 pls.
**693.** Fay, R. O. (1952) Catalogue of conodonts. Univ. Kansas Paleont. Contrib., Vertebrata, art. 3, 206 pp.
**694.** Ellison, S. P., Jr., (1957) Conodonts: An annotated bibliography. *In* Ladd, H. S., ed., Paleoecology, Geol. Soc. Am. Mem. 67, p. 993–994.
**695.** Ellison, S. P., Jr., (1962) Annotated bibliography and index of conodonts. Austin, Univ. Texas, Bur. Econ. Geol., 128 pp., 6 charts.

## Vertebrate Paleontology

**696.** Hay, O. P. (1902) Bibliography and catalogue of the fossil Vertebrata of North America. U.S. Geol. Surv., Bull. 179, 868 pp.
———— (1929–1930) Second bibliography and catalogue of the fossil Vertebrata of North America. Washington, D.C., Carnegie Inst. Publ. 390, v. 1, 916 pp.; v. 2, 1074 pp.
**697.** Dean, B. (1916–1917, 1923) A bibliography of fishes. Enlarged and edited by C. R. Eastman. Am. Mus. Nat. Hist., New York, v. 1, A–K, 718 pp. (1916); v. 2, L–Z, 702 pp. (1917); v. 3, index, addenda, etc., 707 pp. (1923).
**698.** Caterini, F. (1925) I Bovini fossili del Museo di Geologia della R. Universita di Pisa con bibliografia generale sur bovini fossili. Atti Soc. Tosc. Sci. Nat., Mem. 36, pp. 50–70.
**699.** Wood, C. A. (1931) An introduction to the literature of vertebrate zoology. Oxford Univ. Press, 643 pp.
**700.** Ruch, T. C. (1941) Bibliographia primatologica. A classified bibliography of primates other than man: Part I, Anatomy, embryology and quantitative morphology; physiology, pharmacology and psychobiology; primate phylogeny and miscellanea. Yale Medical School, Historical Library, Pub. 4, 241 pp.

**701.** Nichols, R. H. (1943) Bibliography of vertebrate paleontology and related subjects for 1942. Soc. Vert. Paleont., News Bull., A to E, no. 9, p. 21–24; F to P, no. 10, p. 21–24; R to Z, no. 11, p. 19–22. (1944) 1943, including 1942 titles found too late for publication in News Bulletins nos. 9, 10, and 11: A to G, no. 12, p. 29–32; H to Z, no. 13, p. 24–32. (1945) 1944, including earlier titles which came in too late for publication in News Bulletins 9–13: A to F, no. 14, p. 27–32; G to P, no. 15, p. 18–24; R, no. 16, p. 28–32; S to Z, no. 17, p. 29–32. (1946) 1945, including some earlier titles, especially of foreign papers recently received: A to C, no. 18, p. 21–24; C in part to G in part, no. 19, p. 28–32. (1947) 1945–46. Soc. Vert. Paleont., 18 + 24 pp. (1948) 1946–47, 39 pp. (1949) 1947–48, 45 pp. (1950) 1948–49, 44 pp. (1951) 1949–50, 52 pp. (1952) 1950–51, 61 pp. (1953) 1951–52, 58 pp. (1954) 1952–3, 56 pp. (1955) 1953–54, 70 pp. (1956) 1954–55, 81 pp. (1957) 1955–56, 67 pp. (1958) 1956–57, 70 pp. (1959) 1957–58, 80 pp. (1960) 1958–59, 85 pp.

———— and J. M. Lyons (1961) *Ibid.,* 1959–1960, 53 pp.

Lyons, J. M. (1962) *Ibid.,* 1960–61, 69 pp.

Holton, Charlotte (1963) *Ibid.,* 1963, 59 pp.

**702.** Anonymous (1957) Russian translations. Soc. Vert. Paleo. News Bull., no. 51, p. 28–29.

**703.** Williams, Ernest (1942) Reading list on fossils, earth history and human evolution. Soc. Vert. Paleo. News Bull., no. 5, p. 17–19.

**704.** Camp, C. L., and V. L. Vanderhoof (1940) Bibliography of fossil vertebrates, 1928–1933. Geol. Soc. America Sp. Paper 27, 503 pp.

————, D. N. Taylor, and S. P. Welles (1942) *Ibid.,* 1934–1938. Sp. Paper 42, 663 pp.

————, S. P. Welles, and Morton Green (1949) *Ibid.,* 1939–1943. Mem. 37, 371 pp. (1953) *Ibid.,* 1944–1948. Mem. 57, 465 pp.

————, and H. J. Allison (1961) *Ibid.,* 1949–1953. Mem. 84, 532 pp.

**705.** Robertson, G. M. (1957) Agnatha: An annotated bibliography. *In* Ladd, H. S., ed., Paleoecology, Geol. Soc. Am., Mem. 67, p. 995–997.

**706.** David, L. R. (1957) Fishes (other than Agnatha): An annotated bibliography. *In* Ladd, H. S., ed., Paleoecology, Geol. Soc. Am. Mem. 67, p. 999–1010.

**707.** Romer, A. S. (1957) Amphibians: An annotated bibliography. *In* Ladd, H. S., ed., Paleoecology, Geol. Soc. Am. Mem. 67, p. 1011.

**708.** Zangerl, Rainer (1957) Reptiles: An annotated bibliography. *In* Ladd, H. S., ed., Paleoecology, Geol. Soc. Am., Mem. 67, p. 1013–1017.

**709.** Friedmann, Herbert (1957) Birds: An annotated bibliography. *In* Ladd, H. S., ed., Paleoecology, Geol. Soc. Am. Mem. 67, p. 1019–1020.

**710.** Kellogg, Remington, and F. C. Whitmore, Jr. (1957) Mammals: An annotated bibliography. *In* Ladd, H. S., ed., Paleoecology, Geol. Soc. Am. Mem. 67, p. 1021–1024.

**711.** Bader, R. S., and David Techter (1959) A list and bibliography of the fossil mammals of Illinois. Chicago Acad. Sci., Nat. History Misc. no. 162, 8 pp.

**712.** Romer, A. S., N. E. Wright, Tilly Edinger, and R. Van Frank (1962)

Bibliography of fossil vertebrates exclusive of North America, 1509–1927. Geol. Soc. Am., Mem. 87, 2 v., 1544 pp.

**713.** See 83 (Fossil Vertebrates, Florida); 84 (Mammals, Florida); 141 (John Day Region, Oregon); 176, 177 (Paleontology, Canada); 370 (Vertebrate Fauna, Middle East); 415–417, 419 (Paleontology, Japan); 443 (Fossil Mammals, Africa); 486 (Reptilia, Karroo); 567, Pts. 4 (Saurischia et Ornithischia triadica), 9 (Stegosauria), 12 (Aves), 24 (Otolithi Piscium), 27 (Osteologia Reptilium), 33 (Pisces triadici), 45 (Pterosauria), 47 (Post-Mesozoic Marsupialia), 57 (Antiarchi), 58 (Thecodontia), 61 (Labyrinthodortia), 62 (Placodontia), 63 (Icthyosauria), 69 (Sauropterigia), 71 (Rhynchocephalia), 74 (Hominidae fossiles), 75 (Crocodilia), 78 (Ornithischia), 79 (Cotylosauria et Theromorpha), 82, 89, 92 (Fauna fossiles cavernarum) 85 (Protoposauria, Mesosauria), 86 (Squamata), 87 (Saurischia), 90 (Saltatoria Eusifera fossilia), 93 (Mammalia triadica), 97 (Amphibia), 98, 99 (Reptilia), 103 (Serpentes)

## Paleobotany

**714.** Knowlton, F. H. (1898) A catalogue of the Cretaceous and Tertiary plants of North America. U.S. Geol. Surv. Bull. 152, 247 pp.

**715.** ———— (1919) Catalogue of the Mesozoic and Cenozoic plants of North America. U.S. Geol. Surv. Bull. 696. 815 pp.

**716.** Botanical Abstracts. Volumes 1–15, 1918 to 1926. Baltimore, 1918–1926. Contains a section, "Paleobotany and Evolutionary History"; Continued by Biological Abstracts: see entry 584.

**717.** Carpentier, M. A. (1923) Revue des travaux de paléontologie végétale publiés dans le cours des anées 1910–1919. Rev. generale bot., Part 1, Paleozoique, v. 33, p. 437–448, 471–477, 558–576, 653–672, 771–791; v. 34, p. 65–70, 124–133, 166–170, 237–250, 300–310, 367–375, 417–424, 463–470, 508–518, 556–563, 604–611; v. 35, p. 42–47, 101–112, 149–160, 201–208; Part 2., Mésozoique (du Trias an Wealdien inclus), v. 35, p. 254–347.

**718.** Gams, H. (1927) Die Ergebnesse der pollenanalytischen Forschung in bezug auf die Geschichte der Vegetation und des Klimas von Europa. Zeitsch. Gletscherkunde, Bd. 15, p. 161–190. (1929) Zweiter Nachtrag, Bd. 17, p. 244–248; 389–391. (1931) Dritter Nachtrag, Bd. 19, p. 328–334. (1933) Vierter Nachtrag, Bd. 21, p. 188–196. (1935) Fünfter Nachtrag, Bd. 22, p. 267–274. (1937) Sechster Nachtrag, Bd. 25, p. 283–299.

**719.** Erdtman, G. (1927) Literature on pollen-statistics published before 1927. Geol. Foren. Stockholm, Bd. 49, p. 196–211. (1930) During years 1927–1929: Bd. 52, p. 191–213. (1933) 1930–1931, Bd. 54, p. 395–418. (1934) 1932–1933, Bd. 56, p. 463–481. (1935) 1934, Bd. 57, p. 261–274. (1937) 1935–1936, Bd. 59, p. 157–181. (1940) 1937–1939, Bd. 62, p. 61–97. (1944) 1940–1943, Bd. 66, p. 256–276. (1945) 1944, Bd. 67, p. 273–283. (1947) Literature on Palynology X, Jan. 1, 1945-Sept. 25, 1946, Bd. 69, p. 24–40. (1948) XI, Bd. 70, p. 295–328. (1949) XII, Bd. 71, p. 71–90. (1950) XIII, Bd. 72, p. 30–50.

———, O. Hedberg, and J. Terasmäe (1951) *Ibid.,* XIV. Bd. 73, p. 100–131.

Erdtman, G. (1952) *Ibid.,* XV. Bd. 74, p. 25–43. (1953) XVI, Bd. 75, p. 17–38.

720. Mills, F. W. (1933–1935) An index to the genera and species of the Diatomaceae and their synonyms. London, Weldon & Wesley, 3 v.

721. Johnson, J. Harlan (1943) Geologic importance of calcareous algae: With annotated bibliography. Colorado School Mines Quart., v. 38, no. 1, 92 pp.

722. Lamotte, R. S. (1944) A supplement to Catalogue of Mesozoic and Cenozoic plants of North America, 1919–1937. U. S. Geol. Surv. Bull. 924, 330 pp.

723. ——— (1952) Catalogue of the Cenozoic plants of North America through 1950. Geol. Soc. Am., Mem. 51, 381 pp.

724. Just, Theodor Karl, and others (1954) Report of the Committee on Paleobotany, no. 23 (Appendix E of Annual Report of Division), with bibliography of paleobotany in North and South America, 1952; Washington, D.C., Natl. Res. Council, Div. Earth Sci., 33 pp.

725. Andrews, H. N., Jr. (1955) Index of generic names of fossil plants, 1820–1950. U.S. Geol. Surv. Bull. 1013, 262 pp.

726. Johnson, J. H. (1957) Calcareous algae: An annotated bibliography. *In* Ladd, H. S., ed., Paleoecology, Geol. Soc. Am. Mem. 67, p. 699–701.

727. Johnson, J. H. (1957) Bibliography of fossil algae, 1942–1955. Colo. School Mines Quart., v. 52, no. 2, 92 pp.

728. Wilson, L. R. (1957) Spores and pollen of the post-Paleozoic: An annotated bibliography. *In* Ladd, H. S., ed., Paleoecology, Geol. Soc. Am. Mem. 67, p. 719–728.

729. Schopf, J. M. (1957) Spores and related plant microfossils, Paleozoic: An annotated bibliography. *In* Ladd, H. S., ed., Paleoecology, Geol. Soc. Am. Mem. 67, p. 703–707.

730. ——— (1957) "Spores" and problematic plants commonly regarded as marine: An annotated bibliography. *In* Ladd, H. S., ed., Paleoecology, Geol. Soc. Am. Mem. 67, p. 709–717.

731. Brown, R. W. (1957) Nonalgal megascopic marine plants: An annotated bibliography. *In* Ladd, H. S., ed., Paleoecology, Geol. Soc. Am. Mem. 67, p. 729–730.

732. Lohman, K. E. (1957) Diatoms: An annotated bibliography. *In* Ladd, H. S., ed., Paleoecology, Geol. Soc. Am. Mem. 67, p. 731–736.

733. Franklin, S. H. (1959) *Ginkgo biloba* L.: Historical summary and bibliography. Va. Jour. Sci., v. 10, no. 3, p. 131–176.

734. Campo, Madeleine van (1959) Palynologie: Références bibliographiques. Pollen et Spores v. 1, nos. 1, 2, p. 92–144, 317–332.

———, and N. Planchais (1960) Références bibliographiques: Pollen et Spores, suppl., v. 2, nos. 1, 2, p. 133–158, 325–346. (1961) v. 3, nos. 1, 2, p. 165–186, 397–419.

735. Neishtadt, M. I. (1960) Palinologiya v SSSR 1952–1957 gg., Moscow, Akad. Nauk SSSR, Inst. Geog., 272 pp., illus. [An outline of the history

of palynologic research in the USSR during 1952–1957, together with a bibliography (1632 titles), arranged chronologically and accompanied by geographic, subject, and author indexes.]

736. Němejc, František (1960) Úvod do starši paleobotanické literatury. Prague, Ceskoslov. Akad. Věd, 139 pp. [A review of the paleobotanic literature published up through the first half of the 20th century, with bibliographic lists, classified by region.]

737. Vachey, G. (1961) Bibliographie palynologique du crétacé inférieur. Pollen et Spores, v. 3, no. 2, p. 373–383.

738. See 415 (Paleobotany, Japan); 444 (Algae, Africa); 567 (Series II)

**Problematica**

739. Caster, K. E. (1957) Problematica: An annotated bibliography. *In* Ladd, H. S., ed., Paleoecology, Geol. Soc. Am. Mem. 67, p. 1025–1032.

# INDEXES

# SUBJECT INDEX

# INDEX OF NAMES